Elements of Econometrics

Jan Kmenta

PROFESSOR OF ECONOMICS
MICHIGAN STATE UNIVERSITY

Elements of Econometrics

The Macmillan Company · NEW YORK
COLLIER-MACMILLAN LIMITED · LONDON

To Joan

Preface

This book has been written for economists—that is, for people who should understand and may want to use modern econometric techniques—rather than for prospective econometricians who plan to participate in the development and refinement of methods. The contents are designed to cover a one-year course in introductory econometrics offered to first-year economics graduate students in many universities. However, the book may also serve as a text for a course in economic or business statistics for advanced undergraduates, or as a reference book for economists of all specializations who want to keep up with current applied economic research.

Both students and teachers of economics face an increasing need for familiarity with quantitative methods in order to understand current economic literature and to be effective in their own research efforts. I have tried to cover most of the statistical and econometric methods that modern economists might need. In my opinion there appears to be a need for a book which will give the economist as much econometrics as possible without making excessive demands on his mathematical skills. I have found, from my experience with the graduate students at the University of Wisconsin and at Michigan State University, that it is perfectly possible to start at a low level of statistical knowledge and to move rather rapidly to quite sophisticated econometric topics. This, of course, requires a lot of effort on the part of the students as well as on the part of the teacher. I have been fortunate to have had students who were strongly motivated and who derived a lot of pleasure out of being able to do things which only two weeks earlier appeared to be beyond reach. As for the work of the teacher, I think that it is his obligation to emphasize at all times complete understanding rather than a cookbook type of learning, and to spare no effort at making everything as clear as possible. This is the spirit in which this book has been written.

Every textbook writer owes it to his readers to spell out the technical background which he thinks is necessary if the book is to be reasonably well understood. In my case, I have assumed what is coming to be the usual standard for an entering economics graduate student, namely a knowledge of intermediate economic theory, of college algebra and basic calculus, and of some basic descriptive statistics. Because the book is carefully planned to develop the foundations of statistics in a gradual way, these prerequisites will be sufficient for all the material covered in the text except for the last two chapters which require some matrix algebra. A convenient survey of what is needed is provided in Appendix B.

As suggested earlier, the basic philosophy underlying this book is to make everything as simple and clear as possible. All methods are explained and discussed within the simplest framework, and generalizations are presented as logical extensions of the simple cases. This, of course, reduces to a minimum the use of mathematics and particularly of matrix algebra. It represents a conscious and laborious effort on my part. Throughout the book I have tried to present all relevant work from econometric literature in the simplest and clearest form while, at the same time, hopefully avoiding the danger of over-simplification. I hope that this will make the subject aesthetically pleasing, more accessible, and will make the application of it easier. While every attempt has been made to preserve a relatively high degree of rigor, every conflict between rigor and clarity of exposition or understanding was resolved in favor of the latter.

The book consists of two parts. Part One, which contains six chapters, covers the elements of the theory of statistics, while Part Two contains seven chapters on various topics of regression analysis and simultaneous equation problems. The first part should provide the students with a good understanding of the process of scientific generalization from incomplete information. The emphasis is on explaining the basic ideas rather than on presenting formulas and rules to be applied. In line with this, more than usual attention is paid to hypothesis testing and parameter estimation. Part One is a prerequisite for Part Two, but it might also be used as a self-contained unit. Part Two of the book contains a thorough exposition of all basic econometric methods, and includes some of the most recent developments in several areas. While many topics represent standard parts of econometrics texts, several other topics are treated much more extensively than is usually the case. In particular, a great deal of attention is given to models involving binary variables, to nonlinear and distributed lag models, to restricted estimation, and to generalized linear regression.

Since the book has already exceeded its originally intended length by a fair amount, there are a few topics which are not included. One of these is spectral analysis which, while providing an interesting new technique, has not yet been closely integrated with economic theory, and is fairly unwieldy for a non-specialist to manipulate. Further, a discussion of the Bayesian approach to statistics would constitute another worthwhile topic (some of my friends would say *the* worthwhile topic), but to do it justice would require considerable space. A third topic regretfully left out is econometric model simulation. The economist who is interested in these topics may consult more specialized texts. The aim of the present book is to provide him with the basic tools which would make such consultation more easy and more efficient.

There are several direct and less direct acknowledgments that should be made in connection with this book. My long-standing thanks are due to Arthur Goldberger whose excellence in teaching and devotion to research—and clarity in both—have inspired much of the spirit of my work. Several of the topics that I treat in the book have been developed by Arnold Zellner. I owe him thanks not only on this count, but mainly because he has been always most gracious in discussing problems in econometrics and in giving me the benefit of his exceptional insights. I have also received editorial help and encouragement from Lawrence Klein who kindly read the entire manuscript and offered many useful comments and suggestions. Unfortunately, I was not able to incorporate all of them into the book because of limitations of time and space, but the book would undoubtedly have been improved if all of the suggestions were followed up. Indirect but nevertheless important help has been given to me by Robert Basmann and Karl Brunner who made me painfully aware of many methodological shortcomings, and by James Ramsey whose technical knowledge and imaginative insights have been made constantly available to me. Specific thanks are due to Roy Gilbert for aiding me with the computer, to Jeffrey Roth for verifying the examples, and to William Ruble for his assistance with the simultaneous equation programs. Mrs. Elisabeth Belfer of The Macmillan Company deserves special commendation for her painstaking assistance at the proofreading stage. Of course, the largest thanks go to my wife who has served as a most patient proofreader as well as a caretaker of all family affairs that would otherwise intrude upon my work.

Finally, I would like to express my appreciation and indebtedness to Arnold Zellner and Martin Geisel for permission to cite unpublished work, and to J. Zubrzycki for permission to use the data in the examples of Section 9–2. In addition, I am indebted to the Literary Executor of the late Sir Ronald Fisher, F.R.S., and to Oliver & Boyd Ltd., Edinburgh, for their permission to reprint Table D–2 from their book *Statistical Methods for Research Workers*; to Professor E. S. Pearson and the *Biometrika* trustees for permission to reproduce the material in Tables D–3, D–4, and D–5; and to the Rand Corporation for permission to reproduce the material in Table D–6 from their book *A Million Random Digits and One Hundred Thousand Deviates*. The publication of the material in Table D–5 was also authorized by Professor J. Durbin and Professor G. S. Watson.

East Lansing   J. K.

Contents

Part ONE
Basic Statistical Theory

Part TWO
Basic Econometric Theory

Part ONE

Basic Statistical Theory

1

Introduction to Statistical Inference

Until the early part of the nineteenth century, statistics was understood to be concerned with characteristics of the state, particularly those related to political and military institutions. Descriptions of these characteristics were at first mainly in verbal terms, but they gradually became more and more numerical. The change to an increasingly more quantitative character was accompanied by an extension to fields other than those concerned with the affairs of the state. Later advances in probability led to the development of the theory of statistics that permits scientific generalization from incomplete information—in other words, statistical inference.

As a result of this historical development, the subject known as "statistics" consists of two parts, descriptive statistics and statistical inference. Descriptive statistics deals with the collection, organization, and presentation of data, while statistical inference deals with generalizations from a part to the whole. Statistical inference, like any other science, is concerned with the development of methods (statistical theory) as well as with their use (statistical application).

In econometrics we are mainly concerned with statistical inference. Descriptive statistics is relevant only to the extent that measures developed by descriptive statisticians for the purpose of summarizing various characteristics of the data—averages, measures of dispersion, etc.—are also used in statistical inference. The basic difference lies in the fact that in the field of descriptive statistics these measures represent ends in themselves, whereas in statistical inference they are only means in the process of inquiry.

1-1 Basic Concepts of Statistical Inference

Before explaining the nature of statistical inference more specifically, we must introduce a few basic concepts. The most crucial ones are those of a population and of a sample.

A *population* can be defined as the totality of all possible observations on measurements or outcomes. Examples are incomes of all people in a certain country in a specific period of time, national income of a country over a number of periods of time, and all outcomes of repeatedly tossing a coin. A population

3

may be either finite or infinite. A *finite population* is one in which the number of all possible observations is less than infinity. However, the distinction between finite and infinite populations is more subtle than may at first appear. For instance, a series of national income figures for the United States for a number of years, e.g., 1948–1967, represents a finite collection of twenty observations and thus might seem to be a finite population. But this would be a very narrow interpretation of historical events, since it would imply that the twenty measurements of national income were the only possible ones, i.e., that there is only one course that history might have taken. Now there are obviously not many people who would take such an extremely fatalistic view of the world; most people would admit that it was not impossible for some other, even if only slightly different, values of national income to have occurred. This latter view underlies virtually all policy-oriented research in economics and econometrics and will be used throughout this book. Thus a population of national incomes in a given time interval includes not only the actual history represented by the values that were in fact observed but also the potential history consisting of all the values that might have occurred but did not. The population so defined is obviously an infinite one. Similarly, the population of all possible outcomes of coin tosses is also infinite, since the tossing process can generate an infinite number of outcomes, in this case "heads" and "tails." Most of the populations with which we deal in econometrics are infinite.

Related to the concept of a population is the concept of a *sample*, which is a set of measurements or outcomes selected from the population. The selection can be done by the investigator, in which case we can speak of a sampling experiment, or it may happen independently either by design of others or by nature. In the latter case, the investigator is a mere observer, and this situation is particularly frequent in econometrics. While samples from infinite populations can themselves be infinite, the relevance of such samples is at best only a theoretical one. In practice we deal only with finite samples and, regrettably, quite often only very small ones. Since samples are obtained by a selection from a given population, the principle of selection clearly plays an important part in determining the composition of the sample. In econometrics our attention is confined to samples drawn in accordance with some specified chance mechanism. Such samples are called *probability samples*. An important type of probability sample is the *random sample*. In finite populations, the principle of selecting a random sample is that of giving every individual in the population an equal chance of being chosen. In the case of infinite populations, a sample is random if each observation (of a measurement or an outcome) is independent of every other observation. The meaning of *independence* will be given in a rigorous way later; at present it is sufficient to note that two events (which can be either measured or counted) are independent if the occurrence of one in no way influences the occurrence of the other.

Both populations and samples can be described by stating their characteristics. Numerical characteristics of a population are called *parameters*; the characteristics of a sample, given in the form of some summary measure, are called *statistics* (a plural of the word "statistic"). Such characteristics may be, for instance, central tendency of measurements (e.g., the mean or the mode), their dispersion (e.g., standard deviation), or, in the case of qualitative phenomena, the proportion of observations of a given kind. Obviously, the parameters of an infinite population are never observed; the parameters of a finite population could be observed in theory but may be impossible to observe in practice.

From our discussion so far it should be clear that statistics deals with phenomena that can be either measured or counted. With respect to a phenomenon that can be measured, we speak of a *variable*, meaning a homogeneous quantity that can assume different values at different points of observation. If a phenomenon can only be counted but not measured (each observation representing one count), we speak of an *attribute*. Thus an attribute is the presence or absence of a given characteristic. An outcome of an event such as the birth of a child leads to an observation of an attribute of sex (i.e., "male" or "not male"); an outcome of a toss of a die may be classified as a presence or an absence of "1," of "2," and so on. In a way the concept of attribute is redundant because we can, and often do, simply assign the value of 1 to the presence, and 0 to the absence, of a given characteristic. In this case we equate "attribute" with the concept of a *qualitative* or *binary variable*. Another and more colorful name, "dummy variable," has also been used.

The definition of a *variable*, and indeed the name itself, stresses the possibility of variation at different points of observation. On the other hand, a quantity that cannot vary from one observation to another is called a *constant*. (Note that a parameter is also a constant since it does not vary from observation to observation.) If the quantity in question is a variable and not a constant, one may wish to ask about the general source of variation. In particular, it is important to distinguish between those variations that can and those that cannot be fully controlled or manipulated. In the case of a variation that cannot be fully controlled, its existence is due to chance. An obvious example of an uncontrolled variation would be the outcomes of tossing a coin (in the absence of cheating, of course), but many other less obvious instances exist. In fact, as we shall elaborate at length in the rest of this book, most economic variables are always to some extent determined by chance. The variables whose values cannot be fully controlled or determined prior to observation are called *random* or *stochastic variables*; their chief characteristic is that they assume different values (or fall into different value intervals) with some probability other than one. In contrast, a *nonrandom* or *nonstochastic* or *fixed variable* is one that is fully controllable or at least fully predictable. A constant may be regarded as a special case of a fixed variable.

Another important classification of variables is that which distinguishes between continuous and discrete variables. A *continuous variable* is a variable that can assume any value on the numerical axis or a part of it. Typical examples are time and temperature, but income, expenditure, and similar variables can all be classified as continuous. In fact, most economic variables are continuous or at least approximately so. The last qualification is added to take care of such possible objections as those pointing out that money values of less than a dollar (or possibly a cent) are, in fact, not observable. In contrast to a continuous variable, a *discrete variable* is one that can assume only some specific values on the numerical axis. These values are usually (but not always) separated by intervals of equal length. Examples are a number of children in a family, a number of dots on a die after a toss, or any binary variable.

Table 1–1

Number of Children (= Variable)	Number of Families (= Absolute Frequency)	Proportion of Families (= Relative Frequency)
0	4	0.0625
1	12	0.1875
2	20	0.3125
3	16	0.2500
4	8	0.1250
5 and over	4	0.0625
Totals	64	1.0000

The final concept to be introduced at this stage is that of a *distribution*. In the case of a sample we have a frequency distribution, while in the case of a population we speak of a probability distribution. A *frequency distribution* represents an organization of data so as to give the number of observations for each value of the variable (in the case of a discrete variable) or for each interval of values of the variable (in the case of a continuous variable). The number of observations in each class (represented by a point in the case of a discrete variable or by an interval in the case of a continuous variable) is called *absolute frequency*. This can be distinguished from *relative frequency*, which gives the proportion of observations rather than their number for each class. As an example, consider a sample of 64 families being observed with respect to the number of children. The results might be those given in Table 1–1. Another example, this time related to a continuous variable, is given by family income distribution in the United States in 1962 (Table 1–2). Here, absolute frequencies are not shown, and the relative frequencies are stated in percentages rather than in simple proportions. Sample data in the form of a time series, such as national income figures for a number of years, could also be presented in the form of a frequency distribution, although this is usually not done. The fact that different observations are made at different points of time is relevant only to the extent that the population from which the sample was drawn may have changed through time.

In a population the concept corresponding to a sample frequency distribution is known as a *probability distribution*. Consider, for instance, the population of

United States families classified by income received in 1962 as shown in Table 1–2. It is fairly clear that to state that 12.7% of all families received an income of less than $2000 is equivalent to stating that the probability of selecting (at random) a family with an income of less than $2000 is 0.127. If the population is infinite, the probabilities can be represented by *limits* of relative frequencies

Table 1–2

Income After Taxes (= Variable)	Percent Consumer Units* (= Relative Frequency)
Under $2,000	12.7
$2,000 to $4,999	31.9
$5,000 to $9,999	39.7
$10,000 and over	15.7
Total	100.0

Source: *Statistical Abstract of the United States, 1965*, p. 341.
* Includes families and unattached individuals (total number = 57,890,000).

(this will be explained more rigorously in Chapter 3). Picturing, then, the probability distribution of one variable as a counterpart of the frequency distribution in a sample, we can see that it is possible to deal with more than one variable at a time. For example, a distribution giving the probability of death at various ages confines itself to one variable—it is an *univariate distribution.* If, however, we tabulate these probabilities separately for each sex, we are considering two variables and have a *bivariate distribution.* A further classification by other characteristics could produce a *multivariate distribution.*

1–2   The Nature of Statistical Inference

Having introduced, however briefly, some of the most important concepts of statistical theory, we are now in a position to describe the nature of statistical inference. As indicated earlier, statistical inference is concerned with generalizations about the population on the basis of information provided by a sample. Such a procedure is, of course, frequent in everyday life: we make generalizations about the temperature of our soup on the basis of the first spoonful, or about the life expectancy of a pair of tennis shoes on the basis of past experience. This is precisely what is done in statistical inference, except that we go about it in a somewhat more scientific way. What makes the application of statistical inference scientific is that we take into account the way in which the sample was selected, and that we express our generalization in specific probability terms. For example, instead of saying that tennis shoes last five years, we specify a range and state the level of probability associated with it.

To sum up, we use a sample to make a judgment about the population from which the sample comes. If the population is infinite, then it can never be observed as a whole and any judgment about it can only come from a sample. But even if the population is a finite one, there may be a good reason for observing only a sample since making observations (as in the case of tasting soup or measuring the lifetime of light bulbs) is destructive or, at best, expensive. Now, in general we are not interested in knowing everything about a population but are concerned with only *some* of its characteristics, which, it may be recalled, we call parameters. The purpose of sampling, and the business of statistical inference, is to make judgments about population parameters on the basis of sample statistics. These judgments are, in fact, guesses endowed with a specific degree of reliability and they can be of two types, one concerned with estimation of a parameter and the other with testing some hypothesis about it. Estimation is done with the help of an *estimator*, which is a formula describing a procedure of guessing the value of a given population parameter; a specific value of an estimator is called an *estimate*. Judgments in the form of *hypothesis testing* involve an a priori assumption about the value of a parameter. If the sample information provides evidence against the hypothesis, we reject it; otherwise, we keep it. The evidence provided by the observations in the sample is, for the purpose of hypothesis testing, summarized in the form of a *test statistic*; this is then used in arriving at a verdict concerning the hypothesis.

A sample provides evidence about the population from which it was drawn. This evidence can be summarized in the form of an estimator when the problem is one of estimation, or in the form of a test statistic when the problem is one of hypothesis testing. In either case we follow some formula into which we substitute the values observed in our sample. The values thus obtained for an estimator and for a test statistic are closely related, as they ought to be, since they draw upon the same source of information, i.e., the sample. In any case, the value of an estimator or of a test statistic represents a guess concerning the relevant population parameter. Now it is obvious that different samples would lead to different guesses. Some will be closer to the truth (e.g., to the true value of the parameter) than others. In reality we have, of course, usually just one sample and therefore only one guess. But it is obviously important for us to know what the guesses might have been had we had different samples. If all possible samples lead to guesses that are always near the truth, any single guess is obviously quite reliable. On the other hand, if all possible samples lead to widely differing guesses, only some of the guesses can be near the truth and no single guess can be trusted much. The third extreme case is one where all possible guesses are similar to each other but far from the true value of the parameter.

1–3 Sampling Distributions

The preceding paragraph suggests that the way to know the reliability of a guess is by knowing the behavior of all guesses that could be made on the basis of all possible samples. We can envision drawing one sample after another, from each sample calculating the value of our guess (say, an estimate of a certain population parameter), and arranging these guesses in the form of a distribution. If we had an infinite number of such samples, the resulting distribution would be called a *sampling distribution*. Consider, for example, the problem of estimating the mean family income in the United States in a given year on the basis of a sample of, say, 100 families. One possibility is to calculate the mean family income in our sample and use it as our estimate of the population mean. Of course, we could use the mode, or the median, or some other measure as our estimator. Suppose we estimate the population mean by using the sample mean. Then we wish to know how reliable this estimator is. One way to find this out would be by drawing an infinite number of such samples, calculating the value of the sample mean from each sample, and arranging these values in the form of a distribution. Note that although the population of all families in the United States is a finite one, the number of samples that we can draw from this population is infinite as long as we allow each family to be included in any sample. Such sampling is called *sampling with replacement*. By studying the resulting sampling distribution, we would know all about the possible behavior of our guess. If we, in fact, knew the characteristics of the population beforehand, then this exercise would serve the function of extending our knowledge about the relationship between the sample and the population mean; this knowledge could then be used in other cases when we are limited to only one sample.

If each family contained in the sample is selected at random, we do not know beforehand what its income is going to be. Thus, in this case family income is a random variable. Furthermore, the *mean* income observed in a sample is also a random variable. This means that the sampling distribution of sample mean (based on an infinite number of samples) is really a probability distribution. This distribution could be either discrete or continuous depending upon whether the population variable is a discrete or a continuous; in our example the sampling distribution is continuous since income is a continuous variable. Of course, the idea is quite general: *a sampling distribution is a probability distribution of an estimator or of a test statistic.*

It is quite obvious that samples of different sizes give different amounts of information about the population from which they are drawn. Therefore, estimators that use all information contained in a sample and are based on samples of different sizes will display different degrees of reliability. To avoid the effects of changed sample size upon the quality of an estimator, any given sampling distribution always refers to samples of the same size. The effects of changing the sample size are best studied by comparing different sampling distributions.

Suppose we are dealing with a population of all possible values of a variable X (e.g., family incomes in a given year) and are interested in estimating a parameter θ (e.g., the mean family income). To estimate this parameter, we use a sample statistic $\hat{\theta}$. In usual terminology, $\hat{\theta}$ is an estimator of θ, while a specific value of $\hat{\theta}$ (obtained from a specific sample) is called an estimate of θ. Incidentally, a common notation is to use plain Greek letters to describe population parameters and to use Greek letters with hats, tildes, etc., to describe estimators. Then if X is a continuous variable (as in the case of family income), the sampling distribution of $\hat{\theta}$ may look something like the distribution in Figure 1–1. As pointed out earlier, this is really a probability distribution; since we do not intend to define and describe probability distributions until Chapter 3, we are not in a position to discuss sampling distributions with any degree of rigor. However, we may gain a better understanding of the concept of a sampling distribution if we view it for the time being simply as a relative frequency distribution compiled from an infinite number of observations, i.e., samples in this case. In Figure 1–1 the relative frequencies of $\hat{\theta}$ are measured along the $f(\hat{\theta})$ axis.

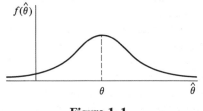

Figure 1–1

A reasonable and generally useful way of judging the quality of a guess is to evaluate the quality of the procedure that produced the guess. Suppose, for example, that a man, who has spent a lot of time learning about horse racing, goes to a race track with his wife, who is completely ignorant of such matters, and in the first race the wife wins her bet whereas the man does not. Then we do not necessarily conclude that the wife's guesses are better in general and that we should bet on the same horse that she does in the next race. Such a conclusion could be reached only after more evidence (i.e., more observations) was gathered and the wife's "system" led to bigger gains (or smaller losses) than that of her husband. Of course, if only one bet—that on the first race, say—was allowed, then there is no question that the wife's guess was better, since it led to a win while her husband lost, but this is obviously a special case of little general interest. In general, the result of any specific act of guessing is considered of little relevance; what is relevant is how often a guessing procedure leads to bad results and how often it leads to good ones. In other words, we need to know about the results of a large number of guesses, each based on the same guessing procedure. This is precisely the information conveyed by a sampling distribution. To compare the quality of guesses we compare the results of the guessing procedures from which these guesses were derived, which means that we compare their sampling distributions.

1–4 Properties of Sampling Distributions

The preceding discussion brings us to the question of what is a good guessing procedure, i.e., a good estimator. Or, to put it slightly differently, we want to know which are the specific features of a sampling distribution that enable us to pass a judgment on a particular estimator. We shall deal with this question quite thoroughly in Chapter 6, but some observations can be made right now. We may start with the simplest case, which is that of a perfect estimator. A perfect estimator is one that is never wrong, i.e., one whose sampling distribution is concentrated entirely in one point, the point that happens to be the true value of the parameter to be estimated. Needless to say, perfect estimators are very rare. One case under which we can have a perfect estimator is that of no variation in the population. In our example on sampling the temperature of a bowl of soup by a spoonful, our guessing would be perfect if the temperature were the same everywhere in the bowl and we used the temperature of the spoonful as an estimate. Normally this would be achieved by a thorough mixing before tasting. In the example on family income, we would have a perfect estimator if all families had the same income and we used the mean of a sample as an estimate of the population mean. Another case that may produce perfect estimation is when the sample is of infinite size. But it should be noted that the existence of either of the two cases does not by itself guarantee perfect estimation results; if a part or all of the sample information is ignored or wrongly used, we may still make mistakes. For instance, if our estimator of mean family income were not the sample mean but the sample mean increased by, say, 10% (perhaps in the belief that people tend to underestimate their incomes), when there was no need for it (people were, in fact, honest about their incomes), then our estimator would not be perfect regardless of the lack of variation in the population or regardless of sample size.

Almost invariably estimators are not perfect but are such that only a small proportion of an estimator's values is at or near the true value of the parameter. This means that we have to be satisfied by lesser achievements; these can be summarized by stating some properties of an estimator that are commonly considered desirable. At this stage we shall only mention the basic idea behind three of these properties; an elaborate and extended discussion will be left for another chapter. Perhaps the best-known desirable property of an estimator is that of *unbiasedness*. An unbiased estimator is one that has a sampling distribution with a mean equal to the parameter to be estimated. A perfect estimator gives a perfect guess every time; an unbiased estimator gives a perfect result only on the average. An unbiased estimator will lead to estimates that are sometimes higher and sometimes lower than the true value of the parameter, but the amount of overstating and understating "averages out" when an infinite number of estimates is made. If the sampling distribution is symmetric, then the fact that an estimator is unbiased implies that half of all possible estimates are higher and half are lower than the value of the parameter. Such a situation (in the case of a continuous estimator) is depicted by Figure 1–1. It should be emphasized that unbiasedness tells us nothing about the distance between the estimates and the value of the parameter, only that all the (positive and negative) distances add up to zero. It is quite possible that an unbiased estimator will never produce an estimate that is, in fact, equal to the value of the parameter. Consider our example on estimating the mean family income by using the mean of a sample. Let us accept the proposition—which we shall prove later—that the sample mean is an unbiased estimator of the population mean. Suppose the population mean family income is $6573.46; obviously, the probability that a sample mean would be *precisely* the same figure is negligible.

A further important desirable property of an estimator is *efficiency*, a property concerned with the distances of the values of an estimator from the value of the

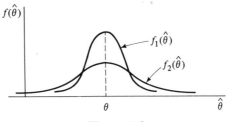

Figure 1–2

parameter. Unfortunately, there is no generally accepted definition of efficiency that would cover all cases. There is, however, a generally accepted definition if we restrict our consideration to unbiased estimators only; in this case, an efficient estimator is one that has the smallest dispersion, i.e., one whose sampling distribution has the smallest variance. In Figure 1–2 we depict two estimators, $\hat{\theta}_1$ with sampling distribution $f_1(\hat{\theta})$ and $\hat{\theta}_2$ with sampling distribution $f_2(\hat{\theta})$. Both estimators are unbiased, but $\hat{\theta}_2$ is obviously more dispersed than $\hat{\theta}_1$ and is, therefore, less efficient. If we could find no other unbiased estimator that would

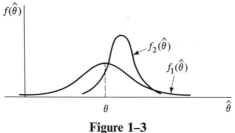

Figure 1–3

have a smaller variance than $\hat{\theta}_1$, then $\hat{\theta}_1$ would be an efficient estimator among the family of all unbiased estimators. If we do not wish to be restricted only to unbiased estimators, then the concept of efficiency becomes ambiguous since in that case it is necessary to consider the trade-off between bias and variance. Figure 1–3 demonstrates a case in point: the estimator $\hat{\theta}_1$ is unbiased but has a large variance, whereas $\hat{\theta}_2$ is biased but has a small variance. We cannot say which of the two estimators is more efficient unless we assign relative weights (i.e., prices) to bias and to variance. It is worth noting, though, that minimum variance by itself is not a desirable property; if it were, we could simply use some constant (which has, by definition, zero variance) regardless of sample evidence. The sampling distribution of such an "estimator" would be concentrated entirely in one point and yet obviously the estimator would be useless.

Another desirable property is *consistency*. This property relates to changes in the sampling distribution as sample sizes are increased. An estimator is said to be consistent if its sampling distribution tends to become concentrated on the true value of the parameter as sample size increases to infinity. Figure 1–4

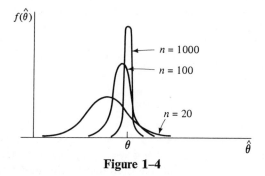

Figure 1–4

shows the sampling distributions of a consistent estimator for different sample sizes. As we move from a smaller sample size to a larger one, two things happen: (a) the bias becomes smaller, and (b) the estimates become less dispersed. Consistency is an important property because it guarantees that our estimates improve with sample size. If it is at all possible to increase sample size, then we can buy greater reliability by spending more on sampling. Even observations from national income accounts can be made more numerous by having data for shorter periods of time.

Estimating a parameter from a sample can be compared to our shooting at a target with a rifle. In this parallel, the bull's-eye represents the true value of the parameter, each shot represents a particular estimate (sample), the rifle is our estimator (i.e., estimation formula), and the distance from the target reflects our sample size. In reality we normally have only one sample and thus can make only one estimate; that is—in our parallel—we are allowed only one shot. However, the quality of any shot before it is made is clearly judged by the quality of the rifle. The rifle can be judged either by its actual performance, i.e., by making a large number of shots, or by examining its construction, the type of material used, etc. The former corresponds to empirical and the latter to theoretical derivation of properties of an estimator. An unbiased rifle is one that produces shots that are randomly scattered around the bull's-eye. If we compare all unbiased rifles, then the one whose shots are most heavily concentrated around the bull's-eye can be considered efficient. Finally, a rifle may be considered consistent if the probability of a shot falling within some (small) distance from the bull's-eye increases when the distance between the shooter and the target is decreased. Note that the quality of a rifle is judged by its repeated performance (actual or expected) and not by a single shot. Given just one shot, it may happen that an inaccurate rifle may hit the bull's-eye while an obviously superior and highly accurate rifle may not. Obviously, this would not affect our judgment of the respective qualities of the two rifles unless it tended to happen repeatedly.

So far we have not considered the question of constructing an estimator. As pointed out earlier, an estimator is a formula for generating estimates. Consider, for instance, sample mean as an estimator of population mean. Here the formula requires that we take all values of the variable observed in our sample, add them up, and divide them by the number of observations. A specific sample will lead to a specific estimate. In this case we have chosen the sample mean for an estimator of population mean more or less because it appears intuitively plausible. This, indeed, is one way of obtaining estimators—namely, by invoking some plausible idea and trying it out—which, in this context, means finding the properties of such estimators. Another way is to construct an estimator by design, to develop a formula so as to satisfy certain conditions that ensure at least some of the desirable properties. Or, finally, we may use some principles that, although not directly guaranteeing desirable properties, nevertheless appear promising on some other grounds. We shall discuss this in detail in Section 6–2.

1–5   Derivation of Sampling Distributions

The main purpose of the preceding discussion was to explain the crucial importance of sampling distributions in statistical inference. The next problem is to derive the sampling distributions of given estimators. In general, this can be done either experimentally or theoretically. The *experimental derivation* is based upon simulation: we create a specific population (which is, therefore, completely known to us) and actually draw from it a large number of random samples. These samples enable us to construct an approximate sampling distribution of the estimator we are examining. While the result is only specific in the sense that it applies solely to the specific population (characterized by specific parameters) with which we are experimenting, we usually hope to be able to generalize our results at least within a certain range. Such generalizations can be tested by further experiments on populations with different parameter values. The *theoretical derivation* of sampling distributions uses probability theory; instead of physically drawing a large number of samples as in the experimental approach, we can find what would happen without actually doing it. Thus, theory may save us a lot of work, which is a great advantage. Another advantage is that theory is more precise: while in experiments we can never produce an infinite number of samples, in theory the concept of infinity may be handled quite easily. And last but not least, in contrast to the experimental method, the results of theoretical derivation are quite general, at least within some well-defined boundaries. Theoretical derivation of sampling distribution is thus clearly superior to the experimental derivation. Its only drawback is that

we may not always be able to manage it. The problem is sometimes so complicated that our knowledge is simply insufficient to deal with it. This has been
particularly the case with estimation problems in modern econometrics, as will
be demonstrated in the discussion of simultaneous economic relations.

The experimental approach will be used in the next chapter to derive the
sampling distributions of two common estimators. Our reason for doing so is
not, in this case, the difficulty of implementing the laws of probability. Rather,
our intention is to familiarize the student with the concept of sampling distribution as much as possible. By first giving the theory a physical content provided
by our experiments, we hope to make the idea much clearer. The theoretical
approach to the same problem will also be demonstrated and compared with
the experimental approach; however, we will need to introduce the basic tools
provided by probability theory before attempting a theoretical derivation.

EXERCISES

In the exposition of the basic principles of statistical inference, we assume that
the reader has a working knowledge of basic algebra. The short questions in Exercises 1–1 through 1–8 are designed to check the validity of this assumption.

1–1. Sketch the graphs of the following functions:

a. $y = x + 1.$ **b.** $y = \sqrt{x}.$ **c.** $\log y = \frac{1}{2} \log x.$

1–2. Solve for x and y:

$$ax + by = b^2 \qquad \text{and} \qquad x + y = a.$$

1–3. Simplify the following expressions:

a. $\dfrac{x^5}{x^2}.$ **b.** $\sqrt[3]{x^6}.$ **c.** $\dfrac{(x/y) - (y/x)}{(x - y)/(x + y)}.$

1–4. What is $\sum_{i=1}^{5} x_i$ if

a. $x_i = i.$ **b.** $x_i = 1 + 2i.$ **c.** $x_i = 2^{i-1}.$

1–5. Solve the following equation: $x^2 - 5x + 6 = 0.$

1–6. Find the maximum value of y given that:

$$y = 1 + 2x - x^2.$$

1–7. Derive the first and second derivatives of y for:

a. $y = (x + a)^2.$ **b.** $y = \sqrt{x}.$ **c.** $y = \dfrac{a - x}{b - x}.$

1–8. Let $x > 0$ and $y > 0$. Prove that

$$(x/y + y/x) > 2.$$

In our exposition we also assume that the reader is familiar with the basic concept of descriptive statistics. Exercises 1–9 through 1–12 provide practice in this respect. (Note that an outline of basic algebra of summations is given in Appendix A.)

1–9. The sum of ten numbers $x_1, x_2, \ldots, x_{10}$ is 60, and the sum of their squares is 396. Find the following:

a. The arithmetic mean $\bar{x}$.

b. The standard deviation of x, say, s (using 10 as the denominator).

c. $\displaystyle\sum_{i=1}^{10} (x_i - \bar{x})/s.$ **d.** $\displaystyle\sum_{i=1}^{10} 2(x_i - 5).$

e. The arithmetic mean of z_i, where $z_i = x_i - (x_i - \bar{x})/s$.

1–10. Draw a rough sketch of each of the frequency distributions characterized as follows:

a. The frequency is the same for all values of the variables.
b. The variable assumes the same value at each observation.
c. The distance between the upper quartile and the median is twice as long as the distance between the lower quartile and the median.
d. The value of the standard deviation is zero.
e. The value of the arithmetic mean is smaller than that of the mode.

1–11. Suppose we wish to determine the mean age in a specified population of individuals. Suppose further that in the census one quarter of the individuals underestimate their ages by one year, one half give their correct ages, and one quarter overestimate their ages by two years. Determine the relationship between the true mean age and the mean age obtained from the census.

1–12. The percentage frequency distributions of industrial workers by the amount of monthly wages in the Soviet Union in the years 1929 and 1934, that is, before and after the wage reform of 1931–1933, are given in Table 1–3.[1] A claim was made that

> "the wages of the lower-paid groups increased most and of the medium-paid groups the least. Although the difference between the wages of the lower-paid workers and the wages of the medium-paid workers lessened somewhat, the gap between the wages of the medium- and higher-paid workers increased."[1]

Check whether the data support this claim.

---

[1] A. Aganbegian, "Methods of Analyzing and Calculating the Distribution of Workers and Employees by the Amount of Wages," *Problems of Economics*, Vol. 3, October 1960, p. 24.

(coffee-drinkers) and the white ones failures. We conduct two experiments with this population. In the first experiment we draw 100 samples of size 4, and in the second experiment 100 samples of size 16. Note that in each experiment we use 100 samples as our approximation of an infinite number of samples, and thus our results will contain errors of approximation. These errors could be decreased by making the number of samples larger if one should so desire. For our purposes the degree of approximation given by 100 samples is sufficient. In describing the results we shall use the following notation:

π = proportion of successes in the population;

$\hat{\pi}$ = proportion of successes in the sample (an estimator of π);

f = relative frequency;

n = size of sample.

In our experiments, $\hat{\pi}$ will assume 100 values, one for each sample. Note that in our population $\pi = 0.7$.

EXPERIMENT A.1: 100 samples of size 4.   Here $n = 4$, so that each sample may give only 1 of 5 possible results (no success, one success, etc.). These results are described in Table 2–1 and Figure 2–1. The last column of Table 2–1 gives the

Table 2–1

Successes		Frequency	
Number	Proportion: $\hat{\pi}$	Absolute	Relative: f
0	0.00	1	0.01
1	0.25	6	0.06
2	0.50	28	0.28
3	0.75	42	0.42
4	1.00	23	0.23
		100	1.00

frequencies that approximate the sampling distribution in question. The main characteristics of this sampling distribution are

$$\text{Mean} = \sum_{i=0}^{4} f_i \hat{\pi}_i = 0.01 \times 0 + 0.06 \times 0.25 + 0.28 \times 0.50$$
$$+ 0.42 \times 0.75 + 0.23 \times 1.00 = 0.700.$$

$$\text{Standard deviation} = \sqrt{\sum_{i=0}^{4} f_i(\hat{\pi}_i - 0.7)^2} = 0.2233.$$

Table 1–3

Monthly Wages, Rubles	March 1929	October 1934
Under 30	2.3	0.0
30 to 49	15.2	0.8
50 to 69	23.6	2.6
70 to 89	21.1	7.9
90 to 109	15.0	12.7
110 to 129	9.4	14.3
130 to 149	5.8	13.3
150 to 169	1.8	10.6
170 to 199	4.1	11.9
200 to 249	1.3	12.0
250 to 299	0.4	6.6
300 and over	0.0	7.3
	100.0	100.0

2 Experimental Derivation of Sampling Distributions

Sampling distribution of an estimator can be viewed as a relative frequency distribution of the values of the estimator obtained from an infinite number of random samples, each sample being of the same size and drawn from the same population. We can do this experimentally as follows. First we create our own population with certain given characteristics, i.e., parameters. Next we choose the parameter to be estimated and the formula for its estimation from the information provided by the sample. Then we draw a large number of random samples of equal size and from each sample calculate the value of the estimator. Finally, we analyze the results in the form of a relative frequency distribution. This will be an approximation of the sampling distribution of the given estimator. We say "an approximation" because we have only a finite, although large, number of samples, while a proper sampling distribution is based upon an infinite number of samples.

The problem of creating or simulating a population is generally a very simple one. For one thing, some populations do not need to exist physically before we start drawing samples. An example would be the population of all possible outcomes of some chance mechanism such as the population of all outcomes of a toss of a coin. Suppose we wish to estimate the probability of getting a head and use as an estimator the proportion of heads in, say, 30 tosses. Then we may take a coin with known probability of getting a head (e.g., an unbiased coin for which the probability of getting a head is one half), toss it 30 times, and record the result. By repeating this a large number of times we should be able to construct a reasonable approximation of the sampling distribution of the proportion of heads in samples of size 30. In the case of other populations, it may be necessary to have a physical representation of each unit before drawing samples. Thus, for instance, the population of United States families may be represented by cards bearing relevant information, one card for each family. A random sample of families would then be given by a random sample of cards.

In this chapter we consider experimental derivation of sampling distributions in two simple cases. In case A we consider sampling of attributes. In particular, we would like to estimate the proportion of people (objects, outcomes, etc.) possessing a certain attribute and to use the proportion found in the sample as

our estimator. Then our task is to derive the sampling distribution of this [esti]mator. To make the case more concrete, we may envision it as a proble[m] estimating the proportion of coffee-drinkers in a given population. In case [B we] shall be concerned with sampling of a (nonbinary) variable. Here we will w[ish] to derive the sampling distribution of sample mean as an estimator of populat[ion] mean. As an illustrative interpretation, we may think of a variable describi[ng] the number of dental appointments for each adult per year, and consider t[he] problem of estimating the mean number of dental appointments per person i[n] the population.

The mechanical aspects of the sampling experiment to be carried out are th[e] same in both cases. We have a container with a large number of differently marked marbles representing units of the population. The container is shaken, and a number of marbles equal to the desired sample size are selected at random. The result is recorded and the marbles are put back into the container. This is repeated a large number of times. Since after each drawing the marbles are returned into the container and shaken before another drawing is made, each sample has the same chance of being chosen. A slight complication arises, however, because our population is finite (although large) and the marbles are not returned until *after* the whole sample has been collected. This means that the second marble has a slightly higher chance of being picked up than the first one, the third marble has a greater chance than the second one, and so on, since, as the number of marbles in the container decreases, the chance for each remaining marble to be selected increases. But if the population is large, the change in the probabilities is so small that it can be disregarded.

It should be noted that simulating a population by using marbles, or any other objects, to represent units of population is possible only if the variable is no[t] continuous. If the population consisted of all possible values within a certai[n] interval, we could not represent it by a collection of discrete objects. For suc[h] cases we would have to use some other ways of simulation. A device that wou[ld] go a long way toward achieving a reasonable simulation for variables with [a] finite range of values is a dial with a needle freely rotating around its cen[ter.] Other methods, particularly those relying on electronic computers, are a[lso] available. In the cases discussed here this problem does not arise since we do [not] use a continuous variable.

2–1 Sampling Distribution of Sample Proportions of Successes

Let us consider the proportion of successes (e.g., coffee-drinkers) in the [sample] as an estimator of the proportion of successes in the population. We wi[ll de]rive the sampling distribution of this estimator by repeated sampling. O[ur popu]lation is a container with a large number of marbles that are identica[l in every] respect except for color. In this particular population, 70% of all m[arbles are] red and 30% are white. We may envision that the red balls represe[nt]

(Note that here $\hat{\pi}_0 = 0$, $\hat{\pi}_1 = 0.25$, $\hat{\pi}_2 = 0.50$, etc., and f_0, f_1, f_2, etc., are the corresponding relative frequencies.) An examination of the derived sampling distribution shows that had we used the sample proportion of successes from sample size 4 as our estimate of the proportion of successes in the population, we would have made a serious underestimate 35% of the time $(0.01 + 0.06 + 0.28 = 0.35)$ and a serious overestimate 23% of the time, and we would have been quite close to the true value 42% of the time. These percentages are, of course, only approximate since our experience is limited to 100 samples.

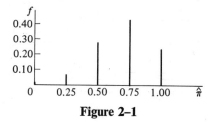

Figure 2–1

EXPERIMENT A.2: 100 samples of size 16.   Here $n = 16$, so that there are 17 different possible results. These are presented in Table 2–2 and Figure 2–2. The main characteristics of the sampling distribution in this case are

$$\text{Mean} = \sum_{i=0}^{16} f_i\hat{\pi}_i = 0.7006.$$

$$\text{Standard deviation} = \sqrt{\sum_{i=0}^{16} f_i(\hat{\pi}_i - 0.7006)^2} = 0.1191.$$

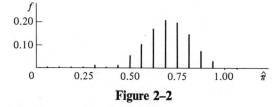

Figure 2–2

(Note that here $\hat{\pi}_0 = 0$, $\hat{\pi}_1 = 1/16$, $\hat{\pi}_2 = 2/16$, etc., and f_0, f_1, f_2, etc., are the corresponding relative frequencies.) The derived sampling distribution shows a fair concentration of estimates around the true value: 95% of all estimates lie in the interval 0.5 to 0.9, and a high percentage is in the near vicinity of the population parameter. In contrast to the previous experiment, the sample evidence never suggests that the population consists entirely of successes or of failures.

The main results of our experiments can be summarized in the following points: (i) in both experiments the mean of the sampling distribution is found to be virtually equal to the value of the population parameter; (ii) the dispersion of the sampling distribution for samples size 16 is less than that for samples size 4, the standard deviation of the former being about one half of that of the latter; and (iii) the sampling distribution for samples size 16 is considerably more symmetric than that for samples size 4.

Table 2–2

Successes		Frequency	
Number	Proportion: $\hat{\pi}$	Absolute	Relative: f
0	0.0000	0	0.00
1	0.0625	0	0.00
2	0.1250	0	0.00
3	0.1875	0	0.00
4	0.2500	0	0.00
5	0.3125	1	0.01
6	0.3750	0	0.00
7	0.4375	1	0.01
8	0.5000	5	0.05
9	0.5625	10	0.10
10	0.6250	17	0.17
11	0.6875	21	0.21
12	0.7500	20	0.20
13	0.8125	15	0.15
14	0.8750	7	0.07
15	0.9375	3	0.03
16	1.0000	0	0.00
		100	1.00

These results have been obtained by repeated sampling from a dichotomous population (i.e., a population containing only two types of individuals) with a proportion of successes equal to 0.7. Only two sampling distributions, those corresponding to samples size 4 and size 16, have been derived. But even given this specific character of our experiments, the results clearly inspire certain generalizations about the sampling distribution of the proportion of successes observed in a sample ($\hat{\pi}$) as an estimator of the proportion of successes in the population (π). These generalizations are

1. $\hat{\pi}$ is an *unbiased estimator* of π (i.e., the mean of the sampling distribution of $\hat{\pi}$ is equal to the population parameter π).
2. As sample size increases, the sampling distribution of $\hat{\pi}$ becomes increasingly more concentrated around π. This implies that $\hat{\pi}$ is a *consistent estimator* of π.
3. Sampling distribution of $\hat{\pi}$ based on larger samples tends to be more symmetric than that based on small samples.

The fourth generalization is less obvious and involves a greater degree of uncertainty than the first three. It arises in connection with generalization 2; since dispersion (or, conversely, concentration) is measured by standard deviation, we would expect some relationship between the change in sample size and the change in the standard deviation. Noting that as sample size is increased fourfold, the standard deviation is halved, we may suspect that the proposition given below also holds:

4. The standard deviation of the sampling distribution of $\hat{\pi}$ decreases with the square root of the sample size.

This final generalization appears to be more risky than the previous three. For one thing, the standard deviation for samples size 16 is only roughly equal to one half of that for sample size 4; for another thing, we only have two sample sizes (i.e., one ratio) from which we generalize. The first difficulty could be remedied by using more than 100 samples and thus sharpening the accuracy, the second by conducting further experiments.

It may have been noticed that our sampling experiment does not allow any generalizations about the efficiency of $\hat{\pi}$. While it would certainly be interesting to see whether any other unbiased estimator has a smaller variance than $\hat{\pi}$, the answer cannot be extracted from our experiments since we considered only one estimator and thus are not able to make comparisons. But even if we did consider several alternative estimators rather than just one, sampling experiments would at best settle the question of efficiency within the small class of estimators actually considered and not with respect to all (unbiased) estimators as desired.

We hope the foregoing generalizations hold for all values of the population parameter π and all sample sizes n. Whether they do or do not will be found when we derive the sampling distribution theoretically in Chapter 4.

2–2 Sampling Distribution of Sample Means

Let us now consider the problem of deriving the sampling distribution of sample mean as an estimator of the population mean. The population we are simulating is that of, say, all adults in a given geographical region, each being characterized by the number of dental appointments in a given year. Our variable X then represents the number of dental appointments by an adult in a year. To simplify the construction of the population we will postulate that X can only assume the values $0, 1, 2, \ldots, 9$, and that each of these values can be observed with equal probability. Such a distribution of values is called a *discrete uniform distribution*. This population is simulated by a container with a large number of marbles that are identical in every respect except for a numeral embossed in the surface. The numerals are $0, 1, 2, \ldots, 9$, and the container includes an equal number of marbles of each denomination. A more elaborate description of the population is given in Table 2–3.

As in case A, we will again conduct two sampling experiments. In the first experiment, we will draw 100 samples of size 5 and derive the sampling distribution of sample mean. To get some idea about its efficiency we will also derive the sampling distribution of an alternative estimator, namely sample median. Thus each sample will be used for producing two estimates of the population mean.

Table 2–3

Value of X	Relative Frequency in the Population	
0	0.1	
1	0.1	
2	0.1	
3	0.1	Population mean: $\mu = 4.5$.
4	0.1	Population standard deviation:
5	0.1	$\sigma = 2.8723$.
6	0.1	
7	0.1	
8	0.1	
9	0.1	
	────	
	1.0	

In the second experiment, we will draw 100 samples of size 10 and derive the distribution of sample mean. As in the experiments in connection with case A, we will again be satisfied with approximating infinity by a mere 100 samples. In describing the results, the following notation will be used:

μ = population mean;

σ = population standard deviation;

$\bar{X}$ = sample mean;

$\tilde{X}$ = sample median;

f = relative frequency;

n = size of sample.

EXPERIMENT B.1 100 samples of size 5. Let us first consider the sampling distribution of sample mean, which is the focal point of our interest. Obviously, even though the variable (and thus individual observations) can assume only integer values 0 to 9, sample means will, in general, not be integers. Thus the sampling distribution will be a frequency distribution with classes defined by intervals and not by points. We may, of course, choose a single value such as the center of each interval to represent each class. The distribution obtained as a result of our experiment is shown in Table 2–4 and illustrated by Figure 2–3.

Table 2–4

Value of Sample Mean: $\bar{X}$		Frequency	
Interval	Midpoint	Absolute	Relative: f
0.5 to 1.499	1	1	0.01
1.5 to 2.499	2	5	0.05
2.5 to 3.499	3	12	0.12
3.5 to 4.499	4	31	0.31
4.5 to 5.499	5	28	0.28
5.5 to 6.499	6	15	0.15
6.5 to 7.499	7	5	0.05
7.5 to 8.499	8	3	0.03
8.5 to 9.499	9	0	0.00
		100	1.00

The main characteristics of this distribution are

$$\text{Mean} = \sum_{i=1}^{9} f_i \bar{x}_i = 4.60.$$

$$\text{Standard deviation} = \sqrt{\sum_{i=1}^{9} f_i(\bar{x}_i - 4.60)^2} = 1.3638.$$

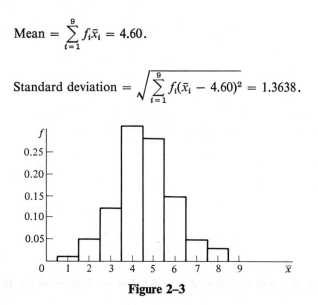

Figure 2–3

The results indicate that 59% of the estimated values $(0.31 + 0.28 = 0.59)$ fall within ± 1 of the true value of 4.5, while 86% of the estimates lie within ± 2 of 4.5.

Next we present the derived sampling distribution of sample median. Since the sample size is an odd number, sample median will always be an integer. The distribution is given in Table 2–5. The main characteristics of this distribution are

$$\text{Mean} = \sum_{i=0}^{9} f_i \tilde{x}_i = 4.68.$$

$$\text{Standard deviation} = \sqrt{\sum_{i=0}^{9} f_i(\tilde{x}_i - 4.68)^2} = 1.8758.$$

Table 2–5

Value of Sample Median: $\tilde{X}$	Frequency	
	Absolute	Relative: f
0	1	0.01
1	4	0.04
2	4	0.04
3	19	0.19
4	23	0.23
5	14	0.14
6	17	0.17
7	11	0.11
8	5	0.05
9	2	0.02
	100	1.00

The distribution is shown graphically in Figure 2–4. To facilitate a comparison with the sampling distribution of sample mean, we reproduce the distribution of

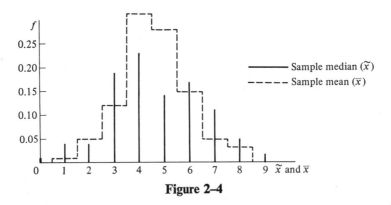

Figure 2–4

Figure 2–3 on the same diagram with dotted lines. It is obvious at first sight that the two distributions are quite different, that of $\tilde{X}$ being much less regular and considerably more dispersed than that of $\bar{X}$.

EXPERIMENT B.2 100 samples of size 10. The results of this experiment are summarized in Table 2–6 and Figure 2–5. The main characteristics of this distribution are

$$\text{Mean} = \sum_{i=2}^{7} f_i \bar{x}_i = 4.57.$$

$$\text{Standard deviation} = \sqrt{\sum_{i=2}^{7} f_i(\bar{x}_i - 4.57)^2} = 1.0416.$$

Table 2–6

Value of Sample Mean: $\tilde{X}$		Frequency	
Interval	Midpoint	Absolute	Relative: f
0.5 to 1.499	1	0	0.00
1.5 to 2.499	2	1	0.01
2.5 to 3.499	3	14	0.14
3.5 to 4.499	4	34	0.34
4.5 to 5.499	5	32	0.32
5.5 to 6.499	6	16	0.16
6.5 to 7.499	7	3	0.03
7.5 to 8.499	8	0	0.00
8.5 to 9.499	9	0	0.00
		100	1.00

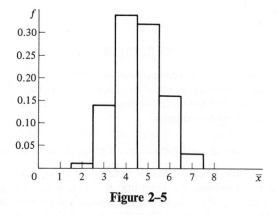

Figure 2–5

The results of our sampling experiments in case B can be summarized as follows: (i) the mean of the sampling distribution of sample mean is approximately equal to the population mean for both sample sizes examined; (ii) the dispersion of the sampling distribution of sample mean for samples size 10 is less than that for samples size 5, the variance of the latter (1.3638^2) being almost twice as large as that of the former (1.0416^2); and (iii) the mean of the sampling distribution of sample median is also approximately equal to the population mean, but its variation is greater than that of the sample mean in samples of equal size.

These results, although based on a specific case, obviously inspire some generalizations:

1. Sample mean $\bar{X}$ is an *unbiased estimator* of the population mean μ.
2. As sample size increases, the sampling distribution of $\bar{X}$ becomes increasingly more concentrated around the population mean; thus $\bar{X}$ is a *consistent estimator* of μ.
3. Sample median $\tilde{X}$ is an unbiased estimator of μ, but its variance is greater than that of $\bar{X}$; thus $\tilde{X}$ is an inefficient estimator of μ.

These generalizations follow quite obviously from the main findings of our experiments. The next generalization is less obvious and somewhat more risky.

4. The standard deviation of the sampling distribution of $\bar{X}$ decreases with the square root of sample size.

Generalization 4 is borne out by our experiment only very roughly; it means that we consider $1.3638 \div 1.0416 = 1.3093$ as "approximately equal" to $\sqrt{2} = 1.4142$.

These four generalizations will be considered again when we discuss theoretical derivations of sampling distributions. For the time being we will hold them only tentatively and hope to be able to confirm or refute them later. Before we do that, we have to master the basic tools of probability theory, and this is the subject of Chapter 3.

EXERCISES

2–1. Using 100 samples, construct experimental sampling distributions of the proportion of heads for samples of 4 and of 16 tosses of a coin. Calculate the mean and the standard deviation of both distributions, and compare the results with those presented under case A of this chapter.

2–2. Consider a population consisting of equal proportions of numbers 1, 2, and 3.

a. Construct all possible samples of size 3, noting that the relative frequency of each sample is the same. Describe the resulting distribution of sample mean and of sample median. Calculate the means and the standard deviations of the two distributions. (HINT: There are 27 different samples of size 3 that can be drawn from this population.)

b. Do the same for samples of size 4. Compare the ratio of the standard deviation of the mean to the standard deviation of the median with the corresponding ratio obtained in **a** above.

2–3. Call getting two heads and a tail in tossing three coins of equal denominations a "success." Make 10 such tosses and record the number of successes. Repeat this 100 times, each time making 10 tosses and recording the number of successes.

a. Present the resulting sampling distribution.

b. Calculate the mean and the standard deviation of the proportion of successes.

2–4. Using the table of random normal deviates provided in Appendix D, construct an empirical sampling distribution of sample mean for samples of size 5 drawn from a normal population.

3 | Probability and Probability Distributions

In spite of the fact that probability is a concept which is frequently used in many branches of science as well as in everyday life, the term itself is very difficult to define and is surrounded by controversy. We will mention the main points of view and illustrate the nature of the difficulties. According to the so-called *classical* view, the probability of a favorable outcome is given by the ratio f/n where n is the number of all possible mutually exclusive and equally likely outcomes and f is the number of those outcomes which are taken as favorable. Two outcomes are mutually exclusive if the occurrence of one rules out the occurrence of the other; for example, the appearance of a head when tossing a coin rules out the appearance of a tail in the same toss. Furthermore, outcomes are "equally likely" if it is expected a priori that each outcome would occur with equal frequency in the long run. Thus the probability of getting a 3 when tossing a fair six-sided die is 1/6 since there are six possible outcomes and, assuming that the die is fair, they are all equally likely. As another example, consider the probability of getting two heads as a result of tossing two unbiased coins. The possible outcomes are

1st Coin	2nd Coin
H	H
H	T
T	H
T	T

Thus there are four (not three!) possible and equally likely outcomes, and the probability of getting two heads is then 1/4. Note that this definition of probability may easily be adapted to continuous cases as well. Consider, for example, a clock dial without the clock and with only one freely rotating hand. Here there is an infinite number of points at which the hand may stop after being rotated. Since a point has no dimension and, in particular, no length, the probability that the hand stops at any specific point is zero. However, any interval (unlike a point) has a nonzero length, and thus the probability that the hand will stop within any interval is positive and can be determined. The probability definition given above is rephrased in terms of length (volume, etc.) instead of numbers; for example, in our illustration the probability that the hand stops between the 10th and the 12th minute is 1/30.

There are two major difficulties associated with the use of the classical definition of probability. The first arises from the crucial dependence of the definition on the assumption that all outcomes are equally likely. If we were asked what is the probability of throwing a head when the coin is biased in an unspecified way, we would not be able to answer. The second difficulty is similar. There exist some events for which it is impossible—with our present knowledge—to derive prior probabilities. Examples are given by mortality tables, labor force participation rates, income changes, and many others. Both of these difficulties are due to the fact that the classical definition relies on prior analysis. In fact, probabilities determined by using the classical definition are sometimes called "prior probabilities" to emphasize their theoretical nature.

The difficulties associated with the classical view of probability are avoided if we adopt the *objectivistic* or *frequency* concept of probability. This view of probability represents a newer development in probability theory; it defines probabilities as the limits of relative frequencies as the number of observations approaches infinity. The relative frequencies in a large number of trials can be used as approximations of probabilities. Thus, if we were to toss an unbiased coin a large number of times, we would notice that the proportion (i.e., relative frequency) of heads tends to become stable and close to 1/2. In this objectivistic view, probabilities are considered as empirically determined; thus they are sometimes labeled "positive probabilities." The difficulty with this view is its dependence on observations; since infinity can never be observed, empirically determined probabilities are necessarily only approximations of the limiting values. Another difficulty is that in some cases the relative frequency may not approach a limiting value.

A third approach to defining probability is one which considers probability as the *degree of rational belief*. This definition covers frequently made or implied probability statements which cannot be justified by the use of either classical or frequency definitions of probability. We are here referring to cases in which it is impossible to count (or measure) favorable as well all possible outcomes. Examples are such statements as "I am almost certain that I will fail the examination tomorrow" or "It is quite probable that we will never know the full truth about the death of President Kennedy." In none of these examples is it possible to use well-defined theory for the development of prior probabilities or to conceive of natural repetitions to obtain probabilities *a posteriori*.

The diversity of views on probability may appear somewhat bewildering, but, fortunately, it causes relatively little difficulty in practice. In part, this is because quite often the specific probability given to an event is the same from all viewpoints. For example, if a respectable person produces a normal-looking coin, the probability of getting a head would be considered as 1/2 regardless of which definition of probability one uses. In cases of disagreement (or where the classical definition fails to give an answer) one can use the frequency interpretation of probability, which is precisely what we shall do.

3–1   Sets and Sample Spaces

The elements of probability theory can be developed rather conveniently with the help of simple *set theory*. This seems desirable also because the language of set theory has acquired great popularity in modern statistics and to some extent in economics as well. A *set* is a collection of definite and well-distinguished objects (members, elements). For example, a set may be three numbers 1, 2, and 3; then we write

$$S = \{1, 2, 3\}.$$

But note that a set for five numbers 1, 2, 2, 3, 3 is also

$$S = \{1, 2, 3\}$$

since only three of the five numbers are well distinguished. Also note that the order in which the elements are listed does not matter. A set can be specified either by listing all its elements, or by giving a rule which would enable us to decide whether any given object does or does not belong to it. Thus we can conceive of a rule to define a set of all families in the United States at a given time instead of having a full list. A *null*, or an *empty set*, is one with no elements in it; we write

$$S = \varnothing.$$

If element a belongs to the set S, we write

$$a \in S;$$

if it does not, then

$$a \notin S.$$

If every element in S_1 is an element of S, then S_1 is a *subset* of S. This is expressed by

$$S_1 \subseteq S.$$

For example, if $S_1 = \{1\}$ and $S = \{1, 2, 3\}$, then $S_1 \subseteq S$. S_1 is a *proper subset* of of S if S contains at least one element not in S_1; this can be written as

$$S_1 \subset S.$$

If $S_1 = \{1\}$ and $S = \{1, 2, 3\}$, then S_1 is a proper subset of S. As an example of the logic and set construction consider the statement

$$\varnothing \subseteq S.$$

This must be true because if it were not true then $\varnothing$ would have at least one element not in S; but $\varnothing$ has no elements, thus the statement must hold. Further, if $S \neq \varnothing$, then S contains at least one element not in $\varnothing$, so $\varnothing$ must be a proper subset of S, i.e., $\varnothing \subset S$.

Let us now define two concepts that are of particular relevance to probability theory. The first of these is the *union of sets*. The union of two sets S_1 and S_2 is defined as the set of elements that belong either to S_1 or to S_2, or to both. If we denote by S the set that is the union of S_1 and S_2, then we can write

$$S = S_1 \cup S_2.$$

For example, if $S_1 = \{a, b, c, 2\}$ and $S_2 = \{1, 2, 3\}$, then $S = S_1 \cup S_2 = \{a, b, c, 1, 2, 3\}$. A diagrammatic representation of the concept is given in Figure 3–1. The other concept of importance in probability theory is that of

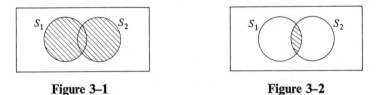

Figure 3–1   **Figure 3–2**

intersection of sets. The intersection of two sets S_1 and S_2 is the set of elements that belong to both S_1 and S_2. If such a set is denoted by S, then we have

$$S = S_1 \cap S_2.$$

For example, if $S_1 = \{a, b, c, 2\}$ and $S_2 = \{1, 2, 3\}$, then $S = S_1 \cap S_2 = \{2\}$. Figure 3–2 illustrates this concept diagrammatically.

The algebra of sets is based upon a few basic postulates or laws. These postulates include, among others, the so-called *commutative* and *associative laws*. Consider the sets $S_1, S_2, S_3, \ldots$, all of which are subsets of some set S. Then the commutative law states:

$$S_1 \cup S_2 = S_2 \cup S_1.$$

$$S_1 \cap S_2 = S_2 \cap S_1.$$

The associative law gives the following:

$$(S_1 \cup S_2) \cup S_3 = S_1 \cup (S_2 \cup S_3),$$

$$(S_1 \cap S_2) \cap S_3 = S_1 \cap (S_2 \cap S_3).$$

These laws allow us to extend the definitions of the union and of the intersection of sets to cover more than two sets.

The most important set in probability and sampling theory is called *sample space*. This is a set whose elements represent all possible well-distinguished outcomes of an experiment (where the experiment may either have been conducted by design or have happened naturally). Thus the sample space corresponding to the experiment of tossing a coin consists of two elements, viz. $\{H, T\}$, the sample space corresponding to the experiment of tossing a die consists of six elements, viz. $\{1, 2, 3, 4, 5, 6\}$; and so on. A sample space that consists of a finite number of elements (or an infinite number but with elements that can be counted) is called a *discrete sample space*. Any other sample space is a *continuous* one. It should be noted that the sample space corresponding to an experiment need not be unique. That is, two or more different sample spaces may refer to the same experiment. Suppose, for example, that the experiment consists of tossing two coins. One sample space corresponding to this experiment is

{no head, one head, two heads},

and another is

{head on both coins, tail on both coins, head on first coin and tail
on second coin, tail on first coin and head on second coin}.

The difference between the first and the second sample space is that one element of the first sample space (one head) is further subdivided into two elements in the second set. In general, it is desirable to use sample spaces whose elements cannot be further subdivided. Finally, in connection with discrete sample spaces, note that an *event* is simply a subset of the sample space.

3–2   Permutations and Combinations

A discrete sample space can be defined, and its elements counted, by making out a complete list. Alternatively, we may develop counting formulas that will simplify this task, particularly where there is a larger number of elements involved. These counting formulas refer to the number of *permutations* and *combinations* of various outcomes; they will be of particular use in the theoretical derivation of sampling distributions when we deal with attributes.

Let us consider permutations first. By a *permutation* we mean an arrangement of objects in a definite order. We are concerned with finding the number of permutations that can be formed using the elements of a given set. Consider, for example, the set $\{A, B, C\}$. In this set there are three types of permutations possible: those consisting of one element, those consisting of two elements, and those consisting of three elements. The complete enumeration is as follows:

1. Possible permutations of *one* element: A, B, C (i.e., three in number).
2. Possible permutations of *two* elements: AB, BA, AC, CA, BC, CB (i.e., six in number).
3. Possible permutations of *three* elements: $ABC, BAC, ACB, CAB, BCA, CBA$ (i.e., six in number).

Next consider the general case of a set with n elements $\{A, B, \ldots, Z\}$.

1. Possible permutations of *one* element: $A, B, \ldots, Z$. There are obviously n of these.
2. Possible permutations of *two* elements: $AB, BA, AC, CA, \ldots, AZ,$

$ZA, BC, CB, \ldots, YZ, ZY$. The construction of these two-element permutations can be shown explicitly as follows:

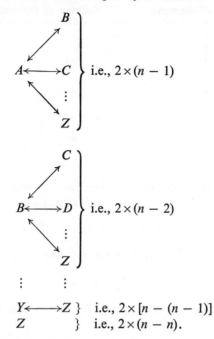

$$\left.\begin{array}{c} B \\ \nearrow \\ A \longleftrightarrow C \\ \vdots \\ Z \end{array}\right\} \quad \text{i.e., } 2 \times (n-1)$$

$$\left.\begin{array}{c} C \\ \nearrow \\ B \longleftrightarrow D \\ \vdots \\ Z \end{array}\right\} \quad \text{i.e., } 2 \times (n-2)$$

$$\vdots \qquad \vdots$$

$$\begin{array}{ll} Y \longleftrightarrow Z \;\} & \text{i.e., } 2 \times [n - (n-1)] \\ Z \qquad\quad \} & \text{i.e., } 2 \times (n-n). \end{array}$$

(The two-way arrows indicate that the associations go both ways; e.g., $A \leftrightarrow B$ stands for *AB as well as BA*.) The sum total of these permutations is

$$2[(n-1) + (n-2) + \cdots + 2 + 1]$$

$$= 2\left[\left(\frac{n-1}{2}\right)n\right] = n(n-1).$$

This result could also be obtained by noting that in the case of two-element permutations each of the n elements gets associated with the remaining $(n-1)$ elements. Since there are altogether n elements, the total must be $n(n-1)$.

3. Possible permutations of *three* elements: $ABC, BAC, ADC, DAC,$ $\ldots, AZX, ZAX, BCA, CBA, \ldots, YZX, ZYX$. That is, each of the $n(n-1)$ permutations obtained in 2 gets associated with the remaining $(n-2)$ elements of the set. The sum total is, therefore, $n(n-1)(n-2)$.

This could be continued but the answers should be quite obvious by now. They can be summarized in Table 3–1. Let us denote by $_nP_r$ the number of permutations of r distinct elements selected from a set of n elements. Then from the formula for permutations of r elements, listed in Table 3–1, we have

$$_nP_r = n(n-1)(n-2)\cdots(n-r+1).$$

Table 3–1

Number of Elements	Number of Permutations
1	n
2	$n(n-1)$
3	$n(n-1)(n-2)$
$\vdots$	$\vdots$
r	$n(n-1)(n-2)\cdots(n-r+1)$
$\vdots$	$\vdots$
$(n-1)$	$n(n-1)(n-2)\cdots2$
n	$n(n-1)(n-2)\cdots2\times1$

This expression can be simplified by using the so-called factorial notation. A *factorial* of a number n is denoted by $n!$ and defined as

$$n! = n(n-1)(n-2)\cdots3\times2\times1,$$

where n can be any positive integer. We also define

$$0! = 1.$$

When we use these symbols, the formula for the number of permutations becomes

(3.1)
$$_nP_r = \frac{n!}{(n-r)!}.$$

The following points are worth noting:

1. $_nP_0 = 1$, i.e., there is only one way in which an empty set can be arranged.
2. Suppose we have n objects of which k objects are exactly the same. Then

(3.2)
$$_nP_n^{(k)} = \frac{n!}{k!}.$$

For example, consider the number of permutations of the four letters in the word POOH:

POOH HPOO OPHO
POHO HOPO OPOH
PHOO HOOP OHPO   Total = 12.
                OHOP
                OOHP
                OOPH

$$_4P_4^{(2)} = \frac{4!}{2!} = \frac{4\times3\times2\times1}{2\times1} = 12.$$

This result can be extended to the case of n objects of which k are of one kind (and all are exactly the same), ℓ are of another kind, etc. Then

(3.3) $$_nP_n^{(k,\ell,\dots)} = \frac{n!}{k!\ell!\cdots}.$$

3. If one set of objects can be arranged in m_1 ways and another set of objects in m_2 ways, then the total number of permutations is $m_1 \times m_2$. This is sometimes known as the *multiplication principle*.

As an example of the multiplication principle, consider the number of permutations given by the outcomes of tossing two coins. Here m_1 is the number of permutations given by the possible outcomes of tossing the first coin (H and T) and is equal to 2, and m_2 refers to the outcomes of tossing the second coin and is also equal to 2. Thus, the total number of permutations is $2 \times 2 = 4$. This can be easily verified: the possible outcomes of tossing two coins are HH, HT, TH, TT, i.e., four in number. As another example, consider the number of permutations given by the outcomes of tossing two six-sided dice. In this case, $m_1 = 6$ and $m_2 = 6$, so that the total number is 36.

All permutations that involve the same elements represent a given combination. More precisely, a *combination* is a subset of r elements selected, without regard to their order, from a set of n different elements. It is assumed that $n \geq r$. Consider the set $\{A, B, C\}$. From the elements of this set we can form combinations of one, two, or three elements. These are as follows.

1. Combinations of *one* element: $\{A\}$, $\{B\}$, $\{C\}$ (i.e., three in number).
2. Combinations of *two* elements: $\{A, B\}$, $\{A, C\}$, $\{B, C\}$ (i.e., three in number).
3. Combinations of *three* elements: $\{A, B, C\}$ (i.e., *one* in number).

Next consider the general case of n elements $\{A, B, C, \dots, Z\}$.

1. Combinations of *one* element: $\{A\}$, $\{B\}, \dots, \{Z\}$. These are n in number.
2. Combinations of *two* elements: $\{A, B\}$, $\{A, C\}, \dots, \{X, Z\}$. These can be depicted as follows:

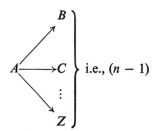

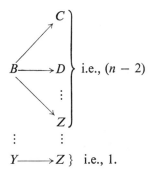

$$Y \longrightarrow Z \} \text{ i.e., 1.}$$

The total is

$$(n - 1) + (n - 2) + \cdots + 1 = \frac{1}{2}n(n - 1) = \frac{1}{2}{}_nP_2.$$

This result could also be obtained by noting that any two-letter combination leads to two permutations. Thus all we have to do to get the total number of two-letter combinations is to divide the total number of two-letter permutations by two.

3. Combinations of *three* elements: $\{A, B, C\}, \{A, B, D\}, \ldots, \{X, Y, Z\}$. Since any three-letter combination leads to $3! = 6$ permutations, the total number of three-letter combinations is

$$\frac{1}{6}{}_nP_3 = \frac{n(n - 1)(n - 2)}{3!}.$$

This could be continued for any number of elements; the results are summarized in Table 3–2. The number of combinations of r distinct elements

Table 3–2

Number of Elements	Number of Combinations
1	n
2	$\dfrac{n(n - 1)}{2}$
3	$\dfrac{n(n - 1)(n - 2)}{3!}$
$\vdots$	
r	$\dfrac{n(n - 1) \cdots (n - r + 1)}{r!}$
$\vdots$	$\vdots$
$(n - 1)$	n
n	1

selected without regard to order from a set of n elements is usually denoted by $\binom{n}{r}$. From Table 3–2 we obviously have

(3.4)
$$\binom{n}{r} = \frac{n!}{(n - r)!r!}.$$

Note that

$$\binom{n}{0} = 1,$$

$$\binom{n}{n} = 1,$$

$$\binom{n}{r} = \binom{n}{n-r}.$$

A well-known use of the formula for the number of combinations is the determination of *binomial coefficients*. Consider the following algebraic expansions:

$$(a + b)^0 = 1,$$
$$(a + b)^1 = a + b,$$
$$(a + b)^2 = a^2 + 2ab + b^2,$$
$$(a + b)^3 = a^3 + 3a^2b + 3ab^2 + b^3,$$
$$(a + b)^4 = a^4 + 4a^3b + 6a^2b^2 + 4ab^3 + b^4,$$

and so on.

The numerical coefficients in the foregoing expansions are known as the binomial coefficients. Note that they are, in fact, given by the formula for the number of combinations, since the expansions could equivalently be written as

$$(a + b)^0 = 1,$$
$$(a + b)^1 = \binom{1}{0}a + \binom{1}{1}b,$$
$$(a + b)^2 = \binom{2}{0}a^2 + \binom{2}{1}ab + \binom{2}{2}b^2,$$
$$(a + b)^3 = \binom{3}{0}a^3 + \binom{3}{1}a^2b + \binom{3}{2}ab^2 + \binom{3}{3}b^3,$$
$$(a + b)^4 = \binom{4}{0}a^4 + \binom{4}{1}a^3b + \binom{4}{2}a^2b^2 + \binom{4}{3}ab^3 + \binom{4}{4}b^4,$$

and so on.

Generalizing we have

$$(3.5) \quad (a + b)^n = \binom{n}{0}a^n + \binom{n}{1}a^{n-1}b + \binom{n}{2}a^{n-2}b^2 + \cdots + \binom{n}{n}b^n$$

$$= \sum_{r=0}^{n} \binom{n}{r}a^{n-r}b^r.$$

An easy way of calculating the binomial coefficients is by using what is known

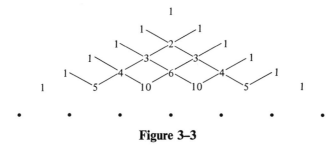

Figure 3–3

as *Pascal's triangle* (Figure 3–3). Each row begins and ends with a 1; each other number is a sum of the two neighboring numbers in the row immediately above.

The binomial formula (3.5) facilitates the determination of the total number of subsets that can be formed from a set of n distinct elements. The first subset is the null set, then there are n subsets of one element each, $n(n-1)/2$ subsets of two elements, and so on. The total number is given by the sum

$$\binom{n}{0} + \binom{n}{1} + \binom{n}{2} + \cdots + \binom{n}{n}.$$

These are the binomial coefficients for the expansion with $a = 1$ and $b = 1$, i.e.,

$$(1 + 1)^n = \binom{n}{0} + \binom{n}{1} + \binom{n}{2} + \cdots + \binom{n}{n}.$$

But, obviously,

$$(1 + 1)^n = 2^n.$$

Thus we have found that *a set of n elements has 2^n subsets.*

3–3 Basic Theorems of Probability Theory

Let us now consider the basic theorems of probability theory. Let $A, B, C, \ldots$ be events represented by subsets of a discrete sample space S and let $P(A)$, $P(B), P(C), \ldots$ be their respective probabilities. We postulate that

$$0 \le P(A) \le 1 \quad \text{for each subset } A \text{ of } S, \qquad \text{and} \qquad P(S) = 1.$$

Theorem 1   *If $\bar{A}$ is an event "not A," then $P(\bar{A}) = 1 - P(A)$.*

This, we hope, needs no elaboration. If the probability that it will rain is 0.40, then it is quite obvious that the probability that it will not rain is 0.60. Theorem 1 is represented by Figure 3–4.

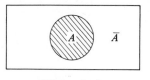

Figure 3–4

Before we proceed any further, we ought to digress in order to clarify the meaning of conditional statements of the form "if . . . , then . . ." and similar, which are frequently used in the language of theorems and proofs. Such a clarification requires that we distinguish between different types of conditions; in particular, we have to distinguish between a "necessary," a "sufficient," and a "necessary and sufficient" condition. This distinction will be illustrated by reference to two nonidentical propositions P_1 and P_2. First, take a *sufficient* condition: if P_1 is true, then P_2 is true. This is sometimes expressed as "P_1 implies P_2." Here P_1 is a sufficient condition for P_2. For instance, P_1 may be "being a mother" and P_2 "being a woman," since motherhood is obviously a sufficient condition for womanhood. Or, as another example, P_1 may be a statement "today is Tuesday" and P_2 a statement "tomorrow is Wednesday." Next, consider a *necessary* condition: if P_1 is not true, then P_2 is not true, or alternatively, P_2 is true *only if* P_1 is true. Here P_1 is a necessary condition for P_2. For instance, "being a woman" is a necessary condition for "being a mother." Note that a sufficient condition may or may not be a necessary one; similarly, a necessary condition may or may not be sufficient. An example of a sufficient but not necessary condition is "being a mother" as a condition for "being a woman," since it is possible to be a woman without being a mother. If we reverse these propositions and put "being a woman" as a condition of "being a mother," we have an example of a necessary but not sufficient condition since being a woman is not enough for being a mother. The last example illustrates a universal property of a sufficiency relation: *if P_1 is sufficient for P_2, then P_2 is necessary for P_1.* Finally, we have the case of a *necessary and sufficient condition*: if P_1, then P_2, and if P_2, then P_1. This condition is described by an "if and only if" statement. For example, "if and only if today is Tuesday, then tomorrow is Wednesday." That is, the truth of "today is Tuesday" is not only sufficient but also necessary for the truth of "tomorrow is Wednesday."

In our discussion the most frequently used conditional statement will be "if P_1, then P_2." This means that P_1 is a sufficient, but may or may not be a necessary, condition for P_2. The fact that this statement omits the clause "and only if" should not be interpreted to mean that P_1 is not a necessary condition for P_2. The omission of this clause is simply an indication that, for our purposes, the fact that P_1 is or is not a necessary condition for P_2 does not matter and thus is of no interest. Only when the condition of necessity is relevant to subsequent arguments shall we insert the "only if" qualification in the statement. With this remark we finish our digression and return to the discussion of basic theorems in probability.

Theorem 2 (*Addition Theorem*) $P(A \cup B) = P(A) + P(B) - P(A \cap B)$

This theorem states that the probability of either A or B or of both is equal to the probability of A *plus* the probability of B *minus* the probability of both A and B occurring simultaneously. It is illustrated by Figure 3–5. Because A and B overlap, the term $P(A \cap B)$ has to be deducted from the sum $P(A) + P(B)$; otherwise it would be counted twice.

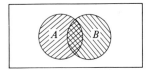

Figure 3–5

EXAMPLE 1   Consider the probability that a card drawn at random from a pack of 52 cards is either a spade or a face card. Let A = spade and B = face card. Note that

$$P(A) = \frac{13}{52} \quad \text{(since there are 13 spades in a pack),}$$

$$P(B) = \frac{12}{52} \quad \text{(since there are 12 face cards in a pack),}$$

$$P(A \cap B) = \frac{3}{52} \quad \text{(since there are 3 face cards in a suit of spades).}$$

Then

$$P(A \cup B) = \frac{13}{52} + \frac{12}{52} - \frac{3}{52} = \frac{22}{52}.$$

EXAMPLE 2   What is the probability that a toss of a six-sided die will result in a "1" or "2"?

$$P(\text{``1''} \cup \text{``2''}) = P(\text{``1''}) + P(\text{``2''}) - P(\text{``1''} \cap \text{``2''})$$

$$= \frac{1}{6} \quad + \quad \frac{1}{6} \quad - \quad 0$$

$$= \frac{1}{3}.$$

The second example brings us to the theorem that deals with the probability of mutually exclusive events already mentioned in connection with the classical definition of probability. In the language of set theory, events (i.e., subsets of the sample space) are mutually exclusive if and only if their interaction is an empty set. The theorem is as follows:

Theorem 3 *If A and B are mutually exclusive, then* $P(A \cup B) = P(A) + P(B)$.

This theorem is illustrated by Figure 3–6. It can be extended to any number of mutually exclusive events. In particular, if $A, B, C, \ldots, Z$ are all mutually exclusive, then

$$P(A \cup B \cup C \cup \ldots \cup Z) = P(A) + P(B) + P(C) + \cdots + P(Z).$$

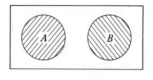

Figure 3–6

Let us now examine events that are not mutually exclusive. Consider, for example, the situation where we randomly select a person from a certain population and record two characteristics, smoking habit (S or $\bar{S}$) and sex (M or F). The two characteristics are obviously not mutually exclusive, at least not in a modern society. The sample space for this experiment is $\{(MS), (FS), (M\bar{S}), (F\bar{S})\}$, where MS represents "male smoker," etc. If the population is a finite one, the distribution may be described by absolute frequencies as follows:

		Smoking Habit		
		S	$\bar{S}$	Totals
Sex	M	a	b	$a + b$
	F	c	d	$c + d$
Totals		$a + c$	$b + d$	N

where $N = a + b + c + d$ is the population total. In terms of probabilities this distribution would be

		Smoking Habit		
		S	$\bar{S}$	
Sex	M	$P(M \cap S)$	$P(M \cap \bar{S})$	$P(M)$
	F	$P(F \cap S)$	$P(F \cap \bar{S})$	$P(F)$
		$P(S)$	$P(\bar{S})$	1

The probabilities in the body of the table, represented by intersections of sets, are called *joint probabilities*. For example, $P(M \cap S)$ is the probability that a person selected at random will be both a male and a smoker, i.e., has the two joint characteristics. The probabilities that appear in the last row and in the last column of the table are known as *marginal probabilities*. Thus, $P(M)$ gives the probability of drawing a male regardless of his smoking habits, $P(S)$ gives the probability of selecting a smoker regardless of sex, and so on. Let us see how the addition theorem given earlier works in this situation:

$$P(M \cup S) = P(M) + P(S) - P(M \cap S) = \frac{a+b}{N} + \frac{a+c}{N} - \frac{a}{N}$$

$$= \frac{a+b+c}{N} = 1 - \frac{d}{N} = 1 - P(F \cap \bar{S}).$$

That is, the probability of drawing either a male or a smoker or both is simply equal to 1 *minus* the probability of drawing a female nonsmoker (the only category not covered by $M \cup S$). Similarly,

$$P(M \cup \bar{S}) = 1 - P(F \cap S),$$

$$P(F \cup S) = 1 - P(M \cap \bar{S}),$$

$$P(F \cup \bar{S}) = 1 - P(M \cap S).$$

Suppose now that we wish to know the probability that a person of *given* sex is a smoker (nonsmoker), or that a person of *given* smoking habits is a male (female). Such probabilities are known as *conditional probabilities*, and we write them as $P(S|M)$, which we read "probability of S, given M," etc. For instance, $P(S|M)$ means that we have a male and want to know the probability that he is a smoker. This probability, in a finite population, is obviously given by the total number of male smokers divided by the total number of males. Thus we have

$$P(S|M) = \frac{a}{a+b}.$$

Similarly,

$$P(\bar{S}|M) = \frac{b}{a+b},$$

$$P(S|F) = \frac{c}{c+d},$$

$$P(\bar{S}|F) = \frac{d}{c+d},$$

$$P(M|S) = \frac{a}{a+c},$$

$$P(F|S) = \frac{c}{a+c},$$

$$P(M|\bar{S}) = \frac{b}{b+d},$$

$$P(F|\bar{S}) = \frac{d}{b+d}.$$

Note that
$$P(S|M) + P(\bar{S}|M) = 1,$$
$$P(S|F) + P(\bar{S}|F) = 1,$$

and so on.

In terms of probabilities we can write

$$P(S|M) = \frac{P(S \cap M)}{P(M)},$$

$$P(\bar{S}|M) = \frac{P(\bar{S} \cap M)}{P(M)},$$

and so on.

This applies whether the population is finite or infinite.

This discussion leads to an important theorem:

Theorem 4 (*Conditional Probability*) *If A and B are subsets of a discrete sample space and* $P(B) \neq 0$, *then* $P(A|B) = P(A \cap B)/P(B)$.

That is, the conditional probability of A, given B, is equal to the joint probability of A and B divided by the (nonzero) marginal probability of B.

The following points should be noted in connection with this theorem on conditional probability:

1. $A|B$ is *not* a set.
2. $P(A|B)$ and $P(B|A)$ are not necessarily the same. In fact, they are equal to each other if and only if $P(A) = P(B) \neq 0$.
3. By writing $P(A|B)$ we do not imply any temporal ordering between A and B. It does not matter whether B occurred prior to, simultaneously with, or after A.
4. Since the conditional probability theorem could also be written in the form $P(A \cap B) = P(A|B)[P(B)]$, it sometimes is called the *multiplication theorem*.

EXAMPLE 1

$$P(\text{face card}|\text{spade}) = \frac{3/52}{13/52} = \frac{3}{13}$$

and

$$P(\text{spade}|\text{face card}) = \frac{3/52}{12/52} = \frac{3}{12}.$$

EXAMPLE 2 Suppose we toss an unbiased coin twice. What is the probability that the outcome of the second toss is a head, given that the outcome of the first toss was a head? Let H_i stand for "head in the ith toss." Then

$$P(H_2|H_1) = \frac{P(H_1 \cap H_2)}{P(H_1)} = \frac{1/4}{1/2} = \frac{1}{2}.$$

Let us consider the second example more closely. The results show that the probability of getting a head in the second toss, given that we obtained a head in the first toss, is 1/2. But 1/2 is precisely the probability of getting a head in *any* toss, regardless of what happened in the first toss. Indeed, we should be very surprised if we got any other answer since the coin obviously has no memory. Therefore, what happened to it in the first toss is irrelevant for determining what is going to happen to it in the second toss. Such events for which the occurrence of one event in no way affects the probability of occurrence of the other event are called *independent events*. Thus, if A is independent of B, we must have

(3.6) $$P(A|B) = P(A).$$

That is, the conditional probability of A, given B, is equal to the marginal probability of A. By using the development of $P(A|B)$ given by *Theorem 4* (under the assumption that $P(B) \neq 0$, we obtain

(3.7) $$\frac{P(A \cap B)}{P(B)} = P(A).$$

If we now also assume that $P(A) \neq 0$, we can rewrite (3.7) as

(3.8) $$\frac{P(A \cap B)}{P(A)} = P(B).$$

But the left-hand side of (3.8) is nothing else than $P(B|A)$, so that we have

(3.9) $$P(B|A) = P(B).$$

That is, if A is independent of B, then B is independent of A. Equations (3.7) and (3.8) lead to the following important theorem:

Theorem 5 (*Independence*)   If $P(A) \neq 0$ and $P(B) \neq 0$, then A and B are independent if and only if $P(A \cap B) = P(A) \times P(B)$.

In other words, A and B are independent if and only if their joint probability is equal to the product of their respective marginal probabilities. The theorem can be extended to any number of events. In particular, $A, B, C, \ldots, Z$, each occurring with nonzero probability, are independent if and only if

$$P(A \cap B \cap C \cdots \cap Z) = P(A) \times P(B) \times P(C) \times \cdots \times P(Z).$$

EXAMPLE 1   Suppose we toss two six-sided dice. What is the probability that one die will show an even and the other an odd number? Let E = even number and O = odd number. Then $P(E) = 1/2$, $P(O) = 1/2$. $P(E \cap O) = 1/2 \times 1/2 = 1/4$.

EXAMPLE 2   What is the probability of getting three heads in three tosses of an unbiased coin?

$$P(H_1 \cap H_2 \cap H_3) = P(H_1) \times P(H_2) \times P(H_3) = \frac{1}{2} \times \frac{1}{2} \times \frac{1}{2} = \frac{1}{8}.$$

EXAMPLE 3   Suppose smoking habits are independent of sex, i.e., $P(M \cap S) = P(M) \times P(S)$. Does this necessarily imply that $P(F \cap \bar{S}) = P(F) \times P(\bar{S})$? We have

	S	$\bar{S}$	
M	$P(M)P(S)$	$P(M \cap \bar{S})$	$P(M)$
F	$P(F \cap S)$	$P(F \cap \bar{S})$	$P(F)$
	$P(S)$	$P(\bar{S})$	1

Now,

$$P(F \cap S) = P(S) - P(M)P(S) = P(S)[1 - P(M)] = P(S)P(F)$$

and

$$P(F \cap \bar{S}) = P(F) - P(F \cap S) = P(F) - P(F)P(S)$$
$$= P(F)[1 - P(S)] = P(F)P(\bar{S}).$$

The answer, then, is yes.

Those not well versed in probability theory often tend to confuse the applicability of the addition theorem for mutually exclusive events with the applicability of the multiplication theorem for independent events. The confusion is due to the failure of distinguishing $P(A \cup B)$ (i.e., probability that *either A or B*

$$P(A \cup B) \qquad\qquad P(A \cap B)$$

Figure 3–7

or *both A and B* will occur) from $P(A \cap B)$ (i.e., probability that *both A* and *B* will occur) (see Figure 3–7). Now if A and B are mutually exclusive, then

(3.10) $P(A \cap B) = 0,$

as implied by *Theorem 3* and illustrated by Figure 3–6. For A and B to be independent we require that

(3.11) $P(A \cap B) = P(A) \times P(B)$

But Equations (3.10) and (3.11) can hold simultaneously only if either $P(A)$ or $P(B)$ (or both) is equal to zero. But according to our *Theorem 5* this is ruled out. Thus, mutually exclusive events cannot be independent at the same time. This should be obvious even by much less formal reasoning. If A and B are mutually exclusive, then the occurrence of one prevents the occurrence of the other, i.e., the occurrence of A makes the probability of occurrence of B zero. However, we described independent events as those for which the occurrence of one in *no way* affects the probability of the other, and this is clearly not the case when two events are mutually exclusive. By the same reasoning it is also quite clear that independent events cannot be mutually exclusive.

3-4   Discrete Random Variables and Probability Functions

Suppose we carry out an experiment that consists of tossing two coins. The sample space associated with this experiment can be described by $S = \{TT, TH, HT, HH\}$. Each element of this sample space is associated with a given number of heads (or tails). Thus we have

Elements of Sample Space	Number of Heads
TT	0
TH	1
HT	1
HH	2

Alternatively, we could present this association as follows:

Number of Heads	Elements of Sample Space
0	*TT*
1	*TH, HT*
2	*HH*

The principle of associating the elements of a sample space with some numerical characteristic can obviously be applied quite generally to any sample space. This numerical characteristic is called a *discrete random* (or *stochastic*) *variable*. Thus a discrete random variable is a variable whose values are associated with the elements of a sample space. A common notation is to denote a random variable by a capital letter (e.g., X) and its values by small letters (e.g., x); if the values follow some ordering (e.g., a sequence of observations), the order is indicated by a subscript (e.g., x_1, x_2, etc.). In our example we associated the number of heads with the elements of the sample space, but we could have equally well chosen the proportion, rather than the number, of heads as the numerical characteristic. Obviously, either the number or the proportion of heads is a random variable.

Since a sample space consists of elements that refer to outcomes of an experiment, each element can be associated with a certain probability value. In addition, since each value of a discrete random variable is associated with (one or more) elements of the sample space, it follows that each value can be associated

Table 1–3

Monthly Wages, Rubles	March 1929	October 1934
Under 30	2.3	0.0
30 to 49	15.2	0.8
50 to 69	23.6	2.6
70 to 89	21.1	7.9
90 to 109	15.0	12.7
110 to 129	9.4	14.3
130 to 149	5.8	13.3
150 to 169	1.8	10.6
170 to 199	4.1	11.9
200 to 249	1.3	12.0
250 to 299	0.4	6.6
300 and over	0.0	7.3
	100.0	100.0

2 | Experimental Derivation of Sampling Distributions

Sampling distribution of an estimator can be viewed as a relative frequency distribution of the values of the estimator obtained from an infinite number of random samples, each sample being of the same size and drawn from the same population. We can do this experimentally as follows. First we create our own population with certain given characteristics, i.e., parameters. Next we choose the parameter to be estimated and the formula for its estimation from the information provided by the sample. Then we draw a large number of random samples of equal size and from each sample calculate the value of the estimator. Finally, we analyze the results in the form of a relative frequency distribution. This will be an approximation of the sampling distribution of the given estimator. We say "an approximation" because we have only a finite, although large, number of samples, while a proper sampling distribution is based upon an infinite number of samples.

The problem of creating or simulating a population is generally a very simple one. For one thing, some populations do not need to exist physically before we start drawing samples. An example would be the population of all possible outcomes of some chance mechanism such as the population of all outcomes of a toss of a coin. Suppose we wish to estimate the probability of getting a head and use as an estimator the proportion of heads in, say, 30 tosses. Then we may take a coin with known probability of getting a head (e.g., an unbiased coin for which the probability of getting a head is one half), toss it 30 times, and record the result. By repeating this a large number of times we should be able to construct a reasonable approximation of the sampling distribution of the proportion of heads in samples of size 30. In the case of other populations, it may be necessary to have a physical representation of each unit before drawing samples. Thus, for instance, the population of United States families may be represented by cards bearing relevant information, one card for each family. A random sample of families would then be given by a random sample of cards.

In this chapter we consider experimental derivation of sampling distributions in two simple cases. In case A we consider sampling of attributes. In particular, we would like to estimate the proportion of people (objects, outcomes, etc.) possessing a certain attribute and to use the proportion found in the sample as

our estimator. Then our task is to derive the sampling distribution of this estimator. To make the case more concrete, we may envision it as a problem of
estimating the proportion of coffee-drinkers in a given population. In case B we
shall be concerned with sampling of a (nonbinary) variable. Here we will wish
to derive the sampling distribution of sample mean as an estimator of population
mean. As an illustrative interpretation, we may think of a variable describing
the number of dental appointments for each adult per year, and consider the
problem of estimating the mean number of dental appointments per person in
the population.

Tiie mechanical aspects of the sampling experiment to be carried out are the
same in both cases. We have a container with a large number of differently
marked marbles representing units of the population. The container is shaken,
and a number of marbles equal to the desired sample size are selected at random.
The result is recorded and the marbles are put back into the container. This is
repeated a large number of times. Since after each drawing the marbles are returned into the container and shaken before another drawing is made, each
sample has the same chance of being chosen. A slight complication arises, however, because our population is finite (although large) and the marbles are not
returned until *after* the whole sample has been collected. This means that the
second marble has a slightly higher chance of being picked up than the first one,
the third marble has a greater chance than the second one, and so on, since, as
the number of marbles in the container decreases, the chance for each remaining
marble to be selected increases. But if the population is large, the change in the
probabilities is so small that it can be disregarded.

It should be noted that simulating a population by using marbles, or any other
objects, to represent units of population is possible only if the variable is not
continuous. If the population consisted of all possible values within a certain
interval, we could not represent it by a collection of discrete objects. For such
cases we would have to use some other ways of simulation. A device that would
go a long way toward achieving a reasonable simulation for variables with a
finite range of values is a dial with a needle freely rotating around its center.
Other methods, particularly those relying on electronic computers, are also
available. In the cases discussed here this problem does not arise since we do not
use a continuous variable.

2-1   Sampling Distribution of Sample Proportions of Successes

Let us consider the proportion of successes (e.g., coffee-drinkers) in the sample
as an estimator of the proportion of successes in the population. We wish to derive the sampling distribution of this estimator by repeated sampling. Our population is a container with a large number of marbles that are identical in every
respect except for color. In this particular population, 70% of all marbles are
red and 30% are white. We may envision that the red balls represent successes

Finally, the probability that X is equal to x, *given* that Y is equal to y, is known as the *conditional probability of x, given y*, and is denoted by $f(x|y)$. Similarly, the *conditional probability of y, given x*, is denoted $f(y|x)$. By applying Theorem 4 we get

$$(3.16) \qquad\qquad f(x|y) = \frac{f(x,y)}{f(y)}.$$

Using our example of drawing a card from a pack, we see that the probability of drawing, say, a Queen, *given* that the card is a Heart, is

$$f(12|1) = \frac{1/52}{13/52} = \frac{1}{13}$$

and the probability that the card is a Heart, *given* that its denomination is Queen, is

$$f(1|12) = \frac{1/52}{4/52} = \frac{1}{4}.$$

When we consider multivariate distributions, the question of dependence or independence becomes relevant. Earlier we defined independence as the condition under which the conditional probability of an event is equal to its marginal probability. Thus X and Y are independent if and only if, for all values of X and Y,

$$f(x|y) = f(x) \qquad [f(y) \neq 0]$$
and
$$f(y|x) = f(y) \qquad [f(x) \neq 0].$$

This means that for each variable the conditional and the marginal distributions are precisely the same. A further implication given by Theorem 5 is that X and Y are independent if and only if

$$(3.17) \qquad\qquad f(x,y) = f(x)f(y)$$

for all values of X and Y. This can be generalized to any number of random variables. In particular, discrete random variables $X, Y, Z, \ldots$ are considered to be independent if and only if

$$(3.18) \qquad\qquad f(x,y,z,\ldots) = f(x)f(y)f(z)\ldots$$

for all values of $X, Y, Z, \ldots$.

Consider, for example, the experiment of tossing two six-sided dice *twice*. Let X be the variable with values given by the number of dots in the first toss, and Y the variable with values given by the number of dots in the second toss. Obviously, the probabilities of various outcomes of the second toss are completely unaffected by the outcome of the first toss, and vice versa, so that X and Y are independent. Note that the (marginal) distribution of X is precisely the same as that of Y and can be found in Table 3–3. From this we find that the probability of throwing 7 twice is $(6/36) \times (6/36) = 1/36$, the probability of throwing 4 followed by 8 is $(3/36) \times (5/36) = 5/432$, and so on.

With the exception of the various examples, our discussion of probability functions in this section has been quite general. It is obvious that different experimental situations may lead to different probability distributions. When describing these distributions, it is not always necessary to write out the whole distribution as we have done in our examples; frequently we may find an algebraic formula for $f(x)$ (or even for the multivariate case) that will provide a complete description of the distribution in question. Some of the distributions are very common in the sense that they describe the probabilities of many experimental situations encountered in practice. One of the most common probability distributions, and the simplest one, is the so-called *uniform distribution*. In this distribution the probability that X will assume any of a number of specific values is the same; i.e., $f(x)$ is a constant for all values of X. This distribution describes the probabilities of various outcomes of a toss of a die, of pulling a card of a given suit from a pack, of winning in a lottery, and many others. Another extremely common distribution is the so-called *binomial distribution*, which is especially important in statistical inference and will be discussed in detail in Section 4–1.

3–5   Continuous Random Variables and Probability Functions

In the discrete case the elements of sample space are represented by points that are separated by finite distances. To each point we can ascribe a numerical value and to each value we can ascribe a given probability. However, there are many experiments for which the sample space does not consist of countable points but covers an entire interval (or collection of intervals). The random variable associated with the outcomes of such experiments is called a *continuous random variable*. An example of such an experiment is that of observing a freely rotating hand on a clock dial. The random variable in this case may be the time (say in hours) indicated by the hand when stopped at random. There is obviously an infinite number of points between 0 and 12 at which the hand may stop, so that the probability that the hand stops at any particular *point* is zero. On the other hand, the probability that the hand stops within an *interval* around any particular point is nonzero and can be found.

The probabilities associated with the clock-dial experiment for all intervals are shown graphically by Figure 3–9. The probabilities that the value of X will

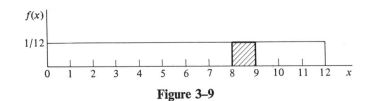

Figure 3–9

fall within any interval are given by the corresponding area under the curve (in this case a straight line). For example, the shaded area in Figure 3–9 gives the probability that x will fall between 8 and 9, which is 1/12. This idea can be generalized to apply to other experiments involving continuous variables. Thus the *probability distribution for a continuous variable X (called the probability density function) is represented by a curve, and the probability that X assumes a value in the interval from a to b (a < b) is given by the area under this curve bounded by a and b.* Most probability distributions that we will encounter will be continuous.

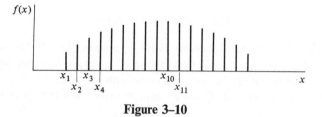

Figure 3–10

To develop the idea of the probability density function further, we can contrast it with the probability function of a discrete variable. Suppose we have a discrete random variable that can assume values $x_1, x_2, \ldots, x_n$, and the values are in ascending order of magnitude. Suppose that the probability function of this variable is given by Figure 3–10. Now the probability that, e.g., X will assume a value greater than x_3 but smaller than or equal to x_{10} is as follows:

$$P(x_3 < x \le x_{10}) = f(x_4) + f(x_5) + \cdots + f(x_{10}) = \sum_{i=4}^{10} f(x_i).$$

Alternatively we could write

$$P(x_3 < x \le x_{10}) = F(x_{10}) - F(x_3),$$

where $F(x)$ represents a cumulative distribution function. Suppose we now have a continuous random variable with probability density given by Figure 3–11. Then the probability that X will assume a value in the interval from x_3 to x_{10} is given by the shaded area under the curve. Now, areas under a curve are determined by integrals so that, given that the algebraic formula describing the

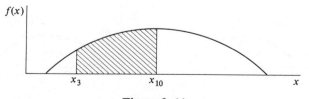

Figure 3–11

density function in Figure 3–11 is $f(x)$, the area under the curve between x_3 and x_{10} is given by the appropriate integral. Thus we have

$$P(x_3 < x < x_{10}) = \int_{x_3}^{x_{10}} f(x)dx.$$

(Since the probability that $x = x_{10}$ is zero, $P(x_3 < x < x_{10})$ and $P(x_3 < x \le x_{10})$ are equivalent.) The integration from x_3 to x_{10} in the case of the continuous variable is analogous to the summation of probabilities in the discrete case. In general, *if X is a continuous random variable, then the probability that it assumes a value in the interval from a to b is determined by the following:*

(3.19) $$P(a < x < b) = \int_a^b f(x)dx,$$

where $f(x)$ is the relevant probability density function. As it turns out, we will have very little need for actual enumeration of integrals, but they do provide a convenient conceptual framework for considering probability densities.

Since the probability that X will assume *any* value is 1 (i.e., it is a certainty),

(3.20) $$P(-\infty < x < +\infty) = \int_{-\infty}^{+\infty} f(x)dx = 1.$$

Furthermore, the probability that X will assume any value less than or equal to some specific x is

(3.21) $$F(x) = \int_{-\infty}^{x} f(x)dx.$$

As in the discrete case, $F(x)$ is called the *cumulative probability* of x. Note that

1. $F(-\infty) = 0$ and $F(+\infty) = 1$.

2. For $a < b$,

$$F(b) - F(a) = \int_{-\infty}^{b} f(x)dx - \int_{-\infty}^{a} f(x)dx = \int_a^b f(x)dx = P(a < x < b).$$

(In other words, the difference between two cumulative probabilities is equal to simple probability.)

A diagrammatic representation of cumulative probability is given in Figure 3–12.

As in the case of discrete variables, continuous sample spaces may involve more than one variable at a time. The corresponding probability distribution is

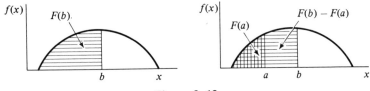

Figure 3–12

called *multivariate probability density*. It gives the *joint probability* that each of the variables involved will fall within specified intervals; if the variables are, e.g., X, Y, Z, then the *joint probability density* would be $f(x, y, z)$. In an analogy with the discrete case, we define *marginal density* of X as the probability density of X whatever the values of the remaining variables. Note that the marginal density of one variable is given by integrating the joint distribution over all values of the other variable, namely,

$$f(x) = \int_{-\infty}^{+\infty} f(x,y)dy \qquad \text{and} \qquad f(y) = \int_{-\infty}^{+\infty} f(x,y)dx.$$

Also, as in the discrete case, the continuous random variables X, Y, Z, ... are *independent* if and only if

(3.22) $$f(x,y,z,\ldots) = f(x)f(y)f(z)\ldots.$$

Some continuous distributions are of special importance because they are frequently encountered in practice. The *continuous uniform distribution*, used in connection with our clock-dial example and depicted by Figure 3–9, is one such distribution. Another one is the so-called *normal distribution*, which is extremely common and will be discussed at length in Section 4–2. Other distributions will be introduced as the occasion arises.

3–6   Mathematical Expectation

Probability distributions, like ordinary frequency distributions, display various characteristics. These characteristics, of which the best known are the mean and the variance, are defined in terms of so-called *expected values* or *mathematical expectations*. An explanation of these terms can best be carried out by analogy to an ordinary frequency distribution. Suppose, for instance, that we have a sample of 64 families classified by the number of children as shown in Table 3–5. Here n represents absolute frequencies and f represents

Table 3–5

Number of children: x	Number of families: n	Proportion of families: f
0	4	0.06250
1	12	0.18750
2	20	0.31250
3	16	0.25000
4	8	0.12500
5	2	0.03125
6	2	0.03125
	64	1.00000

relative frequencies. There are seven different values of X, $x_1 = 0$, $x_2 = 1, \ldots$, $x_7 = 6$, associated with various frequencies. Let us now determine the average number of children per family. Although several different types of averages exist, most people would in this case probably choose the arithmetic mean—the total number of children in the sample divided by the total number of families. This is given by

$$\bar{x} = \frac{\sum_{i=1}^{7} n_i x_i}{\sum_{i=1}^{7} n_i} = \frac{1}{64}(4 \times 0 + 12 \times 1 + \cdots + 2 \times 6) = 2.40625.$$

The same result would be obtained by using relative frequencies:

$$\bar{x} = \sum_{i=1}^{7} f_i x_i = (0.06250 \times 0 + 0.18750 \times 1 + \cdots + 0.03125 \times 6)$$

$$= 2.40625.$$

That is, the arithmetic mean of a frequency distribution is, in fact, a weighted mean of the different values of the variable with weights given by the respective relative frequencies. Consider now a *discrete random variable* X with the following probability function:

x	$f(x)$
x_1	$f(x_1)$
x_2	$f(x_2)$
$\vdots$	$\vdots$
x_n	$f(x_n)$

where n is some finite number. Then the *expected value* or the *mathematical expectation* of X is

$$(3.23) \qquad E(X) = \sum_{i=1}^{n} x_i f(x_i).$$

We can see that $E(X)$ is nothing else but a weighted average of the different values of X with weights given by the respective probabilities. This is the reason why $E(X)$ is identified with the population mean μ; that is,

$$(3.24) \qquad \mu = E(X).$$

The analogy between the mean of an ordinary frequency distribution and the expected value of a discrete random variable X should be clear from our exposition.

The term *expected value* is used to emphasize the relation between the population mean and one's anticipation about the outcome of an experiment. Suppose, for instance, that we are asked to toss a six-sided die and are told that we will receive as many dollars as the number of dots shown. The question is how much do we expect to receive before actually throwing the die. If our expectation is formed in accordance with the rule given by (3.23), the answer is

$$E(X) = 1 \times \frac{1}{6} + 2 \times \frac{1}{6} + \cdots + 6 \times \frac{1}{6} = 3.5.$$

While we cannot actually get (and therefore do not "expect" in the colloquial sense of the word) $3.50, this figure represents a summary of the possible results. If the tosses were repeated an infinite number of times, the average return per toss would be precisely $3.50.

The *expected value of a continuous variable* is defined in a very similar fashion. As we mentioned earlier, we may view a continuous variable as a limiting case of a discrete variable, where the values that the variable can assume get more and more numerous and closer and closer to each other. Therefore, if X is a continuous random variable with probability density $f(x)$, its expected value (or mathematical expectation) is

(3.25) $$E(X) = \int_{-\infty}^{+\infty} xf(x)dx.$$

The integration is carried out from $-\infty$ to $+\infty$ to make sure that all possible values of X are covered.

It should be noted that there are some probability distributions for which the *expected value of the variable does not exist*; that is, $E(X)$ might be equal to infinity. A classical example is given by the following probability function:

x	$f(x)$
2	1/2
4	1/4
8	1/8
16	1/16
⋮	⋮

This is a perfectly legitimate probability function since $f(x) \geq 0$ for every x and

$$\sum_{i=1}^{\infty} f(x_i) = \frac{1}{2} + \frac{1}{4} + \frac{1}{8} + \cdots = 1.$$

In fact, $f(x)$ can be interpreted as representing the probability of getting 1 head in 1 toss of an unbiased coin, 2 heads in 2 tosses, 3 heads in 3 tosses, and so on in an ascending order. The expected value of X is[1]

---

[1] This case is known as the *St. Petersburg paradox*. Suppose somebody asks us to toss a coin and offers to pay us $2 if we get a head in the first toss but not in the second; $4 if we get a head in the first and the second toss but not in the third; $8 if we get a head in the first, second, and third toss but not in the fourth; and so on. How much is the value of this game to us? According to our calculations, the expected value (i.e., the expected gain in this case) is infinity, but it is unlikely that anybody would be willing to pay that amount (or even, say, a mere million dollars) for the privilege of playing this game. This is the paradoxical aspect of the situation.

$$E(X) = 2 \times \frac{1}{2} + 4 \times \frac{1}{4} + 8 \times \frac{1}{8} + \cdots = 1 + 1 + 1 + \cdots = \infty.$$

Fortunately, distributions of this sort are not very frequent. In what follows we shall assume that we are dealing with distributions for which expected values exist. When this is not the case, we shall make the point of emphasizing it.

The concept of mathematical expectation can easily be extended to apply to problems other than simple determination of the mean value of X. In particular, if X is a random variable and $g(X)$ is a single-valued function of this variable, then,

$$(3.26) \qquad Eg(X) = \begin{cases} \displaystyle\sum_{i=1}^{\infty} g(x_i)f(x_i) & (X \text{ discrete}) \\[2ex] \displaystyle\int_{-\infty}^{+\infty} g(x)f(x)dx & (X \text{ continuous}). \end{cases}$$

As an example, we shall prove the following theorem.

Theorem 6   *If X is a random variable and a and b are constants, then*

$$E(aX + b) = aE(X) + b.$$

Proof: (a) X is discrete:

$$\begin{aligned} E(aX + b) &= \sum_{i=1}^{n} (ax_i + b)f(x_i) \\ &= \sum_{i} ax_i f(x_i) + \sum_{i} bf(x_i) \\ &= a \sum_{i} x_i f(x_i) + b \sum_{i} f(x_i) \\ &= aE(X) + b. \end{aligned}$$

(b) X is continuous:

$$\begin{aligned} E(aX + b) &= \int_{-\infty}^{+\infty} (ax + b)f(x)dx \\ &= \int axf(x)dx + \int bf(x)dx \\ &= aE(X) + b. \end{aligned}$$

A direct application of (3.26) enables us to determine special characteristics of a probability distribution called *moments*. These represent a family of parameters which characterize a distribution. Two kinds of moments can be distinguished: moments about the origin (i.e., zero) and moments about the mean (i.e., μ). *Moments about the origin* are defined by

$$(3.27) \qquad \mu_r' = E(X^r) = \begin{cases} \displaystyle\sum_{i} x_i^r f(x_i) & (X \text{ discrete}) \\[2ex] \displaystyle\int_{-\infty}^{+\infty} x^r f(x)dx & (X \text{ continuous}) \end{cases}$$

for $r = 0, 1, 2, \ldots$. That is, substitution of different values for r will lead to moments of different order. In particular,

$$\mu_0' = 1,$$

$$\mu_1' = E(X) = \mu.$$

Thus the *mean is the first moment about the origin.* Moments about the origin of order higher than one are less commonly used and have no special names. *Moments about the mean* are defined by

$$(3.28) \qquad \mu_r = E[(X - \mu)^r] = \begin{cases} \displaystyle\sum_i (x_i - \mu)^r f(x_i) & (X \text{ discrete}) \\[2ex] \displaystyle\int_{-\infty}^{+\infty} (x - \mu)^r f(x)dx & (X \text{ continuous}) \end{cases}$$

for $r = 0, 1, 2, \ldots$. Note that

$$\mu_0 = 1,$$

$$\mu_1 = E(X - \mu) = E(X) - \mu = 0,$$

$$\mu_2 = E(X - \mu)^2 = \text{Var}(X).$$

Thus the *variance is the second moment about the mean.* Its square root is called the *standard deviation* of the distribution.

The most important characteristics of a distribution are noted below.

1. The *mean* $\mu = E(X)$ is a measure of central tendency of a distribution. Its chief distinction is the fact that in the population the deviations of all the values of X from μ average out to zero. This is true whether the variable is discrete or continuous. In particular, we see that in the discrete case we have:

$$\sum_i (x_i - \mu)f(x_i) = \sum_i x_i f(x_i) - \mu = E(X) - \mu = 0.$$

If the distribution is symmetric, then the mean lies in its center.

2. The *variance* σ^2 or $\text{Var}(X)$, frequently presented as

$$(3.29) \qquad\qquad \text{Var}(X) = E[X - E(X)]^2,$$

is a measure of the spread or dispersion of a distribution. It is, in fact, the mean of the squared deviations of X from μ since, by the definition of mathematical expectation,

$$\sigma^2 = \begin{cases} \displaystyle\sum_i (x_i - \mu)^2 f(x_i) & (X \text{ discrete}) \\[2ex] \displaystyle\int_{-\infty}^{+\infty} (X - \mu)^2 f(x)dx & (X \text{ continuous}). \end{cases}$$

Variance, of course, can never be negative. If all values of X are highly concentrated, the point of concentration must be the mean (or at least its neighborhood) and the variance will be very small. In the extreme case where all values of X are the same (i.e., X is a constant), the variance will be equal to zero. Note that an alternative way of determining the variance can be developed as follows:

$$(3.30) \qquad \sigma^2 = E(X - \mu)^2 = E(X^2 - 2\mu X + \mu^2)$$
$$= E(X^2) - 2\mu E(X) + \mu^2 = E(X^2) - \mu^2,$$

since μ is a constant. Further, we have an important theorem:

Theorem 7   *If X is a random variable and a and b are constants, then*

$$Var(aX + b) = a^2 Var(X).$$

Proof:

$$Var(aX + b) = E[(aX + b) - E(aX + b)]^2$$

by the definition of a variance. Now,

$$E(aX + b) = aE(X) + b$$

by Theorem 6, where $E(X) = \mu$ by definition. Therefore,

$$Var(aX + b) = E[aX + b - (a\mu + b)]^2 = E[aX - a\mu]^2$$
$$= E[a^2(X - \mu)^2] = a^2 E[(X - \mu)^2] = a^2 Var(X).$$

Sometimes it is more convenient to use the *standard deviation* of X, which is simply

$$\sigma = \sqrt{Var(X)}.$$

3. A *measure of skewness* (departure from symmetry) is given by

$$(3.31) \qquad \mu_3 = E(X - \mu)^3.$$

If the distribution is symmetric, μ_3 will be equal to zero. If the distribution is skewed to the left (i.e., its left tail is elongated), μ_3 will be negative, and if the distribution is skewed to the right, μ_3 will be positive. In Figure 3–13, the first distribution, $f_1(x)$, is skewed to the left, the second, $f_2(x)$, is symmetric, and the

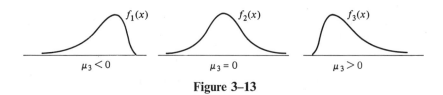

$$f_1(x) \qquad\qquad f_2(x) \qquad\qquad f_3(x)$$
$$\mu_3 < 0 \qquad\qquad \mu_3 = 0 \qquad\qquad \mu_3 > 0$$

Figure 3–13

third, $f_3(x)$, is skewed to the right. For many purposes it is preferable to use a slightly different measure of skewness, called α_3, which is defined as

$$(3.32) \qquad\qquad\qquad \alpha_3 = \frac{\mu_3}{\sigma^3}.$$

The denominator in this expression functions as a scale factor so that comparisons of different distributions with respect to skewness are not distorted by the differences in dispersion. Since $\sigma^3 = [\text{Var}(X)]^{3/2}$ is always positive, the sign of α_3 is fully determined by the sign of μ_3.

So far we have considered only univariate probability distributions, but there is no difficulty in extending the concept of mathematical expectation to distributions involving more than one random variable. Suppose we have two random variables X and Y with a joint distribution $f(x,y)$. We wish to determine the expected value of some single-valued function of X and Y, say $g(X, Y)$. Then,

$$(3.33) \qquad E[g(X, Y)] = \begin{cases} \displaystyle\sum_{i=1}^{\infty} \sum_{j=1}^{\infty} g(x_i, y_j)f(x_i, y_j) & (X \text{ and } Y \text{ discrete}) \\[2ex] \displaystyle\int_{-\infty}^{+\infty} \int_{-\infty}^{+\infty} g(x, y)f(x, y)\,dx\,dy & (X \text{ and } Y \text{ continuous}). \end{cases}$$

This can be generalized for any number of random variables. Some functions of random variables are of special interest; these are given in the following theorems, which are very important in econometric theory. We shall prove them for two discrete random variables, but the extension to other cases is quite straightforward.

Theorem 8 *The expected value of a sum of random variables is equal to the sum of their expected values, i.e.,* $E(X + Y + Z + \cdots) = E(X) + E(Y) + E(Z) + \cdots.$

Proof:

$$E(X + Y) = \sum_i \sum_j (x_i + y_j)f(x_i y_j) = \sum_i \sum_j x_i f(x_i, y_j) + \sum_i \sum_j y_j f(x_i, y_j)$$

$$= \sum_i x_i \sum_j f(x_i, y_j) + \sum_j y_j \sum_i f(x_i, y_j) = \sum_i x_i f(x_i) + \sum_j y_j f(y_j)$$

$$= E(X) + E(Y).$$

Theorem 9 *The expected value of a linear combination of random variables is equal to the linear combination of their expected values, i.e.,*

$$E(aX + bY + cZ + \cdots) = aE(X) + bE(Y) + cE(Z) + \cdots,$$

where $a, b, c, \ldots$ are any constants.

Proof:

$$E(aX + bY) = \sum_i \sum_j (ax_i + by_i)f(x_i, y_j)$$

$$= \sum_i \sum_j ax_i f(x_i, y_j) + \sum_i \sum_j by_j f(x_i, y_j)$$

$$= a \sum_i x_i \sum_j f(x_i, y_j) + b \sum_j y_j \sum_i f(x_i, y_j)$$

$$= aE(X) + bE(Y).$$

Theorem 10 *If X and Y are two independent random variables, then the expected value of their product is equal to the product of their expected values, i.e., $E(XY) = E(X)E(Y)$.*

Proof:

$$E(XY) = \sum_i \sum_j x_i y_j f(x_i, y_j).$$

But if X and Y are independent,

$$f(x_i, y_j) = f(x_i)f(y_j).$$

Therefore,

$$E(XY) = \sum_i \sum_j x_i y_j f(x_i)f(y_j) = \sum_i x_i f(x_i) \sum_j y_j f(y_j) = E(X)E(Y).$$

It is important to note the difference in the expected value of a sum and the expected value of a product. The expected value of a sum is *always* equal to the sum of expected values, whereas the expected value of a product is equal to the product of the expected values *only* if the variables are independent.

The last theorem on expected values that we intend to present requires the definition of a *covariance* between two random variables, say X and Y. This is usually denoted by $Cov(X, Y)$ (or sometimes σ_{XY}) and is defined as

(3.34) $$Cov(X, Y) = E[X - E(X)][Y - E(Y)].$$

The sign of the covariance depends on the direction of association between X and Y. If there is a positive association—that is, if small values of X tend to be associated with small values of Y and large values of X with large values of Y —then the covariance will be *positive*. If, on the other hand, there is a negative association—that is, if small values of X tend to be associated with large values of Y and large values of X with small values of Y—the covariance will be *negative*. (Here by "small" we mean values less than the mean and by "large," values greater than the mean.) That is, if there is a positive association, then $[x - E(X)]$ and $[y - E(Y)]$ will tend to be of the same sign; therefore, their product will tend to be positive and this will make for a positive covariance. But if there is a negative association, $[x - E(X)]$ and $[y - E(Y)]$ will tend to be of opposite signs; therefore, their product will tend to be negative, and this will be reflected in the sign of the covariance. An illustration is given by Figure 3–14. With this introduction we can now present the following theorem:

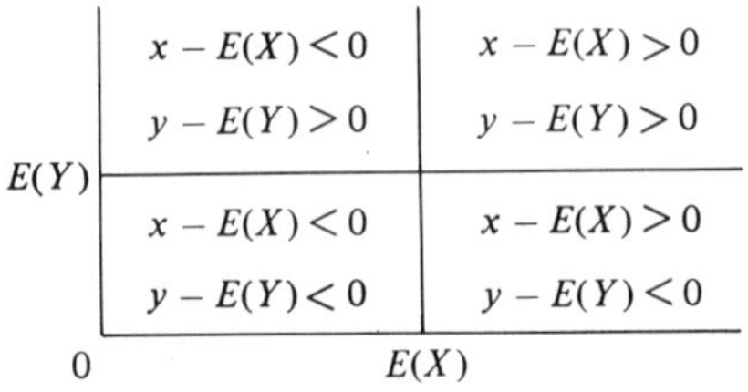

	$x - E(X) < 0$	$x - E(X) > 0$
	$y - E(Y) > 0$	$y - E(Y) > 0$
$E(Y)$		
	$x - E(X) < 0$	$x - E(X) > 0$
	$y - E(Y) < 0$	$y - E(Y) < 0$

0                          $E(X)$

Figure 3–14

Theorem 11   *If X and Y are two independent random variables, then*

$$Cov(X, Y) = 0.$$

Proof:

$$Cov(X, Y) = E[X - E(X)][Y - E(Y)]$$

$$= E[XY - YE(X) - XE(Y) + E(X)E(Y)]$$

$$= E(XY) - E(X)E(Y).$$

But if X and Y are independent, then, by Theorem 10,

$$E(XY) = E(X)E(Y);$$

therefore $$Cov(X, Y) = E(X)E(Y) - E(X)E(Y) = 0.$$

It is important to note that while independence necessarily implies zero covariance, the *converse is not true*. It is not very difficult to find cases for which $Cov(X, Y) = 0$ and yet X and Y are not independent. As an example consider the following distribution:

		Values of Y		$f(x)$
		0	1	
	1	0	1/3	1/3
Values of X	2	1/3	0	1/3
	3	0	1/3	1/3
$f(y)$		1/3	2/3	1

X and Y are obviously not independent since the conditional and the marginal distributions are quite different. Now,

$$Cov(X, Y) = E[X - E(X)][Y - E(Y)] = EXY - E(X)E(Y).$$

But $$E(XY) = \sum_i \sum_j x_i y_j f(x_i, y_j) = 1 \times 1 \times \frac{1}{3} + 2 \times 0 \times \frac{1}{3} + 3 \times 1 \times \frac{1}{3} = \frac{4}{3}.$$

Further, $$E(X) = 1 \times \frac{1}{3} + 2 \times \frac{1}{3} + 3 \times \frac{1}{3} = 2$$

and $$E(Y) = 0 \times \frac{1}{3} + 1 \times \frac{2}{3} = \frac{2}{3}.$$

Therefore, $$Cov(X, Y) = \frac{4}{3} - 2 \times \frac{2}{3} = 0.$$

The variables that have zero covariance are called *noncorrelated*. The point of the preceding discussion was to show that independence is a sufficient but not necessary condition for zero covariance. In a broad sense, the difference between independence and noncorrelation lies in the fact that independence rules out any kind of relationship, whereas noncorrelation rules out only *linear* relations between variables.

As a final point we note that, in analogy to the concept of conditional probability, we have *conditional expectation* of, say, Y given X, which is defined as

$$(3.35) \qquad E(Y|X) = \begin{cases} \sum_i y_i f(y_i|x_i) & (Y \text{ discrete}) \\ \int_{-\infty}^{+\infty} yf(y|x)dy & (Y \text{ continuous}). \end{cases}$$

That is, the conditional expectation of Y given X is equal to the mean of the conditional distribution of Y given X. In terms of the example just given, the conditional expectation of Y given that the value of X is 1 is

$$E(Y|x = 1) = 0 \times \frac{0}{1/3} + 1 \times \frac{1/3}{1/3} = 1.$$

Also

$$E(Y|x = 2) = 0 \times \frac{1/3}{1/3} + 1 \times \frac{0}{1/3} = 0$$

and

$$E(Y|x = 3) = 0 \times \frac{0}{1/3} + 1 \times \frac{1/3}{1/3} = 1,$$

while the unconditional mean of Y is

$$E(Y) = 0 \times \frac{1}{3} + 1 \times \frac{2}{3} = \frac{2}{3}.$$

The concept of the conditional expectation can be generalized to any single-valued function of Y, say $g(Y)$. Then, we have

$$(3.36) \qquad E[g(Y)|X] = \begin{cases} \sum_i g(y_i) f(y_i|x_i) & (Y \text{ discrete}) \\ \int_{-\infty}^{+\infty} g(y)f(y|x)dy & (Y \text{ continuous}). \end{cases}$$

There is one important difference between an unconditional and a conditional expectation: while $E[g(Y)]$ is always a constant, $E[g(Y)|X]$ is not necessarily a constant but may be a function of X.

In the rest of this book, operations involving expected values will be quite frequent. This is because we are very much concerned with the derivation of the properties of sampling distributions, and, as pointed out earlier, sampling distributions are nothing but probability distributions of estimators or test statistics. Expected values are very convenient means of describing the characteristics of these distributions.

EXERCISES

3–1. List the elements of the sample spaces corresponding to the following experiments:

a. Drawing (with replacement) two balls from an urn containing 7 white and 3 red balls.

b. Flipping a coin and, providing a head appears, rolling a six-sided dice (if a tail appears, the experiment is stopped).

c. Drawing cards from a pack of 52 cards until a face card is obtained.

3–2. In how many different ways can three men and three women sit around a dinner table if **(a)** the seating arrangement is not restricted in any way; **(b)** each woman is to be between two men; **(c)** the arrangement is to be the same as in **(b)** but the hostess insists on sitting on the chair nearest to the kitchen?

3–3. How many different samples of size 20 can be drawn (with replacement) from a population of 30 objects?

3–4. The following questions will require probability calculations with a six-sided die. Determine the probability of **(a)** getting an even number or a number in excess of 3; **(b)** getting a 4 followed by a 5; **(c)** not getting a 4 in either of two rolls; **(d)** getting a 4 at least once in two rolls; **(e)** not getting two 7's in two rolls.

3–5. Consider the following set of equally likely outcomes:

$$S = \{1, 2, \ldots, n\}$$

where n is a multiple of six. Define

$$S_1 = \{1, 3, \ldots, (n - 1)\}.$$
$$S_2 = \{2, 4, \ldots, n\}.$$
$$S_3 = \{3, 6, \ldots, n\}.$$

Find the following probabilities:

a. $P(n)$, $P(S_1)$, $P(S_2)$, and $P(S_3)$.   **e.** $P(S_1 \cup S_3)$.

b. $P(S_1 \cap S_3)$.   **f.** $P(S_2 \cup S_3)$.

c. $P(S_2 \cap S_3)$.   **g.** $P[S_1(S_2 \cap S_3)]$.

d. $P(S_1 \cup S_2)$.

3–6. Let S_1 and S_2 be subsets of the sample space S. Given $P(S_1)$, $P(S_2)$, and $P(S_1 \cap S_2)$, find

a. $P(\bar{S}_1 \cup \bar{S}_2)$.   **c.** $P(\bar{S}_1 \cap S_2)$.

b. $P(\bar{S}_1 \cap \bar{S}_2)$.   **d.** $P(\bar{S}_1 \cup S_2)$.

3–7. Three boys are asked to guess which of three jars contains a cookie. If the guess of the first is correct, he will get the cookie. If the guess is incorrect, the empty jar will be removed and the next boy will have his turn at guessing. If his guess is correct, he will get the cookie, otherwise the cookie will go to the third boy. Is there any advantage in being the first, second, or third boy? Give reasons.

3–8. In Michigan, the automobile license plates show two letters followed by four numbers. How many different license plates can be made in this way?

3–9. Show that $\sum_{i=0}^{n} \binom{a}{i}\binom{b}{n-i} = \binom{a+b}{n}$, $\quad a, b > n.$

3–10. The records for a certain large city show the following distribution of applicants for unskilled jobs by the duration of their unemployment:

Duration of unemployment (weeks)	0	1	2	3	4	5	6	7	8	9–12
Proportion of applicants	0.25	0.20	0.15	0.10	0.10	0.05	0.04	0.03	0.02	0.06

a. What is the expected duration of unemployment of an applicant?

b. Calculate the value of the standard deviation and of the α_3-measure of skewness of this distribution.

3–11. If X is a random variable with mean μ and variance σ^2, and if Z is defined as $Z = X - (X - \mu)/\sigma$, find $E(Z)$ and $\text{Var}(Z)$.

3–12. If X is a random variable with mean μ and b is a constant different from μ, prove that $E(X - \mu)^2 < E(X - b)^2$.

3–13. If X and Y are two random variables and a and b are constants, prove that

a. $\text{Var}(X + a) = \text{Var}(X).$

b. $\text{Var}(Y + b) = \text{Var}(Y).$

c. $\text{Cov}[(X + a), (Y + b)] = \text{Cov}(X, Y).$

3–14. Consider a sample of identically and independently distributed variables $X_1, X_2, \ldots, X_n$, each having a mean μ and variance σ^2. Find, for $i = 1, 2, \ldots, n$ and $i \neq j$:

a. $E(X_i \bar{X}).$

f. $E[X_i(X_j - \bar{X})].$

b. $E(X_i^2).$

g. $\text{Var}(X_i - \bar{X}).$

c. $E(\bar{X}^2).$

h. $\text{Cov}(X_i, \bar{X}).$

d. $E[X_i(X_i - \bar{X})].$

i. $\text{Cov}[(X_i - \bar{X}), \bar{X}].$

e. $E[\bar{X}(X_i - \bar{X})].$

j. $\text{Cov}[(X_i - \bar{X}), (X_j - \bar{X})].$

3–15. Consider three random variables X, Y, and Z. Prove that **(a)** the fact that X is uncorrelated with Y and Y is uncorrelated with Z does not imply that X is uncorrelated with Z; **(b)** the fact that X is independent of Y and Y is independent of Z does not imply that X is independent of Z.

3–16. Prove that

$$\mu_r = \mu_r' + (-1)^1 \binom{r}{1}\mu_{r-1}'\mu + \cdots + (-1)^i \binom{r}{i}\mu_{r-i}'\mu^i + \cdots + (-1)^{r-1}(r-1)\mu^r$$

for $r = 1, 2, 3, \ldots$.

(If the proof for the general case is too difficult, give a proof for $r = 1, 2$, and 3.)

3–17. The joint distribution of X and Y is as follows:

		X				
		-2	-1	0	1	2
Y	10	.09	.15	.27	.25	.04
	20	.01	.05	.08	.05	.01

a. Find the marginal distributions of X and Y.

b. Find the conditional distribution of X given $y = 20$.

c. Are X and Y uncorrelated?

d. Are X and Y independent?

3–18. A company has to decide between two investment projects. Project A will yield a $20,000 profit if it is successful or a loss of $2,000 if it is unsuccessful, whereas Project B will yield $25,000 profit if it is successful or $5,000 loss if it is not. The probability of a project being successful is thought to be the same for both projects. Find this probability given that, on the basis of expected profit, the two projects were judged to be equivalent.

4   Theoretical Derivation
of Sampling Distributions

The purpose of the discussion on probability and probability distributions in Chapter 3 was to provide tools for theoretical derivation of the sampling distributions of estimators and test statistics, and also to facilitate our understanding of the process and results of estimation or hypotheses testing. In this chapter we come to the point where we shall *use* probability theory to derive various sampling distributions. As explained in Section 1–5, sampling distributions can be derived either experimentally or theoretically. In the experimental approach we construct our population from which we draw a large number of samples. Each sample then provides us with one value of the estimator or test statistic with which we are concerned. The resulting frequency distribution is our approximation of the probability distribution that we would have obtained had the number of samples been not just large but infinite. The experimental approach has two major disadvantages. The first is that we have to be satisfied with approximations of sampling distributions instead of their exact forms, and the second is that the results are, strictly speaking, applicable only to the specific population underlying the experiment. Theoretically derived sampling distributions are free from both of these difficulties and are, therefore, clearly superior to those that are experimentally derived. The one drawback in using the theoretical approach is that it may not always work—in the sense that our mathematical knowledge and skill may not be sufficient to lead to results. This happens particularly frequently with respect to estimators of a system of economic relations, as we shall see in Chapter 13.

In this chapter we shall limit ourselves to the derivation of the sampling distribution of sample proportions of successes and of sample mean. Both of these distributions were already derived experimentally for specific populations in Chapter 2, and can be derived mathematically for any population without much difficulty. Other sampling distributions will be discussed later as the occasion arises.

4–1   Sampling Distribution of Sample Proportion of Successes: Binomial Distribution

Consider a population in which every unit can be classified as either possessing or not possessing a given attribute. This population may or may not be infinite.

If it is not infinite, then we assume that, when we draw a sample, every unit drawn is replaced before another unit is drawn (i.e., we have sampling with replacement). This means that there is no limit to sample size. A unit that possesses the given attribute will be called a *success*; that which does not, a *failure*. As a concrete example, we may envision that we are dealing with the adult population of the United States at a given point of time and that the attribute of interest is whether a person is a coffee-drinker or a non-coffee-drinker. Drawing a coffee-drinker is considered a success, a non-coffee-drinker a failure. In accordance with Section 2–1 let us use the following notation:

π = proportion (or limit of relative frequency) of successes in the population;

ρ = proportion (or limit of relative frequency) of failures in the population;

n = size of sample;

$\hat{\pi}$ = proportion of successes in the sample;

X = number of successes in the sample.

Note that if we make a single random drawing, the probability of success is π and of failure ρ. Let S stand for "success," and F for "failure." Then we have

$$P(S) = \pi$$

and $\qquad\qquad P(F) = \rho \qquad$ or $\qquad P(F) = 1 - \pi,$

since F is "not S."

Let us now derive the sampling distributions of X and $\hat{\pi}$ for samples of various sizes. Since there is a one-to-one correspondence between X and $\hat{\pi}$ given by the fact that

$$\hat{\pi} = \frac{X}{n} \qquad \text{or} \qquad X = n\hat{\pi},$$

knowledge of the distribution of X gives a complete knowledge of the distribution of $\hat{\pi}$, and vice versa. We will give a full description of sampling distributions for each sample size, using X as the random variable; however, we will determine the main distributional characteristics for both X as well as $\hat{\pi}$. In presenting each distribution, we will determine the values of X, their probability, and the values of $xf(x)$ and $x^2f(x)$ which are needed for calculating the mean and the variance.

Sampling Distribution for Samples Size 1

Number of Successes: x	Probability: $f(x)$	$xf(x)$	$x^2f(x)$
0	$P(F) = \rho$	0	0
1	$P(S) = \pi$	π	π
Sum	$\rho + \pi = 1$	π	π

Mean and variance of X:

$$E(X) = \sum_i x_i f(x_i) = \pi,$$

$$\text{Var}(X) = E(X^2) - [E(X)]^2 = \sum_i x_i^2 f(x_i) - \left[\sum_i x_i f(x_i)\right]^2$$

$$= \pi - \pi^2 = \pi(1 - \pi) = \pi\rho,$$

Mean and variance of $\hat{\pi}$:

$$E(\hat{\pi}) = E\left(\frac{X}{n}\right) = E(X) = \pi,$$

$$\text{Var}(\hat{\pi}) = \text{Var}\left(\frac{X}{n}\right) = \text{Var}(X) = \pi\rho.$$

Sampling Distribution for Samples Size 2

Number of Successes: x	Probability: $f(x)$	$xf(x)$	$x^2f(x)$
0	$P(F)P(F) = \rho^2$	0	0
1	$P(S)P(F) + P(F)P(S) = 2\pi\rho$	$2\pi\rho$	$2\pi\rho$
2	$P(S)P(S) = \pi^2$	$2\pi^2$	$4\pi^2$
Sum	$(\rho + \pi)^2 = 1$	$2\pi(\rho + \pi)$	$2\pi(\rho + 2\pi)$

Note that the "no success" can be obtained only if both the first and second observations are failures. Since drawings are random, the outcomes of the first and the second drawings are independent, therefore the probability of two failures is equal to the product $P(F)P(F)$. The same applies to the probability of two successes. However, "one success and one failure" can be obtained in two ways, either success followed by failure or failure followed by success. The two are mutually exclusive so that the probability of one failure and one success is $P(S)P(F) + P(F)P(S)$, as shown.

Mean and variance of X:

$$E(X) = 2\pi(\rho + \pi) = 2\pi,$$

$$\text{Var}(X) = 2\pi(\rho + 2\pi) - [2\pi]^2 = 2\pi\rho + 4\pi^2 - 4\pi^2 = 2\pi\rho.$$

Mean and variance of $\hat{\pi}$:

$$E(\hat{\pi}) = E\left(\frac{X}{2}\right) = \pi,$$

$$\text{Var}(\hat{\pi}) = \text{Var}\left(\frac{X}{2}\right) = \frac{1}{4}\text{Var}(X) \quad \text{(by Theorem 7)}$$

$$= \frac{\pi\rho}{2}.$$

Sampling Distribution for Samples Size 3

Number of Successes: x	Probability: $f(x)$	$xf(x)$	$x^2f(x)$
0	$P(F)P(F)P(F) = \rho^3$	0	0
1	$P(S)P(F)P(F) + P(F)P(S)P(F) + P(F)P(F)P(S) = 3\pi\rho^2$	$3\rho^2\pi$	$3\rho^2\pi$
2	$P(S)P(S)P(F) + P(S)P(F)P(S) + P(F)P(S)P(S) = 3\pi^2\rho$	$6\rho\pi^2$	$12\rho\pi^2$
3	$P(S)P(S)P(S) = \pi^3$	$3\pi^3$	$9\pi^3$

$$\text{Sum} \quad (\rho + \pi)^3 = 1$$

Mean and variance of X:

$$E(X) = 3\rho^2\pi + 6\rho\pi^2 + 3\pi^3 = 3\pi(\rho^2 + 2\rho\pi + \pi^2) = 3\pi(\rho + \pi)^2 = 3\pi.$$

$$\begin{aligned}\text{Var}(X) &= 3\rho^2\pi + 12\rho\pi^2 + 9\pi^3 - (3\pi)^2 = 3\rho^2\pi + 12\rho\pi^2 + 9\pi^2(\pi - 1) \\ &= 3\rho^2\pi + 12\rho\pi^2 - 9\rho\pi^2 = 3\rho\pi(\rho + 4\pi - 3\pi) = 3\rho\pi.\end{aligned}$$

Mean and variance of $\hat{\pi}$:

$$E(\hat{\pi}) = E\left(\frac{X}{3}\right) = \pi.$$

$$\text{Var}(\hat{\pi}) = \text{Var}\left(\frac{X}{3}\right) = \frac{1}{9}\,\text{Var}(X) = \frac{\pi\rho}{3}.$$

We could continue this for larger and larger sample sizes, but the results are already obvious: the probabilities of drawing 0, 1, 2, ..., n successes in a sample size n are given by the respective terms of $(\rho + \pi)^n$, the so-called *binomial*

Table 4–1

x	Size 1	Size 2	Size 3	Size 4	$\cdots$	Size n
			$f(x)$			
0	ρ	ρ^2	ρ^3	ρ^4		ρ^n
1	π	$2\rho\pi$	$3\rho^2\pi$	$4\rho^3\pi$		$\binom{n}{1}\rho^{n-1}\pi$
2		π^2	$3\rho\pi^2$	$6\rho^2\pi^2$		$\binom{n}{2}\rho^{n-2}\pi^2$
3			π^3	$4\rho\pi^3$		$\binom{n}{3}\rho^{n-3}\pi^3$
4				π^4		$\binom{n}{4}\rho^{n-4}\pi^4$
$\vdots$						$\vdots$
$n-1$						$\binom{n}{n-1}\rho\pi^{n-1}$
n						π^n

expansion. Table 4–1 summarizes the distributions of X for various sample sizes. Note that the first element in the last column could also be written as

$$\rho^n = \binom{n}{0}\rho^n \pi^0,$$

and the last element in the same column as

$$\pi^n = \binom{n}{n}\rho^0 \pi^n.$$

Thus the probability of getting x successes in a sample size n is

(4.1) $$f(x) = \binom{n}{x}\rho^{n-x}\pi^x.$$

Similarly, the probability of obtaining $\hat{\pi}$ proportion of successes in a sample size n is

(4.2) $$f(\hat{\pi}) = \binom{n}{n\hat{\pi}}\rho^{n(1-\hat{\pi})}\pi^{n\hat{\pi}}.$$

These probabilities can be interpreted as limits of relative frequencies, i.e., the frequencies that would be obtained if an infinite number of samples of each size were taken. The distributions defined by these probabilities are, therefore, the true and exact sampling distributions: (4.1) defines the sampling distribution of the number of successes, and (4.2) the sampling distribution of the proportion of successes.

The calculation of the individual probabilities of the binomial distribution becomes quite laborious unless the sample size is very small. Some work can be saved by using *Pascal's triangle* (Figure 3–3), which gives the values of

$$\binom{n}{1}, \quad \binom{n}{2}, \quad \binom{n}{3}, \text{ and so on,}$$

for any n. But we can save ourselves all the calculating work involved if we use the tables of *binomial probabilities* which give the probabilities for different values of n and π.[1] For large values of n, the binomial distribution can be reasonably well approximated by the so-called *normal distribution* (unless π is very small and $n\pi$ remains constant as $n \to \infty$). This will be discussed in detail in Section 4–2.

Let us now derive the basic characteristics of the sampling distribution of X and of $\hat{\pi}$. In particular, we are interested in the mean, the variance, and the skewness of these distributions. The mean and the variance for samples size 1, 2, and 3 are summarized in Table 4–2. The generalization to sample size n is quite straightforward. Its validity could be proved without much difficulty, but the

[1] These are available in quite a few statistical texts or handbooks, including John E. Freund, *Mathematical Statistics* (Englewood Cliffs, N.J.: Prentice-Hall, 1962).

Table 4–2

Sample Size	Mean — Number of Successes: x	Mean — Proportion of Successes: $\hat{\pi}$	Variance — Number of Successes: x	Variance — Proportion of Successes: $\hat{\pi}$
1	π	π	$\pi\rho$	$\pi\rho$
2	2π	π	$2\pi\rho$	$\pi\rho/2$
3	3π	π	$3\pi\rho$	$\pi\rho/3$
⋮	⋮	⋮	⋮	⋮
n	$n\pi$	π	$n\pi\rho$	$\pi\rho/n$

proof would involve a fair amount of tedious algebra and therefore will not be given here. As for the measure of skewness, we can use α_3 given as

$$\alpha_3 = \frac{\mu_3}{(\mu_2)^{3/2}},$$

where μ_2 is the variance and μ_3 is the third moment around the mean. Then it can be shown that, for the distribution of X as well as for that of $\hat{\pi}$, the expression for α_3 is

(4.3) $$\alpha_3 = \frac{2\rho - 1}{\sqrt{n\pi\rho}}.$$

The basic characteristics of the two sampling distributions are summarized in Table 4–3.

Table 4–3

Characteristic	Distribution of X	Distribution of $\hat{\pi}$
Mean	$n\pi$	π
Variance	$n\pi\rho$	$\pi\rho/n$
α_3 (skewness)	$(2\rho - 1)/\sqrt{n\pi\rho}$	$(2\rho - 1)/\sqrt{n\pi\rho}$

Since now we have a complete knowledge of the sampling distribution of $\hat{\pi}$ for *any* specific population parameter π and for *any* sample size n, we can draw definite conclusions about the *properties* of $\hat{\pi}$ (proportion of successes in the sample) as an estimator of π (proportion of successes or the probability of success in the population). The main conclusions are

1. The mean of the sampling distribution of $\hat{\pi}$ is equal to the population parameter π. That is, $\hat{\pi}$ *is an unbiased estimator of* π.

2. Since the standard deviation of the sampling distribution of $\hat{\pi}$ is

$$(4.4) \qquad\qquad\qquad \sigma_{\hat{\pi}} = \sqrt{\frac{\pi \rho}{n}},$$

the distribution becomes more and more concentrated as the sample size is increased. This, together with conclusion 1, implies that $\hat{\pi}$ *is a consistent estimator of* π.

3. Given the formula for $\sigma_{\hat{\pi}}$ it follows that *the dispersion of the sampling distribution of* $\hat{\pi}$ (as measured by its standard deviation) *decreases with the square root of sample size.* This can be seen as follows. Consider two samples, the first of size n and the second of size $2n$. Then using the appropriate formula of Table 4–3, we have

$$\frac{\sigma_{\hat{\pi}} \text{ (2nd sample)}}{\sigma_{\hat{\pi}} \text{ (1st sample)}} = \frac{\sqrt{\pi \rho / 2n}}{\sqrt{\pi \rho / n}} = \frac{1}{\sqrt{2}};$$

i.e., $\qquad\qquad \sigma_{\hat{\pi}} \text{ (2nd sample)} = \frac{\sigma_{\hat{\pi}} \text{ (1st sample)}}{\sqrt{2}}.$

In other words, as the sample size is increased k times, the standard deviation of the sampling distribution decreases $\sqrt{k}$ times.

4. For any given sample size, the sampling distribution of $\hat{\pi}$ is *most dispersed* when the population parameter π is equal to 1/2, and is *least dispersed* when π is 0 or 1. This follows from the fact that $0 \leq \pi \leq 1$ and

$$\sigma_{\hat{\pi}} = \sqrt{\frac{\pi \rho}{n}} = \sqrt{\frac{\pi(1 - \pi)}{n}}$$

is at maximum when $\pi = 1/2$ and at minimum when $\pi = 0$ or 1. In fact, the largest value which $\sigma_{\hat{\pi}}$ can have is $1/(2\sqrt{n})$ and the smallest is 0.

5. *The skewness (asymmetry) of the sampling distribution of* $\hat{\pi}$ *decreases with the square root of sample size.* This clearly follows from (4.3) above.

6. For any *given* sample size, the sampling distribution of $\hat{\pi}$ is *least skewed* when π is equal to 1/2, and is *most skewed* when π is 0 or 1. This can be seen from (4.3) again: α_3 is zero when $\pi = 1/2$ and its departure from zero is greatest when π is either 0 or 1.

These conclusions have been reached with the help of probability theory and apply quite universally. In Section 2–1 we tried to derive the sampling distribution of $\hat{\pi}$ from a sampling experiment related to a population with $\pi = 0.70$. The experiment consisted of drawing 100 samples of size 4 and 100 samples of size 16. It enabled us to construct frequency distributions (one for each sample size), which were supposed to approximate the true sampling distributions. The results led to generalizations about the sampling distribution of $\hat{\pi}$ for any π and any sample size. Now we are in a position, first, to check the results to see how well the experimentally derived distributions fit the theoretical ones and, second, to verify or refute the validity of the generalizations.

Let us first compare the experimental and the theoretical distributions and their characteristics.

Sampling Distribution for Samples Size 4 (Table 4–4). The results for the experimentally determined probabilities are the relative frequencies of Table 2–1.

Table 4–4

Proportion of Successes: $\hat{\pi}$	Experimental $f(\hat{\pi})$	Theoretical $f(\hat{\pi})$
0.00	0.01	0.01
0.25	0.06	0.07
0.50	0.28	0.26
0.75	0.42	0.41
1.00	0.23	0.24
Mean	0.7	0.7
Standard deviation	0.2233	0.2291

The theoretical probabilities were derived from Freund,[2] rounded off to two decimal places. They could be calculated as follows:

$$f(0) = \left(\frac{4!}{4!0!}\right)(0.3)^4(0.7)^0 = (0.3)^4 = 0.0081 \approx 0.01,$$

$$f\left(\frac{1}{4}\right) = \left(\frac{4!}{3!1!}\right)(0.3)^3(0.7)^1 = 4 \times (0.3)^3 \times (0.7) = 0.0756 \approx 0.07,$$

and so on.

Sampling Distribution for Sample Size 16 (Table 4–5). The results for the experimentally determined probabilities have been taken from Table 2–2. The theoretical probabilities are from the same source as those for Table 4–4, again rounded off to two decimal places.

It is clear that the experimental results describe the sampling distributions quite closely; the errors are quite small and are unlikely to be of practical importance. Thus, in this case, distributions based on 100 samples come quite close to those that would result from an infinite number of samples. Furthermore, the generalizations made on the basis of experimental results—namely unbiasedness, consistency, relative change in the standard deviation, and decrease in skewness

[2] *Ibid.*, Table 1.

—all proved to be correct. However, the experimental results compare unfavorably with the theoretical ones in two respects. In the first place, the experimental results fail to give us any formulas for variance, measure of skewness, and, of course, the individual probabilities. In the second place, and this is much

Table 4–5

Proportion of Successes: $\hat{\pi}$	Experimental $f(\hat{\pi})$	Theoretical $f(\hat{\pi})$
0	0	0
1/16	0	0.00
2/16	0	0.00
3/16	0	0.00
4/16	0	0.00
5/16	0.01	0.00
6/16	0	0.01
7/16	0.01	0.02
8/16	0.05	0.05
9/16	0.10	0.10
10/16	0.17	0.17
11/16	0.21	0.21
12/16	0.20	0.20
13/16	0.15	0.15
14/16	0.07	0.07
15/16	0.03	0.02
1	0	0.00
Mean	0.7006	0.7
Standard deviation	0.1191	0.1146

more important, there is no guarantee at all that the generalizations deduced from the experimental distributions are, in fact, valid. The conclusions are not proved, only suggested by the results of isolated experiments.

4–2 Normal Distribution as the Limiting Case of Binomial Distribution

One of the findings of Section 4–1 was that the binomial distribution tends to be increasingly more symmetric as n (size of sample) increases, regardless of the value of π. Even the distributions with π close to zero (or to unity), which for small n are very skewed, tend to become symmetric when n is somewhat larger. This point is demonstrated by Figure 4–1 which shows the binomial probabilities for $\pi = 0.10$ for various values of n. Note also that as n increases, the points become more numerous and the connecting lines become smoother.

In this section, we shall carry the previous point still farther by asserting that *as n approaches infinity, the binomial distribution approaches the so-called normal*

distribution.[3] Normal distribution is a continuous distribution with probability
density

(4.5)
$$f(x) = \frac{1}{\sqrt{2\pi\sigma^2}}\, e^{-(1/2)[(x-\mu)/\sigma]^2},$$

where σ = standard deviation of X,

  μ = mean of X,

  π = 3.14159 ... (not to be confused with π, the population parameter),

  e = 2.71828 ....

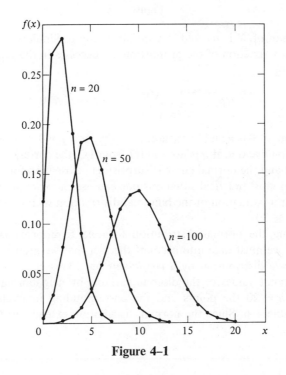

Figure 4–1

Graphical representation of a normal distribution is given in Figure 4–2. This
shows that the distribution is symmetric around its mean μ, and that it extends
from $-\infty$ to $+\infty$. Other properties are discussed on pages 82–83.

The fact that the binomial distribution approaches normal as $n \to \infty$ means,
in effect, that for a large n we can use normal distribution as an approximation to

[3] The proof can be found in many statistical texts. A relatively simple proof is presented
in G. Udny Yule and M. G. Kendall, *An Introduction to the Theory of Statistics* (London:
Charles Griffin, 1950), pp. 177–181.

the binomial distribution. Thus, if X is the number of successes in the sample and if n is large, we can write

(4.6) $$f(x) = \frac{1}{\sqrt{2\pi}} \frac{1}{\sqrt{n\pi\rho}} e^{-(1/2)[(x-n\pi)/\sqrt{n\pi\rho}]^2}$$

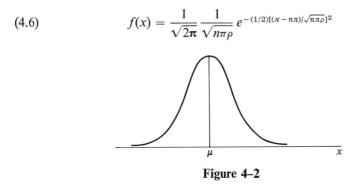

Figure 4–2

since the mean of X is $n\pi$ and the variance is $n\pi\rho$. Similarly, when n is large the probability function of the proportion of successes in the sample $(\hat{\pi})$ can be represented by

(4.7) $$f(\hat{\pi}) = \frac{1}{\sqrt{2\pi}} \frac{\sqrt{n}}{\sqrt{\pi\rho}} e^{-(1/2)[(\hat{\pi}-\pi)\sqrt{n}/\sqrt{\pi\rho}]^2},$$

since the mean of $\hat{\pi}$ is π and its variance is $\pi\rho/n$. How good these approximations are depends on n and π. If π is not too far from $1/2$, the correspondence between the binomial and the normal curve is surprisingly close even for low values of n. In general, in most practical situations one can use the normal distribution as a reasonable approximation of the binomial distribution without much hesitation as long as $n \geq 30$.

When using the normal distribution formula to approximate a binomial distribution, we must take into account the fact that we are trying to approximate a *discrete* distribution by a *continuous* one. This can be done by representing the point values of the discrete variable by neighboring intervals. For example, if $n = 20$ the points and the corresponding intervals would be as shown in Table 4–6. Since the normal distribution extends, in fact, from $-\infty$

Table 4–6

x (Discrete)	x (Continuous Approximation)	$\hat{\pi}$ (Discrete)	$\hat{\pi}$ (Continuous Approximation)
0	$-\frac{1}{2}$ to $\frac{1}{2}$	0	$-1/40$ to $1/40$
1	$\frac{1}{2}$ to $1\frac{1}{2}$	$1/20$	$1/40$ to $3/40$
2	$1\frac{1}{2}$ to $2\frac{1}{2}$	$2/20$	$3/40$ to $5/40$
3	$2\frac{1}{2}$ to $3\frac{1}{2}$	$3/20$	$5/40$ to $7/40$
⋮	⋮	⋮	⋮
20	$19\frac{1}{2}$ to $20\frac{1}{2}$	1	$39/40$ to $41/40$

to $+\infty$, we may start the first intervals at $-\infty$ and end the last intervals at $+\infty$ instead of the lower and upper limits shown.

The reconciliation between the discrete binomial and the continuous normal distribution becomes easier as the sample size gets larger. This can be seen particularly clearly with respect to the distribution of $\hat{\pi}$. As n gets larger, the intervals corresponding to each value of $\hat{\pi}$ become shorter. As an example, consider the intervals corresponding to the point $\hat{\pi} = 0.1$ for various sample sizes:

n	Interval	
10	0.05	to 0.15
20	0.075	to 0.125
50	0.090	to 0.110
100	0.095	to 0.105
1000	0.0995	to 0.1005
	etc.	

Note that, e.g., for $n = 1,000$, we replace the probability of $\hat{\pi}$ being equal to 0.1 by the probability that $\hat{\pi}$ is within 0.1 ± 0.0005, which is certainly not too rough. If we represent the binomial probabilities of $\hat{\pi}$ by rectangles with base equal to the appropriate interval and heights equal to $nf(\hat{\pi})$ (to make the total *area* equal to unity), we can see how the broken curve gets smoother as n gets larger. This is illustrated by Figure 4–3 for π equal to 0.1.

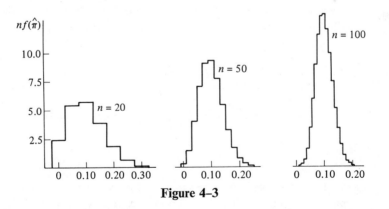

Figure 4–3

In asserting that binomial distribution converges to normal as n approaches infinity, we took it for granted that the population parameter π (and therefore p) is fixed, and that it is different from 0 or 1. If π is *not* fixed but decreases as $n \to \infty$ (so that $n\pi$ remains constant), the limiting form of the binomial distribution is not normal but becomes what is known as the *Poisson distribution*. This distribution became famous because it fitted extremely well the frequency of deaths from the kick of a horse in the Prussian army corps in the last quarter of the nineteenth century. As it is, the Poisson distribution has little relevance to us since our attention is confined to populations with a fixed proportion (probability) of successes. As for the cases in which π is equal to zero or one (i.e., the cases in which the population consists *entirely* of failures or of successes), the proportion of successes ($\hat{\pi}$) is the same in each sample and is equal to π. This means that the sampling distributions are concentrated on one point regardless of sample size, and thus the question of convergence to normal distribution does not arise.

Normal distribution is extremely important in econometrics, not only because it represents the limiting form of the binomial distribution, but because it applies to many other situations as well. This will become apparent in the subsequent section and in further discussions throughout the book. For that reason, it will be useful to consider the normal distribution in greater detail. First, let us describe its *main features*.

1. The distribution is *continuous* and *symmetric* around its mean μ. This has the following implications: (a) the mean, the median and the mode are all equal; and (b) the mean divides the area under the normal curve into exact halves.
2. The range of the distribution extends from $-\infty$ to $+\infty$, i.e., the distribution is *unbounded*.
3. The maximum height of the normal curve is attained at the point $x = \mu$, and the points of inflection (i.e., the points where the distribution starts flattening out) occur at $x = \mu \pm \sigma$. This means that the standard deviation measures the distance from the center of the distribution to a point of inflection, as illustrated in Figure 4-4.

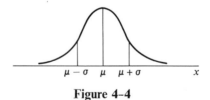

Figure 4-4

4. Normal distribution is *fully specified by two parameters, mean and variance*. This means that if we know μ and σ^2 of a normal distribution, we know all there is to know about it. Note that the binomial distribution is also fully specified by only two parameters, π and n. Figure 4-5 shows various comparisons of two normal distributions. Case (a) represents two normal distributions with different means but equal variances. In case (b) the means are equal but the variances are different, and in (c) both means and variances differ.

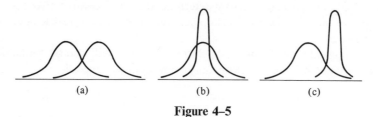

(a)   (b)   (c)

Figure 4–5

5. The last feature to be mentioned will be found particularly useful in later work. We present it here in the form of a theorem:

Theorem 12: *If $X, Y, Z, \ldots$, are normally and independently distributed random variables and a, b, c, $\ldots$, are constants, then the linear combination $aX + bY + cZ + \cdots$ is also normally distributed.*

The proof of this theorem can be found in many texts on mathematical statistics.[4]

Having stated the main properties of the normal distribution, we still have to face the problem of how to operate with it. In particular, we would like to be able to calculate different probabilities for a variable which is normally distributed. This was, at least in principle, no problem in the case of the binomial distribution since the terms of binomial expansion are determined by a straightforward formula. In the case of a normal distribution, however, the probability density formula is quite formidable. Fortunately, we do not have to use the formula; the probabilities, given by the corresponding areas under the curve, can be obtained from tabulated results. Of course, different normal distributions lead to different probabilities but since the differences can only be due to differences in means and variances, this presents no difficulty. If we know the areas under one specific normal curve, we can derive the areas under any other normal curve simply by allowing for the difference in the mean and the variance. The one specific distribution for which areas (corresponding to relatively narrow intervals) have been tabulated is a normal distribution with mean $\mu = 0$ and variance $\sigma^2 = 1$, called *standard normal distribution* (sometimes also called *unit normal distribution*).

The problem of determining the probabilities for a normally distributed variable X can be then stated as follows: given that we know (a) μ and σ^2 of X, and (b) the areas under the standard normal curve, how do we determine the probability that x will lie within some interval bordered by, say, x_1 and x_2?

To develop the solution, let us introduce the following notation:

$Z =$ a normally distributed variable with mean zero and variance equal to unity (i.e., a "standard normal variable");

$P(x_1 < x < x_2) =$ probability that X will lie between x_1 and x_2 $(x_1 < x_2)$;
$P(z_1 < z < z_2) =$ probability that Z will lie between z_1 and z_2 $(z_1 < z_2)$.

[4] See, for example, R. L. Anderson and T. A. Bancroft, *Statistical Theory in Research* (New York: McGraw-Hill, 1952), pp. 63–64.

We will proceed in two steps: first we determine the relationship between X and Z, and then we examine the relationship between corresponding areas under the two curves.

Since X is normally distributed, a linear function of X will also be normal (see Theorem 12). Such a linear function can be represented generally as

$$aX + b,$$

where a and b are some constants. If we find a and b such that they would make the mean of $(aX + b)$ zero and its variance unity, we will have a standard normal variable. That is, we require that

$$E(aX + b) = 0 \quad \text{and} \quad \text{Var}(aX + b) = 1.$$

This can be written as

$$a\mu + b = 0 \quad \text{(by Theorem 6)}$$

and

$$a^2\sigma^2 = 1 \quad \text{(by Theorem 7).}$$

Solving for a and b we obtain

$$a = \frac{1}{\sigma} \quad \text{and} \quad b = -\frac{\mu}{\sigma}.$$

Thus we have

$$aX + b = \frac{X - \mu}{\sigma}.$$

Since $(X - \mu)/\sigma$ has mean zero and variance equal to one, it is a standard normal variable, i.e.,

(4.8)
$$\frac{X - \mu}{\sigma} = Z.$$

Thus any normal variable with mean μ and variance σ^2 can be transformed into a standard normal variable by expressing it in terms of deviations from its mean, each deviation being divided by σ.

Let us consider $P(x_1 < x < x_2)$, where $x_1 < x_2$, which is a probability statement about X. We wish to find an exactly equivalent probability statement about Z. Now

$$\frac{X - \mu}{\sigma} = Z \quad \text{implies} \quad X = \sigma Z + \mu.$$

Therefore, we can write

$$x_1 = \sigma z_1 + \mu \quad \text{and} \quad x_2 = \sigma z_2 + \mu.$$

Consequently, by substitution we have

$$P(x_1 < x < x_2) = P(\sigma z_1 + \mu < \sigma z + \mu < \sigma z_2 + \mu).$$

After canceling out all the common positive terms in the right-hand-side inequality, this becomes

(4.9) $$P(x_1 < x < x_2) = P(z_1 < z < z_2),$$

where $$z_1 = \frac{x_1 - \mu}{\sigma} \quad \text{and} \quad z_2 = \frac{x_2 - \mu}{\sigma}.$$

Thus we have found that the probability that x lies between x_1 and x_2 is equal to the probability that a standard normal variable lies between $(x_1 - \mu)/\sigma$ and $(x_2 - \mu)/\sigma$.

As an example, consider a normally distributed variable X which has a mean of 5 and standard deviation of 2. The problem is to find the probability $P(2 < x < 3)$. To do that we have to find an equivalent probability statement in terms of the standard normal variable Z. Here the lower limit $x_1 = 2$ and the upper limit $x_2 = 3$. Since

$$z_1 = \frac{x_1 - \mu}{\sigma},$$

we have $$z_1 = \frac{2 - 5}{2} = -\frac{3}{2}.$$

Similarly, $$z_2 = \frac{x_2 - \mu}{\sigma} = \frac{3 - 5}{2} = -1.$$

Therefore, $P(2 < x < 3) = P(-3/2 < z < -1)$. This is shown graphically in Figure 4–6. The two shaded areas under the two curves are exactly the same.

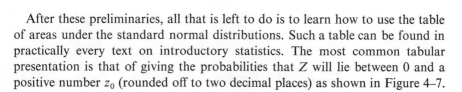

Figure 4–6

After these preliminaries, all that is left to do is to learn how to use the table of areas under the standard normal distributions. Such a table can be found in practically every text on introductory statistics. The most common tabular presentation is that of giving the probabilities that Z will lie between 0 and a positive number z_0 (rounded off to two decimal places) as shown in Figure 4–7.

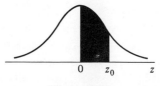

Figure 4–7

The table given in Appendix D of this book is of that form. The probabilities shown refer to only one half of the distribution. Since the distribution is perfectly symmetric this is, of course, sufficient. The largest probability (area) shown could

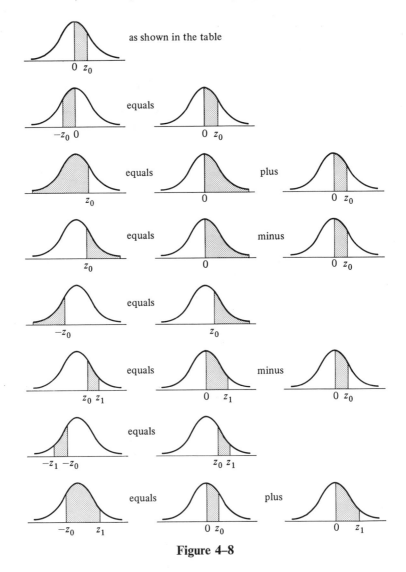

Figure 4–8

then be 0.5 at the point where $z = +\infty$. However, since the tail of the distribution tapers off fairly rapidly, the probability that z lies between 0 and 3 is already very close to 0.5 (in fact, it is 0.4987); therefore, most tables stop there. (Some tables give probabilities that z lies between $-\infty$ and a positive number. In these tables the *lowest* probability shown is 0.5 and the highest is close to 1.) The use of the table for solving various problems is indicated in Figure 4–8.

Note that $z_0 > 0$ and $z_1 > z_0$.

Let us now consider two examples on the use of the table areas under the standard normal curve. The first example will provide us with information that will prove useful in later work. The second example is concerned with the relationship between the binomial and the normal distribution in a specific case which is of interest to us.

EXAMPLE 1   If X is a random normal variable with mean μ and variance σ^2, find the following:

(a) $P(\mu - \sigma < x < \mu + \sigma)$,
(b) $P(\mu - 2\sigma < x < \mu + 2\sigma)$,
(c) $P(\mu - 3\sigma < x < \mu + 3\sigma)$,
(d) the two values of X which cut off the central 95 per cent of the area under the curve.
(e) the two values of X which cut off the central 99 per cent of the area under the curve.

The answers are found as follows.

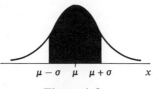

$$\mu - \sigma \quad \mu \quad \mu + \sigma \qquad x$$

Figure 4–9

For (a). We wish to determine the area shown in Figure 4–9. The corresponding lower and upper limits in terms of the standard normal variable are as follows:

$$z_1 = \frac{x_1 - \mu}{\sigma} = \frac{(\mu - \sigma) - \mu}{\sigma} = -1$$

and
$$z_2 = \frac{x_2 - \mu}{\sigma} = \frac{(\mu + \sigma) - \mu}{\sigma} = +1.$$

Then

$$P(-1 < z < +1) = P(0 < z < +1) + P(0 < z < +1) = 0.3413 + 0.3413 = 0.6826.$$

That is, *the probability that x lies within one standard deviation in either direction from its mean is* 68.26%.

For (b)

$$P(\mu - 2\sigma < x < \mu + 2\sigma) = P\left(\left[\frac{(\mu - 2\sigma) - \mu}{\sigma}\right] < z < \left[\frac{(\mu + 2\sigma) - \mu}{\sigma}\right]\right)$$

$$= P(-2 < z < +2) = 0.4772 + 0.4772 = 0.9544.$$

That is, *the probability that x lies within two standard deviations in either direction from its mean is* 95.44%.

For (c)

$$P(\mu - 3\sigma < x < \mu + 3\sigma) = P\left(\left[\frac{(\mu - 3\sigma) - \mu}{\sigma}\right] < z < \left[\frac{(\mu + 3\sigma) - \mu}{\sigma}\right]\right)$$

$$= P(-3 < z < +3) = 0.4987 + 0.4987 = 0.9974.$$

That is, *the probability that x lies within three standard deviations in either direction from its mean is* 99.74%. In other words, practically all values of X are confined to an interval of six standard derivations; the midpoint of this interval is, of course, the mean.

The previous problems were all cases in which we knew the values of X and determined the areas under the curve bounded by these values. The two problems that follow are of just the opposite kind: this time we know the area and want to find the boundary values of X.

For (d). Here we have $P(x_1 < x < x_2) = 0.95$, and the interval x_1 to x_2 is centered around the mean. Our problem is to find x_1 and x_2. We solve it by first finding the corresponding boundaries of the standard normal distribution. Given the probability statement for X, the corresponding probability statement for the standard normal variable Z is $P(z_1 < z < z_2) = 0.95$, and the interval z_1 to z_2 is centered around 0 (Figure 4–10). Because of the centering around zero we have

$$P(0 < z < z_2) = P(z_1 < z < 0) = \frac{0.95}{2} = 0.475.$$

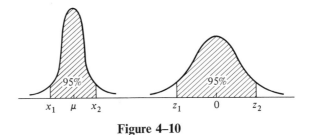

Figure 4–10

Searching the body of the table of areas of standard normal distribution, we find that the value of Z which corresponds to the area of 0.475 is 1.96. Thus,

$$z_2 = 1.96,$$

$$z_1 = -1.96.$$

Therefore
$$\frac{x_2 - \mu}{\sigma} = 1.96,$$

$$\frac{x_1 - \mu}{\sigma} = -1.96.$$

This gives
$$x_2 = \mu + 1.96\,\sigma$$

and
$$x_1 = \mu - 1.96\,\sigma.$$

That is, *the interval $\mu \pm 1.96\sigma$ contains the central 95% of all values of X.*

For (e)

$$P(x_1 < x < x_2) = 0.99,$$

$$P(z_1 < z < z_2) = 0.99,$$

$$P(0 < z < z_2) = 0.495.$$

The value of Z corresponding to the area of 0.495 is 2.57. Thus,

$$z_2 = 2.57,$$

$$z_1 = -2.57,$$

and therefore $\qquad x_2 = \mu + 2.57\,\sigma$

and $\qquad x_1 = \mu - 2.57\,\sigma.$

That is, *the interval $\mu \pm 2.57\sigma$ contains the central 99% of all values of X.*

EXAMPLE 2   Consider the distribution of sample proportion $\hat{\pi}$ for samples of size 16 coming from a population with a proportion of successes $\pi = 0.7$. This is the binomial distribution which was derived earlier; it is given in the last column of Table 4–5 (and reproduced in the last column of Table 4–7). We are supposed to find a normal approximation of this distribution. The solution is as follows. First, we have to replace the points $\hat{\pi}$ of the discrete binomial distribution by intervals that would pertain to the corresponding normal distribution. This was explained and described at the beginning of this section. The next step is to obtain the normal probabilities corresponding to each interval. Since in this case the binomial distribution of $\hat{\pi}$ has a mean of 0.7 and standard deviation of 0.11464, the approximating normal distribution must be characterized by these parametric values. To find the probabilities we have to make a transformation to the standard normal variable given by

$$z = \frac{\hat{\pi} - 0.7}{0.11464} = 8.72872\hat{\pi} - 6.11010.$$

This will enable us to state the intervals in terms of z rather than $\hat{\pi}$, and to find the corresponding probabilities from the table of areas of the standard normal distribution. The results are presented in Table 4–7. It is obvious that the normal approximation to the binomial distribution is extremely close in spite of the fact the size of the sample is only 16.

In our discussion about the normal distribution, we started with the assertion that normal distribution is the limiting form of binomial distribution. It should be pointed out that this is only one way in which the normal distribution may be deduced and that there are other lines of reasoning which would lead to it.[5] Of these the most important one is that in which the derivation is based on the behavior of random errors. For instance, consider the problem of measuring the length of an object. Under ordinary circumstances each measurement may be subject to an error. Now let us suppose that any error is the result of an indefinitely large number of small causes, each producing a small deviation.

[5] For a compact survey, see C. R. Rao, *Linear Statistical Inference and Its Applications* (New York: Wiley, 1965), pp. 126ff.

If we then assume that all of these small deviations are equal and that positive deviations are just as likely as negative deviations, then it can be shown that the *errors are normally distributed* about zero, i.e., that the measurements are normally distributed about the "true" value. The basis of this derivation can, of course, be interpreted quite generally. In particular, the term "error" can

Table 4–7

$\hat{\pi}$ (Discrete Values)	$\hat{\pi}$ (Intervals)	z (Intervals)	$F(\hat{\pi})$ (Cumulative Normal Approximation)*	$f(\hat{\pi})$ (Normal Approximation)†	$f(\hat{\pi})$ (Binomial Distribution)
0	−1/32 to 1/32	−∞ to −5.84	0.0000	0.0000 (0.00)	0.00
1/16	1/32 to 3/32	−5.84 to −5.29	0.0000	0.0000 (0.00)	0.00
2/16	3/32 to 5/32	−5.29 to −4.75	0.0000	0.0000 (0.00)	0.00
3/16	5/32 to 7/32	−4.75 to −4.20	0.0000	0.0000 (0.00)	0.00
4/16	7/32 to 9/32	−4.20 to −3.66	0.0000	0.0000 (0.00)	0.00
5/16	9/32 to 11/32	−3.66 to −3.11	0.0009	0.0009 (0.00)	0.00
6/16	11/32 to 13/32	−3.11 to −2.57	0.0050	0.0041 (0.00)	0.01
7/16	13/32 to 15/32	−2.57 to −2.02	0.0217	0.0167 (0.02)	0.02
8/16	15/32 to 17/32	−2.02 to −1.48	0.0694	0.0477 (0.05)	0.05
9/16	17/32 to 19/32	−1.48 to −0.93	0.1762	0.1068 (0.11)	0.10
10/16	19/32 to 21/32	−0.93 to −0.38	0.3520	0.1758 (0.17)	0.17
11/16	21/32 to 23/32	−0.38 to 0.16	0.5636	0.2116 (0.21)	0.21
12/16	23/32 to 25/32	0.16 to 0.71	0.7611	0.1975 (0.20)	0.20
13/16	25/32 to 27/32	0.71 to 1.25	0.8944	0.1333 (0.13)	0.15
14/16	27/32 to 29/32	1.25 to 1.80	0.9641	0.0697 (0.07)	0.07
15/16	29/32 to 31/32	1.80 to 2.34	0.9904	0.0263 (0.03)	0.02
1	31/32 to 33/32	2.34 to +∞	1.0000	0.0096 (0.01)	0.00

* $F(\hat{\pi})$ is represented by the area from $-\infty$ to the upper limit of each interval.

† $f(\hat{\pi})$ is given by the area corresponding to each interval. The figures in brackets are the probabilities rounded off to two decimal places.

be taken to mean any deviation from some systematic behavior, and this is the interpretation which underlies most theoretical developments in modern econometrics. This will become obvious as soon as we start discussing regression models. For now we ought to mention that the extensive use of the normal distribution has led to the following abbreviated notation:

$X \sim N(\mu, \sigma^2)$ *means that X is a normally distributed random variable with mean μ and variance σ^2. Therefore, $X \sim N(0, 1)$ stands for standard normal variable.* This notation will be followed hereafter.

4–3 Sampling Distribution of Sample Mean

In the case of the sampling distribution of sample proportion discussed in Section 4–1, we dealt with sampling from a dichotomous population. Every observation was classified as a failure or a success, and we considered the proportion of successes in the sample as an estimator of the probability of success in the population. As mentioned earlier, the labeling of observations as failure or success could be replaced by numerical values, namely 0 for failure and 1 for success. Thus instead of dealing with attributes we would be dealing with a *binary variable*. Suppose we call this variable Y and observe the following values in a sample of six observations:

$$y_1 = 0,$$

$$y_2 = 1,$$

$$y_3 = 0,$$

$$y_4 = 0,$$

$$y_5 = 1,$$

$$y_6 = 0.$$

Then the observed proportion of successes is

$$\hat{\pi} = \frac{0 + 1 + 0 + 0 + 1 + 0}{6} = \frac{2}{6} = \frac{1}{n} \sum_{i=1}^{6} y_i = \bar{y}.$$

That is, the proportion of successes in the sample is nothing else but the sample mean of Y. Further, we know that the probability of success in the population is the limit of the relative frequency of successes as the number of observations approaches infinity. Since the limit of relative frequency of y is the probability of y—which we labeled $f(y)$—and since observing a success means that $y = 1$, it follows that

$$\pi = P(\text{success}) = P(y = 1) = f(1),$$

or $\qquad\qquad\qquad \pi = 1 \times f(1).$

This may as well be written as

$$\pi = 0 \times f(0) + 1 \times f(1),$$

since zero times any number is zero. But writing the expression for π in this form shows that π is, in fact, equal to the weighted average of the different values of Y (i.e., 0 and 1) with the weights given by the respective probabilities. This is precisely the definition of the mathematical expectation of Y as stated in (3.23). Therefore, we have

$$\pi = E(Y) = \mu_Y.$$

In other words, the probability of success in the population is the population mean of Y. Therefore, the sampling distribution of sample proportion (as an estimator of the probability of success) can be viewed as a sampling distribution of sample mean (as an estimator of population mean) when the variable is a binary one.

At this stage we are interested in the problem of deriving the sampling distribution of sample mean in cases in which the variable can assume more than two values and have any kind of distribution. In general, we expect that different distributions of the variable in the population (i.e., "parent" distributions) lead to different forms of sampling distributions of sample mean. For example, there is no apparent reason why the distribution of sample mean for samples drawn from a highly skewed population should have the same form as that for samples drawn from a symmetric population. However, we cannot and do not want to discuss every conceivable form of parent distribution individually. For our purpose, it is sufficient if we limit ourselves to a detailed discussion of only two distributions—a discrete uniform and a normal distribution—and consider all the other distributions in general terms. The discrete uniform distribution is of special interest to us because it was used as the basis of our sampling experiment in Section 2–2; it also provides a convenient background for illustrating a way of deriving theoretical sampling distributions. The normal distribution will be discussed because many inference statements in econometrics depend heavily on the assumption of normality in the parent population.

First, we take up the problem of deriving the sampling distribution of sample mean when the variable of interest (say, X) has a *discrete uniform distribution.* This means that X can assume a finite number of different values, each with equal probability. The case of a binary variable represents a special case; we already know that this case leads to a binomial distribution of sample mean (see Section 4–1). Here our concern is with a more general problem. We will start by specifying the parental distribution as that which was used in our sampling experiment in Section 2–2. There, it may be recalled, we let X take on values $0, 1, 2, \ldots, 9$, each with probability of $1/10$. As worked out earlier, the main characteristics of this distribution are:

Mean: $\qquad\qquad\qquad E(X) = 4.5$

Variance: $\qquad\qquad\quad \mathrm{Var}(X) = 2.8723^2 = 8.25.$

Later on we shall generalize this case to allow for any number of different values of X.

Let us then derive the sampling distribution of $\bar{X}$ as an estimator of $\mu = 4.5$. In this we will follow the procedure of Section 4–1 by "building up" the probabilities of individual values of the estimator and by calculating the main characteristics of the resulting distribution. As before, we will do this for different sample sizes and try to discover the pattern that would allow us to develop a general formula to apply to any sample size.

Sampling Distribution of $\bar{X}$ for Sample Size 1. In this case $\bar{X}$ can assume 10 different values: $0, 1, 2, \ldots, 9$, the same as the variable X. The probability of each of these values is $1/10$, as shown in Table 4–8 and Figure 4–11.

Table 4–8

$\bar{x}$	$f(\bar{x})$	$\bar{x}f(\bar{x})$	$\bar{x}^2f(\bar{x})$
0	$P(0) = 1/10$	0	0
1	$P(1) = 1/10$	1/10	1/10
2	$P(2) = 1/10$	2/10	4/10
3	$P(3) = 1/10$	3/10	9/10
4	$P(4) = 1/10$	4/10	16/10
5	$P(5) = 1/10$	5/10	25/10
6	$P(6) = 1/10$	6/10	36/10
7	$P(7) = 1/10$	7/10	49/10
8	$P(8) = 1/10$	8/10	64/10
9	$P(9) = 1/10$	9/10	81/10
	Sum 1	45/10	285/10

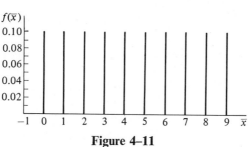

Figure 4–11

Mean and variance of $\bar{X}$:

$$E(\bar{X}) = \sum_i \bar{x}_i f(\bar{x}_i) = 4.5,$$

$$\text{Var}(\bar{X}) = E(\bar{X}^2) - [E(\bar{X})]^2 = \sum_i \bar{x}_i^2 f(\bar{x}_i) - \left[\sum_i \bar{x}_i f(\bar{x}_i)\right]^2 = 28.5 - 4.5^2 = 8.25.$$

The mean and variance of $\bar{X}$ in this case are, of course, the same as those of X in the population.

Sampling Distribution of $\bar{X}$ for Sample Size 2.   Here the possible values of $\bar{X}$ are 0, 1/2, 2/2, ..., 18/2. That is, there are 19 different values that $\bar{X}$ can assume. The probability distribution is given in Table 4–9. The complete enumeration of various probabilities in Table 4–9 can be replaced by combinatorial formulas as developed in Section 3–2. In particular, we can write:

$$P(0, 0) = \binom{1}{1} \bigg/ 10^2$$

$$P(0, 1) + P(1, 0) = \binom{2}{1} \bigg/ 10^2$$

$$P(0, 2) + P(2, 0) + P(1, 1) = \binom{3}{1} \bigg/ 10^2$$

$$P(0, 3) + P(3, 0) + P(1, 2) + P(2, 1) = \binom{4}{1} \Big/ 10^2$$

$$\vdots$$

$$P(0, 9) + P(9, 0) + P(8, 1) + P(1, 8) + P(2, 7)$$
$$+ P(7, 2) + P(3, 6) + P(6, 3) + P(4, 5) + P(5, 4) = \binom{10}{1} \Big/ 10^2$$

$$P(1, 9) + P(9, 1) + P(2, 8) + P(8, 2) + P(3, 7)$$
$$+ P(7, 3) + P(4, 6) + P(6, 4) + P(5, 5) = \left[\binom{11}{1} - 2\right] \Big/ 10^2$$

$$\vdots$$

$$P(8, 9) + P(9, 8) = \left[\binom{18}{1} - 16\right] \Big/ 10^2$$

$$P(9, 9) = \left[\binom{19}{1} - 18\right] \Big/ 10^2 .$$

The resulting distribution has a "triangular" form, as shown in Figure 4–12.

Table 4–9

$\bar{x}$	$f(\bar{x})$		$\bar{x}f(\bar{x})$	$\bar{x}^2 f(\bar{x})$
0	$P(0,0)$	$= 1/10^2$	0.00	0.000
1/2	$P(0,1) + P(1,0)$	$= 2/10^2$	0.01	0.005
2/2	$P(0,2) + P(2,0) + P(1,1)$	$= 3/10^2$	0.03	0.030
3/2	$P(0,3) + P(3,0) + P(1,2) + P(2,1)$	$= 4/10^2$	0.06	0.090
4/2	$\cdots$	$= 5/10^2$	0.10	0.200
5/2	$\cdots$	$= 6/10^2$	0.15	0.375
6/2	$\cdots$	$= 7/10^2$	0.21	0.630
7/2	$\cdots$	$= 8/10^2$	0.28	0.980
8/2	$\cdots$	$= 9/10^2$	0.36	1.440
9/2	$P(0,9) + P(9,0) + P(1,8) + P(8,1)$ $+ P(2,7) + P(7,2) + P(3,6) + P(6,3)$ $+ P(4,5) + P(5,4)$	$= 10/10^2$	0.45	2.025
10/2	$P(1,9) + P(9,1) + P(2,8) + P(8,2)$ $+ P(3,7) + P(7,3) + P(4,6) + P(6,4)$ $+ P(5,5)$	$= 9/10^2$	0.45	2.250
$\vdots$	$\vdots$	$\vdots$	$\vdots$	$\vdots$
17/2	$P(8,9) + P(9,8)$	$= 2/10^2$	0.17	1.445
18/2	$P(9,9)$	$= 1/10^2$	0.09	0.810
		Sum 1	4.50	24.375

Mean and variance of $\bar{X}$:

$$E(\bar{X}) = 4.5,$$

$$\mathrm{Var}(\bar{X}) = 24.375 - 4.5^2 = 24.375 - 20.25 = 4.125.$$

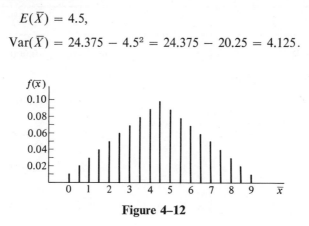

Figure 4–12

Sampling Distribution of $\bar{X}$ for Sample Size 3.   The possible values of $\bar{X}$ in this case are 0, 1/3, 2/3, ..., 27/3. The corresponding probabilities are derived in Table 4–10. The distribution is perfectly symmetric around the point 4.5. Its graphical representation is given in Figure 4–13.

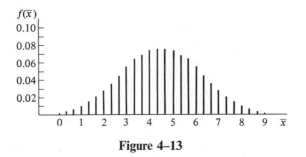

Figure 4–13

Mean and variance of $\bar{X}$:

$$E(\bar{X}) = 4.5,$$

$$\mathrm{Var}(\bar{X}) = 23.00 - 4.5^2 = 2.75.$$

By now it should be clear how to go about constructing the sampling distributions, and there is no need for us to continue in detail. Instead, let us present the distribution for various sample sizes in a summary form. We hope this will inspire a generalization that would enable us to determine the probability of *any* given value of $\bar{X}$ for *any* sample size from one formula.

Table 4–11 has been set up in a way which would make the presentation as concise as possible without a loss of clarity. Since the values of $\bar{X}$ are always of the form $0/n$, $1/n$, $2/n$, ..., $9n/n$, each one of them depends on the sample size n. To avoid having to present a different column of values of $\bar{X}$ for each sample

Table 4–10

$\bar{x}$	$f(\bar{x})$			$\bar{x}f(\bar{x})$	$\bar{x}^2f(\bar{x})$
0	$P(0,0,0)$	$= \binom{2}{2}\big/10^3$	$= 1/10^3$	0.000	0.000 000
1/3	$P(0,0,1) + P(0,1,0)$				
	$\quad + P(1,0,0)$	$= \binom{3}{2}\big/10^3$	$= 3/10^3$	0.001	0.000 333
2/3	$\cdots$	$= \binom{4}{2}\big/10^3$	$= 6/10^3$	0.004	0.002 667
3/3	$\cdots$	$= \binom{5}{2}\big/10^3$	$= 10/10^3$	0.010	0.010 000
4/3	$\cdots$	$= \binom{6}{2}\big/10^3$	$= 15/10^3$	0.020	0.026 667
5/3	$\cdots$	$= \binom{7}{2}\big/10^3$	$= 21/10^3$	0.035	0.058 333
6/3	$\cdots$	$= \binom{8}{2}\big/10^3$	$= 28/10^3$	0.056	0.112 000
7/3	$\cdots$	$= \binom{9}{2}\big/10^3$	$= 36/10^3$	0.084	0.196 000
8/3	$\cdots$	$= \binom{10}{2}\big/10^3$	$= 45/10^3$	0.120	0.320 000
9/3	$\cdots$	$= \binom{11}{2}\big/10^3$	$= 55/10^3$	0.165	0.495 000
10/3	$\cdots$	$= \left[\binom{12}{2} - 3\right]\big/10^3$	$= 63/10^3$	0.210	0.700 000
11/3	$\cdots$	$= \left[\binom{13}{2} - 9\right]\big/10^3$	$= 69/10^3$	0.253	0.927 667
12/3	$\cdots$	$= \left[\binom{14}{2} - 18\right]\big/10^3$	$= 73/10^3$	0.292	1.168 000
13/3	$\cdots$	$= \left[\binom{15}{2} - 30\right]\big/10^3$	$= 75/10^3$	0.325	1.408 333
14/3	$\cdots$	$= \left[\binom{16}{2} - 45\right]\big/10^3$	$= 75/10^3$	0.350	1.633 333
15/3	$\cdots$	$= \left[\binom{17}{2} - 63\right]\big/10^3$	$= 73/10^3$	0.365	1.825 000
$\vdots$		$\vdots$	$\vdots$	$\vdots$	$\vdots$
26/3		$= \left[\binom{28}{2} - 375\right]\big/10^3$	$= 3/10^3$	0.026	0.225 333
27/3		$= \left[\binom{29}{2} - 405\right]\big/10^3$	$= 1/10^3$	0.009	0.081 000
			Sum $\quad$ 1	4.500	23.000 000

Table 4–11

$n\bar{x}$	$n=1$	$n=2$		$n=3$		$n=4$		$n=5$	
				$10^n f(\bar{x})$					
0	1	$\binom{1}{1}$	$= 1$	$\binom{2}{2}$	$= 1$	$\binom{3}{3}$	$= 1$	$\binom{4}{4}$	$= 1$
1	1	$\binom{2}{1}$	$= 2$	$\binom{3}{2}$	$= 3$	$\binom{4}{3}$	$= 4$	$\binom{5}{4}$	$= 5$
2	1	$\binom{3}{1}$	$= 3$	$\binom{4}{2}$	$= 6$	$\binom{5}{3}$	$= 10$	$\binom{6}{4}$	$= 15$
$\vdots$	$\vdots$	$\vdots$		$\vdots$		$\vdots$		$\vdots$	
8	1	$\binom{9}{1}$	$= 9$	$\binom{10}{2}$	$= 45$	$\binom{11}{3}$	$= 165$	$\binom{12}{4}$	$= 495$
9	1	$\binom{10}{1}$	$= 10$	$\binom{11}{2}$	$= 55$	$\binom{12}{3}$	$= 220$	$\binom{13}{4}$	$= 715$
10		$\binom{11}{1}-2$	$= 9$	$\binom{12}{2}-3$	$= 63$	$\binom{13}{3}-4$	$= 282$	$\binom{14}{4}-5$	$= 996$
11		$\binom{12}{1}-4$	$= 8$	$\binom{13}{2}-9$	$= 69$	$\binom{14}{3}-16$	$= 348$	$\binom{15}{4}-25$	$= 1,340$
12		$\binom{13}{1}-6$	$= 7$	$\binom{14}{2}-18$	$= 73$	$\binom{15}{3}-40$	$= 415$	$\binom{16}{4}-75$	$= 1,745$
$\vdots$		$\vdots$		$\vdots$		$\vdots$		$\vdots$	
18		$\binom{19}{1}-18$	$= 1$	$\binom{20}{2}-135$	$= 55$	$\binom{21}{3}-660$	$= 670$	$\binom{22}{4}-2,475$	$= 4,840$
19				$\binom{21}{2}-165$	$= 45$	$\binom{22}{3}-880$	$= 660$	$\binom{23}{4}-3,575$	$= 5,280$
20				$\binom{22}{2}-195$	$= 36$	$\binom{23}{3}-1,138$	$= 633$	$\binom{24}{4}-4,995$	$= 5,631$
21				$\binom{23}{2}-225$	$= 28$	$\binom{24}{3}-1,432$	$= 592$	$\binom{25}{4}-6,775$	$= 5,875$
22				$\binom{24}{2}-255$	$= 21$	$\binom{25}{3}-1,760$	$= 540$	$\binom{26}{4}-8,950$	$= 6,000$
$\vdots$				$\vdots$		$\vdots$		$\vdots$	
28						$\binom{31}{3}-3,330$	$= 165$	$\binom{32}{4}-31,625$	$= 4,335$
29						$\binom{32}{3}-4,840$	$= 120$	$\binom{33}{4}-37,125$	$= 3,795$
30						$\binom{33}{3}-5,240$	$= 84$	$\binom{34}{4}-43,130$	$= 3,246$
31						$\binom{34}{3}-5,928$	$= 56$	$\binom{35}{4}-49,650$	$= 2,710$
32						$\binom{35}{3}-6,510$	$= 35$	$\binom{36}{4}-56,700$	$= 2,205$
$\vdots$						$\vdots$		$\vdots$	
$\sum_i \bar{x}_i f(\bar{x}_i)$	4.5	4.50		4.500		4.5000		4.5000	
$\sum_i \bar{x}_i^2 f(\bar{x}_i)$	28.5	24.375		23.000		22.3125		21.9000	

size, we use only the numerators $0, 1, 2, \ldots$. These are pure numbers independent of sample size in every respect other than the determination of the last one. They are, of course, nothing else but $n\bar{x}$ as shown in the heading of the first column. In writing out the actual numbers in this column, we confine ourselves only to those which center around the "breaking-off" points given by multiples of 10. The individual probabilities themselves are fractions with 10^n for denominator. To avoid repeated rewriting of this denominator, we present only the numerators; this accounts for the label "$10^n f(\bar{x})$" instead of the usual $f(\bar{x})$. In other respects the table is quite conventional.

The best way of analyzing the probability coefficients given in the main body of Table 4–11 is by considering them in groups of 10 at a time. The reason for this is the fact that there are 10 different values of X in the population so that the pattern of probabilities of $\bar{x}$ changes after each 10th, 20th, etc., coefficient. The thresholds separating the groups are represented in the table by horizontal dotted lines. Let us begin by considering the first 10 coefficients where the pattern is the simplest. For sample size 1, all of the coefficients are the same and are equal to 1. To make the notation consistent with that of the other columns, we may as well write out these coefficients as

$$\binom{0}{0}, \binom{1}{0}, \binom{2}{0}, \ldots, \binom{9}{0},$$

since each one is equal to unity anyway (see Section 3–2). Then a simple inspection of the table shows that, for the values of $n\bar{x}$ from 0 to 9, the probabilities are

$$f(\bar{x}) = \binom{n\bar{x} + n - 1}{n - 1} \bigg/ 10^n.$$

For example, the probability that $\bar{x}$ of sample size 5 will be equal to 1 is

$$\binom{5 + 5 - 1}{5 - 1} \bigg/ 10^5 = 0.00126.$$

The formula for the first 10 coefficients applies to the second group of coefficients only after a certain modification has been made. This modification consists of deducting a number which we shall call a correction factor c_1. That is, for $n\bar{x}$ from 10 to 19, we have

$$f(\bar{x}) = \left[\binom{n\bar{x} + n - 1}{n - 1} - c_1\right] \bigg/ 10^n.$$

The problem is to discover a formula for c_1. Note that c_1 is in every case a multiple of the corresponding sample size. Dividing each value of c_1 by the sample size n we find the following sequences:

$n\bar{x}$	$n = 2$	$n = 3$	$n = 4$	$n = 5$
10	1	1	1	1
11	2	3	4	5
12	3	6	10	15
13	4	10	20	35
⋮	⋮	⋮	⋮	⋮

Now it appears that these sequences are simply the probability coefficients given ten places earlier. That is,

$$c_1 = n\binom{n\bar{x} - 10 + n - 1}{n - 1},$$

and, therefore, the probabilities of different values of $\bar{X}$ for $n\bar{x}$ from 10 to 19 are:

$$f(\bar{x}) = \left[\binom{n\bar{x} + n - 1}{n - 1} - n\binom{n\bar{x} - 10 + n - 1}{n - 1}\right]\Big/10^n.$$

For example, the probability that $\bar{x}$ of sample size 4 will be equal to 4.5 is

$$\left[\binom{18 + 4 - 1}{4 - 1} - 4\binom{18 - 10 + 4 - 1}{4 - 1}\right]\Big/10^4 = \left[\binom{21}{3} - 4\binom{11}{3}\right]\Big/10^4$$

$$= 0.0670.$$

Applying the formula developed for the second group of coefficients to determine the coefficients in the third group reveals that a further correction is necessary. Consider, for instance, the coefficient for $n\bar{x} = 20$ in sample size 3. This coefficient is equal to

$$\binom{22}{2} - 195 = 36.$$

But the application of the formula of the preceding paragraph gives

$$\binom{22}{2} - 3\binom{12}{2} = 33 \neq 36.$$

Thus we need another correction factor to be called c_2. Then, for $n\bar{x}$ from 20 to 29, we have

$$f(\bar{x}) = \left[\binom{n\bar{x} + n - 1}{n - 1} - n\binom{n\bar{x} - 10 + n - 1}{n - 1} + c_2\right]\Big/10^n.$$

The values of c_2 are

$n\bar{x}$	$n = 3$	$n = 4$	$n = 5$
20	3	6	10
21	9	24	50
22	18	60	150
23	30	120	350
⋮	⋮	⋮	⋮

Note that all the values in the column "$n = 3$" are multiples of 3, those in the column "$n = 4$" multiples of 6, and those in the column "$n = 5$" multiples of 10. The relationship of these common factors to the respective sample sizes can be identified, after some reflection, as follows: $3 = \binom{3}{2}$, $6 = \binom{4}{2}$, and $10 = \binom{5}{2}$. In general, the common factor is equal to $\binom{n}{2}$. After dividing each column by the respective common factor we get

$n\bar{x}$	$n = 3$	$n = 4$	$n = 5$
20	1	1	1
21	3	4	5
22	6	10	15
23	10	20	35
$\vdots$	$\vdots$	$\vdots$	$\vdots$

These sequences are simply the probability coefficients given twenty places earlier. Therefore, the formula for the probabilities of different values of $\bar{X}$ for $n\bar{x}$ ranging from 20 to 29 is

$$f(\bar{x}) = \left[\binom{n\bar{x} + n - 1}{n - 1} - n\binom{n\bar{x} - 10 + n - 1}{n - 1} \right.$$
$$\left. + \binom{n}{2}\binom{n\bar{x} - 20 + n - 1}{n - 1} \right] \bigg/ 10^n.$$

As an example consider the probability that $\bar{x}$ of sample size 4 will be equal to 6. This is

$$\left[\binom{24 + 4 - 1}{4 - 1} - 4\binom{24 - 10 + 4 - 1}{4 - 1} + 6\binom{24 - 20 + 4 - 1}{4 - 1} \right] \bigg/ 10^4 = 0.0415.$$

We could continue this further but by now the pattern is quite clear. To calculate the probability of *any* value of $\bar{X}$ for *any* sample size n, we simply extend the preceding formula for $f(\bar{x})$ by adding further correction factors of the same type. In general, the probability distribution of $\bar{X}$ will then be

$$(4.10) \quad f(\bar{x}) = \frac{1}{10^n} \left[\binom{n\bar{x} + n - 1}{n - 1} - \binom{n}{1}\binom{n\bar{x} - 10 + n - 1}{n - 1} \right.$$
$$\left. + \binom{n}{2}\binom{n\bar{x} - 20 + n - 1}{n - 1} - \binom{n}{3}\binom{n\bar{x} - 30 + n - 1}{n - 1} + \cdots \right].$$

The sum in (4.10) is to be continued as long as $(n\bar{x} - 10)$, $(n\bar{x} - 20)$, . . . remain positive or zero, i.e., until 10, 20, 30, . . . remain less or equal to $n\bar{x}$.

Equation (4.10) gives us the sampling distribution of $\bar{X}$ for samples drawn from a discrete uniform population with values of X equal to 0, 1, 2, . . . , 9. It is a simple matter to modify the formula to apply to a situation where X can assume, with equal probability, any one of k different values which are separated by equal distances. All that is needed to make this generalization is to replace $10, 20, 30, \ldots$ in formula (4.10) by $k, 2k, 3k, \ldots$ to get

$$(4.11) \quad f(\bar{x}) = \frac{1}{k^n}\left[\binom{n\bar{x} + n - 1}{n - 1} - \binom{n}{1}\binom{n\bar{x} - k + n - 1}{n - 1}\right.$$
$$\left. + \binom{n}{2}\binom{n\bar{x} - 2k + n - 1}{n - 1} - \binom{n}{3}\binom{n\bar{x} - 3k + n - 1}{n - 1} + \cdots\right].$$

Let us now determine the basic characteristics of the sampling distributions given by (4.10) and (4.11). With respect to the former, the values of the means and variances obtained earlier for sample sizes 1, 2, 3, 4, and 5 are summarized in Table 4–12. (The variances for sample sizes 1, 2, and 3 were calculated earlier;

Table 4–12

Sample Size	Mean	Variance
1	4.5	8.25
2	4.5	4.125
3	4.5	2.75
4	4.5	2.0625
5	4.5	1.65

those for sample sizes 4 and 5 can be obtained from the bottom line of Table 4–11 by deducting 4.5^2.) The most obvious feature of Table 4–12 is the fact that the value of the mean is equal to the population mean for all sample sizes examined. As far as the variance is concerned, note that its value for sample size 1 is exactly equal to the population variance and that the remaining values decrease in proportion to sample size, i.e., that

$$4.125 = \frac{8.25}{2},$$

$$2.75 = \frac{8.25}{3},$$

$$2.0625 = \frac{8.25}{4},$$

$$1.65 = \frac{8.25}{5}.$$

Finally, since we found all the sampling distributions to be exactly symmetric, the third moment μ_3 (and, therefore, also α_3) must be equal to zero. These results can easily be generalized to apply to any sample size n. Then we have

$$E(\bar{X}) = \mu,$$

$$\sigma_{\bar{x}}^2 = \frac{\sigma_x^2}{n},$$

$$\alpha_3 = 0,$$

where $\quad \sigma_{\bar{x}}^2 = \mathrm{Var}(\bar{X}) \quad$ and $\quad \sigma_x^2 = \mathrm{Var}(X).$

It can be shown that these generalizations are perfectly valid and, furthermore, that they apply not only to the distribution (4.10) but also to its generalized version given by (4.11). (The proof concerning the mean and the variance will be given toward the end of this section; the proof concerning α_3 is left to the reader.)

Now we are in a position to make definite statements about the properties of sample mean as an estimator of the population mean for samples from a *discrete uniform population* with equally spaced values of X. The following conclusions can be made:

1. $\overline{X}$ *is an unbiased estimator of* μ.
2. *The variance of* $\overline{X}$ *is equal to the variance of* X *divided by sample size.* Thus, as the sample size increases, the distribution of $\overline{X}$ becomes more and more concentrated.
3. Conclusions 1 and 2 together imply that $\overline{X}$ *is a consistent estimator of* μ.
4. *The distribution of* $\overline{X}$ *is perfectly symmetric.*

These properties of $\overline{X}$ have been deduced from the theoretically derived sampling distribution. In Section 2–2 we tried to find these properties by conducting a sampling experiment on a discrete uniform population with values of X equal to 0, 1, 2, ..., 9. The experiment consisted of drawing 100 samples of size 5 and 100 samples of size 10. For sample size 5, we constructed frequency distributions of sample mean and of sample median, and for sample size 10 of sample mean alone. The frequency distributions obtained in this way were assumed to approximate the true sampling distributions of these estimators. The results enabled us to make some tentative conclusions concerning the properties of these estimators. With respect to sample mean we are now in a position to check the experimental results by comparing them with the theoretically derived ones.

First, let us look at the sampling distribution of sample mean for sample size 5. The experimental results for this case are given in Table 2–4. They are reproduced in Table 4–13, alongside the theoretical results obtained from Table 4–11, and presented in a comparable form.

Next we compare the experimental and the theoretical results for sample size 10. The experimental results are given in Table 2–6; the theoretical results have been calculated by using formula (4.10) and the derived expressions for $E(\overline{X})$ and $\sigma_{\overline{x}}$. The distributions are presented in a comparable form in Table 4–14. The theoretical distribution is, of course, perfectly symmetric, although this is not immediately apparent from Table 4–14 because of the way the interval limits are spaced.

Tables 4–13 and 4–14 show that the experimentally derived frequency distributions give a reasonable approximation of the true sampling distributions. The tentative conclusions about $\overline{X}$ as an estimator of the population mean— namely unbiasedness, consistency, and reduction of variance proportional to sample size—all proved to be correct. However, the experimental results did not give us any formulas for the variance and were not clear enough to suggest symmetry. The theoretical results are not only more accurate, but they are also considerably more explicit and more general.

Table 4–13

	Sample Size 5	
Interval: $\bar{x}$	Experimental $f(\bar{x})$	Theoretical $f(\bar{x})$
0.5 to 1.499	0.01	0.01
1.5 to 2.499	0.05	0.05
2.5 to 3.499	0.12	0.16
3.5 to 4.499	0.31	0.28
4.5 to 5.499	0.28	0.28
5.5 to 6.499	0.15	0.16
6.5 to 7.499	0.05	0.05
7.5 to 8.499	0.03	0.01
8.5 to 9.499	0.00	0.00
Mean	4.60	4.5
Standard deviation	1.3638	1.2845

Table 4–14

	Sample Size 10	
Interval: $\bar{x}$	Experimental $f(\bar{x})$	Theoretical $f(\bar{x})$
0.5 to 1.499	0.00	0.00
1.5 to 2.499	0.01	0.01
2.5 to 3.499	0.14	0.11
3.5 to 4.499	0.34	0.35
4.5 to 5.499	0.32	0.37
5.5 to 6.499	0.16	0.14
6.5 to 7.499	0.03	0.02
7.5 to 8.499	0.00	0.00
8.5 to 9.499	0.00	0.00
Mean	4.57	4.5
Standard deviation	1.0416	0.9829

So far we have dealt with sampling from a discrete uniform population. Let us now turn to sampling from *normal populations*. In particular, our task now is to find the sampling distribution of sample mean given that the variable X, whose values make up the sample, is distributed normally with mean μ and variance σ^2, i.e., given that $X \sim N(\mu, \sigma^2)$. Note that we made a slight change in notation: instead of σ_x^2 we use σ^2 to describe the population variance. Now we know that

$$\bar{X} = \frac{1}{n} \sum_{i=1}^{n} X_i = \frac{1}{n}(X_1 + X_2 + \cdots + X_n) = \frac{1}{n} X_1 + \frac{1}{n} X_2 + \cdots + \frac{1}{n} X_n.$$

The n observations $X_1, X_2, \ldots, X_n$ can be viewed as n variables, each having the same distribution, mean, and variance as X. That is, X_1 stands for all possible values of X that can be obtained when drawing the first observation, X_2 for all possible values of X that can be obtained when drawing the second observation, and so on. This way of looking at the sample—which is, of course, perfectly legitimate—makes the subsequent analysis simpler and neater. Since n (and, therefore, $1/n$) is, for a given sample size, a constant, it follows that $\bar{X}$ can be regarded as a linear combination of n independent normal variables $X_1, X_2, \ldots, X_n$. But we know, by Theorem 12 of this chapter, that a linear combination of normally distributed independent random variables is also normally distributed. This saves us all the work of deriving the form of the sampling distribution of $\bar{X}$ because the theorem clearly implies that *if X (and therefore $X_1, X_2, \ldots, X_n$) is normal, then $\bar{X}$ is also normal, whatever the sample size.*

Having obtained this result, our task is reduced to determining the mean and the variance of the sampling distribution of $\bar{X}$. As emphasized in Section 4–2, the knowledge of the mean and the variance of a normal distribution is sufficient for its complete identification. Fortunately, the derivation of these two parameters turns out to be relatively simple. Let us start with the mean:

$$E(\bar{X}) = E \frac{1}{n} \sum_{i=1}^{n} X_i.$$

Since $1/n$ is a constant, we can, according to Theorem 6, write this as

$$E(\bar{X}) = \frac{1}{n} E \sum_{i} X_i.$$

But, by Theorem 8, the expectation of a sum is equal to the sum of expectations so that

$$E(\bar{X}) = \frac{1}{n} \sum_{i} E(X_i) = \frac{1}{n} [E(X_1) + E(X_2) + \cdots + E(X_n)].$$

Now each of $X_1, X_2, \ldots, X_n$ has the same mean as X, i.e., μ. Therefore,

$$E(\bar{X}) = \frac{1}{n} [\mu + \mu + \cdots + \mu] = \frac{n\mu}{n} = \mu.$$

That is, the mean of the sampling distribution of $\bar{X}$ is equal to the population mean μ. Next we derive the variance of $\bar{X}$ denoted by $\sigma_{\bar{x}}^2$. We have

$$\sigma_{\bar{x}}^2 = \text{Var}(\bar{X}) = \text{Var}\left[\frac{1}{n} \sum_{i=1}^{n} X_i\right] = \frac{1}{n^2} \text{Var}\left[\sum_{i} X_i\right] \quad \text{(by Theorem 7)}$$

Since $X_1, X_2, \ldots, X_n$ are, by assumption of random sampling, independent of each other, we can use the following theorem.

Theorem 13   *The variance of a sum of independent random variables is equal to the sum of their variances.*

Proof: Let $X_1, X_2, \ldots, X_n$ be a set of independent random variables. Then

$$\text{Var}\left[\sum_{i=1}^{n} X_i\right] = E[(X_1 + X_2 + \cdots + X_n) - E(X_1 + X_2 + \cdots + X_n)]^2$$

$$= E\{[X_1 - E(X_1)] + [X_2 - E(X_2)] + \cdots + [X_n - E(X_n)]\}^2$$

$$= \sum_i E[X_i - E(X_i)]^2 + 2 \sum_{i<j} E[X_i - E(X_i)][X_j - E(X_j)].$$

But since the variables are independent of each other, their covariances are all equal to zero and we have

$$\text{Var}\left[\sum_{i=1}^{n} X_i\right] = \sum_{i=1}^{n} \text{Var}(X_i).$$

Thus for the variance of $\bar{X}$ we can write

$$\sigma_{\bar{x}}^2 = \frac{1}{n^2}[\text{Var}(X_1) + \text{Var}(X_2) + \cdots + \text{Var}(X_n)].$$

Now each of $X_1, X_2, \ldots, X_n$ has the same variance as X, i.e., σ^2. Therefore,

$$\sigma_{\bar{x}}^2 = \frac{1}{n^2}[\sigma^2 + \sigma^2 + \cdots + \sigma^2] = \frac{\sigma^2}{n}.$$

That is, the variance of the sampling distribution of $\bar{X}$ is equal to the population variance divided by sample size. These results can be summarized as follows:

If $X \sim N(\mu, \sigma^2)$, *then* $\bar{X} \sim N(\mu, \sigma^2/n)$.

This result is very important and will be used frequently throughout the rest of the book.

The preceding result implies certain properties of $\bar{X}$ as an estimator of the mean (μ) of a normal population.

1. Since $E(\bar{X}) = \mu$, $\bar{X}$ *is an unbiased estimator of* μ.
2. Since $\sigma_{\bar{x}}^2 = \sigma^2/n$, the distribution of $\bar{X}$ becomes more and more concentrated as the sample size n increases.
3. The preceding two properties imply that $\bar{X}$ *is a consistent estimator of* μ.
4. Since the distribution of $\bar{X}$ is normal, it is perfectly symmetric.

These properties are the same as those of $\bar{X}$ as an estimator of the mean of a discrete uniform population, although the sampling distributions themselves are somewhat different.

Another interesting implication of the result concerns the relationship between the variance of the sampling distribution of $\bar{X}$ and the variance of X in the population. Note that the dispersion of $\bar{X}$ depends only on two things, the size of the sample and the dispersion of the variable X in the population. For a given sample size, the smaller the population variance happens to be, the less dispersed (that is, the more reliable) are our guesses about the population mean. We use the term "happens to be" to emphasize the fact that the size of the population variance, unlike that of the sample, is not under our control—not even in theory. Thus, if we were to estimate the mean of some normally distributed variable such as, e.g., annual family expenditure of families in a given income bracket, we would obtain a more reliable estimate from a population with similar tastes, values, etc., than from a less conformist population. (The relationship between the variance of $\bar{X}$ and that of X was found to be the same in the case of a discrete uniform parent population as in the case of a normal parent. However, the former case is less interesting in practice, and thus we made no comment about it at the time.)

We have now completed a detailed derivation of the sampling distribution of sample mean for two parent populations—a discrete uniform population and a normal population. The latter is of considerable practical importance but, even so, cases of sampling from nonnormal populations (and from nonuniform populations) arise quite often in econometric work. However, we cannot conceivably pay individual attention to all remaining distributions, nor do we have any useful criterion for singling out some in preference to others. Therefore, we shall deal with the rest of the distributions only in a summary form, while trying to come to as many conclusions of general applicability as possible. Fortunately, we can go quite some way in this direction by establishing results which are independent of the form of the parent distribution of X.

One feature of the sampling distribution of $\bar{X}$, which in no way depends on the form of the distribution of X in the population, has already been obtained in connection with sampling from a normal population. This concerns the mean and the variance of $\bar{X}$. Suppose that the variable X has *any* distribution with mean μ and variance σ^2, and that $X_1, X_2, \ldots, X_n$ are regarded as n variables, each having exactly the same mean and variance as X. Then the mean of $\bar{X}$ is given by

$$E(\bar{X}) = E\frac{1}{n}(X_1 + X_2 + \cdots + X_n) = \mu,$$

and the variance of $\bar{X}$ is

$$\text{Var}(\bar{X}) = \text{Var}\left[\frac{1}{n}(X_1 + X_2 + \cdots + X_n)\right] = \frac{\sigma^2}{n}.$$

These results are summarized in the following theorem.

Theorem 14   *If X is a variable with mean μ and variance σ^2 then, whatever the distribution of X, the sampling distribution of $\bar{X}$ has the same mean μ and variance equal to σ^2/n.*

Another feature of the sampling distribution of $\bar{X}$ which is independent of the distribution of X is described in the next theorem. This theorem, generally referred to as the *central limit theorem*, is one of the most important propositions in the theory of statistics. Its proof can be found in many texts on mathematical statistics and will not be developed here.[6]

Theorem 15 (*Central Limit Theorem*).   *If X has any distribution with mean μ and variance σ^2, then the distribution of $\bar{X}$ approaches the normal distribution with mean μ and variance σ^2/n as sample size n increases.*

This is quite a remarkable result. Its clear implication is that, for large samples, the distribution of $\bar{X}$ can be approximated by a normal distribution whatever the parent distribution of X. It is this implication which gives the central limit theorem practical importance.

As an application of the central limit theorem, we may try to use normal distribution to approximate the sampling distribution of $\bar{X}$ based on samples from a discrete uniform population. In particular, let the parent distribution of X be such that X takes on only the values $0, 1, 2, \ldots, 9$. This is the same parent distribution as that which served as a basis for our sampling experiment described in Section 2–2. In this experiment, we constructed distributions of $\bar{X}$ from 100 samples of size 5 and 100 samples of size 10. The exact formula for the distribution of $\bar{X}$ was derived in the first part of the present section so that we know precisely what the true distribution of $\bar{X}$ is. Let us now try to use normal distribution (with mean $\mu = 4.5$ and variance $\sigma^2/n = 8.25/n$) as an approximation of the true distribution of $\bar{X}$. Although the approximation is presumed to be reasonable only for large samples and samples of size 5 or 10 obviously cannot be considered large, it may be instructive to see how it works in small samples.

First, let us try the sampling distribution of $\bar{X}$ for sample size 5. In this case, the mean and the standard deviation of the distribution are

$$E(\bar{X}) = 4.5$$

$$\sigma_{\bar{x}} = \sqrt{\frac{8.25}{5}} = 1.2845.$$

Therefore, the standard normal variable Z—which we need in order to use the normal probability table—is

$$z = \frac{\bar{x} - \mu}{\sigma_{\bar{x}}} = \frac{\bar{x} - 4.5}{1.2845} = 0.7785\bar{x} - 3.5033.$$

[6] The exact formulation of the central limit theorem varies from text to text. We shall follow that of R. L. Anderson and T. A. Bancroft, *Statistical Theory in Research* (New York: McGraw-Hill, 1952), p. 71, which makes the theorem easier to understand than some other formulations. It ought to be emphasized, though, that the validity of the theorem is restricted by the assumption that the variables X_i are mutually independent and that they are drawn from the same population with constant parameters.

In constructing the normal distribution we shall follow the procedure of Section 4–2 as illustrated in Table 4–7. The results are given in Table 4–15,

Table 4–15

		Sample Size 5			
Interval: $\bar{x}$	Interval: z	$f(z)$ (Cumulative Normal)	$f(\bar{x})$ (Normal Approx.)	$f(\bar{x})$ (Theoretical)	$f(\bar{x})$ (Experimental)
0.5 to 1.499	$-\infty$ to -2.33	0.010	0.01	0.01	0.01
1.5 to 2.499	-2.33 to -1.56	0.059	0.05	0.05	0.05
2.5 to 3.499	-1.56 to -0.78	0.218	0.16	0.16	0.12
3.5 to 4.499	-0.78 to 0.00	0.500	0.28	0.28	0.31
4.5 to 5.499	0.00 to 0.78	0.782	0.28	0.28	0.28
5.5 to 6.499	0.78 to 1.56	0.941	0.16	0.16	0.15
6.5 to 7.499	1.56 to 2.33	0.990	0.05	0.05	0.05
7.5 to 8.499	2.33 to 3.11	0.999	0.01	0.01	0.03
8.5 to 9.499	3.11 to ∞	1.000	0.00	0.00	0.00

together with the experimental and the theoretical probabilities reproduced from Table 4–13. The results given by the normal approximation are very good. In fact, it turns out that the fitted normal distribution is exactly the same—at least up to two decimal places—as the exact, theoretically determined distribution of $\bar{X}$.

Next, let us consider the sampling distribution for sample size 10. The mean and the standard deviation of this distribution are

$$E(\bar{X}) = 4.5,$$

$$\sigma_{\bar{x}} = \sqrt{\frac{8.25}{10}} = 0.9829.$$

The corresponding standard normal variable then is

$$z = \frac{\bar{x} - 4.5}{0.9829} = 1.0174\bar{x} - 4.5782.$$

The calculations are presented in Table 4–16; the columns giving the theoretical and the experimental probabilities are taken from Table 4–14. The results again indicate that normal distribution provides a very good approximation to the sampling distribution of $\bar{X}$. The fit in this case appears slightly worse than in Table 4–15 because, with sample size given by an even number, the theoretical distribution has only one peak at 4.5; when the sample size is odd, the theoretical distribution has two equal peaks, one just below and just above 4.5. With the interval limits as specified, the distributions based on even sample size have a spurious appearance of asymmetry.

The preceding results indicate that normal distribution may provide a reasonable approximation to the sampling distribution of $\bar{X}$ even when the sample size is small, but this is not true in general. The specific feature of the preceding case that made the normal approximation come out so well was the symmetry of the parent distribution and, consequently, of the distribution of $\bar{X}$ for any sample

Table 4–16

		Sample Size 10			
Interval: $\bar{x}$	Interval: z	$f(z)$ (Cumulative Normal)	$f(\bar{x})$ (Normal Approx.)	$f(\bar{x})$ (Theoretical)	$f(\bar{x})$ (Experimental)
0.5 to 1.499	$-\infty$ to -3.05	0.001	0.00	0.00	0.00
1.5 to 2.499	-3.05 to -2.03	0.021	0.02	0.01	0.01
2.5 to 3.499	-2.03 to -1.02	0.154	0.13	0.11	0.14
3.5 to 4.499	-1.02 to 0.00	0.500	0.35	0.35	0.34
4.5 to 5.499	0.00 to 1.02	0.846	0.35	0.37	0.32
5.5 to 6.499	1.02 to 2.03	0.979	0.13	0.14	0.16
6.5 to 7.499	2.03 to 3.05	0.999	0.02	0.02	0.03
7.5 to 8.499	3.05 to 4.07	1.000	0.00	0.00	0.00
8.5 to 9.499	4.07 to ∞	1.000	0.00	0.00	0.00

size. In cases where the parent distribution is highly skewed, it would take a large sample size before one could feel reasonably satisfied with using normal distribution for $\bar{X}$. And this, in fact, is all that one can legitimately expect from the central limit theorem.

Our discussion on sampling distribution of sample mean may best be closed by highlighting the most important results. We started by deriving the sampling distribution of $\bar{X}$ for samples drawn from a *discrete uniform population*. The resulting distribution of $\bar{X}$ turned out to be perfectly symmetric and capable of being closely approximated by a normal distribution, whatever sample size. Next, we found that the distribution of $\bar{X}$ for samples from a *normal population* is itself exactly normal for every sample size. Finally, by invoking the central limit theorem, we concluded that the distribution of $\bar{X}$ of a large sample will be approximately normal whatever the parent population. All these results bring out the importance of a normal distribution in statistical inference. In dealing with large samples we can *always* rely on normal distribution to describe the sampling distribution of $\bar{X}$. (Strictly speaking, the central limit theorem does not hold in the case in which the population variance is not finite. The statement in the text is based on the assumption that such cases are excluded from our discussion. Also, note the qualifying remarks made in footnote 6 on page 107.) If the parent population is not normal, the description will be approximate; if it is normal, the description will be exact. In dealing with small samples, normal distribution will give a perfect description of the distribution of $\bar{X}$ if the parent population is normal, and an approximate description if the parent population is nonnormal but symmetric. Only in the case of small samples and a skewed parent population would it be inadvisable to approximate the distribution of $\bar{X}$ by a normal distribution. Finally, concerning the properties of the sample mean as an estimator of the population mean, we found that, whatever the parent population, the distribution of $\bar{X}$ has a mean equal to the population mean and variance equal to the population variance divided by sample size. Thus $\bar{X}$ is an unbiased and consistent estimator of the population mean.

EXERCISES

4-1. In a certain city, 20% of all consumers are users of Brand D soap. What are the probabilities that in an elevator containing 10 people there will be 0, 1, 2, ..., 10 users of Brand D soap?

4-2. How many times would we have to toss a coin in order that the probability will be at least 0.95 that the proportion of heads will lie between 0.40 and 0.60?

4-3. Given that the mean number of successes in n trials is 8 with standard deviation equal to 2, find n and π.

4-4. Consider a discrete uniform population with $X = 0, 1, \ldots, 5$. Derive the sampling distribution of the range (i.e., the difference between the largest and the smallest observation) for samples of size 4.

4-5. Consider a continuous uniform population with $0 < x < 1$. What is the probability that the mean of 20 observations will lie between 0.4 and 0.6?

4-6. A population consists of 10 balls of which 5 are white and 5 are red. Construct the sampling distribution of the proportion of white balls in a sample of 5 balls which are drawn *without replacement*.

4-7. A company operating in a certain city has been charged with making excessive profits. As evidence, it has been stated that the company's rate of profit last year was 22% while the national average for the industry was 16%. In defense, the officials of the company claimed that the profits in their industry are highly variable and that substantial deviations from the average are not infrequent. They pointed out that, while the mean rate of profit for the industry was 16%, the standard deviation was as large as 4%. Assuming that profits are normally distributed, what is the probability of making a profit of 22% or higher by pure chance?

4-8. If $X \sim N(8, 16)$, find each of the following:

a. $P(6 < X < 10)$.   **b.** $P(10 < X < 12)$.   **c.** $P(X < 0)$.   **d.** $P(X > 20)$.

e. The two values of X which cut off the central 50% of the area under the curve.

4–9. Let Y = income and X = log Y. A frequently made claim is that the distribution of X is approximately normal. Check this claim by fitting a normal curve to the distribution of X obtained from the data in Table 4–17.

Table 4–17 Income of Families and Unattached Individuals, United States, 1962

Income	Percentage Frequency
Under $2,000	12.0
$2,000 to $2,999	8.5
$3,000 to $3,999	9.8
$4,000 to $4,999	10.2
$5,000 to $5,999	10.2
$6,000 to $7,499	14.1
$7,500 to $9,999	15.7
$10,000 to $14,999	12.3
$15,000 and over	7.2

Source: *Statistical Abstract of the United States, 1965* (U.S. Department of Commerce), p. 341.

5 | Tests of Hypotheses

At the beginning of this text we stated that there are essentially two kinds of statistical inference: estimation and tests of hypotheses. Both are concerned with making judgments about some unknown aspect of a given population on the basis of sample information. The unknown aspect may be the value of one or more of the population parameters or, less frequently, the functional form of the population. Whether a problem is one of estimation or one of hypothesis testing is determined by the type of question that is being asked. In the case of estimation, we ask a question about the value of a particular parameter. In hypothesis testing the question is preceded by a statement concerning the population; the question then is whether this statement is true or false. In other respects the two cases are quite similar. In either case we arrive at an answer by combining our prior knowledge and assumptions about the population with the evidence provided by the sample. In either case we make considerable use of the concept of a sampling distribution developed in the previous sections. Finally, whatever the type of question, the answer is always tentative. However, there are some differences in approach which warrant separate discussion. Accordingly, we shall devote this chapter to the problem of testing hypotheses and the next to that of estimation.

5–1 Design and Evaluation of Tests

A hypothesis is defined as an assumption about the population. Typically, we make more than one such assumption, but not all of them are to be tested. Those assumptions that are not intended to be exposed to a test are called the *maintained hypothesis*. They consist of all the assumptions that we are willing to make and to believe in. Of course, we are never absolutely certain that these assumptions are valid; if we were, they would cease to be assumptions and would become facts. The usual situation in this respect is one in which we believe that the assumptions in question very likely hold at least approximately so that the maintained hypothesis is very nearly correct. The remaining assumptions that are to be tested are called the *testable hypothesis*. Usually the testable hypothesis consists of a statement that a certain population parameter is equal to a given value. In statistical theory this hypothesis is called the *null hypothesis* since it implies that there is no difference between the *true* value of the population parameter and that which is being hypothesized.

As an example, consider the statement that "economists and psychologists spend an equal average amount on tipping during their annual conventions." This can be interpreted as a testable hypothesis stating that the population means of the two professional groups are equal. One would normally test this by drawing a random sample of economists and a random sample of psychologists, and by comparing the respective sample means (in a manner to be discussed presently). The maintained hypothesis in this case might consist of the following assumptions.

1. If there is a difference in average tipping behavior, it depends entirely on the profession of the tipper; other factors such as income, sex, and age are of no relevance.
2. In each group the amount spent on tipping is normally distributed with the same variance.
3. There is no definite prior presumption that either of the two population means is greater than the other.

The first of these assumptions implies that no factors other than difference in profession have to be taken into account when the test is carried out. The second assumption is needed in order to determine the sampling distribution of the test statistic. The final assumption determines the alternative to the null hypothesis. In this case the alternative hypothesis is that the means are *not* the same. The specification of the alternative hypothesis is needed when setting up the test.

The idea of an alternative hypothesis is quite important and requires elaboration. Since the null hypothesis is a testable proposition, there must exist a counterproposition to it, otherwise there would be no need for a test. The counterproposition is called the *alternative hypothesis*. Suppose the null hypothesis states that the population mean μ is equal to some value, say, μ_0. Usually we denote the null hypothesis by H_0 and the alternative by H_A. Then the alternative hypothesis may be, for instance, the proposition that μ is equal to some *other* value, say, μ_A. That is, we would have

$$H_0: \quad \mu = \mu_0,$$
$$H_A: \quad \mu = \mu_A.$$

If this is the case, the implication is that μ can be equal to either μ_0 or μ_A, but nothing else. Obviously such a case is very rare since it means that we know really quite a lot about the population mean a priori; the only thing that we are not certain about is which of the two values it has. More frequently, our prior knowledge concerning the population mean (or any other population parameter) is much less. If we know absolutely nothing about μ, then the alternative hypothesis would be that μ is *not* equal to μ_0, as described by

$$H_0: \quad \mu = \mu_0,$$
$$H_A: \quad \mu \neq \mu_0.$$

Sometimes we are reasonably certain that μ is greater (or smaller) than μ_0. Then we would have

$$H_0: \quad \mu = \mu_0,$$

$$H_A: \quad \mu > \mu_0 \qquad (\text{or } H_A: \quad \mu < \mu_0).$$

Hypotheses of a general form such as $\mu \neq \mu_0$, $\mu > \mu_0$, or $\mu < \mu_0$ are called *composite hypotheses*, whereas specific claims such as $\mu = \mu_0$ are called *simple hypotheses*.

Since specific claims are easier to disprove than vague claims, it is desirable—and it has been the common practice—to formulate problems of hypotheses testing so that the null hypothesis is stated as specifically as possible. Thus, if—as very frequently is the case—we have two rival hypotheses, one simple and one composite, we choose the simple one as the null hypothesis to be tested. This means that we often introduce the null hypothesis as that proposition which we actually wish to disprove. A good example of this is a test of a new drug. There is an obvious presumption that the new drug will do better, say in terms of mean percentage of recoveries, than the old drug or therapy used, otherwise there would be no point in testing. Yet the null hypothesis for this case will be the proposition that the new drug leads to the same mean percentage of recoveries as the old drug; the alternative hypothesis will be that the mean percentage is higher for the new drug.

The decision as to which of the two rival hypotheses is to be regarded as the null hypothesis has some implications which ought to be taken into account. According to established methodology, a null hypothesis is a proposition which is considered valid unless evidence throws serious doubt on it. In this respect a statistical test is like a trial in a court of law. A man on trial is considered innocent unless the evidence suggests *beyond reasonable doubt* that he is guilty. Similarly, a null hypothesis is regarded as valid unless the evidence suggests—also beyond reasonable doubt—that it is not true. (However, while in court the definition of "reasonable doubt" is presumably the same from case to case, in statistical tests it may vary depending upon the cost of making an incorrect verdict.) Furthermore, just as in court it is up to the prosecution to prove the accused guilty, so in statistical testing it is up to the statistician to prove the null hypothesis incorrect. Of course, in neither case is the word "prove" to be taken in an absolute sense since a "shadow" of a doubt always exists; only God knows whether a man is really guilty or a null hypothesis is really incorrect. Finally, there is also a similarity in procedure. In court all evidence and other information relevant to the case are produced and weighed in accordance with the rules set by law, and a verdict of "guilty" or "not guilty" is reached. Similarly, when a statistical test is conducted, all evidence and prior information is used in accordance with predetermined rules, and a conclusion of "reject" or "do not reject" the null hypothesis is obtained. Interestingly enough, just as a court pronounces a verdict as "not guilty" rather than "innocent," so the conclusion of a statistical test is "do not reject" rather than "accept."

The parallel between a trial in a court and a statistical test stops abruptly when it comes to the application of the Fifth Amendment of the United States Constitution. Unlike a man on trial who is not to "be subject for the same offense to be twice put in jeopardy of life or limb," a null hypothesis is *always* open to a test. In fact, while a null hypothesis is viewed as valid unless thrown into serious evidence, such a view is always held only tentatively. In this respect, a null hypothesis is like a titleholder who is forever open to challenge. In fact, one can visualize the course of science as a process of establishing hypotheses and then busily collecting evidence to bring about their downfall. Only the sturdiest hypotheses withstand the repeated attacks and become worthy of our faith, at least until the next attack comes along.

So far we have not mentioned the question concerning the source of hypotheses. In principle, this question has a simple answer: economic hypotheses are drawn from economic theory. In practice, however, the matter is much less simple. In the first place, economic theory is rarely sufficiently precise and detailed to lead to hypotheses suitable for application of statistical tests. For instance, one would be hard put to find in economic literature a theoretical development which would lead to a proposition specifying a definite value of the government expenditure multiplier as well as spelling all the assumptions that would be embraced by the maintained hypothesis. Economic theory typically specifies only the interrelationships between different economic variables, usually described in quite general terms. The econometrician, then, must specify the mathematical form of those relationships and spell out the maintained hypothesis more completely and in greater detail. The null hypothesis usually states that the postulated relationship does *not* exist, which normally means that the value of one or more of the parameters is equal to zero, while the alternative hypothesis states that the relationship does exist. The second difficulty with economic theory as a source of hypotheses is that frequently the variables involved are difficult to define, or to measure, or both. This, unfortunately, applies not only to such notoriously difficult concepts as capital, but also to less obviously troublesome concepts such as income or consumption. Finally, there are many problems for which economic theory is not at all well developed, and thus it offers little help in leading to relevant hypotheses. In these situations the researcher usually resorts to ad hoc theorizing, that is, to setting up maintained and testable hypotheses by using his common sense and whatever inspiration he can get from theory. Most of the applied econometric work that has been done so far is of this kind, or at least predominantly so. All these difficulties in setting up economic hypotheses to some extent account for the greater concentration on problems of estimation rather than on problems of hypothesis testing in past econometric research.

Setting up the null hypothesis and its alternative represents the first step in dealing with a problem involving hypothesis testing. The next step consists of devising a criterion that would enable us to decide whether the null hypothesis is or is not to be rejected on the basis of evidence. This criterion or rule is in principle the same regardless of the problem: it defines a test statistic and a boundary for dividing the sample space into a region of rejection and a region of non-rejection. The test statistic is simply a formula telling us how to confront the null hypothesis with the evidence. It is a random variable whose value varies from sample to sample. The *region of rejection*, sometimes called the *critical region*, is a subset of the sample space such that if the value of the test statistic falls in it, the null hypothesis is rejected. Similarly, the *region of nonrejection*, usually called the *acceptance region*, is a subset of the sample space such that if the value of the test statistic falls in it, the null hypothesis is not rejected. The boundary between the rejection and the acceptance regions is determined by prior information concerning the distribution of the test statistic, by the specification of the alternative hypothesis, and by considerations of the costs of arriving at an incorrect conclusion. An important feature of the boundary is the fact that it does not depend on sample information; in fact, its determination comes logically prior to drawing the sample.

Test Criterion

The procedure of devising a criterion for rejecting the null hypothesis can be conveniently explained with reference to a standard textbook problem of hypothesis testing. Consider a null hypothesis which states that the mean of some variable X is equal to μ_0. Suppose that our maintained hypothesis consists of the following assumptions: (1) X is normally distributed; (2) the variance of X is σ^2 and is *known*. Since the maintained hypothesis tells us nothing about μ (for instance, that μ is restricted to positive values or some such information), the alternative hypothesis is then simply that μ is not equal to μ_0. Thus we can write

$$H_0: \quad \mu = \mu_0,$$

$$H_A: \quad \mu \neq \mu_0.$$

Let us now develop a suitable test statistic. The information that we will receive from the sample will obviously tell us *something* about the population mean; the question is how this information should be used. Our discussion in Section 4–3 indicated that sample mean has some desirable properties as an estimator of the population mean. This suggests that we may use the sample mean to summarize the sample evidence about the population mean. Then an obvious criterion for rejecting or not rejecting the null hypothesis will be as follows: if the value of $\bar{X}$ is very different from μ_0, reject the null hypothesis; if it is not very different, do not reject it.

The foregoing criterion is clearly useless for defining the critical and the acceptance region unless we state precisely which values of $\bar{X}$ are to be regarded as "very different" from μ_0 and which are not. To decide that, we have to consider the sampling distribution of $\bar{X}$. If X is normal and has, in fact, mean μ_0 and variance σ^2, then $\bar{X}$ will be normal with mean μ_0 and variance σ^2/n (where n is the sample size). Of course, since the normal distribution extends from $-\infty$ to $+\infty$, *any* value of $\bar{X}$ can be observed whatever the population mean. However, if the true mean is μ_0, then the values of $\bar{X}$ in intervals close to μ_0 will occur with greater probability than those in intervals (of the same length) farther away from μ_0. It is natural then to regard as "very different from μ_0" those values of $\bar{X}$ which—if μ_0 were the true mean—would occur by chance only very rarely. By "very rarely" we mean, at least for the time being, "with probability 0.01."

At this stage we have to introduce the alternative hypothesis which states that $\mu \neq \mu_0$. This, in fact, means that if the null hypothesis does not hold, the true mean may be on either side of μ_0. Therefore, values of $\bar{X}$ that are very much larger than μ_0 *as well as* values that are very much smaller would constitute evidence against the null hypothesis. (If the alternative hypothesis were, for example, that $\mu > \mu_0$, then only those values of $\bar{X}$ that are very much *larger* than μ_0 would represent evidence against the null hypothesis.) That is, the boundaries between the critical and the acceptance regions must be such that we would reject the null hypothesis if the value of $\bar{X}$ turned out to be *either* so low *or* so high compared to μ_0 that its occurrence by chance would be very unlikely. Since we decided to call an event very unlikely (i.e., very rare) if it occurs with probability of only 0.01, this probability must be "shared" equally by excessively low and excessively high values of $\bar{X}$. In other words, the boundaries are to be set in such a way that the probability of $\bar{x}$ being that excessively low is 0.005 and the probability of $\bar{x}$ being that excessively high is also 0.005. Then, by the Addition Theorem (Theorem 2), the probability that $\bar{x}$ will be either excessively high or excessively low compared to μ_0 will be $0.005 + 0.005 = 0.01$, as required.

Let us denote that value below which $\bar{x}$ would be considered excessively low by μ_L, and that value above which $\bar{x}$ would be considered excessively high by μ_H. These points are marked off on the sampling distribution of $\bar{X}$ shown in Figure 5–1. We have

$$P(\bar{x} < \mu_L) = 0.005,$$

$$P(\bar{x} > \mu_H) = 0.005;$$

therefore $$P(\mu_L \leq \bar{x} \leq \mu_H) = 0.99.$$

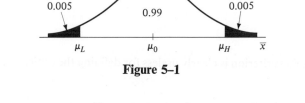

Figure 5–1

We could actually consider $\bar{X}$ as an appropriate test statistic and the interval from μ_L to μ_H as the acceptance region, but this is not very practical since we do not know the location of μ_L and μ_H. We can, however, very easily determine the location of their counterparts in a standard normal distribution for which probabilities are tabulated. How this can be done was described in detail in Section 4–2.

Given that $\bar{X} \sim N(\mu_0, \sigma^2/n)$, the corresponding standard normal variable will be

(5.1)
$$Z = \frac{\bar{X} - \mu_0}{\sqrt{\sigma^2/n}} = \frac{(\bar{X} - \mu_0)\sqrt{n}}{\sigma}.$$

This will be our *test statistic*.

Now we wish to find those values on the z scale which correspond to μ_L and μ_H on the $\bar{x}$ scale. These values of Z, which we will call z_L and z_H, can be found by noting that they have to cut off on each end 0.005 of the area under the curve, as

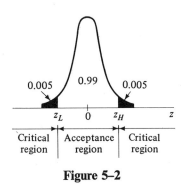

Figure 5–2

shown in Figure 5–2. That is, we have to find from the normal probability tables the value of z_L such that

$$P(z < z_L) = 0.005,$$

or, which amounts to exactly the same,

$$P(z > z_L) = 0.995.$$

Similarly, we have to find z_H such that

$$P(z > z_H) = 0.005,$$

or, equivalently,

$$P(z < z_H) = 0.995.$$

By consulting the normal probability tables we get

$$z_L = -2.575$$

$$z_H = +2.575$$

This completes our task. The interval from -2.575 to $+2.575$ represents the acceptance region, and the intervals from $-\infty$ to -2.575 and from $+2.575$ to $+\infty$ our critical region. (Since the probability of getting a value of Z equal to z_L or z_H is zero, it is of little practical importance whether the acceptance region does or does not include the boundary values.) The criterion for rejecting or not rejecting the null hypothesis is then as follows:

$$reject\ if\ \ \frac{(\bar{x} - \mu_0)\sqrt{n}}{\sigma} < -2.575\ \ or\ if\ \ \frac{(\bar{x} - \mu_0)\sqrt{n}}{\sigma} > +2.575;$$

$$do\ not\ reject\ if\ \ -2.575 \leq \frac{(\bar{x} - \mu_0)\sqrt{n}}{\sigma} \leq +2.575.$$

This division between the critical and the acceptance regions is contingent upon our decision to consider as "very different" from μ_0 only those values of $\bar{X}$ which would occur by chance with probability of 0.01. In other words, if we drew an infinite number of samples from the population with mean μ_0, only 1% of the time would we get a value of $\bar{X}$ that would lead to an incorrect rejection of the null hypothesis. This probability is known as the *significance level* of the test. Of course, there is nothing sacrosanct about the figure of 1% which we chose; in absence of any information, some other figure may just as well have been chosen. Had we chosen a higher percentage, the acceptance region would have been narrower and the critical region wider. As it happens, 1% is one of the "popular" levels of significance but that is all that can be said for it at this stage. We shall discuss the possibility for a more rational choice of the level of significance before the end of the present section, but first let us consider a numerical example of the test procedure that we have just developed.

EXAMPLE Psychological studies indicate that in the population at large intelligence —as measured by IQ—is normally distributed with mean of 100 and standard deviation of 16. Suppose we want to test whether a given subpopulation—for instance, all people who are left-handed—is characterized by a different mean. As our maintained hypothesis, we assume that intelligence among the left-handed is normally distributed with the same standard deviation as that of the population at large, i.e., 16. Let us call the mean IQ among left-handed persons μ. The null and the alternative hypotheses will be

$$H_0:\ \ \mu = 100,$$

$$H_A:\ \ \mu \neq 100.$$

Our test statistic will then be

$$\frac{(\bar{X} - 100)\sqrt{n}}{16}.$$

As the appropriate level of significance we choose 5%, which happens to be the other "popular" level. That is, if the value of $\bar{X}$ should be so different from the hypothesized mean of 100 that it would occur by pure chance only 5% of the time, we will consider the null hypothesis as unlikely and reject it. Now, to find the boundaries of the acceptance region, we have to locate those values of the standard normal variable which cut off 2.5% of total area at each end of the distribution, as shown in Figure 5-3. From the normal probability tables we find

$$z_L = -1.96,$$

$$z_H = +1.96.$$

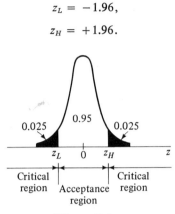

Figure 5–3

Therefore our criterion is:

$$\text{do not reject } H_0 \text{ if } \quad -1.96 \le \frac{(\bar{x} - 100)\sqrt{n}}{16} \le +1.96;$$

otherwise reject it.

At this stage we can draw a sample and calculate the value of $\bar{X}$ and of the test statistic. Suppose the sample consists of 400 observations of left-handed persons, and the mean IQ is 99. Then the value of our test statistic will be

$$\frac{(99 - 100)\sqrt{400}}{16} = -1.25.$$

This obviously falls into the acceptance region so that the sample gives no evidence against the null hypothesis. In other words, there is no evidence that the mean IQ of left-handed persons is any different from that of the population at large. This completes the answer to the problem.

Thus far we have made no assumptions that would help us in formulating the alternative hypothesis. Therefore the alternative hypothesis had to be of the form $\mu \ne \mu_0$. Consequently, the rejection region covered both tail ends of the distribution of the test statistic. A test with this kind of rejection region is called a *two-tail test*. However, sometimes we are able to make assumptions that permit a somewhat less general specification of the alternative hypothesis. In particular, sometimes we are reasonably certain that the only alternative to the claim that $\mu = \mu_0$ is the claim that μ is greater (or smaller) than μ_0. For instance, it has been claimed that the marginal propensity to save (MPS) of "profit makers" is higher than that of the labor force at large. In this case the null hypothesis would be that the two propensities are equal, and the alternative hypothesis would be the claim that the MPS of the profit makers is higher. In such cases the values of $\bar{X}$ (and therefore of the test statistic) that would be regarded as evidence against the null hypothesis would all be concentrated at just one end of the distribution. A test of this kind is called a *one-tail test*.

To illustrate the point, consider again a variable $X \sim N(\mu, \sigma^2)$ where σ^2 is known. Suppose the null and the alternative hypotheses are given as follows:

$$H_0: \quad \mu = \mu_0,$$

$$H_A: \quad \mu > \mu_0.$$

As our test statistic we use

$$Z = \frac{(\bar{X} - \mu_0)\sqrt{n}}{\sigma},$$

as given by (5.1). Suppose now that we wish to carry out the test at 1% level of significance. That is, we will reject the null hypothesis if the value of $\bar{X}$ is so much greater than μ_0 that it would occur by chance with probability of only 0.01. In this case the acceptance and the critical regions will be as shown in Figure 5–4.

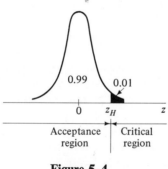

Figure 5–4

The value of z_H, which can be looked up in the normal probability tables, is 2.327. Therefore, the criterion for rejecting H_0 in this case is

$$reject\ if \quad \frac{(\bar{x} - \mu_0)\sqrt{n}}{\sigma} > 2.327;$$

do not reject otherwise.

If the chosen level of significance were 5% instead of 1%, the criterion would be

$$reject\ if \quad \frac{(\bar{x} - \mu_0)\sqrt{n}}{\sigma} > 1.645;$$

do not reject otherwise.

Types of Error

The criterion for rejecting or not rejecting the null hypothesis on the basis of sample evidence is not a guarantee of arriving at a correct conclusion. Let us now consider in detail the kinds of errors that could be made. Suppose we have a problem of testing a hypothesis about the population mean, as in the preceding discussion. The solution of the problem consists essentially of two basic steps: setting up the boundaries between the acceptance and the critical regions and obtaining the sample value of the test statistic. Two outcomes are possible: either the value of the test statistic falls in the acceptance region or it does not. Let us take the second outcome first. In this case the value of the test statistic is such that, if the null hypothesis were in fact true, the probability of this happening by chance would be very small, e.g., 5% or 1%. This means that if the test were repeated an infinite number of times and if the null hypothesis were in fact true, we would *incorrectly reject* the null hypothesis 5% or 1% (or whatever the level of significance) of the time. Such an error is called *Error Type I*. Earlier we compared statistical testing to a trial in a court of law where the innocence of the accused (our null hypothesis) is challenged by the claim of guilt by the prosecution (our alternative hypothesis). Using this parallel, the Error Type I would be represented by the error of convicting an innocent man. In statistical testing the probability of committing this error is given precisely by the chosen level of significance. Consider now the second possible outcome of the test, that is, the case where the value of the test statistic falls inside the acceptance region. In this case we do not reject the null hypothesis, i.e., we keep on believing it to be true. However, the possibility that we came to an incorrect conclusion, namely that the null hypothesis is in fact false, cannot be ruled out. An error of this sort is called *Error Type II*. In terms of the parallel with the court trial, the Error Type II would mean letting a guilty man go. In statistical testing the exact probability of this kind of error is usually unknown.

The general idea behind the two types of error can be clearly illustrated by the —unfortunately not very common—case of testing a simple null hypothesis against a *simple* alternative. Suppose the hypotheses are

$$H_0: \quad \mu = \mu_0,$$

$$H_A: \quad \mu = \mu_A,$$

where μ_0 and μ_A are given numbers and $\mu_A > \mu_0$. As before, we assume X to be normal with a known variance σ^2. Thus the two hypotheses can be identified with two competing populations, both normal with the same variance σ^2 but distinguished by their means. Each population generates—for a given sample size n—its own sampling distribution of $\bar{X}$. To carry out the test we have to establish the boundary between the critical and the acceptance region. This will depend, as we have seen, on the chosen level of significance and on the alternative hypothesis. The level of significance can be chosen a priori as, say, 5%. Since the alternative hypothesis is that $\mu = \mu_A$ and since $\mu_A > \mu_0$, only high values of $\bar{X}$ relative to μ_0 would constitute evidence against H_0. That is, the appropriate test is a one-tail test with the critical region concentrated at the right-hand tail of the distribution. With these considerations in mind, we can determine the boundary between the acceptance and the critical region for the distribution of the test statistic

$$Z = \frac{(\bar{X} - \mu_0)\sqrt{n}}{\sigma}.$$

For the 5% level of significance with the critical region concentrated at the right tail of the distribution, the boundary value z_H is equal to 1.645. Therefore the acceptance region will be

$$z \leq 1.645.$$

If the true mean is μ_0, then the probability that a value of $\bar{X}$ falls inside the acceptance region is 0.95. To determine the probability of Error Type II, we have to find the probability that a value of $\bar{X}$ falls inside the acceptance region if the true mean is *not* μ_0 but μ_A. This can be found as follows. First we note that

$$P(z > 1.645) = 0.05$$

can be written as

$$P\left[\frac{(\bar{x} - \mu_0)\sqrt{n}}{\sigma} > 1.645\right] = 0.05.$$

Consider the inequality inside the square bracket. By multiplying both sides by $\sigma/\sqrt{n}$, we get

$$(\bar{x} - \mu_0) > 1.645\left[\frac{\sigma}{\sqrt{n}}\right].$$

Adding μ_0 to both sides gives

$$\bar{x} > \mu_0 + 1.645\left[\frac{\sigma}{\sqrt{n}}\right].$$

Thus we can write

$$P\left[\bar{x} > \mu_0 + 1.645\left(\frac{\sigma}{\sqrt{n}}\right)\right] = 0.05,$$

which is a probability statement about $\bar{X}$ rather than Z. Thus the boundary between the acceptance and the critical region on the $\bar{x}$ axis is given by $[\mu_0 + 1.645(\sigma/\sqrt{n})]$. Since μ_0, σ, and n are known, the boundary will be a known number. Figure 5–5 shows the two distributions with the boundaries marked off.

Now let us consider the sampling distribution of $\bar{X}$ for samples from the population with mean μ_A. This distribution will be normal with mean equal to the population mean (i.e., μ_A) and variance σ^2/n. Thus the only way in which this distribution differs from the distribution of $\bar{X}$ from the population with mean μ_0

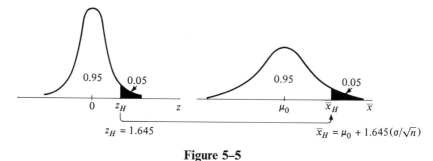

Figure 5–5

is with respect to the mean. The two distributions of $\overline{X}$ are compared in Figure 5–6, which shows clearly the probabilities of the two types of error involved in hypothesis testing. Recall that Error Type I is committed any time we reject H_0 when it is, in fact, the correct hypothesis. This happens whenever $\bar{x}$ falls to the right of the boundary point $\bar{x}_H$. Note that if H_0 is correct, then $\overline{X}$ follows distribution 1 in Figure 5–6. Therefore the probability of Error Type I is given by the chosen level of significance (0.05) and corresponds to the blackened area. The Error Type II occurs whenever we do not reject H_0 when it is in fact false. This happens whenever $\bar{x}$ falls to the left of $\bar{x}_H$. In the present case if H_0 should be false, i.e., if μ_0 were not the true mean, then the only other possibility is that the

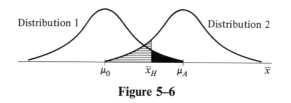

Figure 5–6

true mean is μ_A. But if μ_A should be the true mean, the sample mean $\overline{X}$ would follow distribution 2, and the probability of making Error Type II is given by the striped area in Figure 5–6. In reality we do not know which is the true mean and therefore do not know which is the true distribution of $\overline{X}$. If the true distribution of $\overline{X}$ is "1," then our test will lead to an incorrect conclusion 5% (or whatever the chosen level of significance) of the time. If the true distribution of $\overline{X}$ is "2," then our test will produce incorrect results with a probability given by the striped area to the left of $\bar{x}_H$.

The preceding discussion, although restricted to the case of a simple alternative hypothesis, brings out an important facet of hypothesis testing which remains equally relevant in tests involving composite alternatives. This is the fact that *by decreasing the probability of one type of error we increase the probability of the other type of error*. For instance, we can make the probability of Error Type I (rejecting H_0 when in fact it is true) as small as we like by setting a very low level of significance. In terms of Figure 5–6, this amounts to shifting the boundary point $\bar{x}_H$ farther to the right. But by doing this we would obviously increase the striped area, which represents the probability of Error Type II (not rejecting H_0 when in fact it is false). Similarly, we can reduce the probability of Error Type II by increasing the level of significance, i.e., by shifting $\bar{x}_H$ to the left, but this would increase the probability of Error Type I. By reference to our comparison of statistical testing with trials before a court of law, we could obviously diminish the probability of convicting an innocent man by letting almost everybody go, but this would clearly increase the probability of not convicting a guilty man. Similarly, we could reduce the probability of letting a guilty man go free by requiring less stringent evidence for conviction, but this would increase the probability of convicting an innocent man. In statistical testing, the only way in which we could reduce the probabilities of both kinds of error at the same time is by increasing the sample size (assuming that the test statistic used is the best that can be devised).

EXAMPLE A manufacturer produces two types of tires, one type with a life expectancy of 25,000 miles and the other with a life expectancy of 30,000 miles. The variation in durability around the expected lifetime is the same for both types of tires, the standard deviation being 3,000 miles. The distribution can be assumed to be normal. The two types of tires are indistinguishable except for markings. At the time of inventory taking, it is discovered that there is a forgotten case with 100 tires that do not have any markings. The examining engineer thinks that the tires are of the less durable kind but recommends a test. The test is to be performed on a sample of 4 tires. What should be the appropriate test criterion?

First, we specify the null and the alternative hypotheses as follows:

$$H_0: \quad \mu = 25,000,$$

$$H_A: \quad \mu = 30,000.$$

Next, we set up the boundary between the acceptance and the critical regions. This will depend on the chosen level of significance. We shall consider 1%, 5%, and 10% levels of significance and determine the corresponding probabilities of Error Type II. Because μ_0 ($=25,000$) $< \mu_A$ ($=30,000$), we shall use the upper-tail critical region in every case.

1. If the level of significance is 1%, the boundary point on the z scale (for the standard normal distribution) will be the point which cuts off the top 1% of the area. From the normal probability tables, we find that this is given by

$$z_H = 2.327.$$

To determine the probability of Error Type II we have to find the corresponding point on the $\bar{x}$ scale, $\bar{x}_H$. From the previous discussion, we know that

$$\bar{x}_H = \mu_0 + 2.327\,\frac{\sigma}{\sqrt{n}}.$$

Substituting, we get

$$\bar{x}_H = 25,000 + 2.327\left[\frac{3000}{\sqrt{4}}\right] = 28,490.5.$$

Now we have to determine the probability that $\bar{x} < 28{,}490.5$ *given* that the mean of $\bar{X}$, $E(\bar{X})$, is 30,000. To do that we have to make the appropriate transformation to standard normal variable. We can write

$$P[\bar{x} < 28{,}490.5 \mid E(\bar{X}) = 30{,}000] = P\left[z < \frac{(28{,}490.5 - 30{,}000)\sqrt{4}}{3000}\right]$$

$$= P[z < -1.0063].$$

But from the normal probability tables we find

$$P[z < -1.0063] = 0.1571.$$

This is the probability of making Error Type II.

    2. If the chosen level of significance is 5%, then

$$z_H = 1.645,$$

and $$\bar{x}_H = 25{,}000 + 1.645\left[\frac{3000}{\sqrt{4}}\right] = 27{,}467.5.$$

The probability that $\bar{x} < 27{,}467.5$ *given* that the mean of $\bar{X}$ is 30,000 is

$$P[\bar{x} < 27{,}467.5 \mid E(\bar{X}) = 30{,}000] = P\left[z < \frac{(27{,}467.5 - 30{,}000)\sqrt{4}}{3000}\right]$$

$$= P[z < -1.6883] = 0.0457.$$

    3. Finally, if the level of significance is 10%, then

$$z_H = 1.280,$$

and $$\bar{x}_H = 25{,}000 + 1.280\left[\frac{3000}{\sqrt{4}}\right] = 26{,}920.$$

Consequently

$$P[\bar{x} < 26{,}920 \mid E(\bar{X}) = 30{,}000] = P\left[z < \frac{(26{,}920 - 30{,}000)\sqrt{4}}{3000}\right]$$

$$= P[z < -2.0533] = 0.0200.$$

    In summary, the results are

Boundary		Probability of	
z scale	$\bar{x}$ scale	Error Type I	Error Type II
2.327	28,490.5	0.01	0.1571
1.645	27,467.5	0.05	0.0457
1.280	26,920.0	0.10	0.0200

These results show that, as expected, the two probabilities are inversely related. The question then is which pair of probabilities should be considered as the optimal choice. The answer depends on the cost of making each of the two kinds of error. If the error of rejecting the null hypothesis which is in fact true (Error Type I) is costly relative to the error of not rejecting the null hypothesis which is in fact false (Error Type II), it will be rational to set the probability of the first kind of error low. If, on the other hand, the cost of making Error Type I is low relative to the cost of making Error Type II, it will pay to make the probability of the first kind of error high (thus making the probability of the second type of error low).

A concrete illustration of this point can be given by extending the information in the given example. Suppose the manufacturer sells the less durable tires for $10 and the more durable ones for $12. Suppose further that the more durable tires carries a "money-back" guarantee if the tire should wear out before 25,000 miles, and that there is no guarantee attached to the less durable tire. Given this information, we can estimate the cost of either type of error.

Cost of Error Type I   If the hypothesis that $\mu = 25,000$ is rejected, the manufacturer will sell the tires for the higher price. This will represent a gain of $100 \times (\$12 - \$10) = \$200$. On the other hand, if the true mean actually is 25,000 miles, one half of all tires (in the population) will have a lifetime of less than that. Thus in a shipment of 100 tires the expected number of returns will be 50, and the corresponding outlay will be $50 \times \$12 = \$600$. Therefore, the total cost of making Error Type I is $\$600 - \$200 = \$400$.

Cost of Error Type II   If the hypothesis that the mean is 25,000 miles is *not* rejected while, in fact, the mean is 30,000 miles, the tires will be sold for $1000 instead of $1200. The latter figure, however, has to be adjusted downward because the guarantee does represent a de facto reduction in price. If the mean is 30,000 miles, then 4.78% of the tires will not last for 25,000 miles. This is the result of the fact that

$$P\left[z < \frac{25,000 - 30,000}{3000}\right] = 0.0478.$$

Therefore in a shipment of 100 tires of the more durable kind the expected number of returns will be 4.78. The cost of the guarantee is then $4.78 \times \$12 = \$57.36$. Thus the expected revenue from selling 100 better quality tires is $\$1200 - \$57.36 = \$1142.36$. The total net cost of making Error Type II then is $\$1142.36 - \$1000 = \$142.36$.

With the additional information on the problem on hand, we find that Error Type I is costlier than Error Type II. Thus it will be rational to set the probability of Error Type I lower than that of Error Type II. Just how much lower can be determined by comparing the expected losses for each level of significance. "Expected loss" is defined as the amount of loss multiplied by the probability of its occurrence. For example, if the loss is $400 and the probability of its occurrence is 0.01, the expected loss is $4.00. The calculations of the expected losses in our example are

Error Type I		Error Type II	
Probability	Expected Loss	Probability	Expected Loss
0.01	$4.00	0.1571	$22.36
0.05	$20.00	0.0457	$6.51
0.10	$40.00	0.0200	$2.85

Assuming that the manufacturer gets no utility from gambling as such, the rational choice will be one which gives equal expected loss for each type of error. From the above figures it appears that this would be realized somewhere between the 1% and

5% levels of significance. Carrying out the calculations for levels in this interval leads to the following:

Error Type I		Error Type II	
Probability	Expected Loss	Probability	Expected Loss
0.02	$8.00	0.1006	$14.32
0.03	$12.00	0.0732	$10.42
0.04	$16.00	0.0567	$8.07

It appears, then, that the optimum of significance lies between 2% and 3%. If the level of significance is set at 2.75%, then the expected loss from Error Type I will be approximately the same as that from Error Type II (about $11.00). This then would be optimal level of significance in our example.

The preceding example illustrates the relevance of considering the cost implications of different decisions in setting up statistical tests. Modern statistical theory puts a great emphasis on this and develops a formal apparatus for incorporating loss and risk functions in the determination of a proper test criterion. Unfortunately very little of this is of use or relevance in econometric research since prior (or even posterior) ideas about losses due to incorrect conclusions are either completely nonexistent or are so vague that they offer no guidance at all. For instance, consider the question whether liquid assets do or do not affect consumption expenditure. The econometrician will specify the relevant maintained and testable hypothesis and calculate the value of the appropriate test statistic, but he has absolutely no idea as to what is the cost—to him, to the profession, to the society—of drawing an incorrect conclusion. Consequently, it has been a standard practice in econometrics to use the traditional approach of classical statistics, namely, to fix the level of significance at 1% or 5% and to use a test statistic that would make the probability of Error Type II as small as possible. If the value of the test statistic is such that it falls in the critical region given by the 5% significance level, it is said to be *significant*; if the value of the test statistic falls in the critical region given by the 1% significance level, it is said to be *highly significant*. However, there is nothing superior about these two significance levels other than that they are widely used. And it is only this popularity which stifles the competition from other levels of significance.

Power of a Test

The classification of errors into the two types was explained with reference to the case of a simple null hypotheses and a simple alternative. The idea can easily be extended to the more common case of testing a null hypothesis against a composite alternative. Suppose we have

$$H_0: \quad \mu = \mu_0,$$
$$H_A: \quad \mu \neq \mu_0.$$

As before, the probability of Error Type I (rejecting H_0 when it is true) is given by the level of significance. However, the probability of Error Type II (not rejecting H_0 when it is false) is now no longer a single number for a given level of significance but depends on the value of μ. For values of μ close to μ_0 the probability of Error Type II will be high compared to the probability of this error for values of μ farther away from μ_0. If, for example, the null hypothesis states that the mean is equal to 10, then the probability of *not* rejecting H_0 is obviously greater if the true mean is 15 than if it is 20. This is illustrated by Figure 5–7, where the probability of Error Type II is shown by the striped area.

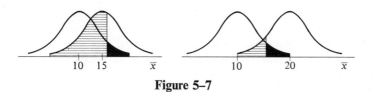

Figure 5–7

Obviously, we can determine the probability of Error Type II for any value of μ. The smaller this probability, the better is the test in discriminating between true and false hypotheses. In the illustration given in Figure 5–7, the test will discriminate more clearly between the null hypothesis and the alternative hypothesis if the alternative mean is 20 than if it is 15. In the common terminology of statistics, the lower the probability of not rejecting H_0 when it is false, the more *powerful* is the test. That is, the *power of a test* is measured by the *probability of rejecting H_0 when it is false*. Since the probability of Error Type II is the probability of *not* rejecting H_0 when it is false, the power of a test is equal to

$$1 - P(\text{Error Type II}).$$

Furthermore, since for composite alternatives the probability of Error Type II depends on the value of μ, the power of a test is likewise dependent on μ. If we plot the probabilities of rejecting H_0 when it is false on the vertical axis against the values of μ on the horizontal axis, we get what is known as the *power function* of a test.

EXAMPLE   Consider the following statement of hypotheses concerning the mean of a variable $X \sim N(\mu, 81)$

$$H_0: \quad \mu = 10,$$

$$H_A: \quad \mu \neq 10.$$

Suppose the test statistic is based on sample size 9 and the chosen level of significance is 5%. The appropriate test is then a two-tail one with the acceptance region given by

$$-1.96 \leq \frac{(\bar{x} - 10)\sqrt{9}}{\sqrt{81}} \leq 1.96$$

or
$$-1.96 \leq \frac{\bar{x} - 10}{3} \leq 1.96.$$

On the $\bar{x}$ scale, the equivalent acceptance region is

$$4.12 \leq \bar{x} \leq 15.88.$$

To find the power function we have to calculate $[1 - P(\text{Error Type II})]$ for the acceptance region for various values of μ. Let us start with some very small value of μ, say -10. Then

$$P[\text{Error Type II}] = P[4.12 \leq \bar{x} \leq 15.88 \mid \mu = -10]$$

$$= P\left[\frac{4.12 - (-10)}{3} \leq z \leq \frac{15.88 - (-10)}{3}\right]$$

$$= P(4.707 \leq z \leq 8.627) = 0.0000,$$

where, as before, z is the value of a standard normal variable. The value of the power function therefore is $1 - 0.0000 = 1.0000$. Carrying out these calculations for other values of μ leads to the following results:

μ	Power	μ	Power
-10	1.0000	10	0.0500
-5	0.9988	12	0.1022
0	0.9152	14	0.2659
2	0.7602	16	0.5159
4	0.5159	18	0.7602
6	0.2659	20	0.9152
8	0.1022	25	0.9988

A graphical representation of this power function is shown in Figure 5–8. The graph confirms our previous contention that the power of a test increases as μ gets farther away from μ_0 in the direction (or directions) specified by the alternative hypothesis.

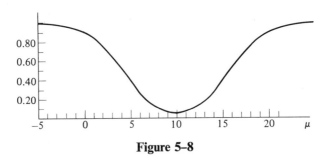

Figure 5–8

In our case we see that if the true value of μ were -5 or $+25$, we would correctly reject the false hypothesis virtually every time. If the true value of μ were equal to 0 or $+20$, we would correctly reject the false hypothesis 91.5% of the time. Note that if the true mean were almost equal to $+10$, we would correctly reject the false hypothesis only about 5% of the time.

The power function in Figure 5–8 has a shape which is typical for symmetric two-tail tests concerning the mean of a normal population. A one-tail test leads to quite a different curve, which we shall not present here. The interested reader can do the calculations and plotting for himself, or he can consult almost any standard test on statistical inference. We only wish to point out that the power function is another way of demonstrating some weaknesses of statistical testing. An ideal power function—which, needless to say, does not exist—would be one that would show a value of 1 for all values of μ (or whatever the relevant parameter) specified by the alternative hypothesis, and a value of 0 for the value of μ specified by the null hypothesis.

Quality of a Test

What is the best test we can design, given the size of the sample and given all the prior information that is available ? We can answer this question by noting the choices that are open to us when we are setting up the test criterion. In general, there are three areas of choice that are relevant:

1. Choice of the level of significance.
2. Choice of the location of the acceptance region.
3. Choice of test statistic.

We have already found that a rational choice can be made in the first area *providing* we have a way of assessing the losses due to an incorrect conclusion. Otherwise—and this is normally the case in econometric research—we have no firm basis for the choice of the level of significance other than tradition.

The second area of choice concerns the location of the acceptance region on the z or the $\bar{x}$ axis. Suppose the problem involves the hypotheses

$$H_0: \quad \mu = \mu_0$$

$$H_A: \quad \mu \neq \mu_0$$

and the chosen level of significance is 5%. Previously, in a problem of this kind, we chose a two-tail test and located the acceptance region symmetrically around 0 on the z axis or, equivalently, around μ_0 on the $\bar{x}$ axis. The acceptance region then covered the central 95% of the area, leaving 2.5% of the area at each tail to be taken up by the critical region. Obviously, we could have the same 5% level of significance—and therefore the same probability of Error Type I—with the acceptance region located in a different position. For instance, we could locate the acceptance region in such a way that it would cut off 1% of the area at the lower tail and 4% of the area at the upper tail. The number of possibilities is clearly infinite. Previously we justified our choice of the symmetric acceptance region largely on intuitive grounds; now we are in a position to make a stronger case for such a choice. Since any acceptance region that preserves the same level of significance automatically preserves the same probability of Error Type I, the argument in favor of the symmetric acceptance region can only run in terms of probabilities of Error Type II. But because the problem involves a composite alternative hypothesis, different values of μ embraced by the alternative hypothesis will be associated with different probabilities of Error Type II. Therefore, we have to compare the *power functions* of tests based on differently located acceptance regions, not just individual probability values. Suppose we compare the power function of a test with a symmetric acceptance region with the power function of a test with an asymmetric acceptance region, such as one which cuts off 1% of the area at the lower tail and 4% of the area at the upper tail. Then, as can be easily confirmed by carrying out the necessary calculations, the symmetric test turns out to be more powerful for values of μ smaller than μ_0. Since the power function measures the capability of a test to discriminate between a true and a false hypothesis, the comparison shows that the symmetric test discriminates better than the asymmetric test (with a smaller lower and a larger upper tail) when $\mu < \mu_0$ and worse when $\mu > \mu_0$. If there is no reason why we should want to be able to discriminate between hypotheses more effectively when μ is on one side of μ_0 than when it is on the other, then a symmetric test is clearly more appropriate than an asymmetric one. If there *is* a reason, it must be included in the prior information relevant to testing and the acceptance region would be then located accordingly. Normally the choice of a symmetric acceptance region (when H_A is $\mu \neq \mu_0$) is the most reasonable one that can be specified. Incidentally, it is interesting to note that this acceptance region is shorter than any other one based on the same test statistic and the same level of significance. By similar reasoning we can also establish that, for problems involving alternative hypothesis of the kind $\mu > \mu_0$ or $\mu < \mu_0$, the most reasonable test is a one-tail test as previously described.

This leaves only the third area of choice, that involving the test statistic. For the problem of testing a hypothesis concerning the population mean of a normal population—the only problem specifically considered in this section—we used as the test statistic the standard normal variable Z constructed as

$$Z = \frac{\bar{X} - \mu_0}{\sigma_{\bar{x}}},$$

where μ_0 is the population mean postulated by the null hypothesis and $\sigma_{\bar{x}} = \sigma/\sqrt{n}$. The use of $\bar{X}$ was justified on the grounds that it is an unbiased and consistent estimate of μ and thus represents a reasonable summary of the sample evidence about the population mean. For, say, a two-tail test with 5% level of significance, the acceptance region for the Z statistic is

$$-1.96 \leq z \leq 1.96;$$

and for $\bar{X}$,

$$\mu_0 - 1.96\sigma_{\bar{x}} \leq \bar{x} \leq \mu_0 + 1.96\sigma_{\bar{x}}.$$

Let us now demonstrate why the desirable properties of an estimator (unbiasedness, etc.) are also desirable when it comes to hypothesis testing. Consider a test statistic similar to Z but one in which instead of $\bar{X}$ we use an unspecified estimator of μ to be called $\hat{\mu}$. The variance of this estimator, which is also unspecified, is $\sigma_{\hat{\mu}}^2$. The only restriction that we place on $\hat{\mu}$ is that it should be normally distributed (at least approximately) so that we can make the transformation to the standard normal variable. The latter will then be given by

$$Z^* = \frac{\hat{\mu} - E(\hat{\mu})}{\sigma_{\hat{\mu}}}.$$

Now in the form in which it is given, Z^* does not involve μ_0 and therefore does not fulfil the basic function of a test statistic, namely confronting the null hypothesis with sample evidence. However, we can introduce μ_0 into the formula quite easily by writing

$$Z^* = \frac{\hat{\mu} - E(\hat{\mu})}{\sigma_{\hat{\mu}}} + \frac{\mu_0}{\sigma_{\hat{\mu}}} - \frac{\mu_0}{\sigma_{\hat{\mu}}} = \frac{(\hat{\mu} - \mu_0) - [E(\hat{\mu}) - \mu_0]}{\sigma_{\hat{\mu}}}.$$

If the null hypothesis is valid and μ_0 is the true mean, $[E(\hat{\mu}) - \mu_0]$ represents the bias and will be equal to zero only if $\hat{\mu}$ is an unbiased estimator of μ. The acceptance region for a two-tail test with 5% level of significance will be

$$-1.96 \leq \frac{(\hat{\mu} - \mu_0) - [E(\hat{\mu}) - \mu_0]}{\sigma_{\hat{\mu}}} \leq 1.96.$$

The equivalent acceptance region on the $\hat{\mu}$ axis will be

$$\mu_0 - 1.96\sigma_{\hat{\mu}} + [E(\hat{\mu}) - \mu_0] \leq \hat{\mu} \leq \mu_0 + 1.96\sigma_{\hat{\mu}} + [E(\hat{\mu}) - \mu_0].$$

The first property of $\hat{\mu}$ which we shall consider is *unbiasedness*. Suppose $\hat{\mu}$ is a biased estimator of μ. The obvious consequence of this is the fact that the above acceptance region is not symmetric around μ_0. For instance, if $\mu_0 = 10$, $E[\hat{\mu}] = 5$, and $\sigma_{\hat{\mu}} = 3$, the acceptance region will be

$$10 - 1.96 \times 3 + (5 - 10) \leq \hat{\mu} \leq 10 + 1.96 \times 3 + (5 - 10),$$

that is, $$-0.88 \leq \hat{\mu} \leq 10.88,$$

which is clearly not symmetric around 10. If such an asymmetric acceptance region were to be used, then the power function of the test would be shifted so that its lowest value would be at the point $E(\hat{\mu})$ and not at μ_0. Unless there is a special reason why we would wish to have the capacity for discriminating between true and false hypotheses so unevenly distributed, a test like this is hardly appropriate. Of course, if the extent of the bias of $\hat{\mu}$ is not known, then we cannot specify the boundary between the acceptance and the critical region as we did above and thus cannot carry out the test. But even more troublesome is the situation when the estimator *is* biased but we are not aware of it. Then we would clearly be using an acceptance region which is incorrect for the chosen level of significance, and our conclusion would be correspondingly distorted. All this applies equally to one-tail tests and points to the desirability of using an unbiased estimator of μ in constructing the test statistic.

Next let us consider *consistency*. Earlier we described an estimator as consistent if its distribution tends to become more and more concentrated around the true value of the parameter as sample size increases. Except for some special cases (i.e., estimators which do not have a finite mean or variance or both), this means that as sample size increases both the bias (if any) and the variance of the distribution will decrease and, in the limit, will approach zero. Therefore, the larger the sample size, the narrower is the acceptance region on the $\hat{\mu}$ scale, and the more powerful is the test. This is illustrated in Figure 5–9. Here μ_0 is the value

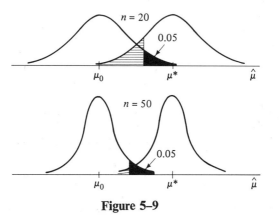

Figure 5–9

of the mean postulated by the null hypothesis, and μ^* is one of the values of the mean postulated by the alternative hypothesis. The blackened area represents the probability of Error Type I and the striped area the probability of Error Type II. The diagram illustrates how, for the same level of significance, the increase in sample size reduces the probability of Error Type II or, equivalently, increases the power of the test. If the variance of the distribution did not decrease with an increase in sample size—i.e., if the estimator were not consistent—then an increase in sample size would not reduce the probability of Error Type II. This would be obviously undesirable since it would mean that the additional cost involved in increasing the size of the sample would result in no additional information about the population mean.

The last property that we shall mention in this context is *efficiency*. If we have two estimators of the population mean, both unbiased and normally distributed but characterized by different variances, then the estimator with the larger variance is not efficient. The acceptance region of this estimator—measured on the $\hat{\mu}$ axis—will be wider than that of the other estimator and the corresponding power of the test will be lower. A demonstration is given in Figure 5–10. In the diagram, $\hat{\mu}_{\mathrm{I}}$ is more efficient compared with $\hat{\mu}_{\mathrm{II}}$. If we were to compare the power functions of the two tests corresponding to these two estimators, we would find that the values of the power function related to μ_{I} are always higher than those of the power function related to μ_{II}. Thus, efficiency is obviously a highly desirable feature in setting up a statistic.

The preceding discussion about an optimal design of a test indicates that, for most problems in econometrics, the only way of getting the best design is by using the best estimator in constructing the appropriate test statistic. Normally, we have no information that would allow us to make a rational choice of the level of significance or of the location of the acceptance region. Thus, for given prior information and for a given sample size, the only avenue of search is that for the best estimator. As we shall see, for some problems the search is already completed; that is, the best estimator has already been found.[1] Unfortunately,

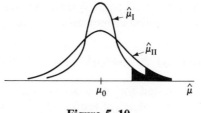

Figure 5-10

this is true only for simple problems—such as estimating the mean of a normal population—but for many problems in econometrics the search still goes on. This, at least in part, is the reason for the heavy concentration of pure econometric research on problems of estimation.

Concluding Remarks

This brings us to the end of the section on design and evaluation of statistical tests. The reader may recall that the discussion started with the division of hypotheses into maintained hypotheses on one hand and testable hypotheses on the other. There is a question about this division that has never been asked, namely why *any* hypothesis should be considered as maintained, that is, beyond challenge. It would appear more reasonable to test all the assumptions involved rather than just some. This certainly would be safer than relying upon our prior beliefs that make up the maintained hypothesis. The difficulty with doing this, however, lies in the fact that our *factual* knowledge of the population is very meager, so that without assumptions the only source of information would be the sample. As a result, the scope for making errors would be greater and, thus, the power of the test would be weakened. Consider, for instance, the problem of testing a hypothesis about the mean of a normal population with known variance—a problem considered throughout this section. A part of the maintained hypothesis is the assumption that the population variance is known. If this assumption is not made, the variance of the distribution of sample mean is not known and we cannot construct the test statistic given by (5.1). We can, of course, estimate the population variance from sample data. But using an estimate rather than the actual value of the variance increases the degree of uncertainty concerning the population and, predictably, results in a wider acceptance region. We still can choose whatever level of significance we desire but, with a wider

---

[1] There is, however, also the question of whether we use *all* prior information as effectively as possible. Some prior knowledge (e.g., the numerical results of previous estimations) is typically not used at all unless one adopts the Bayesian approach to statistical inference.

acceptance region, the power of the test will be diminished (a detailed explanation of this test is given in Section 5–2). Thus, by replacing an assumption with a sample estimate, we lose some information and pay for it by having a less powerful test. Of course, if we have *no idea* about the value of the population variance, then we have no choice. On the other hand, by relying on the assumptions contained in the maintained hypothesis, we get results that are strictly conditional on these assumptions and do not hold without them. This elementary fact seems to be frequently forgotten in applied econometric research.

5–2   Distribution of Selected Test Statistics

In Section 5–1 we illustrated the ideas underlying the test of statistical hypotheses by considering the problem of testing a hypothesis about the mean of a normal population with known variance σ^2. As the test statistic we suggested

$$Z = \frac{(\bar{X} - \mu_0)}{\sigma_{\bar{x}}},$$

where μ_0 is the mean postulated by the null hypothesis, and $\sigma_{\bar{x}}$ is the standard deviation of the distribution of $\bar{X}$ given by $\sigma/\sqrt{n}$. If $\bar{X}$ is the best estimator of the population mean that can be found, then Z is the best test statistic that can be devised. As we shall see in Chapter 6, $\bar{X}$ is—except for special circumstances—the best estimator of the population mean so that we cannot, in general, improve on Z.

Test for the Difference Between Two Means

A test procedure similar to the one just described can be employed in the problem involving *two independent samples* from two normal populations with known variances. The question may arise whether there is any difference between the two population means. Suppose the mean of the first population is μ_1 and the mean of the second population is μ_2. Then the null hypothesis is

$$H_0: \quad \mu_1 = \mu_2,$$

and the alternative hypothesis is

$$H_A: \quad \mu_1 \neq \mu_2 \quad (\text{or } \mu_1 > \mu_2).$$

As the sample summary of evidence about the population means, we can use the respective sample means, say $\bar{X}_1$ and $\bar{X}_2$. If the null hypothesis is true, then $(\mu_1 - \mu_2) = 0$; therefore, the value of $(\bar{X}_1 - \bar{X}_2)$ would seldom be very different from zero. Consequently, sample values of $(\bar{X}_1 - \bar{X}_2)$ which *are* very different from zero could be considered as evidence against the null hypothesis. If we determine the distribution of $(\bar{X}_1 - \bar{X}_2)$, we can specify the appropriate acceptance and critical region. Now, since both $\bar{X}_1$ and $\bar{X}_2$ come from normal populations, their difference must also be normally distributed. The mean of this distribution is

$$E(\bar{X}_1 - \bar{X}_2) = E(\bar{X}_1) - E(\bar{X}_2) = \mu_1 - \mu_2,$$

which, if the null hypothesis is true, is equal to zero. Thus the only thing to determine is the variance. Since $\bar{X}_1$ and $\bar{X}_2$ are means of two independent samples, their covariance is zero and we have

$$\text{Var}(\bar{X}_1 - \bar{X}_2) = \text{Var}(\bar{X}_1) + \text{Var}(\bar{X}_2) = \frac{\sigma_1^2}{n_1} + \frac{\sigma_2^2}{n_2},$$

where σ_1^2 and σ_2^2 are the variances of the two normal populations from which the samples were drawn, and n_1 and n_2 are the respective sample sizes. When the two population means are the same as postulated by the null hypothesis,

$$(\bar{X}_1 - \bar{X}_2) \sim N\left[0, \frac{\sigma_1^2}{n_1} + \frac{\sigma_2^2}{n_2}\right].$$

The corresponding standard normal variable then is

(5.2)
$$Z_{(\bar{x}_1 - \bar{x}_2)} = \frac{\bar{X}_1 - \bar{X}_2}{\sigma_{(\bar{x}_1 - \bar{x}_2)}} = \frac{\bar{X}_1 - \bar{X}_2}{\sqrt{\sigma_1^2/n_1 + \sigma_2^2/n_2}}.$$

This is the appropriate test statistic for which we can define the acceptance and the critical region with the help of normal probability tables.

Estimation of σ^2

In both tests considered so far, we have assumed that the population variance is always known. Usually this is not the case and the variance has to be estimated from the sample. But if we use an *estimate* of the population variance rather than its actual value, the tests concerning the population mean have to be modified. Before developing the necessary modification, we shall discuss the problem of estimating the population variance of $X \sim N(\mu, \sigma^2)$. As a possible candidate we may consider the sample variance, which we shall call $\hat{\sigma}^2$ and which is defined as follows:

(5.3)
$$\hat{\sigma}^2 = \frac{1}{n} \sum_{i=1}^{n} (X_i - \bar{X})^2.$$

Different samples will, of course, lead to different values of $\hat{\sigma}^2$. We are interested to know whether $\hat{\sigma}^2$ has any desirable properties and what its distribution is.

We may start by examining $\hat{\sigma}^2$ for biasedness. This we can do by taking the mathematical expectation of $\hat{\sigma}^2$ and by checking whether it is equal to σ^2 or not. If it is, then $\hat{\sigma}^2$ is unbiased. We have

$$E(\hat{\sigma}^2) = E\frac{1}{n}\sum_i (X_i - \bar{X})^2 = \frac{1}{n}\sum_i E(X_i - \bar{X})^2.$$

As it is, we do not know $E(X_i - \bar{X})^2$. However, we know that

$$E(X_i - \mu)^2 = \text{Var}(X_i) = \sigma^2,$$

since X_i has exactly the same distribution as X and, therefore, the same variance. Also, we know that

$$E(\bar{X} - \mu)^2 = \text{Var}(\bar{X}) = \frac{\sigma^2}{n}.$$

by Theorem 13 (Section 4–3). Therefore, we will rewrite the expression for $E(\hat{\sigma}^2)$ by simultaneously adding and deducting μ:

$$E(\hat{\sigma}^2) = \frac{1}{n} \sum_i E[(X_i - \mu) - (\bar{X} - \mu)]^2$$

$$= \frac{1}{n} \sum_i [E(X_i - \mu)^2 + E(\bar{X} - \mu)^2 - 2E(X_i - \mu)(\bar{X} - \mu)]$$

$$= \frac{1}{n} \sum_i E(X_i - \mu)^2 + \frac{1}{n} \sum_i E(\bar{X} - \mu)^2 - \frac{2}{n} \sum_i E(X_i - \mu)(\bar{X} - \mu)$$

$$= \frac{1}{n} \sum_i \sigma^2 + \frac{1}{n} \sum_i \frac{\sigma^2}{n} - 2E(\bar{X} - \mu)\frac{1}{n} \sum_i (X_i - \mu)$$

$$= \sigma^2 + \frac{\sigma^2}{n} - 2E(\bar{X} - \mu)^2 = \sigma^2 + \frac{\sigma^2}{n} - 2\frac{\sigma^2}{n}.$$

That is,

(5.4) $$E(\hat{\sigma}^2) = \left[\frac{n-1}{n}\right]\sigma^2,$$

which is not equal to σ^2. This means that $\hat{\sigma}^2$ is a *biased* estimator of σ^2.

This result, although negative, is nevertheless helpful since it suggests an easy way of finding an unbiased estimator of $\hat{\sigma}^2$. By multiplying both sides of (5.4) by $n/(n-1)$ we obtain

$$\left[\frac{n}{n-1}\right] E(\hat{\sigma}^2) = \sigma^2,$$

which can be written as

$$E\left[\frac{n}{n-1}\right]\hat{\sigma}^2 = \sigma^2,$$

or $$E\left[\frac{n}{n-1}\right]\frac{1}{n} \sum_i (X_i - \bar{X})^2 = \sigma^2,$$

that is,

(5.5) $$E\frac{1}{n-1} \sum_i (X_i - \bar{X})^2 = \sigma^2,$$

so that an estimator of σ^2, which we shall call s^2 and which is defined as

(5.6) $$s^2 = \frac{1}{n-1} \sum_i (X_i - \bar{X})^2,$$

is an *unbiased* estimator of σ^2.

Because of the property of unbiasedness, we shall use s^2 as our preferred estimator of σ^2. Its distribution, which we shall not derive or present here, is a special case of the so-called gamma distribution.[2] The exact shape of the distribution of s^2 depends on two parameters, the population variance σ^2 and the sample size n. The distribution is always skewed to the right for small sample sizes and becomes more and more symmetric as the sample size increases. The mean of the distribution is, as shown, equal to σ^2 and its variance is given[3] by

$$(5.7) \qquad\qquad\qquad \mathrm{Var}(s^2) = \frac{2\,\sigma^4}{n - 1}.$$

Since s^2 is unbiased and since its variance approaches zero as $n \to \infty$, s^2 is a *consistent* estimator of σ^2. Another feature of s^2 that is worth a passing reference is the fact that s^2 is independent of $\overline{X}$ in the sense that the joint distribution of s^2 and $\overline{X}$ is equal to the product of their respective marginal distributions. That is,

$$f(s^2, \bar{x}) = f(s^2)f(\bar{x}).$$

The Chi-Square Distribution

To determine the probability that s^2 lies within any specific interval, we would have to find the areas under the corresponding gamma curve. This curve would be different for each different combination of σ^2 and n, and the determination of the appropriate area would be quite complicated. This problem has already been encountered in connection with the normal distribution, which also differs from one combination of parameter values—in this case μ and σ^2—to another, and for which the mathematical formula is also highly complicated. In the case of the normal distribution, the problem was solved by transforming a normal variable to one with mean 0 and variance 1 (a "standard normal variable") for which the probabilities are tabulated. In the case of s^2, the solution is similar. The transformation in this case is to a variable called *chi-square*, which is defined as

$$(5.8) \qquad\qquad\qquad \chi^2 = \frac{(n - 1)s^2}{\sigma^2},$$

and for which probabilities are calculated. However, unlike the standard normal distribution, the distribution of χ^2 changes its shape with sample size. For small samples the distribution is skewed to the right, but it becomes more and more symmetric as the sample size increases. No value of χ^2 is, of course, negative. Because of the dependence of the chi-square distribution on sample size, we usually use an identifying subscript. For instance, (5.8) would normally be written as

$$(5.8a) \qquad\qquad\qquad \chi^2_{n-1} = \frac{(n - 1)s^2}{\sigma^2}.$$

---

[2] See, e.g., John E. Freund, *Mathematical Statistics* (Englewood Cliffs, N.J.: Prentice-Hall, 1962), pp. 127–28. For the special case of s^2 we have, in Freund's notation, $\alpha = (n - 1)/2$ and $\beta = 2\sigma^2/(n - 1)$.

[3] *Ibid.*, p. 147. Note that the mean of s^2 is equal to σ^2 regardless of the form of the parent distribution of X but the variance formula (5.7) hinges on the assumption of normality of X.

An equivalent way of writing (5.8a) is

$$\chi_{n-1}^2 = \frac{\sum_{i=1}^{n} (X_i - X)^2}{\sigma^2}.$$

(5.8b)

The subscript of χ^2, which is equal to the sample size reduced by 1, is called the number of *degrees of freedom* and is often designated by ν instead of $(n-1)$. The terms "degrees of freedom" refers to the number of independent squares in the numerator of the chi-square statistics, i.e., in

$$\sum_{i=1}^{n} (X_i - \bar{X})^2.$$

The total number of squares in this expression is n, but only $(n-1)$ of them are independent since after calculating any first $(n-1)$ squares, the value of the nth square will be automatically determined. The reason for this is the presence of $\bar{X}$ and one of the well-known features of $\bar{X}$ is that

$$\sum_i (X_i - \bar{X}) = 0.$$

This represents a restriction that must be fulfilled. For example, suppose we have three squares of which the values of the first two are

$$(x_1 - \bar{x})^2 = 2^2,$$

$$(x_2 - \bar{x})^2 = 4^2.$$

If the third square were independent of the first two, its value could be any number, say 5^2. But that cannot be because in that case we would have

$$\sum_i (x_i - \bar{x}) = 2 + 4 + 5,$$

which adds up to 11 and not to 0 as required. In fact, with the first two squares being 2^2 and 4^2, the third square can only be equal to $(-6)^2 = 36$ because only then we get $2 + 4 - 6 = 0$. This explanation of the determination of the number of degrees of freedom in the present context is relatively straightforward; in other cases the issue is more clouded. For that reason most basic statistical texts do not dwell too much upon the subject and suggest that the reader may think of the degrees of freedom as simply a name given to a parameter.

From the knowledge of the probability distribution of χ^2 we can determine the probabilities for the sampling distribution of s^2. This can be seen as follows. If a and b are any constants such that $0 \le a \le b$, then

$$P(a \le \chi_{n-1}^2 \le b) = P\left[a \le \frac{(n-1)s^2}{\sigma^2} \le b\right]$$

$$= P\left[a\left(\frac{\sigma^2}{n-1}\right) \le s^2 \le b\left(\frac{\sigma^2}{n-1}\right)\right],$$

so that a probability statement about χ^2 can readily be translated into an equivalent probability statement about s^2. Finally, it may be noted that the mean and the variance of the chi-square distribution are

$$E(\chi^2_{n-1}) = n - 1$$

and
$$\mathrm{Var}(\chi^2_{n-1}) = 2(n - 1),$$

and its modal value is $(n - 3)$. A graph of the chi-square distribution for various degrees of freedom ν is given in Figure 5–11.

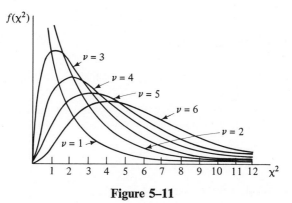

Figure 5–11

The nature of the chi-square distribution can be made clearer by comparing it with the normal distribution. The normal distribution appears in statistics for two principal reasons. First, it is a distribution of some importance on its own right, in the sense that it provides a description of many parent populations. It is not very difficult to find variables which refer to natural or social phenomena and which are—or can be assumed to be—normally distributed. Examples are intelligence, physical height of persons, errors of measurement or behavior, successes in a large number of observations, and many others. The second reason for the use of the normal distribution is the fact that it describes some important sampling distributions, in particular that of sample mean. Thus the normal distribution can serve as a description of a parent population or of a sampling distribution. The chi-square distribution, on the other hand, serves only as a description of certain sampling distributions, one of which is the distribution of the statistic (5.8).[4] There are no noted parent populations whose distributions could be described by the chi-square distribution.

---

[4] Apart from describing the distribution of (5.8), the chi-square distribution also describes the distribution of a certain statistic used in testing for independence in contingency tables and for "goodness of fit" of frequency distributions. The test for independence in contingency tables will be discussed in connection with binary variables in Chapter 11; the goodness-of-fit test is described at the end of this section.

The *t* Distribution

Having settled the problem of estimating the population variance, we may return to the original problem of testing a hypothesis about the population mean of a normally distributed variable with unknown variance. To recapitulate, we know that if

$$X \sim N(\mu, \sigma^2),$$

then

$$\bar{X} \sim N\!\left[\mu, \frac{\sigma^2}{n}\right]\!.$$

Further, if the null hypothesis is given as

$$H_0: \quad \mu = \mu_0,$$

then the appropriate test statistic is

$$\frac{(\bar{X} - \mu_0)\sqrt{n}}{\sigma} \sim N(0,1),$$

providing σ is known. When, as presently supposed, the value of σ is not known, we may replace it by its estimate obtained from

$$s = \sqrt{\frac{1}{n-1} \sum_i (X_i - \bar{X})^2},$$

which follows directly from (5.6). The test statistic then would be

$$\frac{(\bar{X} - \mu_0)\sqrt{n}}{s}.$$

The problem is to find its distribution. Note that by dividing the numerator and the denominator by σ and rearranging the result we get

$$\frac{(\bar{X} - \mu_0)\sqrt{n}/\sigma}{\sqrt{(n-1)s^2/(n-1)\sigma^2}}.$$

The numerator is the standard normal variable Z, and in the denominator $(n-1)s^2/\sigma^2 = \chi_{n-1}$, as we saw from (5.8a). That is, we have

$$\frac{Z \sim N(0,1)}{\sqrt{\chi_{n-1}^2/(n-1)}}.$$

This variable has a distribution known as the *t distribution*. Because of the presence of the chi-square variable in the denominator, the shape of this distribution depends on the size of the sample. Therefore, we usually use an identifying subscript and write

(5.9) $$\frac{(\bar{X} - \mu_0)\sqrt{n}}{s} \sim t_{n-1}.$$

Here $(n-1)$ is referred to as the number of the degrees of freedom. The number of the degrees of freedom is, of course, derived from the chi-square variable in the denominator. But unlike the chi-square distribution, the t distribution is *always* symmetric; its mean is equal to zero and its variance is $(n - 1)/(n - 3)$, which is close to unity when n is large. As the sample size increases, the t distribution approaches the standard normal distribution. The probabilities for different sample sizes are available in tabulated form (see Appendix D).

To carry out a test of a hypothesis that the population mean is equal to a given value, we have to specify the boundary between the acceptance and the critical region for the test statistic (5.9). This will depend on the form of the alternative hypothesis, on the desired level of significance, and on the number of degrees of freedom. Suppose we wish to test

$$H_0: \quad \mu = \mu_0$$
$$H_A: \quad \mu \neq \mu_0.$$

The desired level of significance is some number α. Then the acceptance region is defined as

$$-t_{n-1,\,\alpha/2} \leq \frac{(\bar{X} - \mu_0)\sqrt{n}}{s} \leq t_{n-1,\,\alpha/2}.$$

Here $t_{n-1,\,\alpha/2}$ stands for the value of the t statistic with $(n - 1)$ degrees of freedom which cuts off $\alpha/2$ of the area of the distribution at each tail end. This value can be looked up in the table of probabilities of the t distribution. The table is arranged in such a way that each row corresponds to a different number of the degrees of freedom, and each column corresponds to a different area at the tail end of the distribution. For instance, in the row labeled "14" and column "0.05," the value shown is 1.761. This means that a value of the t statistic—calculated from a sample of size 15—that would exceed 1.761 (or, alternatively, one that would be less than -1.761) would occur with a probability of 0.05. That is, the values of the test statistic are shown in the main body of the table, and the probabilities are given on the margin. This is a different arrangement from that of the normal probability tables where the order is just the reverse. The table of the t values gives, in fact, a description of many different distributions (as many as there are rows) and is therefore much less detailed than the normal probability table.

Consider now the two-tail test mentioned above. If the desired level of significance is 5%, then $\alpha/2$ is 0.025, and the appropriate column in the t table would be headed by this number. Which is the appropriate row would depend on the size of the sample. Some selected values are

Sample Size (n)	Degrees of Freedom (ν)	Value of $t_{n-1,\,0.025}$
5	4	2.776
10	9	2.262
20	19	2.093
30	29	2.045
∞		1.960

Note that the values of t get smaller as n gets larger, and that they approach 1.960, the value that would be assumed by a standard normal variable at the same level of significance. In comparison to the tests in which the population variance is known and therefore does not have to be estimated, the acceptance region based on the t distribution is always wider. This can be seen by noting that in each column of the t table all values are larger than the value in the bottom row which corresponds to standard normal variable. The consequence of having a wider acceptance region is a higher probability of Error Type II and, therefore, a less powerful test.

The test outlined above is a two-tail test. The procedure in the case of a one-tail test is very similar. Instead of giving a general description, we shall illustrate it by a numerical example.

EXAMPLE A worker handling a certain product takes, on the average, 7 minutes to complete his task. An efficiency expert suggests a slightly different way of handling the product and decides to take a sample to see if there is any saving of time. The null and the alternative hypotheses then are

$$H_0: \quad \mu = 7 \text{ min. (or 420 sec.)}$$

$$H_A: \quad \mu < 7 \text{ min.}$$

The level of significance is to be the traditional 5% and the size of the sample 16. Assuming that the parent population is normal, the appropriate test statistic is t of (5.9) with 15 degrees of freedom. The boundary on the t distribution can be looked up in the t table in row "15" and column "0.05." The resulting test criterion is

$$\textit{do not reject if} \quad \frac{(\bar{X} - 420)\sqrt{16}}{s} \geq -1.753;$$

$$\textit{reject otherwise.}$$

Note that $\bar{x}$ and s are to be measured in seconds. The recorded observations are

6 min. 26 sec.	6 min. 0 sec.	7 min. 30 sec.	6 min. 4 sec.
6 min. 38 sec.	7 min. 0 sec.	7 min. 8 sec.	6 min. 42 sec.
6 min. 48 sec.	7 min. 12 sec.	7 min. 20 sec.	7 min. 6 sec.
6 min. 58 sec.	6 min. 46 sec.	6 min. 22 sec.	6 min. 48 sec.

The following results are obtained:

$$\bar{x} = 6{,}528/16 = 408 \text{ (i.e., 6 min. 48 sec.)}$$

$$s = \sqrt{9872/15} = 25.65.$$

Therefore, the value of the test statistic is

$$\frac{(408 - 420)\sqrt{16}}{25.65} = -1.871.$$

This falls outside the acceptance region and thus the "7 minute" hypothesis has to be rejected at the 5% level of significance.

Tests Concerning the Mean of a Nonnormal Population

The preceding discussion involved a test concerning the population of a normally distributed variable with unknown variance. A similar procedure can be devised to deal with the problem concerning the difference between two means of two normal populations and involving two independent samples. This test will not be described because it can be found in any introductory text on mathematical statistics. A test which we will mention here, though, is the test concerning the value of the mean of a variable which is *not necessarily normally distributed* (but has a finite variance). Thus, *if the sample is large,* we can invoke the central limit theorem (our Theorem 15) which states that whatever the distribution of X, the distribution of $\bar{X}$ in large samples will be approximately normal. Given this, and given the fact that for large n the t distribution is approximately normal, it follows that

$$\frac{(\bar{X} - \mu_0)\sqrt{n}}{s} \quad (n \geq 30)$$

has a distribution which can be approximated by the standard normal distribution. Therefore, in this situation we can use the test described in Section 5–1. If the sample size is small and the parent distribution is not known, we can resort to so-called *distribution-free* or *nonparametric* tests, which are described in many texts.

Tests Concerning σ^2

Let us now consider some tests concerning the population variance. Suppose we wish to test the null hypothesis that the variance of a normal population has a specified value against the alternative claim that it has a different value. That is,

$$H_0: \quad \sigma^2 = \sigma_0^2,$$

$$H_A: \quad \sigma^2 \neq \sigma_0^2.$$

This hypothesis can be tested by taking a sample estimate of σ^2 as defined by (5.6), namely,

$$s^2 = \frac{1}{n-1} \sum_{i=1}^{n} (X_i - \bar{X})^2,$$

and by setting up the acceptance and the critical region for the distribution of s^2. We use, as our test statistic, a transformation of s^2 given as

$$\chi_{n-1}^2 = \frac{(n-1)s^2}{\sigma_0^2},$$

where $(n - 1)$ is the number of *degrees of freedom*. The properties of this distribution were discussed earlier. If the chosen level of significance is α, then the acceptance region for a two-tail test is

$$\chi_{n-1,\,1-\alpha/2}^2 \leq \frac{(n-1)s^2}{\sigma_0^2} \leq \chi_{n-1,\,\alpha/2}^2,$$

where the subscripts $1 - \alpha/2$ and $\alpha/2$ refer to the area to the *right* of the particular boundary value of χ^2. The table of the chi-square probabilities is arranged in the same way as the table of the t distribution. The rows refer to different degrees of freedom, the columns to different probabilities, and the entries in the main body of the table are the corresponding values of χ^2. For instance, in the row labeled "4" and the column "0.975" the value shown is 0.484. The row refers to the chi-square distribution for samples of size 5, and the value 0.484 is that value of the chi-square variable which would be exceeded with a probability of 0.975. In other words, 0.484 is the lower limit of an interval which extends to $+\infty$, and 0.975 is the probability that a value of χ_4^2 would fall in that interval. Some selected values of χ^2 for a two-tailed test with 5% level of significance are given below.

Sample Size (n)	Degrees of Freedom (ν)	Values of	
		$\chi_{n-1,\,0.975}^2$	$\chi_{n-1,\,0.025}^2$
5	4	0.484	11.143
10	9	2.700	19.023
20	19	8.907	32.852
30	29	16.047	45.722
1001	1000	914	1090

For large n we can determine the chi-square probabilities by using the fact that $[\sqrt{2\chi^2} - \sqrt{2(n-1)}]$ has a distribution which can be approximated by the standard normal distribution. For instance, when $(n-1) = 1000$, then

$$\sqrt{2 \times 914} - \sqrt{2 \times 1000} = -1.966$$

and $$\sqrt{2 \times 1090} - \sqrt{2 \times 1000} = +1.966$$

which is almost the same as the corresponding values -1.960 and $+1.960$ of a standard normal variable. Our explanation of the above test procedure referred to a two-tail test but can be easily adapted to a one-tail test for $H_A: \sigma^2 > \sigma_0^2$ or $\sigma^2 < \sigma_0^2$; this will be left to the reader.

EXAMPLE   Consider the previous example dealing with the time taken by a worker to perform a certain task. Suppose the variance of this variable, which is assumed to be normally distributed, is claimed to be 30^2 seconds. The efficiency expert contends that the new method of handling the product which he suggested will also change the previous variation in the time. The null and the alternative hypotheses will then be

$$H_0: \quad \sigma^2 = 900,$$

$$H_A: \quad \sigma^2 \neq 900.$$

The null hypothesis is to be tested at the 5% level of significance by using the 16 observations given in the previous example. The acceptance region is defined as

$$6.262 \leq \frac{(n-1)s^2}{900} \leq 27.488,$$

where the boundary values are taken from the chi-square table. From the observations the value of the test statistic is

$$\frac{9872}{900} = 10.97,$$

which falls inside the acceptance region. Thus the sample provides no evidence against the null hypothesis.

The F Distribution

Another test concerning the population variance and one which is widely used involves the hypothesis that two normal populations have the same variance. The most common alternative hypothesis is the claim that one of the variances is larger than the other.[5] That is,

$$H_0: \quad \sigma_1^2 = \sigma_2^2,$$

$$H_A: \quad \sigma_1^2 > \sigma_2^2,$$

where we regard as the *first* population the one which may, according to H_A, have the larger variance. The null hypothesis can be tested by drawing a sample from each of the two populations and calculating the estimates s_1^2 and s_2^2 of the respective variances. The samples are assumed to be independently drawn and to be of size n_1 and n_2 respectively. As the appropriate test statistic, we may consider the ratio s_1^2/s_2^2. If the null hypothesis is true, this ratio would differ from unity only because the sample estimates differ from the respective parameters. In any case, we would expect s_1^2/s_2^2 to approach unity as both sample sizes get larger unless the null hypothesis were false.

To carry out the test we have to set up the boundary between the acceptance and the critical regions, and for that we have to know the sampling distribution of s_1^2/s_2^2. Let us divide the numerator by σ_1^2 and the denominator by σ_2^2; if the null hypothesis is true, the ratio will be unaffected. Thus we can write

$$\frac{s_1^2/\sigma_1^2}{s_2^2/\sigma_2^2},$$

which is equivalent to

$$\frac{(n_1 - 1)s_1^2/(n_1 - 1)\sigma_1^2}{(n_2 - 1)s_2^2/(n_2 - 1)\sigma_2^2} = \frac{\chi_{n_1-1}^2/(n_1 - 1)}{\chi_{n_2-1}^2/(n_2 - 1)}$$

by (5.8a). Since the two samples are independent of each other, the numerator and the denominator of the preceding expression are likewise independent. We mention this because the distribution of a ratio of two independent chi-square variables, each divided by its respective number of degrees of freedom, is the well-known F *distribution*. This distribution is asymmetric and depends on two

[5] A two-sided alternative $\sigma_1^2 \neq \sigma_2^2$ could, of course, also be considered, but it happens to be much less common so it will not be discussed here.

parameters, the number of the degrees of freedom in the numerator and the number of degrees of freedom in the denominator. These two numbers are usually given as subscripts of F to ensure proper identification. Thus we write

$$(5.10) \qquad\qquad \frac{s_1^2}{s_2^2} \sim F_{n_1-1,\,n_2-1}.$$

The values for the F distribution are available in tabulated form. Usually there are two tables, one for 5% and one for 1% level of significance. Each table gives the boundary value of F for a one-tail test. The rows in each table refer to the number of degrees of freedom in the denominator and the columns to the number of degrees of freedom in the numerator. For example, in the table for the 5% level of significance, the entry in the row labeled "10" and column labeled "15" is 2.85. This means that when we have two independent samples, one of size 16 and the other of size 11, the probability that the ratio (s_1^2/s_2^2) would exceed 2.85 is 0.05. That is, the value 2.85 stands for the lower limit of an interval which extends to $+\infty$, and the probability that a value of (s_1^2/s_2^2) would fall within this interval is 0.05.

These tests concerning population variances are strictly true only for normal parent populations. There are some indications, however, that the results apply to a large extent also to other types of parent populations, providing they do not differ from the normal population too markedly.[6] But if there are good reasons to suspect that the parent population is highly skewed or U-shaped, then the tests cannot be applied with much confidence.

Goodness-of-Fit Test

The *goodness-of-fit* test is applicable to problems of deciding whether a sample frequency distribution is compatible with some given theoretical distribution. It would be used, for instance, to test the assumption that some variable is normally distributed. In general, the null hypothesis is the proposition that a certain variable has a specified probability distribution, while the alternative hypothesis states that the proposition is not true. To test the null hypothesis, we use the frequency distribution obtained in the sample as the evidence concerning the form of the distribution in the population. The test statistic commonly used in this case is

$$\sum_{i=1}^{m} \frac{(f_i - e_i)^2}{e_i},$$

where f_i is the sample frequency in the ith interval, e_i is the frequency expected in the theoretical (hypothesized) distribution, and m is the number of intervals. It can be shown that this test statistic has a distribution which for *large samples* can be approximated by the *chi-square distribution*. In particular, if the sample is large, then

$$(5.11) \qquad\qquad \sum_{i=1}^{m} \frac{(f_i - e_i)^2}{e_i} \sim \chi^2_{m-k-1},$$

---

[6] For a discussion on this topic see, e.g., G. Udny Yule and M. G. Kendall, *An Introduction to the Theory of Statistics* (London: Griffin, 1950), p. 486.

where the subscript $(m - k - 1)$ refers to the number of degrees of freedom. The sample frequencies f_i are observed, and the theoretical frequencies e_i can be calculated by using the distribution formula specified by the null hypothesis. This formula will involve some unknown parameters which have to be replaced by their respective sample estimates. For instance, if the null hypothesis specifies that the population distribution is normal, it will be necessary to estimate the mean and the variance of this distribution from the sample. (Actually, if (5.11) is to hold, the estimates must be of a certain kind. Specifically, the estimates should be of "maximum likelihood" type—a term that will be explained in Section 6–2. At this stage it is sufficient to note that $\bar{X}$ *is* a maximum likelihood estimate, and s^2 is approximately so in large samples.) The number of the degrees of freedom is determined as follows:

m = number of intervals;

k = number of parameters that had to be replaced by sample estimates.

For the test to be reasonably satisfactory, it is required that $m \geq 5$ and $e_i \geq 5$ for each i.

If the null hypothesis is true, f_i can be considered as a sample estimate of e_i, and the expression in (5.11) will differ from zero only because we observe a sample rather than the entire population. Therefore, if we observe a sample for which the value of the test statistic (5.11) is large, we consider it as evidence against the null hypothesis. To carry out the test we have to determine the boundary between the acceptance and the critical region. This depends on the number of degrees of freedom and the chosen level of significance and can be looked up in the chi-square table. Note that since the statistic (5.11) cannot be negative, evidence against the null hypothesis can only take the form of very large values (and not very small ones) so that the appropriate test is a *one-tail* test.

EXAMPLE   Economists are often interested in the distribution of personal incomes. Let us consider the hypothesis that family incomes are normally distributed. To test this hypothesis we may use the data in Table 5–1. These data may be considered as a sample from a population that includes all possible incomes that *could* have been received during 1962 in the United States. The statistic to be used for the test is

$$\sum_{i=1}^{9} \frac{(f_i - e_i)^2}{e_i} = \left[\frac{\sum f_i}{100}\right] \sum_i \frac{(p_i - \pi_i)^2}{\pi_i},$$

where p_i = observed percentage frequencies, and π_i = expected percentage frequencies. The expected frequencies have to be calculated by fitting a normal distribution to the observed data. To do that we have to estimate *two* parameters—the mean and the variance—from the sample. For this purpose we shall use the sample mean and the sample variance whose values are

$$\bar{x} = 6507 \quad \text{and} \quad \hat{\sigma}^2 = 4920^2.$$

Table 5-1

Interval	Midpoint*	Percent of Familiest
Under $2,000	1,130	12.7
$2,000 to $2,999	2,560	9.4
$3,000 to $3,999	3,490	10.8
$4,000 to $4,999	4,510	11.7
$5,000 to $5,999	5,480	11.4
$6,000 to $7,499	6,690	14.4
$7,500 to $9,999	8,570	13.9
$10,000 to $14,999	11,960	10.5
$15,000 and over	22,780	5.2
Total		100.0
Total number	57,890,000	

* Midpoints were calculated by dividing total income (after tax) in each income class by the number of recipient families in that class.
† Includes unattached individuals.
Source: *Statistical Abstract of the United States, 1965*, U.S. Department of Commerce, Table 467.

To obtain the frequencies of the normal distribution with the above mean and variance, we shall follow the procedure described in Section 4–2 and illustrated in Table 4–7. First, we form the standard normal variable

$$Z = \frac{X - 6507}{4920}$$

(where X = income), and recalculate the interval limits in terms of this variable. Then we find the normal probabilities for each income class from the table of areas under the normal curve. The results are presented in the Table 5–2. Using these results, we find that

$$\sum_{i=1}^{9} \frac{(f_i - e_i)^2}{e_i} = 9,454,950.$$

The tabulated value of chi-square with $9 - 2 - 1 = 6$ degrees of freedom at 1% level of significance is 16.812. Values smaller than that would fall into the acceptance region and values that are larger into the critical region. Since in our case the value of the test statistic far exceeds the boundary value of 16.812, the null hypothesis is to be rejected. That is, the data do not appear to be consistent with the proposition that family incomes are normally distributed.

Conclusion

This brings us to the end of the present section containing the description of several basic tests. There was a twofold purpose to it. First, we wanted to illustrate the development of test procedures in general so that the reader could see in concrete terms the kind of problems involved and the method of handling them. Actually, the specific problems and related tests given in this section are *not* very frequently encountered in enconometrics. This is because the statistical models used are too simple to satisfy the usual demands of economic theory. In particular, the concentration on one variable to the exclusion of all other factors

Table 5–2

Intervals		Cumulative Normal Probabilities	Normal Probabilities	
x	z		$f(z)$	Percent
Under 2,000	$-\infty$ to -0.92	0.1788	0.1788	17.9
2,000 to 2,999	-0.92 to -0.71	0.2388	0.0600	6.0
3,000 to 3,999	-0.71 to -0.51	0.3050	0.0662	6.6
4,000 to 4,999	-0.51 to -0.31	0.3783	0.0733	7.3
5,000 to 5,999	-0.31 to -0.11	0.4562	0.0779	7.8
6,000 to 7,499	-0.11 to 0.20	0.5793	0.1231	12.3
7,500 to 9,999	0.20 to 0.71	0.7612	0.1819	18.2
10,000 to 14,999	0.71 to 1.73	0.9582	0.1970	19.7
15,000 and over	1.73 to $+\infty$	1.0000	0.0418	4.2
			1.0000	100.0

does not do justice to the complexity of economic relations. There is, however, one common feature between the simple tests discussed in this section and the tests applicable to more complex situations. This common feature is the use of distributions described on the preceding pages: the normal, the chi-square, the *t* and the *F* distributions. This was the second and the more important purpose of this section. The discussion of the simple tests enabled us to introduce these distributions in a natural way, and gave us an opportunity to highlight their main characteristics and to relate them to each other. For this reason this section is really indispensable for a complete understanding of econometric methods.

EXERCISES

5–1. Let $X \sim N(\mu, 81)$. The null and the alternative hypotheses are

$$H_0: \quad \mu = 10,$$

$$H_A: \quad \mu > 10.$$

The test statistic is to be based on a sample of size 9, and the chosen level of significance is to be 5%. Draw a diagram of the power function for this test.

5–2. In conducting a survey of food prices, two samples of prices of a given food item were collected. Sample I came from a congested city area, and Sample II was obtained in the suburbs. The results were as follows:

	Sample I	Sample II
n	14	18
$\sum_{i=1}^{n} p_i$	12.60	14.96
$\sum_{i=1}^{n} p_i^2$	1.68	1.96

where p_i = price recorded in the ith store. Test the hypothesis that there is no difference between the mean price of the particular food item in the two areas. (Use 5% level of significance.)

5–3. When allocating federal subsidies to localities, a certain town was classified as a high-income area. The mayor objected and produced evidence, based on a random sample of 25 families, that the average family income in his town was $7145. A nationwide survey of towns of similar size showed that the average family income is $6500, with standard deviation of $920. Are the sample results produced by the mayor consistent with his claim that the town in question is no more prosperous than other similar towns in the nation?

5–4. Let Y = income and X = log Y. Using the data on income distribution in the United States given in Table 5–1, test the hypothesis that X is normally distributed.

5–5. A claim is made that the cyclical fluctuations in the demand for teenage workers are greater than those in the demand for married males. Test this claim by reference to Table 5–3.

Table 5–3 Unemployment in the United States

	Unemployment Rate, %	
	Married Men	Teenagers 14–19 years
1949	3.4	12.2
1950	4.6	11.3
1951	1.5	7.7
1952	1.4	8.0
1953	1.7	7.1
1954	4.0	11.4
1955	2.6	10.2
1956	2.3	10.4
1957	2.8	10.8
1958	5.1	14.4
1959	3.6	13.2
1960	3.7	13.6
1961	4.6	15.2

Source: *Economic Report of the President, 1965* (Washington, D.C.: U.S. Government Printing Office, 1965), p. 217.

5–6. Design and carry out an experiment, involving the chi-square test, designed to test the randomness of the last digits of the entries in the table of normal deviates in Appendix D.

5–7. The owner of a pizza restaurant wants to start a delivery service for which he needs a van. The choice is eventually confined to two makes, A and B. Van A costs $300 more than van B, but its average mileage is claimed to be 24 miles per gallon, which compares favorably with the 20 miles per gallon expected of B. The restaurant owner is allowed to use each van for four days before making a final commitment. What should be the appropriate test criterion, given that the expected productive life of each van is 50,000 miles and that the cost of gasoline is 40¢ per gallon?

6 | Estimation

In the introduction to this chapter we described the traditional division of the problems of statistical inference into problems of hypothesis testing and problems of estimation. The similarity between the two types of problems lies in the fact that they are both concerned with questions concerning the value of some unknown population parameter or parameters. The difference is that in estimation, unlike in hypothesis testing, we make no prior claims whose credibility would be disputed. In hypothesis testing, the initial ingredients are prior information (in the form of a maintained hypothesis) and a claim concerning the value of the parameter in question. In estimation we also start with prior information (in the form of a model), but we have an open mind as to the value of the parameter. (Prior specification about the possible *range* of the parameter—e.g., a specification that the parameter must be positive—is considered to be a part of the model.) As mentioned earlier, estimation problems have received more attention by the econometricians than problems of hypothesis testing. Thus estimation theory for various types of economic models is quite well developed, although, of course, many difficulties still remain.

The theory of estimation can be divided into two parts, point estimation and interval estimation. In *point estimation* the aim is to use the prior and the sample information for the purpose of calculating a value which would be, in some sense, our best guess as to the actual value of the parameter of interest. In *interval estimation* the same information is used for the purpose of producing an interval which would contain the true value of the parameter with some given level of probability. Since an interval is fully characterized by its limits, estimating an interval is equivalent to estimating its limits. The interval itself is usually called a *confidence interval*. Confidence intervals can also be viewed as possible measures of the precision of a point estimator. This view will be adopted in our discussion of confidence intervals in Section 6–3 at the end of the present chapter.

The problem of point estimation is that of producing an estimate that would represent our best guess about the value of the parameter. To solve this problem we have to do two things: first, we have to specify what we mean by "best guess" and, second, we have to devise estimators that would meet this criterion or at least come close. In other words, we have to specify what we want, and provide a formula that would tell us how to get it or at least how to come close to getting it. The first part of the problem—the definition of the best guess—amounts to specifying various properties of an estimator that can be considered desirable. Since an estimator is a random variable whose value varies from sample to sample, its properties are, in fact, the properties of its sampling distribution. These properties will be discussed in Section 6–1. The second part of the problem involves devising estimators that would have at least some of the desirable properties. This will be the subject of Section 6–2. The last section will be, as mentioned earlier, devoted to a discussion of confidence intervals.

6–1   Properties of Estimators

Let us consider some random variable X whose distribution is characterized, among others, by some parameter θ which we would like to estimate. Thus the parent population consists of all possible values of X, and θ is one of the parametric characteristics of this population. X may be continuous or discrete, or even an attribute (i.e., a binary variable). An example would be family income—which is a continuous variable—and its mean. This specification constitutes a relatively simple estimation problem; a more complicated problem would involve a joint estimation of several parameters related to several variables. As it is, the simple estimation problem is perfectly sufficient for the purpose of describing various properties of estimators and for outlining the basic estimation methods. The more complicated estimation problems, which are typical in econometrics, will be considered in the following chapters.

To estimate a population parameter we combine the prior information that we may have with the information provided by the sample. The prior information is really nothing else but what, in the context of hypothesis testing, was called the "maintained hypothesis." In the context of estimation we usually use the term *model* but the term *maintained hypothesis* is also perfectly acceptable. Such prior information concerns the population of X; it may consist of assumptions about the form of the distributions, the value of some parameters other than θ, or some specification (e.g., range) concerning θ itself. The information provided by the sample is given by the sample observations $X_1, X_2, \ldots, X_n$. The way of utilizing the information to obtain an estimate of θ is prescribed by the estimation formula called the *estimator*. There may be, and generally is, more than one such formula to choose from. In this chapter we will, for the most part, consider only problems with a minimum of prior information. Problems involving more elaborate models will be discussed in the rest of the book.

An estimator of parameter θ, which is one of the characteristics of the distribution of X, may be called $\hat{\theta}$. Since $\hat{\theta}$ is constructed by substituting sample observations of X into a formula, we may write

$$\hat{\theta} = \hat{\theta}(x_1, x_2, \ldots, x_n),$$

which is read "$\hat{\theta}$ is a function of $x_1, x_2, \ldots, x_n$." (If not *all* sample observations are to be used, the expression will be modified accordingly.) This function can be of any form *except* for the restriction that it must not involve any unknown parameters including, of course, θ itself. The basic characteristics of the distribution of $\hat{\theta}$ are its mean $E(\hat{\theta})$ and the variance,

$$\text{Var}(\hat{\theta}) = E[\hat{\theta} - E(\hat{\theta})]^2 = E(\hat{\theta}^2) - [E(\hat{\theta})]^2.$$

The standard deviation of $\hat{\theta}$, defined as $\sqrt{\text{Var}(\hat{\theta})}$, is known as the *standard error* of $\hat{\theta}$. Of special importance are also the following concepts:

$$\text{Sampling error} = \hat{\theta} - \theta,$$

$$\text{Bias} = E(\hat{\theta}) - \theta,$$

$$\text{Mean square error} = E(\hat{\theta} - \theta)^2.$$

Sampling error is simply the difference between the value of the estimator and the true value of the parameter to be estimated. The extent of the sampling error does, of course, vary from sample to sample. *Bias* is the difference between the mean of the sampling distribution of a given estimator and the true value of the parameter. This value is, for any given estimator, a fixed value which may or may not be equal to zero. Finally, the *mean square error* is a concept related to the dispersion of the distribution of an estimator, and, thus, is similar to the concept of the variance. The difference between the variance of an estimator and its mean square error is that while the variance measures the dispersion of the distribution *around the mean*, the mean square error measures the dispersion *around the true value of the parameter*. If the mean of the distribution coincides with the true value of the parameter, then the variance and the mean square error are identical, otherwise they differ.

The relationship between the mean square error (MSE) and the variance can be shown explicitly as follows:

$$\begin{aligned} \text{MSE}(\hat{\theta}) = E(\hat{\theta} - \theta)^2 &= E[\hat{\theta} - E(\hat{\theta}) + E(\hat{\theta}) - \theta]^2 \\ &= E\{[\hat{\theta} - E(\hat{\theta})] + [E(\hat{\theta}) - \theta]\}^2 \\ &= E[\hat{\theta} - E(\hat{\theta})]^2 + E[E(\hat{\theta}) - \theta]^2 + 2E[\hat{\theta} - E(\hat{\theta})][E(\hat{\theta}) - \theta]. \end{aligned}$$

Consider the last term,

$$2E[\hat{\theta} - E(\hat{\theta})][E(\hat{\theta}) - \theta] = 2\{[E(\hat{\theta})]^2 - [E(\hat{\theta})]^2 - \theta E(\hat{\theta}) + \theta E(\hat{\theta})\} = 0.$$

Taking this into account and noting that the expected value of a constant is simply the constant itself, we can write

$$\text{MSE}(\hat{\theta}) = E[\hat{\theta} - E(\hat{\theta})]^2 + [E(\hat{\theta}) - \theta]^2 = \text{variance } plus \text{ squared bias.}$$

That is, the value of the mean square error can never be smaller than that of the variance, and the difference between the two is precisely equal to the squared bias.

Let us now turn to the description of some of the properties of estimators which are commonly considered to be desirable. These can be divided into two groups depending upon the size of sample. *Finite sample* or *small sample properties* refer to the properties of the sampling distribution of an estimator based on any fixed sample size. Finite sample properties may characterize estimates calculated from any number of observations; they are frequently called small sample properties because they may apply *even* if the samples are small. On the other hand, *asymptotic* or *large sample properties* are restricted to sampling distributions based on samples whose size approaches infinity. These properties, when they apply, are assumed to hold only approximately when the sample size is large, and possibly not at all when the samples are small. This will be discussed more fully when we come to the actual description of various asymptotic properties, but first we shall concern ourselves with finite samples.

Small Sample Properties

The first property that we shall mention is *unbiasedness*. This property of an estimator is more widely known among empirical research workers than any other. We already explained the meaning of unbiasedness in Section 1–4, where we stated that an unbiased estimator is one whose mean is equal to the value of the population parameter to be estimated. Now, after having discussed the meaning and terminology of mathematical expectation, we can define unbiasedness in a precise and technical way as follows:

(6.1) $\hat{\theta}$ *is an unbiased estimator of* θ *if* $E(\hat{\theta}) = \theta$.

An illustration of an unbiased estimator is given in Figure 6–1; since the

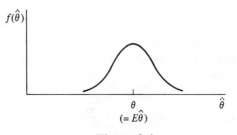

Figure 6–1

distribution shown is a symmetric one, the mean is at the center of the distribution and coincides with the value of the parameter. An example of an unbiased estimator is the sample mean as an estimator of the population mean, since

$$E(\bar{X}) = E\frac{1}{n}\sum_{i=1}^{n} X_i = \frac{1}{n}\sum E(X_i) = \mu.$$

(Note that $E(X_i)$ is the mean of X_i, which is μ.)

It should be emphasized that unbiasedness by itself is not a very comforting property since it implies nothing about the *dispersion* of the distribution of the estimator. An estimator which is unbiased, but one which has a large variance, will frequently lead to estimates that are quite far off the mark. On the other hand, an estimator which has a very small variance but is biased—and the extent of the bias is not known—is even less useful. This can be seen by taking the extreme case of an estimator with zero variance. Such an estimator is not hard to construct since any constant, which has zero variance by definition, qualifies. Thus if we decide that our estimate of θ will always be the number 5, then the sampling distribution of this "estimator" will be entirely concentrated at the point $\hat{\theta} = 5$. Such an estimator makes obviously very little sense since it pays no attention to the evidence provided by the sample and thus disregards all the information from this source. In light of this argument, it would seem desirable that an estimator should minimize the mean square error. Indeed, it can be shown that such an estimator would be an optimal one in the case where the loss of using an estimate in place of the true value of the parameter increases with the distance of $\hat{\theta}$ from θ. Unfortunately, in practice the formula for an estimator that would give the minimum value of mean square error very frequently includes the true value of the parameter to be estimated. This obviously makes the formula quite useless; it would be like a recipe for a cake that starts with "take a cake . . . ." Our definition of an estimator specifically excluded such formulas as not being worthy of the name "estimator."

The preceding discussion provides a background to the introduction of the concept of *efficiency* in estimation. As mentioned in Section 1–4, there is a lack of general agreement as to the most appropriate definition of this concept in statistical literature. Some authors equate efficiency with minimum mean square error in spite of the difficulty just mentioned; others define efficiency only in the context of asymptotic rather than finite sample properties, and others consider an estimator to be efficient if (and only if) it is unbiased and at the same time has a minimum variance. This last view of efficiency is becoming quite common among the econometricians and we will adopt it here. Accordingly, we make the formal definition of efficiency as follows:

(6.2) $\hat{\theta}$ *is an efficient estimator of* θ *if the following conditions are satisfied:*

(a) $\hat{\theta}$ *is unbiased;*

(b) $Var(\hat{\theta}) \leq Var(\tilde{\theta})$, *where* $\tilde{\theta}$ *is any other unbiased estimator of* θ.

An efficient estimator thus defined is also sometimes called "minimum variance unbiased estimator" or "best unbiased estimator." Note that, by our definition, an estimator which is even slightly biased cannot be called efficient no matter how small its variance is. A diagrammatic illustration of efficiency is given in Figure 6–2. Here are shown the distributions of three estimators of θ, namely, $\hat{\theta}_a$, $\hat{\theta}_b$, and $\hat{\theta}_c$. Of these, $\hat{\theta}_a$ has the smallest variance but is not efficient because it is biased. Furthermore, $\hat{\theta}_b$ and $\hat{\theta}_c$ are both unbiased, but $\hat{\theta}_c$ has a larger variance than $\hat{\theta}_b$ so that $\hat{\theta}_c$ is also not efficient. That leaves $\hat{\theta}_b$, which is efficient *providing* there is no other unbiased estimator which would have a smaller variance than $\hat{\theta}_b$.

The last remark brings us to considering one practical aspect of efficiency, and that is the problem of ascertaining whether a given estimator is or is not efficient. We have not worried about this kind of a problem in connection with unbiasedness since there the problem is, at least in principle, quite trivial. All we have to do to check whether an estimator is or is not unbiased is to determine its mathematical expectation, i.e., the mean of its sampling distribution. In connection with efficiency, and in particular with the condition of minimum

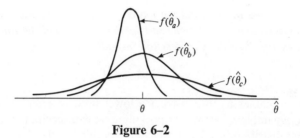

Figure 6–2

variance, the problem is potentially very complex. Since we have to make a statement about the variance of *all* unbiased estimators, of which there may be an infinite number, it may be hard to claim that a particular estimator is efficient. One way of avoiding this difficulty is by lowering our standards and, instead of proclaiming a given unbiased estimator as better—in the sense of having a smaller variance—or at least as good as any other unbiased estimator, we may be satisfied with the claim that the estimator in question is better than some other unbiased estimator. Thus, in comparing two unbiased estimators, we could concern ourselves merely with their *relative efficiency* and declare that estimator which has a smaller variance as more efficient than the other estimator. A case in point is the comparison of sample mean and sample median as estimators of population mean. As we saw in Section 2–2, both estimators are unbiased, but the variance of sample mean is smaller than the variance of sample median. Then we can say that sample mean is a more efficient estimator of the population mean relative to sample median.

Fortunately, in quite a few cases there is no need for us to confine ourselves to comparing the variances of a small number of estimators since we can make a definite statement concerning efficiency in an absolute sense. The reason is the existence of the following theorem, which is known as the *Cramer-Rao inequality*.

Theorem 16 *Let X be a random variable with a probability distribution $f(x)$ characterized by parameters $\theta_1, \theta_2, \ldots, \theta_k$. Let $\hat{\theta}_i$ be any unbiased estimator of θ_i derived from a sample $X_1, X_2, \ldots, X_n$. Define $L = \log f(x_1, x_2, \ldots, x_n)$; L is known* as the logarithmic likelihood function of a given sample. Form the following matrix:

$$
\begin{bmatrix}
-E\left[\dfrac{\partial^2 L}{\partial \theta_1^2}\right] & -E\left[\dfrac{\partial^2 L}{\partial \theta_1 \partial \theta_2}\right] & \cdots & -E\left[\dfrac{\partial^2 L}{\partial \theta_1 \partial \theta_k}\right] \\[2ex]
-E\left[\dfrac{\partial^2 L}{\partial \theta_2 \partial \theta_1}\right] & -E\left[\dfrac{\partial^2 L}{\partial \theta_2^2}\right] & \cdots & -E\left[\dfrac{\partial^2 L}{\partial \theta_2 \partial \theta_k}\right] \\[2ex]
\vdots & \vdots & & \vdots \\[2ex]
-E\left[\dfrac{\partial^2 L}{\partial \theta_k \partial \theta_1}\right] & -E\left[\dfrac{\partial^2 L}{\partial \theta_k \partial \theta_2}\right] & \cdots & -E\left[\dfrac{\partial^2 L}{\partial \theta_k^2}\right]
\end{bmatrix}
$$

The matrix is called the information matrix. Consider now the inverse of the information matrix, and call the element in the ith row and the ith column of this inverse matrix I^{ii}. Then the Cramer-Rao inequality is

$$\operatorname{Var}(\hat{\theta}_i) \geq I^{ii}.$$

This theorem enables us to construct a lower limit (greater than zero) for the variance of *any* unbiased estimator providing we can specify the functional form of the parent distribution.[1] The lower limit specified in the theorem is called the *Cramer-Rao lower bound*. If we can find an unbiased estimator whose variance is equal to the Cramer-Rao lower bound, then we know that no other unbiased estimator can have a smaller variance and the estimator under consideration is efficient. For example, we know that the variance of sample mean $\bar{X}$ is equal to (σ^2/n). Now if the parent population is normal, then it can be shown that (σ^2/n) is, in fact, equal to the Cramer-Rao lower bound for unbiased estimators of the population mean. Therefore $\bar{X}$ is an efficient estimator of the mean of a normal population. It should be noted, though, that the use of the Cramer-Rao inequality need not always work to our satisfaction, because the lower bound need not be *attainable* by any unbiased estimator. For instance, in the case of estimating the variance of a normal population the Cramer-Rao lower bound for an unbiased estimator is $(2\sigma^4/n)$ but there is *no* unbiased estimator of σ^2 that would have a variance as low as that.[2]

The preceding discussion indicates that determining efficiency is not without difficulties. At best we have to be able to specify the form of the parent distribution and hope that there is an unbiased estimator with variance equal to the Cramer-Rao lower bound. If we do not know the form of the parent distribution or if the Cramer-Rao lower bound happens to be unattainable, then we have little hope of establishing that a given estimator is or is not efficient. For this reason we may be willing to abandon the idea of looking for an estimator with minimum variance among *all* unbiased estimators and may confine our attention

---

[1] This inequality holds under very general conditions. Full details are given in, e.g., C. R. Rao, *Linear Statistical Inference and Its Applications* (New York: Wiley, 1965), pp. 265 ff.

[2] *Ibid.*, p. 268.

to a smaller class of unbiased estimators. In fact, it turns out that the problem of finding an unbiased estimator with minimum variance is relatively simple if we confine ourselves to the estimators which are *linear* functions of the sample observations. This has led to the definition of a more specialized concept of efficiency as described below.

(6.3) $\hat{\theta}$ *is a best linear unbiased estimator (or BLUE) of θ if the following three conditions are satisfied:*

    (a) $\hat{\theta}$ *is a linear function of the sample observations;*
    (b) $\hat{\theta}$ *is unbiased;*
    (c) $Var(\hat{\theta}) \leq Var(\tilde{\theta})$, *where $\tilde{\theta}$ is any other linear unbiased estimator of θ.*

The condition of linearity means that, for a sample $X_1, X_2 \ldots, X_n$, the estimator has to be of the form $a_1 X_1 + a_2 X_2 + \cdots + a_n X_n$ where $a_1, a_2, \ldots, a_n$ are some constants. Thus, for instance, $\bar{X}$ is a linear estimator since

$$\bar{X} = \frac{1}{n}\sum_{i=1}^{n} X_i = \frac{1}{n}X_1 + \frac{1}{n}X_2 + \cdots + \frac{1}{n}X_n.$$

It should be noted that the fact that we are limiting ourselves to the class of linear estimators may not be too restrictive since many functions may be reasonably well approximated by a linear function over a wide range of values. In general, one of the following situations may prevail:

1. The efficient estimator is itself linear in the sample observations. In this case the BLUE and the efficient estimator are identical. Thus, for example, since $\bar{X}$ is an efficient estimator of the mean of a normal population, μ, and since $\bar{X}$ is linear in the sample observations, $\bar{X}$ is also the BLUE of μ.
2. The efficient estimator is *approximately* linear. In this case the BLUE is not efficient, but its variance is likely to be close to that of the efficient estimator.
3. The efficient estimator is highly nonlinear. In this case the variance of the efficient estimator may be quite considerably smaller than that of BLUE. This case, it is to be hoped, occurs infrequently.

Another finite sample property of an estimator which is sometimes mentioned is *sufficiency*. An estimator is said to be sufficient if it utilizes all the information about the parameter that is contained in the sample. Since the value of every observation tells us something about the population, an estimator, to be sufficient, must be based on the values of all sample observations. Thus, for instance, sample median is not a sufficient estimator since it uses only the ranking and not the values of sample observations. Note that there is nothing desirable about sufficiency as such; we obviously do not care whether an estimation formula does or does not utilize all the sample observations as long as it produces good estimates of the parameter in question. The real relevance of sufficiency lies in the fact that sufficiency is a necessary condition for efficiency.[3] That is, an estimator cannot be efficient—as defined in (6.2)—unless it makes use of all the sample information. This is the important aspect of sufficiency and the reason for mentioning it.

The three properties—unbiasedness, efficiency, and best linear unbiasedness—represent all the desirable small sample properties of estimators that are important and commonly mentioned in econometric work. They are all defined in terms of means and variances and thus cannot be determined for those estimators whose means or variances do not exist. For instance, let us consider unbiasedness. If $\hat{\theta}$ is an estimator of θ whose distribution is continuous and described by $f(\hat{\theta})$, then, for $\hat{\theta}$ to be unbiased, we would require that

$$E(\hat{\theta}) = \theta.$$

But, by definition,

$$E(\hat{\theta}) = \int_{-\infty}^{+\infty} \hat{\theta} f(\hat{\theta}) d\hat{\theta}.$$

Now, the above integral represents nothing else but the area under the curve $\hat{\theta}f(\hat{\theta})$ measured from $-\infty$ to $+\infty$, and one cannot exclude the possibility that this area is infinite. If this happens, we say that the integral is *divergent* and that the mean of the distribution *does not exist*. We mention this since we will come across estimators whose mean or variance may not exist, and the reader should be clear as to what it means.

Asymptotic Properties

Let us now turn to the asymptotic properties of estimators. As mentioned earlier, these properties relate to the distribution of an estimator when the sample size is large and approaches infinity. In general, the distribution of a given estimator based on one sample size is different from the distribution of this estimator based on a different sample size. The distributions may differ not only with respect to the mean or variance but even with respect to the mathematical form. Take, for example, the distribution of the mean of samples from a discrete uniform population discussed at the beginning of Section 4–3. We found that for samples of size 1, the distribution was uniform, i.e., rectangular in shape; for samples of size 2, the distribution was triangular (see Figure 4–12), and for samples of size 5 and 10 the distribution was close to being normal. The process of change in the distribution of sample mean for samples from *any* population is described by the Central Limit Theorem (i.e., Theorem 15 in Section 4–3). This theorem states, in essence, that as the sample size increases, the distribution of sample mean approaches the normal distribution. Then we say that normal distribution is the *asymptotic* (or *limiting*) *distribution* of sample mean. In general, if the distribution of an estimator tends to become more and more similar in form to some specific distribution as the sample size increases,

---

[3] See, e.g., A. M. Mood and F. A. Graybill, *Introduction to the Theory of Statistics* (New York: McGraw-Hill, 1963), p. 176.

then such a specific distribution is called the *asymptotic distribution* of the estimator in question.

The use of the term "asymptotic" should not lead the reader into thinking that the asymptotic distribution is necessarily the final form that the distribution of an estimator takes as the sample size approaches infinity. In fact, what typically happens to the distribution of an estimator as the sample size approaches infinity is that it collapses on one point—hopefully that representing the true value of the parameter. (A distribution which is entirely concentrated at one point is called a *degenerate* distribution.) Again take the distribution of sample mean as an example. We know (by Theorem 14 of Section 4–3) that for *every* sample size the mean of this distribution is equal to the population mean and its variance is equal to (σ^2/n), where σ^2 is the population variance and n is the sample size. Now, clearly, as the sample size approaches infinity, (σ^2/n) approaches zero, and the distribution will collapse on the population mean. A graphical representation of such a distribution would show a straight vertical line of height equal to 1. This is obviously *not* the normal distribution which, as we know by the Central Limit Theorem, represents the asymptotic distribution of sample mean. What is meant by the asymptotic distribution is not the ultimate form of the distribution, which may be degenerate, but the form that the distribution tends to put on in the last part of its journey to the final collapse (if this occurs). As for the distribution of sample mean, as the sample size increases, the distribution will have a smaller and smaller variance, but it also will look more and more like a normal distribution. Just before the distribution collapses, it will not be discernible from a normal distribution, although one with an extremely small variance.

Having discussed the meaning of "asymptotic distribution," we can now turn to the problem of how to determine its existence and its form. In many cases this is relatively simple. First, some estimators have a distribution which is of the same form regardless of the sample size, and this form is known. If that is the case, then the estimators will also have that form when the sample size is large and approaches infinity. The asymptotic distribution of these estimators is therefore the same as the finite sample distribution. An example is sample mean as an estimator of the mean of a *normal* population. The distribution of sample mean in this case is normal for *every* sample size, with mean equal to the population mean and variance equal to (σ^2/n). Therefore, the asymptotic distribution of sample mean is also normal with mean μ and variance (σ^2/n). Second, some estimators have a distribution which, although not necessarily always of the same form, is known for every sample size. The asymptotic distribution of these estimators is the distribution based on a sample size which tends to infinity. This case is exemplified by the distribution of sample proportion of successes. As we found in Section 4–2, this distribution is binomial but converges to a normal distribution as n approaches infinity. Thus the asymptotic distribution of sample proportion of successes is normal. Third, for some estimators the distribution is not necessarily known for every sample size, but it is known for $n \to \infty$. An example of such an estimator is sample mean as an estimator of the mean of a nonnormal population. We know, by the Central Limit Theorem, that this distribution tends to become normal as $n \to \infty$. The three categories of estimators just enumerated cover most of the problems that are encountered in estimation problems in economics. Furthermore, in practice many asymptotic distributions are normal, which is convenient since the normal distribution is so well known.

Asymptotic distributions, like other distributions, may be characterized by their moments. Of these the most important are the mean, known as the *asymptotic mean*, and the variance, known as the *asymptotic variance*. The asymptotic mean is found simply by determining the limiting value (as $n \to \infty$) of the finite sample mean. Consider an estimator $\hat{\theta}$. By definition, the mean of this estimator is equal to its mathematical expectation, i.e., $E(\hat{\theta})$. Its *asymptotic mean* is equal to its *asymptotic expectation* and is given by $\lim_{n \to \infty} E(\hat{\theta})$. The asymptotic variance, however, is *not* equal to $\lim_{n \to \infty} \mathrm{Var}(\hat{\theta})$. The reason is that in the case of estimators whose variance decreases with an increase in n, the variance will approach zero as $n \to \infty$. This will happen when the distribution collapses on a point. But, as we explained, the asymptotic distribution is *not* the same as the collapsed (degenerate) distribution, and its variance is *not* zero. For example, consider the distribution of sample mean. The asymptotic distribution of sample mean is normal and its variance is (σ^2/n). But $\lim_{n \to \infty}(\sigma^2/n) = 0$, which is not the variance of a normal distribution. The term "asymptotic variance" is thus somewhat misleading; it is, strictly speaking, just an abbreviation for the term "variance of the asymptotic distribution." The formula giving the mathematical definition of asymptotic variance is [4]

$$\text{Asymptotic Var}(\hat{\theta}) = \frac{1}{n} \lim_{n \to \infty} E[\sqrt{n}(\hat{\theta} - \lim_{n \to \infty} E\hat{\theta})]^2 .$$

In what follows we shall describe three so-called asymptotic properties of an estimator which are considered desirable: asymptotic unbiasedness, consistency and asymptotic efficiency. Two of these, asymptotic unbiasedness and asymptotic efficiency, are defined in terms of specific features of the asymptotic distribution of an estimator as just described, while the remaining property, consistency, is defined as a feature of the "collapsed" (i.e., degenerate) distribution given when $n \to \infty$.

Let us begin with the *asymptotic unbiasedness*.

(6.4) $\hat{\theta}$ *is an asymptotically unbiased estimator of* θ *if* $\lim_{n \to \infty} E(\hat{\theta}) = \theta$.

This definition simply states that an estimator is asymptotically unbiased if it becomes unbiased as the sample size approaches infinity. Note that if an estimator is unbiased, it is also asymptotically unbiased, but the reverse is not necessarily true. Unbiasedness implies asymptotic unbiasedness because if an estimator is unbiased, its expectation is equal to the true value of the parameter

---

[4] See A. S. Goldberger, *Econometric Theory* (New York: Wiley, 1964), p. 116.

for *every* sample size, including one close to infinity. A common example of a biased but asymptotically unbiased estimator is the sample variance:

$$\hat{\sigma}^2 = \frac{1}{n} \sum_{i=1}^{n} (X_i - \bar{X})^2$$

and, by (5.4),

$$\lim_{n \to \infty} E(\hat{\sigma}^2) = \lim_{n \to \infty} \left[\frac{n-1}{n} \right] \sigma^2 = \sigma^2,$$

since $(n - 1)/n$ approaches unity as $n \to \infty$.

The next desirable property to consider is *consistency*. As mentioned above, this property is defined in reference to the "collapsed" distribution of an estimator when $n \to \infty$. The point on which the distribution of an estimator, say, $\hat{\theta}$, collapses is called the *probability limit of* $\hat{\theta}$, frequently abbreviated as plim $\hat{\theta}$. More formally, let θ^* be some point which may or may not be equal to θ. Then the statement

$$\text{plim } \hat{\theta} = \theta^*$$

is equivalent to the statement

$$\lim_{n \to \infty} P(\theta^* - \varepsilon \leq \hat{\theta} \leq \theta^* + \varepsilon) = 1$$

where ε is any arbitrarily small positive number. Now, an estimator is considered to be consistent if it collapses on the point of the true value of the parameter. Specifically,

(6.5) $\hat{\theta}$ *is a consistent estimator of* θ *if plim* $\hat{\theta} = \theta$.

A way of finding whether an estimator is consistent is to trace the behavior of the bias and of the variance of an estimator as the sample sizes approach infinity. If the increase in sample size is accompanied by a reduction in bias (if there is one) as well as in variance, and if this continues until both the bias and the variance approach zero when $n \to \infty$, then the estimator in question is consistent. This is depicted in Figure 1–4. Since the sum of squared bias and variance is equal to the mean square error, the disappearance of the bias and the variance as $n \to \infty$ is equivalent to the disappearance of the mean square error. Thus we can state the following:

(6.6) *If* $\hat{\theta}$ *is an estimator of* θ *and if* $\lim_{n \to \infty} MSE(\hat{\theta}) = 0$, *then* $\hat{\theta}$ *is a consistent estimator of* θ.

The condition described by (6.6) is, in general, a sufficient but not necessary condition for consistency. That is, it is possible to find estimators whose mean square error does *not* approach zero when $n \to \infty$, and yet they are consistent. Such a situation may arise when the asymptotic distribution of an estimator is such that its mean or variance does not exist. This complicates the problem of determining whether an estimator is consistent or not. Fortunately, estimators with nonexisting asymptotic means or variances are not frequent.

EXAMPLE   Following is an example[5] of a consistent estimator whose mean square error does not approach zero when $n \to \infty$. Let $\hat{\alpha}$ be an estimator of α, and let the probability distribution of $\hat{\alpha}$ be

$\hat{\alpha}$	$f(\hat{\alpha})$
α	$1 - \dfrac{1}{n}$
n	$\dfrac{1}{n}$

That is, $\hat{\alpha}$ can assume only two different values, α and n. Clearly, $\hat{\alpha}$ is consistent since as $n \to \infty$, the probability that $\hat{\alpha}$ is equal to α will approach unity. But

$$\lim_{n \to \infty} \text{MSE}(\hat{\alpha}) = \lim_{n \to \infty} E(\hat{\alpha} - \alpha)^2$$

$$= \lim_{n \to \infty} \left[(\alpha - \alpha)^2 \left(1 - \frac{1}{n}\right) + (n - \alpha)^2 \left(\frac{1}{n}\right) \right] = \infty.$$

If we expressly exclude such estimators from consideration and confine ourselves to estimators with finite asymptotic means and variances, then condition (6.6) represents a necessary, as well as a sufficient, condition for consistency. Some authors refer to this somewhat more limited concept as the *square-error consistency*.[6] Since the fact that the mean square error of an estimator approaches zero as $n \to \infty$ implies that bias also goes to zero, an estimator which is square error consistent is necessarily asymptotically unbiased. The reverse is not true since asymptotic unbiasedness *alone* is not sufficient for square error consistency.

An important feature of consistent estimators is the fact that any continuous function of a consistent estimator is itself a consistent estimator. This is established by the following theorem:

Theorem 17 (*Slutsky Theorem*)   *If plim $\hat{\theta} = \theta$ and $g(\hat{\theta})$ is a continuous function of $\hat{\theta}$, then plim $g(\hat{\theta}) = g(\theta)$.*

The proof of this theorem is given elsewhere.[7] This property of consistent estimators, sometimes also described as "consistency carries over," is very convenient, and we shall make good use of it later on. It means, for instance, that if $\hat{\theta}$ is a consistent estimator of θ, then $(1/\hat{\theta})$ is a consistent estimator of $(1/\theta)$, log $\hat{\theta}$ is a consistent estimator of log θ, etc. Note carefully that the same does not, in general, apply to unbiasedness. That is to say, unlike consistency, unbiasedness *does not* "carry over." In particular, the fact that $\hat{\theta}$ is an unbiased estimator of θ does not imply that $(1/\hat{\theta})$ is an unbiased estimator of $(1/\theta)$, or that log $\hat{\theta}$ is an unbiased estimator of log θ, and so on.

---

[5] This example was suggested to me by Professor Phoebus Dhrymes.

[6] See, e.g., Mood and Graybill, *op. cit.*, p. 173.

[7] See S. S. Wilks, *Mathematical Statistics* (New York: Wiley, 1962), pp. 102–103.

The last desirable property that we shall mention is *asymptotic efficiency*, which is related to the dispersion of the asymptotic distribution of an estimator. Asymptotic efficiency is defined only for those estimators whose asymptotic mean and variance exist (i.e., are equal to some finite numbers). In fact, it is a property which gives us a criterion of choice within the family of estimators which are square error consistent (and therefore asymptotically unbiased). Given that the distribution of consistent estimators collapses on the true value of the parameter when $n \to \infty$, preference should be given to those estimators which approach this point in the fastest possible way. These will be the estimators whose asymptotic distributions have the smallest variance. This is because asymptotic distribution represents the last stage before the distribution completely collapses, and estimators with the smallest variance are closer to collapsing than the other consistent estimators.

The above considerations lead to the following definition of asymptotic efficiency:

(6.7) *$\hat{\theta}$ is an asymptotically efficient estimator of θ if all of the following conditions are satisfied*:

(a) *$\hat{\theta}$ has an asymptotic distribution with finite mean and finite variance.*

(b) *$\hat{\theta}$ is consistent.*

(c) *No other consistent estimator of θ has a smaller asymptotic variance than $\hat{\theta}$.*

The first two conditions taken together state that an estimator must be square error consistent to qualify for asymptotic efficiency. Whether this is or is not satisfied can be established simply by determining the limiting value (as $n \to \infty$) of the mean square error. The estimator in question is or is not square error consistent depending upon whether the limiting value of its mean square error is or is not equal to zero. To establish whether a consistent estimator satisfies the third condition of asymptotic efficiency is more difficult, very much like the problem of establishing efficiency in the finite sample case. As in the case of finite sample efficiency, the question of the smallest asymptotic variance can be settled only for those estimators for which we know the distributional form of the parent population. For such estimators we can establish asymptotic efficiency by comparing their asymptotic variance with the Cramer-Rao lower bound (as defined in Theorem 16); if the two are equal, then the estimator in question is asymptotically efficient. Thus both efficiency and asymptotic efficiency are established by reference to the Cramer-Rao lower bound—in the case of efficiency by comparing it with ordinary (finite sample) variance and in the case of asymptotic efficiency by comparing it with asymptotic variance. Since an estimator which is efficient is efficient for *any* sample size no matter how large, it follows that efficiency implies asymptotic efficiency. The reverse, however, is not true.

Concluding Remarks

This brings us toward the end of our discussion of desirable properties of an estimator. These properties can be listed as follows:

Finite (Small) Sample Properties	Asymptotic (Large) Sample Properties
Unbiasedness	Asymptotic unbiasedness
Efficiency	Consistency
BLUE	Asymptotic efficiency

In our early discussion of estimation in Section 1–4, we compared estimation of a parameter to shooting at a target with a rifle. The bull's-eye can be taken to represent the true value of the parameter, the rifle the estimator, and each shot a particular estimate (calculated from a particular sample). The distance from the target is inversely related to the size of sample. In this parallel desirable properties of an estimator are described in terms of various qualities of a rifle. An unbiased rifle is one whose shots are scattered around the bull's-eye as the center, whereas the shots from a biased rifle are centered around some other point. If we compare all unbiased rifles, then that rifle whose shots are, on the whole, closest to the bull's-eye is regarded as efficient. If we know what kind of bullet is being used, we can determine the minimum possible scatter of the shots; this corresponds to the Cramer-Rao lower bound. With respect to the BLUE property, the comparison is restricted to rifles of a particular and relatively simple construction. A BLUE rifle is unbiased and produces shots which are closer to the bull's-eye than the shots from any other unbiased rifle of the same construction. Coming now to the asymptotic properties we must consider the effect of decreasing the distance from the target. Asymptotic unbiasedness means that the shots tend to become centered around the bulls'-eye as the distance from the target decreases. Consistency means that the probability of hitting the bull's-eye, or being within some small distance from it, increases with a decrease in distance. Square error consistency (which implies consistency) can be viewed as the tendency for the shots to become centered around the bull's-eye and to be less and less scattered as the distance is decreased. Finally, a rifle can be considered as asymptotically efficient if it is square error consistent, and if its shots are closer to the bull's eye than those from other consistent rifles when the distance from the target is nearly negligible.

The discussion about desirable properties of estimators presented in this section is quite crucial since it provides a basis for much of the work in econometrics. We shall close it by giving an example on the determination of various properties of three estimators of the mean of a normal population.

EXAMPLE Let X be a normally distributed variable with mean μ and variance σ^2.

Consider the problem of estimating μ from a random sample of observations on $X_1, X_2, \ldots, X_n$. Three estimators are proposed:

$$\bar{X} = \frac{1}{n} \sum_{i=1}^{n} X_i,$$

$$\hat{\mu} = \frac{1}{n+1} \sum_{i=1}^{n} X_i,$$

$$\tilde{\mu} = \frac{1}{2} X_1 + \frac{1}{2n} \sum_{i=2}^{n} X_i.$$

What are the desirable properties (if any) of each of these estimators?

1. *Unbiasedness*

$$E(\bar{X}) = E\left[\frac{1}{n} \sum_{i=1}^{n} X_i\right] = \frac{1}{n} \sum_{i=1}^{n} E(X_i) = \mu;$$

i.e., $\bar{X}$ is unbiased.

$$E(\hat{\mu}) = E\left[\frac{1}{n+1} \sum_{i=1}^{n} X_i\right] = \left[\frac{n}{n+1}\right]\mu;$$

i.e., $\hat{\mu}$ is biased.

$$E(\tilde{\mu}) = E\left[\frac{1}{2} X_1 + \frac{1}{2n} \sum_{i=2}^{n} X_i\right] = \frac{1}{2} E(X_1) + \frac{1}{2n} \sum_{i=2}^{n} E(X_i)$$

$$= \frac{1}{2}\mu + \left[\frac{n-1}{2n}\right]\mu = \left[\frac{2n-1}{2n}\right]\mu;$$

i.e., $\tilde{\mu}$ is biased.

2. *Efficiency.* Since $\hat{\mu}$ and $\tilde{\mu}$ are biased, only $\bar{X}$ qualifies as a candidate for efficiency. We know that the variance of $\bar{X}$ is (σ^2/n). We know further that the sample comes from a normal population. Therefore we can determine the Cramer-Rao lower bound for the variance of an unbiased estimator of μ. It can be shown that this is also equal to (σ^2/n), from which it follows that $\bar{X}$ is an efficient estimator of μ.

3. *BLUE.* Here again only $\bar{X}$ qualifies as a candidate since the other two estimators are biased. $\bar{X}$ also satisfies the condition of linearity since

$$\bar{X} = \frac{1}{n} \sum_{i=1}^{n} X_i = \frac{1}{n} X_1 + \frac{1}{n} X_2 + \cdots + \frac{1}{n} X_n.$$

Finally, since $\bar{X}$ is efficient, it has the smallest variance among *all* unbiased estimators. Therefore $\bar{X}$ must also have the smallest variance among those unbiased estimators which are linear in observations. Consequently $\bar{X}$ is BLUE. (A full derivation of the BLUE property of $\bar{X}$ independent of the form of the parent distribution is given in Section 6–2.)

4. *Asymptotic unbiasedness*

$$\lim_{n \to \infty} E(\bar{X}) = \lim_{n \to \infty} \mu = \mu;$$

i.e., $\bar{X}$ is asymptotically unbiased.

$$\lim_{n \to \infty} E(\hat{\mu}) = \lim_{n \to \infty} \left[\frac{n}{n+1}\right]\mu = \mu;$$

i.e., $\hat{\mu}$ is asymptotically unbiased.

$$\lim_{n \to \infty} E(\tilde{\mu}) = \lim_{n \to \infty} \left[\frac{2n-1}{2n}\right]\mu = \mu;$$

i.e., $\tilde{\mu}$ is asymptotically unbiased.

5. *Consistency*

$$\text{MSE}(\bar{X}) = \text{Var}(\bar{X}) = \frac{\sigma^2}{n},$$

$$\lim_{n \to \infty} \text{MSE}(\bar{X}) = 0;$$

i.e., $\bar{X}$ is consistent.

$$\text{MSE}(\hat{\mu}) = \text{Var}(\hat{\mu}) + (\text{Bias of } \hat{\mu})^2 = \text{Var}\left[\frac{1}{n+1}\sum_{i=1}^{n} X_i\right] + \left[\left(\frac{n}{n+1}\right)\mu - \mu\right]^2$$

$$= \left[\frac{1}{n+1}\right]^2 \sum_{i=1}^{n} \text{Var}(X_i) + \left[\frac{-1}{n+1}\right]^2 \mu^2 = \frac{n\sigma^2 + \mu^2}{(n+1)^2},$$

$$\lim_{n \to \infty} \text{MSE}(\hat{\mu}) = 0;$$

i.e., $\hat{\mu}$ is consistent.

$$\text{MSE}(\tilde{\mu}) = \text{Var}(\tilde{\mu}) + (\text{Bias of } \tilde{\mu})^2$$

$$= \text{Var}\left[\frac{1}{2}X_1 + \frac{1}{2n}\sum_{i=2}^{n} X_i\right] + \left[\left(\frac{2n-1}{2n}\right)\mu - \mu\right]^2$$

$$= \frac{1}{4}\text{Var}(X_1) + \left[\frac{1}{2n}\right]^2 \sum_{i=2}^{n} \text{Var}(X_i) + \left[\frac{-1}{2n}\right]^2 \mu^2$$

$$= \frac{(n^2 + n - 1)\sigma^2 + \mu^2}{4n^2},$$

$$\lim_{n \to \infty} \text{MSE}(\tilde{\mu}) = \frac{\sigma^2}{4}.$$

Since $\lim_{n \to \infty} \text{MSE}(\tilde{\mu})$ is not equal to zero, $\tilde{\mu}$ is not square error consistent. In fact, it can be shown that $\tilde{\mu}$ is not consistent in the general sense either, but the proof is beyond the scope of the book.

6. *Asymptotic efficiency.* $\bar{X}$ and $\hat{\mu}$ satisfy the condition of square error consistency and thus qualify as candidates for asymptotic efficiency; $\tilde{\mu}$ does not qualify. Now, since $\bar{X}$ is efficient for *any* sample size, it is also efficient when the sample size increases toward infinity. Thus $\bar{X}$ is asymptotically efficient as well. Note that since $\text{Var}(\bar{X}) = (\sigma^2/n)$ for any n, (σ^2/n) is also the asymptotic variance of $\bar{X}$. Concerning $\hat{\mu}$, we have

$$\text{Var}(\hat{\mu}) = \frac{n\sigma^2}{(n+1)^2} = \left[\frac{n}{n+1}\right]^2 \frac{\sigma^2}{n}.$$

In large samples $n/(n + 1)$ will be close to unity so that the asymptotic variance of $\hat{\mu}$ will be (σ^2/n). Since this is the same as the asymptotic variance of $\bar{X}$, and since $\bar{X}$ is asymptotically efficient, it follows that $\hat{\mu}$ is also asymptotically efficient.

The above results are summarized in Table 6–1. The general conclusion then is that $\bar{X}$ is the superior estimator in small samples, but in large samples $\bar{X}$ and $\hat{\mu}$ are equally good. The third estimator, $\tilde{\mu}$, has none of the desirable properties except for asymptotic unbiasedness.

Table 6–1

Properties	Estimator		
	$\bar{X}$	$\hat{\mu}$	$\tilde{\mu}$
Finite sample			
Unbiasedness	Yes	No	No
Efficiency	Yes	No	No
BLUE	Yes	No	No
Asymptotic properties			
Unbiasedness	Yes	Yes	Yes
Consistency	Yes	Yes	No
Efficiency	Yes	Yes	No

6–2   Methods of Estimation

Having defined the desirable properties of estimators, we come to the problem of devising estimation formulas that would generate estimates with all or at least some of these desirable properties. At the outset of Section 6–1, we defined an estimator as an estimation formula which does not involve any unknown parameters. Estimators can originate in several ways. One possible way is to invoke some more or less intuitively plausible principle, use this principle to derive a formula, and then check whether the resulting estimator possesses any of the desirable properties. The estimators are given names that indicate the nature of the principle used in deriving the formula. The *method of moments*, the *least squares method*, and the *maximum likelihood method*, all lead to estimators of this kind. Another way of devising estimators is to construct an estimation formula in such a way that the desirable properties are built into it in the process of construction. The so-called *BLUE method*, which leads to best linear unbiased estimators, is the most notable representative of this category.

Method of Moments

The *method of moments* is probably the oldest estimation method known in statistics. It is based on a very simple principle which states that one should estimate a moment of the population distribution by the corresponding moment of the sample. Thus the population mean is to be estimated by the sample mean, the population variance by the sample variance, and so on. As for the properties of the moments estimators, it can be shown that, under very general conditions, these estimators are square error consistent (and therefore generally consistent) and asymptotically normal.[8] They may, of course, have other desirable properties as well, but this need not be so. For instance, the sample mean as an estimator of the population mean has other desirable properties in addition to consistency. The method of moments is not applicable when the population moments do not exist, and may be difficult to apply when dealing with more complicated problems of estimation.

Least Squares Estimation

Another method of estimation which has long been used is the *method of least squares*. This method is suitable for estimating moments about zero of a population distribution. The underlying principle is somewhat more involved than in the case of the method of moments. Consider a random variable X and its rth moment about zero:

$$E(X^r) = \mu_r',$$

where $r = 0, 1, 2, \ldots$. The sample to be used is given by $X_1, X_2, \ldots, X_n$. To derive the least squares estimator of μ_r' we form the following sum:

$$\sum_{i=1}^{n} [X_i^r - \mu_r']^2.$$

As the least squares estimator we select that value of μ_r' which makes the above sum as small as possible. For instance, to find the least squares estimator of the population mean $\mu(=\mu_1')$, we find that value of μ which minimizes the sum

$$\sum_{i=1}^{n} [X_i - \mu]^2.$$

Note that since X_i^r is the ith observation on X^r and $E(X_i^r) = \mu_r'$ is the mean of X_i^r, the expression to be minimized is, in fact, equal to the sum of squared deviations of the observed values from their mean. The least squares estimator of this mean is that value which makes the sum as small as possible.

To derive the least squares estimation formula we have to solve the problem of minimizing a function with respect to a given "variable"—in our case with respect to μ_r'. It is well known from elementary calculus, that a necessary condition for the occurrence of a minimum (or a maximum) is that the first derivative of the function to be minimized be equal to zero. That is, we have to differentiate the sum of squares with respect to μ_r', set this derivative equal to zero, and solve the resulting equation for μ_r'. The solution then satisfies the necessary condition for the occurrence of a minimum or a maximum. However, it can be easily shown that what we are getting is really a minimum and not a maximum so that the solution does, in fact, represent the least squares estimator of μ_r'.

We may illustrate the derivation of the least squares estimation formula by

---

[8] See, e.g., Mood and Graybill, *op. cit.*, p. 187.

considering the problem of estimating population mean. Here the sum to be minimized is

$$\sum_{i=1}^{n} (X_i - \mu)^2.$$

Differentiating with respect to μ we get

$$\frac{d \sum_i (X_i - \mu)^2}{d\mu} = \sum_i \left[\frac{d(X_i - \mu)^2}{d\mu}\right] = \sum_i 2(X_i - \mu)(-1) = -2 \sum_i (X_i - \mu).$$

Equating this to zero and putting a "hat" on μ to indicate that it is only the estimator of μ (rather than its true value) which satisfies this equation, we obtain

$$-2 \sum_i (X_i - \hat{\mu}) = 0,$$

$$\left(\sum_i X_i\right) - n\hat{\mu} = 0,$$

$$\hat{\mu} = \frac{1}{n} \sum_i X_i = \bar{X}.$$

Thus we find that the least squares estimator of the population mean is given by the sample mean, i.e., the same as the moments estimator. As another example, let us derive the least squares estimator of $E(X^2) = \mu_2'$. In this case we minimize the sum

$$\sum_{i=1}^{n} (X_i^2 - \mu_2')^2.$$

Differentiating with respect to μ_2' gives

$$\frac{d \sum_i (X_i^2 - \mu_2')^2}{d(\mu_2')} = -2 \sum_i (X_i^2 - \mu_2').$$

Equating this to zero, we have

$$-2 \sum_i (X_i^2 - \hat{\mu}_2') = 0,$$

$$\left(\sum_i X_i^2\right) - n\hat{\mu}_2' = 0,$$

$$\hat{\mu}_2' = \frac{1}{n} \sum_i X_i^2,$$

which is the same as the moments estimator of μ_2'.

The properties of least squares estimators have to be established in each case. In the two examples given in the preceding paragraph, least squares estimators were the same as moments estimators and, therefore, we are justified in claiming that they are consistent. This need not be the case with more complicated models.

Indeed, a large part of modern econometrics owes its existence to the discovery that in many economic models, least squares estimators are, in fact, inconsistent.

Maximum Likelihood Estimation

The third method of estimation is the *maximum likelihood method*. This method is based on the relatively simple idea that different populations generate different samples, and that any given sample is more likely to have come from some populations than from others. To illustrate this idea, let us consider the case of normal populations and a given sample of n observations. The sample observations are points on the numerical axis scattered around their mean. Suppose the observed sample mean is equal to 5. The question is: To which population does this sample most likely belong? In general, any normal population is a candidate. Since normal populations are fully characterized by a mean and a variance, they differ only with respect to these two parameters. Let us, for the time being, consider populations with the same variance. Of these the one with mean 5 will, of course, generate samples with mean equal to or near 5 more frequently than a population with mean 6, a population with mean 6 will generate such samples more frequently than a population with mean 7, and so on. Similar statements could be made by considering populations with means less than 5.

The foregoing argument is shown graphically in Figure 6–3. The points $x_1, x_2, \ldots, x_{10}$ represent some 10 specific sample observations. Strictly speaking, these observations could have come from any normal population whatsoever, since the range of a normal population extends from $-\infty$ to $+\infty$ (three such populations are shown in the diagram). However, if the true population is either

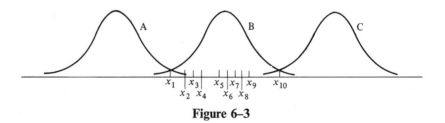

Figure 6–3

A or C, the probability of getting the sample observations in the range shown (i.e., from x_1 to x_{10}) is very small. On the other hand, if the true population is B, then the probability of drawing observations in this range is very high. Thus we conclude that the particular sample is more likely to have come from population B than from population A or C.

In the example just given we have not considered populations that would differ with respect to the variance as well as the mean. Such an extension makes the explanation of the likelihood principle somewhat more complicated but leads to the same conclusion. A given sample may have come from a population characterized by *any* mean and *any* variance, but some populations would generate such a sample more frequently than others. Just as a sample with mean 5 is more likely to have come from a population with mean 5 than from a population with the same variance but with mean 6 or 7, so a sample with a large variance is more likely to have come from a population with a large variance than from a population with a small variance. All that is required is that we consider combinations of specific mean and variance in the population in relation to combinations of specific mean and variance in the sample.

With these introductory remarks in mind we may now define *maximum likelihood estimators*:

If a random variable X has a probability distribution f(x) characterized by parameters $\theta_1, \theta_2, \ldots, \theta_k$ *and if we observe a sample* $x_1, x_2, \ldots, x_n$, *then the maximum likelihood estimators of* $\theta_1, \theta_2, \ldots, \theta_k$ *are those values of these parameters that would generate the observed sample most often.*

In other words, the maximum likelihood estimators of $\theta_1, \theta_2, \ldots, \theta_k$ are those values for which the probability (or probability density) of the given set of sample values is at maximum. That is, to find the maximum likelihood estimators of $\theta_1, \theta_2, \ldots, \theta_k$ we have to find those values which maximize $f(x_1, x_2, \ldots, x_n)$.

Let us take a simple example to illustrate the concept of the maximum likelihood estimator (MLE). Suppose X is a binary variable which assumes a value of 1 with probability π and a value of 0 with probability $(1 - \pi)$. That is,

$$f(0) = 1 - \pi,$$

$$f(1) = \pi.$$

This means that the distribution of X is characterized by a single parameter π, which can be viewed as the proportion of successes (or a probability of success) in the population. Suppose a random sample—drawn by sampling with replacement—consists of the following three observations:

$$\{1, 1, 0\}.$$

Our problem is to find the MLE of π. From the description of the population, it is obvious that π cannot be less than 0 or more than 1. To find which population would generate the given sample $\{1, 1, 0\}$ most often, we can simply consider various values of π between 0 and 1, and for these values determine the probability of drawing our sample. Let us start with $\pi = 0$. If this is the case, there are no "successes" in the population, and it would be impossible to observe two 1's. Thus for $\pi = 0$, the probability of drawing our sample is 0. Consider now $\pi = 1/10$. In this case the probability of drawing a 1 is $1/10$ and the probability of drawing a 0 is $9/10$. Therefore, the probability of drawing our sample in this case is

$$f(1, 1, 0) = f(1)f(1)f(0) = \frac{1}{10} \times \frac{1}{10} \times \frac{9}{10} = \frac{9}{1000},$$

since the sample observations are independent. (Recall that in the case of independence the joint probability is equal to the product of simple—i.e., marginal—
probabilities.) Thus for $\pi = 1/10$ the probability of observing our sample is
9/1000. Similarly, we can calculate the probability of drawing $\{1, 1, 0\}$ for other
values of π. The results are:

π	$f(1, 1, 0)$
0	0
1/10	0.009
2/10	0.032
3/10	0.063
4/10	0.096
5/10	0.125
6/10	0.144
7/10	0.147
8/10	0.128
9/10	0.081
1	0.000

The function $f(1, 1, 0)$ is the *likelihood function* for the sample $\{1, 1, 0\}$. In our
calculations we selected values of π at intervals of one tenth. Obviously, we
could have selected shorter intervals since the likelihood function is continuous.
Figure 6–4, which is based on the preceding calculations, reveals that the
likelihood function for our sample is maximized when π is about 0.7. That is, a

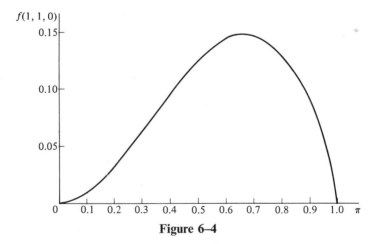

Figure 6–4

population with $\pi = 0.7$ would generate samples $\{1, 1, 0\}$ more frequently than
any other population. Thus the MLE of π is 0.7 (see also Example 1 on page
179).

The concept of a *likelihood function* is crucial for the derivation of maximum likelihood estimates and thus deserves a more general explanation. A likelihood function, usually denoted by ℓ, is a name given to the formula of the joint probability distribution of the sample. The reader may recall our discussion in Sections 3–4 and 3–5 of a joint probability distribution of random variables $X, Y, Z, \ldots$, described as $f(x, y, z, \ldots)$. It was stated that if X, Y, Z, are independent, then we have

$$f(x, y, z, \ldots) = f(x)f(y)f(z) \ldots .$$

Now consider a random variable X with probability distribution $f(x)$ characterized by some parameters $\theta_1, \theta_2, \ldots, \theta_k$. A random sample $X_1, X_2, \ldots, X_n$ represents a set of n independent random variables, each having exactly the same probability distribution as X. Then the likelihood function ℓ is defined by the formula of the joint probability distribution of the sample, i.e.,

(6.8a) $$\ell = f(x_1, x_2, \ldots, x_n).$$

Since the sample observations are independent, we can also write

(6.8b) $$\ell = f(x_1)f(x_2)\ldots f(x_n).$$

While the formula for the joint probability distribution of the sample is exactly the same as that for the likelihood function, the interpretation of the formula is different. In the case of the joint probability distribution the parameters $\theta_1, \theta_2, \ldots, \theta_k$ are considered as fixed and the X's (representing the sample observations) as variable. In the case of the likelihood function the values of the parameters can vary but the X's are fixed numbers as observed in a particular sample. The maximum likelihood estimates are found by maximizing the likelihood function with respect to the parameters.

Obtaining the maximum likelihood estimators involves specifying the likelihood function and finding those values of the parameters which give this function its maximum value. As mentioned in connection with the least squares method, a necessary condition for a function to be at a maximum (or a minimum) is that at this point its first derivative is equal to zero. If there is only one unknown parameter in the likelihood function, then there is only one first derivative for which this applies. In general, however, the number of the unknown parameters in the likelihood function is more than one and we have to resort to partial derivatives. In this case it is required that the partial derivative of ℓ with respect to *each* of the unknown parameters is to be equal to zero. That is, if the unknown parameters are $\theta_1, \theta_2, \ldots, \theta_k$, the equations given by the necessary conditions for the occurrence of a maximum (or a minimum) are:

(6.9a) $$\frac{\partial \ell}{\partial \theta_1} = 0, \quad \frac{\partial \ell}{\partial \theta_2} = 0, \quad \ldots, \quad \frac{\partial \ell}{\partial \theta_k} = 0.$$

Thus we have k equations to solve for the values of the k unknown parameters. These equations are sometimes referred to as the first-order conditions for the occurrence of a maximum (or a minimum). These conditions guarantee that, for the values of $\theta_1, \theta_2, \ldots, \theta_k$ obtained by solving the above equations, we obtain *either* a maximum *or* a minimum value of ℓ. To be sure that the solution of (6.9a) gives, in fact, a maximum value of ℓ, certain second-order conditions have to be fulfilled. A description of these conditions is beyond the scope of our discussion, but it is not very difficult to show that they are fulfilled in the cases with which we shall be dealing.[9] However, an easy way of ascertaining that we do *not* have a minimum (rather than a maximum) is by calculating the value of ℓ corresponding to the solution of (6.9a) and then calculating the value of ℓ for slightly different values of $\theta_1, \theta_2, \ldots, \theta_k$. If the second result gives a smaller number than the first, the first result obviously could *not* have been a minimum.

A final point to be made in connection with the maximization procedure concerns the form of the first-order conditions. In practice these conditions are usually stated somewhat differently than as given in (6.9a). The development of the alternative formulation is based on the fact that the *logarithm* of ℓ is a "monotonic transformation" of ℓ. This means that whenever ℓ is increasing, its logarithm is also increasing, and whenever ℓ is falling, its logarithm is also falling. Therefore, the point corresponding to the maximum of ℓ is also the point which corresponds to the maximum of the logarithm of ℓ. Since ℓ, being a formula for a joint probability distribution, can never be negative, there is no problem about obtaining its logarithm. A sketch illustrating the monotonicity of the logarithmic transformation in the case of one unknown parameter (θ) is given in Figure 6–5. The point $\hat{\theta}$ clearly corresponds to a maximum on both

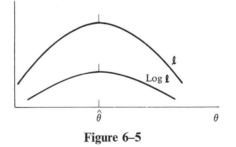

Figure 6–5

the ℓ function as well as the log ℓ function. Therefore, it does not matter whether we maximize ℓ or log ℓ. Since in practice the solution of the first-order conditions turns out to be easier when working with log ℓ than with ℓ, we put

$$L = \log_e \ell,$$

and restate the first-order conditions as

(6.9b) $$\frac{\partial L}{\partial \theta_1} = 0, \quad \frac{\partial L}{\partial \theta_2} = 0, \quad \ldots, \quad \frac{\partial L}{\partial \theta_k} = 0.$$

We shall illustrate the derivation of MLE's by presenting two examples. The

---

[9] A simple description of the second-order conditions can be found in, e.g., T. Yamane, *Mathematics for Economists* (Englewood Cliffs, N.J.: Prentice-Hall, 1962), pp. 344–345.

first of these relates to the problem of estimating the proportion of "successes" in the population and provides a theoretical generalization of the graphical solution given in Figure 6–4. The second example deals with the standard problem of deriving the MLE of the mean of a normal population.

EXAMPLE 1   Suppose X is a binary variable which assumes a value of 1 with probability π and a value of 0 with probability $(1 - \pi)$. Observing a "1" can be considered as a "success," and observing a "0" a "failure." Thus we have

$$f(0) = 1 - \pi,$$
$$f(1) = \pi.$$

Note that the probability distribution of X can be described by

$$f(x) = (1 - \pi)^{1-x}\pi^{x}.$$

We can check the appropriateness of this by substituting the values 0 and 1 for x. We get

$$f(0) = (1 - \pi)^{1-0}\pi^{0} = (1 - \pi)^{1} = (1 - \pi)$$

and

$$f(1) = (1 - \pi)^{1-1}\pi^{1} = \pi^{1} = \pi,$$

which agrees with the earlier specification. Also note that

$$E(X) = 0 \times (1 - \pi) + 1 \times \pi = \pi,$$

so that π can be interpreted as the mean of X. Now suppose we draw a random sample of n values $\{x_1, x_2, \ldots, x_n\}$. Our problem is to find the MLE of π. To this end we first derive the likelihood function:

$$\ell = f(x_1)f(x_2)\ldots f(x_n)$$

$$= [(1 - \pi)^{1-x_1}\pi^{x_1}][(1 - \pi)^{1-x_2}\pi^{x_2}]\ldots[(1 - \pi)^{1-x_n}\pi^{x_n}]$$

$$= (1 - \pi)^{(1-x_1)+(1-x_2)+\ldots+(1-x_n)}\pi^{x_1+x_2+\ldots+x_n}$$

$$= (1 - \pi)^{n-\Sigma x_i}\pi^{\Sigma x_i}.$$

The logarithm of this function is

$$L = (n - \Sigma x_i)\log(1 - \pi) + (\Sigma x_i)\log \pi.$$

The only unknown parameter involved in L is π. Differentiating L with respect to π gives

$$\frac{dL}{d\pi} = (n - \Sigma x_i)\left[\frac{1}{1-\pi}\right](-1) + (\Sigma x_i)\left[\frac{1}{\pi}\right].$$

Equating this to zero and putting a "triangle" on π to indicate that we are solving for an estimator of π and not for π itself, we obtain

$$\frac{(\Sigma x_i) - n}{1 - \overset{\triangle}{\pi}} + \frac{\Sigma x_i}{\overset{\triangle}{\pi}} = 0.$$

For a $\overset{\triangle}{\pi}$ not equal to 0 or 1 we can multiply both sides of the equation by $\overset{\triangle}{\pi}(1 - \overset{\triangle}{\pi})$ to get

$$[(\Sigma x_i) - n]\overset{\triangle}{\pi} + (\Sigma x_i)(1 - \overset{\triangle}{\pi}) = 0,$$

which gives

$$\hat{\pi} = \frac{1}{n} \sum x_i.$$

Since $\sum x_i$ is the number of "successes" and n is the number of all observations in the sample, the MLE of π is simply the proportion of successes found in the sample. In the specific case considered earlier, in which the sample was $\{1, 1, 0\}$, the MLE of π is

$$\hat{\pi} = \frac{2}{3} \approx 0.7.$$

EXAMPLE 2   Consider a normally distributed random variable X with mean μ and variance σ^2, i.e., $X \sim N(\mu, \sigma^2)$. We observe a random sample $\{x_1, x_2, \ldots, x_n\}$. Find the MLE of μ. Now the normal density function is defined as

$$f(x) = (2\pi\sigma^2)^{-1/2} e^{-(1/2)[(x-\mu)/\sigma]^2}$$

where $\pi = 3.14159$. Its logarithm is

$$\log f(x) = -\frac{1}{2} \log (2\pi\sigma^2) - \frac{1}{2}\left[\frac{x - \mu}{\sigma}\right]^2$$

since $\log_e e = 1$. The likelihood function is

$$\ell = f(x_1)f(x_2)\ldots f(x_n),$$

and its logarithm is

$$L = \sum_{i=1}^{n} \log f(x_i).$$

Substituting for $\log f(x_i)$ gives

$$L = \sum_i \left[-\frac{1}{2} \log (2\pi\sigma^2) - \frac{1}{2}\left(\frac{x_i - \mu}{\sigma}\right)^2\right] = -\frac{n}{2} \log (2\pi\sigma^2) - \frac{1}{2\sigma^2} \sum_i (x_i - \mu)^2.$$

There are two unknown parameters involved in L: μ and σ^2. Differentiating with respect to each of them gives

$$\frac{\partial L}{\partial \mu} = -\frac{1}{2\sigma^2} \sum_i 2(x_i - \mu)(-1),$$

$$\frac{\partial L}{\partial (\sigma^2)} = -\frac{n}{2}\frac{1}{\sigma^2} + \frac{1}{2\sigma^4} \sum_i (x_i - \mu)^2.$$

Equating these to zero, we get

(6.10a) $$\frac{1}{\hat{\sigma}^2} \sum_i (x_i - \hat{\mu}) = 0,$$

(6.10b) $$-\frac{n}{2}\frac{1}{\hat{\sigma}^2} + \frac{1}{2\hat{\sigma}^4} \sum_i (x_i - \hat{\mu})^2 = 0.$$

For $\hat{\sigma}^2$ different from zero the first equation reduces to

$$\sum_i (x_i - \hat{\mu}) = 0,$$

giving

$$\hat{\mu} = \frac{1}{n} \sum_i x_i.$$

Thus the maximum likelihood estimator of the mean of a normal population is equal to the sample mean. It should be noted that the two equations (6.10a) and (6.10b) can also be solved for $\hat{\sigma}^2$, which is the MLE of σ^2. Multiplying the second equation by $2\hat{\sigma}^4$ leads to

$$-n\hat{\sigma}^2 + \sum_i (x_i - \hat{\mu})^2 = 0.$$

Substituting $\bar{x}$ for $\hat{\mu}$ and solving for $\hat{\sigma}^2$ gives

$$\hat{\sigma}^2 = \frac{1}{n} \sum_i (x_i - \bar{x})^2.$$

That is, the maximum likelihood estimator of the variance of a normal population is simply equal to the sample variance. As shown earlier, the sample variance is a *biased* estimator of the population variance. In fact, by equation (5.4) we see that

$$E(\hat{\sigma}^2) = \left[\frac{n-1}{n}\right]\sigma^2.$$

We mention this to illustrate the fact that a maximum likelihood estimator need not always be unbiased.

Knowledge of the likelihood function enables us to determine not only the MLE's of μ and σ^2 but also the Cramer-Rao lower bounds for the variances of the unbiased estimators of μ and σ^2. These are obtained by substituting into the formula for the information matrix given in Theorem 16 (Section 6–1) as follows:

$$\begin{bmatrix} -E\dfrac{\partial^2 L}{\partial \mu^2} & -E\dfrac{\partial^2 L}{\partial \mu \partial(\sigma^2)} \\[2ex] -E\dfrac{\partial^2 L}{\partial \mu \partial(\sigma^2)} & -E\dfrac{\partial^2 L}{\partial(\sigma^2)^2} \end{bmatrix}^{-1} = \begin{bmatrix} \dfrac{n}{\sigma^2} & 0 \\[2ex] 0 & \dfrac{n}{2\sigma^4} \end{bmatrix}^{-1} = \begin{bmatrix} \dfrac{\sigma^2}{n} & 0 \\[2ex] 0 & \dfrac{2\sigma^4}{n} \end{bmatrix}$$

The Cramer-Rao lower bound for an unbiased estimator of the mean of a normal population is given by the element in the upper left corner of the last matrix, i.e., it is equal to (σ^2/n).

The maximum likelihood principle is based on the intuitively appealing idea of choosing those parameters from which the actually observed sample is most likely to have come. However, this intuitive appeal by itself is of little value unless the resulting estimators have some desirable properties. This, in fact, is the case. It can be shown[10] that, under quite general conditions, maximum likelihood estimators are

1. Consistent as well as squared-error consistent.
2. Asymptotically efficient.

[10] See, e.g., Wilks, *op. cit.*, pp. 358–365. The general conditions under which the MLE's have the stated properties are not very restrictive. The one condition which may sometimes cause problems and which is frequently neglected is the requirement that the number of parameters in the likelihood function be finite; see E. Malinvaud, *Statistical Methods of Econometrics* (Chicago: Rand McNally, 1966), p. 339.

Another convenient feature of the MLE's is that their asymptotic distribution is normal, and that a formula for determining their asymptotic variances is readily available. In particular, the asymptotic variances of the MLE's are given by the diagonal elements of the inverse of the information matrix; that is, they are equal to the Cramer-Rao lower bounds. In finite samples we use as estimates of the asymptotic variances the diagonal elements of

$$
\begin{bmatrix}
-\dfrac{\partial^2 L}{\partial \theta_1^2} & -\dfrac{\partial^2 L}{\partial \theta_1 \partial \theta_2} & \cdots & -\dfrac{\partial^2 L}{\partial \theta_1 \partial \theta_k} \\[2ex]
-\dfrac{\partial^2 L}{\partial \theta_2 \partial \theta_1} & -\dfrac{\partial^2 L}{\partial \theta_2^2} & \cdots & -\dfrac{\partial^2 L}{\partial \theta_2 \partial \theta_k} \\[2ex]
\vdots & & & \\[2ex]
-\dfrac{\partial^2 L}{\partial \theta_k \partial \theta_1} & -\dfrac{\partial^2 L}{\partial \theta_k \partial \theta_2} & \cdots & -\dfrac{\partial^2 L}{\partial \theta_k^2}
\end{bmatrix}^{-1}
$$

evaluated at $\theta_i = \text{MLE of } \theta_i$ $(i = 1, 2, \ldots, k)$. While all these properties are only asymptotic, in many situations this is frequently all that we can hope for.

Best Linear Unbiased Estimation

The last method of estimation to be discussed at this stage is the *best linear unbiased estimation method*. This method, unlike the preceding ones, leads to an estimation formula which guarantees certain desirable properties by definition. Let $\tilde{\theta}$ be a best linear unbiased estimator (BLUE) of some parameter θ. Then the formula for $\tilde{\theta}$ must satisfy the following conditions:

1. $\tilde{\theta}$ is a linear function of the sample observations;
2. $E(\tilde{\theta}) = \theta$;
3. $\text{Var}(\tilde{\theta}) \leq \text{Var}(\theta^*)$, where θ^* is any other linear unbiased estimator of θ.

In addition, the formula for $\tilde{\theta}$ must not involve θ or any other unknown parameter, otherwise $\tilde{\theta}$ would not qualify as an estimator. To devise a best linear unbiased estimator, we have to find that linear function of the sample observations which satisfies conditions 2 and 3. We shall show how to go about finding such a function by deriving the BLUE of the population mean.

Suppose a random variable X comes from a population with mean μ and variance σ^2. The sample observations are $X_1, X_2, \ldots, X_n$. We wish to find the BLUE of μ, say, $\tilde{\mu}$. To do that we consider each of the three conditions in turn.

1. *Linearity.* Since $\tilde{\mu}$ is to be a linear combination of the sample observations, we can write

$$
(6.11) \qquad\qquad \tilde{\mu} = \sum_{i=1}^{n} a_i X_i,
$$

where $a_1, a_2, \ldots, a_n$ are constants to be determined. Thus the whole problem of finding the BLUE of μ is really a problem of specifying $a_1, a_2, \ldots, a_n$ in such a way that the conditions 2 and 3 are satisfied.

2. *Unbiasedness.*   For $\tilde{\mu}$ to be unbiased we require that

$$E(\tilde{\mu}) = \mu.$$

Now,

$$E(\tilde{\mu}) = E\left[\sum_i a_i X_i\right] = \sum_i a_i E(X_i) = \sum_i a_i \mu = \mu \sum_i a_i.$$

That is, for $E(\tilde{\mu})$ to be equal to μ we require that $\sum_i a_i = 1$. The condition then is that the constants $a_1, a_2, \ldots, a_n$ add up to unity.

3. *Minimum variance.*   Finally, we require that, among all estimators of μ which satisfy the above conditions, $\tilde{\mu}$ is the one with the smallest variance. We have

$$\text{Var}(\tilde{\mu}) = \text{Var}\left[\sum_i a_i X_i\right] = E\left[\sum_i a_i X_i - E\left(\sum_i a_i X_i\right)\right]^2$$

$$= E\left[\sum_i a_i X_i - \mu \sum_i a_i\right]^2 = E\left[\sum_i a_i(X_i - \mu)\right]^2$$

$$= E\left[\sum_i a_i^2(X_i - \mu)^2\right] + E\left[\sum_i \sum_j a_i a_j(X_i - \mu)(X_j - \mu)\right]$$

$$= \sum_i a_i^2 E(X_i - \mu)^2 + \sum_i \sum_j a_i a_j E(X_i - \mu)(X_j - \mu) \qquad (i \neq j).$$

But
$$E(X_i - \mu)^2 = \text{Var}(X_i) = \sigma^2,$$

and since X_i and X_j are independent,

$$E(X_i - \mu)(X_j - \mu) = \text{Cov}(X_i, X_j) = 0.$$

Therefore

(6.12) $$\text{Var}(\tilde{\mu}) = \sum_i a_i^2 \sigma^2 = \sigma^2 \sum_i a_i^2.$$

This means that we have to find $a_1, a_2, \ldots, a_n$ such that $\sum a_i = 1$ (by condition 2) and at the same time $\sigma^2 \sum a_i^2$ is as small as possible. That is, our problem is to minimize $\sigma^2 \sum a_i^2$ subject to the condition that $\sum a_i = 1$. This is a problem of minimizing a function subject to a constraint, and it can be solved with the help of the *Lagrange multiplier method*.[11]

Very briefly, the Lagrange multiplier method works as follows. Suppose we wish to find those values of $z_1, z_2, \ldots, z_m$ which would minimize (maximize) a function $F(z_1, z_2, \ldots, z_m)$ subject to the condition that $G(z_1, z_2, \ldots, z_m) = 0$. The function G is the constraint expressed in such a way that all terms are transferred to the left-hand side of the equation. Then we form a new function, say H, defined as

(6.13) $$H = F(z_1, z_2, \ldots, z_m) - \lambda G(z_1, z_2, \ldots, z_m).$$

[11] See, e.g., Yamane, *op. cit.*, pp. 116–120.

Here λ is the Lagrange multiplier. Its value is to be determined, along with the values of $z_1, z_2, \ldots, z_m$ that minimize (maximize) F subject to the condition G. To obtain the required solution we differentiate H with respect to $z_1, z_2, \ldots, z_m$ and λ and put each of the derivatives equal to zero. This gives us $(m + 1)$ equations to be solved for the $(m + 1)$ unknowns. The solution represents the first-order (necessary) conditions; the second-order conditions, which determine whether the solution is a minimum or a maximum, are given elsewhere.[12] A well-known application of the Lagrange multiplier method in economics arises in connection with the problem of utility maximization subject to the budget constraint.[13]

Let us turn now to the specific problem of minimizing $\sigma^2 \sum a_i^2$ subject to $\sum a_i = 1$. In this problem the function F to be minimized is

$$F(a_1, a_2, \ldots, a_n) = \sigma^2 \sum_i a_i^2,$$

and the constraint G is

$$G(a_1, a_2, \ldots, a_n) = \sum_i a_i - 1.$$

Following the Lagrange multiplier method, we form

$$H = \sigma^2 \sum_i a_i^2 - \lambda\left[\sum_i a_i - 1\right].$$

The first-order conditions are

(6.14a) $\quad \dfrac{\partial H}{\partial a_1} = 0, \quad \dfrac{\partial H}{\partial a_2} = 0, \ldots, \quad \dfrac{\partial H}{\partial a_n} = 0, \quad \dfrac{\partial H}{\partial \lambda} = 0$

or, explicitly,

(6.14b)
$$2a_1\sigma^2 - \lambda = 0,$$
$$2a_2\sigma^2 - \lambda = 0,$$
$$\vdots$$
$$2a_n\sigma^2 - \lambda = 0,$$
$$-\left[\sum_i a_i - 1\right] = 0.$$

This gives us $(n + 1)$ equations to be solved for the unknowns $a_1, a_2, \ldots, a_n$ and λ. From the first n equations we get

$$a_1 = \frac{\lambda}{2\sigma^2}, \quad a_2 = \frac{\lambda}{2\sigma^2}, \quad \ldots, \quad a_n = \frac{\lambda}{2\sigma^2}.$$

Substituting into the last equation gives

$$-\left[\frac{n\lambda}{2\sigma^2} - 1\right] = 0,$$

[12] See, e.g., *ibid.*, pp. 345–348.
[13] See, e.g., M. Friedman, *Price Theory* (Chicago: Aldine, 1962), p. 40.

or
$$\lambda = \frac{2\sigma^2}{n}.$$

Therefore,
$$a_1 = \frac{1}{n}, \quad a_2 = \frac{1}{n}, \quad \ldots \quad a_n = \frac{1}{n}.$$

These are then the constants that make $\tilde{\mu}$ unbiased and minimize its variance. Substituting for $a_1, a_2, \ldots, a_n$ into the formula for $\tilde{\mu}$ given by (6.11) leads to

$$\tilde{\mu} = \sum_i \frac{1}{n} X_i = \frac{1}{n} \sum_i X_i = \bar{X}.$$

In other words, the BLUE of the population mean is given by the sample mean. Further, substituting for a_i into the formula for the variance of $\tilde{\mu}$ given by (6.12), we get

$$\mathrm{Var}(\tilde{\mu}) = \sigma^2 \sum_i \left(\frac{1}{n}\right)^2 = \sigma^2 n \left(\frac{1}{n}\right)^2 = \frac{\sigma^2}{n},$$

which is a well-known expression for the variance of the sample mean.

The best linear unbiased estimator can be considered as a special case of a *linear-minimum-weighted-square-error estimator* (LMWSEE), say, θ^*, obtained by minimizing

$$[w \, \mathrm{Var}(\theta^*) + (1 - w)(\text{Bias of } \theta^*)^2],$$

where w is some preassigned weight such that $0 \le w \le 1$. By selecting $w = 0$ we get the BLUE. As it happens, many values of w are "outlawed" because they lead to formulas involving unknown parameters. As an example, consider a LMWSEE of the population mean when $w = 1/2$. This estimator is

$$\mu^* = \sum_i a_i X_i,$$

where the constants $a_1, a_2, \ldots, a_n$ are to be determined so as to minimize

$$\frac{1}{2} [\mathrm{Var}(\mu^*) + (\text{Bias of } \mu^*)^2].$$

That is, setting $w = 1/2$ implies that we wish to minimize the *mean square error* of μ^*. The resulting formula is

$$\mu^* = \left[\frac{n\mu^2}{n\mu^2 + \sigma^2}\right] \bar{X},$$

which clearly indicates that μ^* does not qualify as an estimator since μ^2 and σ^2 are unknown. However, since for any value of μ^2 and σ^2 other than zero

$$\frac{n\mu^2}{n\mu^2 + \sigma^2} < 1,$$

it follows that the value of the linear-minimum-mean-square-error estimator of μ is less than that of $\bar{X}$, though of course we do not know how much less.

Conclusion

This brings us to the end of our present discussion on methods of estimation. We have confined our attention to four basic methods; additional methods will be developed in the following chapters. The methods discussed do, however, provide the backbone of most if not all of the other estimation methods. The usefulness of the four methods has been illustrated by applying them to the problem of estimating the population mean. By each of the four methods we have obtained exactly the same estimator, namely, the sample mean. This result is rather reassuring since we know from Section 6–1 that sample mean as an estimator of the population mean has all the optimal properties.

6–3   Confidence Intervals

Now we take up the question of the precision of an estimator. Suppose we are interested in a population parameter θ for which there is an estimator $\hat{\theta}$. Suppose further that $\hat{\theta}$ possesses all the optimal properties of an estimator and incorporates all our knowledge concerning the relevant population. Since this knowledge is not complete, we shall be making an error by using $\hat{\theta}$ in place of the true parameter θ. The question then arises as to the size of this error. It is in this context that we speak of the precision of an estimator. That is, having obtained the best estimator that can be constructed given our limited knowledge, we may want to ask how well we can expect this estimator to perform.

The answer is obviously connected with the dispersion of the sampling distribution of the estimator. If this dispersion is small, a large proportion of estimates will lie within a close range from the true value of the parameter; if the dispersion is large, the same proportion of estimates will lie within a wider range. Thus the degree of precision of an estimator could be measured by the standard deviation of its sampling distribution, i.e., by its standard error. In most cases in practice this is not known but can be estimated from the sample along with the value of the estimator itself. Indeed, it is becoming an almost standard practice in econometrics to present not only the value of the estimator but also the calculated standard error. The latter is usually presented in parentheses below the value of the estimator, i.e.,

$$\hat{\theta}.$$
$$(s_{\hat{\theta}})$$

A more systematic and explicit method of indicating the precision of an estimator exists in the case in which we know the form of the sampling distribution of the estimator. We are then able to construct so-called *confidence intervals* for the population parameter. The idea of confidence intervals can best be explained by reference to our discussion on hypothesis testing in Section 5–1, using as an illustration the problem of estimating the mean of a normal population. In this case we use as an estimator the sample mean $\overline{X}$, which has all the optimal properties. We know that if the normal population in question has mean

μ and variance σ^2, the distribution of the sample mean will be normal with mean μ and variance (σ^2/n), i.e., $\bar{X} \sim N(\mu, \sigma^2/n)$. Therefore,

$$\frac{\bar{X} - \mu}{\sqrt{\sigma^2/n}} \sim N(0, 1),$$

where $N(0, 1)$ is the standard normal distribution whose areas have been calculated and tabulated (see Appendix D). With this knowledge we are able to make certain probability statements that, in turn, lead to the construction of confidence intervals for μ.

The reader may recall that in the case of a variable with standard normal distribution, 95% of all values fall within -1.96 and $+1.96$. That is, we can write

$$(6.15) \qquad P(-1.96 \leq \frac{\bar{X} - \mu}{\sqrt{\sigma^2/n}} \leq +1.96) = 0.95.$$

This statement implies that 95% of all samples drawn from a normal population with mean μ and variance σ^2 will have $\bar{X}$ such that

$$(6.16) \qquad -1.96 \leq \frac{\bar{X} - \mu}{\sqrt{\sigma^2/n}} \leq +1.96$$

will be true. Multiplying this inequality by $\sqrt{\sigma^2/n}$ throughout, we get

$$-1.96\sqrt{\sigma^2/n} \leq (\bar{X} - \mu) \leq +1.96\sqrt{\sigma^2/n}.$$

Deducting $\bar{X}$ from all sides gives

$$-1.96\sqrt{\sigma^2/n} - \bar{X} \leq (-\mu) \leq +1.96\sqrt{\sigma^2/n} - \bar{X}.$$

Finally, multiplying throughout by -1 and switching the sides around leads to

$$(6.17) \qquad \bar{X} - 1.96\sqrt{\sigma^2/n} \leq \mu \leq \bar{X} + 1.96\sqrt{\sigma^2/n}.$$

The expression in (6.17) is called the *95% confidence interval* for the population mean μ. The probability that this interval covers the true mean μ is equal to 0.95. This means that if we drew an infinite number of samples from the specified population, and if, for each sample, we computed the interval according to (6.17), then 95% of those intervals would contain the true mean μ. The measure "95%" represents the degree of our confidence that the interval—constructed on the basis of a given sample—will contain the true population mean. Note that we cannot say that "the probability that μ will lie within the stated interval is 0.95" because μ is a fixed number, not a random variable. The only probability statement that can be made about μ is that μ will assume its true value with probability 1 and all other values with probability 0. However, the end points of the interval—and therefore the interval itself—are random.

In setting up a confidence interval we can, of course, choose any level of confidence we like. However, we should realize that the higher the level of confidence, the wider the corresponding confidence interval and, therefore, the less useful is the information about the precision of the estimator. This can be seen by taking an extreme case, namely, that in which the confidence level is 100%. In this case the corresponding confidence interval, derived from a normally distributed estimator, is from $-\infty$ to $+\infty$, which obviously conveys no information about the precision of the estimator. On the other hand, narrower confidence intervals will be associated with lower levels of confidence. The problem here is very much like that of the level of significance in the context of hypothesis testing. A common solution in both cases is to use those levels which are most frequently used by others. In connection with hyhothesis testing, we pointed out that there are two customarily employed levels of significance, 5% and 1%. Similarly, in connection with confidence intervals the two customary levels of confidence are 95% and 99%. For the mean of a normal population—with $\bar{X}$ as an estimator—the 95% confidence interval was given in (6.17); the 99% confidence interval is

$$(6.18) \qquad \bar{X} - 2.57\sqrt{\sigma^2/n} \leq \mu \leq \bar{X} + 2.57\sqrt{\sigma^2/n}.$$

In constructing this interval we have made use of the fact that in the case of the standard normal distribution 99% of all values fall within -2.57 and $+2.57$.

The confidence interval (6.17) has been derived from a probability statement about the standard normal distribution. In particular, we have used the boundary points -1.96 and $+1.96$ that contain 95% of the total area. These boundary points are not unique since we can find other boundaries that also contain 95% of the area, for instance, -2.10 and $+1.85$, or -2.20 and $+1.80$, among others. The difference is that the interval from -1.96 to $+1.96$ contains the *central* portion of the area since it cuts off 2.5% of the area at each end of the distribution, whereas all the other intervals are asymmetric. The fact that the interval from -1.96 to $+1.96$ is symmetric implies that it is the *shortest* of all intervals that contain 95% of the area. This, in turn, means that the resulting 95% confidence interval is shorter than any other interval of the same level of confidence. The same conclusion can be drawn with respect to the 99% confidence interval (6.18). Obviously, given the level of confidence, a shorter interval is more desirable than a longer one.

EXAMPLE   As a numerical example consider the following problem. Suppose we wish to construct a 95% confidence interval for the mean of $X \sim N(\mu, 16)$, having drawn a sample of 400 observations and obtained $\bar{x} = 99$. Then the 95% confidence interval is

$$99 - 1.96\sqrt{16/400} \leq \mu \leq 99 + 1.96\sqrt{16/400}$$

or
$$98.61 \leq \mu \leq 99.39.$$

That is, the probability that the interval from 98.61 to 99.39 will contain the true mean is 0.95. Note that the 99% confidence interval in this case is

$$99 - 2.57\sqrt{16/400} \leq \mu \leq 99 + 2.57\sqrt{16/400}$$

or
$$98.36 \leq \mu \leq 99.64.$$

The reader has probably noticed the similarity between confidence intervals for the population mean and acceptance regions of a test about the population mean. Let us consider this in explicit terms. Suppose, for instance, that we are dealing with a variable $X \sim N(\mu, \sigma^2)$ and that we wish to test the null hypothesis

$$H_0: \quad \mu = \mu_0$$

against the alternative,

$$H_A: \quad \mu \neq \mu_0.$$

Then the acceptance region corresponding to a 5% level of significance is

$$-1.96 \leq \frac{\bar{X} - \mu_0}{\sqrt{\sigma^2/n}} \leq +1.96.$$

This can be rewritten as

$$\bar{X} - 1.96\sqrt{\sigma^2/n} \leq \mu_0 \leq \bar{X} + 1.96\sqrt{\sigma^2/n}.$$

Now compare this with the 95% confidence interval for the population mean μ given by (6.17):

$$\bar{X} - 1.96\sqrt{\sigma^2/n} \leq \mu \leq \bar{X} + 1.96\sqrt{\sigma^2/n}.$$

The implication is that the 95% confidence interval is simply an interval that contains all those hypotheses about the population mean (i.e., all μ_0's) that would be accepted in a two-tail test at the 5% level of significance. A similar case could be made out for a 99% confidence interval and a two-tail test at the 1% level is significance. The difference between the acceptance regions and the confidence intervals is implied by the difference between hypothesis testing and estimation: in one case we make statements about the population and check whether or not they are contradicted by sample evidence; in the other case we regard the population as a blank that is to be filled by the sample.

So far we have assumed that the construction of confidence intervals involves estimators with optimal properties. In discussing confidence intervals for the mean of a normal population, the estimator was represented by the sample mean that satisfies this condition. Now we shall concern ourselves with the desirability of these optimal properties in confidence interval construction. First, if the estimator in question should be biased and the extent of the bias were not known, then the stated level of confidence would be incorrect. This can be easily demonstrated by replacing $\bar{X}$ in (6.17) or (6.18) by ($\bar{X} + B$), where B is the bias and the value of B is not known. It is obvious that the interval involving ($\bar{X} + B$) is associated with a different probability statement than the interval involving only $\bar{X}$ (unless, of course, $B = 0$), and thus the two intervals are characterized by different levels of confidence. Second, if the estimator is unbiased but not efficient, then the confidence interval is wider than otherwise. This follows from the fact that the variance of an inefficient estimator is larger than that of the efficient one and this "pushes" the end points of a confidence interval farther apart. Finally, squared-error consistency guarantees that as the sample size increases, the confidence interval narrows down and, at the limit, completely collapses at the point of the true value of the parameter.

In our discussion about confidence intervals, we have used as an illustration the problem of constructing confidence intervals for the mean of a normal population with *known* variance. In practical applications we rarely know the population variance but rather have to estimate it from the sample. An unbiased estimator of σ^2 was derived earlier and presented by (5.6) as

$$s^2 = \frac{1}{n-1} \sum_{i=1}^{n} (X_i - \bar{X})^2.$$

Furthermore, we know by (5.9) that if

$$\frac{(\bar{X} - \mu)}{\sqrt{\sigma^2/n}} \sim N(0, 1),$$

then

$$\frac{(\bar{X} - \mu)}{\sqrt{s^2/n}} \sim t_{n-1},$$

where t_{n-1} represents the t distribution with $(n-1)$ degrees of freedom. This enables us to make the following probability statement:

$$(6.19) \qquad P\left[-t_{n-1, \alpha/2} \leq \frac{\bar{X} - \mu}{\sqrt{s^2/n}} \leq +t_{n-1, \alpha/2}\right] = 1 - \alpha,$$

where $t_{n-1, \alpha/2}$ stands for the value of the t statistic with $(n-1)$ degrees of freedom that cuts off $\alpha/2$ of the area of the t distribution at each tail end. The term $(1 - \alpha)$ represents the area between the points $-t_{n-1, \alpha/2}$ and $+t_{n-1, \alpha/2}$. From (6.19) we can construct a confidence interval for μ at any level of confidence. For instance, the 95% confidence interval for μ is

$$(6.20) \qquad \bar{X} - t_{n-1, 0.025}\sqrt{s^2/n} \leq \mu \leq \bar{X} + t_{n-1, 0.025}\sqrt{s^2/n}.$$

EXAMPLE   As a numerical example, consider the problem of constructing the 95% confidence interval for the mean μ of $X \sim N(\mu, \sigma^2)$, given that $\bar{X} = 20$, $s^2 = 100$, and $n = 25$. In this case the value of $t_{19,0.025}$ is 2.064 so that the 95% confidence interval for μ is

$$20 - 2.064\sqrt{100/25} \leq \mu \leq 20 + 2.064\sqrt{100/25}$$

or
$$15.872 \leq \mu \leq 24.128.$$

In a similar way we could construct intervals corresponding to 99% level of confidence, or any other level we might desire.

The idea of a confidence interval, developed above with respect to the mean of a normal population, can be used quite generally in connection with any parameter for which we have an estimator with known sampling distribution. For instance, we could construct a confidence interval for the variance of a normal population since we know that $[(n - 1)s^2/\sigma^2]$ has the chi-square distribution with $(n - 1)$ degrees of freedom. In our discussion we have viewed confidence intervals as a certain means of formally measuring the precision of an estimator. An alternative and more traditional view is to regard confidence intervals as more or less a separate subject treated under the heading of "interval estimation," to be distinguished from "point estimation," which is the subject of our Sections 6–1 and 6–2. We do not follow this traditional view since the connection between "point estimation" and "interval estimation" is so intimate as to make the separation rather artificial.

EXERCISES

6–1. Let $X \sim N(\mu, \sigma^2)$. Consider two independent random samples of observations on X. The samples are of size n_1 and n_2 with means $\bar{X}_1$ and $\bar{X}_2$, respectively. Two estimators of the population mean are proposed:

$$\hat{\mu} = \frac{1}{2}(\bar{X}_1 + \bar{X}_2),$$

$$\tilde{\mu} = \frac{n_1 \bar{X}_1 + n_2 \bar{X}_2}{n_1 + n_2}.$$

Compare the properties of these estimators.

6–2. Let $X \sim N(\mu, \sigma^2)$. Consider the following estimator of the population mean obtained from a random sample of n observations on X:

$$\tilde{\mu} = \bar{X} + \frac{a}{n},$$

where a is a finite constant.

a. What are the asymptotic mean and the asymptotic variance of μ?

b. Prove that $\tilde{\mu}$ is consistent and asymptotically efficient.

6–3. Let X be the number of successes in a sample of size n. The observations are assumed to be independent. Two estimators of the population proportion of successes, π, are

$$\hat{\pi} = \frac{X}{n},$$

$$\tilde{\pi} = \frac{(X + 1)}{(n + 1)}.$$

Examine the properties of these estimators.

6–4. A k-sided die has sides marked $1, 2, \ldots, k$. The die is tossed, and the uppermost number shown is 9. On the basis of this observation, obtain the maximum likelihood estimate of k and draw the likelihood function.

6-5. Let X be a random variable with mean μ and variance σ^2. Find a linear estimator of μ, say $\overset{\circ}{\mu}$, such that

$$\frac{\text{Var}(\overset{\circ}{\mu})}{\sigma^2} + \frac{(\text{Bias of } \overset{\circ}{\mu})^2}{\mu^2}$$

is at minimum.

6-6. Let $X \sim N(\mu, \sigma^2)$. Consider the following two estimators of σ^2:

$$\hat{\sigma}^2 = \frac{1}{n} \sum_{i=1}^{n} (X_i - \bar{X})^2,$$

$$s^2 = \frac{1}{n-1} \sum_{i=1}^{n} (X_i - \bar{X})^2.$$

Show that

a. $\text{Var}(\hat{\sigma}^2) < \text{Var}(s^2)$;

b. $\text{MSE}(\hat{\sigma}^2) < \text{MSE}(s^2)$;

c. Both estimators are consistent.

[HINT: $\text{Var}(\hat{\sigma}^2) = 2\sigma^4(n-1)/n^2$.]

6-7. Following are 20 observations drawn from a normal population:

0.464	0.137	2.455	−0.323
0.060	−2.526	−0.531	−0.194
1.486	−0.354	−0.634	0.697
1.022	−0.472	1.279	3.521
1.394	−0.555	0.046	0.321

a. Find the 95% confidence interval for the population mean.

b. Plot the likelihood function for the population mean and the ML estimate of μ.

[NOTE: Since the ML estimate of μ does not depend on σ^2, for the purpose of graphing we can set its value to be some convenient number, e.g., unity.]

6-8. The Air Conditioning Maintenance and Repair Company contemplates opening a branch in Belair Hills. You have been engaged to conduct a sample survey to estimate the percentage of homes with air conditioning in this community. The conditions of the contract between you and A.C.M.R. are as follows:
  1. The required confidence limits for the population proportion are 95%.
  2. The sample used as a basis for the estimate must be strictly random and must contain at least 30 families.
  3. You will get paid $500, *less* $10 for each percentage unit of the estimated interval for the population proportion; for example, if you should find that, with 95% confidence, the population proportion lies between 0.4 and 0.6, you will receive $500 − $10 (60 − 40) = $300.
In the preliminary investigation you have found out that the cost of obtaining sample information is $2 per family included in the sample. The results of the interviews with the families included in your sample can be obtained by using the "census" of Belair Hills presented in Table 6–2. There are 250 families, each occupying a house;

houses with air conditioning are marked by a tick. [NOTE: The large-sample 95% confidence interval for the proportion of successes in a finite population is given as

$$\hat{\pi} \pm 1.96\sqrt{\frac{\hat{\pi}(1-\hat{\pi})}{n}}\,\sqrt{\frac{N-n}{N-1}},$$

where n = sample size, and N = population size.]

a. Draw a full report to A.C.M.R. in which you describe the technique used in selecting the sample and the method of estimation, and present the results.

b. Produce a bill to A.C.M.R.

c. Work out your *net* remuneration for the work carried out.

d. Show an extract from a letter to a friend, whom you wish to entice into partnership, in which you describe how cleverly you applied the profit-maximization principle in connection with the job for A.C.M.R.

Table 6–2 Complete Listing of Families in Belair Hills

Family No.	Family No.	Family No.	Family No.	Family No.	Family No.	Family No.	Family No.
1 √	33	65	96	127	158	189	220
2	34 √	66 √	97 √	128 √	159 √	190	221
3 √	35	67	98	129 √	160 √	191	222
4 √	36 √	68	99	130 √	161	192 √	223
5	37 √	69 √	100	131	162	193	224
6 √	38	70 √	101	132	163	194	225 √
7	39 √	71 √	102 √	133	164 √	195 √	226
8	40 √	72	103	134	165 √	196	227 √
9 √	41 √	73	104	135	166 √	197 √	228 √
10	42	74 √	105	136	167 √	198	229 √
11 √	43	75	106	137 √	168 √	199 √	230
12 √	44	76	107 √	138	169 √	200	231 √
13 √	45	77 √	108	139	170 √	201	232 √
14	46 √	78 √	109 √	140	171 √	202	233 √
15 √	47	79 √	110	141	172	203	234
16	48 √	80	111 √	142	173	204 √	235
17	49	81	112 √	143	174 √	205	236
18	50	82	113	144	175	206 √	237 √
19 √	51	83 √	114 √	145 √	176	207 √	238
20 √	52	84	115	146	177	208	239
21	53	85 √	116 √	147 √	178 √	209 √	240
22	54	86 √	117 √	148 √	179	210	241
23 √	55	87	118	149	180	211	242 √
24 √	56 √	88	119 √	150 √	181	212	243
25 √	57	89	120	151	182	213	244
26 √	58 √	90	121 √	152	183 √	214	245
27 √	59 √	91	122 √	153 √	184	215 √	246 √
28 √	60	92 √	123 √	154	185	216 √	247
29 √	61 √	93 √	124	155 √	186	217 √	248
30 √	62	94 √	125	156	187	218	249 √
31	63	95 √	126	157	188	219	250 √
32 √	64 √						

Part TWO

Basic Econometric Theory

7 | Simple Regression

Economic theory is mainly concerned with relations among variables. Demand and supply relations, cost functions, production functions, and many others are familiar to every student who has taken a course in economics. In fact, the entire body of economic theory can be regarded as a collection of relations among variables.[1] As pointed out in Chapter 1, econometrics is concerned with testing the theoretical propositions embodied in these relations, and with estimating the parameters involved. In the chapters of Part Two we will discuss various methods that can be used in performing this task and the problems encountered in the process. In the present chapter we will discuss the simplest case of a linear relation involving only two measurable variables; the subsequent chapters will contain increasingly more complicated cases.

7–1 Relations Between Variables

An appropriate way to start our discussion is by defining the new concepts with which we will be working. We define a *relation* between variables X and Y as a set of all values of X and Y which are characterized by a given equation. For example, if the characterizing equation is given by

$$y = \alpha + \beta x,$$

where α and β are some constants, then the relation between X and Y is the set $\{x, y\}$ consisting of all possible values of X and Y that satisfy the equation. Typically, the form of the characterizing equation gives the name to the corresponding relation: a linear equation describes a linear relation, an exponential equation describes an exponential relation, and so on. The concept of a relation is closely associated with the concepts of a domain and of a range. If a relation between X and Y is characterized by an equation $y = f(x)$, then the *domain* of this relation is the set of all possible values of X, and the *range* is the set of all possible corresponding values of Y. In practice, relations are usually described

---

[1] See, e.g., Paul A. Samuelson, *Foundations of Economic Analysis* (Cambridge, Mass.: Harvard University Press, 1947).

simply by stating the appropriate characterizing equation, while the domain and the range are implied but unstated.

All relations can be classified as either deterministic or stochastic. A relation between X and Y is *deterministic* if each element of the domain is paired off with *just one* element of the range. That is, a relationship between X and Y characterized as $y = f(x)$ is a deterministic relation if for each value of X there is only one corresponding value of Y. However, the *variables* X and Y may both be nonstochastic (i.e., they may assume values that are fully controllable or predictable), or they may both be stochastic. This means that a relation may be deterministic (i.e., nonstochastic) even if both variables involved are stochastic; however, if both variables are stochastic while the relation is deterministic, the conditional distribution of Y given X is degenerate (see page 163). On the other hand, a relation between X and Y is said to be *stochastic* if for each value of X there is a whole probability distribution of values of Y. Thus, for any given value of X the variable Y may, in this case, assume some specific value—or fall within some specific interval—with a probability smaller than one and greater than zero.

To illustrate the distinction between a deterministic and a stochastic relation, suppose we conduct a series of experiments in class to determine the demand for Mackintosh apples at different prices. Let q_t = quantity of apples sold at time t, and let p_t = price in cents. The apples are offered for sale at a given price every time the class meets during the term. The results at the end of the term may be as follows:

p_t	q_t
25	1
20	3
15	5
10	7
5	9
0	11

These results can be summarized in the form of a "demand equation" as

$$q_t = 11 - 0.4p_t.$$

The relation between price and quantity then is such that *any time* the apples were offered at 25 cents apiece, only one apple was sold. Any time the price was 20 cents, three apples were sold, and so on. This is a deterministic relation, since for each price there is always only one corresponding quantity of apples sold. Now consider a different set of results (Table 7–1). The "demand equation" must now be rewritten as

$$q_t = 11 - 0.4p_t + \varepsilon_t,$$

Table 7–1

p_t	q_t
25	$\begin{cases} \text{0 apples 25\% of the time} \\ \text{1 apple\ \ 50\% of the time} \\ \text{2 apples 25\% of the time} \end{cases}$
20	$\begin{cases} \text{2 apples 25\% of the time} \\ \text{3 apples 50\% of the time} \\ \text{4 apples 25\% of the time} \end{cases}$
$\vdots$	$\vdots$
0	$\begin{cases} \text{10 apples 25\% of the time} \\ \text{11 apples 50\% of the time} \\ \text{12 apples 25\% of the time} \end{cases}$

where ε_t is a random variable having the following probability distribution, whatever the specified price:

ε_t	$f(\varepsilon_t)$
-1	0.25
0	0.50
$+1$	0.25
	1.00

This variable is commonly called a *random disturbance* since it "disturbs" an otherwise deterministic relation (an alternative expression for ε_t is "a random error term"). The last relation is a stochastic one since, because of the presence of the disturbance, there are several quantities demanded for each price, each quantity occurring with a given probability. A diagrammatic representation of the two relations is shown in Figure 7–1.

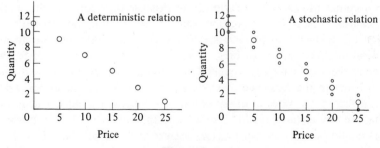

Figure 7–1

Let us now consider the question of dependence between two variables involved in a relation. First, consider a deterministic relation characterized by

$$y = f(x).$$

Then, if $f(x)$ is not constant over all values of X (that is, if $f(x)$ is not constant over all elements of the domain), we say that Y *is dependent on X in the functional sense*. In other words, Y is considered to depend on X if, at least for some values of X, a change in X implies a change in Y. If, in a two-dimensional diagram, the values of Y are measured along the vertical and those of X along the horizontal axis, then Y is dependent on X if all points do not lie on a straight horizontal line. With respect to a *stochastic relation*, we say that Y *is dependent on X in the functional sense* if the probability distribution of Y is not the same for all values of X. A typical case of dependence of Y on X arises when the mean of Y changes as X assumes different values. However, Y would be considered as dependent on X even if the mean of Y remained constant for all values of X, as long as some other characteristic of the distribution of Y would change with X. For instance, if the variance of Y were to increase with increases in X, this alone would make Y dependent on X according to our definition.

It is interesting to note that, in the numerical example on the stochastic demand curve given above, the mean quantity demanded changes with price while the variance remains unchanged. In particular, we have

p_t	$E(q_t)$	$Var(q_t)$
25	1	0.5
20	3	0.5
15	5	0.5
10	7	0.5
5	9	0.5
0	11	0.5

In a more general case of dependence both the mean and the variance of Y may change in response to changes in X.

In economic theory all relations are, as a rule, stated in a deterministic form. This is not because economists would believe in a complete absence of chance when it comes to economic relations, but because they consider the stochastic disturbances to be of less importance than the systematic influences. The introduction of stochastic disturbances into the economic relations would greatly complicate the task of the theorist. However, the stress on the need for *testing* economic theories, which is frequently encountered in economic writings, implies a belief in the existence of stochastic factors. If the theoretical relations were, in fact, deterministic, the question of statistical testing would not arise; all that we would have to do to determine the values of the unknown parameters would be to carry out precise measurements rather than tests. To illustrate this, we may consider a theory that Y is linearly dependent on X. If the relation between Y and X were, in fact, deterministic, we would simply measure two pairs of values of X and Y. If the line connecting these two points were horizontal, the theory would be rejected; in all other cases the theory would be verified. The intercept and the slope of the line could be simply read off the graph. If, however, the relation between X and Y were stochastic, our observations of the values of the two variables would have to be considered as a sample. The sample would then be used to test a proposition about the population, and the slope and the intercept would have to be estimated.

7-2   The Regression Model

In econometrics we deal exclusively with stochastic relations. The simplest form of stochastic relation between two variables X and Y is called a *simple linear regression model*. This model is formally described as

$$(7.1) \qquad\qquad\qquad Y_i = \alpha + \beta X_i + \varepsilon_i,$$

where Y is called the "dependent variable," X the "explanatory variable," and ε the "stochastic disturbance," and α and β are the "regression parameters," which are unknown. The subscript i refers to the ith observation. The values of the variables X and Y are observable, but those of ε are not. Observations on X and Y can be made over time, in which case we speak of having "time-series data," or they can be made over individuals, groups of individuals, objects, or geographical areas, in which case we speak of having "cross-section data." Thus the subscript i may refer to the ith point or period of time, or to the ith individual, object, etc. Of course, data of both kinds can be combined to obtain "pooled time-series and cross-section data"; for example, we may have data on consumption expenditure and income of N individual households for T periods of time. In this case it would be convenient to use a double subscript. However, data of this kind are not very common. Typically, aggregate relations such as aggregate consumption functions, market demand relations, or aggregate production functions are estimated from time-series data, while microrelations such as household expenditure functions or firm production functions are estimated from cross-section data obtained from sample surveys. The origin of the data is not explicitly taken into account in the development of estimators of the regression parameters. But, as we shall see, the properties of these estimators depend on certain assumptions concerning the observations, and some of these assumptions are more likely to be violated when the data are of one kind than another. In this respect the type of data used in estimation is of relevance.

The stochastic nature of the regression model implies that for every value of X there is a whole probability distribution of values of Y. This means that the value of Y can never be forecast exactly. The uncertainty concerning Y arises because of the presence of the stochastic disturbance ε which, being random, imparts randomness to Y. Consider, for example, a production function of a firm. Suppose that output depends in some specified way on the quantity of labor input in accordance with the engineer's blueprint. Such a production function may apply in the short run when the quantities of other inputs are fixed. But, in general, the same quantity of labor will lead to different quantities of output because of variations in weather, human performance, frequency of machine breakdowns, and many other factors. Output, which is the dependent variable in this case, will depend not only on the quantity of labor input, which is the explanatory variable, but also on a large number of random causes, which we summarize in the form of the stochastic disturbance. The probability distribution of Y and its characteristics are then determined by the values of X and by the probability distribution of ε. If the "blueprint" relation between output and labor were completely and correctly specified, then we could measure the value of ε from the observations on X and Y after each production run. In reality this is almost never the case. In fact, we consider ourselves lucky when we know even the mathematical form of the relation without knowing the parameters. Typically, the mathematical form of the relation has to be assumed and the values of the parameters are estimated from observations on X and Y. Using the estimated values of the parameters, we can then "estimate" the values of the stochastic disturbance for each pair of values of X and Y.

It should be clear now that the full specification of the regression model includes not only the form of the regression equation as given in (7.1) but also a specification of the probability distribution of the disturbance and a statement indicating how the values of the explanatory variable are determined. This information is given by what we shall call the *basic assumptions*. These assumptions, which are taken to apply to *all* observations, are as follows:

(7.2) *Normality:* ε_i is normally distributed.

(7.3) *Zero mean:* $E(\varepsilon_i) = 0$.

(7.4) *Homoskedasticity:* $E(\varepsilon_i^2) = \sigma^2$.

(7.5) *Nonautoregression:* $E(\varepsilon_i \varepsilon_j) = 0$ $(i \neq j)$.

(7.6) *Nonstochastic X:* X_i is a nonstochastic variable with values fixed in repeated samples and such that, for *any* sample size,

$$\frac{1}{n} \sum_{i=1}^{n} (X_i - \bar{X})^2$$

is a finite number different from zero.

The full specification of the simple linear regression model then consists of the regression equation (7.1) and the five basic assumptions (7.2) through (7.6).[2] This represents the so-called "classical normal linear regression model," which provides a point of departure for most of the work in econometric theory.

----

[2] Strictly speaking, there is one further assumption, which is made only implicitly, namely, that there exists no other regression model with a disturbance that would be correlated with ε_i of (7.1). The relevance of this assumption will become quite clear when we discuss "seemingly unrelated regressions."

Let us now examine the meaning of the various assumptions. The first two assumptions state that, for each value of X_i, the disturbance is normally distributed around zero. The implications are that ε_i is continuous and ranges from $-\infty$ to $+\infty$, that it is symmetrically distributed around its mean, and that its distribution is fully determined by two parameters, the mean and the variance. The rationalization of normality relies on the same argument as that which applies to the behavior of random errors of measurement and which was mentioned at the end of Section 4-2. In particular, we may consider each value of the stochastic disturbance as the result of a large number of small causes, each cause producing a small deviation of the dependent variable from what it would be if the relation were deterministic. Under these circumstances the analogy with the behavior of errors of measurement may be valid and the assumptions of normality and zero mean appropriate. The third assumption concerning homoskedasticity means that every disturbance has the same variance σ^2 whose value is unknown. This assumption rules out, for example, the possibility that the dispersion of the disturbances would be greater for higher than for lower values of X_i. In terms of our production functions example, the assumption of homoskedasticity implies that the variation in output is the same whether the quantity of labor is 20, 100, or any other number of units. The fourth assumption requires that the disturbances be nonautoregressive. Under this assumption the fact that, say, output is higher than expected today should not lead to a higher (or lower) than expected output tomorrow. Note that assumptions (7.3) and (7.5) together imply that the disturbances are uncorrelated, and assumptions (7.2), (7.3), and (7.5) together imply that the disturbances are independent in the probability sense.[3] The final assumption, which states that the explanatory variable is to be nonstochastic, is quite straightforward. This assumption confines us to considering those situations in which the values of X_i are either controllable or fully predictable. The additional statement that the values of X_i are "fixed in repeated samples" indicates that the set of values of X is taken to be the same from sample to sample. Finally, the requirement that $(1/n) \sum (X_i - \bar{X})^2$ be a finite number different from zero means that the values of X in the sample must not all be equal to the same number, and that they cannot grow or decline without limit as the sample size increases.

The assumptions underlying the classical normal linear regression model are used in deriving estimators of the regression parameters. Since the disturbance is assumed to be normally distributed with a mean equal to zero, the only thing that is not known about this distribution is its variance σ^2. Thus the model described by (7.1) through (7.6) involves altogether three unknown parameters, the regression parameters α and β and the variance of the disturbance σ^2. It should be emphasized, however, that we do not ignore the possibility that any one or more of the basic assumptions may not be fulfilled. In fact, Chapter 8 is devoted to precisely this question. There we shall examine what happens to the properties of the estimators developed in the present chapter when various

[3] For normally distributed random variables, uncorrelatedness implies independence. See, e.g., A. S. Goldberger, *Econometric Theory* (New York: Wiley, 1964), pp. 107–108.

assumptions are violated. We shall also try to develop alternative estimators appropriate to the situation on hand whenever necessary.

Having made a complete specification of the regression model as described by the regression equation and the five basic assumptions, we may take a closer look at some of its basic features. In particular, let us turn to the probability distribution of the dependent variable Y_i. First, the mean of Y_i can be obtained by taking the mathematical expectation of both sides of equation (7.1). We get

$$(7.7) \qquad\qquad E(Y_i) = E(\alpha + \beta X_i + \varepsilon_i) = \alpha + \beta X_i.$$

This follows from the specification that α and β are parameters, X_i is non-stochastic (i.e., some given number), and the mean of ε_i is 0 by (7.3). Further-more, the variance of Y_i is

$$(7.8) \qquad \operatorname{Var}(Y_i) = E[Y_i - E(Y_i)]^2 = E[(\alpha + \beta X_i + \varepsilon_i) - (\alpha + \beta X_i)]^2$$
$$= E(\varepsilon_i^2) = \sigma^2.$$

In this derivation we first used the general definition of a variance, then sub-stituted for Y_i from (7.1) and for $E(Y_i)$ from (7.7), and finally made use of the assumption of homoskedasticity given by (7.4). Concerning the distribution of Y_i, we can see from equation (7.1) that Y_i is merely a linear function of ε_i. Since ε_i is normally distributed, it follows by Theorem 12 that Y_i is also nor-mally distributed. Therefore, we can assert that Y_i is a normally distributed variable with mean $(\alpha + \beta X_i)$ and variance σ^2, i.e., that $Y_i \sim N(\alpha + \beta X_i, \sigma^2)$. This is illustrated graphically by Figure 7–2. Note that the means of the distribu-tions all lie on a straight line, and that each distribution has exactly the same variance.

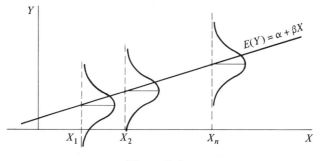

Figure 7–2

Equation (7.7), which gives the mean value of Y for each value of X, is known as the *population regression line*. The intercept of this line, α, measures the mean value of Y corresponding to zero value of X. The slope of the line, β, measures the change in the mean value of Y corresponding to a unit change in the value of X. If, for instance, Y represents aggregate consumption and X aggregate income, then α measures the subsistence level of consumption and β represents the marginal propensity to consume. Since the values of these parameters are not known, the population regression line is not known. When the values of α and β are estimated, we obtain a *sample regression line* that serves as an estimate of the population regression line. If α and β are estimated by $\hat{\alpha}$ and $\hat{\beta}$ respectively, then the sample regression line is given by

$$(7.9) \qquad\qquad \hat{Y}_i = \hat{\alpha} + \hat{\beta} X_i,$$

where $\hat{Y}_i$ is the fitted value of Y_i. Most, if not all, of the observed values of Y_i will not lie exactly on the sample regression line so that the values of Y_i and $\hat{Y}_i$ will differ. This difference is called a *residual* and is designated by e_i. Thus we have to distinguish the following:

$$Y_i = \alpha + \beta X_i + \varepsilon_i \quad \text{(population)};$$

$$Y_i = \hat{\alpha} + \hat{\beta} X_i + e_i \quad \text{(sample)}.$$

Note that, in general, e_i is different from ε_i because $\hat{\alpha}$ and $\hat{\beta}$ differ from the true values of α and β. In fact, one can view the residuals e_i as "estimates" of the disturbances ε_i. (Alternatively, we might say that the distribution of e_i is used to estimate the parameters of the distribution of ε_i.) This is illustrated in Figure 7–3. In Section 7–3 we will develop a procedure for estimating the regression parameters and, therefore, the population regression line.

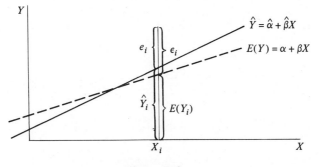

Figure 7–3

7–3   Estimation of the Regression Parameters

The problem of estimating the parameters of the regression model can be viewed as one of estimating the parameters of the probability distribution of the dependent variable Y_i. As we have shown, under the assumptions of the model, Y_i is normally distributed with the mean $E(Y_i) = \alpha + \beta X_i$ and variance $\text{Var}(Y_i) = \sigma^2$. The problem of estimating the regression parameters α and β is thus equivalent to the problem of estimating the mean of Y_i. This can be solved by a number of different estimation methods as described in Section 6–2.

We shall try three such methods—least squares, best linear unbiased estimation, and maximum likelihood—and compare the resulting estimators and their properties. The object is to obtain an estimator that will have as many desirable properties as possible. Such an estimator can then be used to test hypotheses about the regression model and to make predictions.

Least Squares Estimation

Let us begin with the derivation of the *least squares estimators* of α and β. The principle of least squares estimation involves minimizing the sum of squared deviations of the observed values from their mean. That is, we have to find the value of the mean that makes the required sum as small as possible. In our case we have to minimize the sum S given by

$$S = \sum_{i=1}^{n} [Y_i - E(Y_i)]^2,$$

or

$$S = \sum_{i=1}^{n} [Y_i - \alpha - \beta X_i]^2.$$

To find the values of α and β that minimize this sum we have to differentiate S with respect to α and β. This gives

$$\frac{\partial S}{\partial \alpha} = \sum_i \frac{\partial (Y_i - \alpha - \beta X_i)^2}{\partial \alpha} = \sum_i 2(Y_i - \alpha - \beta X_i)(-1)$$

$$= -2 \sum_i (Y_i - \alpha - \beta X_i),$$

and

$$\frac{\partial S}{\partial \beta} = \sum_i \frac{\partial (Y_i - \alpha - \beta X_i)^2}{\partial \beta} = \sum_i 2(Y_i - \alpha - \beta X_i)(-X_i)$$

$$= -2 \sum_i X_i(Y_i - \alpha - \beta X_i).$$

Equating each of these derivatives to zero and putting a "hat" on α and β to indicate that the resulting equations are satisfied by the least squares estimators of α and β, not by their true values, we obtain

$$-2 \sum_i (Y_i - \hat{\alpha} - \hat{\beta} X_i) = 0,$$

$$-2 \sum_i X_i(Y_i - \hat{\alpha} - \hat{\beta} X_i) = 0;$$

or, equivalently,

(7.10) $$\sum Y_i = \hat{\alpha} n + \hat{\beta} (\sum X_i),$$

(7.11) $$\sum X_i Y_i = \hat{\alpha} (\sum X_i) + \hat{\beta} (\sum X_i^2).$$

These equations are generally known as the "least squares normal equations." [4] Since we can write

$$Y_i = \hat{\alpha} + \hat{\beta} X_i + e_i,$$

where e_i represents the "least squares residuals," the least squares normal equations can be presented more simply as

(7.10a) $$\sum e_i = 0,$$

(7.11a) $$\sum X_i e_i = 0.$$

Equations (7.10) and (7.11) can be solved for $\hat{\alpha}$ and $\hat{\beta}$. The solution for $\hat{\beta}$ is

(7.12) $$\hat{\beta} = \frac{n(\sum X_i Y_i) - (\sum X_i)(\sum Y_i)}{n(\sum X_i^2) - (\sum X_i)^2}.$$

This expression can be written in a somewhat different way. Note that

(7.13) $$n \sum (X_i - \bar{X})(Y_i - \bar{Y})$$
$$= n(\sum X_i Y_i) - n\bar{X}(\sum Y_i) - n\bar{Y}(\sum X_i) + n^2 \bar{X}\bar{Y}$$
$$= n(\sum X_i Y_i) - (\sum X_i)(\sum Y_i) - (\sum X_i)(\sum Y_i) + (\sum X_i)(\sum Y_i)$$
$$= n(\sum X_i Y_i) - (\sum X_i)(\sum Y_i),$$

which is the numerator of the expression for $\hat{\beta}$. Also

(7.14) $$n \sum (X_i - \bar{X})^2 = n(\sum X_i^2) - 2n\bar{X}(\sum X_i) + n^2 \bar{X}^2$$
$$= n(\sum X_i^2) - 2(\sum X_i)^2 + (\sum X_i)^2$$
$$= n(\sum X_i^2) - (\sum X_i)^2,$$

which is the denominator of the expression for $\hat{\beta}$. Therefore, we can write

$$\hat{\beta} = \frac{\sum (X_i - \bar{X})(Y_i - \bar{Y})}{\sum (X_i - \bar{X})^2},$$

since the n in the numerator and the denominator cancel out. A further simplification can be achieved by introducing new notation for the deviations of X_i and Y_i from their respective sample means. In particular, let

$$x_i' = X_i - \bar{X} \quad \text{and} \quad y_i' = Y_i - \bar{Y}.$$

---

[4] The following rule may be found useful in memorizing. In the regression equation, $Y_i = \alpha + \beta X_i + \varepsilon_i$, the multiplier of α is 1 and the multiplier of β is X_i. The first least squares normal equation is obtained by multiplying both sides of the regression equation by 1, adding all observations, and omitting the last term involving ε_i. The second equation is obtained by multiplying both sides of the regression equation by X_i, adding all observations, and omitting the last term involving ε_i. This rule can be extended to regression equations with any number of explanatory variables.

Of course, this implies that $\sum x_i' = 0$ and $\sum y_i' = 0$. The expression for the least squares estimator of $\hat{\beta}$ then simplifies to

(7.12a) $$\hat{\beta} = \frac{\sum x_i' y_i'}{\sum x_i'^2}.$$

Once $\hat{\beta}$ is determined, the solution for $\hat{\alpha}$ can be obtained quite easily from equation (7.10). This leads to

(7.15) $$\hat{\alpha} = \frac{1}{n}\left(\sum Y_i\right) - \hat{\beta}\frac{1}{n}\left(\sum X_i\right) = \bar{Y} - \hat{\beta}\bar{X},$$

which means that the sample regression line

$$\hat{Y}_i = \hat{\alpha} + \hat{\beta}X_i$$

passes through the point $(\bar{X}, \bar{Y})$. The value of $\hat{\alpha}$ measures the intercept, and the value of $\hat{\beta}$ the slope of the sample regression line. The sampling properties of these estimators will be discussed at the end of this section.

EXAMPLE   As a numerical example, consider the data in Table 7–2 on prices and quantities of oranges sold in a supermarket on twelve consecutive days. Let X_i be

Table 7–2

Price, ¢/lb	Quantity, lb
100	55
90	70
80	90
70	100
70	90
70	105
70	80
65	110
60	125
60	115
55	130
50	130

the price charged and Y_i the quantity sold on the ith day. Let us further postulate that the demand function is of the form

$$Y_i = \alpha + \beta X_i + \varepsilon_i$$

and such that the basic assumptions of the classical normal regression model are satisfied. We wish to obtain the least squares estimate of α and β. Carrying out the appropriate calculations we get

$$\bar{X} = 70, \qquad \sum x_i' y_i' = -3550,$$
$$\bar{Y} = 100, \qquad \sum x_i'^2 = 2250.$$

(We also note for future reference that $\sum y_i'^2 = 6300$.) The least squares estimates then are

$$\hat{\beta} = \frac{-3550}{2250} = -1.578,$$

$$\hat{\alpha} = 100 - (-1.578) \times 70 = 210.460,$$

so that the estimated sample regression line is

$$\hat{Y}_i = 210.460 - 1.578 X_i.$$

This is our estimated demand curve. Since the function is linear, the price elasticity of demand is different at different prices. At the point of average price (i.e., when $X_i = 70$), the price elasticity η is estimated as

$$\hat{\eta}_{X_i = \bar{X}} = (-1.578) \times \frac{70}{100} = -1.105,$$

indicating that the demand is estimated to be slightly elastic at this point.

Best Linear Unbiased Estimation

Let us now turn to the derivation of the *best linear unbiased estimators* (BLUE) of α and β. The BLU estimation method requires that the estimator be a linear combination of sample observations, that it be unbiased, and that its variance be smaller than that of any other linear unbiased estimator. We shall use this method to derive the BLUE of β, say, $\tilde{\beta}$, first. By the condition of linearity we have

(7.16) $$\tilde{\beta} = \sum_i a_i Y_i,$$

where a_i $(i = 1, 2, \ldots, n)$ are some constants to be determined. Now

$$E(\tilde{\beta}) = E\left(\sum a_i Y_i\right) = \sum a_i E(Y_i) = \sum a_i(\alpha + \beta X_i) = \alpha\left(\sum a_i\right) + \beta\left(\sum a_i X_i\right).$$

This means that for $\tilde{\beta}$ to be unbiased we require that

$$\sum a_i = 0 \qquad \text{and} \qquad \sum a_i X_i = 1.$$

Finally, we require that $\tilde{\beta}$ have a smaller variance than any other estimator that satisfies the above conditions. The variance of $\tilde{\beta}$ is given as

$$\text{Var}(\tilde{\beta}) = \text{Var}\left(\sum_i a_i Y_i\right) = E\left[\left(\sum a_i Y_i\right) - E\left(\sum a_i Y_i\right)\right]^2$$

$$= E\left[\sum a_i(Y - EY_i)\right]^2 = E\left[\sum a_i \varepsilon_i\right]^2.$$

This expression for the sum of squares can be developed further. For example, consider the square of the sum of three numbers called c_1, c_2, and c_3. We have

$$(c_1 + c_2 + c_3)^2 = c_1^2 + c_2^2 + c_3^2 + 2c_1 c_2 + 2c_1 c_3 + 2c_2 c_3.$$

That is, a square of a sum is equal to the sum of squares plus two times the sum of cross products, where the cross products include all possible pairs for which the first subscript is smaller than the second one. We can, in fact, write

$$\left(\sum_i c_i\right)^2 = \sum_i c_i^2 + 2\sum_{i<j} c_i c_j.$$

This result, which is of general interest, can be extended to any number of terms. Thus we obtain

$$(7.17) \qquad \text{Var}(\tilde{\beta}) = E\sum_i (a_i\varepsilon_i)^2 + 2E\sum_{i<j}(a_i\varepsilon_i)(a_j\varepsilon_j)$$

$$= \sum_i a_i^2 E(\varepsilon_i^2) + 2\sum_{i<j} a_i a_j E(\varepsilon_i\varepsilon_j) = \sigma^2 \sum_i a_i^2$$

by the assumptions of homoskedasticity and nonautoregression.

The problem now is to find $a_1, a_2, \ldots, a_n$ such that $\sum a_i = 0$, $\sum_i a_i X_i = 1$, and, at the same time, $\sigma^2 \sum a_i^2$ is as small as possible. That is, we have to minimize

$$\sigma^2 \sum a_i^2$$

subject to the conditions

$$\sum a_i = 0 \qquad \text{and} \qquad \left(\sum a_i\right) - 1 = 0.$$

This is a problem of constrained minimization, which can be solved with the help of *Lagrange multiplier method*. The method for the case of one constraint was outlined earlier in describing the derivation of best linear unbiased estimators (Section 6–2). An extension to the case of two or more constraints can be made by simple analogy.[5] In the problem at hand we form a new function

$$H = \sigma^2 \sum_i a_i^2 - \lambda_1\left(\sum_i a_i\right) - \lambda_2\left[\left(\sum_i a_i X_i\right) - 1\right],$$

which consists of the function to be minimized, the two constraints imposed, and two Lagrange multipliers, λ_1 and λ_2. To obtain the required solution we differentiate H with respect to $a_1, a_2, \ldots, a_n, \lambda_1$, and λ_2, and put each of the derivatives equal to zero. That is,

$$(7.18a) \quad \frac{\partial H}{\partial a_1} = 0, \quad \frac{\partial H}{\partial a_2} = 0, \ldots, \frac{\partial H}{\partial a_n} = 0, \quad \frac{\partial H}{\partial \lambda_1} = 0, \quad \frac{\partial H}{\partial \lambda_2} = 0,$$

or, explicitly,

$$(7.18b) \qquad 2a_1\sigma^2 - \lambda_1 - \lambda_2 X_1 = 0$$
$$2a_2\sigma^2 - \lambda_1 - \lambda_2 X_2 = 0$$
$$\vdots$$
$$2a_n\sigma^2 - \lambda_1 - \lambda_2 X_n = 0$$
$$-\sum_i a_i = 0$$
$$-\left(\sum_i a_i X_i\right) + 1 = 0.$$

[5] See, e.g., T. Yamane, *Mathematics for Economists* (Englewood Cliffs, N.J.: Prentice-Hall, 1962), pp. 119–120.

This gives us $(n + 2)$ equations to be solved for the unknown $a_1, a_2, \ldots, a_n, \lambda_1$, and λ_2. The first n equations can be rewritten as

$$(7.19) \qquad a_1 = \frac{1}{2\sigma^2}(\lambda_1 + \lambda_2 X_1)$$

$$a_2 = \frac{1}{2\sigma^2}(\lambda_1 + \lambda_2 X_2)$$

$$\vdots$$

$$a_n = \frac{1}{2\sigma^2}(\lambda_1 + \lambda_2 X_n).$$

By summing up these equations we get

$$(7.20) \qquad \sum_i a_i = \frac{1}{2\sigma^2}\left(\lambda_1 n + \lambda_2 \sum_i X_i\right).$$

Furthermore, multiplying the first equation of (7.19) by X_1, the second by X_2, the third by X_3, and so on, and then summing up over all n equations leads to

$$(7.21) \qquad \sum_i a_i X_i = \frac{1}{2\sigma^2}\left[\lambda_1\left(\sum_i X_i\right) + \lambda_2\left(\sum_i X_i^2\right)\right].$$

Substituting for $\sum a_i$ and $\sum a_i X_i$ from (7.20) and (7.21) into the last two equations of (7.18b) then gives

$$-\frac{1}{2\sigma^2}\left(\lambda_1 n + \lambda_2 \sum_i X_i\right) = 0,$$

$$-\frac{1}{2\sigma^2}\left[\lambda_1\left(\sum_i X_i\right) + \lambda_2\left(\sum_i X_i^2\right)\right] = -1.$$

Thus we have obtained two equations in two unknowns, λ_1 and λ_2. The reader can easily verify that the solution is

$$\lambda_1 = \frac{-2\sigma^2 \sum X_i}{n(\sum X_i^2) - (\sum X_i)^2},$$

$$\lambda_2 = \frac{2n\sigma^2}{n(\sum X_i^2) - (\sum X_i)^2}.$$

These expressions for λ_1 and λ_2 can be substituted into (7.19) to obtain the solution for $a_1, a_2, \ldots, a_n$. This is

$$(7.22) \qquad a_i = \frac{-(\sum X_i) + nX_i}{n(\sum X_i^2) - (\sum X_i)^2} \qquad (i = 1, 2, \ldots, n).$$

These are then the constants that make $\hat{\beta}$ an unbiased estimator and minimize its variance.[6] Substituting for a_i into the formula for $\hat{\beta}$ given by (7.16) leads to

[6] It can be shown that the second-order conditions for the existence of a minimum are also fulfilled. For an elaboration see, e.g., Yamane, *op. cit.*, pp. 345–348.

$$\tilde{\beta} = \sum_i \left[\frac{-(\sum X_i) + nX_i}{n(\sum X_i^2) - (\sum X_i)^2} \right] Y_i = \sum_i \left[\frac{- Y_i(\sum X_i) + nX_i Y_i}{n(\sum X_i^2) - (\sum X_i)^2} \right]$$

$$= \frac{-(\sum Y_i)(\sum X_i) + n(\sum X_i Y_i)}{n(\sum X_i^2) - (\sum X_i)^2}.$$

This is precisely the same result as that obtained for the least squares estimator of β. By (7.12) we have

$$\tilde{\beta} = \hat{\beta} = \frac{\sum x_i' y_i'}{\sum x_i'^2},$$

utilizing the abbreviated notation of (7.12a).

The application of the BLUE principle leads not only to the derivation of the formula for the estimator in question, but also to the determination of its variance. The formula for the variance of $\tilde{\beta}$ given by (7.17) is

$$\text{Var}(\tilde{\beta}) = \sigma^2 \sum a_i^2.$$

To eliminate the term $\sum a_i^2$ we use the result given in (7.22). Multiplying both sides of (7.22) by a_i and summing over all observations we get

$$\sum a_i^2 = \frac{-(\sum X_i)(\sum a_i) + n(\sum a_i X_i)}{n(\sum X_i^2) - (\sum X_i)^2}.$$

But from the last two equations in (7.18b) we know that

$$\sum a_i = 0 \quad \text{and} \quad \sum a_i X_i = 1.$$

This means that, in fact,

$$\sum a_i^2 = \frac{n}{n(\sum x_i^2) - (\sum X_i)^2},$$

so that

(7.23) $$\text{Var}(\tilde{\beta}) = \frac{n\sigma^2}{n(\sum X_i^2) - (\sum X_i)^2} = \frac{\sigma^2}{\sum x_i'^2},$$

after using the result of (7.14). This then is the variance of the BLUE (and, equivalently, of the LSE) of β.[7]

Having obtained the BLUE of β we are left with the task of finding the BLUE

---

[7] It should be noted that $\tilde{\beta}$ is not, in general, a linear estimator of β *with the minimum mean square error*. The formula for the linear combination of sample observations that gives the minimum MSE is

$$\left(\frac{\beta^2}{(\sigma^2/\sum x_i'^2) + \beta^2} \right) \hat{\beta}.$$

While this expression does not qualify as an estimator (since it involves unknown parameters), it shows that—for β and σ^2 different from zero—the value of the linear minimum MSE estimator of β is less than $\hat{\beta}$ by some unknown amount.

of α, the intercept of the regression line. The derivation of this estimator—to be called $\tilde{\alpha}$—proceeds in exactly the same steps as the derivation of $\tilde{\beta}$ and, therefore, will not be presented here. As in the case of $\tilde{\beta}$, the process of determining the BLUE of α leads not only to the formula for the estimator itself, but also to the formula for its variance. The results are as follows:

$$(7.24) \qquad\qquad \tilde{\alpha} = \bar{Y} - \tilde{\beta}\bar{X},$$

$$(7.25) \qquad \operatorname{Var}(\tilde{\alpha}) = \frac{\sigma^2(\sum X_i^2)}{n(\sum x_i'^2)} = \frac{\sigma^2(\sum x_i'^2 + n\bar{X}^2)}{n(\sum x_i'^2)} = \sigma^2\left[\frac{1}{n} + \frac{\bar{X}^2}{\sum x_i'^2}\right].$$

By noting that $\tilde{\beta}$ and $\hat{\beta}$ are the same, and by comparing (7.24) with (7.15), we can see that the BLUE of α is the same as the least squares estimator of α. The interpretation of the formula for its variance will be discussed in the next section.

Maximum Likelihood Estimation

The last method to be applied is the *maximum likelihood method*. As explained in Section 6–2, the maximum likelihood estimators (MLE's) of the parameters of a given population are considered to be those values of the parameters which would generate the observed sample most often. To find these estimators we have to determine the likelihood function for the observations in the sample and then maximize it with respect to the unknown parameters. In the case of our regression model, the sample consists of observations on the n variables Y_1, $Y_2, \ldots Y_n$. These variables are normally distributed with means $(\alpha + \beta X_1)$, $(\alpha + \beta X_2), \ldots, (\alpha + \beta X_n)$ and with a common variance equal to σ^2. Let us denote these observations by $y_1, y_2, \ldots, y_n$. Then the likelihood function is

$$\ell = f(y_1, y_2, \ldots, y_n).$$

We shall now establish that the observations are mutually independent (in the probability sense) so that their joint probability distribution can be expressed as a product of individual (marginal) distributions.

We may start by pointing out that if the disturbances of the regression model are normally distributed, nonautoregressive, and have zero mean, they must be independent. Thus our only problem is to show that the mutual independence of the disturbances implies mutual independence of the Y's. This can be established with the help of the following theorem.

Theorem 18 (*Change of Variable*). *If a random variable X has a probability density $f(x)$, and if a variable Z is a function of X such that there is a one-to-one correspondence between X and Z, then the probability density of Z is $f(z) = |dx/dz| f(x)$, $dx/dz \neq 0$.*

Here $|dx/dz|$ stands for the absolute value of the derivative of x with respect to z. The proof of this theorem can be found elsewhere.[8] Its importance lies in

---

[8] See, e.g., John E. Freund, *Mathematical Statistics* (Englewood Cliffs, N.J.: Prentice-Hall, 1962), pp. 132–133.

the fact that, under general conditions, it enables us to determine the distribution of one variable from the knowledge of the distribution of a related variable. In the context of our regression model the known distribution is that of ε_i, and the distribution to be determined is that of Y_i. Since we have

$$Y_i = \alpha + \beta X_i + \varepsilon_i,$$

there is obviously a one-to-one correspondence between Y_i and ε_i. Therefore, we can write

$$f(y_i) = \left|\frac{d\varepsilon_i}{dY_i}\right| f(\varepsilon_i).$$

But $\varepsilon_i = Y_i - \alpha - \beta X_i,$

so that $\dfrac{d\varepsilon_i}{dY_i} = 1.$

Consequently, we have

$$f(y_i) = f(\varepsilon_i).$$

Thus if the ε's are independent, the Y's must also be independent.

Armed with this result, we can present the likelihood function as

$$\ell = f(y_1)f(y_2)\ldots f(y_n).$$

Since the values of the parameters which maximize ℓ are the same as those which maximize its logarithm, we can operate with $L = \log \ell$ instead of operating with ℓ itself. Thus we wish to maximize

$$L = \sum_{i=1}^{n} \log f(y_i).$$

Now, since Y_i is normally distributed with mean $(\alpha + \beta X_i)$ and variance σ^2 we have, from the formula for normal distribution,

$$\log f(y_i) = -\frac{1}{2}\log(2\pi\sigma^2) - \frac{1}{2}\left[\frac{Y_i - \alpha - \beta X_i}{\sigma}\right]^2,$$

where $\pi = 3.14159\ldots$. (In writing out the formula, we use a capital letter for the values of the variables Y_i and X_i in order to conform to the notation customarily used in a simple regression model in other texts.) Therefore,

(7.26) $$L = -\frac{n}{2}\log(2\pi) - \frac{n}{2}\log\sigma^2 - \frac{1}{2\sigma^2}\sum_i (Y_i - \alpha - \beta X_i)^2.$$

There are three unknown parameters in L, namely, α, β, and σ^2. Differentiating with respect to each of them, we obtain

$$\frac{\partial L}{\partial \alpha} = -\frac{1}{2\sigma^2}\sum_i 2(Y_i - \alpha - \beta X_i)(-1),$$

$$\frac{\partial L}{\partial \beta^2} = -\frac{1}{2\sigma^2}\sum_i 2(Y_i - \alpha - \beta X_i)(-X_i),$$

$$\frac{\partial L}{\partial \sigma^2} = -\frac{n}{2\sigma^2} + \frac{1}{2\sigma^4}\sum_i (Y_i - \alpha - \beta X_i)^2.$$

Equating these to zero and putting a "triangle" on the parameters to be estimated leads to

$$\frac{1}{2\hat{\sigma}^2} \sum_i (Y_i - \hat{\alpha} - \hat{\beta}X_i) = 0,$$

$$\frac{1}{2\hat{\sigma}^2} \sum_i X_i(Y_i - \hat{\alpha} - \hat{\beta}X_i) = 0,$$

$$-\frac{n}{2\hat{\sigma}^2} + \frac{1}{2\hat{\sigma}^4} \sum_i (Y_i - \hat{\alpha} - \hat{\beta}X_i)^2 = 0.$$

A simple manipulation of the first two equations gives

$$\sum Y_i = \hat{\alpha}n + \hat{\beta}(\sum X_i),$$

$$\sum X_i Y_i = \hat{\alpha}(\sum X_i) + \hat{\beta}(\sum X_i^2).$$

These equations are precisely the same as the least squares normal equations given by (7.10) and (7.11) above. This means that *the maximum likelihood estimators of α and β are the same as the least squares estimators.* The third equation gives the maximum likelihood estimator of σ^2, which is

(7.27)
$$\hat{\sigma}^2 = \frac{1}{n} \sum_i (Y_i - \hat{\alpha} - \hat{\beta}X_i)^2;$$

or, since $\hat{\alpha}$ and $\hat{\beta}$ are equal to the least squares estimators,

(7.27a)
$$\hat{\sigma}^2 = \frac{1}{n} \sum_i e_i^2,$$

where, in accordance with the earlier notation, the terms e_i represent least squares residuals. Since $\sum e_i = 0$, it follows from (7.27a) that the MLE of the variance of the disturbances is equal to the sample variance of the least squares residuals.

Conclusion

In summary, we find then that each of the three estimation methods leads to the same estimates of the regression parameters. In other words, under the assumption of the classical normal linear regression model, the least squares estimators of the regression parameters are equivalent to the best linear unbiased and the maximum likelihood estimators. However, while the least squares method provided us only with the formulas for the estimators of α and β, the BLU estimation method supplied us also with the formulas for their variances, and the ML estimation method gave us a formula for an estimator of σ^2. Both of these subsidiary results are very useful.

Let us now consider the properties of the least squares estimators of α and β.

Beginning with the finite sample properties, we see immediately that the least squares estimators are *unbiased* because they are BLUE. We can also show that they are *efficient*. The Cramer-Rao lower bounds for unbiased estimators of α and β are given by the first two diagonal elements of the following matrix:

$$
\begin{bmatrix}
-E\left(\dfrac{\partial^2 L}{\partial \alpha^2}\right) & -E\left(\dfrac{\partial^2 L}{\partial \alpha \partial \beta}\right) & -E\left(\dfrac{\partial^2 L}{\partial \alpha \partial \sigma^2}\right) \\[2mm]
-E\left(\dfrac{\partial^2 L}{\partial \beta \partial \alpha}\right) & -E\left(\dfrac{\partial^2 L}{\partial \beta^2}\right) & -E\left(\dfrac{\partial^2 L}{\partial \beta \partial \sigma^2}\right) \\[2mm]
-E\left(\dfrac{\partial^2 L}{\partial \sigma^2 \partial \alpha}\right) & -E\left(\dfrac{\partial^2 L}{\partial \sigma^2 \partial \beta}\right) & -E\left(\dfrac{\partial^2 L}{\partial (\sigma^2)^2}\right)
\end{bmatrix}^{-1}
=
\begin{bmatrix}
\dfrac{n}{\sigma^2} & \dfrac{\sum X_i}{\sigma^2} & 0 \\[2mm]
\dfrac{\sum X_i}{\sigma^2} & \dfrac{\sum X_i^2}{\sigma^2} & 0 \\[2mm]
0 & 0 & \dfrac{n}{2\sigma^4}
\end{bmatrix}^{-1}
$$

$$
=
\begin{bmatrix}
\dfrac{\sigma^2 \sum X_i^2}{n(\sum x_i'^2)} & \dfrac{-\bar{X}\sigma^2}{\sum x_i'^2} & 0 \\[2mm]
\dfrac{-\bar{X}\sigma^2}{\sum x_i'^2} & \dfrac{\sigma^2}{\sum x_i'^2} & 0 \\[2mm]
0 & 0 & \dfrac{2\sigma^4}{n}
\end{bmatrix}
$$

Comparison of the first two diagonal elements with the formulas (7.25) and (7.23) of the text shows that these elements are, indeed, equal to the variances of the regression parameters.

Finally, the least squares estimators have all the desirable asymptotic properties since they are the same as the maximum likelihood estimators, and the latter are known to be *asymptotically unbiased, consistent*, and *asymptotically efficient*. Therefore, the least squares estimators of the regression parameters of the classical normal linear regression model have all the desirable finite sample *and* asymptotic properties. In Section 7–4 we shall be concerned with other features of these estimators and discuss further questions of statistical inference in the context of our regression model.

7–4 Further Results of Statistical Inference

In Section 7–3 we derived the least squares estimators of the regression parameters and established their desirable properties. We shall now consider other features of these estimators, and show how the regression model can be used for testing hypotheses about the regression parameters and for prediction.

Distribution of $\hat{\alpha}$ and $\hat{\beta}$

The distribution of the least squares estimators $\hat{\alpha}$ and $\hat{\beta}$ is easy to deduce from the results so far obtained. First, since these estimators are unbiased, their means are equal to the true values of α and β, respectively. Second, from the derivation of the BLUE properties we know what their variances are. Finally, since both $\hat{\alpha}$ and $\hat{\beta}$ are linear combinations of independent normal variables $Y_1, Y_2, \ldots, Y_n$, they must themselves be normally distributed (see Theorem 12). That is, we can write

$$\hat{\alpha} \sim N\left[\alpha, \sigma^2\left(\frac{1}{n} + \frac{\bar{X}^2}{\sum x_i'^2}\right)\right]$$

(7.28)

$$\hat{\beta} \sim N\left[\beta, \frac{\sigma^2}{\sum x_i'^2}\right],$$

using the variance formulas (7.23) and (7.25).

Let us now consider the variances of $\hat{\alpha}$ and $\hat{\beta}$ in greater detail. By examining the formulas we can observe the following:

1. The larger the variance of the disturbance (σ^2), the larger the variances of $\hat{\alpha}$ and $\hat{\beta}$.
2. The more dispersed the values of the explanatory variable X, the smaller the variances of $\hat{\alpha}$ and $\hat{\beta}$.
3. If all the values of X were the same, i.e., if $X_1 = X_2 = \cdots = X_n$, both variances would be infinitely large.
4. The variance of $\hat{\alpha}$ is smallest when $\bar{X} = 0$ ($\sum x_i'^2 \neq 0$).

The first point is obvious; it means that the greater the dispersion of the disturbance around the population regression line, the greater the dispersion of our "guesses" concerning the value of the regression parameters. If all disturbances were completely concentrated at their means—that is, if all disturbances were equal to zero—our "guesses" as to the values of the regression parameters would always be perfect (as long as we observed at least two different values of the dependent variable, of course). The second point is based on the fact that the larger the dispersion of the X's, the larger $\sum x_i'^2$. In fact, if we have an absolutely free choice of selecting a given number of values of X within some interval—say, from a to b ($0 < a < b$)—then *the optimal choice would be to choose one half of the X's equal to a and the other half equal to b*. Such a choice would maximize $\sum x_i'^2$. The third point follows from the fact that if all values of the explanatory variable were the same, the value of $\sum x_i'^2$ would be zero, and any finite number divided by zero is equal to infinity. Another way of making the same point is to state that if all observed values of Y were to lie along a vertical line (as they would do if they all corresponded to the same value of X), we could not make any inference about either the slope or the intercept of the regression line. The final point is somewhat less important in practice since it refers only to the variance of $\hat{\alpha}$. If the range of X includes negative as well as positive values, $\text{Var}(\hat{\alpha})$ would be smallest if the values of X were selected so as to make $\bar{X}$ equal to zero. In this case $\text{Var}(\hat{\alpha})$ would be equal to σ^2/n, which is its lowest attainable value.

EXAMPLE   To illustrate the gain in efficiency that can be achieved by a judicious choice of the values of the explanatory variable, we use the example given in Section 7.3, which involved estimating the demand for oranges. The values of X ($=$ price of oranges) were given as follows: 100, 90, 80, 70, 70, 70, 70, 65, 60, 60, 55, and 50. For these twelve values we found that $\bar{X} = 70$ and $\sum x_i'^2 = 2250$. The variances of the least squares estimators in this case are

$$\text{Var}(\hat{\alpha}) = \sigma^2 \left[\frac{1}{n} + \frac{\bar{X}^2}{\sum x_i'^2} \right] = \sigma^2 \left[\frac{1}{12} + \frac{70^2}{2250} \right] = 2.261111\sigma^2.$$

$$\text{Var}(\hat{\beta}) = \frac{\sigma^2}{\sum x_i'^2} = \frac{\sigma^2}{2250} = 0.000444\sigma^2.$$

Suppose now that instead of the above values we had $X_1 = X_2 = \cdots = X_6 = 100$ and $X_6 = X_7 = \cdots = X_{12} = 50$. Then we would have $\bar{X} = 75$ and $\sum x_i'^2 = 7500$. The resulting variances would then be

$$\text{Var}(\hat{\alpha}) = \sigma^2 \left[\frac{1}{12} + \frac{75^2}{7500} \right] = 0.833333\sigma^2.$$

$$\text{Var}(\hat{\beta}) = \frac{\sigma^2}{7500} = 0.000133.$$

Comparing the variances for these two cases we get

$$\frac{\text{Var}(\hat{\alpha})_{\text{case I}}}{\text{Var}(\hat{\alpha})_{\text{case II}}} = \frac{2.261111\sigma^2}{0.833333\sigma^2} = 2.713.$$

$$\frac{\text{Var}(\hat{\beta})_{\text{case I}}}{\text{Var}(\hat{\beta})_{\text{case II}}} = \frac{0.000444\sigma^2}{0.000133\sigma^2} = 3.338.$$

That is, the variance of $\hat{\alpha}$ in the first case is more than $2\frac{1}{2}$ times, and that of $\hat{\beta}$ $3\frac{1}{3}$ times, as large as the corresponding variance in the second case.

It is clear that the gain in efficiency resulting from an optimal choice of the values of X can be quite considerable. In practice the difficulty is, of course, that the econometrician usually has no choice in the matter because the sampling has been done by somebody else and the econometrician gets only the completed sample results.[9]

Covariance of $\hat{\alpha}$ and $\hat{\beta}$

A question that is of some interest concerns the relationship between $\hat{\alpha}$ and $\hat{\beta}$. By using $\hat{\alpha}$ instead of α and $\hat{\beta}$ instead of β, we are committing sampling errors, and it is of some relevance to know whether these two sampling errors can be expected to be of the same sign or not. That is, we wish to find the sign of

$$E(\hat{\alpha} - \alpha)(\hat{\beta} - \beta),$$

which is, by definition, the covariance of $\hat{\alpha}$ and $\hat{\beta}$. Now, by (7.15) we have

$$\hat{\alpha} = \bar{Y} - \hat{\beta}\bar{X}.$$

[9] It is to be noted, though, that the optimality of the sampling design which "piles up" the values of X at each end of the range is crucially dependent on the linearity of the model. Such a sampling design would be poor for models in which linearity were not to be assumed but to be tested for.

The regression model is, as stated earlier,

$$Y_i = \alpha + \beta X_i + \varepsilon_i.$$

Adding all sample observations and dividing by n we get

(7.29) $$\bar{Y} = \alpha + \beta \bar{X} + \bar{\varepsilon} \quad \text{or} \quad \alpha = \bar{Y} - \beta \bar{X} - \bar{\varepsilon},$$

so that

(7.30) $$\hat{\alpha} - \alpha = (\bar{Y} - \hat{\beta}\bar{X}) - (\bar{Y} - \beta\bar{X} - \bar{\varepsilon}) = -(\hat{\beta} - \beta)\bar{X} + \bar{\varepsilon}.$$

Further, by (7.12a) we have

$$\hat{\beta} = \frac{\sum x_i' y_i'}{\sum x_i'^2};$$

but by deducting (7.29) from (7.1), we get

(7.31) $$(Y_i - \bar{Y}) = \beta(X_i - \bar{X}) + (\varepsilon_i - \bar{\varepsilon}),$$

or, using the abbreviated notation for deviations from sample means,

(7.31a) $$y_i' = \beta x_i' + \varepsilon_i'.$$

Substituting this into the formula for $\hat{\beta}$ gives

$$\hat{\beta} = \frac{\sum x_i'(\beta x_i' + \varepsilon_i')}{\sum x_i'^2} = \beta + \frac{\sum x_i' \varepsilon_i'}{\sum x_i'^2},$$

so that

(7.32) $$\hat{\beta} - \beta = \frac{\sum x_i' \varepsilon_i'}{\sum x_i'^2} = \frac{\sum x_i'(\varepsilon_i - \bar{\varepsilon})}{\sum x_i'^2}$$

$$= \frac{\sum x_i' \varepsilon_i - \bar{\varepsilon} \sum x_i'}{\sum x_i'^2} = \frac{\sum x_i' \varepsilon_i}{\sum x_i'^2},$$

which is the sampling error of $\hat{\beta}$. Thus, combining (7.30) and (7.32), we obtain

$$E(\hat{\alpha} - \alpha)(\hat{\beta} - \beta) = E[-(\hat{\beta} - \beta)\bar{X} + \bar{\varepsilon}](\hat{\beta} - \beta)$$

$$= -\bar{X}E(\hat{\beta} - \beta)^2 + E\bar{\varepsilon}\left[\frac{\sum x_i' \varepsilon_i}{\sum x_i'^2}\right].$$

Let us consider the last term:

$$E\bar{\varepsilon}\left[\frac{\sum x_i' \varepsilon_i}{\sum x_i'^2}\right] = E\left[\frac{\sum x_i' \varepsilon_i \bar{\varepsilon}}{\sum x_i'^2}\right] = \frac{\sum x_i' E\varepsilon_i(1/n)(\varepsilon_1 + \varepsilon_2 + \cdots + \varepsilon_i + \cdots + \varepsilon_n)}{\sum x_i'^2}$$

$$= \frac{(1/n) \sum x_i'(E\varepsilon_i\varepsilon_1 + E\varepsilon_i\varepsilon_2 + \cdots + E\varepsilon_i^2 + \cdots + E\varepsilon_i\varepsilon_n)}{\sum x_i'^2}$$

$$= \frac{(1/n) \sum x_i'(0 + 0 + \cdots + \sigma^2 + \cdots + 0)}{\sum x_i'^2} = \frac{(1/n)\sigma^2 \sum x_i'}{\sum x_i'^2} = 0$$

because $\sum x_i' = 0$. Therefore,

$$(7.33) \quad E(\hat{\alpha} - \alpha)(\hat{\beta} - \beta) = -\bar{X}E(\hat{\beta} - \beta)^2 = -\bar{X}\mathrm{Var}(\hat{\beta}) = -\bar{X}\left[\frac{\sigma^2}{\sum x_i'^2}\right],$$

by (7.23). This, then, is the covariance of $\hat{\alpha}$ and $\hat{\beta}$. From this result we can see that, *as long as $\bar{X}$ is positive*, the sampling errors of $\hat{\alpha}$ and $\hat{\beta}$ can be expected to be of opposite sign. In this case an overstatement of the true value of α can be expected to be associated with an understatement of the true value of β, and vice versa.

Method of Semi-averages

As a matter of interest we may compare the sample regression line fitted by the method of least squares with that fitted by some other method. One such method which has been used in practical applications is the so-called *method of semi-averages*. This method calls for arranging the observations so that the values of X proceed in order of magnitude, dividing them into two equal (or approximately equal) parts, and calculating the average values of X and Y for each part separately. This gives us two points, one for each part. The estimated regression line is the line passing through these two points. For simplicity, we assume that the number of observations is even. Let $\bar{X}_A$ and $\bar{Y}_A$ be the sample means of the first $n/2$ values of X and Y, and $\bar{X}_B$ and $\bar{Y}_B$ the sample means of the last $n/2$ values of X and Y. Further, let a and b be the "semi-average" estimators of α and β, respectively. Then a and b can be calculated from

$$\bar{Y}_A = a + b\bar{X}_A$$
$$\bar{Y}_B = a + b\bar{X}_B,$$

since the estimated regression line is required to pass through the points $(\bar{X}_a, \bar{Y}_A)$ and $(\bar{X}_B, \bar{Y}_B)$. The solution is

$$b = \frac{\bar{Y}_A - \bar{Y}_B}{\bar{X}_A - \bar{X}_B} \quad \text{and} \quad a = \bar{Y}_a - b\bar{X}_A.$$

Let us find the mean and the variance of b. Since

$$Y_i = \alpha + \beta X_i + \varepsilon_i,$$

we have

$$\bar{Y}_A = \alpha + \beta\bar{X}_A + \bar{\varepsilon}_A,$$
$$\bar{Y}_B = \alpha + \beta\bar{X}_B + \bar{\varepsilon}_B,$$

where $\bar{\varepsilon}_A$ and $\bar{\varepsilon}_B$ are the (unobserved) sample means of the regression disturbance for the first and the second half of the observations, respectively. Therefore,

$$\bar{Y}_A - \bar{Y}_B = \beta(\bar{X}_A - \bar{X}_B) + (\bar{\varepsilon}_A - \bar{\varepsilon}_B).$$

Then, we get

$$E(b) = E\left[\frac{\bar{Y}_A - \bar{Y}_B}{\bar{X}_A - \bar{X}_B}\right] = \frac{E[\beta(\bar{X}_A - \bar{X}_B) + (\bar{\varepsilon}_A - \bar{\varepsilon}_B)]}{\bar{X}_A - \bar{X}_B} = \frac{\beta(\bar{X}_A - \bar{X}_B)}{\bar{X}_A - \bar{X}_B} = \beta,$$

so that b is an unbiased estimator of β. Further,

$$\text{Var}(b) = E\left[\frac{\bar{Y}_A - \bar{Y}_B}{\bar{X}_A - \bar{X}_B} - E\left(\frac{\bar{Y}_A - \bar{Y}_B}{\bar{X}_A - \bar{Y}_B}\right)\right]^2 = E\left[\frac{\beta(\bar{X}_A - \bar{X}_B) + (\bar{\varepsilon}_A - \bar{\varepsilon}_B)}{\bar{X}_A - \bar{X}_B} - \beta\right]^2$$

$$= E\left[\frac{\bar{\varepsilon}_A - \bar{\varepsilon}_B}{\bar{X}_A - \bar{X}_B}\right]^2 = \frac{E(\bar{\varepsilon}_A) + E(\bar{\varepsilon}_B)^2 - 2E(\bar{\varepsilon}_A\bar{\varepsilon}_B)}{(\bar{X}_A - \bar{X}_B)^2}.$$

But by the basic assumptions about ε_i we have

$$E(\bar{\varepsilon}_A)^2 = E\left[\frac{1}{n/2}(\varepsilon_1 + \varepsilon_2 + \cdots + \varepsilon_{n/2})\right]^2$$

$$= \left[\frac{1}{n/2}\right]^2\left[E(\varepsilon_1^2) + E(\varepsilon_2^2) + \cdots + E(\varepsilon_{n/2}^2)\right]$$

$$= \left[\frac{1}{n/2}\right]^2(\sigma^2 + \sigma^2 + \cdots + \sigma^2) = \left[\frac{1}{n/2}\right]^2(n/2)\sigma^2 = \frac{\sigma^2}{n/2},$$

and, similarly, $$E(\bar{\varepsilon}_B)^2 = \frac{\sigma^2}{n/2}.$$

Finally,

$$E(\bar{\varepsilon}_A\bar{\varepsilon}_B) = E\left[\frac{1}{n/2}(\varepsilon_1 + \varepsilon_2 + \cdots + \varepsilon_{n/2})\right]\left[\frac{1}{n/2}(\varepsilon_{n/2+1} + \varepsilon_{n/2+2} + \cdots + \varepsilon_n)\right] = 0,$$

by the assumption of nonautoregression. Therefore, we get

$$\text{Var}(b) = \frac{\sigma^2/(n/2) + \sigma^2/(n/2)}{(\bar{X}_A - \bar{X}_B)^2} = \frac{4\sigma^2}{n(\bar{X}_A - \bar{X}_B)^2}.$$

We have, of course,

$$\text{Var}(b) \geq \text{Var}(\hat{\beta}),$$

where $\hat{\beta}$ is the least squares estimator of β.

EXAMPLE   We shall demonstrate the advantage of the least squares method over the method of semi-averages by using the example of the demand for oranges. There are 12 observations which can be divided into two groups with 6 observations in each. The results are

$$\bar{X}_A = 60 \qquad \bar{Y}_A = 115$$
$$\bar{X}_B = 80 \qquad \bar{Y}_B = 85$$

This gives

$$b = \frac{115 - 85}{60 - 80} = -1.5$$

$$a = 115 - (-1.5) \times 60 = 205.$$

The regression line estimated by the method of semi-averages then is

$$\hat{Y}_i = 205 - 1.5X_i.$$

The variance of b is

$$\text{Var}(b) = \frac{4\sigma^2}{12(60-80)^2} = \frac{\sigma^2}{1200}.$$

Comparing $\text{Var}(b)$ with $\text{Var}(\hat{\beta})$ we get

$$\frac{\text{Var}(b)}{\text{Var}(\hat{\beta})} = \frac{\sigma^2/1200}{\sigma^2/2250} = 1.875.$$

Thus we see that the method of semi-averages leads to an estimate of the regression slope with variance 87.5% larger than the variance of the corresponding least squares estimate. In other words, if our "guesses" about the slope of the population regression line in the present instance were formed by using the method of semi-averages, they would be considerably more dispersed about the true value than the "guesses" based on the least squares formula.

Estimation of $\text{Var}(\hat{\alpha})$ and $\text{Var}(\hat{\beta})$

Under the assumptions of the classical normal linear regression model, the least squares estimators of α and β have all the desirable properties of an estimator. But whether or not they are really useful depends on the size of their variances. If their variances were to be very large, the fact that no other unbiased estimator can have a smaller variance is of little consolation. With large variances our guesses about the true values of the parameters are likely to be far off the mark. In Section 7–3 we developed formulas for the variances of $\hat{\alpha}$ and $\hat{\beta}$, but these formulas involve an unknown parameter σ^2 so that their evaluation is impossible. However, σ^2 can be estimated; in fact, we have already derived an estimation formula for it in connection with the maximum likelihood estimators in Section 7–3 above. The estimator of σ^2 was a "by-product" of getting the maximum likelihood estimators of α and β. The formula, given by (7.27), is

$$\hat{\sigma}^2 = \frac{1}{n}\sum_i (Y_i - \hat{\alpha} - \hat{\beta}X_i)^2.$$

Since this is a maximum likelihood estimator of σ^2, it has all the desirable asymptotic properties, but its small sample properties remain to be established. In particular, we may want to check whether $\hat{\sigma}^2$ is or is not an unbiased estimator of σ^2. To do this we rewrite the expression for $\hat{\sigma}^2$ in a somewhat different form. First, substituting for Y_i gives

$$\hat{\sigma}^2 = \frac{1}{n}\sum (\alpha + \beta X_i + \varepsilon_i - \hat{\alpha} - \hat{\beta}X_i)^2 = \frac{1}{n}\sum [-(\hat{\alpha}-\alpha) - (\hat{\beta}-\beta)X_i + \varepsilon_i]^2.$$

Next, substituting for $(\hat{\alpha} - \alpha)$ from (7.30) we get

$$\hat{\sigma}^2 = \frac{1}{n} \sum [(\hat{\beta} - \beta)\bar{X} - \bar{\varepsilon} - (\hat{\beta} - \beta)X_i + \varepsilon_i]^2$$

$$= \frac{1}{n} \sum [-(\hat{\beta} - \beta)x_i' + \varepsilon_i']^2$$

$$= \frac{1}{n} \sum [(\hat{\beta} - \beta)^2 x_i'^2 + \varepsilon_i'^2 - 2(\hat{\beta} - \beta)\,\varepsilon_i' x_i']$$

$$= \frac{1}{n}(\hat{\beta} - \beta)^2 \sum x_i'^2 + \frac{1}{n} \sum \varepsilon_i'^2 - \frac{2}{n}(\hat{\beta} - \beta) \sum \varepsilon_i' x_i'.$$

But from (7.32) we have

$$\sum x_i' \varepsilon_i' = (\hat{\beta} - \beta) \sum x_i'^2,$$

so that we can write

$$\hat{\sigma}^2 = -\frac{1}{n}(\hat{\beta} - \beta)^2 \sum x_i'^2 + \frac{1}{n} \sum \varepsilon_i'^2.$$

Taking mathematical expectation of both sides, we obtain

$$E(\hat{\sigma}^2) = -\frac{1}{n} \sum x_i'^2 E(\hat{\beta} - \beta)^2 + \frac{1}{n} \sum E(\varepsilon_i'^2).$$

Now
$$E(\hat{\beta} - \beta)^2 = \mathrm{Var}(\hat{\beta}) = \frac{\sigma^2}{\sum x_i'^2},$$

and

$$E(\varepsilon_i'^2) = E(\varepsilon_i - \bar{\varepsilon})^2 = E(\varepsilon_i^2) + E(\bar{\varepsilon}^2) - 2E(\varepsilon_i \bar{\varepsilon})$$

$$= \sigma^2 + \frac{\sigma^2}{n} - 2E\varepsilon_i(\varepsilon_1 + \varepsilon_2 + \cdots + \varepsilon_i + \cdots + \varepsilon_n)/n$$

$$= \sigma^2 + \frac{\sigma^2}{n} - 2[E(\varepsilon_i \varepsilon_1) + E(\varepsilon_i \varepsilon_2) + \cdots + E(\varepsilon_i^2) + \cdots + E(\varepsilon_i \varepsilon_n)]/n$$

$$= \sigma^2 + \frac{\sigma^2}{n} - 2(0 + 0 + \cdots + \sigma^2 + \cdots + 0)/n$$

$$= \sigma^2 + \frac{\sigma^2}{n} - \frac{2\sigma^2}{n} = \left[\frac{n-1}{n}\right]\sigma^2.$$

We use these results to get

(7.34) $$E(\hat{\sigma}^2) = -\frac{1}{n}\left(\sum x_i'^2\right)\left[\frac{\sigma^2}{\sum x_i'^2}\right] + \frac{1}{n}\sum\left[\frac{n-1}{n}\right]\sigma^2$$

$$= -\frac{\sigma^2}{n} + \left[\frac{n-1}{n}\right]\sigma^2 = \left[\frac{n-2}{n}\right]\sigma^2.$$

That is, $\hat{\sigma}^2$ is a *biased* estimator of σ^2. However, given the result in (7.34) it is easy to devise an unbiased estimator of σ^2. Multiplying both sides of (7.34) by $n/(n-2)$ gives

$$\left[\frac{n}{n-2}\right] E(\hat{\sigma}^2) = \sigma^2,$$

or

$$E\left[\frac{n}{n-2}\right]\frac{1}{n}\sum(Y_i - \hat{\alpha} - \hat{\beta}X_i)^2 = \sigma^2,$$

which reduces to

$$E\left[\frac{1}{n-2}\right]\sum(Y_i\,\hat{\alpha} - \hat{\beta}X_i)^2 = \sigma^2.$$

Thus an unbiased estimator of σ^2, say, s^2, is given by

(7.35) $$s^2 = \frac{1}{n-2}\sum(Y_i - \hat{\alpha} - \hat{\beta}X_i)^2 = \frac{1}{n-2}\sum e_i^2.$$

Since asymptotically there is no difference between $1/(n-2)$ and $1/n$, s^2 is asymptotically equal to $\hat{\sigma}^2$ and, therefore, has the same optimal asymptotic properties.

For the purpose of computing the value of s^2, the formula (7.35) can be simplified so that we avoid the need for calculating individual e_i''s, the deviations of the observed values from the sample regression line. By substituting for $\hat{\alpha}$ we obtain

$$s^2 = \frac{1}{n-2}\sum[Y_i - (\bar{Y} - \hat{\beta}\bar{X}) - \hat{\beta}X_i]^2 = \frac{1}{n-2}\sum(y_i' - \hat{\beta}x_i')^2$$

$$= \frac{1}{n-2}\left[\sum y_i'^2 + \hat{\beta}^2\sum x_i'^2 - 2\hat{\beta}\sum x_i'y_i'\right];$$

but from (7.12a) we have

$$\hat{\beta}\sum x_i'^2 = \sum x_i'y_i',$$

so that

$$\hat{\beta}^2\sum x_i'^2 = \hat{\beta}\sum x_i'y_i'.$$

Using this result leads to

(7.36) $$s^2 = \frac{1}{n-2}\left[\sum y_i'^2 - \hat{\beta}\sum x_i'y_i'\right],$$

which is much easier to compute than the result given by (7.35).

By using s^2 as the estimator of σ^2, we can obtain estimators of $\text{Var}(\hat{\alpha})$ and $\text{Var}(\hat{\beta})$; these estimators will be unbiased and will have optimal asymptotic properties. Following the customary notation, we denote the estimator of $\mathrm{Var}(\hat{\alpha})$ by $s_{\hat{\alpha}}^2$ and the estimator of $\mathrm{Var}(\hat{\beta})$ by $s_{\hat{\beta}}^2$. The appropriate formulas are

(7.37)

$$s_{\hat{\alpha}}^2 = s^2 \left[\frac{1}{n} + \frac{\bar{X}^2}{\sum x_i'^2} \right]$$

$$s_{\hat{\beta}}^2 = \frac{s^2}{\sum x_i'^2}.$$

The square roots of these estimators, $s_{\hat{\alpha}}$ and $s_{\hat{\beta}}$, represent the estimated standard errors of $\hat{\alpha}$ and $\hat{\beta}$. They are used extensively as measures of precision of $\hat{\alpha}$ and $\hat{\beta}$. (In referring to $s_{\hat{\alpha}}$ and $s_{\hat{\beta}}$ research workers frequently use the term "standard errors" instead of "estimated standard errors." Since the true standard errors are hardly ever known, the omission of the word "estimated" usually creates no confusion.)

Confidence Intervals for α and β

A more formal indication of the precision of $\hat{\alpha}$ and $\hat{\beta}$ can be achieved by constructing the confidence intervals for α and β. Let us begin with β. Since

$$\hat{\beta} \sim N(\beta, \sigma_{\hat{\beta}}^2),$$

where $\sigma_{\hat{\beta}}^2 = \mathrm{Var}(\hat{\beta})$, it follows that

$$\frac{\hat{\beta} - \beta}{\sigma_{\hat{\beta}}} \sim N(0, 1).$$

Furthermore, we know from (5.8b) that

$$\frac{\sum (Y_i - \hat{\alpha} - \hat{\beta} x_i)^2}{\sigma^2} \sim \chi_{n-2}^2.$$

In this case the number of the degrees of freedom of the chi-square distribution is $(n - 2)$, since two degrees of freedom got "used up" for calculating $\hat{\alpha}$ and $\hat{\beta}$. Note that we can write

$$\frac{\sum (Y_i - \hat{\alpha} - \hat{\beta} X_i)^2}{\sigma^2} = \frac{(n-2)s^2}{\sigma^2} = \frac{(n-2)s^2/(\sum x_i'^2)}{\sigma^2/(\sum x_i'^2)} = \frac{(n-2)s_{\hat{\beta}}^2}{\sigma_{\hat{\beta}}^2}.$$

Thus we have

$$\frac{(n-2)s_{\hat{\beta}}^2}{\sigma_{\hat{\beta}}^2} \sim \chi_{n-2}^2.$$

Therefore,

$$\frac{(\hat{\beta} - \beta)/\sigma_{\hat{\beta}}}{\sqrt{(n-2)s_{\hat{\beta}}^2/(n-2)\sigma_{\hat{\beta}}^2}} = \frac{\hat{\beta} - \beta}{s_{\hat{\beta}}}$$

is a ratio in which the numerator is a standard normal variable and the denominator an independent $[\chi^2_{n-2}/(n-2)]^{1/2}$ variable. As explained in Section 5–2,
such a ratio has a t distribution with $(n-2)$ degrees of freedom. That is,

$$(7.38) \qquad \frac{\hat{\beta} - \beta}{s_{\hat{\beta}}} \sim t_{n-2}.$$

By a similar deduction we also get

$$(7.39) \qquad \frac{\hat{\alpha} - \alpha}{s_{\hat{\alpha}}} \sim t_{n-2}.$$

These results enable us to make the following probability statements:

$$P\left[-t_{n-2,\,\lambda/2} \leq \frac{\hat{\alpha} - \alpha}{s_{\hat{\alpha}}} \leq +t_{n-2,\,\lambda/2}\right] = 1 - \lambda,$$

$$P\left[-t_{n-2,\,\lambda/2} \leq \frac{\hat{\beta} - \beta}{s_{\hat{\beta}}} \leq +t_{n-2,\,\lambda/2}\right] = 1 - \lambda,$$

where $t_{n-2,\,\lambda/2}$ stands for the value of the t statistic with $(n-2)$ degrees of freedom, which cuts off $\lambda/2$ of the area of the t distribution at each tail end. This
value can be looked up in the t table for whatever λ we desire. The term $(1-\lambda)$
represents the area of the distribution between the points $-t_{n-2,\,\lambda/2}$ and
$+t_{n-2,\,\lambda/2}$. From these probability statements we can construct the confidence
intervals for α and β as

$$\hat{\alpha} - t_{n-2,\,\lambda/2}s_{\hat{\alpha}} \leq \alpha \leq \hat{\alpha} + t_{n-2,\,\lambda/2}s_{\hat{\alpha}}$$

$$(7.40)$$

$$\hat{\beta} - t_{n-2,\,\lambda/2}s_{\hat{\beta}} \leq \beta \leq \hat{\beta} + t_{n-2,\,\lambda/2}s_{\hat{\beta}}.$$

The probability that the specified confidence interval covers the true value of the
regression parameter is $(1-\lambda)$. This is referred to as the "level of confidence."
As mentioned in Section 6–3, the most commonly used levels are 95% and 99%.

EXAMPLE   As a numerical example, let us construct the 95% confidence intervals
for α and β for the function describing the demand for oranges from the data given
in Section 7–3. To do that we have to calculate the estimates of the standard errors
of $\hat{\alpha}$ and $\hat{\beta}$ using the formulas (7.36) and (7.37). From the data given for this example,
we already calculated

$$\bar{X} = 70,$$

$$\bar{Y} = 100,$$

$$\sum x_i' y_i' = -3550,$$

$$\sum x_i'^2 = 2250,$$

which led to

$$\hat{\alpha} = 210.460,$$

$$= -1.578.$$

In addition we have

$$\sum y_i'^2 = 6300.$$

Substituting into (7.36) gives

$$s^2 = \frac{1}{12 - 2} [6300 - (-1.578)(-3550)] = 69.8.$$

Further substitution into (7.37) leads to

$$s_{\hat{\alpha}}^2 = 69.8\left[\frac{1}{12} + \frac{70^2}{2250}\right] = 157.825555$$

and

$$s_{\hat{\beta}}^2 = \frac{69.8}{2250} = 0.031022.$$

The resulting estimates of the standard errors of $\hat{\alpha}$ and $\hat{\beta}$ are

$$s_{\hat{\alpha}} = 12.563,$$

$$s_{\hat{\beta}} = 0.176.$$

The last piece of information needed for the construction of the confidence intervals is the appropriate t value. Since we had 12 observations, we have 10 degrees of freedom. Furthermore, since the desired level of confidence is 95%, we want to find the value of t that cuts off 0.025 of the area at the tail end of the distribution. Thus we look up the row labeled "10" and the column labeled "0.025" in the t table. The corresponding entry is 2.228. Therefore, the 95% confidence intervals for α and β are

$$210.460 - 2.228 \times 12.563 \le \alpha \le 210.460 + 2.228 \times 12.563$$

$$182.470 \le \alpha \le 238.450,$$

and

$$-1.578 - 2.228 \times 0.176 \le \beta \le -1.578 + 2.228 \times 0.176$$

$$-1.970 \le \beta \le -1.186.$$

Confidence Interval for $E(Y_i)$

We may extend the use of confidence intervals and consider the precision of the entire sample regression line as a representation of the population regression line. The population regression line is given by $E(Y_i) = \alpha + \beta X_i$ and is defined for *any* value of X_i within some range. Its estimator is the sample regression line $\hat{Y}_i = \hat{\alpha} + \hat{\beta} X_i$. Since $E(\hat{Y}_i) = \alpha + \beta X_i$, $\hat{Y}_i$ is an unbiased estimator of $E(Y_i)$. Other desirable properties of $\hat{Y}_i$ as an estimator of $E(Y_i)$ can also be established; heuristically, we may argue that since $\hat{\alpha}$ and $\hat{\beta}$ are the best estimators of α and β we can devise, $(\hat{\alpha} + \hat{\beta} X_i)$ is the best estimator of $(\alpha + \beta X_i)$. To determine the confidence interval for any given point on the population regression line $E(Y_i)$, we have to find the variance of its estimator $\hat{Y}_i$. Let us call this variance $\sigma_{\hat{Y}_i}^2$. It can be determined as follows:

$$\sigma_{\hat{Y}_i}^2 = E[\hat{Y}_i - E(\hat{Y}_i)]^2 = E[(\hat{\alpha} + \hat{\beta}X_i) - (\alpha + \beta X_i)]^2$$
$$= E[(\hat{\alpha} - \alpha) + (\hat{\beta} - \beta)X_i]^2$$
$$= E(\hat{\alpha} - \alpha)^2 + E(\hat{\beta} - \beta)^2 X_i^2 + 2E(\hat{\alpha} - \alpha)(\hat{\beta} - \beta)X_i$$
$$= \text{Var}(\hat{\alpha}) + X_i^2 \text{Var}(\hat{\beta}) + 2X_i \text{Cov}(\hat{\alpha}, \hat{\beta})$$
$$= \sigma^2 \left[\frac{1}{n} + \frac{\bar{X}^2}{\sum x_i'^2} \right] + X_i^2 \left[\frac{\sigma^2}{\sum x_i'^2} \right] - 2X_i \bar{X} \left[\frac{\sigma^2}{\sum x_i'^2} \right].$$

The last result has been obtained by substitution from (7.23), (7.25), and (7.33). Further manipulation gives

$$(7.41) \qquad \sigma_{\hat{Y}_i}^2 = \frac{\sigma^2}{\sum x_i'^2} \left[\frac{\sum x_i'^2}{n} + \bar{X}^2 + X_i^2 - 2X_i \bar{X} \right]$$
$$= \frac{\sigma^2}{\sum x_i'^2} \left[\frac{\sum x_i'^2}{n} + (X_i - \bar{X})^2 \right] = \sigma^2 \left[\frac{1}{n} + \frac{(X_i - \bar{X})^2}{\sum x_i'^2} \right].$$

Having determined the mean and the variance of $\hat{Y}_i$, we should consider its distribution. This turns out to be quite simple: since $(\hat{\alpha} + \hat{\beta}X_i)$ is a linear combination of normally and independently distributed random variables $\varepsilon_1, \varepsilon_2, \ldots,$ ε_n, it will also be normally distributed. Thus we have

$$\hat{Y}_i \sim N \left[\alpha + \beta X_i, \sigma^2 \left(\frac{1}{n} + \frac{(X - \bar{X})^2}{\sum x_i'^2} \right) \right];$$

and, therefore, $$\frac{\hat{Y}_i - (\alpha + \beta X_i)}{\sigma_{\hat{Y}_i}} \sim N(0,1).$$

In general, the expression for $\sigma_{\hat{Y}_i}^2$ given by (7.41) cannot be evaluated because it involves an unknown parameter σ^2. However, we can replace σ^2 by its unbiased, consistent, and asymptotically efficient estimator s^2 given by formula (7.35). This will lead to an estimator of $\sigma_{\hat{Y}_i}^2$, say $s_{\hat{Y}_i}^2$, which has the same desirable properties and which is defined as

$$(7.42) \qquad s_{\hat{Y}_i}^2 = s^2 \left[\frac{1}{n} + \frac{(X_i - \bar{X})^2}{\sum x_i'^2} \right].$$

Then we have $$\frac{\hat{Y}_i - (\alpha + \beta X_i)}{s_{\hat{Y}_i}^2} \sim t_{n-2},$$

and the confidence interval for $(\alpha + \beta X_i)$ will be

$$\hat{Y}_i - t_{n-2, \lambda/2} s_{\hat{Y}_i} \leq (\alpha + \beta X_i) \leq \hat{Y}_i + t_{n-2, \lambda/2} s_{\hat{Y}_i},$$

where $(1 - \lambda)$ is the chosen level of confidence. Since this confidence interval can be calculated for any value of X_i within the applicable domain, we can construct confidence intervals for *any* point on the population regression line. This enables us to construct a *confidence band* for the population regression line as a whole.

EXAMPLE   For an illustration we can use the example of Section 7–3 on the demand for oranges. We will construct the 95% confidence band for the population demand curve. We note that the estimated sample regression line was

$$\hat{Y}_i = 210.460 - 1.578 X_i.$$

The estimate of the variance of $\hat{Y}_i$ is

$$s_{\hat{Y}_i}^2 = 69.8 \left[\frac{1}{12} + \frac{(X_i - 70)^2}{2250} \right],$$

and the value of the t statistic is 2.228 as before. These are all the necessary ingredients for the calculation of the confidence band. Table 7–3 shows the results of these calculations. The last two columns represent the intervals that, we expect, will contain the corresponding population values. Note that the narrowest interval is the one

Table 7–3

				95% Confidence Interval	
X_i	$\hat{Y}_i$	$s_{\hat{Y}_i}$	$2.228 s_{\hat{Y}_i}$	Lower Limit	Upper Limit
0	210.46	12.57	28.01	182.45	238.47
10	194.66	10.84	24.15	170.51	218.81
20	178.88	9.14	20.36	158.52	199.24
30	163.10	7.45	16.60	146.50	179.70
40	147.32	5.81	12.94	134.38	160.26
50	131.54	4.27	9.51	122.03	141.05
60	115.76	2.98	6.64	109.12	122.40
70	99.98	2.41	5.37	94.61	105.35
80	84.20	2.98	6.64	77.56	90.84
90	68.42	4.27	9.51	58.91	77.93
100	52.64	5.81	12.94	39.70	65.58
110	36.86	7.45	16.60	20.26	53.46
120	21.08	9.14	20.36	0.72	41.44

that corresponds to $X_i = 70$, i.e., to $\bar{X}$. The intervals get wider as we move farther away from $\bar{X}$. By connecting the appropriate points we get the lower and the upper boundaries of the confidence band for the population regression line, as illustrated in Figure 7–4.

Decomposition of the Sample Variation of Y

Certain concepts connected with the problem of decomposing the sample variation of the values of the dependent variable[10] can be used to supplement

---

[10] By "variation of the dependent variable" we mean the changes in Y from one sample observation to another. This is to be distinguished from the "variance of Y_i," which refers to the dispersion of the values of Y_i corresponding to one fixed value of X, say X_i. In the case of the sample variation of Y, the values of X may change from observation to observation.

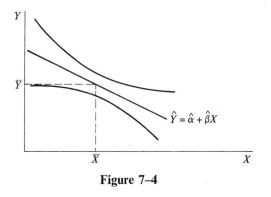

Figure 7–4

the estimation results we have derived. As an illustration, consider the variation of Y as shown in Figure 7–5. Here the values of Y observed in a given sample have been plotted against the corresponding values of X. Such a graph is generally known as a "scatter diagram." In Figure 7–5 we give 10 observations on Y

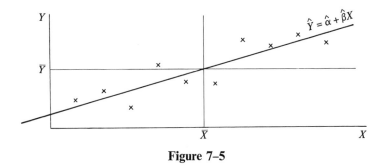

Figure 7–5

corresponding to 10 different values of X. The question that now arises is why the values of Y differ from observation to observation. The answer, in accordance with the hypothesized regression model, is that the variation in Y is partly due to changes in X—which lead to changes in the expected value of Y—and partly due to the effect of the random disturbance. The next question, then, is how much of the observed variation in Y can be attributed to the variation in X and now much to the random effect of the disturbance. This question can be answered with the help of certain measures that we develop below.

First of all, let us define the term "sample variation of Y." If there were no variation, all the values of Y, when plotted against X, would lie on a horizontal line. Since if all values of Y were the same, they would all be equal to their sample mean, the horizontal line would be the one corresponding to $\bar{Y}$ in Figure 7–5. Now, in reality, the observed values of Y will be scattered around this line so that the variation of Y could be measured by the distances of the observed values of Y from $\bar{Y}$. A convenient summary measure of these distances is the sum of their squared values, usually called the "total sum of squares," abbreviated to SST. That is, we define

$$\text{SST} = \sum_i (Y_i - \bar{Y})^2 = \sum_i y_i'^2.$$

Our aim is to decompose this sum of squares into two parts, one designed to account for the variations of Y which can be ascribed to the variations of X, and the other presumed to account for the variations in Y which can be ascribed to random causes.

Let us now return to Figure 7–5 and the sample observations shown therein. Suppose a sample regression line has been obtained by the method of least squares and drawn in the scatter diagram as shown. Since, as the name of the estimation method implies, the line is such that the sum of squares of deviations from it is a minimum, it is sometimes called the "line of the best fit." Consider now a specific observation, say Y_i, which corresponds to the value of X equal to X_i. We are interested in the vertical distance of (X_i, Y_i) from $\bar{Y}$. From Figure 7–6,

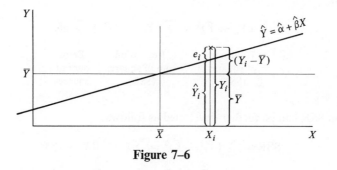

Figure 7–6

we can see that this distance can be divided into two parts, one represented by the distance of the observed point from the sample regression line, and the other by the distance of the sample regression line from $\bar{Y}$. That is, we have

$$Y_i = \hat{Y}_i + e_i,$$

where $\hat{Y}_i$ is the point on the sample regression line corresponding to X_i. Deducting $\bar{Y}$ from both sides we obtain

$$(Y_i - \bar{Y}) = (\hat{Y}_i - \bar{Y}) + e_i.$$

Total distance from $\bar{Y}$	Distance of the regression line from $\bar{Y}$	Residual

This analysis applies to a single observation. Since we want a summary measure for *all* sample observations, we square both sides of this equality and sum over all sample observations. This gives

$$\sum_i (Y_i - \bar{Y})^2 = \sum_i [(\hat{Y}_i - \bar{Y}) + e_i]^2$$

$$= \sum_i (\hat{Y}_i - \bar{Y})^2 + \sum_i e_i^2 + 2 \sum_i (\hat{Y}_i - \bar{Y}) e_i.$$

Consider the last term on the right-hand side. Substituting for $\hat{Y}_i$ we get

$$2 \sum_i (\hat{Y}_i - \bar{Y})e_i = 2 \sum_i (\hat{\alpha} + \hat{\beta} X_i - \bar{Y})e_i$$

$$= \hat{\alpha} \sum_i e_i + \hat{\beta} \sum_i X_i e_i - \bar{Y} \sum_i e_i.$$

But by (7.10a) and (7.11a) we know that $\sum_i e_i = 0$ and $\sum_i X_i e_i = 0$, so we conclude that

$$2 \sum_i (\hat{Y}_i - \bar{Y})e_i = 0.$$

Therefore,

(7.43)
$$\sum_i (Y_i - \bar{Y})^2 = \sum_i (\hat{Y}_i - \bar{Y})^2 + \sum_i e_i^2.$$

| Total sum of squares (SST) | Regression sum of squares (SSR) | Error sum of squares (SSE) |

The term SSR can be further developed as follows:

(7.44)
$$\text{SSR} = \sum (\hat{Y}_i - \bar{Y})^2 = \sum (\hat{\alpha} + \hat{\beta} X_i - \bar{Y})^2$$

$$= \sum [(\bar{Y} - \hat{\beta}\bar{X}) + \hat{\beta} X_i - \bar{Y}]^2$$

$$= \sum [-\hat{\beta}(X_i - \bar{X})]^2$$

$$= \hat{\beta}^2 \sum (X_i - \bar{X})^2 = \hat{\beta}^2 \sum x_i'^2.$$

Thus we have found that the sample variation of Y (SST) can be decomposed into two parts, one describing the variation of the fitted values of Y and the other describing the variation of the regression residuals. That is, SSR represents the estimated effect of X on the variation of Y, and SSE the estimated effect of the random disturbance.

The decomposition of the sample variation of Y leads to a measure of the "goodness of fit," which is known as the *coefficient of determination* and denoted by R^2. This is simply the proportion of the variation of Y that can be attributed to the variation of X. Since

$$\text{SST} = \text{SSR} + \text{SSE},$$

dividing through by SST gives

$$1 = \frac{\text{SSR}}{\text{SST}} + \frac{\text{SSE}}{\text{SST}}.$$

The coefficient of determination is defined as

(7.45)
$$R^2 = \frac{\text{SSR}}{\text{SST}} = \frac{\hat{\beta}^2 \sum x_i'^2}{\sum y_i'^2},$$

or

(7.45a)
$$R^2 = 1 - \frac{\text{SSE}}{\text{SST}} = 1 - \frac{\sum e_i^2}{\sum y_i'^2}.$$

R^2 is a measure commonly used to describe how well the sample regression line fits the observed data. Note that R^2 cannot be negative or greater than one, i.e.,

$$0 \le R^2 \le 1.$$

A zero value of R^2 indicates the poorest, and a unit value the best fit that can be attained.

A necessary but not sufficient condition for R^2 to be zero is that the sample regression line be horizontal—that is, that $\hat{\beta}$ be equal to zero. Note that the sample regression line can be horizontal for several different reasons. This is illustrated in Figure 7–7. In case (a) the observations are scattered randomly

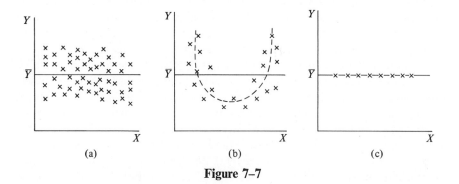

Figure 7–7

around $\bar{Y}$. In case (b) the observations are scattered around a curve such that the best-fitting straight line is a horizontal one. In this case there *is* a relationship between X and Y, but the relationship is highly nonlinear so that a straight line gives a very poor fit. Finally, in case (c) all observed values of Y are the same regardless of X. This is an exceptional case. With all values of Y being constant there is *no* variation to be explained, and thus the question of decomposition of variation is irrelevant. The value of R^2 in this case is indeterminate.

Two final points about decomposing the sample variation of Y should be noted.

First, nowhere in the discussion have we alluded to problems of statistical inference. This omission was deliberate since our purpose was only to provide certain information about the sample. Second, the decomposition of SST as developed above is crucially dependent on the use of the method of least squares to obtain the sample regression line. If we used an estimation method that would lead to a different sample regression line, the decomposition of SST into SSR and SSE would not have been possible. As for R^2, however, we can generalize the formula (7.45a) to apply to *any* estimation method by defining R^2 as

$$(7.45b) \qquad R^2 = 1 - \frac{\text{Sum of Squares of Residuals}}{\text{SST}}.$$

Here the residuals are represented by the deviations from the sample regression line regardless of the method of estimation that is used. But if the sample regression line is different from the one that would be obtained by the least squares method, R^2 can no longer be interpreted as a measure of the proportion of variation of Y attributable to sample regression. In this case, R^2 would be used purely as a measure of the goodness of fit.

If R^2 is regarded as a descriptive statistic, we might ask about the value of the information that it conveys. Suppose, in particular, we find a very low value of R^2 for a given sample. This means that the sample regression line fits the observations rather poorly. One possible explanation is that X is a poor explanatory variable in the sense that variation in X leaves Y unaffected. This is a proposition about the population regression line—a proposition that states that the population regression line is horizontal—and consequently can be tested by reference to the sample. We shall explain how this can be done presently. The validity of the test depends on the validity of the maintained hypothesis—that is, on the correct specification of the regression equation and on the validity of the basic assumptions. In particular, correct specification of the regression equation implies that no other explanatory variable enters into the model and that the effect of X_i on $E(Y_i)$ is a linear one. If we do not reject the hypothesis that the population regression line is horizontal, we are, in fact, claiming that Y is influenced *only* by the random disturbance ε. Another possible explanation of a low value of R^2 is that while X is the relevant explanatory variable, its influence on Y is weak compared to the influence of the random disturbance. This, indeed, seems to be the case for relationships describing household behavior that have been estimated from cross-section data. For example, a typical value of R^2 for various household behavior functions from the University of Michigan's Survey Research Center data (about 3000 observations) is close to 0.20. This would indicate that 80% of the sample behavioral variation from household to household can be accounted for by factors other than the explanatory variable or variables. A third possible explanation of a low value of R^2 is that the regression equation is misspecified. In practice, this is frequently the conclusion that the research worker reaches in this case. The value of R^2 tends to be taken as an indicator of the "correctness" of the specification of the model. This is obviously a purely operational criterion that has no foundation in statistical inference. We shall say more about it when we come to the discussion of specification errors. In any case, it is customary to state the value of R^2 along with the results of the estimation procedure when presenting the regression results.

EXAMPLE   The decomposition of SST and the calculation of R^2 can be illustrated with the example of demand for oranges introduced in Section 7–3. From the previous calculations we have:

$$\sum y_i'^2 = 6300,$$

$$\sum x_i'^2 = 2250,$$

$$\hat{\beta} = -1.578.$$

Thus,
$$\text{SST} = \sum y_i'^2 = 6300,$$

$$\text{SSR} = \hat{\beta}^2 \sum x_i'^2 = 5602,$$

$$\text{SSE} = \text{SST} - \text{SSR} = 698.$$

That is,
$$6300 = 5602 + 698.$$
$$\text{(SST)} \quad \text{(SSR)} \quad \text{(SSE)}$$

The coefficient of determination is

$$R^2 = \frac{\text{SSR}}{\text{SST}} = \frac{5602}{6300} = 0.889.$$

This means that 88.9% of the sample variation of Y can be attributed to the variation of the fitted values of Y, i.e., to $\hat{Y}$. The value of R^2 indicates that the sample regression line fits the observations quite well. This is shown graphically in Figure 7–8.

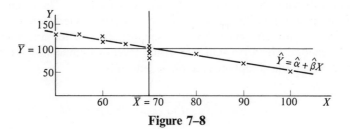

Figure 7–8

Tests of Hypotheses

Let us now turn to the problem of using the regression model for the purpose of *testing hypotheses*. The most common type of hypothesis which is tested with the help of the regression model is that there is no relationship between the explanatory variable X and the dependent variable Y. This hypothesis can be given a more precise interpretation if we first specify the ingredients of the associated maintained hypothesis; that is, if we state all the assumptions about the population that we are willing to make. These assumptions are all those underlying the classical normal linear regression model as specified by statements (7.1) through (7.6). Under this maintained hypothesis the relationship between X and Y is given by the linear dependence of the mean value of Y_i on X_i, i.e., by $E(Y_i) = \alpha + \beta X_i$. Thus the statement that "there is no relationship between X and Y" is to be interpreted as meaning that the mean value of Y_i is *not* linearly dependent on X_i—that is, that the population regression line is horizontal. But this is simply another way of saying that β is equal to zero. Therefore, the *null hypothesis* of no relationship between X and Y is

$$H_0: \quad \beta = 0.$$

If we have no prior knowledge about the values of the regression parameters, the alternative hypothesis would be

$$H_A: \quad \beta \neq 0.$$

If we know a priori that β cannot be positive or negative, the alternative hypothesis would be modified accordingly. To test H_0 we have to develop a test statistic and determine the acceptance and the critical regions. The test statistic can be derived from the least squares estimator of β, which has all the optimal properties under the given assumptions. We can simply utilize the fact that

$$\frac{\hat{\beta} - \beta}{s_\beta} \sim t_{n-2},$$

as given by (7.38). Under the null hypothesis, β equals zero and thus the appropriate test statistic is

$$\frac{\hat{\beta}}{s_{\hat{\beta}}}$$

which has a t distribution with $(n - 2)$ degrees of freedom. The boundary between the acceptance and the critical region can be determined from the table of the t distribution for any given level of significance and for any number of degrees of freedom. For a two-tail test with λ level of significance and $(n - 2)$ degrees of freedom the acceptance region is defined by

(7.46) $$-t_{n-2, \lambda/2} \leq \frac{\hat{\beta}}{s_{\hat{\beta}}} \leq +t_{n-2, \lambda/2}.$$

EXAMPLE As an example, consider the demand for oranges estimated by a linear regression model from the data given in Section 7–3. The null hypothesis of no relationship between X (price) and Y (quantity demanded) is tantamount to the claim that the demand for oranges is not influenced by price. We have

$$H_0: \quad \beta = 0.$$

For the alternative hypothesis, we take

$$H_A: \quad \beta \neq 0.$$

We wish to test H_0 at 1% level of significance. Since the t distribution extends from $-\infty$ to $+\infty$, *any* value of $\hat{\beta}/s_{\hat{\beta}}$ is consistent with the null hypothesis. But if H_0 is true,

values of $\hat{\beta}/s_{\hat{\beta}}$ which are "far" from zero are not very likely. Our decision to use 1%
level of significance means that if the deviation of $\hat{\beta}/s_{\hat{\beta}}$ from zero is so great as to
occur by chance only 1% of the time, we shall reject H_0. Since we have 12 observations, the appropriate value of the t statistic for a two-tail test is the value corresponding to $t_{10,0.005}$. From the table of the t distribution, we find that this is equal to
3.169. The acceptance region for our test then is

$$-3.169 \leq \frac{\hat{\beta}}{s_{\hat{\beta}}} \leq +3.169.$$

From the previous calculations we have

$$\hat{\beta} = -1.578 \qquad \text{and} \qquad s_{\hat{\beta}} = 0.176,$$

so that

$$\frac{\hat{\beta}}{s_{\hat{\beta}}} = -8.965,$$

which clearly lies outside the acceptance region. Therefore, the hypothesis of no
relationship between X and Y is to be rejected. Actually, in a case like this we would
probably want to use a one-sided alternative hypothesis since positive values of β
(that is, an upward-sloping demand curve) can be ruled out on theoretical grounds.
Thus a "sharper" test would be one with the alternative hypothesis stated as

$$H_A: \quad \beta < 0,$$

and the acceptance region given by

$$-t_{n-2,\lambda} \leq \frac{\hat{\beta}}{s_{\hat{\beta}}},$$

or

$$-2.764 \leq \frac{\hat{\beta}}{s_{\hat{\beta}}}.$$

Since -8.965 lies outside this region, the verdict of rejecting H_0 is unchanged.

It should be noted that the hypothesis of no relationship between X and Y can
also be tested by using a different test than the t test. If the null hypothesis is true,
then the variation of Y from observation to observation will not be affected by
changes in X but must be explained by the random disturbance alone. This
means that the "sum of squares due to regression" (SSR) departs from zero only
because we are observing a sample and not the entire population. Indeed, from
the formula (7.44) we have

$$\text{SSR} = \hat{\beta}^2 \sum_i x_i'^2.$$

If $\beta = 0$, the value of SSR in the population would also be zero. Furthermore,
since by (7.43) we have

$$\text{SST} = \text{SSR} + \text{SSE},$$

the corollary of a zero value of SSR is that SST and SSE are equal. Thus, if there
is no relationship between X and Y, the ratio SSR/SSE would be different from

zero only because of sampling. Now it can be shown[11] that under the null hypothesis the statistic

$$\frac{\text{SSR}/1}{\text{SSE}/(n-2)}$$

is a ratio of two independent chi-square variables, each divided by its respective number of degrees of freedom. This means that this ratio has an F distribution (see page 147), i.e., that

(7.47) $$\frac{\text{SSR}/1}{\text{SSE}/(n-2)} \sim F_{1,\,n-2}.$$

The acceptance region for the null hypothesis of no relationship between X and Y would then be

(7.48) $$\frac{\text{SSR}/1}{\text{SSE}/(n-2)} \leq F_{1,\,n-2}^{(\lambda)},$$

where $F_{1,\,n-2}^{(\lambda)}$ is the value of the F statistic with 1 and $(n-2)$ degrees of freedom that corresponds to a level of significance λ. The test (7.48) is equivalent to the two-tail t test (7.46) in the sense that both tests give the same answer as long as the level of significance and the sample data are the same. The difference, as we shall see, is that the F test can be readily generalized to apply to a regression model with more than one explanatory variable, whereas the t test can only be applied to a single regression coefficient.

EXAMPLE   For the numerical example given in the preceding paragraph we have

$$\text{SSR} = 5602,$$

$$\text{SSE} = 698,$$

so that $$\frac{\text{SSR}/1}{\text{SSE}/(n-2)} = \frac{5602}{698/10} = 80.26.$$

Since the value of the F statistic with 1 and 10 degrees of freedom at 1% level of significance is 10.0, the null hypothesis is obviously to be rejected.

In addition to testing a hypothesis about the existence of a relationship between X and Y, we can carry out tests for any specific values of the regression coefficients. For example, a hypothesis that α is equal to zero is, in fact, a hypothesis that the population regression line passes through the origin. The appropriate test statistic would be

$$\frac{\hat{\alpha}}{s_{\hat{\alpha}}}$$

[11] See, e.g., R. L. Anderson and T. A. Bancroft, *Statistical Theory in Research* (New York: McGraw-Hill, 1952), pp. 158–160.

which has a t distribution with $(n - 2)$ degrees of freedom. Or we may wish to test the hypothesis that the regression slope β is equal to some value β_0. In this case the test statistic would be

$$\frac{\hat{\beta} - \beta_0}{s_{\hat{\beta}}} \sim t_{n-2}.$$

Prediction

Apart from estimation and hypotheses testing, the regression model can also be used for prediction. In particular, we are frequently interested in "*forecasting*" the value of Y for a given value of X. For example, the manager of a supermarket may be interested to know what quantity of oranges he can expect to sell when he sets the price at a certain level. To be specific, suppose the given value of the explanatory variable is X_0 so that our task is to predict the value of Y_0. Since Y_0 is a *random* variable with values scattered around the point on the population regression line corresponding to X_0, we will never know its value prior to the experiment, not even if we knew all the population parameters. If the population parameters *were known*, our predictor of Y_0 would be its mean,

$$E(Y_0) = \alpha + \beta X_0,$$

which defines a point on the population regression line. This is the best predictor of Y_0 in the sense that the variance of Y_0 around $E(Y_0)$ is smaller than around any other point. The values of Y_0 will be normally distributed with variance equal to σ^2. This follows from the presence of the random disturbance ε in the regression equation. In reality, $E(Y_0)$ is not known and has to be estimated. The estimator is the corresponding point on the sample regression line,

$$\hat{Y}_0 = \hat{\alpha} + \hat{\beta} X_0,$$

since $\hat{\alpha}$ and $\hat{\beta}$ are the best estimators of α and β that we can devise under given assumptions. Now, the actual value of Y_0 will differ from the predicted value $\hat{Y}_0$ for the following two reasons:

1. The value of Y_0 will not be equal to $E(Y_0)$—i.e., will not lie on the population regression line—because of the random disturbance ε_0.
2. The sample regression will not be the same as the population regression line because of the sampling error.

Formally, we may write

$$Y_0 - \hat{Y}_0 = [Y_0 - E(Y_0)] + [E(Y_0) - \bar{Y}_0].$$

The first type of error is inherent in the mechanism by which the values of the dependent variable are generated, and there is nothing that we can do to diminish it. However, the second type of error would be reduced if we increased the precision of estimating the population regression line by increasing the sample size.

The difference between the actual value of $\hat{Y}_0$ and the predicted value Y_0 is known as the *forecast error*. We note that

$$Y_0 - \hat{Y}_0 = (\alpha + \beta X_0 + \varepsilon_0) - (\hat{\alpha} + \hat{\beta} X_0)$$

is a linear combination of normally and independently distributed random variables $\varepsilon_0, \varepsilon_1, \varepsilon_2 \ldots, \varepsilon_n$. Therefore, the forecast error is also a normally distributed random variable. Thus its distribution is fully determined by its mean and its variance. The mean can be simply determined as follows:

$$E(Y_0 - \hat{Y}_0) = E(\alpha + \beta X_0 + \varepsilon_0 - \hat{\alpha} - \hat{\beta} X_0)$$
$$= \alpha + \beta X_0 + E(\varepsilon_0) - E(\hat{\alpha}) - E(\hat{\beta}) X_0 = 0.$$

The variance of the forecast error is

$$E[(Y_0 - \hat{Y}_0) - E(Y_0 - \hat{Y}_0)]^2 = E(Y_0 - \hat{Y}_0)^2$$
$$= E\{[Y_0 - E(Y_0)] + [E(Y_0) - \hat{Y}_0]\}^2$$
$$= E[Y_0 - E(Y_0)]^2 + E[E(Y_0) - \hat{Y}_0]^2$$
$$+ 2E[Y_0 - E(Y_0)][E(Y_0) - \hat{Y}_0].$$

Taking the last term on the right-hand side,

$$2E[Y_0 - E(Y_0)][E(Y_0) - \hat{Y}_0] = 2E(\varepsilon_0)[E(Y_0) - \hat{Y}_0]$$
$$= 2E(\varepsilon_0)(\alpha + \beta X_0 - \hat{\alpha} - \hat{\beta} X_0)$$
$$= 2E(\varepsilon_0)[-(\hat{\alpha} - \alpha) - (\hat{\beta} - \beta) X_0]$$
$$= 0,$$

since $(\hat{\alpha} - \alpha)$ and $(\hat{\beta} - \beta)$ each depend only on the sample disturbances $\varepsilon_1, \varepsilon_2, \ldots, \varepsilon_n$, and these are independent of ε_0. Thus

(7.49) $$E(Y_0 - \hat{Y}_0)^2 = E[Y_0 - E(Y_0)]^2 + E[E(Y_0) - \hat{Y}_0]^2$$

| Total variance of the forecast error (σ_F^2) | Variance due to random disturbance (σ^2) | Variance due to sampling error $(\sigma_{\hat{Y}_0}^2)$ |

or $$\sigma_F^2 = \sigma^2 + \sigma_{\hat{Y}_0}^2.$$

That is, the variance of the forecast error consists of two parts, one equal to the variance of the disturbance and the other to the variance of the predictor $\hat{Y}_0$ around its mean $E(Y_0)$. The variance of the disturbance is beyond our control, but the variance of the predictor can be diminished by increasing the size of the sample used for estimating the population regression line.

By using the expression for $\sigma_{\hat{Y}_0}^2$ given by (7.41) above, we obtain the following formula for the variance of the forecast error:

(7.50) $$\sigma_F^2 = \sigma^2 + \sigma^2 \left[\frac{1}{n} + \frac{(X_0 - \bar{X})^2}{\sum x_i'^2} \right] = \sigma^2 \left[1 + \frac{1}{n} + \frac{(X_0 - \bar{X})^2}{\sum x_i'^2} \right].$$

This means that the variance of the forecast error will be the smaller:

1. The larger the sample size n.
2. The greater the dispersion of the explanatory variable in the sample (i.e., the larger $\sum x_i'^2$).
3. The smaller the distance between X_0 and the sample mean $\bar{X}$.

The first two conclusions are quite straightforward; they reflect the fact that the better the estimate of the population regression line, the smaller the variance of the forecast error. The third conclusion is more interesting; it means that our forecast will be better for values of X which are close to $\bar{X}$ than for those which lie farther away from $\bar{X}$. This is consistent with the intuitively plausible contention that we are better able to forecast within our range of experience than outside of it. In this case the range of our "experience" is represented by the sample values of the explanatory variable X, and the central point of this range is $\bar{X}$. The farther away we venture with our forecasting, the less reliable the forecast.

   In general, the expression for σ_F^2 given by (7.50) will not be known and must be estimated. This can be done simply by replacing σ^2 by its estimator s^2, which will give an unbiased, consistent, and asymptotically efficient estimator of σ_F^2, say, s_F^2, defined as

$$(7.51) \qquad s_F^2 = s^2 \left[1 + \frac{1}{n} + \frac{(X_0 - \bar{X})^2}{\sum x_i'^2} \right].$$

   In summary, we have found that the forecast error $(Y_0 - \hat{Y}_0)$ is normally distributed, has zero mean, and its variance is σ_F^2. That is,

$$(Y_0 - \hat{Y}_0) \sim N(0, \sigma_F^2);$$

and, therefore

$$\frac{Y_0 - \hat{Y}_0}{\sigma_F} \sim N(0, 1).$$

Replacing σ_F with s_F gives

$$\frac{Y_0 - \hat{Y}_0}{s_F} \sim t_{n-2}.$$

The last result enables us to make definite probability statements about our forecast. In particular, we can set up an interval that will contain the actual value of Y_0 with a given probability. Let this level of probability be $(1 - \lambda)$, where λ is any given number between 0 and 1 that we care to choose. Then we can write

$$P\left[-t_{n-2, \lambda/2} \leq \frac{Y_0 - \hat{Y}_0}{s_F} \leq +t_{n-2, \lambda/2} \right] = 1 - \lambda.$$

The corresponding confidence interval for Y_0 is

$$\hat{Y}_0 - t_{n-2, \lambda/2} s_F \leq Y_0 \leq \hat{Y}_0 + t_{n-2, \lambda/2} s_F.$$

This interval is symmetric around the predictor $\hat{Y}_0$, and can be expected to contain the actual value of Y_0 with a probability $(1 - \lambda)$.

EXAMPLE Suppose we wish to predict the demand for oranges at a price of 110¢ per pound, using the previously estimated demand curve. The predicted quantity demanded will be

$$\hat{Y}_0 = 210.460 - 1.578 \times 110 = 36.88,$$

with standard error

$$s_F = \sqrt{69.9\left[1 + \frac{1}{12} + \frac{(110 - 70)^2}{2250}\right]} = 11.20.$$

The 95% confidence interval for Y_0 is $36.88 \pm 2.228 \times 11.20$ or from 12 to 62 pounds.

Presentation of Regression Results

One last note to be added before we close this chapter concerns the presentation of the results of the regression analysis. Whatever the purpose, operating on sample data will involve estimating the regression coefficients and the standard errors of these estimators. These results are usually supplemented by R^2, the coefficient of determination, which indicates how well the sample regression line fits the observations. It has become customary to present all these results by writing out the estimated regression equation with the estimated standard errors in parentheses under the respective coefficients. This is followed by the value of R^2. That is, we write

$$\hat{Y}_i = \hat{\alpha} + \hat{\beta}X_i, \qquad R^2 = \cdots.$$
$$(s_{\hat{\alpha}}) \quad (s_{\hat{\beta}})$$

In the case of our example on the demand for oranges, we have

$$\hat{Y}_i = 210.460 - 1.578X_i, \qquad R^2 = 0.889.$$
$$(12.563) \quad (0.176)$$

The "hat" on $\hat{Y}_i$ indicates that the equation holds only for the fitted values of the dependent variable, not for the actually observed values. Alternatively, we can write

$$Y_i = \hat{\alpha} + \hat{\beta}X_i + e_i, \qquad R^2 = \cdots,$$
$$(s_{\hat{\alpha}}) \quad (s_{\hat{\beta}})$$

where e_i represents the least squares residuals. But note that writing $Y_i = \hat{\alpha} + \hat{\beta}X_i$ is incorrect. Some researchers present the ratios of the estimated coefficients to their estimated standard errors in place of the estimated standard errors themselves, which is an acceptable alternative.

EXERCISES

All problems in this set of exercises refer to a simple linear regression model,

$$Y_i = \alpha + \beta X_i + \varepsilon_i,$$

for which assumptions (7.2) through (7.6) are all satisfied.

7–1. Derive the best linear unbiased estimator of α and its variance.

7–2. Consider any two regression disturbances ε_t and ε_s ($t \neq s$). By our assumptions, these disturbances have the same variance and are mutually independent. Can the same be asserted about the respective least squares residuals e_t and e_s?

7–3. Using the method of semi-averages and the data on the demand for oranges given in the text, we estimated the regression line as

$$\hat{Y}_i = 205 - 1.5X_i.$$

Calculate the value of R^2.

7–4. Which of the assumptions (7.2) through (7.6) are *necessary* for the least squares estimator of β to be (a) unbiased; (b) best linear unbiased; (c) consistent?

7–5. Suppose $Y_i = $ log value of production per worker, $X_i = $ log wage rate, and the subscript i refers to the ith firm. The parameter β may be interpreted as a measure of the elasticity of substitution between labor and capital. The least squares results for industry A are

$$Y_i = -0.4 + 1.0X_i + e_i \qquad (n = 50).$$
$$(0.1)$$

For industry B the results are

$$Y_i = -0.3 + 0.8X_i + e_i \qquad (n = 50).$$
$$(0.1)$$

The two samples can be considered to be independent.

a. Show that $R_A^2 = 2/3$ and $R_B^2 = 4/7$.

b. Test the hypothesis that both industries are characterized by the same elasticity of substitution, i.e., that $\beta_A = \beta_B$.

7–6. Suppose we have calculated the values of $\hat{\alpha}$, $\hat{\beta}$, $s_{\hat{\alpha}}$, $s_{\hat{\beta}}$, and R^2 on the basis of a sample of n observations. Suppose now that we add another observation to our sample and recalculate these five values. Compare the recalculated values with the original ones—stating whether we get an increase, a decrease, no change, or an uncertain result—given the following situations:

a. $X_{n+1} = \dfrac{1}{n} \displaystyle\sum_{i=1}^{n} X_i.$

b. $X_{n+1} = \max\{X_1, X_2, \ldots, X_n\}.$

c. $X_{n+1} = 0.$

7–7. Suppose the explanatory variable X can only assume the values 0 and 1. The sample consists of n_1 observations for which $X = 0$, and n_2 observations for which $X = 1$. Let $\bar{Y}_1$ be the mean value of Y for the n_1 observations for which $X = 0$, and $\bar{Y}_2$ be the mean value of Y for the n_2 observations for which $X = 1$. Find $\hat{\alpha}$, $\hat{\beta}$, $\text{Var}(\hat{\alpha})$, and $\text{Var}(\hat{\beta})$.

7–8. Three alternative models, designed to explain the changes in aggregate expenditure of food in the United States, have been suggested:

$$\text{Model A:} \qquad Y_t = \alpha + \beta X_t + \varepsilon_{1t}$$

$$\text{Model B:} \qquad Y_t = \gamma + \delta Z_t + \varepsilon_{2t}$$

$$\text{Model C:} \quad \log Y_t = \alpha^* + \beta^* \log X_t + \varepsilon_{3t},$$

where Y = personal expenditure on food (excluding alcoholic beverages), X = personal disposable income, Z = total personal consumption expenditure, and t = time in years. On the basis of the data in Table 7–4,

a. Estimate the three regression equations by the method of least squares.

b. For each model obtain an estimate (given by a single numerical value) of the income elasticity of demand for food defined as

$$\frac{dQ}{dX}\frac{X}{Q},$$

where Q is the quantity of food consumed, i.e., value divided by price.

c. Examine the results obtained in **a** to see whether they help in the choice between the three models.

7–9. The least squares regression equation estimated from 22 observations is

$$Y_i = 10 + 5X_i + e_i, \qquad R^2 = 0.8.$$

Carry out the test for the existence of a relationship between X and Y by using (**a**) the t test; (**b**) the F test.

7–10. Two research workers, working independently of each other, estimated the coefficients of

$$Y_i = \alpha + \beta X_i + \varepsilon_i$$

by the method of least squares. When they found out about each other's work, they decided to pool their results to obtain one joint estimate of β. Two possible ways of doing this were considered:

1. Taking a simple arithmetic mean of their two estimates.
2. Combining their two samples and obtaining a new estimate of β.

Do the two procedures differ? If so, which one would lead to a better estimate of β?

7–11. One test for the existence of a relationship between X and Y is carried out by constructing a t statistic $\hat{\beta}/s_{\hat{\beta}}$. Show that this is exactly equal to

$$[R^2(n - 2)/(1 - R^2)]^{1/2}.$$

7–12. The true relationship between X and Y in the population is given by

$$Y_i = 2 + 3X_i + \varepsilon_i.$$

Table 7–4

| Year | Personal Consumption Expenditure* | | Personal Disposable Income* |
	Total	Food	
1929	79.0	19.5	83.1
1930	71.0	18.0	74.4
1931	61.3	14.7	63.8
1932	49.3	11.4	48.7
1933	46.4	10.9	45.7
1934	51.9	12.2	52.0
1935	56.3	13.6	58.3
1936	62.6	15.2	66.2
1937	67.3	16.4	71.0
1938	64.6	15.6	65.7
1939	67.6	15.7	70.4
1940	71.9	16.7	76.1
1946	147.1	40.7	160.6
1947	165.4	45.8	170.1
1948	178.3	48.2	189.3
1949	181.2	46.4	189.7
1950	195.0	47.4	207.7
1951	209.8	53.4	227.5
1952	219.8	55.8	238.7
1953	232.6	56.6	252.5
1954	238.0	57.7	256.9
1955	256.9	59.2	274.4
1956	269.9	62.2	292.9
1957	285.2	65.2	308.8
1958	293.2	67.4	317.9
1959	313.5	68.1	337.1
1960	328.2	69.7	349.9
1961	337.3	71.0	364.7
1962	356.8	73.9	384.6
1963	375.0	76.0	402.5
1964	399.2	80.0	431.8

Source: *Economic Report of the President*, January, 1965, Tables B–7 and B–9.
* In billions of dollars.

Suppose the values of X in the sample of 10 observations are 1, 2, ..., 10. The values of the disturbances are drawn at random from a normal population with zero mean and unit variance:

$$\varepsilon_1 = 0.464 \qquad \varepsilon_6 = 0.906$$

$$\varepsilon_2 = 0.060 \qquad \varepsilon_7 = -1.501$$

$$\varepsilon_3 = 1.486 \qquad \varepsilon_8 = -0.690$$

$$\varepsilon_4 = 1.022 \qquad \varepsilon_9 = 0.179$$

$$\varepsilon_5 = 1.394 \qquad \varepsilon_{10} = -1.372$$

a. Present the 10 observed values of X and Y.

b. Use the least squares formulas to estimate the regression coefficients and their standard errors, and compare the results with the true values.

c. Carry out a test for the existence of a relationship between X and Y.

d. Obtain the predicted value of Y—and its 95% confidence limits—for $X = 12$.

8

Violations of
Basic Assumptions

In Chapter 7 we have developed a so-called classical normal linear regression model and showed how this model can be used for estimation, hypothesis testing, and prediction. In deriving the results we have made use of certain assumptions, which we termed *basic assumptions*, concerning the stochastic disturbance ε_i and the explanatory variable X_i. The first four assumptions involving the stochastic disturbance are normality, zero mean, homoskedasticity, and non-autoregression. The fifth assumption concerns the explanatory variable, which is assumed to be nonstochastic and such that its sample variance is a finite number, whatever the sample size. Given these assumptions, we have been able to show that the least squares estimators of the regression parameters have all the desirable properties. The main objective of the present chapter is to find how the properties of the least squares estimators are affected when any one of the basic assumptions is violated. Furthermore, if and when we find that the consequences of such a violation are serious, we shall try to develop alternative methods of estimation which would give more satisfactory results.

Perhaps we should start with a warning. While all the results pertaining to the classical normal linear regression model discussed in the preceding chapter are well established, the problems arising in situations in which the basic assumptions do not hold have not been always satisfactorily resolved. In fact, it is the preoccupation with these problems that distinguishes an econometrician from a statistician. The main reason for this is that some of the basic assumptions are likely to be violated because of the particular nature of economic relationships. The resulting problems of estimation and hypotheses testing are thus of special relevance to economics. Many of the results to be presented here are relatively new. Some of the unresolved problems are the subject of current research and hopefully will be solved in the near future; others may stay unresolved for a long time.

Of the five basic assumptions the first two assumptions, normality and zero mean of the disturbance, do not require an extended discussion. If the assumption that the disturbance is normally distributed is dropped, the least squares estimators of the regression coefficients are still BLUE, since this property is independent of the form of the parent population. This means that even without the assumption of normality the least squares estimators are unbiased and have the smallest variance among all linear unbiased estimators of the respective parameters. However, they can no longer be claimed to be efficient because, without the specification of the distributional form, the Cramer–Rao lower bound of their variances is not known. Also, the least squares estimators are no longer maximum likelihood estimators since the likelihood function, based on the assumption of normality, no longer applies. With respect to the asymptotic properties, least squares estimators are consistent and asymptotically efficient regardless of the distribution of the disturbance. This follows from the fact that the distribution of the least squares estimators of the regression coefficients approaches normality as $n \to \infty$. This statement can be proved with the help of the central limit theorem.[1] The implication of this is that the least squares estimators have *asymptotically* the same distribution as the maximum likelihood estimators based on the assumption of normality; therefore, they have the same desirable asymptotic properties. To sum up, when the assumption of normality of the disturbance is dropped, the least squares of the regression coefficients retain most of their desirable properties and the formulas for the variances of these estimators remain unchanged. The confidence intervals and the tests of significance for α and β do, however, depend crucially on the assumption of normality. Without the assumption of normality the least squares estimators are not normally distributed in small samples; strictly speaking, therefore, the confidence limits and the tests described in Section 7–4 no longer apply. Fortunately, if the distribution of the disturbance is not very radically different from normal, the quoted confidence limits and tests of significance are not too badly affected and can be used as reasonable approximations.[2]

The second assumption—zero mean of the regression disturbance—is made in accordance with the specification that the population regression line is

$$E(Y_i) = \alpha + \beta X_i.$$

If the mean of the disturbance is not zero but, say, μ_i, we have

$$E(Y_i) = \alpha + \beta X_i + \mu_i.$$

The implications of this depend on the nature of μ_i. In particular, we have to distinguish between the case where μ_i has the same value for all observations and the case where μ_i may vary. In the first case we can write $\mu_i = \mu$, and the true population regression line is

$$E(Y_i) = \alpha + \mu + \beta X_i$$

or $$E(Y_i) = \alpha^* + \beta X_i.$$

It is clear, then, that while the least squares estimator of β is unaffected, the least squares formula for estimating the intercept gives an estimation of α^* and not of

[1] E. Malinvaud, *Statistical Methods of Econometrics* (Chicago: Rand McNally, 1966), pp. 195–197.

[2] *Ibid.*, pp. 251–254.

α. There is *no* way in which we can estimate α and μ separately and get unbiased or at least consistent estimates. In the second case where μ_i is not a constant, the intercept becomes $(\alpha + \mu_i)$; that is, it may vary from observation to observation. This means that the mean value of the dependent variable, $E(Y_i)$, changes not only because of changes in X_i but also for other reasons; in other words, the relationship between X_i and Y_i has not been correctly specified. This and other kinds of specification errors will be examined in detail in Chapter 10.

After this preliminary discussion we are left with the remaining three assumptions. It may be noted that when the disturbance is not homoskedastic, it is called "heteroskedastic"; this case will be discussed in Section 8–1. Sections 8–2 and 8–3 will deal with autoregressive disturbances and with stochastic explanatory variables.

8–1 Heteroskedasticity

By the assumption (7.4) of the classical normal linear regression model, we have

$$E(\varepsilon_i^2) = \sigma^2 \quad \text{for all } i.$$

Since the mean of ε_i is assumed to be zero, we can write

$$\text{Var}(\varepsilon_i) = \sigma^2.$$

This feature of the regression disturbance is known as homoskedasticity. It implies that the variance of the disturbance is constant for all observations. This assumption may not be too troublesome for models involving observations on aggregates over time, since the values of the explanatory variable are typically of a similar order of magnitude at all points of observation, and the same is true of the values of the dependent variable. For example, in an aggregate consumption function the level of consumption in recent years is of a similar order of magnitude as the level of consumption twenty years ago, and the same is true of income. Unless there are some special circumstances, the assumption of homoskedasticity in aggregate models seems plausible. However, when we are dealing with microeconomic data, the observations may involve substantial differences in magnitude, as, for example, in the case of data on income and expenditure of individual families. Here, the assumption of homoskedasticity is not very plausible on a priori grounds since we would expect less variation in consumption for low-income families than for high-income families. At low levels of income the average level of consumption is low, and variation around this level is restricted: consumption cannot fall too far below the average level because this might mean starvation, and it cannot rise too far above the average because the asset and the credit position does not allow it. These constraints are likely to be less binding at higher income levels. Empirical evidence suggests that these prior considerations are in accord with actual behavior.[3] The appropriate model in this and other similar cases is then one with *heteroskedastic* disturbances.

[3] See S. J. Prais, and H. S. Houthakker, *The Analysis of Family Budgets* (Cambridge, England: The University Press, 1955).

Properties of Least Squares Estimators

If the regression disturbance is heteroskedastic, we have

$$E(\varepsilon_i^2) = \sigma_i^2.$$

This implies that the variance of the disturbance may vary from observation to observation, and we want to know how this behavior of the variance affects the properties of the least squares estimators of the regression coefficients. First, we consider the property of unbiasedness. The least squares estimator of β is

$$\hat{\beta} = \frac{\sum x_i' y_i'}{\sum x_i'^2} = \beta + \frac{\sum x_i' \varepsilon_i}{\sum x_i'^2},$$

as given by (7.32). Then

$$E(\hat{\beta}) = \beta + E\left[\frac{\sum x_i' \varepsilon_i}{\sum x_i'^2}\right] = \beta.$$

Similarly, $$\hat{\alpha} = \bar{Y} - \hat{\beta}\bar{X} = (\alpha + \beta\bar{X} + \bar{\varepsilon}) - \hat{\beta}\bar{X},$$

and $$E(\hat{\alpha}) = \alpha + \beta\bar{X} + E(\bar{\varepsilon}) - E(\hat{\beta})\bar{X} = \alpha.$$

That is, the least squares estimators are *unbiased* even under the conditions of heteroskedasticity.

Next, let us see whether the least squares estimators are still best linear unbiased estimators (BLUE). We can check this by deriving the BLUE formulas for the heteroskedastic case and by comparing them with the least squares formulas. If there is a difference, the least squares estimators are not BLUE. Beginning with the BLUE of β, say $\tilde{\beta}$, we have

$$\tilde{\beta} = \sum_i a_i Y_i$$

by the condition of linearity. Here, a_i ($i = 1, 2, \ldots, n$) are constants to be determined. Furthermore,

$$E(\tilde{\beta}) = E\left(\sum_i a_i Y_i\right) = \sum_i a_i(\alpha + \beta X_i) = \alpha\left(\sum_i a_i\right) + \beta\left(\sum_i a_i X_i\right).$$

For $\tilde{\beta}$ to be unbiased we require, as in the case of homoskedasticity, that

$$\sum_i a_i = 0 \quad \text{and} \quad \sum_i a_i X_i = 1.$$

The variance of $\tilde{\beta}$ is given as

$$\text{Var}(\tilde{\beta}) = E\left[\sum_i a_i Y_i - E\left(\sum_i a_i Y_i\right)\right]^2 = E\left[\sum_i a_i(Y_i - EY_i)\right]^2$$

$$= E\left[\sum_i a_i \varepsilon_i\right]^2 = E\sum_i a_i^2 \varepsilon_i^2 + 2E\sum_{i<j} a_i \varepsilon_i a_j \varepsilon_j,$$

recalling the result in (7.17). Since $E(\varepsilon_i^2) = \sigma_i^2$ and $E(\varepsilon_i \varepsilon_j) = 0$ $(i < j)$, we obtain

$$\text{Var}(\tilde{\beta}) = \sum_i a_i^2 \sigma_i^2.$$

Now we have to find $a_1, a_2, \ldots, a_n$ such that the preceding expression is as small as possible and, at the same time, the conditions $\sum a_i = 0$ and $\sum a_i X_i = 1$ are met. Using the Lagrange multiplier method, we form a function,

$$H = \sum_i a_i^2 \sigma_i^2 - \lambda_1 \left(\sum_i a_i \right) - \lambda_2 \left(\sum_i a_i X_i - 1 \right),$$

which is to be minimized with respect to $a_1, a_2, \ldots, a_n, \lambda_1$ and λ_2. Differentiating H and putting the resulting first derivatives equal to zero, we get

$$2a_1 \sigma_1^2 - \lambda_1 - \lambda_2 X_1 = 0,$$

$$2a_2 \sigma_2^2 - \lambda_1 - \lambda_2 X_2 = 0,$$

$$\vdots$$

$$2a_n \sigma_n^2 - \lambda_1 - \lambda_2 X_n = 0,$$

$$-\sum_i a_i = 0,$$

$$-\left(\sum_i a_i X_i \right) + 1 = 0.$$

This gives $(n + 2)$ equations for the unknowns $a_1, a_2, \ldots, a_n, \lambda_1$ and λ_2. Let us now introduce a more convenient notation by writing

$$\frac{1}{\sigma_i^2} = w_i.$$

Then, the first n of the above equations can be written as

$$a_1 = \tfrac{1}{2}(\lambda_1 w_1 + \lambda_2 w_1 X_1),$$

$$a_2 = \tfrac{1}{2}(\lambda_1 w_2 + \lambda_2 w_2 X_2),$$

$$\vdots$$

$$a_n = \tfrac{1}{2}(\lambda_2 w_n + \lambda_2 w_n X_n).$$

Adding we get

$$\sum_i a_i = \tfrac{1}{2}\left(\lambda_1 \sum_i w_i + \lambda_2 \sum w_i X_i \right).$$

Further, by multiplying the first equation by X_1, the second equation by X_2, the third equation by X_3, and so on, and then adding, we obtain

$$\sum_i a_i X_i = \tfrac{1}{2}\left(\lambda_1 \sum w_i X_i + \lambda_2 \sum w_i X_i^2 \right).$$

Substituting zero for $\sum_i a_i$ and unity for $\sum_i a_i X_i$ gives

$$0 = \tfrac{1}{2}\left(\lambda_1 \sum_i w_i + \lambda_2 \sum_i w_i X_i \right),$$

$$1 = \tfrac{1}{2}\left(\lambda_1 \sum_i w_i X_i + \lambda_2 \sum_i w_i X_i^2 \right).$$

The solution for λ_1 and λ_2 is

$$\lambda_1 = \frac{-2 \sum w_i X_i}{(\sum w_i)(\sum w_i X_i^2) - (\sum w_i X_i)^2},$$

$$\lambda_2 = \frac{2 \sum w_i}{(\sum w_i)(\sum w_i X_i^2) - (\sum w_i X_i)^2}.$$

These expressions can be substituted into the solutions for $a_1, a_2, \ldots, a_n$,

$$a_i = \tfrac{1}{2}(\lambda_1 w_i + \lambda_2 w_i X_i) \qquad (i = 1, 2, \ldots, n),$$

to give

$$a_i = \frac{-w_i(\sum w_i X_i) + w_i X_i(\sum w_i)}{(\sum w_i)(\sum w_i X_i^2) - (\sum w_i X_i)^2}.$$

These are the constants that minimize the variance of $\tilde{\beta}$ and, at the same time, make it an unbiased estimator. Substitution for a_i into $\tilde{\beta} = \sum a_i Y_i$ leads to

(8.1)
$$\tilde{\beta} = \frac{(\sum w_i)(\sum w_i X_i Y_i) - (\sum w_i X_i)(\sum w_i Y_i)}{(\sum w_i)(\sum w_i X_i^2) - (\sum w_i X_i)^2},$$

which is obviously a different formula than that for the least squares estimator of β. The variance of $\tilde{\beta}$ is

(8.2)
$$\mathrm{Var}(\tilde{\beta}) = \sum_i a_i^2 \sigma_i^2 = \frac{(\sum w_i)}{(\sum w_i)(\sum w_i X_i^2) - (\sum w_i X_i)^2}.$$

In a similar way we can derive the best linear unbiased estimator of α and its variance when the disturbance is heteroskedastic. This is

(8.3)
$$\tilde{\alpha} = \frac{\sum w_i Y_i}{\sum w_i} - \tilde{\beta}\left[\frac{\sum w_i X_i}{\sum w_i}\right],$$

which again is different from the least squares estimator of α. The variance of $\tilde{\alpha}$ is

(8.4)
$$\mathrm{Var}(\tilde{\alpha}) = \frac{\sum w_i X_i^2}{(\sum w_i)(\sum w_i X_i^2) - (\sum w_i X_i)^2}.$$

Given these results, we have to conclude that the least squares estimators of the regression coefficients are not BLUE when the assumption of homoskedasticity does not hold. This means that the least squares estimators do not have the smallest variance in a class of unbiased estimators and, therefore, that they are not efficient.

Turning to the asymptotic properties, we can check whether the least squares estimators are consistent under heteroskedasticity by establishing their probability limits as defined in Section 6–1. We have

$$\mathrm{plim}\ \hat{\beta} = \mathrm{plim}\left[\frac{\sum x_i' y_i'}{\sum x_i'^2}\right] = \beta + \mathrm{plim}\left[\frac{\sum x_i' \varepsilon_i'}{\sum x_i'^2}\right]$$

$$= \beta + \frac{\mathrm{plim}(\sum x_i' \varepsilon_i / n)}{\mathrm{plim}(\sum x_i'^2 / n)}$$

by the use of the Slutsky Theorem (Theorem 17 of Section 6–1). In the last term on the right-hand side, the numerator is equal to zero because $(\sum x'_i \varepsilon_i / n)$ is a consistent estimator of the "covariance" of X_i and ε_i which is zero, and the denominator is a finite number different from zero by assumption (7.6).

Therefore,
$$\text{plim } \tilde{\beta} = \beta,$$

indicating that $\tilde{\beta}$ is a consistent estimator of β. Similarly,

$$\text{plim } \tilde{\alpha} = \text{plim } (\bar{Y} - \tilde{\beta}\bar{X}) = \text{plim } (\alpha + \beta\bar{X} + \bar{\varepsilon} - \tilde{\beta}\bar{X})$$
$$= \alpha + \beta\bar{X} + \text{plim } (\bar{\varepsilon}) - \text{plim } (\tilde{\beta}\bar{X}) = \alpha.$$

That is, the least squares estimators of the regression coefficients are *consistent* even if the disturbance is not *homoskedastic*.

To find whether the least squares estimators are asymptotically efficient under the condition of heteroskedasticity, we derive the appropriate maximum likelihood estimators which are known to be asymptotically efficient. Then, we will check whether the variances of the maximum likelihood estimators are asymptotically equivalent to those of the least squares estimators. If they are not, the least squares estimators are not asymptotically efficient. Setting up the likelihood function as in (7.26) but allowing for heteroskedasticity, we get

$$(8.5) \qquad L = -\frac{n}{2} \log (2\pi) - \frac{1}{2} \sum_{i=1}^{n} \log \sigma_i^2 - \frac{1}{2} \sum_{i=1}^{n} \left[\frac{Y_i - \alpha - \beta X_i}{\sigma_i} \right]^2.$$

The first derivatives of L with respect to α and β are

$$\frac{\partial L}{\partial \alpha} = \sum_i \left[\frac{Y_i - \alpha\beta X_i}{\sigma_i^2} \right],$$

$$\frac{\partial L}{\partial \beta} = \sum_i \left[\frac{X_i(Y_i - \alpha - \beta X_i)}{\sigma_i^2} \right].$$

Putting these derivatives equal to zero and solving for the estimators of α and β leads to the formulas (8.1) and (8.3) for the best linear unbiased estimators. Consequently, the variances of the maximum likelihood estimators are also the same as those of the best linear unbiased estimators. These are given by formulas (8.2) and (8.4). We should compare these variances with those of the least squares estimators. The variance of the least squares estimator of β under heteroskedasticity is

$$(8.6) \qquad \text{Var}(\hat{\beta}) = E(\hat{\beta} - \beta) = E\left[\frac{\sum x'_i \varepsilon_i}{\sum x_i'^2} \right]^2$$

$$= E\left[\frac{\sum x_i'^2 \varepsilon_i^2}{(\sum x_i'^2)^2} \right] + 2E \sum_{i<j} \left[\frac{x'_i \varepsilon_i x'_j \varepsilon_j}{\sum x_i'^2} \right]$$

$$= \frac{\sum x_i'^2 \sigma_i^2}{(\sum x_i'^2)^2} = \frac{\sum (x_i'^2 / w_i)}{(\sum x_i'^2)^2}.$$

This variance obviously differs from the variance of $\tilde{\beta}$ given by (8.2), *whatever the sample size.* A similar conclusion can be reached with respect to the variance of the least squares estimator of α. Therefore, since the variances of the least squares estimators are not asymptotically equivalent to the variances of the maximum likelihood estimators, the least squares estimators are *not* asymptotically efficient when the disturbance is not homoskedastic.

Properties of the Estimated Variances of the Least Squares Estimators

We have found that under heteroskedasticity the least squares estimators of the regression coefficients are unbiased and consistent but not efficient or asymptotically efficient. Thus, if the disturbance is heteroskedastic and we do not know it (or know it but disregard it) and use the least squares formulas, the resulting estimators will still have some desirable properties. But when we come to using these estimators for testing hypotheses or constructing confidence intervals, we require not only that the estimators themselves be unbiased, but also that their estimated variances be unbiased. Otherwise, the tests are invalid and the constructed confidence intervals incorrect. Therefore, the next question concerns the biasedness or unbiasedness of the estimated variances obtained from the conventional formulas for the least squares estimators. For the least squares estimator of the regression slope, $\hat{\beta}$, the conventional formula for calculating the variance is given by (7.37) as

$$s_{\hat{\beta}}^2 = \frac{s^2}{\sum x_i'^2},$$

where $s^2 = [\sum (Y_i - \hat{\alpha} - \hat{\beta}X_i)^2]/(n-2)$. Under homoskedasticity, this is an unbiased estimator of the variance of $\hat{\beta}$. We wish to know whether the property of unbiasedness of $s_{\hat{\beta}}^2$ is preserved when the assumption of homoskedasticity does not hold. To answer this we have to find the mathematical expectation of s^2. We have

$$E(s^2) = E\left[\frac{1}{n-2}\right] \sum_i [\alpha + \beta X_i + \varepsilon_i - \hat{\alpha} - \hat{\beta}X_i]^2$$

$$= \frac{1}{n-2} \sum_i E[-(\hat{\alpha} - \alpha) - (\hat{\beta} - \beta)X_i + \varepsilon_i]^2.$$

Substituting for $(\hat{\alpha} - \alpha)$ from (7.30) we get

$$E(s^2) = \frac{1}{n-2} \sum_i E[-(\hat{\beta} - \beta)x_i' + \varepsilon_i']^2$$

$$= \frac{1}{n-2} \left[E(\hat{\beta} - \beta)^2 \sum_i x_i'^2 + E\sum_i \varepsilon_i'^2 - 2E(\hat{\beta} - \beta)\sum x_i'\varepsilon_i'\right].$$

Now, under heteroskedasticity

$$E(\hat{\beta} - \beta)^2 = \frac{\sum x_i'^2 \sigma_i^2}{(\sum x_i'^2)^2}$$

by (8.6). Further,

$$E(\varepsilon_i'^2) = E(\varepsilon_i^2) + E(\bar\varepsilon)^2 - 2E(\varepsilon_i\bar\varepsilon) = E(\varepsilon_i^2) + \frac{1}{n^2}E\Big[\sum_i \varepsilon_i^2 + 2\sum_{i<j}\varepsilon_i\varepsilon_j\Big]$$

$$-\frac{2}{n}E\varepsilon_i(\varepsilon_1 + \varepsilon_2 + \cdots + \varepsilon_i + \cdots + \varepsilon_n)$$

$$= \sigma_i^2 + \frac{\sum\sigma_i^2}{n^2} - \frac{2\sigma_i^2}{n} = \Big[\frac{n-2}{n}\Big]\sigma_i^2 + \frac{\sum\sigma_i^2}{n^2}.$$

Finally,

$$E(\hat\beta - \beta)\sum x_i'\varepsilon_i' = E\Big[\frac{\sum x_i'\varepsilon_i'}{\sum x_i'^2}\Big]\Big(\sum x_i'\varepsilon_i'\Big) = E\Big[\frac{\sum x_i'\varepsilon_i'}{\sum x_i'^2}\Big]^2\Big(\sum x_i'^2\Big)$$

$$= [\mathrm{Var}(\hat\beta)]\Big(\sum x_i'^2\Big) = \Big[\frac{\sum x_i'^2\sigma_i^2}{(\sum x_i'^2)^2}\Big]\Big(\sum x_i'^2\Big).$$

Substituting these results into the expression for $E(s^2)$, we obtain

(8.7) $$E(s^2) = \frac{1}{n-2}\Big\{\Big[\frac{\sum x_i'^2\sigma_i^2}{(\sum x_i'^2)^2}\Big]\Big(\sum x_i'^2\Big) + \sum\Big[\sigma_i^2 + \frac{\sum\sigma_i^2}{n^2} - \frac{2\sigma_i^2}{n}\Big]$$

$$-2\Big[\frac{\sum x_i'^2\sigma_i^2}{(\sum x_i'^2)^2}\Big]\Big(\sum x_i'^2\Big)\Big\}$$

$$= \frac{1}{n-2}\Big[-\frac{\sum x_i'^2\sigma_i^2}{\sum x_i'^2} + \sum\sigma_i^2 + \frac{\sum\sigma_i^2}{n} - \frac{2\sum\sigma_i^2}{n}\Big]$$

$$= \frac{-n(\sum x_i'^2\sigma_i^2) + (n-1)(\sum x_i'^2)(\sum\sigma_i^2)}{n(n-2)(\sum x_i'^2)}$$

and

(8.8) $$E(s_\beta^2) = \frac{E(s^2)}{\sum x_i'^2} = \frac{-n(\sum x_i'^2\sigma_i^2) + (n-1)(\sum x_i'^2)(\sum\sigma_i^2)}{n(n-2)(\sum x_i'^2)^2}.$$

Since this expression is *not* the same as the expression for the variance of $\hat\beta$ given by (8.6), we have to conclude that the conventionally calculated variance of $\hat\beta$ is *biased* when the disturbance is heteroskedastic. A similar conclusion can be reached with respect to $\hat\alpha$.

The consequence of the preceding result is that if we use the least squares estimators of the regression coefficients when the assumption of homoskedasticity is not satisfied, the confidence limits and the tests of significance developed in Chapter 7 *do not apply*. This means that if we proceed with our regression analysis under the false belief that the disturbance is homoskedastic, our inferences about the population coefficients are incorrect—that is, the calculated confidence intervals and acceptance regions will be wrong. It would be interesting to know the direction of error in this case because then we would be able to say whether the incorrect confidence intervals and acceptance regions are likely to be wider or narrower than the correct ones. We can find the answer by determining the direction of the bias of the calculated variance. If the bias is positive, the incorrect intervals and acceptance regions will be wider than the correct ones; if the bias is negative, they will be narrower. The bias is given by

$$(8.9) \quad E(s_{\hat{\beta}}^2) - \text{Var}(\hat{\beta}) = \frac{-n(\sum x_i'^2 \sigma_i^2) + (n-1)(\sum x_i'^2)(\sum \sigma_i^2)}{n(n-2)(\sum x_i'^2)^2} - \frac{\sum x_i'^2 \sigma_i^2}{(\sum x_i'^2)^2}$$

$$= \frac{-n(n-1)(\sum x_i'^2 \sigma_i^2) + (n-1)(\sum x_i'^2)(\sum \sigma_i^2)}{n(n-2)(\sum x_i'^2)^2}.$$

The direction of the bias depends on the sign of this expression. Since for $n > 2$ the denominator is always positive, it is only the sign of the numerator which is decisive. The latter depends on the direction of the association between $x_i'^2$ and σ_i^2. It can be shown—by setting $\sigma_i^2 = a + bx_i'^2$ ($b > 0$) and making the appropriate substitution in (8.9)—that when $x_i'^2$ and σ_i^2 are *positively* associated, the bias is negative. In cases like this, a reliance on the conventionally calculated standard errors will tend to lead to confidence intervals and acceptance regions that are narrower than the correct ones. This means that the estimators will then be presented as having a greater precision than is justified by the chosen level of confidence, and that the probability of rejecting the null hypothesis will be higher than indicated by the stated level of significance.

Assumptions Concerning σ_i^2

Having examined the properties of the least squares estimators of the regression coefficients under the conditions of heteroskedasticity, we come to considering alternative methods of estimation. The reader will recall that we already developed estimation formulas for the heteroskedastic case earlier in the present section. These formulas, given by (8.1) and (8.3), satisfy both the BLUE and the maximum likelihood principles. At this point, we may note an alternative and simpler way of deriving these formulas. The regression equation is

$$Y_i = \alpha + \beta X_i + \varepsilon_i,$$

where, in the case of heteroskedasticity, $\varepsilon_i \sim N(0, \sigma_i^2)$. Now, let us write

$$\varepsilon_i = \frac{u_i}{\sigma\sqrt{w_i}},$$

where $u_i \sim N(0, \sigma^2)$ and w_i are nonstochastic quantities. Then,

$$\sigma_i^2 = \frac{E(u_i^2)}{\sigma^2 w_i} = \frac{\sigma^2}{\sigma^2 w_i} = \frac{1}{w_i}.$$

The regression equation can then be written as

$$Y_i = \alpha + \beta X_i + \frac{u_i}{\sigma\sqrt{w_i}}.$$

Multiplying both sides of this equation by $\sigma\sqrt{w_i}$, we get

$$(8.10) \quad (Y_i \sigma\sqrt{w_i}) = \alpha(\sigma\sqrt{w_i}) + \beta(X_i \sigma\sqrt{w_i}) + u_i.$$

Equation (8.10) may be viewed as a regression equation in which the dependent variable is $(Y_i\sigma\sqrt{w_i})$ and which includes two explanatory variables $(\sigma\sqrt{w_i})$ and $(X_i\sigma\sqrt{w_i})$. Note that these variables can be measured only if $\sigma\sqrt{w_i}$ are known, and that the intercept of the regression equation is zero. The purpose of the transformation leading to (8.10) is to make the regression equation satisfy the condition of homoskedasticity, since the new disturbance u_i has a constant variance. By applying the least squares principle, we obtain the following "least squares normal equations" (see fn. 4, page 207)

$$(8.11) \qquad \sum_i (w_i Y_i) = \tilde{\alpha} \sum_i (w_i) + \tilde{\beta} \sum_i (w_i X_i)$$

$$\sum_i (w_i X_i Y_i) = \tilde{\alpha} \sum_i (w_i X_i) + \tilde{\beta} \sum_i (w_i X_i^2)$$

because the term σ^2 cancels out. By solving these equations for $\tilde{\alpha}$ and $\tilde{\beta}$ we obtain the formulas (8.1) and (8.3). We may note in passing that these formulas are sometimes called "weighted least squares" formulas since the sample observations are, in fact, given differential weights.

The difficulty with estimation formulas (8.1) and (8.3) is that they involve the terms σ_i^2 (or their reciprocals w_i), which are generally unknown. Thus the expressions do not qualify as estimators since they cannot be evaluated. In many cases this difficulty can be overcome either by making certain assumptions about σ_i^2 or by estimating σ_i^2 from the sample. We will first discuss the situations in which we are able to bring in additional information about σ_i^2. The information is frequently in the form of an assumption stating that σ_i^2 is associated with some variable, say Z_i. For instance, in the case of the microconsumption function the variance of the disturbance is often assumed to be positively associated with the level of income. In this case the place of Z_i would be taken by the explanatory variable of the regression equation, X_i (income). An alternative, though similar, assumption would be that the variance of the disturbance is positively associated with the mean level of consumption, in which case the place of Z_i would be taken by $E(Y_i)$. Or the changes in the variance of the disturbance may be thought to be associated with changes in some "outside" variable, for instance the size of the family. Using Z_i just gives us a way of formulating the assumption about σ_i^2 in a fairly general manner. However, to make the assumption operational, we have to specify the form of the association. One form that is very convenient and may be quite plausible is

$$(8.12) \qquad \sigma_i^2 = \sigma^2 Z_i^\delta,$$

which involves two parameters, σ^2 and δ. Of particular importance is the parameter δ, which measures the strength of heteroskedasticity: the lower its magnitude, the smaller the differences between individual variances. When $\delta = 0$, the model is homoskedastic.

The two parameters in (8.12) may both be unknown, in which case they have to be estimated along with the regression coefficients α and β, or the value of at least one of them may be specified a priori. For example, the value of δ is some-times assumed to be 2 since this makes the standard deviation of the disturbance proportional to Z_i. We shall first discuss the estimation problem in general, and then consider some special cases. The complete regression model for this kind of heteroskedastic condition then is

$$Y_i = \alpha + \beta X_i + \varepsilon_i,$$

$$\varepsilon_i \sim N(0, \sigma_i^2),$$

$$\sigma_i^2 = \sigma^2 Z_i^\delta \qquad (\sigma > 0; Z_i > 0).$$

The disturbance ε_i is, of course, assumed to be nonautoregressive, and X_i and Z_i are considered to be nonstochastic. Then we can obtain the maximum likelihood estimators of α, β, σ^2, and δ by a simple substitution for σ_i^2 in the likelihood function (8.5), which then becomes

(8.13) $$L = -\frac{n}{2} \log 2\pi - \frac{1}{2} \sum_{i=1}^{n} (\log \sigma^2 + \delta \log Z_i)$$

$$-\frac{1}{2} \sum_{i=1}^{n} \left[\frac{Y_i - \alpha - \beta X_i}{\sigma Z_i^{\delta/2}} \right]^2.$$

The first derivatives of L are

(8.14) $$\frac{\partial L}{\partial \alpha} = \frac{1}{\sigma^2} \sum_i \left[\frac{Y_i - \alpha - \beta X_i}{Z_i^\delta} \right]$$

$$\frac{\partial L}{\partial \beta} = \frac{1}{\sigma^2} \sum_i \left[\frac{(Y_i - \alpha - \beta X_i) X_i}{Z_i^\delta} \right]$$

$$\frac{\partial L}{\partial \sigma^2} = -\frac{n}{2\sigma^2} + \frac{1}{2\sigma^4} \sum_i \left[\frac{Y_i - \alpha - \beta X_i}{Z_i^{\delta/2}} \right]^2$$

$$\frac{\partial L}{\partial \delta} = -\frac{1}{2} \sum_i \log Z_i + \frac{1}{2\sigma^2} \sum_i \left[\frac{(Y_i - \alpha - \beta X_i)^2 \log Z_i}{Z_i^\delta} \right].$$

By putting each of these derivatives equal to zero, we obtain four equations to be solved for the four unknown values of α, β, σ^2, and δ. However, these equations are highly nonlinear and their solution may be quite troublesome.

Let us now consider some special cases of (8.12) that have been used in practical applications.

Case A: $\delta = 2$ *and* $Z_i = X_i$. In this case, $\sigma_i^2 = \sigma^2 X_i^2$; that is, the variance of the disturbance is assumed to be proportional to the squared value of the explanatory variable. The likelihood function (8.13) now contains only three unknown parameters, α, β, and σ^2. We can substitute for δ and Z_i in the first three expressions of (8.14), put each of these expressions equal to zero, and solve for the three unknowns. It is easily seen that the solution is exactly the same as that given by (8.1) and (8.3) except that w_i is replaced by $1/(\sigma^2 X_i^2)$. That is, we have

$$(8.15) \qquad \hat{\beta}_A = \frac{[\sum (1/X_i^2)][\sum (Y_i/X_i)] - [\sum (1/X_i)][\sum (Y_i/X_i^2)]}{n \sum (1/X_i^2) - [\sum (1/X_i)]^2};$$

$$(8.16) \qquad \hat{\alpha}_A = \frac{\sum (Y_i/X_i^2)}{\sum (1/X_i^2)} - \hat{\beta}_A \left[\frac{\sum (1/X_i)}{\sum (1/X_i^2)}\right],$$

where the subscript A indicates that the estimators have been derived for the specification of Case A. If the specification of the model is correct, these estimators are BLUE, consistent, and asymptotically efficient. The estimator of σ^2 is

$$(8.17) \qquad \hat{\sigma}_A^2 = \frac{1}{n} \sum_i \left[\left(\frac{Y_i}{X_i}\right) - \hat{\alpha}_A\left(\frac{1}{X_i}\right) - \hat{\beta}_A\right]^2$$

$$= \frac{1}{n}\left[\sum_i \left(\frac{Y_i}{X_i}\right)^2 - \hat{\alpha}_A \sum \left(\frac{Y_i}{X_i^2}\right) - \hat{\beta}_A \sum \left(\frac{Y_i}{X_i}\right)\right].$$

This estimator is consistent and asymptotically efficient but not unbiased. An unbiased estimator of σ^2, say, s_A^2, is

$$(8.18) \qquad s_A^2 = \left[\frac{n}{n-2}\right]\hat{\sigma}_A^2.$$

The variances of $\hat{\alpha}_A$ and $\hat{\beta}_A$ are given by (8.2) and (8.4), after w_i is replaced by $1/(\sigma^2 X_i^2)$. Unbiased estimators of these variances can be obtained by replacing σ^2 by s_A^2. This gives

$$(8.19) \qquad s_{\hat{\beta}_A}^2 = \frac{s_A^2 \sum (1/X_i^2)}{n \sum (1/X_i^2) - [\sum (1/X_i)]^2}$$

and

$$(8.20) \qquad s_{\hat{\alpha}_A}^2 = \frac{n s_A^2}{n \sum (1/X_i^2) - [\sum (1/X_i)]^2}.$$

EXAMPLE   Consider the following sample data on annual expenditures for clothing and on income, collected from a sample of 20 families.

Income, $	Number of Families	Clothing Expenditures, $
2000	8	160, 160, 180, 200, 210, 220, 230, 250
4000	7	200, 220, 230, 300, 310, 340, 350
6000	5	300, 300, 400, 450, 540

These observations are shown graphically in Figure 8–1. The relationship between expenditure on clothing and income is hypothesized to be

$$Y_i = \alpha + \beta X_i + \varepsilon_i,$$

where Y = expenditure on clothing, X = income, ε = random disturbance, and the subscript i refers to the ith family. The explanatory variable X_i is considered to be nonstochastic, and the disturbance ε_i is assumed to be a normally distributed, non-autoregressive random variable with zero mean and variance σ_i^2. The ordinary least squares estimators of the regression coefficients are

$$\hat{\beta} = \frac{\sum y_i' x_i'}{\sum x_i'^2} = \frac{2{,}425{,}000}{50{,}200{,}000} = 0.0483\,,$$

$$\hat{\alpha} = \bar{Y} - \hat{\beta}\bar{X} = 277.5 - 0.0483 \times 3700 = 98.79\,,$$

and the coefficient of determination is

$$R^2 = \frac{\hat{\beta}\sum x_i' y_i'}{\sum y_i'^2} = \frac{0.0483 \times 2{,}425{,}000}{190{,}975} = 0.6133\,.$$

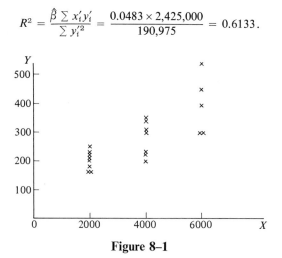

Figure 8–1

Given that the model is a heteroskedastic one, the least squares estimators are unbiased but not efficient or asymptotically efficient. Their conventionally calculated standard errors are biased and, therefore, are not presented. Note that the above value of R^2 is the maximum value for the given sample since the least squares regression line gives the best fit of any line by definition.

Now, if we assume that

$$\sigma_i^2 = \sigma^2 X_i^2\,,$$

we can obtain efficient estimators of the regression coefficients by using formulas (8.15) and (8.16). These call for the following quantities calculated from the sample data:

$$\sum_i \left[\frac{1}{X_i}\right] = \frac{8}{2000} + \frac{7}{4000} + \frac{5}{6000} = 0.006583\,;$$

$$\sum_i \left[\frac{1}{X_i}\right]^2 = \frac{8}{2000^2} + \frac{7}{4000^2} + \frac{5}{6000^2} = 0.000002567\,;$$

$$\sum_i \left[\frac{Y_i}{X_i}\right] = \frac{160}{2000} + \frac{160}{2000} + \cdots + \frac{540}{6000} = 1.624167\,;$$

$$\sum_i \left[\frac{Y_i}{X_i^2}\right] = \frac{160}{2000^2} + \frac{160}{2000^2} + \cdots + \frac{540}{6000^2} = 0.000579630\,.$$

Also we note that

$$\sum_i \left[\frac{Y_i}{X_i}\right]^2 = 0.141388.$$

Substitution then gives

$$\hat{\beta}_A = 0.0451 \quad \text{and} \quad \hat{\alpha}_A = 109.82.$$

Further, using formulas (8.19) and (8.20) we obtain estimates of the standard errors of $\hat{\alpha}_A$ and $\hat{\beta}_A$:

$$s^2_{\hat{\beta}_A} = 0.00017932, \quad s_{\hat{\beta}_A} = 0.0134,$$

$$s^2_{\hat{\alpha}_A} = 1{,}391.7020, \quad s_{\hat{\alpha}_A} = 37.30$$

Finally, $\quad R^2 = 1 - \dfrac{\sum (Y_i - \hat{\alpha}_A - \hat{\beta}_A X_i)^2}{\sum y_i'^2} = 1 - \dfrac{74{,}364}{190{,}975} = 0.6106.$

These results can be summarized as follows:

$$Y_i = 109.82 + 0.0451 X_i + e_i, \quad R^2 = 0.6106.$$
$$(37.30) \quad (0.0134)$$

As expected, the value of R^2 is lower than that for the least squares regression, but the difference is very small. Note that the implied estimate of the average income elasticity of demand for clothing is

$$\hat{\eta}_{INC} = \hat{\beta}_A \left[\frac{\bar{X}}{\bar{Y}}\right] = 0.6013,$$

which suggests that the demand for clothing is income-inelastic.

Case B: $\delta = 2$ *and* $Z_i = E(Y_i)$.   In this case it is assumed that the variance of the disturbance is proportional to the squared mean of Y_i. That is, we assume that

$$\sigma_i^2 = \sigma^2 [E(Y_i)]^2 = \sigma^2 (\alpha + \beta X_i)^2$$

The likelihood function (8.13) in this case becomes

$$(8.21) \qquad L = -\frac{n}{2} \log(2\pi) - \frac{n}{2} \log \sigma^2 - \sum_i \log(\alpha + \beta X_i)$$

$$- \frac{1}{2\sigma^2} \sum_i \left[\frac{Y_i - \alpha - \beta X_i}{(\alpha + \beta X_i)}\right]^2.$$

This function, as in Case A, involves only three unknown parameters, α, β, and σ^2. We could take the first derivatives of L with respect to each of the three parameters, put each of them equal to zero, and solve for the three unknown values.[4] However, the resulting equations are highly nonlinear and their solution

---

[4] Note that it would be incorrect simply to substitute for Z_i (and for δ) in the expressions for the first derivatives given in (8.14) because these were derived on the understanding that Z_i does not involve any of the unknown parameters. This is not true when, as in the present case, $Z_i = \alpha + \beta X_i$.

is difficult. We can simplify the problem by replacing $E(Y_i)$ with $\hat{Y}_i$, which represents the values of Y calculated from the least squares regression. That is, we take the standard deviation of the disturbance to be proportional to the distance of the least squares regression line from the horizontal axis. Since $\hat{Y}_i$ is a consistent estimator of $E(Y_i)$, we can write

$$\sigma_i = \sigma E(Y_i)$$

as

$$\sigma_i = \sigma \text{ plim } \hat{Y}_i,$$

so that putting

$$\sigma_i = \sigma \hat{Y}_i$$

does not damage the consistency of the resulting estimators of the regression coefficients. Strictly speaking, these estimators are not *exactly* maximum likelihood estimators but serve as their approximations.

By allowing ourselves the foregoing simplification, we can use formulas (8.1) and (8.3) for estimating α and β, providing we replace w_i by $1/(\sigma^2 \hat{Y}_i^2)$. Then we obtain

$$(8.22) \qquad \hat{\beta}_B = \frac{\sum (1/\hat{Y}^2) \sum (XY/\hat{Y}^2) - \sum (X/\hat{Y}^2) \sum (Y/\hat{Y}^2)}{\sum (1/\hat{Y}^2) \sum (X^2/\hat{Y}^2) - [\sum (X/\hat{Y}^2)]^2},$$

and

$$(8.23) \qquad \hat{\alpha}_B = \frac{\sum (Y/\hat{Y}^2)}{\sum (1/\hat{Y}^2)} - \hat{\beta}_B \left[\frac{\sum (X/\hat{Y}^2)}{\sum (1/\hat{Y}^2)} \right],$$

where the subscript B indicates that the estimators apply to the specification of Case B. If the specification of the model is correct, these estimators approximate the maximum likelihood estimators which are known to be consistent and asymptotically efficient. The estimator of σ^2 is

$$(8.24) \qquad s_B^2 = \frac{1}{n-2} \left[\sum_i \left(\frac{Y_i^2}{\hat{Y}_i^2} \right) - \hat{\alpha}_B \sum \left(\frac{Y_i}{\hat{Y}_i^2} \right) - \hat{\beta}_B \sum \left(\frac{X_i Y_i}{\hat{Y}_i^2} \right) \right].$$

Finally, the estimators of the standard errors of $\hat{\alpha}_B$ and $\hat{\beta}_B$ are given by

$$(8.25) \qquad s_{\hat{\beta}_B}^2 = \frac{s_B^2 \sum (1/\hat{Y}_i^2)}{\sum (1/\hat{Y}_i^2) \sum (X_i^2/\hat{Y}_i^2) - [\sum (X_i/\hat{Y}_i^2)]^2}$$

and

$$(8.26) \qquad s_{\hat{\alpha}_B}^2 = \frac{s_B^2 \sum (X_i^2/\hat{Y}_i^2)}{\sum (1/\hat{Y}_i^2) \sum (X_i^2/\hat{Y}_i^2) - [\sum (Y_i/\hat{Y}_i^2)]^2}.$$

EXAMPLE   In the example on the relationship between family expenditure on clothing and income given in connection with Case A, we assumed that $\sigma_i = \sigma X_i$. Let us change this assumption to $\sigma_i = \sigma E(Y_i)$ in accordance with Case B. In carrying out the calculations we shall approximate $E(Y_i)$ by $\hat{Y}_i$, previously determined to be

$$\hat{Y}_i = 98.79 + 0.0483 X_i.$$

The following quantities have been calculated from the sample data:

$$\sum_i \left[\frac{1}{\hat{Y}_i^2}\right] = 0.000322729,$$

$$\sum_i \left[\frac{X_i}{\hat{Y}_i^2}\right] = 0.946107,$$

$$\sum_i \left[\frac{X_i^2}{\hat{Y}_i^2}\right] = 3{,}271.421,$$

$$\sum_i \left[\frac{Y_i}{\hat{Y}_i^2}\right] = 0.077417,$$

$$\sum_i \left[\frac{Y_i^2}{\hat{Y}_i^2}\right] = 20.503404,$$

$$\sum_i \left[\frac{X_i Y_i}{\hat{Y}_i^2}\right] = 250.091731.$$

By making the appropriate substitutions into formulas (8.22) through (8.26) we get

$$\hat{\beta}_B = 0.0465,$$

$$\hat{\alpha}_B = 103.56,$$

and

$$s^2_{\hat{\beta}_B} = 0.00009558, \qquad s_{\hat{\beta}_B} = 0.0098,$$

$$s^2_{\hat{\alpha}_B} = 968.9202, \qquad s_{\hat{\alpha}_B} = 31.13.$$

Finally,

$$R^2 = 1 - \frac{\sum (Y_i - \hat{\alpha}_B - \hat{\beta}_B X_i)^2}{\sum y_i'^2} = 1 - \frac{74{,}063}{190{,}975} = 0.6122.$$

In summary, the results for Case B are

$$Y_i = 103.56 + 0.0465 X_i + e_i, \qquad R^2 = 0.6122.$$
$$(31.13) \quad (0.0098)$$

Case C: $Z_i = X_i$. This case is more general than the previous two cases since we do not make any prior specification concerning the value of δ. The assumption about the nature of heteroskedasticity in this case is

$$\sigma_i^2 = \sigma^2 X_i^\delta,$$

or

$$\log \sigma_i = \log \sigma + \frac{\delta}{2} \log X_i.$$

The likelihood function (8.13) then involves *four* unknown parameters, α, β, σ^2, and δ. As mentioned earlier, δ measures the strength of heteroskedasticity in the sense that the smaller the value of δ, the smaller the difference between the individual variances of the disturbance. In Case C, unlike Cases A and B, we are letting the data tell us what this strength seems to be, rather than specifying it a priori. The only prior specification that we make is that the standard deviation of the disturbance is related to the explanatory variable—and that this relationship is log-linear. The price that we pay for a greater generality in the present case is the higher degree of complexity of estimation.

The problem of obtaining maximum likelihood estimates of the regression coefficients, although more complicated than in the previous two cases, is manageable if we use an electronic computer. A relatively simple way of handling it is as follows. By putting each of the first three derivatives of (8.14) equal to zero, substituting X_i for Z_i, and rearranging terms we obtain the following three equations:

$$(8.27) \qquad \sum_i \left[\frac{Y_i}{X_i^\delta} \right] = \hat{\alpha} \sum_i \left[\frac{1}{X_i^\delta} \right] + \hat{\beta} \sum_i \left[\frac{X_i}{X_i^\delta} \right],$$

$$(8.28) \qquad \sum_i \left[\frac{X_i Y_i}{X_i^\delta} \right] = \hat{\alpha} \sum_i \left[\frac{X_i}{X_i^\delta} \right] + \hat{\beta} \sum_i \left[\frac{X_i^2}{X_i^\delta} \right].$$

$$(8.29) \qquad \hat{\sigma}^2 = \frac{1}{n} \left[\sum_i \left(\frac{Y_i^2}{X_i^\delta} \right) - \hat{\alpha} \sum_i \left(\frac{Y_i}{X_i^\delta} \right) - \hat{\beta} \sum_i \left(\frac{X_i Y_i}{X_i^\delta} \right) \right].$$

If δ were known, equations (8.27) through (8.29) could be solved for $\hat{\alpha}$, $\hat{\beta}$, and $\hat{\sigma}^2$. Therefore, by selecting different values of δ we obtain different estimates of the remaining three parameters. In this way we can obtain estimates of α, β, and σ^2 for $\delta = 0$, $\delta = 0.1$, $\delta = 0.2$, and so on until we come to values of δ that are clearly unreasonable (in most practical situations this would be perhaps 5.0 or 6.0). For each value of δ—and the corresponding values of $\hat{\alpha}$, $\hat{\beta}$, and $\hat{\sigma}^2$—we also calculate the value of L as given by (8.13). Then, of all the solutions, we select the one that gives the largest value of L. This solution will maximize the likelihood function as desired. The standard errors of $\hat{\alpha}$ and $\hat{\beta}$ can be estimated by using formulas (8.2) and (8.4), after replacing w_i by $(1/\hat{\sigma}^2 X_i^{\hat{\delta}})$. The variance of $\hat{\delta}$ can be estimated by $s_{\hat{\delta}}^2 = 2/[\sum_i (\log_e X_i)^2]$, where $\log_e X_i = 2.302585 \log_{10} X_i$. This formula represents the asymptotic variance of $\hat{\delta}$ as defined on page 182. Incidentally, if the precision of one decimal place for $\hat{\delta}$ is not sufficient, we can choose finer intervals for the successive values of δ in the vicinity of the solution.

Estimation of σ_i^2

When no assumptions about the nature of heteroskedasticity are made, we have to rely entirely on the sample information and estimate the variances of the disturbance from the data. Since for each specific value of X the value of the variance of the disturbance may be different, we need several observations on the dependent variable for each X_i. If we had only one observation for each value of X, we could obviously find no information about the dispersion of *all* potential observations. Suppose, therefore, that there are m different values of X in the sample, and that for each X_i we have n_i observations on the dependent variable.

Then the regression equation can be written as

$$Y_{ij} = \alpha + \beta X_i + \varepsilon_{ij} \qquad (i = 1, 2, \ldots, m; j = 1, 2, \ldots, n_i),$$

$$n = \sum_{i=1}^{m} n_i,$$

$$X_i \neq X_j \qquad (i \neq j).$$

To illustrate the new subscript notation, we use the data on family expenditure on clothing and income on page 259. There we have

$$m = 3,$$
$$n_1 = 8,$$
$$n_2 = 7,$$
$$n_3 = 5,$$
$$n = 20.$$

Also, for example, $Y_{25} = 310$ is the value of the dependent variable for the fifth family in the $4000 income bracket. In general, there are $(m + 2)$ parameters to be estimated: $\alpha, \beta, \sigma_1^2, \sigma_2^2, \ldots, \sigma_m^2$. The appropriate likelihood function is given by

$$(8.30) \qquad L = -\frac{n}{2} \log (2\pi) - \frac{1}{2} \sum_{i=1}^{m} n_i \log \sigma_i^2 - \frac{1}{2} \sum_{i=1}^{m} \sum_{j=1}^{n_i} \left[\frac{Y_{ij} - \alpha - \beta X_i}{\sigma_i} \right]^2.$$

By differentiating L with respect to the unknown parameters, and by putting the resulting derivatives equal to zero, we would obtain $(m + 2)$ equations that could be solved for the $(m + 2)$ values of the parameters. However, the solution is quite difficult to compute.

One way of overcoming the computational difficulty is to use an iterative procedure, as follows.

1. Obtain ordinary least squares estimates of α and β, to be called $\hat{\alpha}$ and $\hat{\beta}$. Use these to get "first round" estimates of σ_i^2, say $\hat{\sigma}_i^2$, given as

$$\hat{\sigma}_i^2 = \frac{1}{n_i} \sum_{j=1}^{n_i} (Y_{ij} - \hat{\alpha} - \hat{\beta} X_i)^2.$$

2. In formulas (8.1) and (8.3), replace w_i with $1/\hat{\sigma}_i^2$, and obtain new estimates of α and β, say $\hat{\hat{\alpha}}$ and $\hat{\hat{\beta}}$. Use these to obtain "second round" estimates of σ_i^2, say $\hat{\hat{\sigma}}_i^2$, given as

$$\hat{\hat{\sigma}}_i^2 = \frac{1}{n_i} \sum_{j=1}^{n_i} (Y_{ij} - \hat{\hat{\alpha}} - \hat{\hat{\beta}} X_i)^2.$$

3. In formulas (8.1) and (8.3), replace w_i by $1/\hat{\hat{\sigma}}_i^2$, and obtain a new set of estimates of α and β. Use these estimates to obtain "third round" estimates of σ_i^2.

This is to be continued until the values of the estimates converge, that is, until the differences between successive sets of estimates are negligible.[5] The standard errors of the estimated regression coefficients can be estimated by putting $w_i = 1/\hat{\sigma}_i^2$ (where $\hat{\sigma}_i^2$ is the "final round" estimate of σ_i^2) in formulas (8.2) and (8.4).

This iterative procedure is obviously quite laborious. A simple alternative is to estimate σ_i^2 by

$$(8.31) \qquad s_i^2 = \frac{1}{n_i} \sum_{j=1}^{n_i} (Y_{ij} - \bar{Y}_i)^2,$$

where

$$\bar{Y}_i = \frac{1}{n_i} \sum_{j=1}^{n_i} Y_{ij}.$$

It is easy to show that s_i^2 is a consistent estimator of σ_i^2. By replacing w_i with $1/s_i^2$ in (8.1) and (8.3), we obtain estimates of the regression coefficients; and by making the same substitution in (8.2) and (8.4), we obtain their estimated standard errors. The price that we are paying for this simplification is that the resulting estimates are not exactly equal to the maximum likelihood estimates, but only asymptotically so.

EXAMPLE   Returning to the data on family expenditure on clothing and income, we can consider estimating the variances of the disturbance from the data rather than making any assumptions about them. Using (8.31) we obtain

$$s_1^2 = 935.94,$$
$$s_2^2 = 3183.67,$$
$$s_3^2 = 8416.00.$$

Formulas (8.1) through (8.4) require the following quantities:

$$\sum_{i=1}^{m} \sum_{j=1}^{n_i} w_i = \sum_{i=1}^{m} n_i w_i = \frac{n_1}{s_1^2} + \frac{n_2}{s_2^2} + \frac{n_3}{s_3^2} = 0.011340725;$$

$$\sum_{i=1}^{m} \sum_{j=1}^{n_i} w_i X_i Y_{ij} = \sum_{i=1}^{m} w_i X_i \sum_{j=1}^{n_i} Y_{ij} = \frac{X_1}{s_1^2} \sum_{j=1}^{8} Y_{1j} + \frac{X_2}{s_2^2} \sum_{j=1}^{7} Y_{2j} + \frac{X_3}{s_3^2} \sum_{j=1}^{5} Y_{3j}$$
$$= 7{,}309.240;$$

$$\sum_{i=1}^{m} \sum_{j=1}^{n_i} w_i X_i = \sum_{i=1}^{m} n_i w_i X_i = \frac{n_1 X_1}{s_1^2} + \frac{n_2 X_2}{s_2^2} + \frac{n_3 X_3}{s_3^2} = 29.455270;$$

$$\sum_{i=1}^{m} \sum_{j=1}^{n_i} w_i Y_{ij} = \sum_{i=1}^{m} w_i \sum_{j=1}^{n_i} Y_{ij} = \frac{1}{s_1^2} \sum_{j=1}^{8} Y_{1j} + \frac{1}{s_2^2} \sum_{j=1}^{7} Y_{2j} + \frac{1}{s_3^2} \sum_{j=1}^{5} Y_{3j}$$
$$= 2{,}569218;$$

$$\sum_{i=1}^{m} \sum_{j=1}^{n_i} w_i X_i^2 = \sum_{i=1}^{m} n_i w_i X_i^2 = \frac{n_1 X_1^2}{s_1^2} + \frac{n_2 X_2^2}{s_2^2} + \frac{n_3 X_3^2}{s_3^2} = 90{,}758.660.$$

[5] The correctness of this procedure rests on two assertions; namely, (a) that the procedure always leads to convergence and (b) that the final values of the estimates coincide with the values of the maximum likelihood estimators. While the author is not aware of the existence of a formal proof of these assertions, they did appear to hold in every case that has been tried.

Then, the estimates of the regression coefficients are

$$\tilde{\beta} = 0.0446 \qquad \text{and} \qquad \tilde{\alpha} = 110.63,$$

and
$$s_{\tilde{\beta}}^2 = 0.00007015, \qquad s_{\tilde{\beta}} = 0.0084;$$

$$s_{\tilde{\alpha}}^2 = 561.4306, \qquad s_{\tilde{\alpha}} = 23.69.$$

Finally,
$$R^2 = 1 - \frac{\sum_i \sum_j (Y_{ij} - \tilde{\alpha} - \tilde{\beta} X_i)^2}{\sum_i \sum_j (Y_{ij} - \bar{Y})^2} = 1 - \frac{74{,}591}{190{,}975} = 0.6094.$$

In summary, the results are

$$Y_{ij} = 110.63 + 0.0446 X_i + e_{ij}, \qquad R^2 = 0.6094.$$
$$\phantom{Y_{ij} = }(23.69) \quad (0.0084)$$

These results are similar to those obtained in Case A and Case B under various assumptions concerning σ_i^2.

Tests for Homoskedasticity

Up to this point, our discussion has been concerned with the implications of heteroskedasticity in a linear regression model. We have examined the effects of heteroskedasticity on the properties of ordinary least squares estimators and their conventionally calculated standard errors, and we have discussed various alternative estimators designed for heteroskedastic models. However, if we do not know whether the model under investigation is or is not homoskedastic, and if we are unwilling to make an assumption about it, we may not be able to decide which estimation procedure to use. In such cases we have to resort to the information provided by the sample, and carry out a test. Specifically, we may want to test the null hypothesis,

$$H_0: \quad \sigma_1^2 = \sigma_2^2 = \cdots = \sigma_m^2 \qquad (m \leq n),$$

where m is the number of different values of the explanatory variable. The nature of the test will depend upon the specification of the maintained hypothesis. If the maintained hypothesis is

$$\sigma_i^2 = \sigma^2 Z_i^\delta \qquad (i = 1, 2, \ldots, m),$$

where Z_i is some known nonstochastic variable (e.g., X_i), then the null hypothesis may be stated as

$$H_0: \quad \delta = 0.$$

This is because if $\delta = 0$, then $\sigma_i^2 = \sigma^2$, and this means homoskedasticity. We have already discussed the problem of obtaining a maximum likelihood estimator of δ and its estimated standard error. In large samples this estimator will be normally distributed (at least approximately) so that the test of H_0 is rather simple. At the 5% level of significance, the acceptance region for H_0 will be

$$-1.96 \leq \frac{\hat{\delta}}{s_{\hat{\delta}}} \leq +1.96,$$

where $\hat{\delta}$ is the maximum likelihood estimator of δ, and $s_{\hat{\delta}}$ its estimated standard error.

A test of the homoskedasticity hypothesis when no specification is made concerning the nature of heteroskedasticity, can be carried out if we have several observations on the dependent variable for each specific value of the explanatory variable. If this is the case, we can form the following test statistic:

$$(8.32) \qquad\qquad \hat{\lambda} = \frac{-4.60517 \log M}{1 + N},$$

where

$$\log M = \left\{ \sum_i \left[\frac{n_i - 1}{2} \right] \log \left[\frac{n_i s_i^2}{n_i - 1} \right] \right\} - \left\{ \sum_i \left[\frac{n_i - 1}{2} \right] \right\} \left\{ \log \left[\frac{\sum n_i s_i^2}{\sum (n_i - 1)} \right] \right\},$$

$$N = \frac{1}{3(m-1)} \left\{ \sum_i \left[\frac{1}{n_i} \right] - \frac{1}{n} \right\} \qquad (i = 1, 2, \ldots, m),$$

and s_i^2 is defined as in (8.31). This test statistic is approximately distributed as chi-square distribution with $(m - 1)$ degrees of freedom.[6] The acceptance region for H_0 at the 5% level of significance then is

$$\hat{\lambda} \le \chi^2_{m-1, 0.5}.$$

EXAMPLE   In our example on family expenditure and income we have three different values of X so that the test statistic $\hat{\lambda}$ will have a chi-square distribution with two degrees of freedom. The 5% acceptance region for the hypothesis of homoskedasticity then is

$$\hat{\lambda} \le 5.991,$$

where the value 5.991 has been taken from the chi-square table. By substitution from the sample data we obtain

$$\log M = \frac{7}{2} \log \left[\frac{8 \times 935.94}{7} \right] + \frac{6}{2} \log \left[\frac{7 \times 3183.67}{6} \right] + \frac{4}{2} \log \left[\frac{5 \times 8416}{4} \right]$$

$$- \left[\frac{7}{2} + \frac{6}{2} + \frac{4}{2} \right] \left\{ \log \left[\frac{8 \times 935.94 + 7 \times 3183.67 + 5 \times 8416}{7 + 6 + 4} \right] \right\}$$

$$= -1.46505$$

$$N = \frac{1}{3 \times 2} \left[\frac{1}{8} + \frac{1}{7} + \frac{1}{5} - \frac{1}{20} \right] = 0.06964.$$

[6] See Paul G. Hoel, *Introduction to Mathematical Statistics*, 2nd ed. (New York: Wiley, 1955), p. 195. Note that in our definition (8.32) we use *common* logarithms. A modification of (8.32) to deal with the case in which we observe only one value of Y for each specific value of X is suggested in J. B. Ramsey, "Tests for Specification Errors in Classical Linear Least-squares Regression Analysis," *Journal of the Royal Statistical Society*, Series B, Vol. 31, 1969, pp. 350–371. Some special tests can also be found in S. M. Goldfeld and R. E. Quandt, "Some Tests for Homoscedasticity," *Journal of the American Statistical Association*, Vol. 60, September, 1965, pp. 539–547.

Therefore,

$$\hat{\lambda} = \frac{(-4.60517) \times (-1.46505)}{1.06964} = 6.305.$$

Since the value of $\hat{\lambda}$ lies outside the acceptance region, we reject the hypothesis of homoskedasticity at the 5% level of significance. The evidence suggests that the variance of the disturbance is not constant.

8–2   Autoregressive Disturbances

By the assumption (7.5) of the classical normal linear regression model, we have

$$E(\varepsilon_i \varepsilon_j) = 0 \quad \text{for all } i \neq j.$$

Since the mean of ε_i and of ε_j is assumed to be zero, we can write

$$\text{Cov}(\varepsilon_i, \varepsilon_j) = E[\varepsilon_i - E(\varepsilon_i)][\varepsilon_j - E(\varepsilon_j)] = E(\varepsilon_i \varepsilon_j) = 0.$$

This feature of the regression disturbances is known as nonautoregression; some authors refer to it as the absence of serial correlation. It implies that the disturbance occurring at one point of observation is not correlated with any other disturbance. This means that when observations are made over time, the effect of the disturbance occurring at one period does not carry over into another period. For instance, in a study of the relationship between output and inputs of a firm or industry from monthly observations, nonautoregression of the disturbance implies that the effect of machine breakdown is strictly temporary in the sense that only the current month's output is affected. In the case of cross-sectional observations such as those on income and expenditure of different families, the assumption of nonautoregression means that if the expenditure behavior of one family is "disturbed"—for example, by the visit of a relative—this does not affect the expenditure behavior of any other family.

Our present task is to consider the plausibility of the assumption of non-autoregression, to examine the consequences of its violation on the properties of the least squares estimators, and to develop alternative methods of estimation if needed. In Section 8–1 we argued that the assumption of homoskedasticity is frequently reasonable in the case of models describing the behavior of aggregates over time, but that its plausibility is questionable when microeconomic relations are estimated from cross-sectional data. Here, in connection with the assumption of nonautoregression, the argument is just the reverse. The usual contention is that the assumption of nonautoregression is more frequently violated in the case of relations estimated from time series data than in the case of relations estimated from cross-sectional data. This contention relies largely on the interpretation of the disturbance as a summary of a large number of random and independent factors that enter into the relationship under study, but which are not measurable. Then, one would suspect that the effect of these factors operating in one period would, in part, carry over to the following periods. This seems more likely than that the effect would carry over from one family, firm, or other similar unit to another—assuming, of course, that the units are selected at random from a large population.

Autoregression of the disturbances can be compared with the sound effect of tapping a musical string: while the sound is loudest at the time of impact, it does not stop immediately but lingers on for a time until it finally dies off. This may also be the characteristic of the disturbance, since its effect may linger for some time after its occurrence. But while the effect of one disturbance lingers on, other disturbances take place, as if the musical string were tapped over and over, sometimes harder than at other times. The shorter the time between the tappings, the greater the likelihood that the preceding sound can still be heard. Similarly, the shorter the periods of individual observations, the greater the likelihood of encountering autoregressive disturbances. Thus we would be more suspicious of the presence of autoregression when dealing with monthly or quarterly observations than when the data are given at annual intervals.

The presumption that relationships estimated from observations over time involve autoregressive disturbances is so common that, in any discussion of autoregression in the literature, the variables are given a subscript t (for "time") rather than the subscript i that is used in the general case. We shall follow this custom in our discussion. Thus, if the disturbances are autoregressive, we have

$$E(\varepsilon_t \varepsilon_{t-s}) \neq 0 \qquad (t > s).$$

This expression implies that the disturbance occurring at time t is related to the disturbance occurring at time $(t - s)$. The consequences of autoregression for estimation are difficult to trace unless its nature is specified more precisely. Most of the work in this context has been done on the assumption that

(8.33) $E(\varepsilon_t \varepsilon_{t-s}) = \rho^s \sigma^2 \qquad (s < t)$

or $\mathrm{Cov}(\varepsilon_{t,}\, \varepsilon_{t-s}) = \rho^s \sigma^2,$

where ρ is a parameter whose value is less than $+1$ and more than -1, and σ^2 is the variance of ε_t as before.[7] The successive covariances of the disturbances are

$$\mathrm{Cov}(\varepsilon_{t,}\, \varepsilon_{t-1}) = \rho \sigma^2,$$

$$\mathrm{Cov}(\varepsilon_{t,}\, \varepsilon_{t-2}) = \rho^2 \sigma^2,$$

$$\mathrm{Cov}(\varepsilon_{t,}\, \varepsilon_{t-3}) = \rho^3 \sigma^2,$$

$$\vdots$$

$$\mathrm{Cov}(\varepsilon_{t,}\, \varepsilon_1) = \rho^{t-1} \sigma^2.$$

If the value of ρ is equal to some number between 0 and 1, ρ^2 will be smaller than ρ, ρ^3 will be smaller than ρ^2, and so on. This means that the greater the number of periods between two disturbances, the smaller their covariance. If ρ is

---

[7] To suppose that $|\rho| = 1$ would mean that the covariances do not diminish as s increases; it would also mean that the variance of the disturbance would grow infinitely large (see (8.37)). In most economic contexts this is implausible.

equal to zero, each covariance will be equal to zero, so that the assumption of nonautoregression is preserved. If ρ lies between -1 and 0, the values of $\rho, \rho^2, \rho^3, \ldots$ will decrease in absolute magnitude, but they will alternate in sign. The same will be true of the respective covariances.

Generation of the Disturbances

The question that has to be answered now concerns the manner in which the disturbances are generated so that they are related to each other as specified by (8.33). In the case where all the basic assumptions hold, each disturbance represents an independent random drawing from a normal population with zero mean and variance σ^2. When the disturbances are autoregressive, the drawings are no longer independent. Specifically, we shall postulate that the disturbances are generated in accordance with the following scheme:

$$(8.34) \qquad \varepsilon_t = \rho\varepsilon_{t-1} + u_t \qquad (t = 1, 2, \ldots),$$

where u_t is a normally and independently distributed random variable with mean zero and a variance σ_u^2 that is assumed to be independent of ε_{t-1}. That is,

$$(8.35) \qquad u_t \sim N(0, \sigma_u^2) \quad \text{for all } t,$$

$$E(u_t u_s) = 0 \qquad \text{for all } t \neq s.$$

$$E(u_t \varepsilon_{t-1}) = 0 \qquad \text{for all } t.$$

A relationship such as (8.34) is known as a *first-order autoregressive scheme*. It implies that each current disturbance is equal to a "portion" of the preceding disturbance *plus* a random effect represented by u_t. By a successive substitution for $\varepsilon_{t-1}, \varepsilon_{t-2}, \ldots, \varepsilon_1$, we obtain

$$\varepsilon_t = \rho\varepsilon_{t-1} + u_t$$
$$= \rho(\rho\varepsilon_{t-2} + u_{t-1}) + u_t$$
$$= \rho^2\varepsilon_{t-2} + \rho u_{t-1} + u_t$$
$$= \rho^2(\rho\varepsilon_{t-3} + u_{t-2}) + \rho u_{t-1} + u_t$$
$$= \rho^3\varepsilon_{t-3} + \rho^2 u_{t-2} + \rho u_{t-1} + u_t$$
$$\vdots$$
$$= \rho^t\varepsilon_0 + \rho^{t-1}u_1 + \rho^{t-2}u_2 + \cdots + \rho^2 u_{t-2} + \rho u_{t-1} + u_t.$$

This means that each disturbance ε_t is generated as a linear function of the random effects $u_1, u_2, \ldots, u_t$ and the "initial disturbance" ε_0. We have already specified how the u's are generated; to complete the description of ε_t we have to make an additional specification concerning the initial value of ε_0. For reasons that will become clear later, we assume that ε_0 is a normally distributed random variable with mean zero and variance $\sigma_u^2/(1 - \rho^2)$. That is,

$$(8.36) \qquad \varepsilon_0 \sim N\left[0, \frac{\sigma_u^2}{1 - \rho^2}\right].$$

Let us now demonstrate that the first-order autoregressive scheme as specified by (8.34) through (8.36) does, in fact, lead to the covariances between successive disturbances as stated in (8.33) and, at the same time, does not conflict with the assumptions of normality, zero mean, and homoskedasticity of the ε's. First, since ε_t is a linear combination of $\varepsilon_0, u_1, u_2, \ldots, u_t$, all of which are normal and independent of each other, ε_t itself must be normal. Furthermore, we have

$$E(\varepsilon_t) = \rho^t E(\varepsilon_0) + \rho^{t-1} E(u_1) + \cdots + \rho E(u_{t-1}) + E(u_t) = 0,$$

so that the assumption of zero mean of ε_t is also preserved. Next, we note that

$$(8.37) \qquad \mathrm{Var}(\varepsilon_t) = (\rho^t)^2 \mathrm{Var}(\varepsilon_0) + (\rho^{t-1})^2 \mathrm{Var}(u_1) + (\rho^{t-2})^2 \mathrm{Var}(u_2) + \cdots$$

$$= \rho^{2t} \left[\frac{\sigma_u^2}{1 - \rho^2} \right] + \rho^{2(t-1)} \sigma_u^2 + \cdots + \rho^2 \sigma_u^2 + \sigma_u^2$$

$$= \rho^{2t} \left[\frac{\sigma_u^2}{1 - \rho^2} \right] + \sigma_u^2 [\rho^{2(t-1)} + \rho^{2(t-2)} + \cdots + \rho^2 + 1]$$

$$= \sigma_u^2 \left[\frac{\rho^{2t}}{1 - \rho^2} + \frac{1 - \rho^{2t}}{1 - \rho^2} \right] = \frac{\sigma_u^2}{1 - \rho^2}.$$

Since σ_u^2 is constant through time, $\mathrm{Var}(\varepsilon_t)$ will also be constant, so that the assumption of homoskedasticity also holds. Note that this result has been obtained by making use of (8.36). Finally, from (8.34) we have

$$\varepsilon_t = \rho \varepsilon_{t-1} + u_t$$

$$= \rho^2 \varepsilon_{t-2} + \rho u_{t-1} + u_t$$

$$\vdots$$

$$= \rho^s \varepsilon_{t-s} + \rho^{s-1} u_{t-s+1} + \cdots + \rho u_{t-1} + u_t.$$

Multiplying both sides of the above expression by ε_{t-s} and taking mathematical expectations, we obtain

$$E(\varepsilon_t \varepsilon_{t-s}) = \rho^s E(\varepsilon_{t-s}^2) + \rho^{s-1} E(\varepsilon_{t-s} u_{t-s+1}) + \cdots + \rho E(\varepsilon_{t-s} u_{t-1}) + E(\varepsilon_{t-s} u_t)$$

$$= \rho^s \mathrm{Var}(\varepsilon_{t-s}) = \rho^s \sigma^2,$$

which is the same as the specification (8.33). Therefore, the generating mechanism (8.34) through (8.36) does give the correlation between the disturbances as specified earlier, and does not in any way conflict with the remaining basic assumptions.

The preceding remarks make it clear that the relationships between disturbances are crucially dependent on the value of the parameter ρ. This dependence is particularly emphasized by the following interpretation of ρ. In (8.33), the covariance between any two successive disturbances, say ε_t and ε_{t-1}, is given by

$$\mathrm{Cov}(\varepsilon_t, \varepsilon_{t-1}) = \rho \sigma^2.$$

Therefore,

$$\rho = \frac{\text{Cov}(\varepsilon_t, \varepsilon_{t-1})}{\sigma^2},$$

which, since $\sigma^2 = \text{Var}(\varepsilon_t) = \text{Var}(\varepsilon_{t-1})$, can be written as

$$\rho = \frac{\text{Cov}(\varepsilon_t, \varepsilon_{t-1})}{\sqrt{\text{Var}(\varepsilon_t)}\sqrt{\text{Var}(\varepsilon_{t-1})}}.$$

Now, an expression in which the covariance of two variables is divided by the product of the standard deviations of these variables is known as the *coefficient of correlation* between the two variables. This coefficient measures the degree of the relationship between two random variables and its values range from -1 to $+1$. Positive values of the coefficient reflect the existence of a positive relationship, and negative values the presence of a negative relationship. The coefficient of correlation whose value is close to $+1$ or to -1 indicates a high degree of relationship between the variables, and the coefficient whose value is close to zero indicates a low degree of relationship. This means that ρ is, in fact, the coefficient of correlation between ε_t and ε_{t-1}, ρ^2 is the coefficient of correlation between ε_t and ε_{t-2}, ρ^3 is the coefficient of correlation between ε_t and ε_{t-3}, and so on. Note that $\rho = +1$ or $\rho = -1$ is ruled out by the maintained hypothesis specified in connection with (8.33). *When ρ is equal to zero*, we have

$$\varepsilon_t = u_t,$$

$$\text{Var}(\varepsilon_t) = \sigma_u^2,$$

$$\text{Var}(\varepsilon_0) = \sigma_u^2.$$

and since u_t is a normally and independently distributed variable with zero mean and constant variance, *all* the basic assumptions concerning ε hold.

Properties of the Least Squares Estimators

Let us now examine the properties of the least squares estimators of α and β in

$$Y_t = \alpha + \beta X_t + \varepsilon_t,$$

when the disturbance ε_t is autoregressive. The least squares estimator of β is

$$\hat{\beta} = \frac{\sum x_t' y_t'}{\sum x_t'^2} = \beta + \frac{\sum x_t' \varepsilon_t}{\sum x_t'^2},$$

as given by (7.32). Then,

$$E(\hat{\beta}) = \beta + \frac{\sum x_t' E(\varepsilon_t)}{\sum x_t'^2} = \beta.$$

The least squares estimator of α is

$$\hat{\alpha} = \bar{Y} - \hat{\beta}\bar{X} = (\alpha + \beta\bar{X} + \bar{\varepsilon}) - \hat{\beta}\bar{X};$$

and

$$E(\hat{\alpha}) = \alpha + \beta\bar{X} + E(\bar{\varepsilon}) - E(\hat{\beta})\bar{X} = \alpha.$$

This means that the least squares estimators are *unbiased* even when the disturbances are autoregressive.

Next, we determine whether the least squares estimators are still best linear unbiased estimators (BLUE) by deriving the BLUE formulas for the autoregressive case and by comparing them with the least squares formulas. If the two sets of formulas differ, then the least squares estimators are not BLUE. Let us start by considering the BLUE of β. By the condition of linearity, we have

$$\tilde{\beta} = \sum_{t=1}^{n} a_t Y_t,$$

where a_t ($t = 1, 2, \ldots, n$) are constants to be determined. Further,

$$E(\tilde{\beta}) = E\left(\sum_t a_t Y_t\right) = \sum_t a_t(\alpha + \beta X_t) = \alpha\left(\sum_t a_t\right) + \beta\left(\sum_t a_t X_t\right).$$

By the condition of unbiasedness, we require that

$$\sum a_t = 0 \quad \text{and} \quad \sum a_t X_t = 1.$$

The variance of $\tilde{\beta}$ is given as

$$\text{Var}(\tilde{\beta}) = E\left[\sum_t a_t Y_t - E\left(\sum_t a_t Y_t\right)\right]^2 = E\left[\sum_t a_t \varepsilon_t\right]^2$$

$$= E\sum_t a_t^2 \varepsilon_t^2 + 2E\sum_{s<t} a_t \varepsilon_t a_{t-s} \varepsilon_{t-s}$$

$$= \sigma^2 \sum_t a_t^2 + 2\sigma^2 \sum_{s<t} a_t a_{t-s} \rho^s.$$

To minimize $\text{Var}(\tilde{\beta})$ subject to the conditions that $\sum a_t = 0$ and that $\sum a_t X_t = 1$, we use the Lagrange multiplier technique and form a function H as follows:

$$H = \sigma^2 \sum_t a_t^2 + 2\sigma^2 \sum_{s<t} a_t a_{t-s} \rho^s - \lambda_1\left(\sum_t a_t\right) - \lambda_2\left(\sum_t a_t X_t - 1\right).$$

This function is to be minimized with respect to $a_1, a_2, \ldots, a_n, \lambda_1$ and λ_2. Differentiating and putting each of the derivatives equal to zero, we obtain

$$2a_1\sigma^2 + 2\sigma^2(a_2\rho + a_3\rho^2 + \cdots + a_n\rho^{n-1}) - \lambda_1 - \lambda_2 X_1 = 0$$

$$2a_2\sigma^2 + 2\sigma^2(a_1\rho + a_3\rho + \cdots + a_n\rho^{n-2}) - \lambda_1 - \lambda_2 X_2 = 0$$

$$\vdots$$

$$2a_n\sigma^2 + 2\sigma^2(a_1\rho^{n-1} + a_2\rho^{n-2} + \cdots + a_{n-1}\rho) - \lambda_1 - \lambda_2 X_n = 0$$

$$-\sum_t a_t = 0$$

$$-\sum_t a_t X_t + 1 = 0$$

These $(n + 2)$ equations can be solved for the $(n + 2)$ unknown values of $a_1, a_2, \ldots, a_n, \lambda_1$ and λ_2. The solution is algebraically rather cumbersome and will not be developed here;[8] but just by looking at the equations, it is obvious that the solution for $a_1, a_2, \ldots, a_n$ will involve the parameter ρ. This means that the formula for the BLUE of β will also involve ρ, and thus will differ from the formula for the least squares estimator of β. In fact, it can be shown[9] that the BLUE of β is given by

$$(8.38) \qquad \hat{\beta} = \frac{(1 - \rho^2)x_1'y_1' + \sum (x_t' - \rho x_{t-1}')(y_t' - \rho y_{t-1}')}{(1 - \rho^2)x_1'^2 + \sum (x_t' - \rho x_{t-1}')^2}$$

$$= \frac{\sum (x_t' - \rho x_{t-1}')(y_t' - \rho y_{t-1}')}{\sum (x_t' - \rho x_{t-1}')^2} + \tilde{\delta}_{\hat{\beta}},$$

where the subscript t runs from $t = 2$ to $t = n$, and $\tilde{\delta}$ is a correction factor that, for most practical purposes, can be disregarded. Other results are

$$(8.39) \qquad \mathrm{Var}(\hat{\beta}) = \frac{\sigma_u^2}{\sum (x_t' - \rho x_{t-1}')^2} + \tilde{\delta}_{\mathrm{Var}(\hat{\beta})},$$

$$(8.40) \qquad \tilde{\alpha} = \frac{1}{1 - \rho}\left\{\frac{1}{n-1}\sum (Y_t - \rho Y_{t-1}) \right.$$

$$\left. - (\hat{\beta} - \tilde{\delta}_{\hat{\beta}})\left[\frac{1}{n-1}\sum (X_t - \rho X_{t-1})\right]\right\} + \tilde{\delta}_{\tilde{\alpha}},$$

and

$$(8.41) \quad \mathrm{Var}(\tilde{\alpha}) = \frac{\sigma_u^2}{(1 - \rho)^2}\left\{\frac{1}{n-1} + \frac{[\sum (X_t - \rho X_{t-1})/(n-1)]^2}{\sum (x_t' - \rho x_{t-1}')^2}\right\} + \tilde{\delta}_{\mathrm{Var}(\tilde{\alpha})},$$

where in each expression, as in (8.38), the subscript t runs from $t = 2$ to $t = n$, and $\tilde{\delta}$ represents a correction factor which may be disregarded in practice. These results are clearly different from those given by the least squares formulas. Thus, we have to conclude that the least squares estimators are *not* BLUE when the disturbances are autoregressive. This implies that in this case the least squares estimators are *not efficient* estimators. (Intuitively, the loss of efficiency can be explained as a result of the fact that the dependence among the disturbances reduces the *effective* number of independent pieces of information in the sample.) It may be noted that when $\rho = 0$, formulas (8.38) through (8.41)—including the correction factors—reduce to the least squares formulas; if the correction factors are disregarded, these formulas are the same as those obtained by the least squares method *after* discarding the first observation.

Let us now turn to the asymptotic properties of the least squares estimators of the regression coefficients under autoregression in the disturbances. With respect to consistency, we may check whether the variances of these estimators approach zero as the sample size grows to infinity. Since the least squares estimators are

---

[8] The interested reader may consult, e.g., J. Johnston, *Econometric Methods* (New York: McGraw-Hill, 1963), pp. 179–187.

[9] *Ibid.*

unbiased, this is a sufficient condition for consistency. Starting with the variance of $\hat{\beta}$, the least squares estimator of β, we have

$$(8.42) \quad \text{Var}(\hat{\beta}) = E(\hat{\beta} - \beta)^2 = E\left[\frac{\sum x_t' \varepsilon_t}{\sum x_t'^2}\right]^2$$

$$= \frac{1}{(\sum x_t'^2)^2} E\left[\sum_t x_t'^2 \varepsilon_t^2 + 2 \sum_{s<t} x_t' \varepsilon_t x_{t-s}' \varepsilon_{t-s}\right]$$

$$= \frac{\sigma^2}{(\sum x_t'^2)^2} \left[\sum_t x_t'^2 + 2 \sum_{s<t} x_t' x_{t-s}' \rho^s\right]$$

$$= \frac{\sigma^2}{\sum x_t'^2} + \frac{2\sigma^2}{(\sum x_t'^2)^2} \left[\rho \sum_{t=2}^{n} x_t' x_{t-1}' + \rho^2 \sum_{t=3}^{n} x_t' x_{t-2}' + \cdots\right].$$

To simplify notation, we introduce the coefficient of correlation between X_t and X_{t-s}, say, r_s, which we define as

$$r_s = \frac{(1/n) \sum x_t' x_{t-s}'}{\sqrt{(1/n) \sum x_t'^2} \sqrt{(1/n) \sum x_{t-s}'^2}} = \frac{\sum x_t' x_{t-s}'}{\sqrt{\sum x_t'^2} \sqrt{\sum x_{t-s}'^2}},$$

where $s = 1, 2, \ldots, n - 1$; $t = s + 1, s + 2, \ldots, n$; and $s < t$. It can easily be shown that the maximum value of r_s^2 (like that of any squared coefficient of correlation) is unity. Then we can write $\text{Var}(\hat{\beta})$ as

$$(8.42a) \quad \text{Var}(\hat{\beta}) = \frac{\sigma^2}{\sum x_t'^2}$$

$$+ \frac{2\sigma^2}{(\sum x_t'^2)^2} \left[\rho r_1 \sqrt{\sum x_t'^2} \sqrt{\sum x_{t-1}'^2} + \rho^2 r_2 \sqrt{\sum x_t'^2} \sqrt{\sum x_{t-2}'^2} + \cdots\right]$$

$$= \frac{(\sigma^2/n)}{(1/n) \sum x_t'^2} + \frac{2(\sigma^2/n)}{[(1/n) \sum x_t'^2]^2} \left[\rho r_1 \sqrt{\frac{1}{n} \sum x_t'^2} \sqrt{\frac{1}{n} \sum x_{t-1}'^2}\right.$$

$$\left. + \rho^2 r_2 \sqrt{\frac{1}{n} \sum x_t'^2} \sqrt{\frac{1}{n} \sum x_{t-2}'^2} + \cdots\right].$$

As n approaches infinity, the terms

$$\frac{1}{n} \sum x_t'^2, \quad \frac{1}{n} \sum x_{t-1}'^2, \quad \frac{1}{n} \sum x_{t-2}'^2, \quad \ldots,$$

will all approach the same finite positive number, say, m_{xx}, and the terms $r_1, r_2, r_3, \ldots$, will approach some numbers with an absolute value less than or equal to one, say, $r_1^*, r_2^*, r_3^*, \ldots$. Therefore, we have

$$\lim_{n \to \infty} \text{Var}(\hat{\beta}) = \frac{\lim (\sigma^2/n)}{m_{xx}} + \frac{2 \lim (\sigma^2/n)}{m_{xx}} [\rho r_1^* + \rho^2 r_2^* + \cdots]$$

$$= \frac{\lim (\sigma^2/n)}{m_{xx}} [1 + 2\rho r_1^* + 2\rho^2 r_2^* + \cdots].$$

Now, since ρ lies between -1 and $+1$ and r_1^*, r_2^*, ..., are each less than one in absolute value, the sum of the infinite series

$$[1 + 2\rho r_1^* + 2\rho^2 r_2^* + \cdots]$$

will be a finite number.

Thus, since $\lim_{n \to \infty}(\sigma^2/n) = 0$,

$$\lim_{n \to \infty} \mathrm{Var}(\hat{\beta}) = 0.$$

By using a similar argument we can also show that

$$\lim_{n \to \infty} \mathrm{Var}(\hat{\alpha}) = 0.$$

This means that the least squares estimators of the regression coefficients are *consistent* even when the regression disturbances are autoregressive.

The last property that is of interest to us is asymptotic efficiency. This can be examined by comparing the asymptotic variances of the least squares estimators with the asymptotic variances of the best linear unbiased estimators (or, rather, their approximations) given by (8.38) and (8.40). Using the formula for the asymptotic variance of an estimator given in Section 6–1, we can determine the asymptotic variance of the least squares estimator of β as follows:

$$\mathrm{Asympt.\ Var}(\hat{\beta}) = \frac{1}{n} \lim_{n \to \infty} En \left[\frac{\sum x_t' \varepsilon_t}{\sum x_t'^2} \right]^2$$

$$= \frac{1}{n} \lim_{n \to \infty} \frac{n}{(\sum x_t'^2)^2} \left[\sigma^2 \sum_t x_t'^2 + 2\sigma^2 \sum_{s<t} x_t' x_{t-s}' \rho^s \right]$$

$$= \frac{\sigma^2}{n} \left[\frac{m_{xx} + 2\rho r_1^* m_{xx} + 2\rho^2 r_2^* m_{xx} + \cdots}{m_{xx}^2} \right]$$

$$= \frac{\sigma^2}{n m_{xx}} [1 + 2\rho r_1^* + 2\rho^2 r_2^* + \cdots].$$

As an alternative estimator of β, consider $\tilde{\tilde{\beta}}$ defined as

(8.43) $$\tilde{\tilde{\beta}} = \tilde{\beta} - \delta_{\tilde{\beta}},$$

where $\tilde{\beta}$ is the best linear unbiased estimator given in (8.38), and δ is the correction factor, which is considered to be unimportant. The variance of $\tilde{\tilde{\beta}}$ is

(8.44) $$\mathrm{Var}(\tilde{\tilde{\beta}}) = \mathrm{Var}(\tilde{\beta}) - \delta_{\mathrm{Var}(\tilde{\beta})},$$

as defined in (8.39). The asymptotic variance of $\tilde{\tilde{\beta}}$ then is

$$\mathrm{Asympt.\ Var}(\tilde{\tilde{\beta}}) = \frac{1}{n} \lim_{n \to \infty} n \left[\frac{\sigma^2(1 - \rho^2)}{\sum (x_t' - \rho x_{t-1}')^2} \right] = \frac{1}{n} \left[\frac{\sigma^2(1 - \rho^2)}{m_{xx} - 2\rho r_1^* m_{xx} + \rho^2 m_{xx}} \right]$$

$$= \frac{\sigma^2}{n m_{xx}} \left[\frac{1 - \rho^2}{1 - 2\rho r_1^* + \rho^2} \right]$$

The asymptotic variances of $\hat{\beta}$ and $\tilde{\beta}$ can be compared by forming the ratio

$$\frac{\text{Asympt. Var}(\hat{\beta})}{\text{Asympt. Var}(\tilde{\beta})} = \frac{(\sigma^2/nm_{xx})[1 + 2\rho r_1^* + 2\rho^2 r_2^* + \cdots]}{(\sigma^2/nm_{xx})[(1 - \rho^2)/(1 - 2\rho r_1^* + \rho^2)]}$$

$$= \frac{1 + 2\rho r_1^* + 2\rho^2 r_2^* + \cdots}{[(1 - \rho^2)/(1 - 2\rho r_1^* + \rho^2)]}.$$

If this ratio is greater than one, then $\hat{\beta}$ cannot be considered to be asymptotically efficient. (Strictly speaking, this statement is true only if ρ is known or can be consistently estimated; otherwise $\tilde{\beta}$ would not qualify as an estimator. The problem of developing a consistent estimator of ρ will be discussed in the latter part of the present section.) Suppose we evaluate the above ratio for $1 > \rho > 0$ and $r_2^* = r_1^{*2}, r_3^* = r_1^{*3}, \ldots$. That is, we consider a situation in which the disturbances are positively autocorrelated, and the coefficients of correlation between X_t and X_{t-1}, X_t and X_{t-2}, etc., follow a geometrical progression. Such situations are thought to be quite common with economic time series.[10] With this specification we obtain

$$\frac{\text{Asympt. Var}(\hat{\beta})}{\text{Asympt. Var}(\tilde{\beta})} = \frac{1 + 2\rho r_1^* + 2\rho^2 r_1^{*2} + \cdots}{[(1 - \rho^2)/(1 - 2\rho r_1^* + \rho^2)]}$$

$$= \frac{1 - \rho r_1^* - 2\rho^2 r_1^{*2} + \rho^2 + \rho^3 r_1^*}{1 - \rho r_1^* - \rho^2 + \rho^3 r_1^*}.$$

This expression will be greater than or equal to one if

$$1 - \rho r_1^* - 2\rho^2 r_1^{*2} + \rho^2 + \rho^3 r_1^* \geq 1 - \rho r_1^* - \rho^2 + \rho^3 r_1^*$$

or

$$-2\rho^2 r_1^{*2} + \rho^2 \geq -\rho^2;$$

that is, if

$$2\rho^2(1 - r_1^{*2}) \geq 0.$$

This condition will always be satisfied. For example, when $\rho = 0.6$ and $r_1^* = 0.8$, $r_2^* = 0.64$, $r_3^* = 0.512$, etc., the ratio of the two asymptotic variances is equal to 1.78, i.e., the asymptotic variance of $\hat{\beta}$ is 78 percent larger than that of $\tilde{\beta}$. A similar result can be obtained with respect to $\hat{\alpha}$. Thus we have to conclude that the least squares estimators of the regression coefficients are *not asymptotically efficient* when the disturbances are autoregressive.

Properties of the Estimated Variances of the Least Squares Estimators

To sum up, we have established that when the disturbances are autoregressive, the least squares estimators of the regression coefficients are unbiased and consistent, but they are not efficient or asymptotically efficient. Thus, if we use

[10] See E. Ames and S. Reiter, "Distributions of Correlation Coefficients in Economic Time Series," *Journal of the American Statistical Association*, Vol. 56, September 1961, pp. 637–656. The authors consider 100 annual series of 25 observations selected at random from the abstract of statistics of the United States. They find that, on the average, the first five autocorrelation coefficients were 0.84, 0.71, 0.60, 0.53 and 0.45.

the least squares formulas when the disturbances are autoregressive, the resulting estimators will still have some desirable properties. However, if we want to use these estimators for the purpose of testing hypotheses or constructing confidence intervals, we require unbiasedness not only of the estimators themselves, but also of their estimated variances. The question then is whether the conventional formulas for estimating the variances of the least squares estimators do, in fact, guarantee unbiasedness even under autoregression in the disturbances. We note that the conventional least squares formula for estimating the variance of $\hat{\beta}$ is

$$s_{\hat{\beta}}^2 = \frac{s^2}{\sum x_t'^2},$$

where s^2 is an estimator of σ^2 defined as the sum of squares of the least squares residuals divided by $(n-2)$. Since $\sum x_t'^2$ is nonstochastic, we only have to concern ourselves with s^2. For that, we have

$$s^2 = \frac{1}{n-2} \sum_t (y_t' - \hat{\beta}x_t')^2 = \frac{1}{n-2} \sum_t (\beta x_t' + \varepsilon_t' - \hat{\beta}x_t')^2$$

$$= \frac{1}{n-2} \sum_t [-(\hat{\beta} - \beta)x_t' + \varepsilon_t']^2$$

$$= \frac{1}{n-2} \Big[(\hat{\beta} - \beta)^2 \sum_t x_t'^2 + \sum_t \varepsilon_t'^2 - 2(\hat{\beta} - \beta) \sum_t x_t'\varepsilon_t'\Big]$$

$$= \frac{1}{n-2} \Big[\sum_t \varepsilon_t'^2 - (\hat{\beta} - \beta)^2 \sum_t x_t'^2\Big]$$

and

$$E(s^2) = \frac{1}{n-2} \Big[\sum_t E(\varepsilon_t'^2) - \Big(\sum_t x_t'^2\Big)\text{Var}(\hat{\beta})\Big].$$

Now we know what $\text{Var}(\hat{\beta})$ is from (8.42) so that our only problem is to find $E(\varepsilon_t'^2)$. We have

$$E(\varepsilon_t'^2) = E(\varepsilon_t - \bar{\varepsilon})^2 = E(\varepsilon_t^2) + E\Big[\frac{1}{n}\sum_t \varepsilon_t\Big]^2 - 2E\Big[\varepsilon_t \frac{1}{n}\sum_t \varepsilon_t\Big]$$

$$= \sigma^2 + \frac{\sigma^2}{n} + \frac{2}{n^2} E\Big[\sum_{s<t} \varepsilon_{t-s}\varepsilon_t\Big]$$

$$- \frac{2}{n} E[\varepsilon_t(\varepsilon_1 + \varepsilon_2 + \cdots + \varepsilon_t + \cdots + \varepsilon_n)]$$

$$= \sigma^2 + \frac{\sigma^2}{n} + \frac{2}{n^2} [E(\varepsilon_1\varepsilon_2) + E(\varepsilon_1\varepsilon_3) + \cdots + E(\varepsilon_1\varepsilon_n) + E(\varepsilon_2\varepsilon_3)$$

$$+ E(\varepsilon_2\varepsilon_4) + \cdots + E(\varepsilon_2\varepsilon_n) + E(\varepsilon_3\varepsilon_4) + \cdots + E(\varepsilon_{n-1}\varepsilon_n)]$$

$$- \frac{2}{n} [E(\varepsilon_t\varepsilon_1) + E(\varepsilon_t\varepsilon_2) + \cdots + E(\varepsilon_t^2) + \cdots + E(\varepsilon_t\varepsilon_n)]$$

$$= \frac{(n+1)\sigma^2}{n} + \frac{2\sigma^2}{n^2}[(n-1)\rho + (n-2)\rho^2 + \cdots + \rho^{n-1}]$$

$$- \frac{2\sigma^2}{n}[\rho^{t-1} + \rho^{t-2} + \cdots + \rho + 1 + \rho + \cdots + \rho^{n-t}].$$

Then

$$\sum_t E(\varepsilon_t'^2) = (n+1)\sigma^2 + \frac{2\sigma^2}{n}[(n-1)\rho + (n-2)\rho^2 + \cdots + \rho^{n-1}]$$

$$- \frac{2\sigma^2}{n}\sum_t [\rho^{t-1} + \rho^{t-2} + \cdots + \rho + 1 + \rho + \cdots + \rho^{n-t}].$$

Consider the last summation:

$$\sum_t [\rho^{t-1} + \rho^{t-2} + \cdots + \rho + 1 + \rho + \cdots + \rho^{n-t}]$$

$$= (1 + \rho + \rho^2 + \cdots + \rho^{n-1})$$

$$+ (\rho + 1 + \rho + \cdots + \rho^{n-2})$$

$$+ (\rho^2 + \rho + 1 + \cdots + \rho^{n-3})$$

$$\vdots$$

$$+ (\rho^{n-1} + \rho^{n-2} + \rho^{n-3} + \cdots + 1)$$

$$= n + 2(n-1)\rho + 2(n-2)\rho^2 + \cdots + 4\rho^{n-2} + 2\rho^{n-1}.$$

Therefore,

$$\sum_t E(\varepsilon_t'^2) = (n+1)\sigma^2 + \frac{2\sigma^2}{n}\{[(n-1)\rho + (n-2)\rho^2 + \cdots + \rho^{n-1}]$$

$$- [n + 2(n-1)\rho + 2(n-2)\rho^2 + \cdots + 4\rho^{n-2} + 2\rho^{n-1}]\}$$

$$= (n+1)\sigma^2 - \frac{2\sigma^2}{n}A,$$

where $\quad A = n + (n-1)\rho + (n-2)\rho^2 + \cdots + 2\rho^{n-2} + \rho^{n-1}.$

Now, since

$$A - \rho A = n + (n-1)\rho + (n-2)\rho^2 + \cdots + 2\rho^{n-2} + \rho^{n-1}$$

$$- n\rho - (n-1)\rho^2 - \cdots - 3\rho^{n-2} - 2\rho^{n-1} - \rho^n$$

$$= n - \rho - \rho^2 - \cdots - \rho^{n-1} - \rho^{n-2} - \rho^n = n - \frac{\rho(1-\rho^n)}{(1-\rho)}$$

$$= \frac{n(1-\rho) - \rho(1-\rho^n)}{(1-\rho)},$$

we have

$$A = \frac{n(1 - \rho) - \rho(1 - \rho^n)}{(1 - \rho)^2}$$

and
$$\sum_t E(\varepsilon_t'^2) = (n + 1)\sigma^2 - \frac{2\sigma^2}{n}\left[\frac{n(1 - \rho) - \rho(1 - \rho^n)}{(1 - \rho)^2}\right]$$

$$= (n - 1)\sigma^2 - \frac{2\sigma^2}{n}\left[\frac{n\rho(1 - \rho) - \rho(1 - \rho^n)}{(1 - \rho)^2}\right].$$

Substituting this result and the expression for $\text{Var}(\hat{\beta})$ into $E(s^2)$, we obtain

$$(8.45) \quad E(s^2) = \frac{1}{n - 2}\left\{(n - 1)\sigma^2 - \frac{2\sigma^2}{n}\left[\frac{n\rho(1 - \rho) - \rho(1 - \rho^n)}{(1 - \rho)^2}\right]\right\}$$

$$- \frac{1}{n - 2}\sum_t x_t'^2\left\{\frac{\sigma^2}{\sum x_t'^2} + \frac{2\sigma^2}{(\sum x'^2)^2}\left[\rho\sum_{t=2}^{n} x_t'x_{t-1}'\right.\right.$$

$$\left.\left. + \rho^2\sum_{t=3}^{n} x_t'x_{t-2}' + \cdots\right]\right\}$$

$$= \sigma^2 - \frac{2\sigma^2}{n - 2}\left[\frac{n\rho(1 - \rho) - \rho(1 - \rho^n)}{n(1 - \rho)^2}\right.$$

$$\left. + \frac{\rho\sum x_t'x_{t-1}' + \rho^2\sum x_t'x_{t-2}' + \cdots}{\sum x_t'^2}\right],$$

so that

$$(8.46) \quad E(s_{\hat{\beta}}^2) = \frac{\sigma^2}{\sum x_t'^2} - \frac{2\sigma^2}{(n - 2)\sum x_t'^2}\left[\frac{n\rho(1 - \rho) - \rho(1 - \rho^n)}{n(1 - \rho)^2}\right.$$

$$\left. + \frac{\rho\sum x_t'x_{t-1}' + \rho^2\sum x_t'x_{t-2}' + \cdots}{\sum x_t'^2}\right].$$

Since the expression for $E(s_{\hat{\beta}}^2)$ differs from that for $\text{Var}(\hat{\beta})$ given by (8.42), we conclude that the conventionally calculated variance of $\hat{\beta}$ is *biased* when the disturbances are autoregressive. A similar result can be obtained with respect to $\hat{\alpha}$.

The preceding result implies that when the disturbances are autoregressive, the conventional formulas for carrying out tests of significance or constructing confidence intervals with respect to the regression coefficients lead to incorrect statements. That is, the calculated acceptance regions or confidence intervals will be either narrower or wider than the correct ones, depending on whether the bias in estimating the variance is negative or positive. Therefore, let us see whether we can determine the direction of the bias. By deducting (8.42) from

(8.46) we obtain an expression for the bias in estimating the variance of $\hat{\beta}$ as given by

$$(8.47)\qquad E(s_{\hat{\beta}}^2) - \text{Var}(\hat{\beta}) = \frac{-2\sigma^2}{\sum x_t'^2}\left\{\left[\frac{n\rho(1-\rho) - \rho(1-\rho^n)}{n(n-2)(1-\rho)^2}\right]\right.$$

$$+ \frac{(n-1)}{(n-2)\sum x_t'^2}\left[\rho\sum_{t=2}^{n} x_t'x_{t-1}'\right.$$

$$\left.\left. + \rho^2\sum_{t=3}^{n} x_t'x_{t-2}' + \cdots\right]\right\}.$$

From this it can be seen that when $\rho > 0$ and X_t is positively correlated with $X_{t-1}, X_{t-2}, \ldots$, the bias is negative. As pointed out earlier, such a situation is fairly common with economic time series. Thus, if the disturbances are auto-regressive and we persist in using the conventional least squares formulas, the calculated acceptance regions or confidence intervals will be often *narrower* than they should be for the specified level of significance or confidence. To obtain an idea about the extent of the bias, take, for example, the case when $\rho = 0.6$ and $r_1 = 0.8$, $r_2 = (0.8)^2$, $r_3 = (0.8)^3$, etc. Assuming that $\sum x_t'^2$, $\sum x_{t-1}'^2$, $\sum x_{t-2}'^2, \ldots$ are all approximately equal, the biases in estimating $\text{Var}(\hat{\beta})$ for various sample sizes would be as given in Table 8–1. These results indicate that the extent of the bias may be quite substantial.

Table 8–1

Sample Size	$E(s_{\hat{\beta}}^2)$	$\text{Var}(\hat{\beta})$	Bias	$\dfrac{E(s_{\hat{\beta}}^2)}{\text{Var}(\hat{\beta})}$
20	$0.752\left[\dfrac{\sigma^2}{\sum x_t'^2}\right]$	$2.846\left[\dfrac{\sigma^2}{\sum x_t'^2}\right]$	$-2.094\left[\dfrac{\sigma^2}{\sum x_t'^2}\right]$	0.264
50	$0.902\left[\dfrac{\sigma^2}{\sum x_t'^2}\right]$	$2.846\left[\dfrac{\sigma^2}{\sum x_t'^2}\right]$	$-1.944\left[\dfrac{\sigma^2}{\sum x_t'^2}\right]$	0.317
100	$0.951\left[\dfrac{\sigma^2}{\sum x_t'^2}\right]$	$2.846\left[\dfrac{\sigma^2}{\sum x_t'^2}\right]$	$-1.895\left[\dfrac{\sigma^2}{\sum x_t'^2}\right]$	0.334

BLU and Maximum Likelihood Estimations

The preceding discussion has enabled us to uncover the shortcomings of the least squares estimators of the regression coefficients in the case when the disturbance does not satisfy the assumption of nonautoregression. Now we shall turn to the problem of developing alternative estimators that would not suffer from these shortcomings. In the process we shall confine ourselves to the case in which the disturbance ε_t follows a first-order autoregressive scheme as described by (8.34) and (8.35). The reader will recall that we·have already de-veloped the formulas for the best linear unbiased estimators for the auto-regressive model. These estimators, which we labeled $\tilde{\alpha}$ and $\tilde{\beta}$, and their variances are given by (8.38) through (8.41). If we disregard the correction factors appended to each formula, the resulting expressions are simpler, though, of course, no longer *exactly* BLUE. If $\tilde{\alpha}$ and $\tilde{\beta}$ are used to represent $\hat{\alpha}$ and $\hat{\beta}$ *minus* the respective correction factors, we have

$$(8.48) \qquad \tilde{\beta} = \frac{\sum(y'_t - \rho y'_{t-1})(x'_t - \rho x'_{t-1})}{\sum(x'_t - \rho x'_{t-1})^2},$$

$$(8.49) \qquad \mathrm{Var}(\tilde{\beta}) = \frac{\sigma_u^2}{\sum(x'_t - \rho x'_{t-1})^2},$$

$$(8.50) \qquad \tilde{\alpha} = \frac{1}{1 - \rho}[(\bar{Y} - \rho\bar{Y}_{-1}) - \tilde{\beta}(\bar{X} - \rho\bar{X}_{-1})],$$

and

$$(8.51) \qquad \mathrm{Var}(\tilde{\alpha}) = \frac{\sigma_u^2}{(1 - \rho)^2}\left[\frac{1}{n - 1} + \frac{(\bar{X} - \rho\bar{X}_{-1})^2}{\sum(x'_t - \rho x'_{t-1})^2}\right],$$

where the subscript t runs from $t = 2$ to $t = n$, and

$$\bar{Y} = \frac{1}{n - 1}\sum_t Y_t,$$

$$\bar{Y}_{-1} = \frac{1}{n - 1}\sum_t Y_{t-1},$$

$$\bar{X} = \frac{1}{n - 1}\sum_t X_t,$$

$$\bar{X}_{-1} = \frac{1}{n - 1}\sum_t X_{t-1}.$$

Before considering the feasibility and the usefulness of these estimators, we may note an alternative and simpler way of deriving them. The value of the dependent variable in period t is determined by

$$Y_t = \alpha + \beta X_t + \varepsilon_t,$$

and that in period $t - 1$ by

$$Y_{t-1} = \alpha + \beta X_{t-1} + \varepsilon_{t-1}.$$

Multiplying the latter by ρ and subtracting the result from the former, we obtain

$$Y_t - \rho Y_{t-1} = \alpha(1 - \rho) + \beta(X_t - \rho X_{t-1}) + (\varepsilon_t - \rho\varepsilon_{t-1}).$$

But since, by (8.34),

$$\varepsilon_t - \rho\varepsilon_{t-1} = u_t,$$

we can write

$$(8.52) \quad Y_t - \rho Y_{t-1} = \alpha(1 - \rho) + \beta(X_t - \rho X_{t-1}) + u_t \qquad (t = 2, 3, \ldots, n).$$

Equation (8.52) may be viewed as a regression equation in which the dependent variable is $(Y_t - \rho Y_{t-1})$ and the explanatory variable is $(X_t - \rho X_{t-1})$. Both of these variables can be measured if ρ is a known quantity. Since u_t is a normally and independently distributed random variable with mean zero and a constant variance, and $(X_t - \rho X_{t-1})$ is nonstochastic and bounded, all the basic assumptions of the classical normal linear regression model are satisfied. Therefore, least squares estimators of (8.52) would have all the desirable properties except for the fact that, by using as variables $(Y_t - \rho Y_{t-1})$ instead of Y_t and $(X_t - \rho X_{t-1})$ instead of X_t, we lose one observation. This loss implies that these estimators are not exactly BLUE, a fact that has already been noted.

The difficulty with the estimation formulas (8.48) and (8.50) is that they involve the parameter ρ whose value is rarely known. If ρ is not known, these formulas cannot be evaluated, and, consequently, $\tilde{\alpha}$ and $\tilde{\beta}$ do not qualify as estimators. This difficulty can be overcome by estimating ρ (along with α and β) from the sample observations. Several estimation methods are available and will be discussed. First, let us consider maximum likelihood estimation of (8.52). Since

$$u_t = (Y_t - \rho Y_{t-1}) - \alpha(1 - \rho) - \beta(X_t - \rho X_{t-1}) \qquad (t = 2, 3, \ldots, n),$$

the logarithmic likelihood function for $Y_2, Y_3, \ldots, Y_n$ is

$$(8.53) \quad L = -\frac{n-1}{2} \log(2\pi) - \frac{n-1}{2} \log \sigma_u^2$$

$$-\frac{1}{2\sigma_u^2} \sum_{t=2}^{n} [(Y_t - \rho Y_{t-1}) - \alpha(1 - \rho) - \beta(X_t - \rho X_{t-1})]^2.$$

Note that

$$f(y_2, y_3, \ldots, y_n) = \left|\frac{\partial u}{\partial Y}\right| f(u_2, u_3, \ldots, u_n),$$

where $|\partial u / \partial Y|$ is the absolute value of the determinant

$$\begin{vmatrix} \dfrac{\partial u_2}{\partial Y_2} & \dfrac{\partial u_2}{\partial Y_3} & \cdots & \dfrac{\partial u_2}{\partial Y_n} \\[2mm] \dfrac{\partial u_3}{\partial Y_2} & \dfrac{\partial u_3}{\partial Y_3} & \cdots & \dfrac{\partial u_3}{\partial Y_n} \\[1mm] \vdots & \vdots & & \vdots \\[1mm] \dfrac{\partial u_n}{\partial Y_2} & \dfrac{\partial u_n}{\partial Y_3} & \cdots & \dfrac{\partial u_n}{\partial Y_n} \end{vmatrix}.$$

This is an extension of Theorem 18 (the "change-of-variable" theorem) from one variable to several variables. The determinant is known as the *Jacobian* of the transformation from $u_2, u_3, \ldots, u_n$ to $Y_2, Y_3, \ldots, Y_n$. It has been set up as *conditional* upon a given value of Y_1, i.e., as if Y_1 were a constant. This enabled us to ignore $\partial u_2 / \partial Y_1$. It is easy to show that $|\partial u / \partial Y| = 1$ so that $f(u_2, u_3, \ldots, u_n) = f(y_2, y_3, \ldots, y_n)$.

By differentiating L with respect to α, β, ρ, and σ_u^2 and putting each derivative equal to zero, we obtain four equations to solve for the values of the four unknown parameters. However, these equations are highly nonlinear and their solution is rather difficult. A relatively simple way of handling this problem is available if we utilize the fact that *if* ρ were known, the maximum likelihood estimators of α and β would be equal to $\tilde{\alpha}$ and $\tilde{\tilde{\beta}}$ as given by (8.48) and (8.50), and the maximum likelihood estimator of σ_u^2, say, $\tilde{\sigma}_u^2$, would be

$$(8.54)\qquad \tilde{\sigma}_u^2 = \frac{1}{n-1} \sum_{t=2}^{n} [(Y_t - \rho Y_{t-1}) - \tilde{\alpha}(1-\rho) - \tilde{\tilde{\beta}}(X_t - \rho X_{t-1})].$$

This means that different values of ρ lead to different values of $\tilde{\alpha}$, $\tilde{\tilde{\beta}}$, and $\tilde{\sigma}_u^2$. Thus we can obtain different solutions for, say, $\rho = -0.95, -0.90, -0.85, \ldots,$ $+0.85, +0.90, +0.95$, and then select that value of ρ—as well as the corresponding values of $\tilde{\alpha}$ and $\tilde{\tilde{\beta}}$—that leads to the smallest value of $\tilde{\sigma}_u^2$. This solution will maximize the likelihood function L as required. The estimators obtained in this way will be called $\hat{\alpha}$, $\hat{\tilde{\beta}}$, $\hat{\rho}$, and $\hat{\sigma}_u^2$. The estimated standard errors of $\hat{\alpha}$ and $\hat{\beta}$ can be obtained by using formulas (8.49) and (8.51), after replacing ρ by $\hat{\rho}$ and σ_u^2 by $\hat{\sigma}_u^2$. The variance of $\hat{\rho}$ can be estimated by

$$(8.55)\qquad\qquad\qquad s_{\hat{\rho}}^2 = \frac{1 - \hat{\rho}^2}{n}.$$

Formula (8.55) represents estimated asymptotic variance as defined in Section 6-1.

Under quite general conditions, maximum likelihood estimators are known to possess optimal properties in large samples. These optimal properties are assured by general theorems on maximum likelihood estimation. However, in the present case there is some question whether the general theorems apply because $Y_2, Y_3, \ldots, Y_n$ are not independent, i.e.,

$$f(y_2, y_3, \ldots, y_n) \neq f(y_2)f(y_3)\cdots f(y_n).$$

This means that the likelihood function is not the product of independent identical distributions.[11] Nevertheless, it can be shown that the maximum likelihood estimators of (8.52) are consistent and asymptotically equivalent to best-linear-unbiased estimators.[12] An indication of the small sample properties of the maximum likelihood estimators will be given on page 293.

EXAMPLE   Friedman and Meiselman[13] estimated an equation representing a simple form of the quantity theory of money:

$$C_t = \alpha + \beta M_t + \varepsilon_t$$

[11] This point is particularly emphasized in C. Hildreth and J. Y. Lu, "Demand Relations with Autocorrelated Disturbances," *Technical Bulletin 276*, Michigan State University Agricultural Experiment Station, November 1960, p. 14.

[12] Consistency has been proved; *ibid.*, Appendix B. Asymptotic equivalence to BLUE has been demonstrated in Malinvaud, *op. cit.*, pp. 440-441.

[13] Milton Friedman and David Meiselman, "The Relative Stability of Monetary Velocity and the Investment Multiplier in the United States, 1897-1958," in Commission on Money and Credit, *Stabilization Policies* (Englewood Cliffs, N.J.: Prentice-Hall, 1963).

where C = consumer expenditure and M = stock of money, both measured in billions of current dollars. We shall re-estimate this relation using the quarterly data in Table 8–2 and assuming that the disturbance follows a first-order autoregressive scheme.

Table 8–2

Year and Quarter		Consumer Expenditure*	Money Stock*	Year and Quarter		Consumer Expenditure*	Money Stock*
1952	I	214.6	159.3	1954	III	238.7	173.9
	II	217.7	161.2		IV	243.2	176.1
	III	219.6	162.8				
	IV	227.2	164.6	1955	I	249.4	178.0
					II	254.3	179.1
1953	I	230.9	165.9		III	260.9	180.2
	II	233.3	167.9		IV	263.3	181.2
	III	234.1	168.3				
	IV	232.3	169.7	1956	I	265.6	181.6
					II	268.2	182.5
1954	I	233.7	170.5		III	270.4	183.3
	II	236.5	171.6		IV	275.6	184.3

Source: Milton Friedman and David Meiselman, "The Relative Stability of Monetary Velocity and the Investment Multiplier in the United States, 1897–1958," in Commission on Money and Credit, *Stabilization Policies* (Englewood Cliffs, N.J.: Prentice-Hall, 1963), p. 266.

* In billions of dollars.

Following the procedure for obtaining the maximum likelihood estimates of α and β, we calculate the values of $\tilde{\sigma}_u^2$—or, rather, $(n-1)\tilde{\sigma}_u^2$—for different values of ρ. The computer results are given in Table 8–3. We can see that the value of ρ that gives the smallest $\tilde{\sigma}_u^2$ is 0.85. The corresponding least squares estimates of the coefficients and their estimated standard errors are

$$(C_t - 0.85C_{t-1}) = -38.256 + 2.859(M_t - 0.85M_{t-1}) + \hat{u}_t, \qquad R^2 = 0.647.$$
$$\phantom{(C_t - 0.85C_{t-1}) = }(13.926) \quad (0.512)$$

Table 8–3

ρ	$(n-1)\tilde{\sigma}_u^2$	ρ	$(n-1)\tilde{\sigma}_u^2$	ρ	$(n-1)\tilde{\sigma}_u^2$
-0.95	919.30	-0.05	302.75	0.75	85.26
-0.90	874.77	0.00	279.99	0.80	82.71
-0.85	831.45	0.05	258.44	**0.85**	**82.14**
$\vdots$	$\vdots$	0.10	238.10	0.90	84.48
-0.10	326.73	$\vdots$	$\vdots$	0.95	88.67

From these results we obtain:

$$\hat{\beta} = 2.859, \qquad\qquad \text{and} \qquad s_{\hat{\beta}} = 0.512,$$

$$\hat{\alpha} = \frac{-38.256}{1-0.85} = -255.040, \qquad \text{and} \qquad s_{\hat{\alpha}} = \frac{13.926}{1-0.85} = 92.840.$$

$$\hat{\rho} = 0.85, \qquad\qquad \text{and} \qquad s_{\hat{\rho}} = 0.178.$$

To obtain an idea of how well the estimated regression line fits the sample observations, we also calculate the value of R^2. From formula (7.45b)

$$R^2 = 1 - \frac{\text{SSE}}{\text{SST}}.$$

where

$$\text{SSE} = \sum_{t=2}^{20} (C_t - \hat{\alpha} - \hat{\beta}M_t)^2 = \sum_{t=2}^{20} (c_t' - \hat{\beta}m_t')^2$$

$$= \sum_{t=2}^{20} c_t'^2 - 2\hat{\beta}\sum_{t=2}^{20} c_t'm_t' + \hat{\beta}^2 \sum_{t=2}^{20} m_t'^2,$$

and

$$\text{SST} = \sum_{t=2}^{20} c_t'^2.$$

In the following calculations we let the summations extend from $t = 2$ to $t = n$ because the values of these summations are available as by-products of the least squares estimation with $\rho = 0$. In this case we get

$$\sum_{t=2}^{20} c_t'^2 = 5,803.63,$$

$$\sum_{t=2}^{20} m_t'^2 = 1,013.07,$$

and

$$\sum_{t=2}^{20} c_t'm_t' = 2.335 \times 1,013.07 = 2,365.52,$$

so that

$$R^2 = 0.904.$$

The complete result then is

$$C_t = -255.040 + 2.859\, M_t + e_t, \qquad R^2 = 0.904.$$
$$\quad\ (92.840) \quad (0.512)$$

Iterative and Two-Stage Estimation

An alternative estimation procedure for estimating regression equations with autoregressive disturbances is an *iterative method*,[14] which consists of the

[14] See D. Cochrane and G. H. Orcutt, "Application of Least Squares Regressions to Relationships Containing Autocorrelated Error Terms," *Journal of the American Statistical Association*, Vol. 44, March 1949, pp. 32–61.

VIOLATIONS OF BASIC ASSUMPTIONS [Ch. 8

following steps:

1. Obtain ordinary least squares estimates of

$$Y_t = \alpha + \beta X_t + \varepsilon_t,$$

and calculate the residuals $\hat{\varepsilon}_1, \hat{\varepsilon}_2, \ldots, \hat{\varepsilon}_n$. Use these to get the "first round" estimate of ρ, say, $\hat{\rho}$, given as

$$\hat{\rho} = \frac{\sum \hat{\varepsilon}_t \hat{\varepsilon}_{t-1}}{\sum \hat{\varepsilon}_{t-1}^2} \qquad (t = 2, 3, \ldots, n).$$

2. Construct new variables $(Y_t - \hat{\rho} Y_{t-1})$ and $(X_t - \hat{\rho} X_{t-1})$, and obtain ordinary least squares estimates of

$$(Y_t - \hat{\rho} Y_{t-1}) = \alpha^* + \beta(X_t - \hat{\rho} X_{t-1}) + u_t,$$

where $\alpha^* = \alpha(1 - \hat{\rho})$. These "second round" estimates, which may be called $\hat{\hat{\alpha}}$ and $\hat{\hat{\beta}}$, lead to "second round" residuals $\hat{\hat{\varepsilon}}_1, \hat{\hat{\varepsilon}}_2, \ldots, \hat{\hat{\varepsilon}}_n$ (calculated as $\hat{\hat{\varepsilon}}_t = Y_t - \hat{\hat{\alpha}} - \hat{\hat{\beta}} X_t$). The latter then are used to obtain a new estimate of ρ:

$$\hat{\hat{\rho}} = \frac{\sum \hat{\hat{\varepsilon}}_t \hat{\hat{\varepsilon}}_{t-1}}{\sum \hat{\hat{\varepsilon}}_{t-1}^2} \qquad (t = 2, 3, \ldots, n).$$

3. Construct new variables $(Y_t - \hat{\hat{\rho}} Y_{t-1})$ and $(X_t - \hat{\hat{\rho}} X_{t-1})$, and then proceed as in Step 2.

The steps are to be followed until the values of the estimators converge. It can be shown that the procedure is convergent and that, in fact, the "final round" estimates of α and β coincide with the values of the maximum likelihood estimators described above.[15] Thus the only difference between the maximum likelihood estimators developed above and the iterative estimators suggested by Orcutt and others is in the computational design.

The iterative procedure can be reduced to a *two-stage procedure* by stopping after obtaining the "second round" estimates of $\hat{\hat{\alpha}}$ and $\hat{\hat{\beta}}$, based on the "first round" value of ρ. The two-stage estimators will have the same asymptotic properties as the maximum likelihood estimators; some evidence concerning their small sample properties is presented on page 293. The estimates of the standard errors of $\hat{\hat{\alpha}}$ and $\hat{\hat{\beta}}$ can be obtained by using the formulas (8.49) and (8.51), with ρ replaced by $\hat{\rho}$.

EXAMPLE We can use the "quantity theory" relation and the data of the previous example to illustrate the two-stage estimation procedure. The "first round" estimate of ρ is

$$\hat{\rho} = 0.827.$$

[15] See J. D. Sargan, "Wages and Prices in the United Kingdom: A Study in Econometric Methodology," in P. E. Hart, G. Mills, and J. K. Whitaker (eds.), *Econometric Analysis for National Economic Planning* (London: Butterworths, 1964).

Note that this value is numerically very close to the maximum likelihood estimate of ρ of the previous example. The least squares estimates of the regression coefficients based on transformed data are

$$(C_t - 0.827C_{t-1}) = -42.290 + 2.805(M_t - 0.827M_{t-1}) + e_t, \qquad R^2 = 0.703.$$
$$\qquad\qquad\qquad (13.760) \quad (0.442)$$

This leads to the following estimates for the untransformed observations:

$$C_t = -244.450 + 2.805M_t + e_t, \qquad R^2 = 0.912.$$
$$\qquad (79.537) \quad (0.442)$$

These results are very similar to those obtained earlier by the maximum likelihood method.

Durbin's Method

A different estimation method has been suggested by Durbin.[16] Like the preceding method, *Durbin's procedure* consists of two steps. First, we rewrite (8.52) as

$$Y_t = \alpha(1 - \rho) + \rho Y_{t-1} + \beta X_t - \beta\rho X_{t-1} + u_t$$

or

$$Y_t = \alpha^* + \rho Y_{t-1} + \beta X_t + \gamma X_{t-1} + u_t.$$

This expression can be treated as a regression equation with three explanatory variables, X_t, X_{t-1} and Y_{t-1}, and estimated by the ordinary least squares method (as described in Chapter 10). The resulting estimator of ρ, say, $\tilde{\rho}$, is to be used to construct new variables $(Y_t - \tilde{\rho}Y_{t-1})$ and $(X_t - \tilde{\rho}X_{t-1})$. In the second step, we estimate

$$(Y_t - \tilde{\rho}Y_{t-1}) = \alpha^* + \beta(X_t - \tilde{\rho}X_{t-1}) + u_t^*,$$

where $\alpha^* = \alpha(1 - \rho)$. The estimators of α and β that we get will have the same *asymptotic* properties as the maximum likelihood estimators described earlier.

The Use of First Differences

In earlier applied studies, research workers frequently attempted to deal with the problem of autoregression in disturbances by using the *method of first differences*. This method calls for transforming the original data on Y and X into first differences $(Y_t - Y_{t-1})$ and $(X_t - X_{t-1})$, and for setting up the regression equation as

(8.56) $(Y_t - Y_{t-1}) = \alpha^{**} + \beta(X_t - X_{t-1}) + v_t.$

α^{**} and β are then estimated by the method of least squares. Note that since

$$Y_t = \alpha + \beta X_t + \varepsilon_t$$

and

$$Y_{t-1} = \alpha + \beta X_{t-1} + \varepsilon_{t-1},$$

it follows that $\alpha^{**} = 0$ and $v_t = \varepsilon_t - \varepsilon_{t-1}$. The rationale of the method of first differences is the belief that the true value of ρ is close to unity. Since $\alpha^{**} = 0$,

[16] J. Durbin, "Estimation of Parameters in Time-Series Regression Models," *Journal of the Royal Statistical Society*, Series B, Vol. 22, January 1960, pp. 139–153.

one does not expect that its estimate in (8.56) would be significantly different from zero. The implication is that α cannot be estimated by this method. We note in passing that a result giving the estimate of α^{**} as significantly different from zero has often been rationalized by the claim that the original model had been misspecified and that, in addition to X_t, it should have included a trend as an explanatory variable. If that were the case and the trend were measured by the "time variable" t, we would have

$$Y_t = \alpha + \beta X_t + \delta t + \varepsilon_t,$$

$$Y_{t-1} = \alpha + \beta X_{t-1} + \delta(t-1) + \varepsilon_{t-1},$$

and $$Y_t - Y_{t-1} = \beta(X_t - X_{t-1}) + \delta + (\varepsilon_t - \varepsilon_{t-1}),$$

so that the intercept in (8.56) would measure the coefficient of the trend variable.

Let us consider the properties of the estimator of β when using the method of first differences. We assume, as before, that ε_t follows a first-order autoregressive scheme as described by (8.34) through (8.36). Now the disturbance in (8.56) is

$$v_t = \varepsilon_t - \varepsilon_{t-1},$$

so that

$$E(v_t) = 0,$$

$$E(v_t^2) = E(\varepsilon_t^2 + \varepsilon_{t-1}^2 - 2\varepsilon_t\varepsilon_{t-1}) = \sigma^2 + \sigma^2 - 2\rho\sigma^2 = 2\sigma^2(1-\rho)$$

$$= \frac{2\sigma_u^2(1-\rho)}{(1-\rho^2)} = \frac{2\sigma_u^2}{(1+\rho)},$$

$$E(v_t v_{t-1}) = E(\varepsilon_t - \varepsilon_{t-1})(\varepsilon_{t-1} - \varepsilon_{t-2})$$

$$= E(\varepsilon_t\varepsilon_{t-1} - \varepsilon_{t-1}^2 - \varepsilon_t\varepsilon_{t-2} + \varepsilon_{t-1}\varepsilon_{t-2}) = \rho\sigma^2 - \sigma^2 - \rho^2\sigma^2 + \rho\sigma^2$$

$$= -\sigma^2(1-\rho)^2 = \frac{-\sigma_u^2(1-\rho)}{(1+\rho)}.$$

It follows, then, that the disturbance in (8.56) has zero mean and a constant variance but is still autoregressive, although, of course, the extent of autoregression would be small if ρ were close to unity.

The least squares estimator of β based on first differences, say $\bar{\beta}$, is

(8.57) $$\bar{\beta} = \frac{\sum (y_t' - y_{t-1}')(x_t' - x_{t-1}')}{\sum (x_t' - x_{t-1}')^2}$$

$$= \beta + \frac{\sum z_t'(\varepsilon_t - \varepsilon_{t-1})}{\sum z_t'^2} \qquad (t = 2, 3, \ldots, n)$$

where $$z_t' = x_t' - x_{t-1}'.$$

Now $$E(\bar{\beta}) = \beta,$$

so that $\bar{\beta}$ is unbiased. Further,

$$\text{Var}(\bar{\beta}) = E\left[\frac{\sum z_t'(\varepsilon_t - \varepsilon_{t-1})}{\sum z_t'^2}\right]^2 = \frac{1}{(\sum z_t'^2)^2}\left[E\sum_t z_t'^2(\varepsilon_t^2 - 2\varepsilon_t\varepsilon_{t-1} + \varepsilon_{t-1}^2)\right.$$

$$\left. + 2E\sum_{s<t} z_t'z_{t-s}'(\varepsilon_t\varepsilon_{t-s} - \varepsilon_{t-1}\varepsilon_{t-s} - \varepsilon_t\varepsilon_{t-s-1} + \varepsilon_{t-1}\varepsilon_{t-s-1})\right]$$

$$= \frac{2\sigma^2}{(\sum z_t'^2)^2}\left[(1 - \rho)\sum_t z_t'^2 + \sum_{s<t} z_t'z_{t-s}'\rho^{s-1}(2\rho - 1 - \rho^2)\right]$$

$$= \frac{2\sigma^2(1 - \rho)}{\sum z_t'^2}\left\{1 - \frac{(1 - \rho)}{\sum z_t'^2}\left[\sum_{t=3}^{n} z_t'z_{t-1}' + \rho\sum_{t=4}^{n} z_t'z_{t-2}' + \cdots\right]\right\}.$$

The estimator $\bar{\beta}$ is based on the assumption that $\rho \to 1$, while the ordinary least squares estimator $\hat{\beta}$ can be considered as based on the assumption that $\rho = 0$. Thus it may be interesting to compare the variances of these two estimators for different values of ρ. We shall restrict the comparison to the situations characterized as follows.

1. The samples are large enough so that, for all practical purposes,

$$\sum_t x_t'^2 = \sum_t x_{t-1}'^2 = \sum_t x_{t-2}'^2 = \cdots.$$

2. $0 \le \rho < 1$.
3. $r_s = r^s \; (s = 1, 2, \ldots)$, where

$$r_s = \frac{\sum x_t'x_{t-s}'}{\sqrt{\sum x_t'^2}\sqrt{\sum x_{t-s}'^2}} = \frac{\sum x_t'x_{t-s}'}{\sum x_t'^2} \quad \text{(using 1 above)}.$$

With these simplifications we have

$$\sum z_t'^2 = \sum x_t'^2 - 2\sum x_t'x_{t-1}' + \sum x_{t-1}'^2 = 2(1 - r)\sum x_t'^2,$$

$$\sum z_t'z_{t-1}' = \sum x_t'x_{t-1}' - \sum x_{t-1}'^2 - \sum x_t'x_{t-2}' + \sum x_{t-1}'x_{t-2}' = -(1 - r)^2\sum x_t'^2,$$

$$\sum z_t'z_{t-2}' = -r(1 - r)^2\sum x_t'^2,$$

$$\sum z_t'z_{t-3}' = -r^2(1 - r)^2\sum x_t'^2,$$

$$\vdots$$

so that

$$\text{Var}(\bar{\beta}) = \frac{2\sigma^2(1 - \rho)}{2(1 - r)\sum x_t'^2}\left\{1 + \frac{(1 - \rho)(1 - r)^2\sum x_t'^2}{2(1 - r)\sum x_t'^2}[1 + \rho r + \rho^2 r^2 + \cdots]\right\}$$

$$= \frac{\sigma^2(1 - \rho)}{\sum x_t'^2}\left[\frac{1}{1 - r} + \frac{(1 - \rho)}{2(1 - \rho r)}\right].$$

The variance of the ordinary least squares estimator of β is given by (8.42). With the above simplification this becomes

$$\text{Var}(\hat{\beta}) = \frac{\sigma^2}{\sum x_t'^2} [1 + 2\rho r + 2\rho^2 r^2 + \cdots] = \frac{\sigma^2}{\sum x_t'^2} \left[\frac{1 + \rho r}{1 - \rho r} \right].$$

To facilitate the comparison, we evaluate these variances for selected values of ρ and r. The results of the calculations are shown in Table 8–4, with λ representing $\sigma^2 / \sum x_t'^2$. As anticipated, $\text{Var}(\bar{\beta})$ is relatively small when ρ is close to

Table 8–4

Value of ρ	$r = 0.4$		$r = 0.8$	
	$\text{Var}(\bar{\beta})$	$\text{Var}(\hat{\beta})$	$\text{Var}(\bar{\beta})$	$\text{Var}(\hat{\beta})$
0.0	2.17λ	1.00λ	5.50λ	1.00λ
0.3	1.44λ	1.27λ	3.82λ	1.63λ
0.6	0.77λ	1.63λ	2.15λ	2.85λ
0.9	0.17λ	2.12λ	0.52λ	6.14λ

unity, and relatively large when ρ is small. However, it should be emphasized that the *estimator* of the variance of $\bar{\beta}$, like that of the variance of $\hat{\beta}$, is biased. Therefore, the use of $\bar{\beta}$ for testing hypotheses or constructing confidence intervals is inappropriate.[17] For this reason, the use of the method of first differences is not recommended unless it is really believed that ρ is very close to unity.

Small Sample Properties of Alternative Estimators

The small sample properties of the alternative estimators of the regression coefficients in models with autoregressive disturbances are generally unknown because the determination of the sampling distributions of these estimators is very complicated. Nevertheless, we can get some idea about the small-sample behavior of these estimators by deriving their sampling distributions *experimentally*. This can, of course, be done only for specific models and specific populations of the disturbances. The experimental derivation of sampling distributions for the case of discrete variables was discussed in Section 2–2. In the case of normally distributed disturbances, the variables are continuous, but the principle of experimental sampling remains the same. Sampling experiments of this sort have become known as *Monte Carlo experiments* because of their similarity to games of chance. We now describe one such experiment, which was designed for the purpose of comparing several estimators of the regression coefficients in a model with an autoregressive disturbance.

---

[17] The reader can determine the bias in estimating the variance of $\bar{\beta}$ by the conventional formula as an exercise. It may also be interesting to note that if ρ is positive, the values of $\bar{\beta}$ and $\hat{\beta}$ contain between them the value of $\tilde{\beta}$ that would be obtained if ρ were known. See Malinvaud, *op. cit.*, pp. 444–445.

Consider the population regression equation

$$Y_t = 10 + 2X_t + \varepsilon_t \qquad (t = 1, 2, \ldots)$$

with
$$\varepsilon_t = 0.8\varepsilon_{t-1} + u_t,$$

where
$$u_t \sim N(0, 0.36),$$

$$E(u_t\varepsilon_{t-1}) = 0,$$

and
$$\varepsilon_0 \sim N(0, 1).$$

Therefore,

$$E(\varepsilon_t) = 0,$$

$$\mathrm{Var}(\varepsilon_t) = 1,$$

$$\rho = 0.8.$$

The values of X, which were selected more or less arbitrarily, are

$X_1 = 2,$	$X_6 = 1,$	$X_{11} = X_1,$
$X_2 = 0,$	$X_7 = 4,$	$X_{12} = X_2,$
$X_3 = 1,$	$X_8 = 9,$	$\vdots$ $\quad$ $\vdots$
$X_4 = 3,$	$X_9 = 4,$	$X_{99} = X_9,$
$X_5 = 9,$	$X_{10} = 3,$	$X_{100} = X_{10}.$

The experiment consists of drawing 100 samples of size 10, 20, and 100. The random drawings for the disturbances were obtained from the table *One Million Random Digits and One Hundred Thousand Deviates* (published by the Rand Corporation, Santa Monica, Calif., 1950). From each sample we calculated the values of the ordinary least squares (OLS), maximum likelihood (ML), and two-stage (TS) estimators of the regression coefficients. After 100 samples of a given size were drawn, we obtained the mean and the standard deviation for each of the estimators. The results of estimating the regression slope—whose true value is 2—are presented in Table 8–5. From these results it

Table 8–5

	Estimator					
	OLS		ML		TS	
Sample Size	Mean	S.D.	Mean	S.D.	Mean	S.D.
10	2.0070	0.1029	2.0079	0.0634	2.0058	0.0754
20	2.0008	0.0634	1.9995	0.0402	1.9997	0.0412
100	2.0001	0.0201	1.9990	0.0136	1.9990	0.0136

Source: J. Kmenta and R. F. Gilbert, "Estimation of Seemingly Unrelated Regressions with Autoregressive Disturbances," Michigan State University Econometrics Workshop Paper No. 6805, December 1968, p. 18.

is apparent that all three estimators are unbiased, and that the OLS estimator is inefficient relative to the ML and TS estimators. The latter two have identical standard deviations in large samples and nearly the same standard deviations in samples size 20, but in samples size 10 the ML estimator is more efficient. Although generalizations from particular experiments are somewhat hazardous, the results nevertheless offer some evidence concerning the small sample behavior of the estimators considered.

Tests for the Absence of Autoregression

Thus far in this section we have been concerned with the implications of the presence of autoregressive disturbances in a linear regression model. We have examined the properties of the ordinary least squares estimators of the regression coefficients and, having uncovered their shortcomings, we discussed various alternative estimation methods. However, if we do not know—or are not willing to assume—that the model is or is not autoregressive, we may not be able to decide which estimation method to use. In such a case we have to turn to the sample for information. In particular, we may want to test the hypothesis of no autoregression,

$$H_0: \quad \rho = 0,$$

against a one-sided or a two-sided alternative. The usual alternative hypothesis in economic relations is that of positive autoregression, i.e.,

$$H_A: \quad \rho > 0.$$

One test for the presence of autoregression follows, at least implicitly, from our discussion of the maximum likelihood estimation. Since, when using the maximum likelihood method, we estimate the value of ρ along with the values of the regression coefficients, we may simply test whether the estimated value of ρ is significantly different from zero. In large samples the maximum likelihood estimator of ρ is approximately normally distributed with variance given by (8.55) as

$$s_{\hat{\rho}}^2 = \frac{1 - \hat{\rho}^2}{n}.$$

This can be used in smaller samples as an approximation.

EXAMPLE   In illustrating maximum likelihood estimation under autoregression, we used the "quantity theory" equation of Friedman and Meiselman. The maximum likelihood estimate of ρ was found to be 0.85. Its estimated large-sample standard error is

$$\sqrt{\frac{1 - 0.85^2}{20}} = 0.178.$$

If we use a 5% test against the one-sided alternative of positive autoregression, the acceptance region for the null hypothesis is

$$\frac{\hat{\rho}}{s_{\hat{\rho}}} < 1.645.$$

In our case, we have

$$\frac{\hat{\rho}}{s_{\hat{\rho}}} = \frac{0.85}{0.178} = 4.77.$$

Since this lies clearly outside the acceptance region, the hypothesis of no auto-regression has to be rejected.

An alternative test, which has been widely used in econometric applications, is known as the *Durbin-Watson test*. To apply this test we calculate the value of a statistic d given by

$$d = \frac{\sum\limits_{t=2}^{n} (e_t - e_{t-1})^2}{\sum\limits_{t=1}^{n} e_t^2},$$

where the e's represent the ordinary least squares residuals. If the alternative hypothesis is that of positive autoregression, the decision rules are:

1. Reject if $d < d_L$.
2. Do not reject if $d > d_U$.
3. The test is inconclusive if $d_L \leq d \leq d_U$.

The values of d_L (for "lower limit") and d_U (for "upper limit") are given in the table provided by Durbin and Watson and reproduced in Appendix D.[18] These values vary with the number of observations and the number of explanatory variables in the regression equation. If the alternative hypothesis is a two-sided one, the decision rules for the Durbin-Watson test are:

1. Reject if $d < d_L$, or if $d > 4 - d_L$.
2. Do not reject if $d_U < d < 4 - d_U$.
3. The test is inconclusive if $d_L \leq d \leq d_U$, or if $4 - d_U \leq d \leq 4 - d_L$.

A diagrammatic representation of the test is shown in Figure 8–2. Incidentally, it should be noted that the Durbin-Watson test is not applicable to regression equations in which the place of the explanatory variable is taken by the lagged value of the dependent variable.

---

[18] A table that is free of the inconclusive region, but is based on certain assumptions concerning the explanatory variable or variables, is given in H. Theil and A. L. Nagar, "Testing the Independence of Regression Disturbances," *Journal of the American Statistical Association*, Vol. 56, December 1961, pp. 793–806.

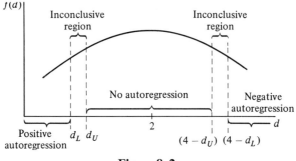

Figure 8–2

EXAMPLE   Consider again estimation of the "quantity theory" equation. Suppose we wish to test the hypothesis

$$H_0: \quad \rho = 0$$

against

$$H_A: \quad \rho > 0$$

at the 5% level of significance, using the Durbin-Watson test. From the table, the appropriate values of d_L and d_U for twenty observations and one explanatory variable are

$$d_L = 1.20, \quad \text{and} \quad d_U = 1.41.$$

This means that we will reject H_0 if $d < 1.20$, and not reject H_0 if $d > 1.41$. The calculated value of the d statistic is

$$d = 0.321,$$

so that the hypothesis of no autoregression ($\rho = 0$) has to be rejected under this test as well.

As mentioned earlier, the Durbin-Watson test has been widely used in econometric applications. In fact, in most studies concerned with estimating regression equations from time-series data, the value of the d statistic is presented along with the other estimates. The question then is what action, if any, is to be taken in response to a particular outcome of the test. If no autoregression is indicated, we can retain the least squares estimates without fearing a loss of efficiency and a bias of the estimated standard errors. However, if the test indicates autoregression, then we have some reason to be concerned. One response is to re-estimate the equation, using one of the estimation methods designed for this situation (e.g., maximum likelihood or the two-stage procedure). Alternatively, we may take a second look at the specification of the regression model, since the autoregression of the disturbance may simply reflect the presence of some unexplained systematic influence on the dependent variable. A fairly commonly adopted ad hoc way of searching for this influence is to plot

the residuals and then to try finding a variable whose peaks and troughs resemble those of the plotted residuals. Finally, if the result of the test is inconclusive, we may or may not respond. There is some evidence [19] that when the
explanatory variable evolves gradually without any sharp, short, regular fluctuations, the appropriate boundary region is nearer d_U.

8–3   Stochastic Explanatory Variable

Assumption (7.6) of the classical normal linear regression model consists of
the following:

1. X is nonstochastic.
2. Values of X are fixed in repeated samples.
3. $(1/n) \sum_i (X_i - \bar{X})^2$ is equal to a finite, nonzero number for any
sample size.

In this section we shall be concerned mainly with 1; 2 and 3 deserve only a
brief mention. To start with, the requirement that the values of X are fixed in
repeated samples is only of theoretical interest since, in reality, we rarely draw
or observe more than one sample for a given set of values of X. The purpose of
this requirement is to set the framework for the sampling distributions of the
various estimators that we discuss. It really amounts to saying that *if* we drew
an infinite number of samples of one size (i.e., an infinite number of sets of values
of $Y_1, Y_2, \ldots, Y_n$) for a fixed set of values of X (i.e., *one* set of values of X_1,
$X_2, \ldots, X_n$), then the sampling distributions and properties of the estimators
would be as we asserted. Thus we avoid the complications that would arise if
the values of X were to change from sample to sample. Note that the values of X
can be considered to be held fixed from sample to sample even if X is a stochastic
variable (as long as holding X fixed does not make Y fixed as well).

By the assumption that for any sample size $\sum_i (X_i - \bar{X})^2/n$ is a finite number
different from zero, it is required that the values of X in the sample are not all
the same, and that they do not grow or decline without limit. The first requirement—that not all values of X are the same—is crucial, since otherwise the
determination of the least squares regression coefficients would become
impossible, as pointed out in Section 7–4. If the values of X are not all the
same but the differences between them are very small, $\sum (X_i - \bar{X})^2$ will be
small, and the variances of the estimators are likely to be very large. This, in
turn, implies that in the tests of significance the probability of Error Type II
(accepting H_0 when it is false) is high, and that the confidence intervals for the
population parameters are wide. This is what the researchers mean when, in
commenting on their regression results, they say: "Unfortunately, there was
very little variation in the explanatory variable." As to the second requirement,
the restriction that the values of X should be bounded is less crucial. It is

---

[19] See *ibid.*; also Malinvaud, *op. cit.*, p. 425.

utilized mainly in proving that an estimator is consistent, but it is *not* a necessary condition for consistency in all cases.

As an example of a case where the values of the explanatory variable are not bounded, consider the equation for a "linear trend" given as

$$Y_t = \alpha + \beta t + \varepsilon_t \qquad (t = 1, 2, \ldots, n),$$

where t measures time in terms of specified periods. Assume that all the basic assumptions about the disturbance ε_t hold. Then, obviously, as n increases to infinity, so do the values of t. In fact,

$$\frac{1}{n} \sum_{t=1}^{n} (t - \bar{t})^2 = \frac{1}{n} \sum_t t^2 - \left[\frac{1}{n} \sum_t t \right]^2$$

$$= \frac{1}{n} [1^2 + 2^2 + \cdots + n^2] - \frac{1}{n^2} [1 + 2 + \cdots + n]^2$$

$$= \frac{1}{n} \left[\frac{n}{6} (n + 1)(2n + 1) \right] - \frac{1}{n^2} \left[\frac{n}{2} (1 + n) \right] = \frac{n^2 - 1}{12}.$$

The small sample properties of the least squares estimators are not affected by this. As for consistency, we have

$$\mathrm{Var}(\hat{\beta}) = \frac{\sigma^2}{\sum (t - \bar{t})^2} = \frac{\sigma^2/n}{\sum (t - \bar{t})^2/n} = \frac{12\sigma^2}{n(n^2 - 1)},$$

so that

$$\lim_{n \to \infty} \mathrm{Var}(\hat{\beta}) = 0.$$

This implies that $\hat{\beta}$ is a consistent estimator of β.

The foregoing discussion leaves only the requirement of a nonstochastic explanatory variable to be considered. Let us now deal with the problem of estimating the coefficients of a regression equation when this is violated, i.e., when X is a stochastic variable. In this case the values of X are not fixed; instead, different values of X—or intervals of values of X—occur with certain probabilities. Regressions with stochastic explanatory variables are common, if not predominant, in econometrics. In many economic relations the values of the explanatory variable are determined, along with those of the dependent variable, as a result of some probability mechanism rather than being controlled by the experimenter or other persons or institutions. If X is stochastic, the important thing is whether it is or is not independent of the disturbance ε, and if dependent, what is the nature of the dependence. We shall distinguish between three possibilities:

1. X and ε are independent.
2. X and ε are contemporaneously uncorrelated.
3. X and ε are *not* independent *or* contemporaneously uncorrelated.

In each case we shall be concerned with the properties of the least squares estimators of the regression coefficients, given that all the basic assumptions about the disturbance term hold. We shall also make the assumption that the variance of X is a finite number different from zero.

Let us start with the case where X and ε are *independent*. As an example, consider the relationship

$$Y_i = \alpha + \beta X_i + \varepsilon_i,$$

with X_i and Y_i defined as follows:

$$Y_i = \log \left[\frac{V}{PL}\right]_i,$$

$$X_i = \log \left[\frac{W}{P}\right]_i,$$

where V = value added in production, L = labor input, P = price of product, W = money wage rate, and the subscript i refers to the ith region. The observations are made for a particular industry and a given period of time. The coefficient β represents the elasticity of substitution between labor and capital.[20] Here X is a stochastic variable which can be assumed to be independent of ε. The least squares estimator of β is

$$\hat{\beta} = \beta + \frac{\sum x_i' \varepsilon_i}{\sum x_i'^2}$$

and

$$E(\hat{\beta}) = \beta + E\left[\frac{\sum x_i'}{\sum x_i'^2}\right] E(\varepsilon_i) = \beta.$$

This result follows from the assumptions that X and ε are independent and that $E(\varepsilon_i) = 0$, using Theorem 10 of Section 3-6. Similarly,

$$E(\hat{\alpha}) = E(\bar{Y} - \hat{\beta}\bar{X}) = E(\alpha + \beta\bar{X} + \bar{\varepsilon} - \hat{\beta}\bar{X})$$

$$= \alpha + \beta E(\bar{X}) + E(\bar{\varepsilon}) - E\left[\beta + \frac{\sum x_i' \varepsilon_i}{\sum x_i'^2}\right]\bar{X} = \alpha,$$

so that $\hat{\alpha}$ and $\hat{\beta}$ retain their property of unbiasedness.

Since X is a stochastic variable, $\hat{\alpha}$ and $\hat{\beta}$ are no longer linear functions of $Y_1, Y_2, \ldots, Y_n$; that is, they can no longer be described as equal to $\sum_i a_i Y_i$ where $a_1, a_2, \ldots, a_n$ are *constants*. Therefore, in the strictest sense, $\hat{\alpha}$ and $\hat{\beta}$ cannot be considered as best-*linear*-unbiased estimators. However, it is not difficult to see that $\hat{\alpha}$ and $\hat{\beta}$ are efficient if we consider their variances as being conditional on a given set of values of $X_1, X_2, \ldots, X_n$. We may think of the population of all pairs of values of X and Y as an enormous card file with each card representing a specific pair. Then we can specify one set of values of $X_1, X_2, \ldots, X_n$ and have the sorting machine pull out all the cards with these values of X. This subset of cards represents a population from which samples can be drawn. Each such sample can be used to estimate the regression coefficients. If we drew an infinite number of these samples, we could construct sampling distributions for these estimators and determine their properties. Obviously, the properties of the estimators determined in this way would be conditional on the chosen values $X_1, X_2, \ldots, X_n$. This means that these values can be treated *as if* they were fixed numbers, which in fact they are *after* we pull out all the appropriate cards from the original file. Now we know that for a fixed set of values $X_1, X_2, \ldots, X_n$, the least squares estimators of the regression coefficients are efficient. We also know that this is true for *any* fixed set of values of X. Therefore, since the least squares estimators of the regression coefficients are unconditionally unbiased, and since for *each* set of values of $X_1, X_2, \ldots, X_n$ they are efficient, it follows that they are *efficient* unconditionally, too.

It is easy to show that the least squares estimators of the regression coefficients also retain their desirable asymptotic properties when X is stochastic but independent of ε. One way is by relying upon the maximum likelihood principle. The probability distribution for a single observation, say the ith, is given by $f(x_i, \varepsilon_i)$. For n independent observations, we have

$$f(x_1, \varepsilon_1)f(x_2, \varepsilon_2) \ldots f(x_n, \varepsilon_n),$$

which, since X and ε are independent, can be written as

$$f(x_1)f(x_2) \ldots f(x_n)f(\varepsilon_1)f(\varepsilon_2) \ldots f(\varepsilon_n).$$

The probability transformation from the ε's, which are not observable, to the Y's is

$$f(y_i) = \left| \frac{\partial \varepsilon_i}{\partial Y_i} \right| f(\varepsilon_i) = f(\varepsilon_i),$$

so that the logarithmic likelihood function becomes

$$L = \log \left[f(x_1)f(x_2) \ldots f(x_n) \right] + \log \left[f(\varepsilon_1)f(\varepsilon_2) \ldots f(\varepsilon_n) \right]$$

$$= \sum_i \log f(x_i) - \frac{n}{2} \log (2\pi) - \frac{n}{2} \log \sigma^2 - \frac{1}{2\sigma^2} \sum_i (Y_i - \alpha - \beta X_i)^2.$$

As long as the distribution of X does not involve any of the parameters α, β, or σ^2, maximizing the likelihood function with respect to these parameters will not be affected by the presence of the term $\sum \log f(x_i)$. The resulting estimators of α and β will then be the same as the least squares estimators. Thus, the least squares estimators of the regression coefficients are consistent, asymptotically efficient, and asymptotically normal whether X is nonstochastic or stochastic, provided X and ε are independent.

As a final point, consider the variances of the least squares estimators of α and β. For $\hat{\beta}$ we have

$$\mathrm{Var}(\hat{\beta}) = E\left[\frac{\sum x_i' \varepsilon_i}{\sum x_i'^2} \right]^2 = E\left[\frac{\sum x_i'^2 \varepsilon_i^2}{(\sum x_i'^2)^2} \right] + 2E\left[\frac{\sum\limits_{i<j} x_i' x_j' \varepsilon_i \varepsilon_j}{(\sum x_i'^2)^2} \right] = \sigma^2 E\left[\frac{1}{\sum x_i'^2} \right].$$

Similarly, we can show that

$$\text{Var}(\hat{\alpha}) = \sigma^2 E\left[\frac{1}{n} + \frac{\bar{X}^2}{\sum x_i'^2}\right].$$

That is, the variances of $\hat{\alpha}$ and $\hat{\beta}$ are the same as when X is nonstochastic, *except that the terms involving X are replaced by their mathematical expectations*. The formulas for unbiased estimators of $\text{Var}(\hat{\alpha})$ and $\text{Var}(\hat{\beta})$ are given by (7.37). Also, the classical procedures for interval estimation and hypothesis testing developed in Chapter 7 remain valid when X is stochastic but independent of ε. Thus, *relaxing the assumption that X is nonstochastic and replacing it by the assumption that X is stochastic but independent of ε does not change the desirable properties and feasibility of least squares estimation.*

Now we come to the second possibility concerning the explanatory variable, namely, the case where X and ε are *contemporaneously uncorrelated*. That is, we assume that

$$\text{Cov}(X_1, \varepsilon_1) = \text{Cov}(X_2, \varepsilon_2) = \cdots = \text{Cov}(X_n, \varepsilon_n) = 0.$$

Note that we do not assume that X and ε are contemporaneously independent, which would be a stronger requirement. As an example, consider the following highly simplified model of income determination:

$$C_t = \gamma_0 + \gamma_1 Y_t + \varepsilon_{1t} \qquad \text{(consumption function)},$$

$$I_t = \delta_0 + \delta_1 Y_{t-1} + \varepsilon_{2t} \quad \text{(investment function)},$$

$$Y_t = C_t + I_t \qquad\qquad\quad \text{(income identity)},$$

where $C =$ consumption, $Y =$ income, $I =$ investment, and ε_{1t} and ε_{2t} are random disturbances that satisfy the basic assumptions. The three-equation model can be reduced to one equation by solving for Y_t to get

$$Y_t = (\gamma_0 + \gamma_1 Y_t + \varepsilon_{1t}) + (\delta_0 + \delta_1 Y_{t-1} + \varepsilon_{2t}).$$

This can be written as

(8.58) $$Y_t = \alpha + \beta Y_{t-1} + \varepsilon_t,$$

where $$\alpha = \frac{\gamma_0 + \delta_0}{1 - \gamma_1},$$

$$\beta = \frac{\delta_1}{1 - \gamma_1},$$

and $$\varepsilon_t = \frac{\varepsilon_{1t} + \varepsilon_{2t}}{1 - \gamma_1}.$$

In (8.58) the explanatory variable is represented by the lagged value of the dependent variable. A model of this kind is generally known as a "model autoregressive in variables." In our case, we shall confine it to the situations where $-1 < \beta < 1$. By carrying out successive substitutions we can express Y_t as

$$Y_t = \alpha(1 + \beta + \beta^2 + \cdots + \beta^{t-1}) + \beta^t Y_0$$

$$+ \varepsilon_t + \beta\varepsilon_{t-1} + \beta^2\varepsilon_{t-2} + \cdots + \beta^{t-1}\varepsilon_1.$$

As $t \to \infty$, Y_t becomes

$$Y_t = \frac{\alpha}{1-\beta} + \varepsilon_t + \beta\varepsilon_{t-1} + \beta^2\varepsilon_{t-2} + \cdots;$$

that is, in the long run Y_t "settles down" to random fluctuations around a fixed level. Note that in (8.58) the explanatory variable Y_{t-1} is *not* correlated with the current disturbance ε_t since Y_{t-1} depends on $Y_0, \varepsilon_1, \varepsilon_2, \ldots, \varepsilon_{t-1}$ but not on ε_t.

Consider now the least squares estimator of β in (8.58). We have

$$\hat{\beta} = \beta + \frac{\sum y'_{t-1}\varepsilon_t}{\sum y'^2_{t-1}}.$$

Now y'_{t-1} and ε_t are not independent since

$$y'_{t-1} = Y_{t-1} - \frac{1}{n}(Y_0 + Y_1 + \cdots + Y_t + \cdots + Y_{n-1});$$

that is, y'_{t-1} involves Y_t, which is *not* independent of ε_t. This means that we cannot separate out ε_t when taking mathematical expectation of $\hat{\beta}$ as we could in case of independence. Thus $\hat{\beta}$ cannot be said to be unbiased. However, the probability limit of $\hat{\beta}$ is

$$\text{plim } \hat{\beta} = \beta + \frac{\text{plim }(\sum y'_{t-1}\varepsilon_t)/n}{\text{plim }(\sum y'^2_{t-1})/n} = \beta,$$

since $(\sum y'_{t-1}\varepsilon_t)/n$ is a consistent estimator of the population covariance of Y_{t-1} and ε_t, which is zero, and $(\sum y'^2_{t-1})/n$ is a consistent estimator of the variance of Y_{t-1}, which is a finite number different from zero. Thus $\hat{\beta}$ is a consistent estimator of β. Similarly, $\hat{\alpha}$ can be shown to be a consistent estimator of α. Asymptotic efficiency and asymptotic normality of the least squares estimators of α and β are more difficult to prove, but they also have been established.[21] The conclusion then is that *when the explanatory variable and the disturbance are contemporaneously uncorrelated (as in the model which is autoregressive in variables), the classical results of least squares estimation established in Chapter 7 hold only asymptotically.*

The last possibility concerning the explanatory variable is the case where X and ε are *neither independent nor contemporaneously uncorrelated*. In this case,

$$\text{plim } \hat{\beta} = \beta + \frac{\text{plim }(\sum x'_t\varepsilon_t)/n}{\text{plim }(\sum x'^2_t)/n} \neq \beta$$

and $$\text{plim } \hat{\alpha} \neq \alpha,$$

[21] For details and relevant references see Malinvaud, *op. cit.*, pp. 452–453.

so that the least squares estimators of the regression coefficients are not even consistent. An intuitive explanation for this is that the least squares estimation method is designed in such a way that the total variation of Y (SST) can always be divided into two parts, one representing the variation due to the explanatory variable (SSR) and the other representing the variation due to other factors. But when the explanatory variable and the disturbance are correlated, such a division is not valid since it does not allow for the *joint* effect of X and ε on Y.

EXAMPLE   As an example of a situation in which the explanatory variable and the disturbance are contemporaneously correlated, consider a market demand equation given by

$$Q_t = \alpha + \beta P_t + \varepsilon_t \qquad (\alpha > 0, \beta < 0),$$

where Q = quantity and P = price of a given commodity. If the market is in equilibrium, the quantity of the commodity sold in the market and the equilibrium price are determined by the intersection of the demand and the supply functions. Suppose the supply function is

$$Q_t = \gamma + \delta P_t + \eta_t \qquad (\gamma > 0, \delta > 0),$$

where $\eta_t \sim N(0, \sigma_\eta^2)$ is a stochastic disturbance which is nonautoregressive and independent of ε_t. The demand and the supply equations can be solved for the equilibrium quantity and price to give

$$Q_t = \frac{\alpha\delta - \beta\gamma}{\delta - \beta} + \frac{\delta\varepsilon_t - \beta\eta_t}{\delta - \beta},$$

$$P_t = \frac{\alpha - \gamma}{\delta - \beta} + \frac{\varepsilon_t - \eta_t}{\delta - \beta}.$$

From the last result we can see that P_t and ε_t are correlated; in particular,

$$\text{Cov}(P_t, \varepsilon_t) = E[P_t - E(P_t)][\varepsilon_t - E(\varepsilon_t)] = E\left[\frac{\varepsilon_t - \eta_t}{\delta - \beta}\right]\varepsilon_t = \frac{\sigma^2}{\delta - \beta}.$$

The least squares estimator of the slope of the demand equation is

$$\hat{\beta} = \beta + \frac{\sum p_t' \varepsilon_t'}{\sum p_t'^2},$$

where

$$p_t' = P_t - \bar{P} = \frac{\varepsilon_t' - \eta_t'}{\delta - \beta}.$$

Substitution for p_t' into $\hat{\beta}$ gives

$$\hat{\beta} = \beta + \frac{\left[\dfrac{1}{\delta - \beta}\right]\sum \varepsilon_t'(\varepsilon_t' - \eta_t')}{\left[\dfrac{1}{\delta - \beta}\right]^2 \sum (\varepsilon_t' - \eta_t')^2} = \beta + \frac{(\delta - \beta)\left[\dfrac{1}{n}\sum \varepsilon_t'^2 - \dfrac{1}{n}\sum \varepsilon_t'\eta_t'\right]}{\dfrac{1}{n}\sum \varepsilon_t'^2 + \dfrac{1}{n}\sum \eta_t'^2 - \dfrac{2}{n}\sum \varepsilon_t'\eta_t'}.$$

Therefore,

$$\text{plim } \hat{\beta} = \beta + \frac{(\delta - \beta)\sigma^2}{\sigma^2 + \sigma_\eta^2},$$

which proves that the least squares estimator of β is inconsistent. This example illustrates the so-called "simultaneous equation problem," which occurs when estimating certain economic relationships.

Regression equations in which the explanatory variable and the disturbance are correlated are rather common in econometrics, most notoriously in the area of simultaneous equation models, illustrated by the preceding example. However, the problem arises also in connection with some single equation models, such as the "distributed lag" model or the "errors-in-variables" model, which will be discussed in the following chapters. In each case the breakdown of the least squares estimation method has led to development of alternative methods of estimation that provide us with consistent estimates. These methods will be discussed in connection with the models for which they were developed or to which they were found to be applicable.

EXERCISES

8-1. Derive the formulas (8.3) and (8.4).

8-2. Prove that if $x_i'^2$ and σ_i^2 are positively associated, the bias in (8.9) is negative.

8-3. Consider the following model:

$$Y_i = \alpha + \varepsilon_i,$$

where

$$\varepsilon_i \sim N(0, \sigma^2 X_i),$$

$$E(\varepsilon_i \varepsilon_j) = 0 \qquad (i \neq j),$$

and X_i is nonstochastic. Find the best linear unbiased estimator of α and its variance.

8-4. Using the data in Table 8-6 on income (X) and expenditure (Y) of a sample of households, estimate the regression equation

$$Y_i = \alpha + \beta X_i + \varepsilon_i$$

for the following heteroskedastic models:

a. $\text{Var}(\varepsilon_i) = \sigma^2 X_i^2$.   **b.** $\text{Var}(\varepsilon_i) = \sigma^2 [E(Y_i)]^2$.   **c.** $\text{Var}(\varepsilon_i) = \sigma_i^2$.

Table 8-6

X	\multicolumn{10}{c}{Y}	
	14	19	21	23	25	27	29	31	33	35	Total
18	74	13	7	1							95
23	6	4	2	7	4						23
25	2	3	2	2	4						13
27	1	1	2	3	3	2					12
29	2		1	3	2		6				14
31	2		2	1			1	2	1		9
33				2			1	1	3		7
35		1		1					2		4
37					1	1		1		1	4

8-5. Prove the validity of the formula (8.38).

8-6. Prove that formulas (8.38) through (8.41) reduce to the least squares formulas when $\rho = 0$.

8-7. Prove that the conventional least squares formula for estimating the variance of the estimator in (8.57) leads to biased results.

8-8. One representation of the aggregate consumption function for the United States economy is:

$$C_t = \alpha + \beta Y_t + \varepsilon_t,$$

where $C =$ personal consumption expenditure in constant prices, $Y =$ personal disposable income in constant prices, and $t =$ time in years.

a. Assume that all the basic assumptions of the simple regression model are satisfied. Estimate the relationship from the data in Table 8-7, following the computational design given in Appendix C.

b. On the basis of the results obtained in **a**, carry out the Durbin-Watson test for the presence of autoregression among the disturbances.

c. Assume that the disturbance follows a first-order autoregressive scheme and obtain asymptotically efficient estimates of the regression coefficients and their estimated standard errors.

Table 8-7

Year	Personal Consumption Expenditure*		Personal Disposable Income* in Current Prices†
	In Current Prices (1)	In Constant 1954 Prices (2)	(3)
1948	178.3	199.3	189.3
1949	181.2	204.3	189.7
1950	195.0	216.8	207.7
1951	209.8	218.5	227.5
1952	219.8	224.2	238.7
1953	232.6	235.1	252.5
1954	238.0	238.0	256.9
1955	256.9	256.0	274.4
1956	269.9	264.3	292.9
1957	285.2	271.2	308.8
1958	293.2	273.2	317.9
1959	313.5	288.9	337.1
1960	328.2	298.1	349.9
1961	337.3	303.8	364.7
1962	356.8	318.5	384.6
1963	375.0	330.6	402.5
1964	399.3	347.5	431.8

Sources: 1948–1960: *Business Statistics*, 1963 ed. (U.S. Department of Commerce); 1961–1964: *Statistical Abstract of the United States*, 1965 (U.S. Department of Commerce).
* In billions of dollars.
† To obtain "real" personal disposable income, deflate by the price deflator given implicitly by columns (1) and (2).

8–9. Derive the formula given in (8.55).

8–10. An aggregate food consumption function is specified as

$$Y_t = \alpha + \beta Z_t + \varepsilon_t,$$

where Y = personal expenditure on food, and Z = total personal consumption expenditure. The data for the United States for the years 1929–1964 are given in Exercise **7–8** (Table 7–4). Conduct a test for the absence of positive autoregression of the disturbances by

a. Using the Durbin-Watson test.

b. Using the maximum likelihood large-sample test.

9

Estimation with
Deficient Data

In Chapter 8 we dealt with the problem of estimating the coefficients of a linear regression equation when one of the basic assumptions of the classical normal linear regression model does not hold. The discussion in the present chapter deals with the estimation problem in situations where the sample data are in some respect deficient. The particular deficiencies that we discuss are:

1. Presence of errors of measurement.
2. Grouped data.
3. Missing observations.

These deficiencies, which are likely to be encountered in empirical work, give rise to estimation problems that deserve our special attention.

9–1   Errors of Measurement

Up to this point, we have always taken for granted that the values of the variables in the regression model are measured without error. This presumption has been implicit in our entire discussion, and all of our formulas are based on it. Here we are investigating what happens to the estimators of the regression coefficients when this is not true and what can be done to cope with such a situation. In doing so, we restrict ourselves to cases in which the errors of measurement can be assumed to be random and to have specific probability characteristics. This fairly standard way of treating errors of measurement in the statistical and econometric literature corresponds to a wide variety of situations encountered in real life.

Let us start by considering the problem of errors of measurement in the context of the classical normal linear regression model of Chapter 7. As before, the regression equation is

$$Y_i = \alpha + \beta X_i + \varepsilon_i.$$

We also retain all the basic assumptions (7.2) through (7.6). Suppose, now, that our observations on Y and X contain errors, so that instead of Y_i and X_i we observe Y_i^* and X_i^*, which are given as

$$Y_i^* = Y_i + v_i,$$
$$X_i^* = X_i + w_i,$$

where v_i and w_i represent the errors in measuring the ith value of Y and of X. The behavioral characteristics of the errors are assumed to be as follows:

(9.1) $$v_i \sim N(0, \sigma_v^2),$$
$$w_i \sim N(0, \sigma_w^2);$$

(9.2) $$E(v_i v_j) = 0 \quad (i \neq j),$$
$$E(w_i w_j) = 0 \quad (i \neq j);$$

(9.3) $$E(v_i w_i) = 0,$$
$$E(v_i \varepsilon_i) = 0,$$
$$E(w_i \varepsilon_i) = 0.$$

Assumption (9.1) states that each error is a random normal variable with zero mean and a constant variance. Assumption (9.2) rules out situations in which the errors are autoregressive; together with (9.1), this assumption implies that errors made at one point of observation are independent of errors made at other points of observation. Assumption (9.3) states how the errors are related—or, rather, unrelated—to each other. Assumptions (9.1) through (9.3) and the basic assumptions about the disturbance ε jointly imply that the errors of measurement are independent of each other, of the disturbance in the regression equation, and of the true values of X and Y.

Let us now consider the problem of estimating the regression coefficients from data on Y^* and X^*. Since

$$Y_i = Y_i^* - v_i$$

and

$$X_i = X_i^* - w_i,$$

the regression equation can be rewritten as

$$(Y_i^* - v_i) = \alpha + \beta(X_i^* - w_i) + \varepsilon_i$$

or

(9.4) $$Y_i^* = \alpha + \beta X_i^* + \varepsilon_i^*,$$

where $$\varepsilon_i^* = \varepsilon_i + v_i - \beta w_i.$$

Now, when the regression model is written in the form (9.4) where the dependent and the explanatory variables are observable, the explanatory variable X_i^* is contemporaneously correlated with the disturbance ε_i^*. In particular,

$$\text{Cov}(X_i^*, \varepsilon_i^*) = E[X_i^* - E(X_i^*)]\varepsilon_i^* = E[w_i(\varepsilon_i + v_i - \beta w_i)] = -\beta \sigma_w^2.$$

This means that the least squares estimator of β is *inconsistent*. The same is true of the least squares estimator of α.

Instrumental Variables Estimation

Equation (9.4) is sometimes referred to as a model with *errors in variables and errors in equation*. An attempt to estimate this model by using the maximum likelihood method breaks down in the sense that the resulting estimators are not consistent.[1] One method known to give consistent estimates in this case is the *method of instrumental variables*. This method is available whenever we can find a new variable Z_i such that

1. $\operatorname{plim} \left(\sum z_i' \varepsilon_i^{*\prime} \right)/n = 0$.

2. $\operatorname{plim} \left(\sum z_i' x_i^{*\prime} \right)/n$ is a finite number different from zero.

Here, in accordance with the previously adopted notation, we define

$$z_i' = Z_i - \bar{Z},$$
$$x_i^{*\prime} = X_i^* - \bar{X}^*.$$

The first condition will be satisfied if Z_i is uncorrelated with ε_i, v_i, and w_i. The second condition will be satisfied if Z_i and X_i^* are correlated with each other. An additional condition, which is not necessary for consistency but helps to reduce the asymptotic variance of the instrumental variables estimator, is that the $\operatorname{plim} \left(\sum z_i' x_i^{*\prime} \right)/n$ is as large as possible—that is, that the degree of correlation between Z_i and X_i^* is high. The variable Z_i, which is called an "instrumental variable," may be either stochastic or nonstochastic. Finally, it does not matter whether Z_i is or is not measured without error as long as the specified conditions are satisfied with respect to the observable values of Z. The estimators of α and β, say, $\alpha^\dagger$ and $\beta^\dagger$, are then defined as follows:

(9.5a)
$$\beta^\dagger = \frac{\sum y_i^{*\prime} z_i'}{\sum x_i^{*\prime} z_i'},$$

(9.5b)
$$\alpha^\dagger = \bar{Y}^* - \beta^\dagger \bar{X}^*,$$

where
$$y_i^{*\prime} = Y_i^* - \bar{Y}^*.$$

For reasons of computational convenience we usually measure the values of the instrumental variable in such units that $\bar{Z}$ is equal to $\bar{X}^*$. This can be easily achieved by multiplying each value of the instrumental variable by the factor $(\bar{X}^*/\bar{Z}^*)$, where $\bar{Z}^*$ is the sample mean of the values of the instrumental variable

---

[1] See J. Johnston, *Econometric Methods* (New York: McGraw-Hill, 1963), pp. 151–152. The breakdown of the maximum likelihood method occurs because the likelihood function includes the "true" values of the explanatory variable, which are not known and therefore have to be treated as unknown parameters. This means that as the sample size increases, so does the number of unknown parameters. In this case the likelihood function does not have a maximum.

measured in terms of original units. Such a transformation leaves unaffected the correlations between Z and ε^* and between Z and X^*.

The idea behind the method of instrumental variables can be explained by reference to the least squares "normal equations" given by (7.10) and (7.11). For the regression equation (9.4) the least squares normal equations are:

$$\sum Y_i^* = \hat{a}n + \hat{\beta}\sum X_i^*,$$

$$\sum Y_i^* X_i^* = \hat{a}\sum X_i^* + \hat{\beta}\sum X_i^{*2}.$$

A rule for obtaining these equations is as follows. To obtain the first normal equation, multiply both sides of (9.4) by the multiplier of α (which is 1), add all observations, and omit the last term involving the disturbance. To obtain the second normal equation, multiply both sides of (9.4) by the multiplier of β (which is X_i^*), add all observations, and omit the last term involving the disturbance. In obtaining the normal equations for the instrumental variables estimators, we proceed in a similar way. The first normal equation is obtained in exactly the same way as the first normal equation in the least squares method. The second normal equation is obtained by multiplying both sides of (9.4) by Z_i instead of X_i^* as in the case of least squares. The result is:

$$\sum Y_i^* = \alpha^\dagger n + \beta^\dagger \sum X_i^*,$$

$$\sum Y_i^* Z_i = \alpha^\dagger \sum Z_i + \beta^\dagger \sum X_i^* Z_i.$$

This leads to the formulas for instrumental variables estimators as given by (9.5a) and (9.5b).

Note that in the case of a regression equation in which the explanatory variable X_i is independent of the disturbance ε_i, a suitable instrumental variable would be X_i itself since, in this case, X_i is uncorrelated with ε_i and at the same time is (perfectly) correlated with itself; therefore, conditions 1 and 2 are satisfied. Thus, an ordinary least squares estimator may be thought of as an instrumental variables estimator with $Z_i = X_i$.

Let us now demonstrate that the instrumental variables estimators are consistent. With respect to $\beta^\dagger$, we have

$$\beta^\dagger = \frac{\sum y_i^{*\prime} z_i^\prime}{\sum x_i^{*\prime} z_i^\prime} = \beta + \frac{\sum \varepsilon_i^{*\prime} z_i^\prime}{\sum x_i^{*\prime} z_i^\prime},$$

and

$$\text{plim } \beta^\dagger = \beta + \frac{\text{plim }(\sum \varepsilon_i^{*\prime} z_i^\prime)/n}{\text{plim }(\sum x_i^{*\prime} z_i^\prime)/n} = \beta$$

by making use of the conditions that Z_i is supposed to satisfy. Similarly,

$$\text{plim } \alpha^\dagger = \text{plim }(\bar{Y}^* - \beta^\dagger \bar{X}^*) = \text{plim }(\alpha + \beta\bar{X}^* + \bar{\varepsilon}^* - \beta^\dagger \bar{X}^*) = \alpha.$$

This shows that $\alpha^\dagger$ and $\beta^\dagger$ are consistent. Note that we cannot prove that $\beta^\dagger$ is unbiased, because in the last term of

$$\beta^\dagger = \beta + \frac{\sum \varepsilon_i^{*\prime} z_i^\prime}{\sum x_i^{*\prime} z_i^\prime}$$

we cannot separate z'_i from the rest (even if Z_i is nonstochastic) when taking the mathematical expectation.

The asymptotic variances of the instrumental variables estimators can be derived from the appropriate formulas.[2] The results are:

$$(9.6a) \qquad \text{Asympt. Var}(\beta^\dagger) = \frac{\sigma_{\varepsilon^*}^2 \sum z_i'^2}{(\sum x_i^{*\prime} z_i')^2},$$

$$(9.6b) \qquad \text{Asympt. Var}(\alpha^\dagger) = \sigma_{\varepsilon^*}^2 \left[\frac{1}{n} + \frac{\bar{X}^{*2} \sum z_i'^2}{(\sum x_i^{*\prime} z_i')^2} \right],$$

where
$$\sigma_{\varepsilon^*}^2 = \text{Var}(\varepsilon_i^*) = \sigma^2 + \sigma_v^2 + \sigma_w^2.$$

In these derivations we have made use of the fact that Z is measured in such a way that $\bar{Z} = \bar{X}^*$. Since $\sigma_{\varepsilon^*}^2$ is not known, it has to be estimated. A consistent estimator of $\sigma_{\varepsilon^*}^2$, say, s^{*2}, is given by

$$(9.7) \qquad s^{*2} = \frac{1}{n-2} \sum_i (Y_i^* - \alpha^\dagger - \beta^\dagger X_i^*)^2,$$

i.e., by dividing the sum of squared residuals by $(n-2)$. This enables us to obtain estimators of the asymptotic variances of $\alpha^\dagger$ and $\beta^\dagger$ as

$$(9.8a) \qquad s_{\beta^\dagger}^2 = \frac{s^{*2} \sum z_i'^2}{(\sum x_i^{*\prime} z_i')^2},$$

$$(9.8b) \qquad s_{\alpha^\dagger}^2 = s^{*2} \left[\frac{1}{n} + \frac{\bar{X}^{*2} \sum z_i'^2}{(\sum x_i^{*\prime} z_i')^2} \right].$$

Although these estimators refer to asymptotic variances, they have been used in finite samples as approximations. It can be shown that the results (9.5), (9.7), and (9.8) also apply when the "true" explanatory variable X is stochastic but independent of ε^*.

The choice of the instrumental variable is limited only by the requirement that it should be uncorrelated with ε^* and correlated with X^*. There can be, and in general there will be, many variables that may qualify as instruments. We will try to choose the one that has the highest correlation with X^*, since this will give smaller asymptotic variances of the estimators than otherwise. For instance, when the data are in the form of a time series, a suitable choice may be that of $Z_t = X_{t-1}^*$, i.e., the lagged value of the explanatory variable. If ε_t^* is nonautoregressive, X_{t-1}^* would be uncorrelated with ε_t^* and, at the same time, probably highly correlated with X_t^*. However, we can never be sure that we may not do better by choosing a different instrumental variable from the one we had selected. Therefore, we cannot assert that our particular instrumental variables estimator has the minimum asymptotic variance, i.e., that it is asymptotically efficient. Thus the only desirable property of instrumental variables estimators is consistency. This limitation, combined with the arbitrariness in the choice of

[2] For details see A. S. Goldberger, *Econometric Theory* (New York: Wiley, 1964), pp. 285–286.

instrumental variables and the difficulty of checking that the chosen variable is indeed uncorrelated with ε^*, makes the method somewhat unattractive. Unfortunately, when it comes to models with errors in variables and errors in equation, we have no better method available to us—at least in the context of classical sampling theory. In previous econometric work, the tendency has been to avoid the issue by assuming that the errors of measurement are so small that they can be safely neglected.

EXAMPLE In a well-known paper on capital-labor substitution,[3] the authors estimate the following relationship:

$$Y_i = \alpha + \beta X_i + \varepsilon_i,$$

with X_i and Y_i defined as

$$X_i = \log (W/P)_i,$$

$$Y_i = \log (V/PL)_i,$$

where W = money wage rate, P = price of product, V = value added in production, L = labor input, and the subscript i refers to the ith country. The observations are made for a particular industry and a given year. In their estimation, the authors used the method of least squares. Since it is quite likely that the observations on X and Y contain errors of measurement, we may re-estimate the relationship by using the method of instrumental variables. We shall confine our attention to the *furniture manufacturing industry* (group 260), which is one of two industries for which price data are given in the paper. As the instrumental variable we shall use $\log (W/P)_i$ for the knitting-mill products (group 232), with an appropriate adjustment so that $\bar{Z} = \bar{X}$. This instrumental variable is very likely to satisfy the two requirements for consistency: the wage rate in knitting mills is unlikely to be related to the disturbance (and errors of measurement) in the furniture manufacturing industry, but is likely to be related to the wage rate in that industry. The relevant data are given in Table 9–1. The price variable is expressed as an index, with the value for the United States equal to 1. If the errors of measurement are negligible, i.e., if $X_i^* = X_i$ and $Y_i^* = Y_i$, then least squares estimates are appropriate. These are

$$Y_i = -2.2877 + 0.8401 X_i + e_i, \qquad R^2 = 0.986.$$
$$\quad\;\; (0.0996) \quad (0.0331)$$

If, on the other hand, there are serious errors of measurement present, estimates obtained by the method of instrumental variables would be preferable since they are consistent. The regression equation estimated by this method is

$$Y_i^* = -2.2978 + 0.8435 X_i^* + e_i^*, \qquad R^2 = 0.985.$$
$$\quad\;\; (0.1025) \quad (0.0342)$$

The results obtained by the method of instrumental variables are very similar to those obtained by the least squares method.

[3] K. J. Arrow, et al., "Capital-Labor Substitution and Economic Efficiency," *Review of Economics and Statistics*, Vol. 43, August 1961, pp. 225–250.

Table 9-1

Country	Furniture Manufacturing Industry					Knitting Mill Products			
	L/V	P	W (\$)	$\log(V/PL)$ $= Y^*$	$\log(W/P)$ $= X^*$	P	W (\$)	$\log(W/P)$ $= Z^*$	$Z^*\bar{X}^*/\bar{Z}^*$ $= Z$
United States	0.1706	1.0000	3515	0.7680	3.5459	1.0000	2698	3.4310	3.4241
Canada	0.2385	1.5470	2668	0.4330	3.2367	1.4891	2260	3.1812	3.1748
New Zealand	0.3678	0.9482	1834	0.4575	3.2865	1.0346	1548	3.1750	3.1686
Australia	0.3857	0.8195	1713	0.5002	3.3202	0.7358	1487	3.3055	3.2989
Denmark	0.5040	0.8941	1288	0.3462	3.1585	0.7713	1169	3.1806	3.1742
Norway	0.5228	0.9437	1342	0.3068	3.1529	0.8990	1021	3.0553	3.0492
United Kingdom	0.6291	0.6646	1078	0.3787	3.2101	0.6030	802	3.1238	3.1175
Colombia	0.7200	1.8260	738	−0.1188	2.6066	2.2570	845	2.5733	2.5681
Brazil	0.9415	1.4590	448	−0.1379	2.4872	0.9720	364	2.5734	2.5682
Mexico	0.9017	1.7580	471	−0.2001	2.4280	1.2458	546	2.6417	2.6364
Argentina	1.0863	2.2300	464	−0.3845	2.3182	1.3901	523	2.5755	2.5703

Generalized Errors-in-Equation Model

When describing Equation (9.4), we referred to it as a model with "errors in variables and errors in equation." The term *errors in variables* is used to describe the measurement errors v_i and w_i, while the term *errors in equation* refers to the stochastic disturbance ε_i. Thus a regression model in which the variables are measured without errors may be called a model with "errors in equation." Let us now consider a model in which measurement errors occur only with respect to the dependent variable. That is, let

$$w_i = 0 \quad \text{for all } i.$$

Then, a substitution of

$$Y_i = Y_i^* - v_i$$

into the regression equation

$$Y_i = \alpha + \beta X_i + \varepsilon_i$$

gives

(9.9) $$Y_i^* = \alpha + \beta X_i + \eta_i,$$

where $$\eta_i = \varepsilon_i + v_i.$$

Since ε_i and v_i are assumed to be normal and independent of each other, we have

$$\eta_i \sim N(0, \sigma_\eta^2),$$

where $$\sigma_\eta^2 = \sigma^2 + \sigma_v^2.$$

Equation (9.9) can be described as a *generalized errors-in-equation model.* Since η_i can be viewed as a random variable that behaves precisely like ε_i, equation (9.9) is formally equivalent to the regression equation (7.1) of the classical normal linear regression model. This means that the least squares estimators of the regression coefficients have the desirable properties. However, there are two differences between η_i and ε_i that are worth noting:

A. The variance of ε_i reflects the behavioral characteristics of the factors that influence the dependent variable in addition to the systematic influence of the explanatory variable. As a rule, this variance cannot be altered by the observer. On the other hand, the variance of the measurement error v_i—and therefore the variance of η_i—can be reduced by improving the methods of measurement.

B. Since, in fact, the methods of measuring economic variables have been improving over the last decades, the variance of v_i—and therefore the variance of η_i—may have been diminishing over time. Thus if v_i is not negligible, η_i may be heteroskedastic when the observations are in the form of time series.

These differences, however, do not create any estimating problems serious enough to warrant extended discussion.

Suppose now that, instead of the dependent variable, the explanatory variable is measured with errors. That is, we consider a situation where

$$v_i = 0 \quad \text{for all } i.$$

Then, we have

$$X_i = X_i^* - w_i,$$

which can be substituted into the regression equation,

$$Y_i = \alpha + \beta X_i + \varepsilon_i$$

to get

(9.10) $$Y_i = \alpha + \beta X_i^* + \zeta_i,$$

where $$\zeta_i = \varepsilon_i - \beta w_i.$$

Here X_i^* and ζ_i are contemporaneously correlated. In fact,

$$\text{Cov}(X_i^*, \zeta_i) = E[X_i^* - E(X_i^*)][\zeta_i - E(\zeta_i)] = E(w_i \zeta_i) = -\beta \sigma_w^2 \neq 0,$$

so that the least squares estimators of α and β in (9.10) are *inconsistent*. Consistent estimators can be obtained by using the method of instrumental variables described earlier.

Errors-in-Variables Model

Finally, we come to a model that is used quite frequently in the natural sciences but very rarely in modern econometrics. We consider it here partly for the sake of completeness and partly because it has an important application in connection with the so-called "permanent income hypothesis." The model is generally known as a model with *errors in variables*. The presumption underlying this model is that the relationship between the dependent and the explanatory variable is a deterministic one, and that the only reason why sample points do not all lie on a straight line is that we do not have exact measurements on X and Y. In our terminology, the errors-in-variables model is characterized by the assumption that

$$\varepsilon_i = 0 \quad \text{for all } i.$$

This model is not generally used in econometrics because it is commonly believed that a stochastic disturbance is an essential part of economic relations. One exception is the formulation of the "permanent income" hypothesis by Friedman[4] who postulated a deterministic relation between "permanent consumption" and "permanent income." In this case our measurements of actual consumption and actual income are erroneous, since they contain "transient components," which can be viewed as errors of measurement. There are also

[4] Milton Friedman, *A Theory of Consumption Function* (Princeton: Princeton University Press, 1957).

other cases in which the errors of measurement may reasonably be expected to be substantial, while the regression disturbance may be considered relatively unimportant. International statistics, for example, are often highly inaccurate. In such cases we may prefer to use the errors-in-variables model, on the assumption that the inaccuracies due to the neglect of the regression disturbance are not serious.

Suppose, then, that the relationship between X and Y is

$$(9.11) \qquad\qquad\qquad Y_i = \alpha + \beta X_i,$$

where X_i may be stochastic or nonstochastic. If X_i is stochastic, we assume it to be independent of v_i and w_i. Since we do not measure X_i and Y_i but only X_i^* and Y_i^*, we have to substitute

$$Y_i = Y_i^* - v_i \qquad \text{and} \qquad X_i = X_i^* - w_i,$$

to get

$$(9.12) \qquad\qquad\qquad Y_i^* = \alpha + \beta X_i^* + \xi_i,$$

where

$$\xi_i = v_i - \beta w_i.$$

Since X_i^* and ξ_i are obviously correlated, least squares estimators of α and β are *inconsistent*. To obtain consistent estimators, we can use the method of instrumental variables providing we can find an instrument that would satisfy the conditions of being uncorrelated with ξ_i while being correlated with X_i^*.

Method of Group Averages

An alternative way of estimating (9.12) is by the *method of group averages*, which, in its simplest form, requires ordering the observed pairs (X_i^*, Y_i^*) by the magnitude of the X_i^*'s so that

$$X_1^* \leq X_2^* \leq \cdots \leq X_n^*.$$

The pairs are then divided into three groups of approximately equal size. The group-averages estimators of the regression coefficients are

$$(9.13a) \qquad\qquad\qquad \beta^{\dagger\dagger} = \frac{\bar{Y}_3^* - \bar{Y}_1^*}{\bar{X}_3^* - \bar{X}_1^*},$$

$$(9.13b) \qquad\qquad\qquad \alpha^{\dagger\dagger} = \bar{Y}^* - \beta^{\dagger\dagger}\bar{X}^*,$$

where $\bar{Y}_1^*$ and $\bar{Y}_3^*$ are the calculated means of Y of the first and the third group, respectively, and $\bar{X}_1^*$ and $\bar{X}_3^*$ are the corresponding means of X. The group-averages estimators are consistent providing the grouping is such that, had we grouped the data by the unobserved X's rather than by the observed X^*'s, no pairs in the first group would have to be re-allocated to the third group and vice versa. It is interesting to note that the method of group averages can be viewed as a special case of the method of instrumental variables. If the three groups of observations are of equal size, and if the values of the instrumental variable Z_i are such that

$$Z_i = -1 \quad \text{if } i \text{ belongs to the 1st group,}$$
$$= 0 \quad \text{if } i \text{ belongs to the 2nd group,}$$
$$= 1 \quad \text{if } i \text{ belongs to the 3rd group,}$$

we find that (9.5a) and (9.5b) are equivalent to (9.13a) and (9.13b), respectively. We can then utilize formulas (9.8a) and (9.8b) to estimate the variances of $\alpha^{\dagger\dagger}$ and $\beta^{\dagger\dagger}$.

EXAMPLE   Let us calculate the group-averages estimates for the relationship between $\log(V/PL)$ and $\log(W/P)$ discussed in the previous example. From the data in Table 9–1, we see that there are eleven observations; we shall use four observations for the first and third groups, leaving three observations unused. The calculations are

$$\bar{X}_1^* = \frac{1}{4}(2.3182 + 2.4280 + 2.4872 + 2.6066) = 2.4600,$$

$$\bar{X}_3^* = \frac{1}{4}(3.2367 + 3.2865 + 3.3202 + 3.5459) = 3.3473,$$

$$\bar{Y}_1^* = \frac{1}{4}(-0.3845 - 0.2001 - 0.1379 - 0.1188) = -0.2103,$$

$$\bar{Y}_3^* = \frac{1}{4}(0.4330 + 0.4575 + 0.5002 + 0.7680) = 0.5397.$$

Then,

$$\beta^{\dagger\dagger} = \frac{0.5397 - (-0.2103)}{3.3473 - 2.4600} = 0.8453$$

$$\alpha^{\dagger\dagger} = \frac{1}{11}(2.3491 - 0.8453 \times 32.7508) = -2.3031.$$

The estimated relationship would then be

$$Y_i^* = -2.3031 + 0.8453 X_i^* + \xi_i,$$

which is numerically quite similar to the result obtained previously.

Weighted Regression

Another way to obtain consistent estimators of the coefficients of the errors-in-variables model is available if we can make a prior assumption about the ratio of the error variances. In particular, let

$$\frac{\sigma_w^2}{\sigma_v^2} = \lambda,$$

where λ is known. For example, at times we may reasonably expect that the errors in measuring X have about the same dispersion as the errors in measuring

Y. In such a case, we may be willing to assume that $\lambda = 1$. Let us now develop consistent estimators of α and β for a given λ. These estimators are frequently called *weighted regression estimators*. We may start by considering the least squares estimator of β, which is

$$\hat{\beta} = \frac{\sum y_i^{*'} x_i^{*'}}{\sum x_i^{*'2}}.$$

Since

$$y_i^{*'} = y_i' + v_i' = \beta x_i' + v_i',$$

and

$$x_i^{*'} = x_i' + w_i',$$

we can write $\hat{\beta}$ as

$$\hat{\beta} = \frac{\sum (\beta x_i' + v_i')(x_i' + w_i')}{\sum (x_i' + w_i')^2} = \frac{\beta \sum x_i'^2 + \sum x_i' v_i' + \beta \sum x_i' w_i' + \sum v_i' w_i'}{\sum x_i'^2 + 2 \sum x_i' w_i' + \sum w_i'^2}.$$

The probability limit of $\hat{\beta}$ is

(9.14) $$\operatorname{plim} \hat{\beta} = \frac{\beta \sigma_x^2}{\sigma_x^2 + \sigma_w^2},$$

where the term σ_x^2 is used for the variance of X if X is stochastic, or for $\lim (\sum x_i'^2)/n$ if X is nonstochastic. In deriving (9.14) we have made use of the assumptions of independence between v_i, w_i, and X_i. Formula (9.14) indicates that the cause of inconsistency of $\hat{\beta}$ is the presence of the term σ_w^2 in the denominator. If that term were not there, σ_x^2 in the numerator would cancel against the σ_x^2 in the denominator and the estimator would be consistent. This suggests that a consistent estimator of β would be given by

(9.15) $$\tilde{\beta} = \frac{(\sum y_i^{*'} x_i^{*'})/n}{(\sum x_i^{*'2})/n - \tilde{\sigma}_w^2},$$

where $\tilde{\sigma}_w^2$ is a consistent estimator of σ_w^2. The problem thus reduces to finding an expression for a consistent estimator of σ_w^2 in terms of X^*, Y^*, and $\tilde{\beta}$. By substituting this expression into (9.15), we could solve for $\tilde{\beta}$, which then would be consistent.

If λ is known, we have

$$\sigma_w^2 = \lambda \sigma_v^2,$$

which can be written as

$$\operatorname{plim} \frac{1}{n} \sum w_i'^2 = \lambda \operatorname{plim} \frac{1}{n} \sum v_i'^2 = \lambda \operatorname{plim} \frac{1}{n} \sum (y_i^{*'} - y_i')^2$$

$$= \lambda \operatorname{plim} \frac{1}{n} \sum (y_i^{*'} - \beta x_i')^2$$

$$= \lambda \left[\operatorname{plim} \frac{1}{n} \sum y_i^{*'2} - 2\beta \operatorname{plim} \frac{1}{n} \sum y_i^{*'} x_i' + \beta^2 \operatorname{plim} \frac{1}{n} \sum x_i'^2 \right]$$

Now, we need to get rid of x_i', which is not observable. Substituting $x_i' = x_i^{*\prime} - w_i'$, we get

$$\operatorname{plim} \frac{1}{n} \sum y_i^{*\prime} x_i' = \operatorname{plim} \frac{1}{n} \sum y_i^{*\prime}(x_i^{*\prime} - w_i') = \operatorname{plim} \frac{1}{n} \sum y_i^{*\prime} x_i^{*\prime}$$

and

$$\operatorname{plim} \frac{1}{n} \sum x_i'^2 = \operatorname{plim} \frac{1}{n} \sum (x_i^{*\prime} - w_i')^2 = \operatorname{plim} \frac{1}{n} \sum x_i^{*\prime 2} - \operatorname{plim} \sum \frac{1}{n} w_i'^2.$$

At this stage, we shall introduce the following abbreviated notation:

$$\frac{1}{n} \sum y_i^{*\prime 2} = m_{yy}^*,$$

$$\frac{1}{n} \sum x_i^{*\prime 2} = m_{xx}^*,$$

$$\frac{1}{n} \sum x_i^{*\prime} y_i^{*\prime} = m_{xy}^*.$$

Using this notation, and replacing the probability limits by their sample counterparts, we get

$$\tilde{\sigma}_w^2 = \lambda[m_{yy}^* - 2\tilde{\beta} m_{xy}^* + \tilde{\beta}^2(m_{xx}^* - \tilde{\sigma}_w^2)].$$

Solving this expression for $\tilde{\sigma}_w^2$, we obtain

(9.16) $$\tilde{\sigma}_w^2 = \frac{\lambda}{1 + \lambda \tilde{\beta}^2} [m_{yy}^* - 2\tilde{\beta} m_{xy}^* + \tilde{\beta}^2 m_{xx}^*].$$

This is the desired expression for $\tilde{\sigma}_w^2$ in terms of the observable quantities, m_{yy}^*, m_{xy}^*, and m_{xx}^* and in terms of $\tilde{\beta}$. A substitution for $\tilde{\sigma}_w^2$ from (9.16) into (9.15) gives

$$\tilde{\beta} = \frac{m_{xy}^*}{m_{xx}^* - [\lambda/(1 + \lambda \tilde{\beta}^2)](m_{yy}^* - 2\tilde{\beta} m_{xy}^* + \tilde{\beta}^2 m_{xx}^*)}.$$

which can be expressed as a quadratic equation,

(9.17) $$\tilde{\beta}^2 \lambda m_{xy}^* + \tilde{\beta}(m_{xx}^* - \lambda m_{yy}^*) - m_{xy}^* = 0.$$

The solution leads to two values for $\tilde{\beta}$, one positive and one negative. The choice between the two is determined by the value of

$$\sum (y_i^{*\prime} - \tilde{\beta} x_i^{*\prime})^2 = m_{yy}^* - 2\tilde{\beta} m_{xy}^* + \tilde{\beta}^2 m_{xx}^*,$$

that is, by the value of the sum of squared deviations from the fitted regression line. Since we want this to be small, we choose that value of $\tilde{\beta}$ which has the same sign as m_{xy}^*. The corresponding consistent estimator of α is

(9.18) $$\tilde{\alpha} = \bar{Y}^* - \tilde{\beta} \bar{X}^*.$$

It can be shown that $\tilde{\alpha}$ and $\tilde{\beta}$ represent the maximum likelihood estimators of the respective parameters and, therefore, are asymptotically efficient.[5]

We can gain some insight into the principle of weighted regression estimation —and explain the basis for the name—by comparing it with the least squares estimation. Suppose the "explanatory" variable X is measured without error. Then the errors-in-variables model reduces to

$$Y_i^* = \alpha + \beta X_i + v_i,$$

and ordinary least squares estimators are consistent, besides having all other desirable properties. Note that here the least squares estimation is based on the idea of minimizing the sum of squared deviations of the observed Y^*'s from the regression line. This procedure is called "minimizing in the direction of Y"; it amounts to minimizing the sum of squares of the *vertical* distances of the observed points from the regression line. A case where X is observed without errors is one where σ_w^2 equal zero since if there are no errors of measurement, their variance is clearly zero. This implies that $\lambda = 0$. Substituting zero for λ into (9.17) leads to

$$\tilde{\beta} = \frac{m_{xy}^*}{m_{xx}^*},$$

which is the formula for the least squares estimator. At the other extreme, suppose that there are no errors in measuring Y. In this case, the errors-in-variables model reduces to

$$Y_i = \alpha + \beta(X_i^* - w_i)$$

or
$$X_i^* = -\frac{\alpha}{\beta} + \frac{1}{\beta}Y_i + w_i.$$

Here we can regard X_i^* as the "dependent" variable, and Y_i as the "explanatory" variable. The least squares estimator of $(1/\beta)$, which is consistent, is

$$\left(\frac{\hat{1}}{\beta}\right) = \frac{m_{xy}^*}{m_{yy}^*}.$$

This leads to a consistent estimator of β, given as

$$\hat{\hat{\beta}} = \frac{m_{yy}^*}{m_{xy}^*}.$$

In obtaining this estimator we are, in fact, minimizing the sum of the squares of deviations of the observed X^*'s from the regression line, i.e., we are "minimizing in the direction of X." This amounts to minimizing the sum of squares of the *horizontal* distances of the observed points from the regression line. Note that

---

[5] See Johnston, *op. cit.*, pp. 152–155. A rough (and highly complicated) formula for the asymptotic variances of these estimators is presented in A. Madansky, "The Fitting of Straight Lines When Both Variables Are Subject to Error," *Journal of the American Statistical Association*, Vol. 54, March 1959, pp. 179–180.

observing Y without errors means that $\sigma_v^2 = 0$ and therefore that $\lambda \to \infty$. Dividing (9.17) by λ gives

$$\tilde{\beta}^2 m_{xy}^* + \tilde{\beta}\left(\frac{m_{xx}^*}{\lambda} - m_{yy}\right) - \frac{m_{xy}^*}{\lambda} = 0.$$

As $\lambda \to \infty$, this reduces to

$$\tilde{\beta}^2 m_{xy}^* - \tilde{\beta} m_{yy}^* = 0$$

or

$$\tilde{\beta} = \frac{m_{yy}^*}{m_{xy}^*},$$

which is exactly the same result as for $\hat{\beta}$. This shows how the size of λ determines the direction of the minimization. When the value of λ lies between 0 and ∞, it serves as a "weighting" factor in placing the direction of the minimization between X and Y.

EXAMPLE   Continuing with the example on the relationship between log (V/PL) and log (W/P), let us calculate the weighted regression estimates of α and β on the assumption that $\lambda = 1$. The relevant calculations are

$$m_{xx}^* = 20.1834/11^2,$$

$$m_{yy}^* = 14.4456/11^2,$$

$$m_{xy}^* = 16.9577/11^2,$$

and therefore

$$m_{xx}^* - m_{yy}^* = 5.7378/11^2.$$

Substitution into (9.17) gives

$$\tilde{\beta} = \frac{-5.7378 + \sqrt{5.7378^2 + 4 \times 16.9577^2}}{2 \times 16.9577} = 0.8452.$$

Similarly, using (9.18), we obtain

$$\tilde{\alpha} = -2.3023.$$

Conclusion

This completes our discussion on errors of measurement. As pointed out at the outset, measurement errors are likely to be present in most, if not all, economic observations. We have found that it is very difficult to deal with the estimation problem where there are stochastic disturbances as well as errors of measurement—a situation described by the model with "errors in variables and errors in equation." The common practice in modern econometrics has been to neglect the errors of measurement and to concentrate on the "errors-in-equation model." The motivation has been not so much the belief that our data are perfect, but the belief that errors of measurement are unimportant compared with the role of the stochastic disturbances in economic relations. We shall carry on in the same spirit, realizing that the area of errors of measurement represents a challenge in the econometric work of the future.

9–2 Estimation from Grouped Data

Survey data are frequently presented in the form of a table summarizing the values for individual observations. Such tabular information has often been used for estimating the coefficients of a regression equation. One reason for this is the fact that tabular results are likely to be readily accessible, whereas the retrieval of the individual observations may be time-consuming and costly. Another reason for using condensed summaries of the sample observations is often the desire to avoid large-scale computations that may otherwise be necessary. In this section we shall inquire how the use of condensed sample information affects the properties of the estimators of the regression coefficients in a simple regression model. We shall consider two types of condensed tabular information, one representing the case where the observations are grouped according to the value of one variable, and the other where the observations are grouped according to the values of both variables. The respective tables are usually distinguished as *one-way* or *two-way* classification tables. Obviously, a one-way classification table represents a greater amount of condensation of the sample information than a two-way classification table. Another way of stating this is to say that a one-way classification table involves a greater loss of information than a two-way classification table.

One-Way Grouping

Consider a simple linear regression model as described by (7.1) through (7.6). As will be recalled, this means that the explanatory variable X is nonstochastic and that the regression disturbance ε has zero mean and is normal, homoskedastic, and nonautoregressive. (The conclusions of this section, however, also apply to the case where X is stochastic but independent of ε.) Suppose the n sample observations are divided into G groups. Let n_1 be the number of observations in the first group, n_2 the number of observations in the second group, and so on. Since there are altogether n observations, we must have

$$\sum_{g=1}^{G} n_g = n.$$

Let us denote the ith observation in the gth group by the double subscript ig, so that the regression equation can be written as

$$(9.19)\qquad Y_{ig} = \alpha + \beta X_{ig} + \varepsilon_{ig} \qquad (i = 1, 2, \ldots, n_g;\ g = 1, 2, \ldots, G).$$

Suppose now that instead of being given a complete enumeration of all observations in each group, we are only given their number and the mean values (or totals) of X and Y, presented as follows:

Group	Number of Observations	Mean of X	Mean of Y
1	n_1	$\bar{X}_1$	$\bar{Y}_1$
2	n_2	$\bar{X}_2$	$\bar{Y}_2$
$\vdots$	$\vdots$	$\vdots$	$\vdots$
G	n_g	$\bar{X}_G$	$\bar{Y}_G$

where

$$\bar{X}_g = \frac{1}{n_g} \sum_{i=1}^{n_g} X_{ig} \quad \text{and} \quad \bar{Y}_g = \frac{1}{n_g} \sum_{i=1}^{n_g} Y_{ig} \quad (g = 1, 2, \ldots, G).$$

The problem now is to derive estimation formulas for the regression coefficients using the group means, and to determine how the properties of the resulting estimators compare with the properties of the ordinary least squares estimators based on individual observations. Let us take the regression equation (9.19) and "condense" it by averaging over all observations within each group. In this way we obtain

$$(9.20) \qquad \bar{Y}_g = \alpha + \beta \bar{X}_g + \bar{\varepsilon}_g \quad (g = 1, 2, \ldots, G).$$

That is, we are replacing the original n observations with a smaller number of G groups means. Now, if X_{ig} is nonstochastic, $\bar{X}_g$ will also be nonstochastic so that we have to worry only about $\bar{\varepsilon}_g$. First, we note that

$$E(\bar{\varepsilon}_g) = E \frac{1}{n_g} (\varepsilon_{1g} + \varepsilon_{2g} + \cdots + \varepsilon_{n_g g}) = 0,$$

which means that ordinary least squares estimators of α and β based on group means are unbiased. Next, for $g \neq h$,

$$E(\bar{\varepsilon}_g \bar{\varepsilon}_h) = E\left[\frac{1}{n_g}(\varepsilon_{1g} + \varepsilon_{2g} + \cdots + \varepsilon_{n_g g})\right]\left[\frac{1}{n_h}(\varepsilon_{1h} + \varepsilon_{2h} + \cdots + \varepsilon_{n_h h})\right] = 0,$$

which means that $\bar{\varepsilon}_g$ is nonautoregressive. Finally,

$$\text{Var}(\bar{\varepsilon}_g) = \frac{1}{n_g^2}(\sigma^2 + \sigma^2 + \cdots + \sigma^2) = \frac{n_g \sigma^2}{n_g^2} = \frac{\sigma^2}{n_g},$$

which means that, unless the number of observations is the same in every group, the disturbance in (9.20) is *heteroskedastic*.

The heteroskedastic nature of $\bar{\varepsilon}_g$ implies that ordinary least squares estimators of α and β using group means as "observations" are not efficient. To make efficient use of the group means, we have to use the estimation formulas designed for heteroskedastic regressions. These formulas were developed earlier and are given by (8.1) through (8.4). With respect to $\bar{\varepsilon}_g$, we are in a fortunate position of knowing exactly how its variance changes from "observation" to "observation," i.e., from group to group, because n_g is known. To adapt formulas (8.1) through (8.4) to the use of group means, we replace the subscript i by g, put "bars" over the X's and the Y's, and replace w by (n_g/σ^2). The resulting estimators of α and β, say, $\tilde{\alpha}$ and $\tilde{\beta}$, are

$$(9.21) \quad \tilde{\beta} = \frac{[(\sum n_g)(\sum n_g \bar{X}_g \bar{Y}_g) - (\sum n_g \bar{X}_g)(\sum n_g \bar{Y}_g)]/\sigma^4}{[(\sum n_g)(\sum n_g \bar{X}_g^2) - (\sum n_g \bar{X}_g)^2]/\sigma^4} = \frac{\sum n_g \bar{X}_g \bar{Y}_g - n\bar{X}\bar{Y}}{\sum n_g \bar{X}_g^2 - n\bar{X}^2}$$

$$= \frac{\sum n_g(\bar{X}_g - \bar{X})(\bar{Y}_g - \bar{Y})}{\sum n_g(\bar{X}_g - \bar{X})^2}$$

and

$$(9.22) \qquad \tilde{\alpha} = \frac{(\sum n_g \bar{Y}_g)/\sigma^2}{(\sum n_g)/\sigma^2} - \tilde{\beta}\frac{(\sum n_g \bar{X}_g)/\sigma^2}{(\sum n_g)/\sigma^2} = \bar{Y} - \tilde{\beta}\bar{X},$$

where $\bar{X}$ is the overall sample mean of X and $\bar{Y}$ the overall sample mean of Y. In simplifying the expressions for $\tilde{\alpha}$ and $\tilde{\beta}$ we have made use of the following equalities:

$$\sum_g n_g = n_1 + n_2 + \cdots + n_G = n,$$

$$\sum_g n_g \bar{X}_g = n_1 \bar{X}_1 + n_2 \bar{X}_2 + \cdots + n_G \bar{X}_G = \sum_i X_{i1} + \sum_i X_{i2} + \cdots + \sum_i X_{iG}$$

$$= \sum_i \sum_g X_{ig} = n\bar{X},$$

$$\sum_g n_g \bar{Y}_g = n_1 \bar{Y}_1 + n_2 \bar{Y}_2 + \cdots + n_G \bar{Y}_G = n\bar{Y}.$$

The variances of $\tilde{\alpha}$ and $\tilde{\beta}$ are

$$(9.23) \qquad \text{Var}(\tilde{\beta}) = \frac{(\sum n_g)/\sigma^2}{[(\sum n_g)(\sum n_g \bar{X}_g^2) - (\sum n_g \bar{X}_g)^2]/\sigma^4}$$

$$= \frac{\sigma^2}{\sum n_g(\bar{X}_g - \bar{X})^2}$$

and

$$(9.24) \qquad \text{Var}(\tilde{\alpha}) = \frac{(\sum n_g \bar{X}_g^2)/\sigma^2}{[(\sum n_g)(\sum n_g \bar{X}_g^2) - (\sum n_g \bar{X}_g)^2]/\sigma^4}$$

$$= \sigma^2 \left[\frac{1}{n} + \frac{\bar{X}^2}{\sum n_g(\bar{X}_g - \bar{X})^2}\right].$$

A question of particular interest to us is how the variances of $\tilde{\alpha}$ and $\tilde{\beta}$ compare with the variances of the ordinary least squares estimators based on ungrouped observations. We know that by grouping the observations and estimating the regression coefficients from group means rather than from the individual observations, we are losing some information contained in the sample, namely, the information about the variation of the observations *within* each group. Therefore, we would expect that we would lose some efficiency in going from estimation based on all individual observations to estimation based on group means. We shall see whether, and to what extent, this is true by evaluating the ratio of $\mathrm{Var}(\tilde{\beta})$ to $\mathrm{Var}(\hat{\beta})$, where $\hat{\beta}$ denotes the least squares estimator of β based on individual observations. Now, from (7.23) the variance of $\hat{\beta}$ is

$$\mathrm{Var}(\hat{\beta}) = \frac{\sigma^2}{\sum_i \sum_g (X_{ig} - \bar{X})^2}.$$

Note that the denominator on the right-hand side of this expression can be written as

$$\sum_i \sum_g (X_{ig} - \bar{X})^2 = \sum_i \sum_g [(X_{ig} - \bar{X}_g) + (\bar{X}_g - \bar{X})]^2$$

$$= \sum_i \sum_g (X_{ig} - \bar{X}_g)^2 + \sum_i \sum_g (\bar{X}_g - \bar{X})^2$$

$$+ 2 \sum_i \sum_g (X_{ig} - \bar{X}_g)(\bar{X}_g - \bar{X})$$

$$= \sum_i \sum_g (X_{ig} - \bar{X}_g)^2 + \sum_g n_g (\bar{X}_g - \bar{X})^2.$$

The ratio of the two variances then is

(9.25) $$\frac{\mathrm{Var}(\tilde{\beta})}{\mathrm{Var}(\hat{\beta})} = \frac{\sigma^2 \Big/ \sum_g n_g (\bar{X}_g - \bar{X})^2}{\sigma^2 \Big/ \Big[\sum_i \sum_g (X_{ig} - \bar{X}_g)^2 + \sum_g n_g (\bar{X}_g - \bar{X})^2 \Big]}$$

$$= 1 + \frac{\sum_i \sum_g (X_{ig} - \bar{X}_g)^2}{\sum_g n_g (\bar{X}_g - \bar{X})^2}.$$

This ratio is always greater than, or at best equal to, unity. The last term on the right-hand side measures the loss of efficiency resulting from the use of grouped data instead of individual observations. Note that the size of the numerator reflects the variation of the values of X *within* each group around the group mean, while the size of the denominator reflects the variation of the group means of X around the overall sample mean. Thus we will lose no efficiency by grouping if there is no variation of the values of X within each group, and the loss of efficiency will be small if this variation is small compared with the variation of the group means of X around the overall mean. In other words, there will always be some loss of efficiency by going from individual observations to groups unless the X's within each group are all equal. *This conclusion holds whether the groups contain the same number of observations or not.* Having groups of equal size would make $\bar{\varepsilon}_g$ homoskedastic but would not prevent a loss of efficiency as a result of grouping.

When estimating the regression coefficients from grouped data, we can use formulas (9.21) and (9.22) since they can be readily evaluated, but the expressions for the variances of these estimators involve an unknown parameter σ^2. To find an unbiased estimator of σ^2, we first determine the mathematical expectation of the weighted sum of squared residuals, using as weights the number of observations in each group. That is,

$$E \sum_{g=1}^{G} n_g(\bar{Y}_g - \tilde{\alpha} - \tilde{\beta}\bar{X}_g)^2 = E \sum_g n_g[(\bar{Y}_g - \bar{Y}) - \tilde{\beta}(\bar{X}_g - \bar{X})]^2$$

$$= E \sum_g n_g[-(\tilde{\beta} - \beta)(\bar{X}_g - \bar{X}) + (\bar{\varepsilon}_g - \bar{\varepsilon})]^2$$

$$= E(\tilde{\beta} - \beta)^2 \sum_g n_g(\bar{X}_g - \bar{X})^2 + E \sum_g n_g(\bar{\varepsilon}_g - \bar{\varepsilon})^2$$

$$- 2E(\tilde{\beta} - \beta) \sum_g n_g(\bar{X}_g - \bar{X})(\bar{\varepsilon}_g - \bar{\varepsilon}).$$

Now,

$$E(\tilde{\beta} - \beta)^2 \sum_g n_g(\bar{X}_g - \bar{X})^2 = \left[\frac{\sigma^2}{\sum_g n_g(\bar{X}_g - \bar{X})^2}\right] \sum_g n_g(\bar{X}_g - \bar{X})^2 = \sigma^2,$$

$$E \sum_g n_g(\bar{\varepsilon}_g - \bar{\varepsilon})^2 = E \sum_g n_g\bar{\varepsilon}_g^2 + E\bar{\varepsilon}^2 \sum_g n_g - 2E\bar{\varepsilon} \sum_g n_g\bar{\varepsilon}_g$$

$$= \sum_g n_g\left(\frac{\sigma^2}{n_g}\right) + \left(\frac{\sigma^2}{n}\right) \sum_g n_g - 2\left(\frac{\sigma^2}{n}\right) \sum_g n_g$$

$$= G\sigma^2 + \sigma^2 - 2\sigma^2 = (G - 1)\sigma^2,$$

and

$$-2E(\tilde{\beta} - \beta) \sum_g n_g(\bar{X}_g - \bar{X})(\bar{\varepsilon}_g - \bar{\varepsilon}) = -2E(\tilde{\beta} - \beta)^2 \sum_g n_g(\bar{X}_g - \bar{X})^2 = -2\sigma^2.$$

Therefore,

$$E \sum_g n_g(\bar{Y}_g - \tilde{\alpha} - \tilde{\beta}\bar{X}_g)^2 = \sigma^2 + (G - 1)\sigma^2 - 2\sigma^2 = (G - 2)\sigma^2.$$

Thus an unbiased estimator of σ^2, say, $\tilde{s}^2$, is

(9.26) $$\tilde{s}^2 = \frac{1}{G - 2} \sum_g n_g(\bar{Y}_g - \tilde{\alpha} - \tilde{\beta}\bar{X}_g)^2.$$

For the purpose of calculation, this expression may be simplified as follows:

(9.26a) $$\tilde{s}^2 = \frac{1}{G - 2} \sum_g n_g[\bar{Y}_g - (\bar{Y} - \tilde{\beta}\bar{X}) - \tilde{\beta}\bar{X}_g]^2$$

$$= \frac{1}{G - 2} \left[\sum_g n_g(Y_g - \bar{Y})^2 - \tilde{\beta}^2 \sum_g n_g(\bar{X}_g - \bar{X})^2\right].$$

By using $\tilde{s}^2$ as the estimator of σ^2 in (9.23) and (9.24), we obtain estimators of the variances of $\tilde{\alpha}$ and $\tilde{\beta}$. These are

(9.27)
$$\tilde{s}_{\tilde{\beta}}^2 = \frac{\tilde{s}^2}{\sum n_g(\bar{X}_g - \bar{X})^2},$$

(9.28)
$$\tilde{s}_{\tilde{\alpha}}^2 = \tilde{s}^2 \left[\frac{1}{n} + \frac{\bar{X}^2}{\sum n_g(\bar{X}_g - \bar{X})^2} \right].$$

These estimators are unbiased, consistent, and asymptotically efficient among the class of all estimators that are based on the same information.

A final point of interest in connection with sample data grouped in the form of a one-way classification table concerns the behavior of the coefficient of determination (R^2) as we go from individual observations to group means. When the estimation is done on the basis of individual observations, the value of R^2 is calculated as

(9.29)
$$R^2 = \frac{\hat{\beta}^2 \sum_i \sum_g (X_{ig} - \bar{X})^2}{\sum_i \sum_g (Y_{ig} - \bar{Y})^2},$$

where $\hat{\beta}$ is an ordinary least squares estimator of β based on individual observations. On the other hand, when we estimate the regression coefficients by using group means, the value of R^2 is calculated as

(9.30)
$$R^2 = 1 - \frac{\sum_g (\bar{Y}_g - \tilde{\alpha} - \tilde{\beta}\bar{X}_g)^2}{\sum_g (\bar{Y}_g - \bar{\bar{Y}})^2},$$

where

$$\sum_g (\bar{Y}_g - \tilde{\alpha} - \tilde{\beta}\bar{X}_g)^2 = \sum_g [\bar{Y}_g - (\bar{Y} - \tilde{\beta}\bar{X}) - \tilde{\beta}\bar{X}_g]^2$$

$$= \sum_g (\bar{Y}_g - \bar{Y})^2 - 2\tilde{\beta} \sum_g (\bar{Y}_g - \bar{Y})(\bar{X}_g - \bar{X})$$

$$+ \tilde{\beta}^2 \sum_g (\bar{X}_g - \bar{X})^2$$

and
$$\sum_g (\bar{Y}_g - \bar{\bar{Y}})^2 = \sum_g \bar{Y}_g^2 - \frac{1}{G}\left(\sum_g \bar{Y}_g\right)^2.$$

It has been shown that the value of R^2 calculated by (9.30) tends to be higher than that calculated by (9.29).[6] That is, as we go from individual observations to group means, the value of R^2 tends to increase. Since the underlying sample is the same whether we use individual observations or group means, the increase in

[6] See J. S. Cramer, "Efficient Grouping, Regression and Correlation in Engel Curve Analysis," *Journal of the American Statistical Association*, Vol. 59, March 1964, pp. 233–250.

the value of R^2 is entirely due to grouping and should be interpreted as such. It simply reflects the fact that the group means tend to be less dispersed around the fitted regression line than the individual observations.

EXAMPLE   A sample survey of immigrants in Australia conducted in 1959 by the Department of Demography of the Australian National University contained information on weekly income and consumption expenditure of immigrant families. The results for the 181 British immigrants included in the sample survey are given in Table 9–2.

Table 9–2

Income Class	Number of Observations (n_g)	Mean Income* ($\bar{X}_g$)	Mean Consumption Expenditure* ($\bar{Y}_g$)
Under 18	51	15.5	13.900
18 and under 20	22	19.0	15.291
20 and under 22	22	21.0	18.195
22 and under 24	23	23.0	20.104
24 and under 26	13	25.0	20.985
26 and under 28	12	27.0	22.742
28 and under 30	14	29.0	24.414
30 and under 32	9	31.0	24.089
32 and under 34	7	33.0	29.286
34 and under 36	4	35.0	27.000
36 and over	4	37.0	29.500

Data made available by Dr. J. Zubrzycki of the Australian National University.
* In Australian pounds per week.

Suppose we wish to estimate the coefficients of a linear consumption function,

$$Y = \alpha + \beta X + \varepsilon,$$

from this information. The results of the basic calculations are

$$\bar{X} = \frac{1}{181} \sum_g n_g \bar{X}_g = 22.390,$$

$$\bar{Y} = \frac{1}{181} \sum_g n_g \bar{Y}_g = 19.024,$$

$$\bar{\bar{Y}} = \frac{1}{11} \sum_g \bar{Y}_g = 22.319,$$

$$\sum_g n_g (\bar{X}_g - \bar{X})(\bar{Y}_g - \bar{Y}) = \sum_g n_g \bar{X}_g \bar{Y}_g - 181(\bar{X}\bar{Y}) = 82{,}153.2 - 77{,}096.5$$

$$= 5056.7,$$

$$\sum_g n_g(\bar{X}_g - \bar{X})^2 = \sum_g n_g \bar{X}_g^2 - 181(\bar{X}^2) = 97,358.8 - 90,735.5$$

$$= 6623.3,$$

$$\sum_g n_g(\bar{Y}_g - \bar{Y})^2 = \sum_g n_g \bar{Y}_g^2 - 181(\bar{Y}^2) = 69,475.8 - 65,506.2$$

$$= 3969.6,$$

$$\sum_g (\bar{Y}_g - \bar{\bar{Y}})^2 = 273.7,$$

$$\sum_g (\bar{Y}_g - \tilde{\alpha} - \tilde{\beta}\bar{X}_g)^2 = 12.069.$$

Therefore,

$$\tilde{\beta} = \frac{5056.7}{6623.3} = 0.763,$$

$$\tilde{\alpha} = 19.024 - 0.763 \times 22.390 = 1.940,$$

$$\tilde{s}^2 = \frac{113.7201}{9} = 12.6356,$$

$$\tilde{s}_{\tilde{\alpha}}^2 = 12.6356\left[\frac{1}{181} + \frac{22.390^2}{6623.3}\right] = 1.026188,$$

$$\tilde{s}_{\tilde{\beta}}^2 = \frac{12.6356}{6623.3} = 0.001908,$$

$$R^2 = 1 - \frac{12.069}{273.7} = 0.956.$$

The estimated regression equation then is

$$\bar{Y}_g = 1.940 + 0.763\bar{X}_g + e_g, \qquad R^2 = 0.956.$$
$$\phantom{\bar{Y}_g = }(1.012)\quad(0.044)$$

Two-Way Grouping

Let us now consider the case where the sample information is condensed in the form of a "two-way" classification table. In this case, the observations are grouped according to the values of the explanatory and the dependent variable. Suppose the values of X are divided into G groups, and those of Y into H groups. Each of the G groups is represented by the respective group mean of X and corresponds to one row, and each of the H groups is represented by the respective group mean of Y and corresponds to one column. The body of the table consists of $G \times H$ cells, each cell showing the appropriate number of observations. A cell with no observations is called "empty." There is at least one nonempty cell in each row and in each column. The following notation will be adopted:

$\bar{X}_{g\cdot}$ group mean of X in the gth row

$\bar{Y}_{\cdot h}$ group mean of Y in the hth column

J total number of nonempty cells $(J \le G \times H)$

n_{gh} number of observations in the cell corresponding to gth row and hth column

$n_{g\cdot}$ number of observations in gth row

$n_{\cdot h}$ number of observations in hth column

n total number of all observations in the sample

This implies that

$$\sum_{g=1}^{G} \sum_{h=1}^{H} n_{gh} = n,$$

$$\sum_{g=1}^{G} n_{g\cdot} = n,$$

and

$$\sum_{h=1}^{H} n_{\cdot h} = n.$$

The tabular information is presented in the following form:

	$\bar{Y}_{\cdot 1}$	$\bar{Y}_{\cdot 2}$	$\cdots$	$\bar{Y}_{\cdot H}$	
$\bar{X}_{1\cdot}$	n_{11}	n_{12}	$\cdots$	n_{1H}	$n_{1\cdot}$
$\bar{X}_{2\cdot}$	n_{21}	n_{22}	$\cdots$	n_{2H}	$n_{2\cdot}$
$\vdots$	$\vdots$	$\vdots$		$\vdots$	$\vdots$
$\bar{X}_{G\cdot}$	n_{G1}	n_{G2}	$\cdots$	n_{GH}	$n_{G\cdot}$
	$n_{\cdot 1}$	$n_{\cdot 2}$	$\cdots$	$n_{\cdot H}$	n

If we use a triple subscript igh to designate the ith observation in the gth row and hth column, the regression equation describing the relationship between X and Y can be written as

$$(9.31) \qquad Y_{igh} = \alpha + \beta X_{igh} + \varepsilon_{igh} \qquad (i = 1, 2, \ldots, n_{gh};$$

$$g = 1, 2, \ldots, G; h = 1, 2, \ldots, H).$$

Since we are not given the individual observations, we have to estimate the regression coefficients α and β from the row and column averages. Let us consider this in detail. For any row (i.e., for any group mean of X), say, the gth, we can have H different values of the dependent variable, namely,

$$\bar{Y}_{\cdot 1} = \alpha + \beta \bar{X}_{g\cdot} + \bar{\varepsilon}_{g1}$$

$$\bar{Y}_{\cdot 2} = \alpha + \beta \bar{X}_{g\cdot} + \bar{\varepsilon}_{g2}$$

$$\vdots$$

$$\bar{Y}_{\cdot H} = \alpha + \beta \bar{X}_{g\cdot} + \bar{\varepsilon}_{gH} ,$$

or, in a summary form,

(9.32) $\bar{Y}_{\cdot h} = \alpha + \beta \bar{X}_{g\cdot} + \bar{\varepsilon}_{gh}$ $(g = 1, 2, \ldots, G; h = 1, 2, \ldots, H)$,

where $\bar{\varepsilon}_{gh} = \dfrac{1}{n_{gh}} \sum_{i=1}^{n_{gh}} \varepsilon_{igh}$.

It is easy to see that $\bar{\varepsilon}_{gh}$ satisfies all the basic assumptions *except* homoskedasticity. In fact, we have

$$\mathrm{Var}(\bar{\varepsilon}_{gh}) = \frac{\sigma^2}{n_{gh}},$$

which means that the variance of $\bar{\varepsilon}_{gh}$ does, in general, change from cell to cell.

Because of the heteroskedasticity of $\bar{\varepsilon}_{gh}$, the appropriate estimation formulas for the regression coefficients and their variances are (8.1) through (8.4). To adapt these formulas to the problem at hand, we replace the subscript i by $g\cdot$ in the case of X and by $\cdot h$ in the case of Y, put "bars" over the X's and the Y's, carry out all the summations over both g *and* h, and replace the term w by (n_{gh}/σ^2). The resulting estimators of α and β, say, $\tilde{\alpha}$ and $\tilde{\beta}$, are

(9.33) $\tilde{\beta} = \dfrac{[(\sum_g \sum_h n_{gh})(\sum_g \sum_h n_{gh} \bar{X}_{g\cdot} \bar{Y}_{\cdot h}) - (\sum_g \sum_h n_{gh} \bar{X}_{g\cdot})(\sum_g \sum_h n_{gh} \bar{Y}_{\cdot h})]/\sigma^4}{[(\sum_g \sum_h n_{gh})(\sum_g \sum_h n_{gh} \bar{X}_{g\cdot}^2) - (\sum_g \sum_h n_{gh} \bar{X}_{g\cdot})^2]/\sigma^4}$

and

(9.34) $\tilde{\alpha} = \dfrac{(\sum_g \sum_h n_{gh} \bar{Y}_{\cdot h})/\sigma^2}{(\sum_g \sum_h n_{gh})/\sigma^2} - \tilde{\beta} \dfrac{(\sum_g \sum_h n_{gh} \bar{X}_{g\cdot})/\sigma^2}{(\sum_g \sum_h n_{gh})/\sigma^2}$.

Now,

$$\sum_g \sum_h n_{gh} \bar{X}_{g\cdot} \bar{Y}_{\cdot h} = \sum_g (n_{g1} \bar{X}_{g\cdot} \bar{Y}_{\cdot 1} + n_{g2} \bar{X}_{g\cdot} \bar{Y}_{\cdot 2} + \cdots + n_{gH} \bar{X}_{g\cdot} \bar{Y}_{\cdot H})$$

$$= \sum_g n_{g\cdot} \bar{X}_{g\cdot} \left[\frac{n_{g1} \bar{Y}_{\cdot 1} + n_{g2} \bar{Y}_{\cdot 2} + \cdots + n_{gH} \bar{Y}_{\cdot H}}{n_{g\cdot}} \right]$$

$$= \sum_g n_{g\cdot} \bar{X}_{g\cdot} \bar{Y}_{g\cdot},$$

where $\bar{Y}_{g\cdot}$ is the mean of Y over the gth row, i.e., the mean of the values of Y belonging to the gth group of values of X. Similarly,

$$\sum_g \sum_h n_{gh} \bar{X}_{g\cdot} = \sum_g (n_{g1} \bar{X}_{g\cdot} + n_{g2} \bar{X}_{g\cdot} + \cdots + n_{gH} \bar{X}_{g\cdot}) = \sum_g n_{g\cdot} \bar{X}_{g\cdot},$$

$$\sum_g \sum_h n_{gh} \bar{Y}_{\cdot h} = \sum_g (n_{g1} \bar{Y}_{\cdot 1} + n_{g2} \bar{Y}_{\cdot 2} + \cdots + n_{gH} \bar{Y}_{\cdot H}) = \sum_g n_{g\cdot} \bar{Y}_{g\cdot},$$

$$\sum_g \sum_h n_{gh} \bar{X}_{g\cdot}^2 = \sum_g (n_{g1} \bar{X}_{g\cdot}^2 + n_{g2} \bar{X}_{g\cdot}^2 + \cdots + n_{gH} \bar{X}_{g\cdot}^2) = \sum_g n_{g\cdot} \bar{X}_{g\cdot}^2,$$

and, of course,

$$\sum_g \sum_h n_{gh} = \sum_g n_{g\cdot}.$$

Substituting these results into (9.33) and (9.34), we obtain

(9.35)
$$\tilde{\tilde{\beta}} = \frac{\left(\sum_g n_{g\cdot}\right)\left(\sum_g n_{g\cdot}\bar{X}_{g\cdot}\bar{Y}_{g\cdot}\right) - \left(\sum_g n_{g\cdot}\bar{X}_{g\cdot}\right)\left(\sum_g n_{g\cdot}\bar{Y}_{g\cdot}\right)}{\left(\sum_g n_{g\cdot}\right)\left(\sum_g n_{g\cdot}X_{g\cdot}^2\right) - \left(\sum_g n_{g\cdot}X_{g\cdot}\right)^2}$$

and

(9.36)
$$\tilde{\tilde{\alpha}} = \left[\frac{\sum_g n_{g\cdot}\bar{Y}_{g\cdot}}{\sum_g n_{g\cdot}}\right] - \tilde{\tilde{\beta}}\left[\frac{\sum_g n_{g\cdot}\bar{X}_{g\cdot}}{\sum_g n_{g\cdot}}\right] = \bar{Y} - \tilde{\tilde{\beta}}\bar{X}.$$

These results are precisely the same as those given by (9.21) and (9.22). *This means that the regression coefficients estimated from a two-way classification table are exactly the same as those estimated from a one-way classification table.* In other words, the information contained in the two-way classification table that is in addition to the information provided by the one-way classification table is irrelevant to the construction of efficient estimators of the regression coefficients.

Since the formulas for $\tilde{\tilde{\alpha}}$ and $\tilde{\tilde{\beta}}$ are the same as those for $\tilde{\alpha}$ and $\tilde{\beta}$, the formulas for their variances will also be the same. These are given by (9.23) and (9.24). As pointed out earlier, these formulas contain an unknown parameter σ^2 that has to be estimated. What we have to do, then, is to check whether the *estimator* of σ^2 obtained from a one-way classification table, i.e., $\tilde{s}^2$ defined by (9.26), will also remain the same when a two-way classification table is used. First, we determine the mathematical expectation of the weighted sum of squared residuals, using as weights the number of observations in each cell. That is,

$$E\sum_g \sum_h n_{gh}(\bar{Y}_{\cdot h} - \tilde{\alpha} - \tilde{\beta}\bar{X}_{g\cdot})^2 = E\sum_g \sum_h n_{gh}[(\bar{Y}_{\cdot h} - \bar{Y}) - \tilde{\beta}(\bar{X}_{g\cdot} - \bar{X})]^2$$

$$= E\sum_g \sum_h n_{gh}[-(\tilde{\beta} - \beta)(\bar{X}_{g\cdot} - \bar{X})$$

$$+ (\bar{\varepsilon}_{gh} - \bar{\varepsilon})]^2$$

$$= E(\tilde{\beta} - \beta)^2 \sum_g \sum_h n_{gh}(\bar{X}_{g\cdot} - \bar{X})^2$$

$$+ E\sum_g \sum_h n_{gh}(\bar{\varepsilon}_{gh} - \bar{\varepsilon})^2$$

$$- 2E(\tilde{\beta} - \beta)\sum_g \sum_h n_{gh}(\bar{X}_{g\cdot} - \bar{X})(\bar{\varepsilon}_{gh} - \bar{\varepsilon}).$$

Now,

$$E(\tilde{\beta} - \beta)^2 \sum_g \sum_h n_{gh}(\bar{X}_{g\cdot} - \bar{X})^2 = \sigma^2,$$

$$E \sum_g \sum_h n_{gh}(\bar{\varepsilon}_{gh} - \bar{\varepsilon})^2 = E \sum_g \sum_h n_{gh}\bar{\varepsilon}_{gh}^2 + E\bar{\varepsilon}^2 \sum_g \sum_h n_{gh}$$

$$- 2E\bar{\varepsilon} \sum_g \sum_h n_{gh}\bar{\varepsilon}_{gh}$$

$$= J\sigma^2 + \sigma^2 - 2\sigma^2 = (J - 1)\sigma^2,$$

and

$$-2E(\tilde{\beta} - \beta) \sum_g \sum_h n_{gh}(\bar{X}_{g\cdot} - \bar{X})(\bar{\varepsilon}_{gh} - \bar{\varepsilon})$$

$$= -2E(\tilde{\beta} - \beta)^2 \sum_g \sum_h n_{gh}(\bar{X}_{g\cdot} - \bar{X})^2 = -2\sigma^2.$$

Therefore,

$$E \sum_g \sum_h n_{gh}(\bar{Y}_{\cdot h} - \alpha - \tilde{\beta}\bar{X}_{g\cdot})^2 = \sigma^2 + (J - 1)\sigma^2 - 2\sigma^2 = (J - 2)\sigma^2.$$

Thus, an unbiased estimator of σ^2, say, $\tilde{s}^2$, is

$$(9.37) \qquad \tilde{s}^2 = \frac{1}{J - 2} \sum_g \sum_h n_{gh}(\bar{Y}_{\cdot h} - \tilde{\alpha} - \tilde{\beta}\bar{X}_{g\cdot})^2,$$

which is different from $\bar{s}^2$, the estimator of σ^2 from a one-way classification table. For the purpose of calculation, we note that

$$\sum_g \sum_h n_{gh}(\bar{Y}_{\cdot h} - \tilde{\alpha} - \tilde{\beta}\bar{X}_{g\cdot})^2 = \sum_g \sum_h n_{gh}(\bar{Y}_{\cdot h} - \bar{Y})^2 - \tilde{\beta}^2 \sum_g \sum_h n_{gh}(\bar{X}_{g\cdot} - \bar{X})^2$$

$$= \sum_h n_{\cdot h}(\bar{Y}_{\cdot h} - \bar{Y})^2 - \tilde{\beta}^2 \sum_g n_{g\cdot}(\bar{X}_{g\cdot} - \bar{X})^2.$$

Although we shall not give a formal proof, it is obvious that $\tilde{s}^2$ is a more efficient estimator of σ^2 than $\bar{s}^2$. This is because $\tilde{s}^2$ uses more information about the *variation* of the dependent variable than $\bar{s}^2$. The use of $\tilde{s}^2$ as an estimator of σ^2 in (9.23) and (9.24) leads to new estimators of $\text{Var}(\tilde{\alpha})$ and $\text{Var}(\tilde{\beta})$, namely,

$$(9.38) \qquad \tilde{s}_{\tilde{\beta}}^2 = \frac{\tilde{s}^2}{\sum_g n_{g\cdot}(\bar{X}_{g\cdot} - \bar{X})^2}$$

and

$$(9.39) \qquad \tilde{s}_{\tilde{\alpha}} = \tilde{s}^2 \left[\frac{1}{n} + \frac{\bar{X}^2}{\sum_g n_{g\cdot}(\bar{X}_{g\cdot} - \bar{X})^2} \right].$$

Again, these estimators are unbiased, consistent, and asymptotically efficient among all estimators that use the same information.

Finally, we may want to determine the value of the coefficient of determination. By analogy with (9.30), the formula for R^2 calculated from a two-way classification table is

$$(9.40) \qquad R^2 = 1 - \frac{\sum_g \sum_h (\bar{Y}_{.h} - \tilde{\alpha} - \tilde{\beta}\bar{X}_{g.})^2}{\sum_g \sum_h (\bar{Y}_{.h} - \bar{\bar{Y}})^2},$$

where

$$\sum_g \sum_h (\bar{Y}_{.h} - \tilde{\alpha} - \tilde{\beta}\bar{X}_{g.})^2 = \sum_g \sum_h (\bar{Y}_{.h} - \bar{\bar{Y}})^2 + \tilde{\beta}^2 \sum_g \sum_h (\bar{X}_{g.} - \bar{X})^2$$

$$- 2\tilde{\beta} \sum_g \sum_h (\bar{Y}_{.h} - \bar{\bar{Y}})(\bar{X}_{g.} - \bar{X})$$

and

$$\sum_g \sum_h (\bar{Y}_{.h} - \bar{\bar{Y}})^2 = \sum_g \sum_h \bar{Y}_{.h}^2 - \frac{1}{J} \sum_g \sum_h \bar{Y}_{.h}.$$

All these summations are carried out over the nonempty cells only. Since the two-way classification table allows for greater dispersion of the observations than the one-way classification table, we would expect the value of R^2 calculated by (9.40) to be smaller than that calculated by (9.30).

If X is a stochastic variable (independent of the regression disturbance), we may be interested in calculating the value of the coefficient of correlation between X and Y. For a two-way classification table this value, unlike that of R^2 in (9.40), is usually calculated by taking into account the frequencies in individual cells. If the coefficient of correlation between X and Y is denoted by r_{XY}, then its value can be obtained from

$$(9.41) \qquad r_{XY}^2 = \frac{[\sum n_{g.}(\bar{X}_{g.} - \bar{X})(\bar{Y}_{g.} - \bar{Y})]^2}{[\sum n_{g.}(\bar{X}_{g.} - \bar{X})^2][\sum n_{g.}(\bar{Y}_{g.} - \bar{Y})^2]}.$$

The formulas for the estimated regression coefficients and their standard errors, of course, remain unchanged.

EXAMPLE   The sample survey results on income and expenditure of 181 British migrants in Australia used in the previous example are also available in the form of a two-way classification table, as given in Table 9–3. Here X = income and Y = consumption expenditure. The estimates of the coefficients of a linear consumption function will be the same as those calculated from Table 9–2. However, we have to calculate new estimates of the standard errors and a new value of R^2. The basic results are

$$J = 45,$$

$$\sum_g \sum_h n_{gh}(\bar{Y}_{.h} - \bar{Y})^2 = 6150.8,$$

$$\sum_g \sum_h n_{gh}(\bar{Y}_{.h} - \tilde{\alpha} - \tilde{\beta}\bar{X}_{g.})^2 = 2292.5,$$

$$\sum_g \sum_h (\bar{Y}_{.h} - \bar{\bar{Y}})^2 = 1538.0,$$

$$\sum_g \sum_h (\bar{Y}_{.h} - \tilde{\alpha} - \tilde{\beta}\bar{X}_{g.})^2 = 983.0.$$

Then,
$$\tilde{s}^2 = \frac{1}{45-2} \times 2292.5 = 53.31,$$

$$\tilde{s}_{\tilde{\alpha}}^2 = 4.3298,$$

$$\tilde{s}_{\tilde{\beta}}^2 = 0.008050,$$

and
$$R^2 = 1 - \frac{983.0}{1538.0} = 0.361.$$

Table 9-3

X	Y										$n_g.$
	13.9	19.0	21.0	23.0	25.0	27.0	29.0	31.0	33.0	35.0	
15.5	51										51
19.0	16	6									22
21.0	7	7	7	1							22
23.0	6	4	2	7	4						23
25.0	2	3	2	2	4						13
27.0	1	1·	2	3	3	2					12
29.0	2		1	3	2		6				14
31.0	2		2	1			1	2	1		9
33.0				2			1	1	3		7
35.0		1		1					2		4
37.0					1	1		1		1	4
$n._h$	87	22	16	20	14	3	8	4	6	1	181

The estimated consumption function then is

$$\bar{Y}._h = 1.940 + 0.763\,\bar{X}_g. + e_{gh}, \qquad R^2 = 0.361, \qquad r_{XY}^2 = 0.628.$$
$$\phantom{\bar{Y}._h = 1.}(2.079) \quad (0.090)$$

Concluding Remarks

The preceding analysis provided us with an interesting result, namely, that regression coefficients can be estimated just as efficiently from a two-way classification table as from a one-way classification table. However, the variances of these estimators can be estimated more efficiently from a two-way table than from a one-way table. Note that the results of the tests of significance of the estimated regression coefficients based on a two-way table may be different from the results based on the corresponding one-way table, since congesting the data amounts to throwing away sample information. In this way the researcher may (consciously or not) falsify the picture. Another point to be noted is that in our discussion we have taken for granted that the group means are the actual sample means for the respective groups. However, if instead of the group means, the table shows only the *limits* of the corresponding intervals, the group means are not known. The usual practice in this case is to use the midpoint of each interval as representing the respective group mean. But if this is not true, then the mid-point is an incorrect measure of the group mean, and we have the problem of errors of measurement on our hands. As pointed out in Section 9.1, this may not be harmful if the errors occur only in measuring the values of the dependent variable, but if the explanatory variable is measured with error, then we have a real problem. This ought to be kept in mind when dealing with tabular information.

9–3   Estimation When Some Observations Are Missing

We shall consider now the question of estimating the parameters of the regression equation

$$Y_i = \alpha + \beta X_i + \varepsilon_i$$

when some of the sample values are missing. That is, we shall be concerned with the situation where some of the pairs of observations $(X_1, Y_1), (X_2, Y_2), \ldots,$ (X_n, Y_n) are incomplete in the sense that *one* of the values is missing. Missing observations are sometimes encountered in the case of cross-section or time-series data. For instance, when estimating a family consumption function from survey data, one finds that some families may have failed to report their income, while others may have omitted to state their consumption expenditure. Or, in the case of time series, the values of either variable may not be given for certain periods of time because of a change in the recording procedure, or for a number of other reasons. The question then is whether, when estimating the regression coefficients, we should discard the incomplete pairs of observations or whether the partial information contained in them could be put to some use.

In discussing the problem of using the information contained in the incomplete pairs of observations, we shall confine ourselves to situations where all the basic assumptions about the disturbance term—that is, assumptions (7.2) through (7.5)—are valid. However, we shall distinguish between the case where X is nonstochastic and the case where X is stochastic but independent of the disturbance. If we use only the complete pairs of observations, then the least squares estimators of α and β are

$$(9.42) \qquad \hat{\beta}_c = \frac{\sum_c (X_i - \bar{X}_c)(Y_i - \bar{Y}_c)}{\sum_c (X_i - \bar{X}_c)^2},$$

and

$$(9.43) \qquad \hat{\alpha}_c = \bar{Y}_c - \hat{\beta}_c \bar{X}_c,$$

where $\bar{X}_c$ and $\bar{Y}_c$ are the sample means of X and of Y calculated from the complete pairs, and $\sum_c$ denotes the summation over all such pairs. The estimators $\hat{\alpha}_c$ and $\hat{\beta}_c$ are unbiased and efficient in the class of all estimators of α and β that use the same information.

Nonstochastic Explanatory Variable

In the case where X is nonstochastic, the values of X are under the control either of the investigator or of the original "experimenter." Of course, this is to be interpreted in a broad sense—for instance, viewing the government as conducting an "experiment" whenever it incurs some expenditure. The implication of this is that those pairs of observations for which the values of Y are not shown give no information about the outcome of the "experiment" and should not be counted as a part of the sample at all. Thus the only interesting case in this context is that where some of the X's are missing while all the values of Y are available. The incomplete pairs give us information about Y, i.e., about the outcome of the "experiment," but not about the conditioning variable X. We will first determine the loss of efficiency that results from using only the complete pairs instead of all of the pairs *if* they were all complete. Then we will try to use the incomplete pairs in an effort to make the loss of efficiency smaller. In the process, and throughout this section, we will use the following notation, in addition to the symbols already used in (9.42) and (9.43):

$\displaystyle\sum_x$ the summation over all pairs for which X is observed

$\displaystyle\sum_y$ the summation over all pairs for which Y is observed

$\displaystyle\sum_{0x}$ the summation over all pairs for which X is not observed

$\displaystyle\sum_{0y}$ the summation over all pairs for which Y is not observed

n_c number of complete pairs

n_x number of pairs for which X is observed

n_y number of pairs for which Y is observed

m_x number of pairs for which X is not observed

m_y number of pairs for which Y is not observed

$\displaystyle \bar{X}_x = \frac{1}{n_x}\sum_x X_i$, etc.

Note that

$$n_c + m_x + m_y = n,$$

$$n_c + m_y = n_x,$$

$$n_c + m_x = n_y.$$

In the present context, where all of the values of Y are available, we have

$$n_x = n_c,$$

$$n_y = n,$$

$$m_y = 0,$$

$$\bar{X}_x = \bar{X}_c.$$

If we use only the complete pairs of observations, the variance of the least squares estimator of β is

(9.44)
$$\text{Var}(\hat{\beta}_c) = \frac{\sigma^2}{\sum_x (X_i - \bar{X}_x)^2},$$

If *all* pairs were complete, the variance of the least squares estimator of β, say, $\hat{\beta}_y$, would be

(9.45)
$$\text{Var}(\hat{\beta}_y) = \frac{\sigma^2}{\sum_y (X_i - \bar{X}_y)^2}.$$

The loss of efficiency due to the fact that some pairs of observations do not show a value for X (and we use only the complete pairs) can be measured by the ratio $\text{Var}(\hat{\beta}_c)$ to $\text{Var}(\hat{\beta}_y)$, i.e., by

(9.46)
$$\frac{\text{Var}(\hat{\beta}_c)}{\text{Var}(\hat{\beta}_y)} = \frac{\sum_y (X_i - \bar{X}_y)^2}{\sum_x (X_i - \bar{X}_x)^2}.$$

Now,

$$\sum_y (X_i - \bar{X}_y)^2 = \sum_x (X_i - \bar{X}_y)^2 + \sum_{0x} (X_i - \bar{X}_y)^2$$

$$= \sum_x [(X_i - \bar{X}_x) + (\bar{X}_x - \bar{X}_y)]^2$$

$$+ \sum_{0x} [(X_i - \bar{X}_{0x}) + (\bar{X}_{0x} - \bar{X}_y)]^2$$

$$= \sum_x (X_i - \bar{X}_x)^2 + n_x(\bar{X}_x - \bar{X}_y)^2 + \sum_{0x} (X_i - \bar{X}_{0x})^2$$

$$+ m_x(\bar{X}_{0x} - \bar{X}_y)^2.$$

By using the fact that

$$\bar{X}_y = \frac{1}{n}(n_x \bar{X}_x + m_x \bar{X}_{0x}),$$

we can write

$$n_x(\bar{X}_x - \bar{X}_y)^2 = n_x\left[\bar{X}_x - \frac{1}{n}(n_x\bar{X}_x + m_x\bar{X}_{0x})\right]^2 = \frac{n_x m_x^2}{n^2}(\bar{X}_x - \bar{X}_{0x})^2,$$

and

$$m_x(\bar{X}_{0x} - \bar{X}_y)^2 = m_x\left[\bar{X}_{0x} - \frac{1}{n}(n_x\bar{X}_x + m_x\bar{X}_{0x})\right]^2 = \frac{n_x^2 m_x}{n^2}(\bar{X}_x - \bar{X}_{0x})^2.$$

Therefore,

$$(9.46a) \qquad \frac{\text{Var}(\hat{\beta}_c)}{\text{Var}(\hat{\beta}_y)} = 1 + \frac{\sum_{0x}(X_i - \bar{X}_{0x})^2 + (n_x m_x/n)(\bar{X}_x - \bar{X}_{0x})^2}{\sum_x(X_i - \bar{X}_x)^2}.$$

This result shows that the loss of efficiency will be small if the missing values of X have a small dispersion and, at the same time, the mean of the missing values of X is close to the mean of the available values of X. There will be no loss of efficiency involved (in finite samples) if and only if each one of the missing values of X is equal to the mean of the available values of X. Of course, since the missing values of X are not known, the ratio (9.46a) cannot be evaluated, but it can be estimated from the available sample information as shown below.

Let us try now to utilize the information contained in the pairs of observations for which the values of X are missing. These missing values can be viewed as unknown parameters that can be estimated along with the regression coefficients and σ^2. We will denote the missing values of X by ξ_i; according to our notation, their number will be m_x. The likelihood function for $(Y_1, Y_2, \ldots, Y_n)$ then is

$$L = -\frac{n}{2}\log 2\pi - \frac{n}{2}\log \sigma^2 - \frac{1}{2\sigma^2}\sum_x(Y_i - \alpha - \beta X_i)^2 - \frac{1}{2\sigma^2}\sum_{0x}(Y_i - \alpha - \beta\xi_i)^2.$$

By differentiating L with respect to α, β, σ^2, and each of the ξ_i's, putting each of the derivatives equal to zero, and solving for the values of the unknown parameters, we obtain the respective maximum likelihood estimators. It is a matter of simple algebra to show that the maximum likelihood estimators of α and β are exactly the same as the least squares estimators (9.42) and (9.43), that the estimator of σ^2 is the same as that based on complete pairs only, and that the estimators of ξ_i are

$$(9.47) \qquad \hat{\xi}_i = \frac{Y_i - \hat{\alpha}_c}{\hat{\beta}_c}.$$

This means that the maximum likelihood estimation method applied to all observations for which Y is observed provides estimates of the missing values of X but leaves the estimates of α, β, and σ^2 as they are when estimated only from the complete pairs. This is somewhat disappointing. Nevertheless, we are a little ahead because we can at least use the estimates of the missing values of X to get some idea about the loss of efficiency resulting from the presence of incomplete pairs of observations. This can be done by substituting $\hat{\xi}_i$ for the missing values of X in (9.46a). The result is

$$(9.48) \qquad \text{Est.} \left[\frac{\text{Var}(\hat{\beta}_c)}{\text{Var}(\hat{\beta}_y)} \right] = 1 + \frac{\sum_{0x} (\hat{\xi}_i - \bar{\hat{\xi}})^2 + (n_x m_x/n)(\bar{X}_x - \bar{\hat{\xi}})^2}{\sum_x (X_i - \bar{X}_x)^2}.$$

The estimator $\hat{\xi}_i$ has the desirable asymptotic properties possessed by other maximum likelihood estimators, provided the number of missing values of X does not grow with sample size.

EXAMPLE   In the example in Section 7–3, we were concerned with estimating the coefficients of a linear relation between price (X) and quantity or oranges sold (Y) in a given supermarket over twelve consecutive days. The observations were:

X:	100	90	80	70	70	70	70	65	60	60	55	50
Y:	55	70	90	100	90	105	80	110	125	115	130	130

The results of the relevant calculations were as follows:

$$\bar{X} = 70,$$

$$\sum (X_i - \bar{X})^2 = 2250,$$

$$\hat{\alpha} = 210.460,$$

$$\hat{\beta} = -1.578.$$

Suppose now that, in addition to the 12 pairs of observations, we also had the information that the quantity sold on the thirteenth day was 37 pounds but that no price has been reported. That is, $Y_{13} = 37$. This observation has been discarded. We wish to know how much efficiency we would have gained in estimating β if X_{13} had been known. First, we use (9.47) to estimate X_{13} as

$$\hat{\xi}_{13} = \frac{Y_{13} - \hat{\alpha}}{\hat{\beta}} = \frac{37 - 210.460}{-1.578} = 110.$$

Then, the estimated ratio of $\text{Var}(\hat{\beta}_c)$ to $\text{Var}(\hat{\beta}_y)$ is

$$1 + \frac{0 + [(12 \times 1)/13](70 - 110)^2}{2250} = 1.6564,$$

which means that the loss of efficiency is estimated to be 65.64%.

An alternative way of using the information contained in the incomplete pairs of observations is to fill in the gaps by using some approximations of the missing values of X. This approach is probably fairly common in practice. The approximations are obtained by, e.g., interpolation from the observed values of X, or by reference to some other variable Z that is correlated with X. However, if we replace the missing values of X with some approximations, we introduce errors of measurement into the values of the explanatory variable and, as a consequence, obtain inconsistent estimates of the regression coefficients. This was explained in detail in Section 9–1. How serious this inconsistency will be depends, of course, on the extent of the errors of approximation. In fact, what is being done in this case is giving up consistency in the hope of reducing the variance of the estimator. If we are reasonably certain that the errors of approximation are small while the gain in efficiency is potentially large, this may be a rational procedure. Otherwise, the trade may result in a loss.

Stochastic Explanatory Variable

Let us now turn to the case where X is a stochastic variable that is distributed independently of the disturbance. The formulas for the least squares estimators of the regression coefficients based on complete pairs of observations remain unchanged, and so do the formulas for their variances—except that the latter have to be interpreted as conditional upon the given set of available values of X. Each pair of the observed values of X and Y now comes from a bivariate probability distribution. Our problem is to estimate the regression coefficients when some of the pairs of observations are incomplete. Other than disregarding the incomplete pairs, we may try to fill in the gaps and *then* apply the least squares estimation. One way of filling the gaps is to ask which value of X, or of Y, would one expect to observe *before* making the observation. Commonly, this would be the mathematical expectation of X or of Y, i.e., their means. Since the means are unknown, we can use the available sample means as estimators. That is, we may complete the missing observations in the incomplete pairs by using the available sample means of the respective variables. The least squares estimators of α and β obtained from the sample completed in this way are called *zero order regression estimators*.[7] They are defined as follows:

$$(9.49) \quad \hat{\beta}_0 = \frac{\sum_c (X_i - \bar{X}_x)(Y_i - \bar{Y}_y) + \sum_{0x} (\bar{X}_x - \bar{X}_x)(Y_i - \bar{Y}_y)}{\sum_c (X_i - \bar{X}_x)^2 + \sum_{0x} (\bar{X}_x - \bar{X}_x)^2 + \sum_{0y} (X_i - \bar{X}_x)^2}$$

$$+ \frac{\sum_{0y} (X_i - \bar{X}_x)(\bar{Y}_y - \bar{Y}_y)}{\sum_c (X_i - \bar{X}_x)^2 + \sum_{0x} (\bar{X}_x - \bar{X}_x)^2 + \sum_{0y} (X_i - \bar{X}_x)^2}$$

$$= \frac{\sum_c (X_i - \bar{X}_x)(Y_i - \bar{Y}_y)}{\sum_x (X_i - \bar{X}_x)^2}$$

and

$$(9.50) \qquad\qquad \hat{\alpha}_0 = \bar{Y}_y - \hat{\beta}_0 \bar{X}_x.$$

[7] See A. A. Afifi and R. M. Elashoff, "Missing Observations in Multivariate Statistics II. Point Estimation in Simple Linear Regression," *Journal of the American Statistical Association*, Vol. 62, March 1967, pp. 10–29.

In order to see whether these estimators are unbiased, we substitute

$$Y_i - \bar{Y}_y = \beta(X_i - \bar{X}_y) + (\varepsilon_i - \bar{\varepsilon}_y)$$

into (9.49) to get

$$\hat{\beta}_0 = \frac{\sum_c (X_i - \bar{X}_x)[\beta(X_i - \bar{X}_y) + (\varepsilon_i - \bar{\varepsilon}_y)]}{\sum_x (X_i - \bar{X}_x)^2}.$$

The mathematical expectation of $\hat{\beta}_0$, conditional upon the observed values of X, is

$$E(\hat{\beta}_0) = \frac{\beta \sum_c (X_i - \bar{X}_c + \bar{X}_c - \bar{X}_x)[X_i - \bar{X}_c + \bar{X}_c - E(\bar{X}_y)]}{\sum_x (X_i - \bar{X}_x)^2}$$

$$= \frac{\beta \sum_c (X_i - \bar{X}_c)^2 + n_c(\bar{X}_c - \bar{X}_x)[\bar{X}_x - E(\bar{X}_y)]}{\sum_x (X_i - \bar{X}_x)^2}.$$

But

$$E(\bar{X}_y) = E\left[\frac{1}{n_y}\left(\sum_c X_i + \sum_{0x} X_i\right)\right] = \frac{1}{n_y}(n_c\bar{X}_c + m_x\mu_x),$$

where μ_x, which is the population mean of X, is used to replace $E(\bar{X}_{0x})$, since $\bar{X}_{0x}$ is not observed. Therefore,

$$E(\hat{\beta}_0) = \frac{\beta[\sum_c (X_i - X_c)^2 + (n_c m_x/n_y)(\bar{X}_c - \bar{X}_x)(\bar{X}_c - \mu_x)]}{\sum_x (X_i - \bar{X}_x)^2} \neq \beta.$$

The conclusion, then, is that the zero order regression estimator of β is, in general, *biased*. The same is true of the zero order regression estimator of α.

Before we leave the zero order regression method, let us consider some special cases. First, suppose that the values of X are all available and only some of the Y's are missing. In this case,

$$n_x = n,$$

$$n_y = n_c,$$

$$m_x = 0,$$

$$\bar{X}_{0x} = 0.$$

Then,

$$E(\hat{\beta}_0) = \beta\frac{\sum_c (X_i - \bar{X}_c)^2}{\sum_x (X_i - \bar{X}_x)^2},$$

so that, unless $\bar{X}_c = \bar{X}_x$, $\hat{\beta}_0$ is still biased. Alternatively, suppose that the values of Y are all available but some of the X's are missing. Then,

$$n_x = n_c,$$

$$n_y = n,$$

$$m_y = 0,$$

$$\bar{X}_x = \bar{X}_c,$$

and

$$E(\hat{\beta}_0) = \frac{\beta\sum_c (X_i - \bar{X}_c)^2}{\sum_c (X_i - \bar{X}_c)^2} = \beta,$$

so that in this case the zero order regression estimator of β is unbiased. However, the variance of $\hat{\beta}_0$, conditional upon the observed X's, in this case is

$$\mathrm{Var}(\hat{\beta}_0) = E(\hat{\beta}_0 - \beta)^2 = E\left[\frac{\sum_x (X_i - \bar{X}_x)(\varepsilon_i - \bar{\varepsilon}_y)}{\sum_x (X_i - \bar{X}_x)^2}\right]^2 = \frac{\sigma^2}{\sum_x (X_i - \bar{X}_x)^2},$$

which is the same as the expression for $\mathrm{Var}(\hat{\beta}_c)$ given by (9.44). This means that we have nothing to gain in the way of efficiency by using $\hat{\beta}_0$ instead of $\hat{\beta}_c$.

The zero order regression method of estimation is based on the idea of replacing each of the missing values of X by $\bar{X}_x$, and each of the missing values of Y by $\bar{Y}_y$. An alternative idea is to replace the missing values of X by a parameter ξ, and the missing values of Y by a parameter η. Since each of the missing values of X is replaced by the same parameter ξ and each of the missing values of Y is replaced by the same parameter η, this procedure brings in only two additional unknown parameters, regardless of sample size and the number of missing values. The regression coefficients α and β can then be estimated simultaneously with ξ and η. This can be done by minimizing

$$\sum_c (Y_i - \alpha - \beta X_i)^2 + \sum_{0x} (Y_i - \alpha - \beta\xi)^2 + \sum_{0y} (\eta - \alpha - \beta X_i)^2$$

with respect to α, β, ξ, and η. The resulting estimators, known as *modified zero order regression estimators*,[8] are

(9.51) $$\hat{\beta}_m = \frac{\sum_c (X_i - \bar{X}_c)(Y_i - \bar{Y}_c)}{\sum_c (X_i - \bar{X}_c)^2 + \sum_{0y} (X_i - \bar{X}_{0y})^2}$$

and

(9.52) $$\hat{\alpha}_m = \bar{Y}_c - \hat{\beta}_m \bar{X}_c.$$

[8] *Ibid.*

The estimators of ξ and η, which are of only incidental interest, are

$$\hat{\xi} = \frac{\bar{Y}_{0x} - \hat{\alpha}_m}{\hat{\beta}_m}$$

and

$$\hat{\eta} = \hat{\alpha}_m + \hat{\beta}_m \bar{X}_{0y}.$$

Let us examine $\hat{\alpha}_m$ and $\hat{\beta}_m$ for unbiasedness. For $\hat{\beta}_m$ we have

(9.51a)
$$\hat{\beta}_m = \frac{\beta \sum_c (X_i - \bar{X}_c)^2 + \sum_c (X_i - \bar{X}_c)(\varepsilon_i - \bar{\varepsilon}_c)}{\sum_c (X_i - \bar{X}_c)^2 + \sum_{0y} (X_i - \bar{X}_{0y})^2}$$

and the mathematical expectation of $\hat{\beta}_m$, conditional upon the observed X's, is

$$E(\hat{\beta}_m) = \frac{\beta \sum_c (X_i - \bar{X}_c)^2}{\sum_c (X_i - \bar{X}_c)^2 + \sum_{0y} (X_i - \bar{X}_y)^2} \neq \beta.$$

This means that the modified zero order regression estimator of β is, in general, *biased*. The same is true of the modified zero order regression estimator of α.

Again, let us examine some special cases. First, suppose that all of the values of X are available and only some of the Y's are missing. In this case it is easy to show that formulas (9.51) and (9.52) remain the same, which means that we do not get any further ahead. Suppose, on the other hand, that all of the values of Y are available and only some of the X's are missing. In this case formulas (9.51) and (9.52) become the same as (9.42) and (9.43). This means that the estimators $\hat{\alpha}_m$ and $\hat{\beta}_m$ are exactly equal to the ordinary least squares estimators based on complete pairs of observations only.

Summary

To sum up, when we deal with samples in which some pairs of observations are incomplete, the information contained in the incomplete pairs is of relatively little use when estimating the regression coefficients. When X is nonstochastic, the information contained in the pairs for which only the Y's are given enables us to get an estimate of the loss of efficiency due to the fact that some of the X's are missing. If this loss is substantial, it may be worthwhile to go to the trouble of attempting to recover the missing values of X, or to find some good approximations for them. When X is stochastic and we use either the zero order regression method or its modified version, we get estimators that are generally biased. If only values of X are missing, both methods will lead to unbiased estimates of β, but these will be no more efficient than the ordinary least squares estimates based on complete pairs only. One redeeming feature of the estimators of the regression coefficients obtained by the zero order regression method or its modified version is the fact that when the correlation between X and Y is low, the mean square error of these estimators is less than that of the ordinary least squares estimators based on complete pairs.[9] Thus, under certain circumstances,

---

[9] For a proof and an elaboration of this statement, see *ibid.*

either one of the former methods may be preferable to estimation from complete pairs only.

EXERCISES

9–1. Assuming the "errors-in-variables" model, estimate the relationship between $\log(V/PL)$ and $\log(W/P)$ from the data for the furniture industry given in Table 9–1. Use the weighted regression method with $\lambda = 2$.

9–2. Suppose the income classes given in Table 9–2 in the text are combined as follows:

Income Class	Number of Observations (n_g)
Under 18	51
18 and under 22	44
22 and under 26	36
26 and under 30	26
30 and under 34	16
34 and over	8

Calculate the appropriate values of $\bar{X}_g$ and $\bar{Y}_g$ and use these to estimate the coefficients of

$$Y = \alpha + \beta X + \varepsilon$$

and their standard errors. Compare your results with those based on the information as originally given in Table 9–2.

9–3. Provide a derivation of formula (9–47).

9–4. Consider the following observations on X (price of oranges) and Y (quantity of oranges sold):

X	Y
100	55
90	70
80	90
70	100
70	90
70	105
70	80
65	110
60	125
60	115
55	130
50	130
—	130
—	140

Estimate the loss of efficiency in estimating β as a result of disregarding the last two incomplete observations.

9-5. Given the sample moments of the observed values of X and Y, the weighted regression estimator of β—as defined by (9-7)—becomes a function of λ. For the example presented in the text we found

$$m_{xx} = 20.1834/121,$$

$$m_{yy} = 14.4456/121,$$

$$m_{xy} = 16.9577/121.$$

Calculate the values of $\hat{\beta}$ for different values of λ and plot the results in a diagram.

10 | Multiple Regression

The regression model introduced in Chapter 7 is applicable to relationships that include only one explanatory variable. When the model is extended to include more than one explanatory variable, we speak of a *multiple regression* model. Relationships that can be described by a multiple regression model are very common in economics. For example, in production functions, output is typically a function of several inputs; in consumption functions, the dependent variable may be influenced by income as well as other factors; and in demand functions, the traditional explanatory variables are the price of the product, the prices of substitutes, and income.

The multiple regression model designed to describe these relationships is a natural extension of the simple regression model. In fact, most of the results derived for the simple regression model can easily be generalized so that they apply to the multiple regression case. The basic results concerning estimation are presented in Section 10–1; hypothesis testing and prediction are discussed in Section 10–2. The subject of Section 10–3 is multicollinearity—a feature that characterizes regression models with two or more explanatory variables. Finally, in Section 10–4 we examine the validity of the results of the preceding sections when the regression equation is not correctly specified.

10–1 Estimation of Regression Parameters

A common type of theoretical proposition in economics states that changes in one variable can be explained by reference to changes in *several* other variables. Such a relationship is described in a simple way by a multiple linear regression equation of the form

$$(10.1) \qquad Y_i = \beta_1 + \beta_2 X_{i2} + \beta_3 X_{i3} + \cdots + \beta_K X_{iK} + \varepsilon_i,$$

where Y denotes the dependent variable, the X's denote the explanatory variables, and ε is a stochastic disturbance. The subscript i refers to the ith observation; the second subscript used in describing the explanatory variables identifies the variable in question. The number of the explanatory variables is $K - 1$, so that for $K = 2$ equation (10.1) reduces to a simple regression equation. An alternative way of writing (10.1) is

(10.1a) $Y_i = \beta_1 X_{i1} + \beta_2 X_{i2} + \cdots + \beta_K X_{iK} + \varepsilon_i,$

where $X_{i1} = 1$ for all $i = 1, 2, \ldots, n$. Writing X_{i1} for 1 as the multiplication factor of β_1 makes the regression equation look symmetric without bringing about any real change. To complete the specification of the regression model, we add the following *basic assumptions*:

(10.2) ε_i is normally distributed,

(10.3) $E(\varepsilon_i) = 0,$

(10.4) $E(\varepsilon_i^2) = \sigma^2,$

(10.5) $E(\varepsilon_i \varepsilon_j) = 0 \quad (i \neq j),$

(10.6)   Each of the explanatory variables is nonstochastic with values fixed in repeated samples and such that, for any sample size, $\sum_{i=1}^{n} (X_{ik} - \bar{X}_k)^2/n$ is a finite number different from zero for every $k = 2, 3, \ldots, K$.

(10.7)   The number of observations exceeds the number of coefficients to be estimated.

(10.8)   No exact linear relation exists between any of the explanatory variables.

These assumptions are taken to apply to all observations. The full specification of the model given by (10.1) through (10.8) describes the so-called "classical normal linear regression model" in the context of multiple regression. Assumptions (10.2) through (10.5) involve the disturbance term and are exactly the same as assumptions (7.2) through (7.5) of the simple regression model. The last three assumptions refer to the explanatory variables. Assumption (10.6) is the same as assumption (7.6) except that it is extended to a larger number of explanatory variables. Assumptions (10.7) and (10.8) are new. Assumption (10.7) makes a provision for a sufficient number of "degrees of freedom" in estimation. Assumption (10.8) states that none of the explanatory variables is to be perfectly correlated with any other explanatory variable or with any linear combination of other explanatory variables. This assumption is also necessary for estimation, as will soon become clear.

Given the above specification of the multiple regression model, the distribution of Y_i is normal, as in the case of the simple regression model.

The mean of Y_i is

(10.9) $E(Y_i) = \beta_1 + \beta_2 X_{i2} + \beta_3 X_{i3} + \cdots + \beta_K X_{iK},$

and its variance is

(10.10) $\text{Var}(Y_i) = E[Y_i - E(Y_i)]^2 = \sigma^2.$

Note that by using (10.9) we can interpret the regression coefficients as follows:

β_1 = the mean of Y_i when each of the explanatory variables is equal to zero;

β_k = the change in $E(Y_i)$ corresponding to a unit change in the kth explanatory variable, holding the remaining explanatory variables constant

$$= \frac{\partial E(Y_i)}{\partial X_{ik}} \quad (k = 2, 3, \ldots, K).$$

β_1 is sometimes called the *intercept* (or the *regression constant*), and $\beta_2, \beta_3, \ldots, \beta_K$ are referred to as the *regression slopes* (or the *partial regression coefficients*).

This interpretation of the regression coefficients has an important implication for their estimation. Consider, for instance, the problem of estimating β_K. Given that β_K measures the effect of X_{iK} on $E(Y_i)$ while $X_{i2}, X_{i3}, \ldots, X_{i, K-1}$ are being held constant, an obvious way of estimating β_K would be by using observations made when all the explanatory variables other than X_{iK} are, in fact, constant. That is, the observations would be obtained from a controlled experiment in which all explanatory variables other than X_{iK} were kept at fixed and unchanged levels. Let us see what would happen to the estimation problem in such a case. In particular, let the level of X_{i2} be kept at ξ_2, that of X_{i3} at ξ_3, and so on, and let X_{iK} vary. Then the regression equation (10.1) can be written as

$$Y_i = \beta_1 + \beta_2\xi_2 + \beta_3\xi_3 + \cdots + \beta_{K-1}\xi_{K-1} + \beta_K X_{iK} + \varepsilon_i$$

or $Y_i = \alpha + \beta_K X_{iK} + \varepsilon_i,$

which clearly shows that in this case we are back in the realm of simple regression. This is precisely what the laboratories conducting experiments in natural sciences are frequently trying to do. It follows then that if we want to keep the assumption of nonstochastic explanatory variables and at the same time have a justification for the existence of a multiple regression model, we have to exclude the possibility that the values of the explanatory variables are controllable by the investigator. Thus we consider only those situations in which the "experiment" has been conducted by somebody other than the econometrician, and for a purpose other than estimating the regression coefficients or testing hypotheses about them. Of course, this is a common way in which economic data are acquired. The "laboratory" is the society and the econometrican is, by and large, a mere onlooker.

The description of the classical normal linear regression model is commonly presented in *matrix notation*. First, equation (10.1a) can be written as

(10.1b) $\mathbf{Y} = \mathbf{X}\boldsymbol{\beta} + \boldsymbol{\epsilon},$

where

$$\mathbf{Y} = \begin{bmatrix} Y_1 \\ Y_2 \\ \vdots \\ Y_n \end{bmatrix}, \quad \mathbf{X} = \begin{bmatrix} X_{11} & X_{12} & \cdots & X_{1K} \\ X_{21} & X_{22} & \cdots & X_{2K} \\ \vdots & \vdots & & \vdots \\ X_{n1} & X_{n2} & \cdots & X_{nK} \end{bmatrix}, \quad \boldsymbol{\beta} = \begin{bmatrix} \beta_1 \\ \beta_2 \\ \vdots \\ \beta_K \end{bmatrix}, \quad \boldsymbol{\epsilon} = \begin{bmatrix} \varepsilon_1 \\ \varepsilon_2 \\ \vdots \\ \varepsilon_n \end{bmatrix}.$$

This means that the dimensions of the matrices and vectors involved are as follows:

$$\mathbf{Y} \rightarrow (n \times 1),$$

$$\mathbf{X} \rightarrow (n \times K),$$

$$\boldsymbol{\beta} \rightarrow (K \times 1),$$

$$\boldsymbol{\epsilon} \rightarrow (n \times 1).$$

Note in particular that each row in the $\mathbf{X}$ matrix represents a set of values of the explanatory variables pertaining to one observation, while each column represents a set of values for one explanatory variable over the n sample observations. The first column of $\mathbf{X}$ consists entirely of 1's. The assumptions (10.2) through (10.5) can be stated in matrix notation as

(10.2a–3a) $\boldsymbol{\epsilon} \sim N(\mathbf{0}, \boldsymbol{\Sigma})$, where $\mathbf{0}$ is a column vector of zeros and $\boldsymbol{\Sigma} \rightarrow (n \times n)$,

(10.4a–5a) $\boldsymbol{\Sigma} = \sigma^2 \mathbf{I_n}$, where $\mathbf{I_n}$ is an identity matrix of order $(n \times n)$, with units in the principal diagonal and zeros everywhere else.

The statement in (10.4a–5a) combines the assumptions of homoskedasticity and nonautoregression; the disturbances that satisfy both of these assumptions are called "spherical." Finally, assumptions (10.6) through (10.8) concerning the explanatory variables can be transcribed as

(10.6a–8a) The elements of the matrix $\mathbf{X}$ are nonstochastic with values fixed in repeated samples, and the matrix $(1/n)(\mathbf{X'X})$ is nonsingular and such that, for any sample size, its elements are finite.

Least Squares Estimation

Consider now the derivation of the *least squares estimators* of the regression coefficients. The sum of squares to be minimized is

$$S = \sum_{i=1}^{n} (Y_i - \beta_1 - \beta_2 X_{i2} - \beta_3 X_{i3} - \cdots - \beta_K X_{iK})^2.$$

Differentiating S with respect to $\beta_1, \beta_2, \ldots, \beta_K$, we get

$$\frac{\partial S}{\partial \beta_1} = -2 \sum_i (Y_i - \beta_1 - \beta_2 X_{i2} - \beta_3 X_{i3} - \cdots - \beta_K X_{iK}),$$

$$\frac{\partial S}{\partial \beta_2} = -2 \sum_i X_{i2}(Y_i - \beta_1 - \beta_2 X_{i2} - \beta_3 X_{i3} - \cdots - \beta_K X_{iK}),$$

$$\vdots$$

$$\frac{\partial S}{\partial \beta_K} = -2 \sum_i X_{iK}(Y_i - \beta_1 - \beta_2 X_{i2} - \beta_3 X_{i3} - \cdots - \beta_K X_{iK}).$$

Equating each derivative to zero and rearranging terms gives us the following least squares normal equations:

$$\sum_i Y_i = \hat{\beta}_1 n + \hat{\beta}_2 \sum_i X_{i2} + \hat{\beta}_3 \sum_i X_{i3} + \cdots + \hat{\beta}_K \sum_i X_{iK},$$

$$\sum_i X_{i2} Y_i = \hat{\beta}_1 \sum_i X_{i2} + \hat{\beta}_2 \sum_i X_{i2}^2 + \hat{\beta}_3 \sum_i X_{i2} X_{i3} + \cdots + \hat{\beta}_K \sum_i X_{i2} X_{iK},$$

$$\vdots$$

$$\sum_i X_{iK} Y_i = \hat{\beta}_1 \sum_i X_{iK} + \hat{\beta}_2 \sum_i X_{i2} X_{iK} + \hat{\beta}_3 \sum_i X_{i3} X_{iK} + \cdots + \hat{\beta}_K \sum_i X_{iK}^2.$$

These equations represent a simple generalization of (7.10) and (7.11). (A simple rule for memorizing the formation of the least squares normal equations is given in footnote 4 on page 207.) Note that this system of normal equations could not be solved for the unknown $\hat{\beta}$'s if either (1) the number of explanatory variables *plus* one exceeded the number of observations or (2) any one of the explanatory variables represented an exact linear combination of other explanatory variables. In the former case, the number of equations would be less than the number of unknowns; in the latter case, the equations would not be independent.

To solve the least squares normal equations, we note that the first equation can be written as

(10.11) $$\hat{\beta}_1 = \bar{Y} - \hat{\beta}_2 \bar{X}_2 - \hat{\beta}_3 \bar{X}_3 - \cdots - \hat{\beta}_K \bar{X}_K,$$

where $\bar{Y} = \dfrac{1}{n} \sum_i Y_i$ and $\bar{X}_k = \dfrac{1}{n} \sum_i X_{ik}$ $(k = 2, 3, \ldots, K).$

Substitution of (10.11) into the remaining normal equations gives, after some simplifications,

$$m_{Y2} = m_{22} \hat{\beta}_2 + m_{23} \hat{\beta}_3 + \cdots + m_{2K} \hat{\beta}_K,$$

$$m_{Y3} = m_{23} \hat{\beta}_2 + m_{33} \hat{\beta}_3 + \cdots + m_{3K} \hat{\beta}_K,$$

$$\vdots$$

$$m_{YK} = m_{2K} \hat{\beta}_2 + m_{3K} \hat{\beta}_3 + \cdots + m_{KK} \hat{\beta}_K,$$

where $$m_{Yk} = \sum_i (Y_i - \bar{Y})(X_{ik} - \bar{X}_k)$$

and $$m_{jk} = \sum_i (X_{ij} - \bar{X}_j)(X_{ik} - \bar{X}_k) \quad (j, k = 2, 3, \ldots, K).$$

These equations can be solved for $\hat{\beta}_2, \hat{\beta}_3, \ldots, \hat{\beta}_K$. The solution is quite straightforward but somewhat laborious. For the case of two explanatory variables (i.e., $K = 3$), we have

(10.12) $$\hat{\beta}_2 = \frac{\begin{vmatrix} m_{Y2} & m_{23} \\ m_{Y3} & m_{33} \end{vmatrix}}{\begin{vmatrix} m_{22} & m_{23} \\ m_{23} & m_{33} \end{vmatrix}} = \frac{m_{Y2} m_{33} - m_{Y3} m_{23}}{m_{22} m_{33} - m_{23}^2},$$

$$(10.13) \qquad \hat{\beta}_3 = \frac{\begin{vmatrix} m_{22} & m_{Y2} \\ m_{23} & m_{Y3} \end{vmatrix}}{\begin{vmatrix} m_{22} & m_{23} \\ m_{23} & m_{33} \end{vmatrix}} = \frac{m_{Y3}m_{22} - m_{Y2}m_{23}}{m_{22}m_{33} - m_{23}^2}.$$

The least squares normal equations can be presented in matrix notation as

$$(\mathbf{X}'\mathbf{Y}) = (\mathbf{X}'\mathbf{X})\hat{\boldsymbol{\beta}},$$

where

$$(\mathbf{X}'\mathbf{Y}) = \begin{bmatrix} \sum Y_i \\ \sum X_{i2} Y_i \\ \vdots \\ \sum X_{iK} Y_i \end{bmatrix}, \qquad (\mathbf{X}'\mathbf{X}) = \begin{bmatrix} n & \sum X_{i2} & \cdots & \sum X_{iK} \\ \sum X_{i2} & \sum X_{i2}^2 & \cdots & \sum X_{i2}X_{iK} \\ \vdots & \vdots & & \vdots \\ \sum X_{iK} & \sum X_{i2}X_{iK} & \cdots & \sum X_{iK}^2 \end{bmatrix},$$

$$\hat{\boldsymbol{\beta}} = \begin{bmatrix} \hat{\beta}_1 \\ \hat{\beta}_2 \\ \vdots \\ \hat{\beta}_K \end{bmatrix}.$$

The solution for $\hat{\boldsymbol{\beta}}$ then simply becomes

$$(10.14) \qquad \hat{\boldsymbol{\beta}} = (\mathbf{X}'\mathbf{X})^{-1}(\mathbf{X}'\mathbf{Y}).$$

Alternatively, we can eliminate $\hat{\beta}_1$ by substitution from (10.11), and then solve the reduced system of equations to get

$$(10.15) \qquad \underline{\hat{\boldsymbol{\beta}}} = (\underline{\mathbf{X}'\mathbf{X}})^{-1}(\underline{\mathbf{X}'\mathbf{Y}}),$$

where

$$\underline{\hat{\boldsymbol{\beta}}} = \begin{bmatrix} \hat{\beta}_2 \\ \hat{\beta}_3 \\ \vdots \\ \hat{\beta}_K \end{bmatrix}, \qquad (\underline{\mathbf{X}'\mathbf{X}}) = \begin{bmatrix} m_{22} & m_{23} & \cdots & m_{2K} \\ m_{23} & m_{33} & \cdots & m_{3K} \\ \vdots & \vdots & & \vdots \\ m_{2K} & m_{3K} & \cdots & m_{KK} \end{bmatrix}, \qquad (\underline{\mathbf{X}'\mathbf{Y}}) = \begin{bmatrix} m_{Y2} \\ m_{Y3} \\ \vdots \\ m_{YK} \end{bmatrix}.$$

EXAMPLE   In Section 7–3, we illustrated the method of least squares in the simple regression context by estimating the relationship between price and quantity of oranges sold in a supermarket on twelve consecutive days. Let us modify this example by postulating that the quantity sold depends not only on price but also on the amount spent on advertising the product. That is, let

$$Y_i = \beta_1 + \beta_2 X_{i2} + \beta_3 X_{i3} + \varepsilon_i,$$

where Y_i = quantity (pounds) of oranges sold, X_{i2} = price in cents per pound, and X_{i3} = advertising expenditure in dollars. The data are given in Table 10-1. The

Table 10-1

Quantity, lb	Price, ¢/lb	Advertising Expenditure, $
55	100	5.50
70	90	6.30
90	80	7.20
100	70	7.00
90	70	6.30
105	70	7.35
80	70	5.60
110	65	7.15
125	60	7.50
115	60	6.90
130	55	7.15
130	50	6.50

results of the basic calculations are

$$\bar{Y} = 100, \qquad m_{22} = 2250, \qquad m_{Y2} = -3550,$$

$$\bar{X}_2 = 70, \qquad m_{33} = 4.86, \qquad m_{Y3} = 125.25,$$

$$\bar{X}_3 = 6.7, \qquad m_{23} = -54, \qquad m_{YY} = 6300.$$

(The quantity $m_{YY} = \Sigma_i (Y_i - \bar{Y})^2$ will be used in later examples.) The estimates of the regression coefficients are

$$\hat{\beta}_2 = \frac{-3550 \times 4.86 - (-54) \times 125.25}{2250 \times 4.86 - (-54)^2} = \frac{-10,631.5}{8019} = -1.326,$$

$$\hat{\beta}_3 = \frac{2250 \times 125.25 - (-54) \times (-3550)}{8019} = \frac{90,112.5}{8019} = 11.237,$$

and $\hat{\beta}_1 = 100 - (-1.326) \times 70 - 11.237 \times 6.7 = 117.532.$

Therefore, the estimated regression equation is

$$Y_i = 117.532 - 1.326 \, X_{i2} + 11.237 \, X_{i3} + e_i.$$

This implies that we estimate that a 10¢ reduction in the price of oranges, with advertising expenditure unchanged, would increase sales by about 13 pounds, while a $1 increase in advertising expenditure, with price unchanged, would increase sales by about 11 pounds.

Best Linear Unbiased Estimation

Let us now derive the *best linear unbiased estimators* (BLUE) for the multiple regression model. For simplicity, we shall use a model with two explanatory variables; an extension to the general case only requires more involved algebraic expressions. Suppose, then, that we wish to derive the BLUE of, say, β_2, of the model

$$Y_i = \beta_1 + \beta_2 X_{i2} + \beta_3 X_{i3} + \varepsilon_i.$$

By the condition of linearity, we have

$$\tilde{\beta}_2 = \sum_i a_i Y_i,$$

where a_i $(i = 1, 2, \ldots, n)$ are some constants to be determined. The mathematical expectation of $\tilde{\beta}_2$ is

$$E(\tilde{\beta}_2) = E \sum_i a_i Y_i = E \sum_i a_i(\beta_1 + \beta_2 X_{i2} + \beta_3 X_{i3} + \varepsilon_i)$$

$$= \beta_1 \sum_i a_i + \beta_2 \sum_i a_i X_{i2} + \beta_3 \sum_i a_i X_{i3},$$

so that, for $\tilde{\beta}_2$ to be unbiased, we require

$$\sum_i a_i = 0,$$

$$\sum_i a_i X_{i2} = 1,$$

$$\sum_i a_i X_{i3} = 0.$$

The variance of $\tilde{\beta}_2$ is

$$\text{Var}(\tilde{\beta}_2) = E\left[\sum_i a_i Y_i - E\left(\sum_i a_i Y_i\right)\right]^2 = E\left(\sum_i a_i \varepsilon_i\right)^2 = \sigma^2 \sum_i a_i^2.$$

That is, we have to find those values of a_i that would minimize

$$\sigma^2 \sum_i a_i^2,$$

subject to the conditions that

$$\sum_i a_i = 0,$$

$$\sum_i a_i X_{i2} = 1,$$

$$\sum_i a_i X_{i3} = 0.$$

Using the Lagrange multiplier method, we form

$$H = \sigma^2 \sum_i a_i^2 - \lambda_1\left(\sum_i a_i\right) - \lambda_2\left(\sum_i a_i X_{i2} - 1\right) - \lambda_3\left(\sum_i a_i X_{i3}\right).$$

Differentiating H with respect to $a_1, a_2, \ldots, a_n, \lambda_1, \lambda_2$, and λ_3 and putting each derivative equal to zero, we obtain

$$(10.16) \qquad 2a_i\sigma^2 - \lambda_1 - \lambda_2 X_{i2} - \lambda_3 X_{i3} = 0 \qquad (i = 1, 2, \ldots, n),$$

$$(10.17) \qquad -\Big(\sum_i a_i\Big) = 0,$$

$$(10.18) \qquad -\Big(\sum_i a_i X_{i2}\Big) + 1 = 0,$$

$$(10.19) \qquad -\Big(\sum_i a_i X_{i3}\Big) = 0.$$

This gives us $(n + 3)$ equations to be solved for the unknown $a_1, a_2, \ldots, a_n, \lambda_1, \lambda_2$, and λ_3. We start by adding the n equations of (10.16). This leads to

$$(10.20) \qquad 2\sigma^2 \sum_i a_i - n\lambda_1 - \lambda_2 \sum_i X_{i2} - \lambda_3 \sum_i X_{i3} = 0.$$

Next, we multiply both sides of (10.16) by X_{i2} and add the resulting equations to get

$$(10.21) \qquad 2\sigma^2 \sum_i a_i X_{i2} - \lambda_1 \sum_i X_{i2} - \lambda_2 \sum_i X_{i2}^2 - \lambda_3 \sum_i X_{i2} X_{i3} = 0.$$

Finally, we multiply both sides of (10.16) by X_{i3} and add again:

$$(10.22) \qquad 2\sigma^2 \sum_i a_i X_{i3} - \lambda_1 \sum_i X_{i3} - \lambda_2 \sum_i X_{i2} X_{i3} - \lambda_3 \sum_i X_{i3}^2 = 0,$$

Substitution for $\sum_i a_i$, $\sum_i a_i X_{i2}$, and $\sum_i a_i X_{i3}$ from (10.17), (10.18), and (10.19) into (10.20), (10.21), and (10.22) then leads to

$$(10.20a) \qquad -n\lambda_1 - \lambda_{2i} \sum_i X_{i2} - \lambda_3 \sum_i X_{i3} = 0,$$

$$(10.21a) \qquad -\lambda_1 \sum_i X_{i2} - \lambda_2 \sum_i X_{i2}^2 - \lambda_3 \sum_i X_{i2} X_{i3} = -2\sigma^2,$$

$$(10.22a) \qquad -\lambda_1 \sum_i X_{i3} - \lambda_2 \sum_i X_{i2} X_{i3} - \lambda_3 \sum_i X_{i3} = 0.$$

Now from (10.20a) we get

$$\lambda_1 = -\lambda_2 \bar{X}_2 - \lambda_3 \bar{X}_3.$$

We can then substitute this expression for λ_1 into (10.21a) and (10.22a), which yields

$$\lambda_2 m_{22} + \lambda_3 m_{23} = 2\sigma^2,$$
$$\lambda_2 m_{23} + \lambda_3 m_{33} = 0.$$

Therefore,
$$\lambda_2 = \frac{2\sigma^2 m_{33}}{m_{22} m_{33} - m_{23}^2}$$

and
$$\lambda_3 = \frac{-2\sigma^2 m_{23}}{m_{22} m_{33} - m_{23}^2},$$

which implies that

$$\lambda_1 = \frac{2\sigma^2(-\bar{X}_2 m_{33} + \bar{X}_3 m_{23})}{m_{22} m_{33} - m_{23}^2}.$$

In this way, we have obtained the solution for λ_1, λ_2, and λ_3. Now from (10.16), we have

$$a_i = \frac{1}{2\sigma^2}(\lambda_1 + \lambda_2 X_{i2} + \lambda_3 X_{i3}),$$

which, after substituting for the λ's, becomes

$$(10.23) \qquad a_i = \frac{-\bar{X}_2 m_{33} + \bar{X}_3 m_{23} + m_{33} X_{i2} - m_{23} X_{i3}}{m_{22} m_{33} - m_{23}^2}.$$

Therefore

$$\tilde{\beta}_2 = \sum_i a_i Y_i = \frac{-n\bar{Y}\bar{X}_2 m_{33} + n\bar{Y}\bar{X}_3 m_{23} + m_{33} \sum X_{i2} Y_i - m_{23} \sum X_{i3} Y_i}{m_{22} m_{33} - m_{23}^2}$$

$$= \frac{m_{33} m_{Y2} - m_{23} m_{Y3}}{m_{22} m_{33} - m_{23}^2},$$

which is precisely the same formula as that for the least squares estimator of β_2 given by (10.12). Similarly, we could show that $\tilde{\beta}_3 = \hat{\beta}_3$ and $\tilde{\beta}_1 = \hat{\beta}_1$. Therefore, *least squares estimators of the regression coefficients are* BLUE. This conclusion applies to regression models with any number of explanatory variables.

The BLUE method provides us not only with a formula for $\tilde{\beta}_2$ but also one for the variance of $\tilde{\beta}_2$. In particular,

$$\text{Var}(\tilde{\beta}_2) = \sigma^2 \sum_i a_i^2.$$

Now, by multiplying both sides of (10.23) by a_i, adding over all observations, and substituting for $\sum a_i$, $\sum a_i X_{i2}$, and $\sum a_i X_{i3}$, we obtain

$$\sum_i a_i^2 = \frac{m_{33}}{m_{22} m_{33} - m_{23}^2}.$$

This means that

$$(10.24) \qquad \text{Var}(\tilde{\beta}_2) = \frac{\sigma^2 m_{33}}{m_{22} m_{33} - m_{23}^2}.$$

The result for the variance of $\tilde{\beta}_3$, which will not be derived here, is

$$(10.25) \qquad \text{Var}(\tilde{\beta}_3) = \frac{\sigma^2 m_{22}}{m_{22} m_{33} - m_{23}^2}.$$

Maximum Likelihood Estimation

Next we come to the derivation of the *maximum likelihood estimators* of the parameters of a multiple normal linear regression model. This represents a direct extension of the procedure developed in connection with the simple regression model. When we set up the likelihood function as in (7.26) but allow for more than one explanatory variable, we get

$$L = -\frac{n}{2} \log (2\pi) - \frac{n}{2} \log \sigma^2$$

$$- \frac{1}{2\sigma^2} \sum_i (Y_i - \beta_1 - \beta_2 X_{i2} - \beta_3 X_{i3} - \cdots - \beta_K X_{iK})^2.$$

The maximum likelihood estimators are obtain by differentiating L with respect to $\beta_1, \beta_2, \ldots, \beta_K$, and σ^2, and by putting each of these derivatives equal to zero. It is easy to see that the first K of these equations, which can be solved for the values of the β's, are exactly the same as the least squares normal equations. This means that the *maximum likelihood estimators of the regression coefficients are equivalent to the least squares estimators*. The maximum likelihood estimator of σ^2 is

(10.26) $$\hat{\sigma}^2 = \frac{1}{n} \sum_i (Y_i - \hat{\beta}_1 - \hat{\beta}_2 X_{i2} - \hat{\beta}_3 X_{i3} - \cdots - \hat{\beta}_K X_{iK})^2$$

or

(10.26a) $$\hat{\sigma}^2 = \frac{1}{n} \sum_i e_i^2,$$

where the terms e_i represent the least squares residuals.

10–2   Further Results of Statistical Inference

From the preceding discussion on estimation of the coefficients of a multiple regression model, we conclude that, as in the case of the simple regression model, each of the three estimation methods considered leads to exactly the same formulas. The implication is that the least squares estimators of the regression coefficients have all the desirable properties. We shall now describe some other features of these estimators and discuss their use for testing hypotheses and for prediction.

Variances and Covariances of the Least Squares Estimators

The formulas for the variances of the estimated regression coefficients of a model with two explanatory variables are presented in (10.24) and (10.25). Generalization of these formulas to models with a larger number of explanatory variables is quite straightforward. For the case of $(K - 1)$ variables, the result is

(10.27) $$E(\hat{\underline{\beta}} - \underline{\beta})(\hat{\underline{\beta}} - \underline{\beta})' = \sigma^2 (\mathbf{X'X})^{-1},$$

or, explicitly,

(10.27a)

$$
\begin{bmatrix}
\text{Var}(\hat{\beta}_2) & \text{Cov}(\hat{\beta}_2, \hat{\beta}_3) & \cdots & \text{Cov}(\hat{\beta}_2, \hat{\beta}_K) \\
\text{Cov}(\hat{\beta}_2, \hat{\beta}_3) & \text{Var}(\hat{\beta}_3) & \cdots & \text{Cov}(\hat{\beta}_3, \hat{\beta}_K) \\
\vdots & \vdots & & \vdots \\
\text{Cov}(\hat{\beta}_2, \hat{\beta}_K) & \text{Cov}(\hat{\beta}_3, \hat{\beta}_K) & \cdots & \text{Var}(\hat{\beta}_K)
\end{bmatrix}
= \sigma^2
\begin{bmatrix}
m_{22} & m_{23} & \cdots & m_{2K} \\
m_{23} & m_{33} & \cdots & m_{3K} \\
\vdots & \vdots & & \vdots \\
m_{2K} & m_{3K} & \cdots & m_{KK}
\end{bmatrix}^{-1}.
$$

The matrix $[\sigma^2(\mathbf{X'X})^{-1}]$, whose dimension is $(K - 1) \times (K - 1)$, represents the *variance-covariance matrix* of the least squares estimators of the regression slopes. In this matrix the variances of the estimators are displayed along the main diagonal, while the covariances of the estimators are given by the off-diagonal terms.

So far we have not derived the formula for the variance of the regression intercept. We shall do this now, first for the model with two explanatory variables and then for the general case. In the case of two explanatory variables, we have

$$\hat{\beta}_1 = \bar{Y} - \hat{\beta}_2\bar{X}_2 - \hat{\beta}_3\bar{X}_3 = \beta_1 + \beta_2\bar{X}_2 + \beta_3\bar{X}_3 + \bar{\varepsilon} - \hat{\beta}_2\bar{X}_2 - \hat{\beta}_3\bar{X}_3,$$

so that

$$\hat{\beta}_1 - \beta_1 = -(\hat{\beta}_2 - \beta_2)\bar{X}_2 - (\hat{\beta}_3 - \beta_3)\bar{X}_3 + \bar{\varepsilon}.$$

This means that

$$(10.28) \quad \text{Var}(\hat{\beta}_1) = \bar{X}_2^2\text{Var}(\hat{\beta}_2) + \bar{X}_3^2\text{Var}(\hat{\beta}_3) + 2\bar{X}_2\bar{X}_3\text{Cov}(\hat{\beta}_2,\hat{\beta}_3)$$
$$- 2\bar{X}_2 E\bar{\varepsilon}(\hat{\beta}_2 - \beta_2) - 2\bar{X}_3 E\bar{\varepsilon}(\hat{\beta}_3 - \beta_3) + \text{Var}(\bar{\varepsilon}).$$

The first three terms on the right-hand side of (10.28) can be determined from (10.27). To determine the next two terms, we note first that

$$m_{Y2} = \sum_i (Y_i - \bar{Y})(X_{i2} - \bar{X}_2)$$

$$= \sum_i [\beta_2(X_{i2} - \bar{X}_2) + \beta_3(X_{i3} - \bar{X}_3) + (\varepsilon_i - \bar{\varepsilon})](X_{i2} - \bar{X}_2)$$

$$= \beta_2 m_{22} + \beta_3 m_{23} + \sum_i (X_{i2} - \bar{X}_2)\varepsilon_i$$

and $m_{Y3} = \beta_2 m_{23} + \beta_3 m_{33} + \sum_i (X_{i3} - \bar{X}_3)\varepsilon_i.$

These expressions can be substituted into (10.12) to get

$$\hat{\beta}_2 = \frac{m_{33}[\beta_2 m_{22} + \beta_3 m_{23} + \sum (X_{i2} - \bar{X}_2)\varepsilon_i]}{m_{22}m_{33} - m_{23}^2}$$
$$- \frac{m_{23}[\beta_2 m_{23} + \beta_3 m_{33} + \sum (X_{i3} - \bar{X}_3)\varepsilon_i]}{m_{22}m_{33} - m_{23}^2}$$

or

$$(10.29) \quad \hat{\beta}_2 - \beta_2 = \frac{m_{33} \sum (X_{i2} - \bar{X}_2)\varepsilon_i - m_{23} \sum (X_{i3} - \bar{X}_3)\varepsilon_i}{m_{22}m_{33} - m_{23}^2}.$$

Similarly, by substituting for m_{Y2} and m_{Y3} into (10.13), we obtain

$$(10.30) \quad \hat{\beta}_3 - \beta_3 = \frac{m_{22} \sum (X_{i3} - \bar{X}_3)\varepsilon_i - m_{23} \sum (X_{i2} - \bar{X}_2)\varepsilon_i}{m_{22}m_{33} - m_{23}^2}.$$

Therefore,

$$E(\hat{\beta}_2 - \beta_2)\bar{\varepsilon} = \frac{m_{33} \sum (X_{i2} - \bar{X}_2)E(\varepsilon_i\bar{\varepsilon}) - m_{23} \sum (X_{i3} - \bar{X}_3)E(\varepsilon_i\bar{\varepsilon})}{m_{22}m_{33} - m_{23}^2} = 0,$$

and also

$$E(\hat{\beta}_3 - \beta_3)\bar{\varepsilon} = 0.$$

Finally, we know that

$$\text{Var}(\bar{\varepsilon}) = \frac{\sigma^2}{n}.$$

Collecting all these results and substituting into (10.28) gives

$$(10.31) \qquad \text{Var}(\hat{\beta}_1) = \bar{X}_2^2\text{Var}(\hat{\beta}_2) + \bar{X}_3^2\text{Var}(\hat{\beta}_3) + 2\bar{X}_2\bar{X}_3\text{Cov}(\hat{\beta}_2,\hat{\beta}_3) + \frac{\sigma^2}{n}$$

$$= \sigma^2\left[\frac{1}{n} + \frac{\bar{X}_2^2 m_{33} + \bar{X}_3^2 m_{22} - 2\bar{X}_2\bar{X}_3 m_{23}}{m_{22}m_{33} - m_{23}^2}\right].$$

By analogy, the variance of $\hat{\beta}_1$ in a model with $(K - 1)$ explanatory variables is

$$(10.32) \qquad \text{Var}(\hat{\beta}_1) = \sum_k \bar{X}_k^2\text{Var}(\hat{\beta}_k) + 2\sum_{j<k} \bar{X}_j\bar{X}_k\text{Cov}(\hat{\beta}_j,\hat{\beta}_k) + \frac{\sigma^2}{n}$$

$$(j, k = 2, 3, \ldots, K; \quad j < k).$$

This expression can be rewritten in matrix notation as

$$(10.32a) \qquad \text{Var}(\hat{\beta}_1) = \bar{\mathbf{X}}'E(\hat{\boldsymbol{\beta}} - \boldsymbol{\beta})(\hat{\boldsymbol{\beta}} - \boldsymbol{\beta})'\bar{\mathbf{X}} = \sigma^2\bar{\mathbf{X}}'(\mathbf{X}'\mathbf{X})^{-1}\bar{\mathbf{X}},$$

where

$$\bar{\mathbf{X}} = \begin{bmatrix} \bar{X}_2 \\ \bar{X}_3 \\ \vdots \\ \bar{X}_K \end{bmatrix}.$$

An alternative way of writing the formulas for the variances and covariances of the least squares estimators of the regression coefficients is

$$(10.33) \qquad E(\hat{\boldsymbol{\beta}} - \boldsymbol{\beta})(\hat{\boldsymbol{\beta}} - \boldsymbol{\beta})' = \sigma^2(\mathbf{X}'\mathbf{X})^{-1}$$

or, explicitly,

$$(10.33a) \quad \begin{bmatrix} \text{Var}(\hat{\beta}_1) & \text{Cov}(\hat{\beta}_1,\hat{\beta}_2) & \cdots & \text{Cov}(\hat{\beta}_1,\hat{\beta}_K) \\ \text{Cov}(\hat{\beta}_1,\hat{\beta}_2) & \text{Var}(\hat{\beta}_2) & \cdots & \text{Cov}(\hat{\beta}_2,\hat{\beta}_K) \\ \vdots & \vdots & & \vdots \\ \text{Cov}(\hat{\beta}_1,\hat{\beta}_K) & \text{Cov}(\hat{\beta}_2,\hat{\beta}_K) & \cdots & \text{Var}(\hat{\beta}_K) \end{bmatrix}$$

$$= \sigma^2\begin{bmatrix} n & \sum X_{i2} & \cdots & \sum X_{iK} \\ \sum X_{i2} & \sum X_{i2}^2 & \cdots & \sum X_{i2}X_{iK} \\ \vdots & \vdots & & \vdots \\ \sum X_{iK} & \sum X_{i2}X_{iK} & \cdots & \sum X_{iK}^2 \end{bmatrix}^{-1}.$$

Formula (10.33), which represents the variance-covariance matrix of the estimated regression coefficients, contains the variances and covariances of *all*
estimated coefficients, including the regression constant. Of course, this formula
gives the same values for the variance of $\hat{\beta}_1$ and for the variances and covariances
of $\hat{\beta}_2, \hat{\beta}_3, \ldots, \hat{\beta}_K$ as formulas (10.27) and (10.32). In addition, (10.33) gives the
covariances of $\hat{\beta}_1$ with $\hat{\beta}_2, \hat{\beta}_3, \ldots, \hat{\beta}_K$. If the latter is not needed and we wish to
minimize the calculation required, then formulas (10.27) and (10.32) are prefer-
able to (10.33).

Estimation of σ^2

The variances and covariances of the least squares estimators of the regression
coefficients all involve the parameter σ^2, the value of which has to be estimated.
To find an unbiased estimator of σ^2, we first determine the mathematical expectation of the sum of squares of the least squares residuals. For the case of two
explanatory variables, this is

$$
\begin{aligned}
E \sum_i (Y_i - \hat{\beta}_1 - \hat{\beta}_2 X_{i2} - \hat{\beta}_3 X_{i3})^2 &= E \sum_i [(Y_i - \bar{Y}) - \hat{\beta}_2(X_{i2} - \bar{X}_2) \\
&\qquad - \hat{\beta}_3(X_{i3} - \bar{X}_3)]^2 \\
&= E \sum_i [\beta_2(X_{i2} - \bar{X}_2) + \beta_3(X_{i3} - \bar{X}_3) \\
&\qquad + (\varepsilon_i - \bar{\varepsilon}) - \hat{\beta}_2(X_{i2} - \bar{X}_2) \\
&\qquad - \hat{\beta}_3(X_{i3} - \bar{X}_3)]^2 \\
&= m_{22}\mathrm{Var}(\hat{\beta}_2) + m_{33}\mathrm{Var}(\hat{\beta}_3) \\
&\qquad + 2m_{23}\mathrm{Cov}(\hat{\beta}_2, \hat{\beta}_3) \\
&\qquad - 2E(\hat{\beta}_2 - \beta_2) \sum_i (X_{i2} - \bar{X}_2)\varepsilon_i \\
&\qquad - 2E(\hat{\beta}_3 - \beta_3) \sum_i (X_{i3} - \bar{X}_3)\varepsilon_i \\
&\qquad + E \sum_i (\varepsilon_i - \bar{\varepsilon})^2.
\end{aligned}
$$

Now by (10.29) we have

$$
-2E(\hat{\beta}_2 - \beta_2) \sum_i (X_{i2} - \bar{X}_2)\varepsilon_i = \frac{-2\sigma^2(m_{22}m_{33} - m_{23}^2)}{m_{22}m_{33} - m_{23}^2} = -2\sigma^2,
$$

and by (10.30) we have

$$
-2E(\hat{\beta}_3 - \beta_3) \sum_i (X_{i3} - \bar{X}_3)\varepsilon_i = -2\sigma^2.
$$

Also,

$$
E \sum_i (\varepsilon_i - \bar{\varepsilon})^2 = E\left(\sum \varepsilon_i^2\right) - 2E\left(\sum \varepsilon_i \bar{\varepsilon}\right) + nE(\bar{\varepsilon}^2) = n\sigma^2 - 2\sigma^2 + \sigma^2
$$

$$
= (n - 1)\sigma^2.
$$

Therefore,

$$E \sum_i (Y_i - \hat{\beta}_1 - \hat{\beta}_2 X_{i2} - \hat{\beta}_3 X_{i3})^2 = \frac{\sigma^2(m_{22}m_{33} + m_{22}m_{33} - 2m_{23}^2)}{m_{22}m_{33} - m_{23}^2}$$

$$- 2\sigma^2 - 2\sigma^2 + (n - 1)\sigma^2$$

$$= (n - 3)\sigma^2.$$

An unbiased estimator of σ^2, say, s^2, for a regression model with two explanatory variables then is

$$(10.34) \qquad s^2 = \frac{1}{n - 3} \sum_i (Y_i - \hat{\beta}_1 - \hat{\beta}_2 X_{i2} - \hat{\beta}_3 X_{i3})^2.$$

This formula can be generalized to apply to the case of $(K - 1)$ explanatory variables as follows:

$$(10.35) \qquad s^2 = \frac{1}{n - K} \sum_i (Y_i - \hat{\beta}_1 - \hat{\beta}_2 X_{i2} - \hat{\beta}_3 X_{i3} - \cdots - \hat{\beta}_K X_{iK})^2.$$

Since asymptotically s^2 is equivalent to $\hat{\sigma}^2$, the maximum likelihood estimator of σ^2, it follows that s^2 has the same optimal asymptotic properties as $\hat{\sigma}^2$.

For computing the value of s^2, formulas (10.34) and (10.35) can be simplified to avoid the calculation of individual residuals. Let us begin with the case of two explanatory variables,

$$s^2 = \frac{1}{n - 3} \sum_i [(Y_i - \bar{Y}) - \hat{\beta}_2(X_{i2} - \bar{X}_2) - \hat{\beta}_3(X_{i3} - \bar{X}_3)]^2$$

$$= \frac{1}{n - 3} (m_{YY} + \hat{\beta}_2^2 m_{22} + \hat{\beta}_3^2 m_{33} - 2\hat{\beta}_2 m_{Y2} - 2\hat{\beta}_3 m_{Y3} + 2\hat{\beta}_2 \hat{\beta}_3 m_{23}).$$

But from the least squares normal equations, we have

$$m_{Y2} = \hat{\beta}_2 m_{22} + \hat{\beta}_3 m_{23},$$

$$m_{Y3} = \hat{\beta}_2 m_{23} + \hat{\beta}_3 m_{33}.$$

Therefore,

$$\hat{\beta}_2^2 m_{22} + \hat{\beta}_2 \hat{\beta}_3 m_{23} - \hat{\beta}_2 m_{Y2} = 0,$$

$$\hat{\beta}_2 \hat{\beta}_3 m_{23} + \hat{\beta}_3^2 m_{33} - \hat{\beta}_3 m_{Y3} = 0.$$

Thus s^2 becomes

$$(10.34a) \qquad s^2 = \frac{1}{n - 3} (m_{YY} - \hat{\beta}_2 m_{Y2} - \hat{\beta}_3 m_{Y3}).$$

This can be generalized to the case of $(K - 1)$ explanatory variables so that (10.35) becomes

$$(10.35a) \qquad s^2 = \frac{1}{n - K} (m_{YY} - \hat{\beta}_2 m_{Y2} - \hat{\beta}_3 m_{Y3} - \cdots - \hat{\beta}_K m_{YK}).$$

These formulas are computationally more convenient than (10.34) and (10.35). By using s^2 in place of σ^2 in (10.27) and (10.32)—or in (10.33)—we obtain unbiased estimators of the variances and covariances of the least squares estimators of the regression coefficients. The *confidence intervals* for the regression coefficients can be constructed by noting that

$$\frac{\hat{\beta}_k - \beta_k}{s_{\hat{\beta}_k}} \sim t_{n-K} \qquad (k = 1, 2, \ldots, K),$$

where $s_{\hat{\beta}_k}$ represents the estimated standard error of $\hat{\beta}_k$.

EXAMPLE   To illustrate the use of the preceding formulas, let us construct the 95% confidence intervals for the coefficients of the regression model described in the previous example. Substituting the numerical results into (10.34a), we get

$$s^2 = \frac{1}{12 - 3}[6300 - (-1.326) \times (-3550) - 11.237 \times 125.25]$$

$$= \frac{185.27}{9} = 20.586.$$

This result, combined with formulas (10.24), (10.25), and (10.31), gives

$$s_{\hat{\beta}_2}^2 = \frac{20.586 \times 4.86}{2250 \times 4.86 - (-54)^2} = 0.012476,$$

$$s_{\hat{\beta}_3}^2 = \frac{20.586 \times 2250}{2250 \times 4.86 - (-54)^2} = 5.7761,$$

and $s_{\hat{\beta}_1}^2 = 20.586\left[\frac{1}{12} + \frac{70^2 \times 4.86 + 6.7^2 \times 2250 - 2 \times 70 \times 6.7 \times (-54)}{2250 \times 4.86 - (-54)^2}\right]$

$$= 452.1700.$$

Therefore, the estimated standard errors of $\hat{\beta}_1$, $\hat{\beta}_2$, and $\hat{\beta}_3$ are

$$s_{\hat{\beta}_1} = 21.264,$$

$$s_{\hat{\beta}_2} = 0.112,$$

$$s_{\hat{\beta}_3} = 2.403.$$

The tabulated t value for $12 - 3 = 9$ degrees of freedom and 0.025 two-tail probability is 2.262. Therefore, the 95% confidence intervals for the regression coefficient are

$$117.532 - 2.262 \times 21.264 \leq \beta_1 \leq 117.532 + 2.262 \times 21.264$$

or $69.43 \leq \beta_1 \leq 165.63,$

$$-1.326 - 2.262 \times 0.112 \leq \beta_2 \leq -1.326 + 2.262 \times 0.112$$

or $-1.58 \leq \beta_2 \leq -1.07,$

$$11.237 - 2.262 \times 2.403 \leq \beta_3 \leq 11.237 + 2.262 \times 2.403$$

or $5.80 \leq \beta_3 \leq 16.67.$

Confidence Interval for $E(Y_i)$

The confidence intervals that we have described indicate the precision of the estimators of each of the regression coefficients considered separately. The precision of the estimated regression equation as a whole is indicated by a *confidence band*. This can be derived as a confidence interval for $E(Y_i)$, using the fitted value $\hat{Y}_i$ as its estimator. We note that $\hat{Y}_i$ is normally distributed with mean equal to $E(Y_i)$. Its variance, in the case of two explanatory variables, is

$$\sigma^2_{\hat{Y}_i} = E[\hat{Y}_i - E(\hat{Y}_i)]^2 = E[\hat{Y}_i - E(Y_i)]^2$$

$$= E[(\hat{\beta}_1 - \beta_1) + (\hat{\beta}_2 - \beta_2)X_{i2} + (\hat{\beta}_3 - \beta_3)X_{i3}]^2.$$

But $\hat{\beta}_1 - \beta_1 = -(\hat{\beta}_2 - \beta_2)\bar{X}_2 - (\hat{\beta}_3 - \beta_3)\bar{X}_3 + \bar{\varepsilon}$,

which gives

(10.36) $\sigma^2_{\hat{Y}_i} = E[(\hat{\beta}_2 - \beta_2)(X_{i2} - \bar{X}_2) + (\hat{\beta}_3 - \beta_3)(X_{i3} - \bar{X}_3) + \bar{\varepsilon}]^2$

$$= (X_{i2} - \bar{X}_2)^2 \mathrm{Var}(\hat{\beta}_2) + (X_{i3} - \bar{X}_3)^2 \mathrm{Var}(\hat{\beta}_3)$$

$$+ 2(X_{i2} - \bar{X}_2)(X_{i3} - \bar{X}_3)\mathrm{Cov}(\hat{\beta}_2, \hat{\beta}_3) + \frac{\sigma^2}{n}.$$

For a model with $(K - 1)$ explanatory variables, we have

(10.37) $\sigma^2_{\hat{Y}_i} = \sum_k (X_{ik} - \bar{X}_k)^2 \mathrm{Var}(\hat{\beta}_k)$

$$+ 2 \sum_{j<k} (X_{ij} - \bar{X}_j)(X_{ik} - \bar{X}_k)\mathrm{Cov}(\hat{\beta}_j, \hat{\beta}_k) + \frac{\sigma^2}{n}$$

$$(j, k = 2, 3, \ldots, K; \quad j < k),$$

or, in matrix notation,

(10.37a) $\sigma^2_{\hat{Y}_i} = (\underline{X}_i - \underline{\bar{X}})'E(\underline{\hat{\beta}} - \underline{\beta})(\underline{\hat{\beta}} - \underline{\beta})'(\underline{X}_i - \underline{\bar{X}}) + \dfrac{\sigma^2}{n}$

$$= \sigma^2 \left[(\underline{X}_i - \underline{\bar{X}})'(\underline{X}'\underline{X})^{-1}(\underline{X}_i - \underline{\bar{X}}) + \frac{1}{n} \right],$$

where

$$(\underline{X}_i - \underline{\bar{X}}) = \begin{bmatrix} X_{i2} - \bar{X}_2 \\ X_{i3} - \bar{X}_3 \\ \vdots \\ X_{ik} - \bar{X}_K \end{bmatrix}.$$

The expression for $\sigma^2_{\hat{Y}_i}$ involves the parameter σ^2 whose value is not known. If we replace σ^2 by its unbiased estimator s^2, we obtain an unbiased estimator of $\sigma^2_{\hat{Y}_i}$, say $s^2_{\hat{Y}_i}$. The confidence band for $E(Y_i)$ can then be constructed by noting that

$$\frac{\hat{Y}_i - E(Y_i)}{s_{\hat{Y}_i}} \sim t_{n-K}.$$

From this, we can determine the confidence interval for $E(Y_i)$ for *any* set of values of the explanatory variables. Note that this interval will be narrowest when the value of each explanatory variable is equal to its sample mean (in which case $s_{\hat{Y}_i}$ will be equal to $s/\sqrt{n}$) and that the interval will get wider and wider as we move away from the sample means of the X's in either direction.

Decomposition of the Sample Variation of Y

Defining, as in the case of simple regression, the sample variation of Y by $\sum(Y_i - \bar{Y})^2$, we have

$$\sum_i (Y_i - \bar{Y})^2 = \sum_i [(\hat{Y}_i + e_i) - \bar{Y}]^2$$

$$= \sum_i (\hat{Y}_i - \bar{Y})^2 + \sum_i e_i^2 + 2\sum_i (\hat{Y}_i - \bar{Y})e_i,$$

where, as before, the terms e_i represent the least squares residuals. Now, from the least squares normal equations we find that

$$\sum_i (\hat{Y}_i - \bar{Y})e_i = \sum_i (\hat{\beta}_1 + \hat{\beta}_2 X_{i2} + \hat{\beta}_i X_{i3} + \cdots + \hat{\beta}_K X_{iK})e_i - \bar{Y}\sum_i e_i = 0.$$

Thus
$$\underbrace{\sum_i (Y_i - \bar{Y})^2}_{\text{SST}} = \underbrace{\sum_i (\hat{Y}_i - \bar{Y})^2}_{\text{SSR}} + \underbrace{\sum_i e_i^2}_{\text{+ SSE}}.$$

Now, for the case of two explanatory variables we decompose SSR as follows:

(10.38) $$\text{SSR} = \sum_i (\hat{\beta}_1 + \hat{\beta}_2 X_{i2} + \hat{\beta}_3 X_{i3} - \bar{Y})^2$$

$$= \sum_i [(\bar{Y} - \hat{\beta}_2 \bar{X}_2 - \hat{\beta}_3 \bar{X}_3) + \hat{\beta}_2 X_{i2} + \hat{\beta}_3 X_{i3} - \bar{Y}]^2$$

$$= \hat{\beta}_2^2 m_{22} + \hat{\beta}_3^2 m_{33} + 2\hat{\beta}_2\hat{\beta}_3 m_{23}.$$

In this case SSR, which represents the estimated regression effect on Y, consists of three terms. The first term corresponds to the effect of X_{i2}, the second to the effect of X_{i3}, and the third to the combined effect of both variables. The combined effect of X_{i2} and X_{i3} reflects the fact that X_{i2} and X_{i3} may vary together to some extent. This joint variation of X_{i2} and X_{i3} accounts for a part of the variation of Y_i. The individual contributions of X_{i2} and X_{i3} to the variation of Y_i cannot be separated completely unless X_{i2} and X_{i3} are uncorrelated, that is, unless m_{23} is equal to zero. The decomposition of SSR given in (10.38) can be generalized to the case of $(K - 1)$ explanatory variables:

(10.39) $$\text{SSR} = \sum_k \hat{\beta}_k^2 m_{kk} + 2\sum_{j<k} \hat{\beta}_j\hat{\beta}_k m_{jk} \qquad (j, k = 2, 3, \ldots, K; \ j < k),$$

or, in matrix notation,

(10.39a) $$\text{SSR} = \hat{\underline{\beta}}'(\mathbf{X}'\mathbf{X})^{-1}\hat{\underline{\beta}}.$$

If we are interested only in the total value of SSR and not in its components then we can obtain a computationally more convenient formula from (10.39) by a substitution from the least squares normal equation:

$$(10.40) \qquad \text{SSR} = \sum_{k=2}^{K} \hat{\beta}_k m_{Yk},$$

or, in matrix notation,

$$(10.40a) \qquad \text{SSR} = \underline{\hat{\beta}}'(\mathbf{X}'\mathbf{Y}).$$

The previous results are also utilized in calculating the value of the *coefficient of determination*. This is defined, as in (7.45), by

$$R^2 = \frac{\text{SSR}}{\text{SST}} = 1 - \frac{\text{SSE}}{\text{SST}}.$$

Some research workers prefer to measure the "goodness of fit" in the case of multiple regression by a somewhat different formula known as the "*corrected coefficient of determination*." This is usually denoted by $\bar{R}^2$ and defined by

$$(10.41) \qquad \bar{R}^2 = R^2 - \frac{K-1}{n-K}(1 - R^2).$$

This measure takes into account the number of explanatory variables in relation to the number of observations. The purpose of $\bar{R}^2$ is to facilitate comparisons of the "goodness of fit" of several regression equations that may vary with respect to the number of explanatory variables and the number of observations. Note that

$$\bar{R}^2 \leq R^2,$$

with $\bar{R}^2$ being equal to R^2 in finite samples only if R^2 is equal to unity. Asymptotically the two measures are, of course, equal. Also note that, unlike R^2, $\bar{R}^2$ may have negative values. For instance, if $n = 10$, $K = 2$, and $R^2 = 0.1$, then $\bar{R}^2 = -0.0125$.

EXAMPLE   From the data of the previous example, we can decompose the sample variation of Y as follows.

Source	Formula	Value	
X_{i2}	$\hat{\beta}_2^2 m_{22}$	$(-1.326)^2 \times 2250$	$= 3956$
X_{i3}	$\hat{\beta}_3^2 m_{33}$	$(11.237)^2 \times 4.86$	$= 614$
X_{i2} and X_{i3}	$2\hat{\beta}_2\hat{\beta}_3 m_{23}$	$2 \times (-1.326) \times 11.237 \times (-54)$	$= 1609$
SSR		$3956 + 614 + 1609$	$= 6179$
SSE	$m_{YY} - \text{SSR}$	$6300 - 6179$	$= 121$
SST	m_{YY}		6300

The value of the coefficient of determination is

$$R^2 = \frac{6179}{6300} = 0.981,$$

which indicates that 98% of the sample variation of the quantity of oranges sold can be attributed to the estimated effect of price variation and of variation in advertising expenditure.

Testing Hypotheses

With respect to *testing hypotheses*, the multiple regression model offers more opportunities than the simple regression model. First of all, there is the test of the hypothesis that the value of, say, β_k, is equal to some specific number. That is,

$$H_0: \quad \beta_k = \gamma_k,$$

which is to be tested against a two-sided or a one-sided alternative. The statistic that we can use to test H_0 is

$$(10.42) \qquad\qquad \frac{\hat{\beta}_k - \gamma_k}{s_k} \sim t_{n-K} \quad (k = 2, 3, \ldots, K).$$

Most frequently we are interested in testing the hypothesis that β_k is equal to zero. When $k = 1$, such a hypothesis implies that the intercept is equal to zero, namely, that the regression plane passes through the origin. When $k = 2, 3, \ldots,$ K, the hypothesis that $\beta_k = 0$ means that the variable X_{ik} has no influence on the mean of Y_i; if the hypothesis is not rejected, we conclude that X_{ik} is not a relevant variable in the regression equation.

A more extensive hypothesis is that *none* of the explanatory variables has an influence on the mean of Y_i. In this case we test

$$H_0: \quad \beta_2 = \beta_3 = \cdots = \beta_K = 0$$

against the alternative that H_0 is not true; i.e., that at least one of the regression slopes is different from zero. If H_0 is true, then the variation of Y from observation to observation is not affected by changes in any one of the explanatory variables, but is purely random. However, if that is true, then the observed value of SSR ("sum of squares due to regression") differs from zero only because of sampling. Since by (10.39)

$$\text{SSR} = \sum_k \hat{\beta}_k^2 m_{kk} + 2 \sum_{j<k} \hat{\beta}_j \hat{\beta}_k m_{jk} \qquad (j, k = 2, 3, \ldots, K; \quad j < k),$$

it is obvious that if the $\hat{\beta}$'s were replaced by the β's and the null hypothesis were correct, SSR would be equal to zero and, therefore, SSE would be equal to SST. Now, it can be shown[1] that if the null hypothesis is true, then

$$(10.43) \qquad\qquad \frac{\text{SSR}/(K - 1)}{\text{SSE}/(n - K)} \sim F_{K-1 \ n-K},$$

[1] See, e.g., J. Johnston, *Econometric Methods* (New York: McGraw-Hill, 1963), pp. 119–122.

where $F_{K-1, n-K}$ represents the F distribution with $(K - 1)$ and $(n - K)$ degrees of freedom. If the value of the expression in (10.43) is not significantly different from zero, the sample offers no evidence that the explanatory variables have any effect on the mean of Y_i. Incidentally, the value of the F statistic in (10.43) can be calculated by using R^2 since

$$\frac{\text{SSR}/(K - 1)}{\text{SSE}/(n - K)} = \left[\frac{n - K}{K - 1}\right]\left[\frac{\text{SSR}/\text{SST}}{1 - (\text{SSR}/\text{SST})}\right] = \left[\frac{n - K}{K - 1}\right]\left[\frac{R^2}{1 - R^2}\right].$$

Note that if any one of the estimated regression coefficients $\hat{\beta}_2, \hat{\beta}_3, \ldots, \hat{\beta}_K$ is significantly different from zero according to the t test of (10.42), then the value of the F statistic in (10.43) will also be significantly different from zero, providing the tests are carried out at the same level of significance and against the same alternative.[2] However, it is quite possible to find that *none* of $\hat{\beta}_2, \hat{\beta}_3, \ldots, \hat{\beta}_K$ is significantly different from zero according to the t test and, at the same time, to reject the hypothesis that $\beta_2 = \beta_3 = \cdots = \beta_K = 0$ by the F test. This could arise in the case where the explanatory variables are highly correlated with each other. In such a situation the separate influences of each of the explanatory variables on the dependent variable may be weak while their joint influence may be quite strong.

The relationship between the values of the individual t statistics in the test of

$$H_0: \quad \beta_k = 0 \qquad (k = 2, 3, \ldots, K)$$

and the value of the F statistic in the test of

$$H_0: \quad \beta_2 = \beta_3 = \cdots = \beta_K$$

can be made explicit by expressing the F statistic in terms of the t statistics. We shall do this for the case of two explanatory variables. From (10.38) we have

$$\text{SSR} = \hat{\beta}_2^2 m_{22} + \hat{\beta}_3^2 m_{33} + 2\hat{\beta}_2\hat{\beta}_3 m_{23},$$

and from (10.34) we know that

$$\frac{\text{SSE}}{(n - 3)} = s^2.$$

Therefore,

(10.44) $\qquad F_{2, n-3} = \dfrac{\text{SSR}/2}{\text{SSE}/(n - 3)} = \dfrac{\hat{\beta}_2^2 m_{22} + \hat{\beta}_3^2 m_{33} + 2\hat{\beta}_2\hat{\beta}_3 m_{23}}{2s^2}.$

---

[2] Strictly speaking, this is not absolutely true. R. C. Geary and C. E. V. Leser in "Significance Tests in Multiple Regression," *The American Statistician*, Vol. 22, February 1968, pp. 20–21, give an example where all t values are significant but the F value is not. They note, however, that this situation is rare and "the possibility of its existence represents little more than a curiosity."

Now let us denote the values of the t statistics for β_2 and β_3 by t_2 and t_3 respectively. Then

$$t_2 = \frac{\hat{\beta}_2}{s_{\hat{\beta}_2}} \quad \text{and} \quad t_3 = \frac{\hat{\beta}_3}{s_{\hat{\beta}_3}}.$$

By reference to (10.24) and (10.25) we can write

$$t_2^2 = \frac{\hat{\beta}_2^2(m_{22}m_{33} - m_{23}^2)}{s^2 m_{33}},$$

$$t_3^2 = \frac{\hat{\beta}_3^2(m_{22}m_{33} - m_{23}^2)}{s^2 m_{22}},$$

or

$$\hat{\beta}_2^2 = \frac{t_2^2 s^2 m_{33}}{m_{22}m_{33} - m_{23}^2},$$

$$\hat{\beta}_3^2 = \frac{t_3^2 s^2 m_{22}}{m_{22}m_{33} - m_{23}^2},$$

and also

$$\hat{\beta}_2\hat{\beta}_3 = \frac{t_2 t_3 s^2 \sqrt{m_{22}}\sqrt{m_{33}}}{m_{22}m_{33} - m_{23}^2}.$$

Substitution into (10.44) then gives

(10.44a) $$F_{2,\,n-3} = \frac{t_2^2 s^2 m_{22}m_{33} + t_3^2 s^2 m_{22}m_{33} + 2t_2 t_3 s^2 (\sqrt{m_{22}}\sqrt{m_{33}})m_{23}}{2s^2(m_{22}m_{33} - m_{23}^2)}.$$

If we use the symbol r_{23} to represent the sample coefficient of correlation between X_{i2} and X_{i3}, that is, if we define

$$r_{23} = \frac{m_{23}}{\sqrt{m_{22}}\sqrt{m_{33}}},$$

then (10.44a) simplifies to

(10.44b) $$F_{2,\,n-3} = \frac{t_2^2 + t_3^2 + 2t_2 t_3 r_{23}}{2(1 - r_{23}^2)}.$$

This shows quite clearly that if r_{23}^2 is not far from unity, the value of $F_{2,\,n-3}$ will be quite large even if both t_2 and t_3 are small. Thus neither $\hat{\beta}_2$ nor $\hat{\beta}_3$ may be significantly different from zero and yet the value of $F_{2,\,n-3}$ may be highly significant.[3]

EXAMPLE   Consider a regression model

$$Y_i = \beta_1 + \beta_2 X_{i2} + \beta_3 X_{i3} + \varepsilon_i.$$

---

[3] For a systematic exploration of this point, see K. Fox, *Intermediate Economic Statistics* (New York: Wiley, 1968), pp. 259–265. Our example given in the text represents a slight modification of one of the many illustrations given by Fox.

Suppose $n = 20$, and the calculated sample moments are

$$m_{YY} = 100, \qquad m_{22} = 100,$$
$$m_{Y2} = 90, \qquad m_{33} = 100,$$
$$m_{Y3} = 90, \qquad m_{23} = 95.$$

Then
$$\hat{\beta}_2 = \frac{90 \times 100 - 90 \times 95}{100 \times 100 - 95^2} = 0.461,$$

and
$$\hat{\beta}_3 = \frac{90 \times 100 - 90 \times 95}{100 \times 100 - 95^2} = 0.461.$$

Further,

$$\text{SSR} = 0.461^2 \times 100 + 0.461^2 \times 100 + 2 \times 0.461 \times 0.461 \times 95 = 83,$$
$$\text{SST} = 100,$$
$$\text{SSE} = 17.$$

Therefore,
$$s^2 = \frac{17}{17} = 1,$$

and
$$s_{\hat{\beta}_2}^2 = \frac{1 \times 100}{100 \times 100 - 95^2} = 0.102564,$$

$$s_{\hat{\beta}_3}^2 = \frac{1 \times 100}{100 \times 100 - 95^2} = 0.102564.$$

Consequently,
$$t_2 = \frac{0.461}{\sqrt{0.102564}} = 1.444,$$

$$t_3 = \frac{0.461}{\sqrt{0.102564}} = 1.444.$$

Since the tabulated t value for 17 degrees of freedom at the 5% level of significance (i.e., $t_{17, 0.025}$) is 2.110, which exceeds 1.444, neither $\hat{\beta}_2$ nor $\hat{\beta}_3$ is significantly different from zero at the 5% level of significance. On the other hand, the value

$$F = \frac{83/2}{1} = 41.5$$

is very much higher than the tabulated value of $F_{2, 17}$ at the 5% level of significance, which is 3.59. Thus, by the t test we cannot reject the hypothesis that $\beta_2 = 0$ or the hypothesis that $\beta_3 = 0$, and yet by the F test we reject the hypothesis that $\beta_2 = \beta_3 = 0$. The reason is the fact that the separate contributions of X_{i2} and X_{i3} to the explanation of the variation of Y_i are weak, whereas their joint contribution, which cannot be decomposed, is quite strong. In fact,

$$\hat{\beta}_2^2 m_{22} = 21.3$$
$$\hat{\beta}_3^2 m_{33} = 21.3$$
$$\underline{2\hat{\beta}_2\hat{\beta}_3 m_{23} = 40.4}$$
$$\text{SSR} = 83.0,$$

which shows that the joint contribution of X_{i2} and X_{i3} to SSR is almost twice as large as the separate contribution of either X_{i2} or X_{i3}. Note that in this example $r_{23} = 0.95$, indicating a high degree of sample correlation between X_{i2} and X_{i3}.

A somewhat different test concerns the influence of additional explanatory variables on the mean of Y_i. In particular, consider two theories, one stating that the regression equation is

$$Y_i = \beta_1 + \beta_2 X_{i2} + \beta_3 X_{i3} + \cdots + \beta_K X_{iK} + \varepsilon_i,$$

while the competing theory states that Y_i depends not only on $X_{i2}, X_{i3}, \ldots, X_{iK}$ but also on additional explanatory variables $X_{i, K+1}, X_{i, K+2}, \ldots, X_{iQ}$ $(Q > K)$, that is,

$$Y_i = \beta_1 + \beta_2 X_{i2} + \beta_3 X_{i3} + \cdots + \beta_K X_{iK} + \beta_{K+1} X_{i, K+1} + \cdots + \beta_Q X_{iQ} + \varepsilon_i.$$

In this case, the second theory can be tested by testing the hypothesis

$$H_0\colon \quad \beta_{K+1} = \beta_{K+2} = \cdots = \beta_Q$$

against the alternative that H_0 is not true. To formulate the appropriate test, we introduce a new notation, using the subscript K to denote the values pertaining to the original set of explanatory variables, and the subscript Q to denote the values to the extended set of explanatory variables. Values with no subscript apply to either set. We can write

$$\text{SST} = \text{SSR}_K + \text{SSE}_K$$

and also

$$\text{SST} = \text{SSR}_Q + \text{SSE}_Q.$$

If the additional explanatory variables are not relevant in explaining the variation of Y_i, then, in the population, SSR_K and SSR_Q would be the same and the observed difference between them would be entirely due to sampling error. If the null hypothesis is true, then it can be shown[4] that

(10.45)
$$\frac{(\text{SSR}_Q - \text{SSR}_K)/(Q - K)}{\text{SSE}_Q/(n - Q)} \sim F_{Q-K, n-Q}.$$

This can be used to test H_0 at a specified level of significance. It is not difficult to show that

$$\text{SSR}_Q \geq \text{SSR}_K$$

so that the expression in (10.45) can never be negative. An implication of this is

that

$$\frac{\text{SSR}_Q}{\text{SST}} \geq \frac{\text{SSR}_K}{\text{SST}};$$

that is,

$$R_Q^2 \geq R_K^2.$$

[4] See, e.g., A. S. Goldberger, *Econometric Theory* (New York: Wiley, 1964), pp. 174–175.

This means that adding new explanatory variables into a regression equation can never result in a reduction in the value of the coefficient of determination. However, this is not necessarily true of $\bar{R}^2$.

EXAMPLE   In a paper on the short-run consumption function for the United States,[5] two of the proposed functions were

$$C_t = \beta_1 + \beta_2 Y_t + \varepsilon_t$$

and

$$C_t = \beta_1 + \beta_2 Y_t + \beta_3 C_{t-1} + \beta_4 L_{t-1} + \varepsilon_t,$$

where C = consumption, Y = income, and L = liquid assets. Let us test the hypothesis

$$H_0: \quad \beta_3 = \beta_4 = 0$$

against the alternative that H_0 is not true at, say, the 1% level of significance. To use the F test of (10.45), we have to calculate

$$F = \left[\frac{\mathrm{SSR}_Q - \mathrm{SSR}_K}{\mathrm{SSE}_Q} \right]\left[\frac{n - Q}{Q - K} \right].$$

We have $n = 31$, $Q = 4$, $K = 2$. The values of SSR and SSE are not given in the paper but can be determined from the values of $\bar{R}^2$'s, which are

$$\bar{R}_Q^2 = 0.984 \quad \text{and} \quad \bar{R}_K^2 = 0.944.$$

First, we find the values of "uncorrected" R^2's. Since

$$\bar{R}_K^2 = R_K^2 - \frac{K-1}{n-K}(1 - R_K^2),$$

we can solve for R_K^2 to get

$$R_K^2 = \frac{(n-K)\bar{R}_K^2 + (K-1)}{n-1} = 0.946$$

and, similarly,

$$R_Q^2 = 0.986.$$

The value of the appropriate F statistic then is

$$F = \frac{(\mathrm{SSR}_Q/\mathrm{SST}) - (\mathrm{SSR}_K/\mathrm{SST})}{1 - (\mathrm{SSR}_Q/\mathrm{SST})}\left[\frac{n-Q}{Q-K} \right] = \left[\frac{R_Q^2 - R_K^2}{1 - R_Q^2} \right]\left[\frac{n-Q}{Q-K} \right] = 38.57.$$

Since the tabulated value of $F_{2,\,27}$ at the 1% level of significance is 5.49, the null hypothesis has to be rejected. That is, the evidence strongly suggests that the addition of lagged consumption and lagged liquid assets contributes to the explanation of variations in current consumption.

Another hypothesis that is sometimes of interest is

$$H_0: \quad \beta_j = \beta_k \quad (j \neq k),$$

[5] Arnold Zellner, "The Short-Run Consumption Function," *Econometrica*, Vol. 25, October 1957, pp. 552–567.

which can be tested against a one-sided or a two-sided alternative. For instance, one form of the aggregate consumption function proposed in the literature is

$$C_t = \beta_1 + \beta_2 W_t + \beta_3 P_t + \beta_4 C_{t-1} + \varepsilon_t,$$

where C = consumption, W = wage income, and P = nonwage income. An interesting hypothesis is that the marginal propensity to consume of the wage earners is equal to that of the nonwage earners, i.e., that $\beta_2 = \beta_3$. To test the hypothesis that two regression coefficients are equal, we consider the distribution of the difference of the corresponding least squares estimators. In general we have

$$E(\hat{\beta}_j - \hat{\beta}_k) = \beta_j - \beta_k$$

and $$\text{Var}(\hat{\beta}_j - \hat{\beta}_k) = \text{Var}(\hat{\beta}_j) + \text{Var}(\hat{\beta}_k) - 2\,\text{Cov}(\hat{\beta}_j, \hat{\beta}_k).$$

Thus, if the null hypthesis is true,

$$(\hat{\beta}_j - \hat{\beta}_k) \sim N(0, \sigma^2_{\hat{\beta}_j - \hat{\beta}_k}).$$

An unbiased estimator of $\sigma^2_{\hat{\beta}_j - \hat{\beta}_k}$, say, $s^2_{\hat{\beta}_j - \hat{\beta}_k}$, can be obtained by using s^2 as an estimator of σ^2. It then follows that

(10.46) $$\frac{\hat{\beta}_j - \hat{\beta}_k}{s_{\hat{\beta}_j - \hat{\beta}_k}} \sim t_{n-K}.$$

If the value of this statistic is significantly different from zero, the hypothesis that the two regression coefficients are equal is to be rejected. A test of the hypothesis that more than two regression coefficients are equal is described by Goldberger.[6]

A hypothesis which is similar to the preceding one is the proposition that the sum of two regression coefficients is equal to a given number. For instance, in the Cobb-Douglas production function

$$Y_i = \beta_1 + \beta_2 X_{i2} + \beta_3 X_{i3} + \varepsilon_i,$$

where Y_i = log output, X_{i2} = log labor input, and X_{i3} = log capital input, the hypothesis of constant returns to scale is equivalent to the hypothesis

$$H_0: \quad \beta_2 + \beta_3 = 1.$$

In general, the hypothesis

$$H_0: \quad \beta_j + \beta_k = a$$

can be tested by noting that

(10.47) $$\left[\frac{\hat{\beta}_j + \hat{\beta}_k - a}{s_{\hat{\beta}_j + \hat{\beta}_k}}\right] \sim t_{n-k},$$

where $$s_{\hat{\beta}_j + \hat{\beta}_k} = \sqrt{s^2_{\hat{\beta}_j} + s^2_{\hat{\beta}} + 2\,\text{Est. Cov}(\hat{\beta}_j, \hat{\beta}_k)}.$$

This test can easily be extended to a sum of more than two regression coefficients.

---

[6] Goldberger, *op. cit.*, p. 175, theorem (7.19).

The final test concerns the equality of two regression equations. In particular, consider a regression equation

$$Y_i = \beta_1 + \beta_2 X_{i2} + \beta_3 X_{i3} + \cdots + \beta_K X_{iK} + \varepsilon_i,$$

which has been estimated from a sample of n observations. Suppose now that we obtain $m \, (> K)$ additional observations and wish to test the hypothesis that the additional observations come from the same population as the first n observations. For example, data on the aggregate consumption function frequently cover the prewar as well as the postwar period. If we concede the possibility that the parameters of the postwar consumption function may be different from those of the prewar consumption function, we would test the null hypothesis that the parameters of the consumption function have *not* changed. In particular, we may write

$$Y_i = \beta_1 + \beta_2 X_{i2} + \beta_3 X_{i3} + \cdots + \beta_K X_{iK} + \varepsilon_i \quad (i = 1, 2, \ldots, n)$$

and

$$Y_i = \gamma_1 + \gamma_2 X_{i2} + \gamma_3 X_{i3} + \cdots + \gamma_K X_{iK} + \varepsilon_i \quad (i = n + 1, n + 2, \ldots, n + m).$$

The null hypothesis then would be

$$H_0: \quad \beta_1 = \gamma_1, \quad \beta_2 = \gamma_2, \quad \ldots, \quad \beta_K = \gamma_K.$$

This is to be tested against the hypothesis that H_0 is not true. The derivation of the appropriate test is described in the literature.[7] The relevant test statistic is obtained by applying the least squares estimation method to the first set of data $(i = 1, 2, \ldots, n)$, to the second set of data $(i = n + 1, n + 2, \ldots, n + m)$, and to the two sets of data combined $(i = 1, 2, \ldots, n + m)$. To estimate the regression coefficients from the combined set of data, let us write the regression equation as

$$Y_i = \delta_1 + \delta_2 X_{i2} + \delta_3 X_{i3} + \cdots + \delta_K X_{iK} + \varepsilon_i \quad (i = 1, 2, \ldots, n + m).$$

Further, let us denote the sum of squares of the least squares residuals as follows:

$$\text{SSE}_1 = \sum_{i=1}^{n} (Y_i - \hat{\beta}_1 - \hat{\beta}_2 X_{i2} - \hat{\beta}_3 X_{i3} - \cdots - \hat{\beta}_K X_{iK})^2,$$

$$\text{SSE}_2 = \sum_{i=n+1}^{n+m} (Y_i - \hat{\gamma}_1 - \hat{\gamma}_2 X_{i2} - \hat{\gamma}_3 X_{i3} - \cdots - \hat{\gamma}_K X_{iK})^2,$$

and $\quad \text{SSE}_C = \sum_{i=1}^{n+m} (Y_i - \hat{\delta}_1 - \hat{\delta}_2 X_{i2} - \hat{\delta}_3 X_{i3} - \cdots - \hat{\delta}_K X_{iK})^2.$

It has been shown, then, that

(10.48) $$\frac{(\text{SSE}_C - \text{SSE}_1 - \text{SSE}_2)/K}{(\text{SSE}_1 + \text{SSE}_2)/(n + m - 2K)} \sim F_{K, \, n+m-2K}.$$

[7] See, e.g., Johnston, *op. cit.*, pp. 136–138.

This can be used in testing H_0, but there are two points to be noted:

1. The test statistic in (10.48) is applicable only if the number of additional observations exceeds the number of explanatory variables *plus* one; i.e., if $m > K$. If $m < K$, a somewhat different test must be used.[8]
2. The formulation of the hypothesis leading to (10.48) is such that it allows for *all* of the regression parameters to change as we go from one set of data to another. Tests of the hypothesis involving only *some* of the regression coefficients will be described in Section 11-1 dealing with binary variables.

Prediction

Having discussed some of the most useful tests that can be carried out with the help of a multiple regression model, we turn our attention to the problem of *forecasting* the value of the dependent variable for a given set of values of the explanatory variables. More formally, let the given values of the explanatory variables be $X_{02}, X_{03}, \ldots, X_{0K}$, and let the corresponding value of the dependent variable be Y_0. We are interested in forecasting Y_0. As pointed out in connection with the simple regression model, the best predictor of Y_0 is $E(Y_0)$ because the variance of Y_0 around $E(Y_0)$ is smaller than around any other point. Since $E(Y_0)$ is not known, we use $\hat{Y}_0$, the least squares fitted value of Y_0, in its place. Since

$$\hat{Y}_0 = \hat{\beta}_1 + \hat{\beta}_2 X_{02} + \hat{\beta}_3 X_{03} + \cdots + \hat{\beta}_K X_{0K},$$

it follows that $\hat{Y}_0$ is normally distributed with mean

$$E(\hat{Y}_0) = \beta_1 + \beta_2 X_{02} + \beta_3 X_{03} + \cdots + \beta_K X_{0K}.$$

The variance of $\hat{Y}_0$ is, according to (10.37),

$$\begin{aligned}
\text{Var}(\hat{Y}_0) &= \sigma_{\hat{Y}_0}^2 \\
&= \sum_k (X_{0k} - \bar{X}_k)^2 \, \text{Var}(\hat{\beta}_k) + 2 \sum_{j<k} (X_{0j} - \bar{X}_j)(X_{0k} - \bar{X}_k) \, \text{Cov}(\hat{\beta}_j, \hat{\beta}_k) \\
&\quad + \frac{\sigma^2}{n} \qquad\qquad\qquad\qquad (j, k = 2, 3, \ldots, K; \quad j < k),
\end{aligned}$$

or, in matrix notation,

$$\text{Var}(\hat{Y}_0) = \sigma^2 \left[(\mathbf{X}_0 - \bar{\mathbf{X}})'(\mathbf{X}'\mathbf{X})^{-1}(\mathbf{X}_0 - \bar{\mathbf{X}}) + \frac{1}{n} \right],$$

where

$$(\mathbf{X}_0 - \bar{\mathbf{X}}) = \begin{bmatrix} X_{02} - \bar{X}_2 \\ X_{03} - \bar{X}_3 \\ \vdots \\ X_{0K} - \bar{X}_K \end{bmatrix}.$$

[8] *Ibid.*, p. 138, eq. (4-65).

We are, of course, primarily interested in the *forecast error*, that is, in $(Y_0 - \hat{Y}_0)$. This random variable is normally distributed with mean

$$E(Y_0 - \hat{Y}_0) = 0$$

and variance

$$\sigma_F^2 = \text{Var}(Y_0 - \hat{Y}_0) = \text{Var}(Y_0) + \text{Var}(\hat{Y}_0) - 2\,\text{Cov}(Y_0, \hat{Y}_0).$$

Now $\text{Var}(Y_0) = \sigma^2,$

$\text{Var}(\hat{Y}_0) = \sigma_{\hat{Y}_0}^2,$

and

$$-2\,\text{Cov}(Y_0, \hat{Y}_0) = -2E[Y_0 - E(Y_0)][\hat{Y}_0 - E(\hat{Y}_0)]$$

$$= -2E\varepsilon_0[\hat{Y}_0 - E(Y_0)] = 0.$$

Therefore,

(10.49) $$\sigma_F^2 = \sigma^2 + \frac{\sigma^2}{n} + \sum_k (X_{0k} - \bar{X}_k)^2\,\text{Var}(\hat{\beta}_k)$$

$$+ 2\sum_{j<k}(X_{0j} - \bar{X}_j)(X_{0k} - \bar{X}_k)\,\text{Cov}(\hat{\beta}_j, \hat{\beta}_k),$$

or, in matrix notation,

(10.49a) $$\sigma_F^2 = \sigma^2\left[1 + \frac{1}{n} + (\mathbf{X_0} - \bar{\mathbf{X}})'(\mathbf{X'X})^{-1}(\mathbf{X_0} - \bar{\mathbf{X}})\right].$$

As with the simple regression model, the shorter the distance between the given values of the explanatory variables and their respective sample means, the smaller the variance of the forecast error. An unbiased estimator of σ_F^2 can be obtained by replacing σ^2 by s^2. If we denote the resulting estimator by s_F^2, then

(10.50) $$\frac{Y_0 - \hat{Y}_0}{s_F} \sim t_{n-K}.$$

From this result, we can construct a forecast interval that will contain the actual value of Y_0 with whatever probability we choose. Designating one *minus* the chosen probability level by λ $(0 < \lambda < 1)$, we have

$$\hat{Y}_0 - t_{n-K,\lambda/2}s_F \le Y_0 \le \hat{Y}_0 + t_{n-K,\lambda/2}s_F.$$

The expression in (10.50) can also be used to test the hypothesis that a new observation, say, $(n + 1)$th, comes from the same population as the n observations that were used for estimating the regression parameters.

EXAMPLE   In the first example of this section, we estimated a regression equation describing the demand for oranges. The sample consisted of twelve observations on the quantity of oranges sold, their price, and the amount spent on advertising (see Table 10–1). The estimated regression equation is

$$\hat{Y}_i = 117.532 - 1.326X_{i2} + 11.237X_{i2},$$

where Y_i = quantity of oranges sold, X_{i2} = price, and X_{i3} = advertising expenditure. Now suppose that no oranges are sold until a new shipment arrives, which is several weeks later. Then, the record for the first day of trading shows

$$Y_0 = 100, \qquad X_{02} = 80, \qquad \text{and} \qquad X_{03} = 7.$$

The problem is to decide whether the demand function has changed since the time of the previous shipment of oranges. Here, we have

$$\hat{Y}_0 = 117.532 - 1.326 \times 80 + 11.237 \times 7 = 90.111.$$

This is the "forecast" value of Y. The estimated variance of the forecast error is

$$s_F^2 = \left[s^2 + \frac{s^2}{n} + (X_{02} - \bar{X}_2)^2 s_{\hat{\beta}_2}^2 + (X_{03} - \bar{X}_3)^2 s_{\hat{\beta}_3}^2 \right.$$
$$\left. + 2(X_{02} - \bar{X}_2)(X_{03} - \bar{X}_3)\text{Est. Cov}(\hat{\beta}_2,\hat{\beta}_3) \right].$$

Now, from the previous calculations, we have

$$s^2 = 20.586, \qquad\qquad\qquad s_{\hat{\beta}_2}^2 = 0.012476,$$

$$\bar{X}_2 = 70, \qquad\qquad\qquad\qquad s_{\hat{\beta}_3}^2 = 5.7761,$$

$$\bar{X}_3 = 6.7, \qquad\qquad \text{Est. Cov}(\hat{\beta}_2,\hat{\beta}_3) = 0.138628.$$

Therefore,

$$s_F^2 = 20.586\left[1 + \frac{1}{12} + (80 - 70)^2 \times 0.012476 + (7 - 6.7)^2 \times 5.7761 \right.$$

$$\left. + 2 \times (80 - 70) \times (7 - 6.7) \times 0.138628 \right]$$

$$= 75.808974,$$

$$s_F = 8.706.$$

The 95% confidence interval for Y_0 can be constructed by noting that the tabulated value of $t_{9,0.025}$ is 2.262. Therefore we have

$$90.111 - 2.262 \times 8.706 \leq Y_0 \leq 90.111 + 2.262 \times 8.706$$

or

$$70.418 \leq Y_0 \leq 109.804.$$

The observed value of Y_0 is 100, which falls well within the 95% interval.

Change in the Units of Measurement

Let us now consider the effect of *changing the units of measurement* on the previously derived results. Let

$$Y_i, X_{i2}, X_{i3}, \ldots, X_{iK}$$

denote the values of the respective variables measured in terms of some "original" units, and let

$$Y_i^*, X_{i2}^*, X_{i3}^*, \ldots, X_{iK}^*$$

denote the values of these variables in terms of some "new" units. First, we shall discuss the case

$$Y_i^* = d_Y Y_i,$$

$$X_{i2}^* = d_2 X_{i2}$$

$$X_{i3}^* = d_3 X_{i3},$$

$$\vdots$$

$$X_{iK}^* = d_K X_{iK},$$

where the d's are some known positive numbers. (Note that when for any particular variable $d = 1$, no change in the units of measurement has occurred.) This case of multiplicative changes in the units of measurement covers changes such as switching from cents to dollars ($d = 0.01$), or expressing a variable in terms of a simple index (for example, $d_k = 1/X_{1k}$). The sample means and second moments for the "starred" variables are

$$\bar{Y}^* = d_Y \bar{Y},$$

$$\bar{X}_k^* = d_k \bar{X}_k,$$

$$m_{jk}^* = \sum_i (d_j X_{ij} - d_j \bar{X}_j)(d_k X_{ik} - d_k \bar{X}_k) = d_j d_k m_{jk},$$

$$m_{Yk}^* = d_Y d_k m_{Yk},$$

$$m_{YY}^* = d_Y^2 m_{YY} \qquad (j, k = 2, 3, \ldots, K).$$

Let us see how these changes affect the values of the estimated coefficients and their standard errors. For the regression model with two explanatory variables we have, from (10.11), (10.12), and (10.13),

$$\hat{\beta}_2^* = \frac{(d_Y d_2 m_{Y2})(d_3^2 m_{33}) - (d_Y d_3 m_{Y3})(d_2 d_3 m_{23})}{(d_2^2 m_{22})(d_3^2 m_{33}) - (d_2 d_3 m_{23})^2} = \left(\frac{d_Y}{d_2}\right)\hat{\beta}_2,$$

$$\hat{\beta}_3^* = \frac{(d_Y d_3 m_{Y3})(d_2^2 m_{22}) - (d_Y d_2 m_{Y2})(d_2 d_3 m_{23})}{(d_2^2 m_{22})(d_3^2 m_{33}) - (d_2 d_3 m_{23})^2} = \left(\frac{d_Y}{d_3}\right)\hat{\beta}_3,$$

and $$\hat{\beta}_1^* = d_Y \bar{Y} - \hat{\beta}_2^*(d_2 \bar{X}_2) - \hat{\beta}_3^*(d_3 \bar{X}_3) = d_Y \hat{\beta}_1.$$

For the estimator of σ^2 we have, from (10.34a),

$$s^{*2} = \frac{1}{n - K}(m_{YY}^* - \hat{\beta}_2^* m_{Y2}^* - \hat{\beta}_3^* m_{Y3}^*) = d_Y^2 s^2.$$

Therefore, by reference to (10.24) and (10.25),

$$s_{\hat{\beta}_2}^{*2} = \frac{(d_Y^2 s^2)(d_3^2 m_{33})}{(d_2^2 m_{22})(d_3^2 m_{33}) - (d_2 d_3 m_{23})^2} = \left(\frac{d_Y}{d_2}\right)^2 s_{\hat{\beta}_2}^2,$$

$$s_{\hat{\beta}_3}^{*2} = \frac{(d_Y^2 s^2)(d_2^2 m_{22})}{(d_2^2 m_{22})(d_3^2 m_{33}) - (d_2 d_3 m_{23})^2} = \left(\frac{d_Y}{d_3}\right)^2 s_{\hat{\beta}_3}^2,$$

and, by reference to (10.31),

$$s_{\hat{\beta}_1}^{*2} = (d_2 \bar{X}_2)^2 \left(\frac{d_Y}{d_2}\right)^2 s_{\hat{\beta}_2}^2 + (d_3 \bar{X}_3)^2 \left(\frac{d_Y}{d_3}\right)^2 s_{\hat{\beta}_3}^2$$

$$+ 2(d_2 \bar{X}_2)(d_3 \bar{X}_3)\left[\frac{(d_Y^2 s^2)(d_2 d_3 m_{23})}{(d_2^2 m_{22})(d_3^2 m_{33}) - (d_2 d_3 m_{23})^2}\right] + \frac{d_Y^2 s^2}{n} = d_Y^2 s_{\hat{\beta}_1}^2.$$

This means that the values of the estimated regression coefficients and of their standard errors are affected by changes in the units of measurement. However, these changes do not affect the value of the t statistic, which is used for testing the hypothesis that $\beta_k = 0$ ($k = 1, 2, \ldots, K$):

$$\frac{\hat{\beta}_k^*}{s_{\hat{\beta}_k}^*} = \frac{(d_Y/d_k)\hat{\beta}_k}{(d_Y/d_k)s_{\hat{\beta}_k}} = \frac{\hat{\beta}_k}{s_{\hat{\beta}_k}}.$$

The same is also true of the F statistic:

$$\frac{\text{SSR}^*/(K-1)}{\text{SSE}^*/(n-K)} = \left[\frac{n-K}{K-1}\right]\left[\frac{\text{SST}^* - \text{SSE}^*}{\text{SSE}^*}\right] = \left[\frac{n-K}{K-1}\right]\left[\frac{m_{YY}^* - (n-K)s^*}{(n-K)s^*}\right]$$

$$= \left[\frac{n-K}{K-1}\right]\left[\frac{(d_Y^2 m_{YY}) - (n-K)(d_Y^2 s^2)}{(n-K)(d_Y^2 s^2)}\right] = \frac{\text{SSR}/(K-1)}{\text{SSE}/(n-K)}.$$

Finally, the value of R^2 is also unchanged:

$$R^{*2} = 1 - \frac{\text{SSE}^*}{\text{SST}^*} = 1 - \frac{(n-K)d_Y^2 s^2}{d_Y^2 m_{YY}} = R^2.$$

It can be demonstrated that these results apply to regression equations with *any* number of explanatory variables as well.

EXAMPLE   In an earlier example we estimated the demand equation for oranges as

$$Y_i = 117.532 - 1.326 X_{i2} + 11.237 X_{i3} + e_i, \qquad R^2 = 0.981,$$
$$(21.264) \quad (0.112) \qquad\quad (2.403)$$

where Y_i = quantity in pounds, X_{i2} = price in cents, and X_{i3} = advertising expenditure in dollars. Suppose we wish to measure the price (X_{i2}) in dollars instead of cents. Then, we have

$$d_Y = 1, \qquad d_2 = 0.01, \qquad \text{and} \qquad d_3 = 1.$$

The estimated regression equation becomes

$$Y_i = 117.532 - 132.6 X_{i2}^* + 11.237 X_{i3} + e_i, \qquad R^2 = 0.981.$$
$$(21.264) \quad (11.2) \qquad\quad (2.403)$$

Sometimes the change in the units of measurement is additive rather than multiplicative. This happens frequently when the variables enter into the regression equation in a logarithmic form. For instance, in the case of the Cobb-Douglas production function, the traditional model is

$$Y_i = \beta_1 + \beta_2 X_{i2} + \beta_3 X_{i3} + \varepsilon_i,$$

where $Y_i = \log$ output, $X_{i2} = \log$ labor input, and $X_{i3} = \log$ capital input. Then, if the units of measuring the labor input are changed, say, from thousands of workers to millions of workers, we have

$$X_{i2}^* = \log L_i^* = \log d_L L_i = \log d_L + \log L_i = (\log d_L) + X_{i2}.$$

In general, let

$$Y_i^* = g_Y + Y_i,$$

$$X_{i2}^* = g_2 + X_{i2},$$

$$X_{i3}^* = g_3 + X_{i3}.$$

$$\vdots$$

$$X_{iK}^* = g_K + X_{iK}.$$

In this case,

$$\bar{Y}^* = g_Y + \bar{Y},$$

$$\bar{X}_k^* = g_k + \bar{X}_k,$$

$$m_{jk}^* = m_{jk},$$

$$m_{Yk}^* = m_{Yk},$$

$$m_{YY}^* = m_{YY} \qquad (j, k = 2, 3, \ldots, K).$$

Therefore, $$\hat{\beta}_k^* = \hat{\beta}_k \qquad \text{for } k = 2, 3, \ldots, K;$$

but

$$\hat{\beta}_1^* = \bar{Y}^* - \hat{\beta}_2^* \bar{X}_2^* - \hat{\beta}_3^* \bar{X}_3^* - \cdots - \hat{\beta}_K^* \bar{X}_K^*$$

$$= \hat{\beta}_1 + (g_Y - \hat{\beta}_2 g_2 - \hat{\beta}_3 g_3 - \cdots - \hat{\beta}_K g_K).$$

That is, the estimates of the regression slopes remain unaffected but the estimate of the intercept is changed. Similarly, the estimates of the variances of $\hat{\beta}_2^*$, $\hat{\beta}_3^*, \ldots, \hat{\beta}_K^*$ remain unchanged but the estimated variance of $\hat{\beta}_1^*$ will change. The values of t statistics, of the F statistic, and of R^2 stay the same.

To sum up, the general principle concerning units of measurement is that a linear transformation of the variables in a linear regression equation does not affect the values of the essential test statistics and of R^2. The values of the estimated regression coefficients might change, but the change can easily be determined by reference to the parameters of the linear transformation.

A Note on Basic Assumptions and Data

In Chapter 8 we discussed the consequences of violating the basic assumptions of the classical normal linear regression model in the context of simple regression. The conclusions reached there hold either completely or only with simple and obvious modifications in the context of multiple regression. In particular, the remarks concerning the assumption of normal distribution and of zero mean of ε_i apply equally to the multiple regression model. With respect to heteroskedasticity, the discussion and the findings of Section 8–1 can be extended to the multiple regression case simply by allowing for more than one explanatory variable. The same is true of the results for models with autoregressive disturbances (Section 8–2) and for models with stochastic regressors (Section 8–3).

The problems of data deficiency studied in Chapter 9 also arise in multiple regression models. The derivations and the statements made in the context of simple regression models can, for the most part, be extended to multiple regression without much difficulty.

10–3 Multicollinearity

By assumption (10.8) of the classical normal linear regression model we require that none of the explanatory variables be perfectly correlated with any other explanatory variable *or* with any linear combination of other explanatory variables. When this assumption is violated, we speak of *perfect multicollinearity*. On the other hand, whenever all explanatory variables are uncorrelated with each other, we speak of *absence of multicollinearity*. The cases in between are then described by various degrees of multicollinearity. Of particular interest are cases of a *high degree of multicollinearity*, which arise whenever one explanatory variable is highly correlated with another explanatory variable *or* with a linear combination of other explanatory variables.

Before discussing multicollinearity in detail, two points should be made clear.

1. Multicollinearity is a question of degree and not of kind. The meaningful distinction is not between the presence and the absence of multicollinearity, but between its various degrees.
2. Since multicollinearity refers to the condition of the explanatory variables that are assumed to be nonstochastic, it is a feature of the sample and not of the population.[9]

Therefore, we do not "test for multicollinearity" but can, if we wish, measure its degree in any particular sample. In the discussion that follows, we will be concerned with the implication of various degrees of multicollinearity for estimation of the regression coefficients.

---

[9] If the explanatory variables are stochastic and there is an underlying relation among them in the population, such a relation should be specified as a part of the model. If such a relation does not exist in the population, we still may (and generally will) find *some* relation between the explanatory variables in the sample. Then again, multicollinearity is a feature of the sample, not of the population.

Absence of Multicollinearity

Let us start with the case of *no multicollinearity*, when the explanatory variables are uncorrelated with each other. In this case the matrix $(\mathbf{X}'\mathbf{X})$ is diagonal. In a regression model with two explanatory variables

$$Y_i = \beta_1 + \beta_2 X_{i2} + \beta_3 X_{i3} + \varepsilon_i,$$

where $m_{23} = 0$, the least squares normal equations for $\hat{\beta}_2$ and $\hat{\beta}_3$ become

$$m_{Y2} = \hat{\beta}_2 m_{22}, \qquad m_{Y3} = \hat{\beta}_3 m_{33}.$$

Therefore,
$$\hat{\beta}_2 = \frac{m_{Y2}}{m_{22}}, \qquad \hat{\beta}_3 = \frac{m_{Y3}}{m_{33}}.$$

These formulas are exactly the same as those for the *simple* regression of Y_i on X_{i2}, and of Y_i on X_{i3}.

The preceding result seems to suggest that, when X_{i2} and X_{i3} are uncorrelated, we might abandon the multiple regression model with two explanatory variables and replace it by two simple regression models

$$Y_i = \alpha_2 + \beta_2 X_{i2} + \varepsilon_i.$$

and
$$Y_i = \alpha_3 + \beta_3 X_{i3} + \varepsilon_i.$$

However, this would create difficulties. In the first place, neither one of the simple regressions will enable us to get an estimator of the regression constant β_1, although this is not so important since the least squares estimator of β_1 is simply

$$\hat{\beta}_1 = \bar{Y} - \hat{\beta}_2 \bar{X}_2 - \hat{\beta}_3 \bar{X}_3.$$

More important is that using the simple regressions for estimating the variances of $\hat{\beta}_2$ and $\hat{\beta}_3$ results in *biased* estimates. This can be seen as follows. From (10.24) we know that the variance of $\hat{\beta}_2$ is

$$\text{Var}(\hat{\beta}_2) = \frac{\sigma^2 m_{33}}{m_{22}m_{33} - m_{23}^2},$$

which for $m_{23} = 0$ becomes

$$\text{Var}(\hat{\beta}_2) = \frac{\sigma^2}{m_{22}}.$$

Now the estimator of $\text{Var}(\hat{\beta}_2)$ based on the simple regression is

$$s_{\hat{\beta}_2}^2 = \frac{s_2^2}{m_{22}},$$

where
$$s_2^2 = \frac{1}{n-2} \sum_i [(Y_i - \bar{Y}) - \hat{\beta}_2(X_{i2} - \bar{X}_2)]^2.$$

Taking the mathematical expectation of s_2^2, we get

$$E(s_2^2) = \frac{1}{n-2} E \sum_i [\beta_2(X_{i2} - \bar{X}_2) + \beta_3(X_{i3} - \bar{X}_3)$$

$$+ (\varepsilon_i - \bar{\varepsilon}) - \hat{\beta}_2(X_{i2} - \bar{X}_2)]^2$$

$$= \frac{1}{n-2} [m_{22}\text{Var}(\hat{\beta}_2) + \beta_3^2 m_{33} - 2m_{22}\text{Var}(\hat{\beta}_2) + (n-1)\sigma^2]$$

$$= \frac{1}{n-2} [(n-2)\sigma^2 + \beta_3^2 m_{33}],$$

so that

$$E(s_{\hat{\beta}_2}^2) = \text{Var}(\hat{\beta}_2) + \frac{\beta_3^2 m_{33}}{m_{22}(n-2)}.$$

Similarly,

$$E(s_{\hat{\beta}_3}^2) = \text{Var}(\hat{\beta}_3) + \frac{\beta_2^2 m_{22}}{m_{33}(n-2)}.$$

This means that the simple regression estimators of the variances of $\hat{\beta}_2$ and $\hat{\beta}_3$ have an upward bias. This result can be generalized to regression models with any number of mutually uncorrelated explanatory variables.

Perfect Multicollinearity

Next we turn our attention to the case of *perfect multicollinearity*. For the multiple regression model with two explanatory variables, perfect multicollinearity means that we can write

(10.51) $$X_{i2} = a + bX_{i3},$$

where a and b are some fixed numbers and $b \neq 0$. In this case, the sample coefficient of correlation between X_{i2} and X_{i3} is

$$r_{23} = \frac{\sum (a + bX_{i3} - a - b\bar{X}_3)(X_{i3} - \bar{X}_3)}{\sqrt{\sum (a + bX_{i3} - a - b\bar{X}_3)^2}\sqrt{\sum (X_{i3} - \bar{X}_3)^2}} = \frac{bm_{33}}{\sqrt{b^2 m_{33}}\sqrt{m_{33}}},$$

so that $$r_{23}^2 = 1.$$

Consider now the least squares estimators of the regression coefficients. The least squares normal equations for the model with two explanatory variables are

$$m_{Y2} = \hat{\beta}_2 m_{22} + \hat{\beta}_3 m_{23},$$

$$m_{Y3} = \hat{\beta}_2 m_{23} + \hat{\beta}_3 m_{33}.$$

But by (10.51) we have

$$m_{Y2} = bm_{Y3},$$

$$m_{22} = b^2 m_{33},$$

$$m_{23} = bm_{33}.$$

Therefore, the least squares normal equations become

$$bm_{Y3} = b(\hat{\beta}_2 bm_{33} + \hat{\beta}_3 m_{33}),$$

$$m_{Y3} = \hat{\beta}_2 bm_{33} + \hat{\beta}_3 m_{33}.$$

This shows that the first normal equation is exactly equal to the second normal equation multiplied by b. Therefore, the two equations are not independent, and the solution for $\hat{\beta}_2$ and $\hat{\beta}_3$ is indeterminate.

Let us now consider the case of three explanatory variables to illustrate a special feature of multicollinearity that does not show up in the two-variable case. In this case the presence of perfect multicollinearity means that we can write

(10.52) $$X_{i2} = a + b_3 X_{i3} + b_4 X_{i4},$$

where a, b_3, and b_4 are some fixed numbers. Suppose both b_3 and b_4 are different from zero. The sample coefficient of correlation between X_{i2} and X_{i3} is

$$r_{23} = \frac{m_{23}}{\sqrt{m_{22}}\sqrt{m_{33}}},$$

$$= \frac{b_3 m_{33} + b_4 m_{34}}{\sqrt{b_3^2 m_{33} + b_4^2 m_{44} + 2b_3 b_4 m_{34}}\sqrt{m_{33}}},$$

$$= \frac{b_3\sqrt{m_{33}} + b_4 r_{34}\sqrt{m_{44}}}{\sqrt{(b_3\sqrt{m_{33}} + b_4 r_{34}\sqrt{m_{44}})^2 + b_4^2 m_{44}(1 - r_{34}^2)}},$$

where r_{34} is the sample coefficient of correlation between X_{i3} and X_{i4}. Similarly, the sample coefficient of correlation between X_{i2} and X_{i4} is

$$r_{24} = \frac{b_3 r_{34}\sqrt{m_{33}} + b_4\sqrt{m_{44}}}{\sqrt{(b_3 r_{34}\sqrt{m_{33}} + b_4\sqrt{m_{44}})^2 + b_3^2 m_{33}(1 - r_{34}^2)}}.$$

These results clearly show that the presence of perfect multicollinearity does *not* necessarily mean that the correlation between any two explanatory variables must be perfect, or even particularly high, when the total number of explanatory variables is greater than two. For example, when

$$X_{i2} = X_{i3} + X_{i4},$$

$$m_{33} = m_{44},$$

and $$r_{34} = -0.5,$$

then $$r_{23} = \frac{1 - 0.5}{\sqrt{(1 - 0.5)^2 + (1 - 0.5^2)}} = 0.5$$

and $$r_{24} = \frac{-0.5 + 1}{\sqrt{(-0.5 + 1)^2 + (1 - 0.5^2)}} = 0.5.$$

In this case we have perfect multicollinearity, and yet none of the correlation coefficients is greater than one half in absolute value. This is important because it means that when there are more than two explanatory variables, we cannot simply look at the coefficients of correlation and conclude that the sample is *not* perfectly (or highly) multicollinear. On the other hand, if the correlation between any one pair of explanatory variables is perfect, then there *is* perfect multicollinearity present in the sample. For perfect correlation between, say, X_{i2} and X_{i3}, implies that X_{i2} is an exact linear function of X_{i3} so that we can write

$$X_{i2} = a + b_3 X_{i3} \quad (b_3 \neq 0),$$

which is equivalent to (10.52) with $b_4 = 0$. Thus, *perfect correlation between two explanatory variables is a sufficient but not necessary condition for the presence of perfect multicollinearity* in the sample when the number of explanatory variables exceeds two.

Now let us see what happens to the least squares estimators of the regression coefficients under conditions of perfect multicollinearity when the regression model contains three explanatory variables. The least squares normal equations are

$$m_{Y2} = \hat{\beta}_2 m_{22} + \hat{\beta}_3 m_{23} + \hat{\beta}_4 m_{24},$$
$$m_{Y3} = \hat{\beta}_2 m_{23} + \hat{\beta}_3 m_{33} + \hat{\beta}_4 m_{34},$$
$$m_{Y4} = \hat{\beta}_2 m_{24} + \hat{\beta}_3 m_{34} + \hat{\beta}_4 m_{44}.$$

But from (10.52) we have

$$m_{Y2} = b_3 m_{Y3} + b_4 m_{Y4},$$
$$m_{22} = b_3^2 m_{33} + b_4^2 m_{44} + 2b_3 b_4 m_{34},$$
$$m_{23} = b_3 m_{33} + b_4 m_{34},$$
$$m_{24} = b_3 m_{34} + b_4 m_{44}.$$

Substitution of these expressions into the least squares normal equations leads to

$$b_3 m_{Y3} + b_4 m_{Y4} = \hat{\beta}_2 (b_3^2 m_{33} + b_4^2 m_{44} + 2b_3 b_4 m_{34}) + \hat{\beta}_3 (b_3 m_{33} + b_4 m_{34})$$
$$+ \hat{\beta}_4 (b_3 m_{34} + b_4 m_{44}),$$
$$m_{Y3} = \hat{\beta}_2 (b_3 m_{33} + b_4 m_{34}) + \hat{\beta}_3 m_{33} + \hat{\beta}_4 m_{34},$$
$$m_{Y4} = \hat{\beta}_2 (b_3 m_{34} + b_4 m_{44}) + \hat{\beta}_3 m_{34} + \hat{\beta}_4 m_{44}.$$

Thus the first normal equation is simply equal to the second normal equation multiplied by b_3 *plus* the third normal equation multiplied by b_4. Therefore, under perfect multicollinearity, the three normal equations are not independent and cannot be solved by $\hat{\beta}_2$, $\hat{\beta}_3$, and $\hat{\beta}_4$. This result can be extended to regression models with any number of explanatory variables. Since by (10.14) the vector of the least squares estimators of the regression coefficients is

$$\hat{\beta} = (X'X)^{-1}(X'Y),$$

the existence of an exact linear relation between the explanatory variables means that one of the columns of $(X'X)$ is an exact linear function of another one or more columns. Thus $(X'X)$ is a singular matrix and its inverse does not exist.

Given that the least squares estimators of the regression coefficients are indeterminate when there is perfect multicollinearity in the sample, what else can be done? Unfortunately, not very much. When there is perfect multicollinearity, the sample simply does not give us any information about the response of the dependent variable to changes in one of the explanatory variables while "holding the remaining explanatory variables constant." The traditional suggestion has been to use information about the regression coefficients from sources other than the sample on hand. For instance, if in the model

$$Y_i = \beta_1 + \beta_2 X_{i2} + \beta_3 X_{i3} + \varepsilon_i,$$

the two explanatory variables are perfectly correlated but we know—or are willing to assume—that

$$\frac{\beta_3}{\beta_2} = k,$$

where k is a known fixed number, then estimation of the regression coefficients becomes possible. By substituting

$$\beta_3 = k\beta_2$$

into the regression model, we obtain

$$Y_i = \beta_1 + \beta_2 X_{i2} + k\beta_2 X_{i3} + \varepsilon_i$$

or $$Y_i = \beta_1 + \beta_2 Z_i + \varepsilon_i,$$

where Z_i is measured by $(X_{i2} + kX_{i3})$. In this case, we can obtain a least squares estimator of β_1 and β_2, and infer an estimator of β_3. These estimators can be viewed as conditional upon the given value of k. If there are several values of k that appear as likely candidates, we may obtain a set of different estimators, each conditional upon a different value of k.[10]

Cases in which we know the ratio of, or have some other exact information about, two regression coefficients are relatively rare. More frequently, we may have an estimate of one or more of the regression coefficients from a different sample. For instance, we may have a sample of time-series observations to estimate a regression model, together with an unbiased estimate of one of the regression coefficients from cross-section survey data. This might be the case in the estimation of a demand function for a particular commodity as a function of price and income. If the observations are made over time, an estimate of the income

---

[10] In a case like this the Bayesian approach to estimation may appear particularly attractive. See, e.g., D. V. Lindley, *Introduction to Probability and Statistics from a Bayesian Viewpoint, Part 2—Inference* (Cambridge, England: The University Press, 1964), Chapter 8.

coefficient is frequently available from a cross-section sample. Suppose the regression model to be estimated is

$$Y_t = \beta_1 + \beta_2 X_{t2} + \beta_3 X_{t3} + \varepsilon_t,$$

and we have an unbiased estimator of β_3, say $\hat{\hat{\beta}}_3$, from an independent cross-section sample. Then, the regression model can be rewritten as

$$(Y_t - \hat{\hat{\beta}}_3 X_{t3}) = \beta_1 + \beta_2 X_{t2} - (\hat{\hat{\beta}}_3 - \beta_3) X_{t3} + \varepsilon_t$$

or

$$Y_t^* = \beta_1 + \beta_2 X_{t2} + u_t.$$

The least squares estimator of $\hat{\beta}_2$ becomes

$$(10.53) \qquad \hat{\beta}_2 = \frac{\sum (Y_t^* - \bar{Y}^*)(X_{t2} - \bar{X}_2)}{\sum (X_{t2} - \bar{X}_2)^2}$$

$$= \frac{\sum (Y_t - \hat{\hat{\beta}}_3 X_{t3} - \bar{Y} + \hat{\hat{\beta}}_3 \bar{X}_3)(X_{t2} - \bar{X}_2)}{\sum (X_{t2} - \bar{X}_2)^2}$$

$$= \frac{m_{Y2} - \hat{\hat{\beta}}_3 m_{23}}{m_{22}}.$$

The mean and the variance of $\hat{\beta}_2$ are

$$(10.54) \qquad E(\hat{\beta}_2) = \frac{1}{m_{22}} E[\beta_2 m_{22} + \beta_3 m_{33} + \sum_t (X_{t2} - \bar{X}_2)\varepsilon_t - \hat{\hat{\beta}}_3 m_{23}] = \beta_2,$$

$$(10.55) \qquad \mathrm{Var}(\hat{\beta}_2) = E(\hat{\beta}_2 - \beta_2)^2$$

$$= \frac{1}{m_{22}^2} E[-(\hat{\hat{\beta}}_3 - \beta_3) m_{23} + \sum_t (X_{t2} - \bar{X}_2)\varepsilon_t]^2$$

$$= \frac{1}{m_{22}^2} [m_{23}^2 \mathrm{Var}(\hat{\hat{\beta}}_3) + \sigma^2 m_{22}]$$

$$= \frac{\sigma^2}{m_{22}} + \frac{m_{23}^2 \mathrm{Var}(\hat{\hat{\beta}}_3)}{m_{22}^2}.$$

Since, under perfect multicollinearity,

$$m_{23}^2 = m_{22} m_{33},$$

the variance of $\hat{\beta}_2$ becomes

$$(10.56) \qquad \mathrm{Var}(\hat{\beta}_2) = \frac{\sigma^2}{m_{22}} + \frac{m_{33} \mathrm{Var}(\hat{\hat{\beta}}_3)}{m_{22}}.$$

In empirical applications the formula for the variance of $\hat{\beta}_2$ has often been simplified by being viewed as conditional upon the given value of $\hat{\hat{\beta}}_3$, which amounts to treating $\hat{\hat{\beta}}_3$ as a fixed number.

An objection to dealing with the multicollinearity problem by obtaining information from sources other than the sample on hand is that it calls for something that should be done in any case. Normally, we suppose that in specifying the regression model and the estimation procedure we use *all* of the available information about the population. There is no reason for us to wait for the presence of perfect multicollinearity before we search for all the relevant information, except when the search is very costly. Had we exhausted all sources of information by the time we came to estimation, the proposed remedy for the multicollinearity problem would not apply. Furthermore, with respect to the use of an estimate from another sample, we might also question the wisdom of using only this information from such a sample and disregarding the rest.

High Degree of Multicollinearity

So far we have considered the two extreme cases of multicollinearity, the case of no multicollinearity and the case of perfect multicollinearity. Neither extreme is very frequent in practical applications, but most data exhibit some—though not perfect—multicollinearity. In a regression model with two explanatory variables, the relation between the explanatory variables in the sample can be described in a general way as

$$(10.57) \qquad\qquad X_{i2} = a + bX_{i3} + v_i,$$

where a and b are some fixed numbers and v_i is a "residual" such that $\sum v_i = \sum v_i X_{i3} = 0$. If we define m_{vv} as

$$m_{vv} = \sum_i v_i^2,$$

then the case of $m_{vv} = 0$ represents perfect multicollinearity, and the case of $m_{vv} = m_{22}$ signifies the absence of multicollinearity. (Note that m_{22} is equal to the maximum attainable value of m_{vv}.) Both of these are special cases of (10.57). The sample coefficient of correlation between X_{i2} and X_{i3} is

$$r_{23} = \frac{\sum (a + bX_{i3} + v_i - a - b\bar{X}_3)(X_{i3} - \bar{X}_3)}{\sqrt{\sum (a + bX_{i3} + v_i - a - b\bar{X}_3)^2}\sqrt{\sum (X_{i3} - \bar{X}_3)^2}}$$

$$= \frac{bm_{33}}{\sqrt{b^2 m_{33} + m_{vv}}\sqrt{m_{33}}}$$

or $\qquad\qquad r_{23}^2 = \dfrac{b^2 m_{33}}{b^2 m_{33} + m_{vv}}.$

When $m_{vv} = 0$, then $r_{23}^2 = 1$; and when $m_{vv} = m_{22}$ (which implies that $b = 0$), then $r_{23}^2 = 0$. Most frequently, m_{vv} will lie between these two extremes, with r_{23}^2 lying between 0 and 1. Consider now the least squares normal equations for the model with two explanatory variables. First, from (10.57) we have

$$m_{Y2} = bm_{Y3} + m_{Yv} \quad \left(\text{where } m_{Yv} = \sum_i (Y_i - \bar{Y})v_i\right),$$

$$m_{22} = b^2 m_{33} + m_{vv},$$

$$m_{23} = bm_{33}.$$

Therefore, the least squares normal equations can be written as

$$bm_{Y3} + m_{Yv} = \hat{\beta}_2(b^2 m_{33} + m_{vv}) + \hat{\beta}_3 b m_{33},$$

$$m_{Y3} = \hat{\beta}_2 b m_{33} + \hat{\beta}_3 m_{33}.$$

When $m_{vv} = 0$ (and therefore $m_{Yv} = 0$), the solution for $\hat{\beta}_2$ and $\hat{\beta}_3$ becomes indeterminate; for all other values of m_{vv} a solution exists. It is easy to see that this is also true for models with more than two explanatory variables. This means that as long as there is no *perfect* multicollinearity (and $n \geq K$), we can always obtain a determinate solution for the least squares estimators of the regression coefficients, unless we run into the problem of rounding errors.

Let us now examine the connection between the degree of multicollinearity and the properties of the least squares estimators of the regression coefficients. Under the basic assumptions of the classical normal linear regression model, the least squares estimators of the regression coefficients have all the desirable properties. But, as pointed out in Section 7–4, knowing that the least squares estimators have these properties is only cold comfort to us if their variances are such that the resulting estimates are highly unreliable. That is, knowing that our estimators have the smallest possible variance (among all unbiased estimators) is not very helpful if, at the same time, this variance happens to be very large. And this is how multicollinearity comes in. Consider a regression model with two explanatory variables. According to (10.24) and (10.25) the variances of $\hat{\beta}_2$ and $\hat{\beta}_3$ are

$$\text{Var}(\hat{\beta}_2) = \frac{\sigma^2 m_{33}}{m_{22}m_{33} - m_{23}^2} = \frac{\sigma^2}{m_{22}(1 - r_{23}^2)},$$

$$\text{Var}(\hat{\beta}_3) = \frac{\sigma^2 m_{22}}{m_{22}m_{33} - m_{23}^2} = \frac{\sigma^2}{m_{33}(1 - r_{23}^2)},$$

and by (10.27) their covariance is

$$\text{Cov}(\hat{\beta}_2, \hat{\beta}_3) = \frac{-\sigma^2 m_{23}}{m_{22}m_{33} - m_{23}^2} = \frac{-\sigma^2 r_{23}}{\sqrt{m_{22}}\sqrt{m_{33}}(1 - r_{23}^2)},$$

This shows clearly that when r_{23}^2 is close to unity, the variances and the covariance of $\hat{\beta}_2$ and $\hat{\beta}_3$ are very large. (In the case when $r_{23}^2 = 1$, they would be infinite.) Since in the case of two explanatory variables the value of r_{23}^2 indicates the degree of multicollinearity, the preceding result implies that the higher the degree of multicollinearity, the larger the variances and the covariance of $\hat{\beta}_2$ and $\hat{\beta}_3$. When there are more than two explanatory variables, the variance-covariance matrix of the least squares estimators of the regression coefficients is

$$E(\hat{\beta} - \beta)(\hat{\beta} - \beta)' = \sigma^2(\mathbf{X}'\mathbf{X})^{-1},$$

as given by (10.33). A high degree of multicollinearity means that in the matrix $(\mathbf{X}'\mathbf{X})$ one column is close to being a linear combination of one or more of the remaining columns. This implies that the determinant of $(\mathbf{X}'\mathbf{X})$ is numerically small so that the elements of $(\mathbf{X}'\mathbf{X})^{-1}$—and, therefore, the variances and covariances of the estimated regression coefficients—are large.

We thus conclude that a high degree of multicollinearity is harmful in the sense that the estimates of the regression coefficients are highly imprecise. The imprecision arises because of the large variances of the least squares estimators. Although these variances are not known, their estimates can be obtained by using formula (10.35a) for estimating σ^2. However, it should be noted that large variances of the estimated regression coefficients may exist even if there is no multicollinearity at all, either because the explanatory variables have a small dispersion or because σ^2 itself is large. If we want to put the blame on multicollinearity, we ought to be able to measure its degree. In the case of models with two explanatory variables, we can use the value of r_{23}^2 for this purpose, but when there are more than two explanatory variables, measurement of the degree of multicollinearity becomes more complicated. This is because, as we demonstrated earlier, the presence of a high degree of multicollinearity, or even of perfect multicollinearity, does not generally imply that the correlation between any two explanatory variables must be particularly high.

Measures of Multicollinearity

The problem of measuring multicollinearity in models with more than two explanatory variables has been attacked in a number of ways. Some research workers have used the value of the determinant of $(\mathbf{X}'\mathbf{X})$ since this is low when the degree of multicollinearity is high, and it is zero when multicollinearity is perfect. This measure has the disadvantage of not being bounded and of being affected by the dispersion of the explanatory variables in addition to their interrelation. For instance, if we used this measure for the model with two explanatory variables, we would get

$$\text{Det} \begin{bmatrix} n & \sum X_{i2} & \sum X_{i3} \\ \sum X_{i2} & \sum X_{i2}^2 & \sum X_{i2}X_{i3} \\ \sum X_{i3} & \sum X_{i2}X_{i3} & \sum X_{i3}^2 \end{bmatrix} = n(m_{22}m_{33} - m_{23}^2) = nm_{22}m_{33}(1 - r_{23}^2).$$

Thus two sets of sample data with the same number of observations and the *same value of* r_{23}^2 would give different values of the determinant if the product of m_{22} and m_{33} were not the same in the two samples.

Another measure of multicollinearity, which is built into some of the least squares regression programs for electronic computers, is defined in terms of what is called " R^2 delete." In these programs the computer calculates not only the usual R^2 for the regression equation in question, but also those R^2's that are obtained by omitting each of the explanatory variables in turn. The R^2's obtained in this way are called the " R^2 deletes." Thus, for example, for a regression equation with three explanatory variables, X_{2i}, X_{3i}, and X_{4i}, we would have three " R^2 deletes," one from regressing Y_i on X_{2i} and X_{3i}, one from regressing Y_i on X_{2i} and X_{4i}, and one from regressing Y_i on X_{3i} and X_{4i}. If there is a high degree of multicollinearity in the sample, then at least one of the explanatory variables will vary largely in accordance with the variation of some other one or more explanatory variables. The introduction of this variable into the regression equation will therefore lead to only a small increase in the value of R^2. Thus a high degree of multicollinearity will be reflected by the fact that the difference between R^2 and the highest of the "R^2 deletes" will be small.

A relatively simple measure of the degree of multicollinearity is suggested by the fact that a high degree of multicollinearity simply means that at least one of the explanatory variables can be represented as a linear function of one or more of the remaining explanatory variables *plus* a small residual. If we "regress" each of the explanatory variables on all the remaining explanatory variables, we can obtain a measure of the "goodness of fit" by calculating the value of R^2 in each case. If any one of these R^2's is close to unity, the degree of multicollinearity is high. Or, in general, the highest of these R^2's can be taken as a measure of the degree of multicollinearity present in the sample. However, this measure, as well as all the other measures we have described, suffers from the lack of a clear definition of what constitutes a "high" degree of multicollinearity. Given that *some* multicollinearity almost always exists, the question is, At what point does the degree of multicollinearity cease to be "normal" and become "harmful"? This question has not been satisfactorily resolved. According to one criterion sometimes used in practice, multicollinearity is regarded as harmful if at, say, the 5% level of significance, the value of the F statistic is significantly different from zero but none of the t statistics for the regression coefficients (other than the regression constant) is. In this case we would *reject* the hypothesis that there is no relationship between Y_i on one side and $X_{i2}, X_{i3}, \ldots, X_{iK}$ on the other side, but we would *not reject* the hypothesis that any one of the explanatory variables is irrelevant in influencing Y_i. Such a situation indicates that the separate influence of each of the explanatory variables is weak relative to their joint influence on Y_i. This is symptomatic of a high degree of multicollinearity, which prevents us from disentangling the separate influences of the explanatory variables. The disadvantage of this criterion is that it is too strong in the sense that multicollinearity is considered as harmful only when all of the influences of the explanatory variables on Y cannot be disentangled.

Let us now assume that we have a sample with a degree of multicollinearity that is definitely considered as harmful. What can be done about it? If we have used up all the prior information in specifying the model and have no information from other samples, there is not very much that we can do. Some applied research workers, faced with this problem in time-series observations, have transformed the data to first differences. That is, instead of estimating

$$Y_t = \beta_1 + \beta_2 X_{t2} + \beta_3 X_{t3} + \cdots + \beta_K X_{tK} + \varepsilon_t,$$

the least squares estimation method is applied to

$$Y_t - Y_{t-1} = \alpha + \beta_2(X_{t2} - X_{t-1, 2}) + \beta_3(X_{t3} - X_{t-1, 3})$$
$$+ \cdots + \beta_K(X_{tK} - X_{t-1, K}) + (\varepsilon_t - \varepsilon_{t-1}).$$

Under some circumstances, this transformation may reduce the degree of multi-collinearity. However, it introduces autoregression in the disturbances that are otherwise independent. As noted, autoregression has undesirable consequences for the properties of least squares estimators. This makes working with first differences instead of the original data a dubious practice.

Since very little can be done about multicollinearity after all of the information on hand has been used, the only thing left is to increase the stock of information. One possible way of doing this is to increase the sample size. For instance, consider the variances of $\hat{\beta}_2$ and $\hat{\beta}_3$ in a model with two explanatory variables. These are

$$\text{Var}(\hat{\beta}_2) = \frac{\sigma^2}{m_{22}(1 - r_{23}^2)},$$

$$\text{Var}(\hat{\beta}_3) = \frac{\sigma^2}{m_{33}(1 - r_{23}^2)}.$$

An increase in sample size may increase m_{22} and m_{33}, or reduce r_{23}^2, or do both at the same time. The increase in m_{22} and m_{33} will occur in all cases in which the additional values of X_{i2} and X_{i3} are different from $\bar{X}_2$ and $\bar{X}_3$, as they are quite likely to be. On the other hand, it is difficult to foresee what will happen to r_{23}^2 as n increases, given that the X's are nonstochastic and not under our control. In fact, r_{23}^2 might increase to the extent that the variances of $\hat{\beta}_2$ and $\hat{\beta}_3$ actually *increase*. One way of avoiding this is to enlarge the size of the sample in such a way that m_{22} and m_{33} are *substantially* increased, for example, by combining time-series and cross-section data.

The problem of encountering a high degree of multicollinearity in the sample is frequently surrounded by a confusion in the applied literature. There is a tendency on the part of some applied research workers to point to the high degree of multicollinearity in the sample as the reason why the estimated regression coefficients are not significantly different from zero. The reader is led to believe that if the degree of multicollinearity were lower, the estimated regression coefficients would turn out to be significant. This may be so, but it certainly does not follow from the presented results. For this reason it is important to realize that a high degree of multicollinearity is simply a feature of the sample that contributes to the unreliability of the estimated coefficients, but has no relevance for the conclusions drawn as a *result* of this unreliability. If the estimated regression coefficients are highly unreliable—that is, if they have large variances—the acceptance region for the hypothesis that a given regression coefficient is zero will be wide. In turn, this means that the power of the test is weak. Thus the test is not very helpful in discriminating between true and false hypotheses. This is all that can be said regardless of the reason for the large variances in the first place.

10–4   Specification Errors

The specification of a regression model consists of a formulation of the regression equation and of statements or assumptions concerning the regressors and the disturbance term. A "specification error," in the broad sense of the term, occurs whenever the formulation of the regression equation or one of the underlying assumptions is incorrect. In a narrower sense of the term, *specification error* refers only to the errors in formulating the appropriate regression equation, and this is the interpretation adopted here. Several kinds of such errors will be considered, in particular those resulting from:

1. Omission of a relevant explanatory variable.
2. Disregard of a qualitative change in one of the explanatory variables.
3. Inclusion of an irrelevant explanatory variable.
4. Incorrect mathematical form of the regression equation.
5. Incorrect specification of the way in which the disturbance enters the regression equation.

Although we shall consider only the cases in which the explanatory variables are nonstochastic, the conclusions would remain essentially unchanged even if the explanatory variables were stochastic, providing they were independent of the regression disturbance. Our main concern will be with determining the consequences of each type of specification error for the least squares estimators of the regression coefficients and their standard errors.

Omission of a Relevant Explanatory Variable

Let us consider a specification error due to *omitting a relevant explanatory variable* from the regression equation. In particular, suppose the correct specification of the regression equation is

$$(10.58) \qquad Y_i = \beta_1 + \beta_2 X_{i2} + \beta_3 X_{i3} + \varepsilon_i,$$

but we estimate

$$(10.59) \qquad Y_i = \beta_1 + \beta_2 X_{i2} + \varepsilon_i^*.$$

Such an error may be committed when no observations on X_{i3} are available, or when the researcher is not aware of the fact that X_{i3} should be included in the regression equation if the maintained hypothesis is to be correctly specified. Now if (10.59) were correct, the least squares estimators of β_1 and β_2 would be unbiased and efficient for all sample sizes. Let us see what happens to these estimators given that (10.58) rather than (10.59) is the correct formulation. For $\hat{\beta}_2$ we have

$$E(\hat{\beta}_2) = E\left[\frac{\sum (X_{i2} - \bar{X}_2)(Y_i - \bar{Y})}{\sum (X_{i2} - \bar{X}_2)^2}\right].$$

But from (10.58) we know that

$$(Y_i - \bar{Y}) = \beta_2(X_{i2} - \bar{X}_2) + \beta_3(X_{i3} - \bar{X}_3) + (\varepsilon_i - \bar{\varepsilon})$$

so that

$$E(\hat{\beta}_2) = \beta_2 + \beta_3 d_{32},$$

where

$$d_{32} = \frac{\sum (X_{i2} - \bar{X}_2)(X_{i3} - \bar{X}_3)}{\sum (X_{i2} - \bar{X}_2)^2}.$$

Similarly, for $\hat{\beta}_1$ we have

$$E(\hat{\beta}_1) = E(\bar{Y} - \hat{\beta}_2\bar{X}_2) = \beta_1 + \beta_2\bar{X}_2 + \beta_3\bar{X}_3 - (\beta_2 + \beta_3d_{32})\bar{X}_2$$

$$= \beta_1 + \beta_3d_{31},$$

where
$$d_{31} = \bar{X}_3 - d_{32}\bar{X}_2.$$

Note that the expressions for d_{31} and d_{32} are, in fact, the formulas for the least squares coefficients of the equation

(10.60) $$X_{i3} = d_{31} + d_{32}X_{i2} + \text{residual}.$$

Since X_{i2} and X_{i3} are nonstochastic, equation (10.60) can be viewed only as a purely descriptive regression equation. In this equation the "dependent' variable is represented by the omitted variable X_{i3}, and the "explanatory" variable by the included variable X_{i2}. Given that β_3 is different from zero, the least squares estimator of β_2 based on (10.59) will be *biased* unless d_{32} equals zero, i.e., unless X_{i2} and X_{i3} are uncorrelated. If β_3 and d_{32} are both of the same sign, the bias of $\hat{\beta}_2$ will be positive; otherwise it will be negative. This means that the direction of the bias of $\hat{\beta}_2$ depends on

1. The sign of β_3.
2. The direction of the correlation between the omitted and the included explanatory variable.

If the correlation between X_{i2} and X_{i3} does not disappear as the sample size increases, i.e., if

$$\lim_{n\to\infty} d_{32} \neq 0,$$

$\hat{\beta}_2$ will also be inconsistent. Furthermore, the least squares estimator of β_1 based on (10.59) will be biased as long as

$$\bar{X}_3 - d_{32}\bar{X}_2 \neq 0,$$

and it will be inconsistent as long as

$$\lim_{n\to\infty} (\bar{X}_3 - d_{32}\bar{X}_2) \neq 0.$$

The foregoing seems to suggest that if the omitted explanatory variable is *uncorrelated* with the included explanatory variable, its omission may not lead to serious consequences for least squares estimation. Let us examine this point in detail. Suppose that X_{i2} and X_{i3} are uncorrelated; that is, suppose $d_{32} = 0$. Then $\hat{\beta}_2$ based on (10.59) is unbiased, and its variance is

$$\text{Var}(\hat{\beta}_2) = E(\hat{\beta}_2 - \beta_2) = \frac{\sigma^2}{\sum(X_{i2} - \bar{X}_2)^2}.$$

The estimator of $\mathrm{Var}(\hat{\beta}_2)$ based on (10.59) is

$$
s_{\hat{\beta}_2}^2 = \frac{s^2}{\sum(X_{i2} - \bar{X}_2)^2} = \frac{\sum[(Y_i - \bar{Y}) - \hat{\beta}_2(X_{i2} - \bar{X}_2)]^2/(n - 2)}{\sum(X_{i2} - \bar{X}_2)^2}
$$

$$
= \frac{\sum[-(\hat{\beta}_2 - \beta_2)(X_{i2} - \bar{X}_2) + \beta_3(X_{i3} - \bar{X}_3) + (\varepsilon_i - \bar{\varepsilon})]^2}{(n - 2)\sum(X_{i2} - \bar{X}_2)^2}.
$$

The mathematical expectation of $s_{\hat{\beta}_2}^2$ is then given by

$$
E(s_{\hat{\beta}_2}^2) = \frac{m_{22}\mathrm{Var}(\hat{\beta}_2) + \beta_3^2 m_{33} - 2m_{22}\mathrm{Var}(\hat{\beta}_2) + (n - 1)\sigma^2}{(n - 2)m_{22}}
$$

$$
= \mathrm{Var}(\hat{\beta}_2) + \frac{\beta_3^2 m_{33}}{(n - 2)m_{22}}.
$$

This implies that in this case the estimator of $\mathrm{Var}(\hat{\beta}_2)$ is positively biased. Therefore, the usual tests of significance concerning β_2 are not valid, since they will tend to reject the null hypothesis more frequently than is justified by the given level of significance. Further, the mathematical expectation of the least squares estimator of β_1 based on (10.59) is

$$
E(\hat{\beta}_1) = E(\bar{Y} - \hat{\beta}_2\bar{X}_2) = \beta_1 + \beta_2\bar{X}_2 + \beta_3\bar{X}_3 - \beta_2\bar{X}_2 = \beta_1 + \beta_3\bar{X}_3,
$$

which means that $\hat{\beta}_1$ is biased unless $\bar{X}_3 = 0$.

Our results concerning the least squares estimation of β_1 and β_2 on the basis of (10.59), given that (10.58) is the correct specification, can be summarized as follows: if the omitted explanatory variable is correlated with the included explanatory variable, the estimators of β_1 and β_2 will be biased and inconsistent. If the omitted explanatory variable is *not* correlated with the included variable, the estimator of β_1 will still be biased and inconsistent, at least in general, but the estimator of β_2 will be unbiased. However, the estimator of the *variance* of $\hat{\beta}_2$ will contain an upward bias, so that the usual tests of significance and confidence intervals for β_2 will tend to lead to unduly conservative conclusions.

The preceding analysis can easily be extended to the case involving a larger number of explanatory variables. Suppose the correct specification of the regression equation is

(10.61) $Y_i = \beta_1 + \beta_2 X_{i2} + \beta_3 X_{i3} + \beta_4 X_{i4} + \varepsilon_i,$

but we estimate

(10.62) $Y_i = \beta_1 + \beta_2 X_{i2} + \beta_3 X_{i3} + \varepsilon_i^*.$

The least squares estimator of β_2 based on (10.62) is

$$
\hat{\beta}_2 = \frac{m_{Y2}m_{33} - m_{Y3}m_{23}}{m_{22}m_{33} - m_{23}^2}.
$$

Now, $E(m_{Y2}) = \beta_2 m_{22} + \beta_3 m_{23} + \beta_4 m_{24},$

$$
E(m_{Y3}) = \beta_2 m_{23} + \beta_3 m_{33} + \beta_4 m_{34},
$$

so that

$$E(m_{Y2}m_{33} - m_{Y3}m_{23}) = \beta_2(m_{22}m_{33} - m_{23}^2) + \beta_4(m_{24}m_{33} - m_{34}m_{23}).$$

Therefore,

$$E(\hat{\beta}_2) = \beta_2 + \beta_4 d_{42},$$

where
$$d_{42} = \frac{m_{42}m_{33} - m_{43}m_{23}}{m_{22}m_{33} - m_{23}^2}.$$

Note that the expression for d_{42} is exactly the same as the formula of the least squares coefficient of X_{i2} in the equation

(10.63) $X_{i4} = d_{41} + d_{42}X_{i2} + d_{43}X_{i3} + \text{residual}.$

In (10.63) the omitted explanatory variable X_{i4} is "regressed" on the two included explanatory variables X_{i2} and X_{i3}. Similarly,

$$E(\hat{\beta}_3) = \beta_3 + \beta_4 d_{43} \qquad \text{and} \qquad E(\hat{\beta}_1) = \beta_1 + \beta_4 d_{41}.$$

Thus the conclusion in this case is the same as when a smaller number of explanatory variables is involved.

EXAMPLE   In a study of production functions for Indian industry, Murti and Sastry [11] use data on outputs and inputs for a sample of 320 firms, and obtain the following estimates of the Cobb-Douglas production function:

$$\log x_i = \log 0.68 + 0.53 \log n_i + 0.50 \log k_i + e_i,$$

where x = net value of output, n = wages and salaries, k = value of net assets, and the subscript i refers to the ith firm. If the "management" input varies systematically from firm to firm so that it cannot be regarded as a part of the random disturbance, the above equation is misspecified. If the management input—which, of course, is very difficult to measure—were brought into the production function in the same way as n_i and k_i, the sign of its coefficient clearly would be positive. The descriptive least squares regression linking the "management" input m_i with the two included explanatory variables n_i and k_i is

$$\log m_i = d_{41} + d_{42} \log n_i + d_{43} \log k_i + \text{residual}.$$

We can then speculate about the signs of d_{42} and d_{43}. If the firms with a high level of capital input possess a superior management input compared to the firms that are more labor-intensive, d_{42} would be negative and d_{43} positive. Under those circumstances—and in the absence of other violations of the assumptions of the classical normal linear regression model—the estimate of the coefficient of $\log n_i$ would be biased downward and that of the coefficient of $\log k_i$ would be biased upward.

Qualitative Change in Explanatory Variables

Consider now the specification error that arises as a result of a *qualitative*

---

[11] V. N. Murti and V. K. Sastry, "Production Functions for Indian Industry," *Econometrica*, Vol. 25, April 1957, pp. 205–221.

change in one or more of the explanatory variables as we go from one observation to another. In particular, suppose the correctly specified regression equation is

$$(10.64) \qquad Y_i = \beta_1 + \beta_2 X_{i2} + \beta_3 X_{i3} + \varepsilon_i,$$

but we do not observe X_{i2} and use X_{i2}^*, which is defined as

$$(10.65) \qquad X_{i2}^* = X_{i2} + Q_{i2},$$

where Q_{i2} is a factor representing the quality change in X_{i2}^*. Suppose also that Q_{i2} is nonstochastic and that it cannot be measured. Such a situation may arise in the case of a production function where the quality of the labor input has been improving over time. Yet the theoretical concept of a production function refers to a relationship between homogeneous output and homogeneous inputs. The effect of such a change on least squares estimation can be determined as follows. Substituting for X_{i2} from (10.65) into (10.64), we obtain

$$
\begin{aligned}
(10.66) \qquad Y_i &= \beta_1 + \beta_2(X_{i2}^* - Q_{i2}) + \beta_3 X_{i3} + \varepsilon_i \\
&= \beta_1 + \beta_2 X_{i2}^* + \beta_3 X_{i3} - \beta_2 Q_{i2} + \varepsilon_i.
\end{aligned}
$$

If we then estimate

$$(10.67) \qquad Y_i = \beta_1 + \beta_2 X_{i2}^* + \beta_3 X_{i3} + \varepsilon_i^*,$$

instead of (10.66), we encounter the same specification error as if we left out a relevant explanatory variable. The mathematical expectations of the least squares estimators of β_1, β_2, and β_3 based on (10.67) then are

$$
\begin{aligned}
E(\hat{\beta}_1) &= \beta_1 - \beta_2 d_{41}, \\
E(\hat{\beta}_2) &= \beta_2 - \beta_2 d_{42}, \\
E(\hat{\beta}_3) &= \beta_3 - \beta_2 d_{43},
\end{aligned}
$$

where the d's are the least squares coefficients of

$$(10.68) \qquad Q_{i2} = d_{41} + d_{42} X_{i2}^* + d_{43} X_{i3} + \text{residual}.$$

In the case of a production function all the β's would be positive. Furthermore, for observations in the form of a time series, d_{42} and d_{43} may be expected to be positive since all three variables in (10.68) have been growing over time, at least since the Second World War. This would imply that both $\hat{\beta}_2$ and $\hat{\beta}_3$ are biased downward. This analysis can be extended easily to the case where the number of explanatory variables is larger than two, or to the case involving a qualitative change in more than one explanatory variable.

Inclusion of an Irrelevant Explanatory Variable

Another type of specification error occurs when the set of relevant explanatory variables is enlarged by the inclusion of one or more *irrelevant variables*. (Regression equations that are formulated by including all conceivable candidates in the set of explanatory variables without much attention to the underlying theory are, for obvious reasons, sometimes called "kitchen sink models.") For instance, suppose the correctly specified regression equation is

$$(10.69) \qquad\qquad Y_i = \beta_1 + \beta_2 X_{i2} + \varepsilon_i,$$

but we estimate

$$(10.70) \qquad\qquad Y_i = \beta_1 + \beta_2 X_{i2} + \beta_3 X_{i3} + \varepsilon_i^*.$$

The specification error involved in using (10.70) rather than (10.69) occurs because we ignore the restriction that $\beta_3 = 0$ in formulating our maintained hypothesis. Let us see what happens to the least squares estimators of the regression coefficients if we base our estimation on (10.70). First the mathematical expectation of $\hat{\beta}_3$ is

$$E(\hat{\beta}_3) = E\left[\frac{m_{Y3}m_{22} - m_{Y2}m_{23}}{m_{22}m_{33} - m_{23}^2}\right].$$

But from (10.69) we know that

$$E(m_{Y2}) = \beta_2 m_{22} \qquad \text{and} \qquad E(m_{Y3}) = \beta_2 m_{23}$$

so that

$$E(\hat{\beta}_3) = \frac{\beta_2 m_{22}m_{23} - \beta_2 m_{22}m_{23}}{m_{22}m_{33} - m_{23}^2} = 0.$$

That is, the mean of $\hat{\beta}_3$ is equal to the true value of β_3, which is zero. The probability that in any given sample we observe a value of $\hat{\beta}_3$ that is significantly different from zero is then equal to the chosen level of significance. Next, the mathematical expectation of $\hat{\beta}_2$ is

$$E(\hat{\beta}_2) = E\left[\frac{m_{Y2}m_{33} - m_{Y3}m_{23}}{m_{22}m_{33} - m_{23}^2}\right] = \beta_2.$$

Also, $\qquad E(\hat{\beta}_1) = E(\bar{Y} - \hat{\beta}_2 \bar{X}_2 - \hat{\beta}_3 \bar{X}_3) = (\beta_1 + \beta_2 \bar{X}_2) - \beta_2 \bar{X}_2 = \beta_1.$

These results show that the estimators of the coefficients of (10.70) are all unbiased. As for their variances, we have

$$\text{Var}(\hat{\beta}_2) = \frac{\sigma^2 m_{33}}{m_{22}m_{33} - m_{23}^2} = \frac{\sigma^2}{m_{22}(1 - r_{23}^2)},$$

where r_{23} is the coefficient of correlation between X_{i2} and X_{i3}. Now, if β_2 were estimated on the basis of the correctly specified regression equation (10.69), its variance, say, $\text{Var}(\hat{\beta}_2^*)$, would be equal to

$$\text{Var}(\hat{\beta}_2^*) = \frac{\sigma^2}{m_{22}}.$$

The ratio of the two variances is

$$\frac{\text{Var}(\hat{\beta}_2)}{\text{Var}(\hat{\beta}_2^*)} = \frac{1}{1 - r_{23}^2}.$$

Since $0 \leq r_{23}^2 \leq 1$, it follows that

$$\frac{\text{Var}(\hat{\beta}_2)}{\text{Var}(\hat{\beta}_2^*)} \geq 1,$$

where the equality holds only for $r_{23} = 0$, i.e., only if X_{i2} and X_{i3} are uncorrelated. The implication of this result is that $\hat{\beta}_2$ is generally *not efficient*. Similarly, by working through the formulas for $\text{Var}(\hat{\beta}_1)$ and $\text{Var}(\hat{\beta}_1^*)$—where $\hat{\beta}_1$ and $\hat{\beta}_1^*$ refer to the least squares estimators of β_1 from (10.70) and (10.69) respectively—we could show that $\hat{\beta}_1$ is also not efficient unless

$$(\bar{X}_3\sqrt{m_{22}} - \bar{X}_2 r_{23}\sqrt{m_{33}}) = 0.$$

Consider now the estimated variances of the least squares coefficients of (10.70). The formulas for $\text{Var}(\hat{\beta}_1)$, $\text{Var}(\hat{\beta}_2)$, and $\text{Var}(\hat{\beta}_3)$ involve only one unknown parameter, σ^2, which is estimated by

$$s^2 = \frac{1}{n-3}\sum_i [(Y_i - \bar{Y}) - \hat{\beta}_2(X_{i2} - \bar{X}_2) - \hat{\beta}_3(X_{i3} - \bar{X}_3)]^2$$

$$= \frac{1}{n-3}\sum_i [\beta_2(X_{i2} - \bar{X}_2) + (\varepsilon_i - \bar{\varepsilon}) - \hat{\beta}_2(X_{i2} - \bar{X}_2) - \hat{\beta}_3(X_{i3} - \bar{X}_3)]^2$$

$$= \frac{1}{n-3}\sum_i [-(\hat{\beta}_2 - \beta_2)(X_{i2} - \bar{X}_2) - \hat{\beta}_3(X_{i3} - \bar{X}_3) + (\varepsilon_i - \bar{\varepsilon})]^2.$$

The mathematical expectation of s^2 is

$$E(s^2) = \frac{1}{n-3}\Big[m_{22}\text{Var}(\hat{\beta}_2) + m_{33}\text{Var}(\hat{\beta}_3) + (n-1)\sigma^2 + 2m_{23}\text{Cov}(\hat{\beta}_2,\hat{\beta}_3)$$
$$- 2E(\hat{\beta}_2 - \beta_2)\sum_i (X_{i2} - \bar{X}_2)\varepsilon_i - 2E\hat{\beta}_3\sum_i (X_{i3} - \bar{X}_3)\varepsilon_i\Big].$$

But

$$-2E(\hat{\beta}_2 - \beta_2)\sum_i (X_{i2} - \bar{X}_2)\varepsilon_i$$

$$= -2E\left[\frac{m_{33}\sum(X_{i2} - \bar{X}_2)\varepsilon_i - m_{23}\sum(X_{i3} - \bar{X}_3)\varepsilon_i}{m_{22}m_{33} - m_{23}^2}\right]\sum (X_{i2} - \bar{X}_2)\varepsilon_i = -2\sigma^2,$$

$$-2E\hat{\beta}_3\sum_i (X_{i3} - \bar{X}_3)\varepsilon_i$$

$$= -2E\left[\frac{m_{22}\sum(X_{i3} - \bar{X}_3)\varepsilon_i - m_{23}\sum(X_{i2} - \bar{X}_2)\varepsilon_i}{m_{22}m_{33} - m_{23}^2}\right]\sum (X_{i3} - \bar{X}_3)\varepsilon_i = -2\sigma^2,$$

so that

$$E(s^2) = \frac{1}{n-3}\left[\frac{\sigma^2(m_{22}m_{33} + m_{33}m_{22} - 2m_{23}^2)}{m_{22}m_{33} - m_{23}^2} + (n-1)\sigma^2 - 4\sigma^2\right] = \sigma^2.$$

This means that the estimator of σ^2 based on (10.70) is unbiased. Therefore, the estimators of $\text{Var}(\hat{\beta}_1)$, $\text{Var}(\hat{\beta}_2)$, and $\text{Var}(\hat{\beta}_3)$ are also unbiased. This result holds whether X_{i2} and X_{i3} are correlated or not. The conclusion, then, is that if the specification error consists of including some irrelevant explanatory variables in the regression equation, the least squares estimators of the regression coefficients are unbiased but not efficient. The estimators of their variances are also unbiased, so that, in the absence of other complications, the usual tests of significance and confidence intervals for the regression parameters are valid. These results have been derived for a simple regression model, but it is not difficult to show that they apply to models with a larger number of explanatory variables as well.

Nonlinearity

Another specification error arises in the case where the correctly specified regression equation is *nonlinear* but we estimate what may be viewed as its linear approximation. Since linear relations are widely used in applied econometric research, this kind of error is likely to be committed quite often. Suppose that the correctly specified regression equation is given by

$$(10.71) \qquad\qquad Y_i = f(X_i) + \varepsilon_i,$$

where $f(X_i)$ is some function of X_i. We assume that this function is continuous and possesses a continuous pth derivative, p being some positive integer. Then, with the use of Taylor's theorem [12] we can expand $f(X_i)$ around, say $\bar{X}$, and write (10.71) as

$$(10.71a) \qquad Y_i = f(\bar{X}) + (X_i - \bar{X})f'(\bar{X}) + \frac{(X_i - \bar{X})^2}{2!}f''(\bar{X})$$

$$+ \cdots + \frac{(X_i - \bar{X})^p}{p!}f^{(p)}(\bar{X}) + R_{p+1} + \varepsilon_i,$$

where

$$f(\bar{X}) = f(X_i)\Big|_{X_i = \bar{X}},$$

$$f'(\bar{X}) = \frac{df(X_i)}{dX_i}\Big|_{X_i = \bar{X}},$$

$$f''(\bar{X}) = \frac{d^2f(X_i)}{dX_i^2}\Big|_{X_i = \bar{X}},$$

$$\vdots$$

$$R_{p+1} = \text{remainder}.$$

By rearranging the terms on the right-hand side of (10.71a), we end up with

$$(10.71b) \qquad\qquad Y_i = \beta_1 + \beta_2 X_i + \beta_3 X_i^2 + \cdots + \varepsilon_i,$$

where

$$\beta_1 = f(\bar{X}) - \bar{X}f'(\bar{X}) + \frac{\bar{X}^2}{2!}f''(\bar{X}) - \cdots,$$

---

[12] See, e.g., A. C. Chiang, *Fundamental Methods of Mathematical Economics* (New York: McGraw-Hill, 1967), pp. 256–260.

$$\beta_2 = f'(\bar{X}) - \bar{X}f''(\bar{X}) + \frac{\bar{X}^2}{2!}f'''(\bar{X}) - \cdots,$$

and so on. That is, the β's are expressions in terms of $\bar{X}$ and the parameters of $f(X_i)$ and can be regarded as parametric regression coefficients. If we then estimate a linear approximation of (10.71), i.e.,

(10.72) $$Y_i = \beta_1 + \beta_2 X_i + \varepsilon_i^*,$$

we are, in fact, omitting the relevant "explanatory variables" from the regression equation. The consequences of such an error were discussed in the early part of this section.

The preceding finding can be illustrated as follows. Suppose the correctly specified regression equation is represented by a parabolic function,

(10.73) $$Y_i = \beta_1 + \beta_2 X_i + \beta_3 X_i^2 + \varepsilon_i.$$

If we then approximate (10.73) by (10.72) and use the least squares estimation method, we can determine the properties of the resulting estimators in the same way as with (10.58) and (10.59). The specification error involved in estimating (10.72) in place of (10.73) is simply the omission of X_i^2 from the regression equation. Therefore, we have

$$E(\hat{\beta}_2) = \beta_2 + \beta_3 d_{32} \quad \text{and} \quad E(\hat{\beta}_1) = \beta_1 + \beta_3 d_{31},$$

where d_{31} and d_{32} represent the least squares coefficients of

(10.74) $$X_i^2 = d_{31} + d_{32}X_i + \text{residual}.$$

In general, d_{32} will be different from zero, so that the estimator of β_2 (and of β_1) will be biased and inconsistent. The magnitude of the bias will depend on the size of β_3, which determines the curvature of the correctly specified regression equation, and on the values of X in the sample.

Incorrect Specification of the Disturbance Term

For another type of misspecification, consider the situation in which the *stochastic disturbance is brought into the regression equation in an incorrect way.* In particular, let the correctly specified regression equation be

(10.75) $$Y_i = f(X_i)\varepsilon_i,$$

where ε_i follows a log-normal distribution with mean zero and variance σ^2, i.e.,

$$\log_e \varepsilon_i \sim N(0, \sigma^2).$$

Note that here we have[13]

$$E(\varepsilon_i) = e^{\sigma^2/2},$$
$$\text{Var}(\varepsilon_i) = e^{\sigma^2}(e^{\sigma^2} - 1).$$

[13] See Goldberger, *op. cit.*, p. 215.

Suppose now that instead of (10.75) we assume

(10.76) $Y_i = f(X_i) + \varepsilon_i^*.$

Then we have

$$\varepsilon_i^* = Y_i - f(X_i) = f(X_i)\varepsilon_i - f(X_i) = f(X_i)(\varepsilon_i - 1).$$

Consequently, $E(\varepsilon_i^*) = f(X_i)(e^{\sigma^2/2} - 1)$

and $\text{Var}(\varepsilon_i^*) = [f(X_i)]^2[e^{\sigma^2}(e^{\sigma^2} - 1)].$

This means that ε_i^* does not satisfy the assumptions of zero mean and of homoskedasticity. Also, if ε_i is log-normal, ε_i^* cannot be normally distributed. The
implications for the properties of the estimators of the parameters of (10.75) can
be determined in detail when the mathematical form of $f(X_i)$ is spelled out. For
example, let the correctly specified regression equation be

(10.77) $Y_i = \gamma X_i \varepsilon_i,$

with $\log_e \varepsilon_i$ satisfying all the assumptions of the classical normal regression
model. Suppose that instead of (10.77), we postulate

(10.78) $Y_i = \gamma X_i + \varepsilon_i^*.$

Then the least squares estimator of γ based on (10.78) is

$$\hat{\gamma} = \frac{\sum Y_i X_i}{\sum X_i^2} = \frac{\gamma \sum X_i^2 \varepsilon_i}{\sum X_i^2}.$$

The mathematical expectation of $\hat{\gamma}$ is

$$E(\hat{\gamma}) = \gamma e^{\sigma^2/2},$$

which means that $\hat{\gamma}$ is *biased*. Also,

$$\text{plim } \hat{\gamma} = \frac{\gamma \, \text{plim}(\sum X_i^2 \varepsilon_i)/n}{\text{plim}(\sum X_i^2)/n} = \gamma e^{\sigma^2/2},$$

which means that $\hat{\gamma}$ is inconsistent.

   In the preceding case we assumed that the disturbance term in the correctly
specified regression equation entered in a multiplicative way, while in the misspecified regression equation the disturbance was additive. Let us now examine
the reverse situation. Suppose that the correctly specified regression equation is

(10.79) $Y_i = f(X_i) + \varepsilon_i,$

where ε_i satisfies all the assumptions of the classical normal regression model,
and suppose that we incorrectly assume

(10.80) $Y_i = f(X_i)\varepsilon_i^*.$

Then, we have

$$\varepsilon_i^* = \frac{Y_i}{f(X_i)} = 1 + \frac{\varepsilon_i}{f(X_i)}.$$

Consequently, $E(\varepsilon_i^*) = 1$

and $\text{Var}(\varepsilon_i^*) = \dfrac{\sigma^2}{[f(X_i)]^2}.$

To illustrate this case, consider that the correctly specified regression equation is of the form

(10.81) $Y_i = \alpha X_i^\beta + \varepsilon_i,$

but we estimate

(10.82) $\log Y_i = \log \alpha + \beta \log X_i + \varepsilon_i^*.$

The least squares estimator of β based on (10.82) is

$$\hat{\beta} = \frac{\sum [\log Y_i - (\sum \log Y_i)/n][\log X_i - (\sum \log X_i)/n]}{\sum [\log X_i - (\sum \log X_i)/n]^2}.$$

But from (10.81) we have

$$\log Y_i = \log(\alpha X_i^\beta + \varepsilon_i) = \log \alpha + \beta \log X_i + \log[1 + (\varepsilon_i/\alpha X_i^\beta)].$$

Therefore,

$$\hat{\beta} = \beta + \frac{\{\sum [\log X_i - (\sum \log X_i)/n]\log[1 + (\varepsilon_i/\alpha X_i^\beta)]\}/n}{\{\sum [\log X_i - (\sum \log X_i)/n]^2\}/n}.$$

With the help of Taylor's expansion, we can write[14]

$$E\log[1 + (\varepsilon_i/\alpha X_i^\beta)] = E[(\varepsilon_i/\alpha X_i^\beta) - \tfrac{1}{2}(\varepsilon_i/\alpha X_i^\beta)^2 + \tfrac{1}{3}(\varepsilon_i/\alpha X_i^\beta)^3 - \cdots]$$
$$= -[\tfrac{1}{2}E(\varepsilon_i^2)/(\alpha X_i^\beta)^2 + \tfrac{1}{4}E(\varepsilon_i^4)/(\alpha X_i^\beta)^4 + \cdots].$$

Then it follows that

$$E(\hat{\beta}) \neq \beta$$

and also $\text{plim } \hat{\beta} \neq \beta.$

Thus we reach the conclusion that $\hat{\beta}$ is biased and inconsistent.

Specification Error Tests

The above examination of the consequences of committing different types of specification errors has shown that, with the exception of the case of including irrelevant explanatory variables in the regression equation, all the specification errors that we have considered lead to biasedness and inconsistency of the least squares estimators. In the case of including irrelevant explanatory variables, the least squares estimators are unbiased and consistent but not efficient. Thus it is important that we try to avoid specification errors as much as possible or, if they are unavoidable, that we at least become aware of their presence. We have mentioned two possible reasons for committing a specification error. One is that the

---

[14] See, e.g., T. Yamane, *Mathematics for Economists* (Englewood Cliffs, N.J.: Prentice-Hall, 1962), p. 170.

regression equation cannot be estimated in its correctly specified form because of data limitations. In such a case the preceding analysis, adapted to the problem at hand, may enable us to get at least some idea about the seriousness of the bias and its direction. The second reason for committing a specification error is our lack of knowledge as to the correct specification of the regression equation. In this case we would like to be able to *test* whether or not we have misspecified the regression equation. This is precisely how we approached the problem in connection with the assumptions about the regression disturbance in Chapter 8, where we described some of the tests for homoskedasticity and for nonauto-regression. Here we consider some tests for specification errors involving inclusion of irrelevant and omission of relevant explanatory variables; tests for linearity of the regression equation will be discussed in Section 11–3.

Let us start with the problem of *testing the hypothesis that the regression equation as specified includes some irrelevant explanatory variables.* Suppose the regression equation is specified as

$$Y_i = \beta_1 + \beta_2 X_{i2} + \cdots + \beta_K X_{iK} + \beta_{K+1} X_{i,K+1} + \cdots + \beta_Q X_{iQ} + \varepsilon_i.$$

Suppose further that there exists a competing theory according to which the variables $X_{i,K+1}, X_{i,K+2}, \ldots, X_{iQ}$ are irrelevant. Then, the null hypothesis can be stated as

$$H_0: \quad \beta_{K+1} = \beta_{K+2} = \cdots = \beta_Q = 0,$$

and the alternative hypothesis as

$$H_A: \quad H_0 \text{ is not true.}$$

The appropriate test is the F test described by (10.45). This test will enable us to discriminate between the two theories. The difficulty about applying this test in practice is that our theories are often not as sharply formulated as presupposed by the test. Quite frequently we know of no unique way of classifying the explanatory variables into two groups, one containing the variables that should be included and the other the variables that are candidates for exclusion. For instance, if our regression equation is specified as

$$Y_i = \beta_1 + \beta_2 X_{i2} + \beta_3 X_{i3} + \beta_4 X_{i4} + \varepsilon_i,$$

we may concede, as possible alternatives, regression equations that contain any one or any two of X_{i2}, X_{i3}, and X_{i4} as the explanatory variables. If all three variables are highly intercorrelated, trying out all possible regressions will not help either. What may happen is that, in regressions with more than one explanatory variable, we do *not reject* the hypotheses

$$\beta_2 = 0,$$

$$\beta_3 = 0,$$

$$\beta_4 = 0,$$

but we *do reject* the hypotheses

$$\beta_2 = \beta_3 = \beta_4 = 0,$$

$$\beta_2 = \beta_3 = 0,$$

$$\beta_2 = \beta_4 = 0,$$

$$\beta_3 = \beta_4 = 0.$$

That is, we may find that the joint variation of the X's explains a high proportion of the variation of Y, but that this joint variation cannot be disentangled to allocate credits to individual variables.

The preceding problem is difficult to resolve by the existing sample data alone. However, it may be possible to distinguish between alternative regression models by reference to their respective forecasting performances. To illustrate this, consider the following set of alternative models:

Model 1: $Y_i = \beta_1 + \beta_2 X_{i2} + \beta_3 X_{i3} + \beta_4 X_{i4} + \varepsilon_i;$

Model 2: $Y_i = \beta_1 + \beta_2 X_{i2} + \beta_3 X_{i3} + \varepsilon_i;$

Model 3: $Y_i = \beta_1 + \beta_2 X_{i2} + \beta_4 X_{i4} + \varepsilon_i;$

Model 4: $Y_i = \beta_1 + \beta_3 X_{i3} + \beta_4 X_{i4} + \varepsilon_i.$

Suppose now that we expect to observe an additional value of Y, say, Y_{n+1}, for which the appropriate values of the X's are known. Then, for each of the models we can construct the forecast interval

$$\hat{Y}_{n+1} \pm t s_F,$$

as given by (10.50). The value of Y_{n+1} will fall within the forecast interval corresponding to the correct model with a given level of probability, say, 95%. After observing Y_{n+1}, we shall find one of the following:

(1) None of the intervals contains Y_{n+1}.
(2) Y_{n+1} lies within the interval corresponding to Model 1 but not within any other interval.
(3) The outcome is different from (1) and (2).

If the outcome is that described by (1), we have to reject all the models and look for another theory. If (2) occurs, we reject Models 2, 3, and 4, and our test is completed. In case of (3), the result of the test is inconclusive. Then, we have to wait for further observations and continue testing. If the correct model is 1, the other models will be eventually eliminated. If the correct model is, say, Model 2, then Models 3 and 4 will be eventually eliminated, and the contest will be confined to Models 1 and 2. Given that Model 2 is correct, both 1 and 2 will give unbiased forecasts, but the variance of the forecast error will be greater for 1 than for 2. It should be noted, though, that if forecasts are made more than once, the appropriate test is an F test, which is described elsewhere.[15]

---

[15] See Johnston, *op. cit.*, pp. 137–138.

Let us now consider *testing for the specification error that involves omitting a relevant explanatory variable from the regression equation.* For instance, suppose that we have two competing models,

$$\text{Model A:} \quad Y_i = \beta_1 + \beta_2 X_{i2} + \varepsilon_i,$$

$$\text{Model B:} \quad Y_i = \beta_1 + \beta_3 X_{i3} + \varepsilon_i.$$

If Model A is correct, β_3 must be equal to zero. To carry out a test that would discriminate between these models, we can form a "general" model,

$$Y_i = \beta_1 + \beta_2 X_{i2} + \beta_3 X_{i3} + \varepsilon_i,$$

and test the hypothesis that $\beta_3 = 0$. However, if X_{i2} and X_{i3} are highly correlated, we may well find that neither $\hat{\beta}_2$ nor $\hat{\beta}_3$ is significantly different from zero, but that the joint effect of X_{i2} and X_{i3} is definitely significant. If that is the case, we may have to wait for additional observations. If there is only *one* model, the problem of testing for a specification error involving the omission of a relevant explanatory variable becomes more difficult. We can wait for additional observations and consider each one of them as potential evidence against the model. If the model is correct, the probability that a future value of Y will fall outside the forecast interval is small. The difficulty is that there may be other models—about which we do not know—whose forecast intervals may largely overlap the forecast interval of the model that we are testing. In this case it may take many additional observations before our model is rejected even if it is incorrect.

There is an obvious disadvantage to waiting for additional observations before making a pronouncement concerning the presence of specification errors. An alternative approach involves reliance on the fact that, if the model is correctly specified, the regression disturbances (and, therefore, the residuals that represent their sample counterparts) have to exhibit certain properties. In particular, if we omit some relevant explanatory variables from the regression equation, the mean of the disturbance will no longer be equal to zero and its variance will no longer be constant. We can test for this kind of specification error by examining the behavior of the regression residuals. Several such tests have been developed recently by J. B. Ramsey and can be used in this context.[16] These tests require a somewhat involved description, which will not be presented here, but they are very useful and represent an important advance in dealing with the problem of specification errors.

EXERCISES

10–1. Consider the following multiple regression equation:

$$Y_i = \beta_1 + \beta_2 X_{i2} + \beta_3 X_{i3} + \cdots + \beta_K X_{iK} + \beta_{K+1} X_{i,K+1} + \cdots + \beta_Q X_{iQ} + \varepsilon_i.$$

---

[16] See James B. Ramsey, "Tests for Specification Errors, in Classical Linear Least Squares Regression Analysis," *Journal of the Royal Statistical Society*, Series B, Vol. 31, 1969, pp. 350–371.

Prove that

a. $SSR_Q \geq SSR_K$.

b. $R_Q^2 \geq R_K^2$.

10–2. Given the definitions of $\hat{\boldsymbol{\beta}}$, $\mathbf{X}$, and $\mathbf{Y}$ as stated in connection with (10.15), prove that

a. $\hat{\boldsymbol{\beta}} = (\mathbf{X'X})^{-1}(\mathbf{X'Y})$.

b. $Var(\hat{\boldsymbol{\beta}}) = \sigma^2(\mathbf{X'X})^{-1}$.

c. $\underline{\mathbf{Y}}'\underline{\mathbf{Y}} = \mathbf{Y'Y} - \left(\sum_t Y_t\right)^2 / n$.

10–3. Given the least squares estimates

$$Y_t = 5 + 3X_{t1} + 10X_{t2} + e_t \qquad (n = 100),$$
$$\quad\;\; (1) \qquad\;\; (2)$$

and given that the sample coefficient of correlation between the two explanatory variables is 0.5, find the value of R^2.

10–4. Consider $\mathbf{Y} = \mathbf{X}\boldsymbol{\beta} + \boldsymbol{\epsilon}$ with K (the number of explanatory variables including the constant) equal to two. Show, by writing out all matrices in full, that the least squares formulas for the multiple regression model give the same answer as the formulas for the simple regression model developed in Section 7–3 without the use of matrix algebra.

10–5. It has been suggested that corporate investment behavior can be described by the relationship

$$I_t = \beta_1 + \beta_2 F_{t-1} + \beta_3 K_{t-1} + \varepsilon_t,$$

where I_t = current gross investment, F_{t-1} = end-of-period value of outstanding shares, and K_{t-1} = end-of-period capital stock. From the data for General Motors Corporation given in Table 10–2:

a. Obtain least squares estimates of the regression coefficients and their estimated standard errors.

b. Calculate the value of R^2 and test for the existence of a relationship.

c. The values of F_{t-1} and K_{t-1} for the year 1954 are 5593.6 and 2226.3, respectively. What is the forecast value of I_{1954} and its 95% forecast interval? (The actual value of I_{1954} was 1486.7.)

10–6. For the regression model

$$Y_i = \beta_1 + \beta_2 X_{i2} + \beta_3 X_{i3} + \varepsilon_i,$$

derive the formula for the best-linear-unbiased estimator of β_1 and its variance.

10–7. Consider a regression model with three explanatory variables, i.e., with $K = 4$. Derive the expression for the F statistic,

$$F_{3, n-4} = \frac{SSR/3}{SSE/(n-4)}$$

in terms of the t statistics.

Table 10–2*

Year	I_t	F_{t-1}	K_{t-1}
1935	317.6	3078.5	2.8
1936	391.8	4661.7	52.6
1937	410.6	5387.1	156.9
1938	257.7	2792.2	209.2
1939	330.8	4313.2	203.4
1940	461.2	4643.9	207.2
1941	512.0	4551.2	255.2
1942	448.0	3244.1	303.7
1943	499.6	4053.7	264.1
1944	547.5	4379.3	201.6
1945	561.2	4840.9	265.0
1946	688.1	4900.9	402.2
1947	568.9	3526.5	761.5
1948	529.2	3254.7	922.4
1949	555.1	3700.2	1020.1
1950	642.9	3755.6	1099.0
1951	755.9	4833.0	1207.7
1952	891.2	4924.9	1430.5
1953	1304.4	6241.7	1777.3

Source: J. C. G. Boot and G. M. deWitt, "Investment Demand: An Empirical Contribution to the Aggregation Problem," *International Economic Review*, Vol. 1, January 1960, pp. 3–30.

* All values (in millions of dollars) are deflated by appropriate price indexes.

10–8. Suppose a correctly specified regression model is given as

$$Y_t = \alpha + \beta X_t + \varepsilon_t.$$

All assumptions of the classical normal linear regression model are satisfied. Now suppose that we do not have observations on X, and that in its place we use as a "proxy" some other nonstochastic variable Z; i.e., we estimate

$$Y_t = \alpha + \beta Z_t + \varepsilon_t^*.$$

a. What are the properties of the resulting least squares estimates of α and β, and of their estimated variances?

b. Does the replacement of X_t by Z_t affect the validity of the standard test of the hypothesis that $\beta = 0$? Would it make any difference if Z_t were not a "good proxy" for X_t, that is, if X_t and Z_t were not highly correlated?

10–9. Let E_i = total weekly planned expenditure of the ith household, X_{ig} = expenditure of the ith household on the gth commodity, and N_i = number of persons in the ith household. The variable N_i is nonstochastic. Consider the following model:

$$X_{ig} = \alpha_g + \beta_g E_i + \gamma_g N_i + u_{ig} \quad (i = 1, 2, \ldots, n; \ g = 1, 2, \ldots, G; \ n > G).$$

Further,

$$E_i = \sum_{g=1}^{G} X_{ig} + v_i,$$

$$v_i = - \sum_{g=1}^{G} u_{ig}.$$

We assume that

$$E(u_{ig}) = 0,$$

$$E(\mathbf{u_g u_g'}) = \sigma_{gg} \mathbf{I_n},$$

$$E(\mathbf{u_g u_h'}) = \mathbf{0} \quad (g \neq h),$$

where $\mathbf{u_g'} = [u_{1g} \quad u_{2g} \quad \ldots \quad u_{ng}].$

Suppose we have obtained observations on E_i and X_{ig} and have fitted the following equation by the ordinary least squares method:

$$X_{ig} = a_g + b_g E_i + e_{ig}, \quad g = 1, 2, \ldots, G.$$

a. Under what conditions, if any, will b_g be an unbiased estimate of β_g ?

b. Under what conditions, if any, will a_g be an unbiased estimate of a_g ?

11

Formulation and Estimation of Special Models

Multiple regression, because of its flexibility, is a suitable analytical tool for problems of statistical inference under conditions in which the imposition of prior knowledge about the regression equation leads to a departure from the standard linear regression model. In this chapter we consider four types of departures. Section 11–1 deals with the formulation and estimation of relationships that involve qualitative or binary variables. Included here are the well-known statistical techniques of "analysis of variance" and "analysis of covariance," both of which can be regarded as regression models with qualitative explanatory variables. In Section 11–2 we take up the problem of incorporating various prior restrictions on the coefficients of a linear relationship when carrying out the estimation. Section 11–3 contains description of some nonlinear models and deals with the problems of estimation and of testing for linearity. Finally, in Section 11–4 we examine models in which the response of the dependent variable to changes in the explanatory variables may be delayed. These models, which are known as "distributed lag models," have recently assumed an important place in many areas of applied economic research.

11–1   Models with Binary Variables

Some phenomena that we observe cannot be measured but only counted. This is true of all qualitative characteristics of objects, people, time periods, etc. Our observation then consists of noting whether the given characteristic is or is not present. For instance, when the unit of observation is an adult man, we may note whether he is or is not a house owner, whether he has or has not a college degree, whether he does or does not smoke, or anything else that is relevant to the problem at hand. Since we can assign a value of 1 to the presence, and 0 to the absence of the attribute in question, we may view it as a variable that is restricted to two values. (Of course, it is not necessary that the two values be 0 and 1. We may, if we wish, choose any other two values to represent the presence and the absence of the given attribute. For obvious reasons, 0 and 1 are chosen most commonly.) Such a variable is then called a "binary" or a "dummy" variable. We will discuss the problem of formulating and estimating models in which qualitative variables appear on either side of the regression equation, starting with simple models and progressing to more complex ones.

Single Qualitative Explanatory Variable

A simple regression model in which the explanatory variable is represented by a binary variable can be illustrated by the salaries offered to economics graduate students entering the academic labor market. Assume that these salaries are normally distributed with variance σ^2 and mean equal to μ_1 for candidates who have already received their Ph.D., and μ_0 for those who have not. This situation can be described by a regression model, with salary as the dependent variable and degree qualification as the explanatory variable. Formally,

$$(11.1) \qquad Y_i = \alpha + \beta X_i + \varepsilon_i,$$

where Y_i is the salary of the ith candidate, and X_i is a binary variable such that

$$X_i = 1 \quad \text{if the candidate has a Ph.D.},$$

$$= 0 \quad \text{otherwise}.$$

The disturbance ε_i is a random variable that satisfies all the basic assumptions of the classical normal linear regression model. The mean values of Y_i corresponding to the two values of X_i are

$$E(Y_i \mid X_i = 0) = \alpha,$$

$$E(Y_i \mid X_i = 1) = \alpha + \beta.$$

Therefore,

$$\alpha = \mu_0,$$

and

$$\alpha + \beta = \mu_1,$$

or

$$\beta = \mu_1 - \mu_0.$$

This means that the intercept of the population regression line (11.1) measures the mean salary of a non-Ph.D., and the slope measures the difference between the mean salary of a Ph.D. and that of a non-Ph.D. A test of the hypothesis that β is zero is then equivalent to the test that there is no difference between the mean salary of a Ph.D. and that of a non-Ph.D.

The coefficients of the regression equation (11.1) can be estimated by the method of least squares. Under the assumptions of the classical normal linear regression model, the resulting estimates will have all the desirable properties. Recall that the formulas for the least squares estimators are

$$\hat{\beta} = \frac{\sum (X_i - \bar{X})(Y_i - \bar{Y})}{\sum (X_i - \bar{X})^2},$$

$$\hat{\alpha} = \bar{Y} - \hat{\beta}\bar{X}.$$

Let n_1 = number of candidates with a Ph.D. in the sample,

n_0 = number of candidates without a Ph.D. in the sample,

$\bar{Y}_1$ = sample mean salary of a candidate with a Ph.D.,

$\bar{Y}_0$ = sample mean salary of a candidate without a Ph.D.

Then
$$\sum_{i=1}^{n} X_i = n_1,$$

$$\sum_{i=1}^{n} X_i^2 = n_1,$$

$$\sum_{i=1}^{n} Y_i = n_1 \bar{Y}_1 + n_0 \bar{Y}_0,$$

$$\sum_{i=1}^{n} X_i Y_i = n_1 \bar{Y}_1.$$

Therefore,

$$\sum_i (X_i - \bar{X})(Y_i - \bar{Y}) = \sum_i X_i Y_i - \frac{1}{n}\left(\sum_i X_i\right)\left(\sum_i Y_i\right)$$

$$= n_1 \bar{Y}_1 - \frac{n_1}{n}(n_1 \bar{Y}_1 + n_0 \bar{Y}_0) = \frac{n_0 n_1}{n}(\bar{Y}_1 - \bar{Y}_0)$$

and
$$\sum_i (X_i - \bar{X})^2 = \sum_i X_i^2 - \frac{1}{n}\left(\sum_i X_i\right)^2 = n_1 - \frac{n_1^2}{n} = \frac{n_0 n_1}{n}.$$

This gives

$$\hat{\beta} = \frac{(n_0 n_1/n)(\bar{Y}_1 - \bar{Y}_0)}{n_0 n_1/n} = \bar{Y}_1 - \bar{Y}_0$$

and
$$\hat{\alpha} = \frac{1}{n}(n_1 \bar{Y}_1 + n_0 \bar{Y}_0) - (\bar{Y}_1 - \bar{Y}_0)\frac{n_1}{n} = \bar{Y}_0.$$

Thus the least squares estimator of the regression slope is equal to the difference between the sample mean salary of a Ph.D. and that of a non-Ph.D., and the least squares estimator of the regression intercept is equal to the sample mean salary of a non-Ph.D. The t test of the hypothesis that β is equal to zero described in (7.46) is in this case exactly the same as the t test of the hypothesis that two population means are equal. The latter is derived from (5.2). (The test statistic $\hat{\beta}/s_{\hat{\beta}}$ is the same as the test statistic in (5.2), after replacing σ_1^2 and σ_2^2 by s^2.)

In the preceding illustration the characteristic represented by the explanatory variable was dichotomous; i.e., only two possibilities were considered as relevant. But we can handle equally well models in which the explanatory characteristic is polychotomous. The only consequence of this complication is that we need more than one binary variable to describe such a characteristic. For instance, suppose the starting salaries of the high school teachers of English are normally distributed with variance σ^2, the mean depending on whether the highest degree attained by the candidate is a B.A., an M.A., or a Ph.D. Let the mean starting salary for a B.A. be equal to μ_A; that for an M.A., μ_B; and that for a Ph.D., μ_C. The appropriate regression equation can be represented by

(11.2) $$Y_i = \beta_1 + \beta_2 X_{i2} + \beta_3 X_{i3} + \varepsilon_i,$$

where Y_i is the salary of the ith candidate, and

$X_{i2} = 1$ if the highest degree of the candidate is a Ph.D.,

   $= 0$ otherwise;

$X_{i3} = 1$ if the highest degree of the candidate is an M.A.,

   $= 0$ otherwise.

Note that when $X_{i2} = 1$, X_{i3} must be equal to zero, and vice versa. The mean values of Y_i corresponding to different values of the regressors are

$$E(Y_i \mid X_{i2} = 1, X_{i3} = 0) = \beta_1 + \beta_2,$$

$$E(Y_i \mid X_{i2} = 0, X_{i3} = 1) = \beta_1 + \beta_3,$$

$$E(Y_i \mid X_{i2} = 0, X_{i3} = 0) = \beta_1.$$

It follows then that

$$\beta_1 = \mu_A,$$

$$\beta_2 = \mu_C - \mu_A,$$

$$\beta_3 = \mu_B - \mu_A.$$

This result is analogous to that obtained for the dichotomous classification of (11.1).

Note that the trichotomy in the preceding model is represented by *two* binary variables, each assuming a value of 0 or 1. It would be incorrect to use *one* variable with three values, say, 0 for a B.A., 1 for an M.A., and 2 for a Ph.D. If we did that and formed the regression model as

$$Y_i = \alpha + \beta W_i + \varepsilon_i,$$

where W_i is the explanatory variable with values 0, 1, and 2, we would have

$$E(Y_i \mid W_i = 0) = \alpha,$$

$$E(Y_i \mid W_i = 1) = \alpha + \beta,$$

$$E(Y_i \mid W_i = 2) = \alpha + 2\beta.$$

However, this implies that the difference between the mean salary of an M.A. and a B.A. is

$$(\alpha + \beta) - \alpha = \beta,$$

and the difference between the mean salary of a Ph.D. and an M.A. is

$$(\alpha + 2\beta) - (\alpha + \beta) = \beta.$$

That is, by using one variable with values 0, 1, and 2 (or any three equidistant values) we are, in fact, assuming that the difference between the salary of a Ph.D. and an M.A. is the same as that between the salary of an M.A. and a B.A. Unless we know a priori that this is the case, we are not justified in making such an assumption.

Note also that we cannot represent the trichotomy by three rather than by two binary variables (unless we drop the constant term in the regression equation). For if we did and formed the regression model as

$$Y_i = \beta_1 + \beta_2 X_{i2} + \beta_3 X_{i3} + \beta_4 X_{i4} + \varepsilon_i,$$

where X_{i2} and X_{i3} are defined as before and

$$X_{i4} = 1 \quad \text{if the highest degree of the candidate is a B.A.,}$$

$$= 0 \quad \text{otherwise,}$$

the solution for $\hat{\beta}_1$, $\hat{\beta}_2$, $\hat{\beta}_3$, and $\hat{\beta}_4$ would be indeterminate. The reason is that

$$X_{i4} = 1 - X_{i2} - X_{i3}$$

and the least squares normal equations are not independent, or (what amounts to the same thing) $\mathbf{X'X}$ is a singular matrix. This holds quite generally: when the explanatory characteristic leads to a classification into G types, we use $(G - 1)$ binary variables for its representation.

Models with a single qualitative variable have been traditionally formulated in statistical texts as "one-way analysis of variance" models rather than as regression models with binary regressors. The two approaches are equivalent in the sense that they describe the same phenomenon and lead to the same test results about it. Consider a normally distributed random variable Y whose mean depends on a given polychotomous characteristic that leads to a classification into G types. The variance of Y is constant, and the observations are assumed to be independent. By the "analysis of variance" approach we divide all of the observed values of Y into G groups according to the given characteristic, and formulate the model as

$$(11.3) \qquad Y_{tg} = \mu + \alpha_g + \varepsilon_{tg} \qquad (t = 1, 2, \ldots, n_g; g = 1, 2, \ldots, G).$$

Here Y_{tg} is the tth observation on Y in the gth group, μ is the "grand mean," α_g is the deviation of the mean of the gth group from μ, and ε_{tg} is a stochastic disturbance. Note that

$$\sum_{g=1}^{G} \alpha_g = 0.$$

Let us now compare the "analysis of variance" model with the corresponding regression model. The latter is given by

(11.4) $Y_{tg} = \beta_1 + \beta_2 X_{t2} + \beta_3 X_{t3} + \cdots + \beta_G X_{tG} + \varepsilon_{tg},$

where $X_{tg} = 1$ if the observation belongs to the gth group,

          $= 0$ otherwise $(g = 2, 3, \ldots, G).$

To specify the coefficients of (11.4) in terms of the parameters of (11.3) and vice versa, we compare the two formulations for each group separately (Table 11-1).

Table 11-1

Group	Analysis of Variance Model	Regression Model
1	$E(Y_{t1}) = \mu + \alpha_1$	$E(Y_{t1}) = \beta_1$
2	$E(Y_{t2}) = \mu + \alpha_2$	$E(Y_{t2}) = \beta_1 + \beta_2$
⋮	⋮	⋮
G	$E(Y_{tG}) = \mu + \alpha_G$	$E(Y_{tG}) = \beta_1 + \beta_G$

That is,

$$\mu + \alpha_1 = \beta_1,$$

$$\mu + \alpha_2 = \beta_1 + \beta_2,$$

$$\vdots$$

$$\mu + \alpha_G = \beta_1 + \beta_G,$$

or

$$\mu = \beta_1 + \frac{1}{G}(\beta_2 + \beta_3 + \cdots + \beta_G),$$

$$\alpha_1 = -\frac{1}{G}(\beta_2 + \beta_3 + \cdots + \beta_G),$$

$$\alpha_2 = \beta_2 - \frac{1}{G}(\beta_2 + \beta_3 + \cdots + \beta_G),$$

$$\vdots$$

$$\alpha_G = \beta_G - \frac{1}{G}(\beta_2 + \beta_3 + \cdots + \beta_G).$$

The hypothesis, tested with the help of the analysis of variance model, is that there is no difference between the group means; i.e.,

$$H_0: \quad \alpha_1 = \alpha_2 = \cdots = \alpha_G = 0,$$

$$H_A: \quad H_0 \text{ is not true.}$$

It is easy to see that this null hypothesis is exactly equivalent to the hypothesis that the slopes of the regression equation (11.4) are jointly equal to zero; that is,

$$H_0: \quad \beta_2 = \beta_3 = \cdots = \beta_G = 0,$$

$$H_A: \quad H_0 \text{ is not true.}$$

As we have shown earlier, to carry out a test of H_0 within the framework of the regression model, we use the F test described by (10.43). This is equivalent to the F test for the analysis of variance models that is traditionally given in the textbooks on statisticis.[1] The regression model can also be used for testing the hypothesis that any one of the β coefficients is singly equal to zero, but the analysis of variance model is not readily suited for such a test.

Several Qualitative Explanatory Variables

Let us now extend the formulation of the regression models with qualitative explanatory variables to take into account more than one characteristic. Consider the following modification of the earlier example on the salaries of high school English teachers. Suppose the mean salary depends not only on the highest degree attained by the candidate, but also on whether the high school making the offer is public or private. The difference between the mean salaries in the public and the private school systems is presumed to be the same whatever the degree qualification. Again, we assume that salaries are normally distributed with variance σ^2 and that the observations are independent. Let

$$\mu_{A0} = \text{mean salary for a B.A. in a private school};$$

$$\mu_{A1} = \text{mean salary for a B.A. in a public school};$$

$$\mu_{B0} = \text{mean salary for an M.A. in a private school};$$

$$\mu_{B1} = \text{mean salary for an M.A. in a public school};$$

$$\mu_{C0} = \text{mean salary for a Ph.D. in a private school};$$

$$\mu_{C1} = \text{mean salary for a Ph.D. in a public school.}$$

Then a regression model can be formulated as

$$(11.5) \qquad Y_i = \beta_1 + \beta_2 X_{i2} + \beta_3 X_{i3} + \gamma Z_i + \varepsilon_i,$$

where Y_i, X_{i2} and X_{i3} are defined as in (11.2), and

$Z_i = 1$ if the school to which the ith candidate is applying is a public school,

$\quad = 0$ otherwise.

---

[1] See, e.g., J. E. Freund, *Mathematical Statistics* (Englewood Cliffs, N.J.: Prentice-Hall, 1962), p. 335, formula (14.2.5).

Note again that when $X_{i2} = 1$, X_{i3} must be equal to zero. The mean values of Y_i corresponding to different values of the regressors are

$$E(Y_i \mid X_{i2} = 1, X_{i3} = 0, Z_i = 1) = \beta_1 + \beta_2 + \gamma,$$

$$E(Y_i \mid X_{i2} = 0, X_{i3} = 1, Z_i = 1) = \beta_1 + \beta_3 + \gamma,$$

$$E(Y_i \mid X_{i2} = 0, X_{i3} = 0, Z_i = 1) = \beta_1 + \gamma,$$

$$E(Y_i \mid X_{i2} = 1, X_{i3} = 0, Z_i = 0) = \beta_1 + \beta_2,$$

$$E(Y_i \mid X_{i2} = 0, X_{i3} = 1, Z_i = 0) = \beta_1 + \beta_3,$$

$$E(Y_i \mid X_{i2} = 0, X_{i3} = 0, Z_i = 0) = \beta_1.$$

From this it follows that

$$\beta_1 = \mu_{A0},$$

$$\beta_2 = \mu_{C0} - \mu_{A0} = \mu_{C1} - \mu_{A1},$$

$$\beta_3 = \mu_{B0} - \mu_{A0} = \mu_{B1} - \mu_{A1},$$

$$\gamma = \mu_{A1} - \mu_{A0} = \mu_{B1} - \mu_{B0} = \mu_{C1} - \mu_{C0}.$$

That is, β_1 measures the mean salary of a B.A. in a private high school, β_2 measures the difference between the mean salary of a Ph.D. and a B.A. (which is presumed to be the same in both school systems), β_3 measures the difference between the mean salary of an M.A. and a B.A. (also the same in both school systems), and γ represents the difference between the mean salaries in the public and the private schools.

The preceding regression model is represented in statistical texts as a "two-way analysis of variance" model. The two approaches are again equivalent. Consider a random variable Y with values that can be classified according to two criteria, one criterion leading to a classification into G groups and the other to a classification into H groups. The observations on Y can then be arranged in the form of a two-way classification table with G columns and H rows. In this table each cell contains all observations belonging to the appropriate row and column. (The "analysis of variance" model usually assumes an equal number of observations per cell. This assumption is not needed for the regression formulation.) The two-way analysis of variance model is formulated as

$$(11.6) \qquad Y_{tgh} = \mu + \alpha_g + \lambda_h + \varepsilon_{tgh}$$

$$(t = 1, 2, \ldots, n_{gh}; \, g = 1, 2, \ldots, G; \, h = 1, 2, \ldots, H).$$

Here Y_{tgh} is the tth observation on Y in the gth column and hth row, μ is the "grand mean," α_g is the deviation of the mean of the gth column from μ, λ_h is the deviation of the mean of the hth row from μ, and ε_{tgh} is a stochastic disturbance. Note that

$$\sum_{g=1}^{G} \alpha_g = 0, \qquad \sum_{h=1}^{H} \lambda_h = 0.$$

We may compare this formulation with the corresponding regression model:

$$(11.7) \qquad Y_{tgh} = \beta_1 + \beta_2 X_{t2} + \beta_3 X_{t3} + \cdots + \beta_G X_{tG}$$

$$+ \gamma_2 Z_{t2} + \gamma_3 Z_{t3} + \cdots + \gamma_H Z_{tH} + \varepsilon_{tgh},$$

where $\quad X_{tg} = 1 \quad$ if the observation belongs to the gth column,

$\qquad\qquad = 0 \quad$ otherwise $\quad (g = 2, 3, \ldots, G)$;

$\qquad Z_{th} = 1 \quad$ if the observation belongs to the hth row,

$\qquad\qquad = 0 \quad$ otherwise $\quad (h = 2, 3, \ldots, H)$.

To determine the relationship between the coefficients of (11.6) and the parameters of (11.7), we compare the means of Y for each cell, as shown in Table 11-2.

Table 11-2

Column	Row	Analysis of Variance Model	Regression Model
1	1	$E(Y_{t11}) = \mu + \alpha_1 + \lambda_1$	$E(Y_{t11}) = \beta_1$
1	2	$E(Y_{t12}) = \mu + \alpha_1 + \lambda_2$	$E(Y_{t12}) = \beta_1 + \gamma_2$
$\vdots$	$\vdots$	$\vdots$	$\vdots$
1	H	$E(Y_{t1H}) = \mu + \alpha_1 + \lambda_H$	$E(Y_{t1H}) = \beta_1 + \gamma_H$
2	1	$E(Y_{t21}) = \mu + \alpha_2 + \lambda_1$	$E(Y_{t21}) = \beta_1 + \beta_2$
2	2	$E(Y_{t22}) = \mu + \alpha_2 + \lambda_2$	$E(Y_{t22}) = \beta_1 + \beta_2 + \gamma_2$
$\vdots$	$\vdots$	$\vdots$	$\vdots$
G	H	$E(Y_{tGH}) = \mu + \alpha_G + \lambda_H$	$E(Y_{tGH}) = \beta_1 + \beta_G + \gamma_H$

From this, we find that

$$\mu = \beta_1 + \frac{1}{G}(\beta_2 + \beta_3 + \cdots + \beta_G) + \frac{1}{H}(\gamma_2 + \gamma_3 + \cdots + \gamma_H),$$

$$\alpha_1 = -\frac{1}{G}(\beta_2 + \beta_3 + \cdots + \beta_G),$$

$$\alpha_2 = \beta_2 - \frac{1}{G}(\beta_2 + \beta_3 + \cdots + \beta_G),$$

$$\vdots$$

$$\alpha_G = \beta_G - \frac{1}{G}(\beta_2 + \beta_3 + \cdots + \beta_G),$$

$$\lambda_1 = -\frac{1}{H}(\gamma_2 + \gamma_3 + \cdots + \gamma_H),$$

$$\lambda_2 = \gamma_2 - \frac{1}{H}(\gamma_2 + \gamma_3 + \cdots + \gamma_H),$$

$$\vdots$$

$$\lambda_H = \gamma_H - \frac{1}{H}(\gamma_2 + \gamma_3 + \cdots + \gamma_H).$$

The two-way analysis of variance model is used for testing the hypotheses

$$H_0: \quad \alpha_1 = \alpha_2 = \cdots = \alpha_G = 0$$

and

$$H_0: \quad \lambda_1 = \lambda_2 = \cdots = \lambda_H = 0.$$

These hypotheses have their exact counterparts in terms of the coefficients of the regression model (11.7). The first hypothesis is equivalent to the hypothesis that $\beta_2, \beta_3, \ldots, \beta_G$ are jointly equal to zero; i.e.,

$$H_0: \quad \beta_2 = \beta_3 = \cdots = \beta_G = 0.$$

The second hypothesis is equivalent to the hypothesis that $\gamma_2, \gamma_3, \ldots, \gamma_H$ are jointly equal to zero; i.e.,

$$H_0: \quad \gamma_2 = \gamma_3 = \cdots = \gamma_H = 0.$$

The appropriate test for these hypotheses is the F test described by (10.45). This test is equivalent to the F test for the analysis of variance models given in the statistical texts. The models (11.6) and (11.7), and the comparison, can be generalized to a larger number of explanatory characteristics by simple analogy.

Interaction Terms

The regression model with two, or more, explanatory characteristics can be generalized further by introducing "interaction terms." Consider the preceding example on the starting salaries of the high school English teachers. In this example we presume that the mean salary depends on the degree qualification of the candidate and on the type of high school, and that the difference between the mean salaries in the public and in the private school systems is the same for all degree qualifications. Suppose now that we do not wish to make the latter presumption. Then the regression model (11.5) can be modified as follows:

$$(11.8) \qquad Y_i = \beta_1 + \beta_2 X_{i2} + \beta_3 X_{i3} + \gamma Z_i + \delta_2 X_{i2} Z_i + \delta_3 X_{i3} Z_i + \varepsilon_i,$$

where all the variables are defined as in (11.5). The mean values of Y_i corresponding to different values of the regressors are

$$E(Y_i \mid X_{i2} = 1, X_{i3} = 0, Z_i = 1) = \beta_1 + \beta_2 + \gamma + \delta_2,$$

$$E(Y_i \mid X_{i2} = 0, X_{i3} = 1, Z_i = 1) = \beta_1 + \beta_3 + \gamma + \delta_3,$$

$$E(Y_i \mid X_{i2} = 0, X_{i3} = 0, Z_i = 1) = \beta_1 + \gamma,$$

$$E(Y_i \mid X_{i2} = 1, X_{i3} = 0, Z_i = 0) = \beta_1 + \beta_2,$$

$$E(Y_i \mid X_{i2} = 0, X_{i3} = 1, Z_i = 0) = \beta_1 + \beta_3,$$

$$E(Y_i \mid X_{i2} = 0, X_{i3} = 0, Z_i = 0) = \beta_1.$$

This means that we can define the regression coefficients in terms of the mean salaries as follows:

$$\beta_1 = \mu_{A0},$$

$$\beta_2 = \mu_{C0} - \mu_{A0},$$

$$\beta_3 = \mu_{B0} - \mu_{A0},$$

$$\gamma = \mu_{A1} - \mu_{A0},$$

$$\delta_2 = (\mu_{C1} - \mu_{C0}) - (\mu_{A1} - \mu_{A0}),$$

$$\delta_3 = (\mu_{B1} - \mu_{B0}) - (\mu_{A1} - \mu_{A0}).$$

The differences in the mean salary in the public and the private systems are

$$\text{B.A.:} \quad \mu_{A1} - \mu_{A0} = \gamma,$$

$$\text{M.A.:} \quad \mu_{B1} - \mu_{B0} = \gamma + \delta_3,$$

$$\text{Ph.D.:} \quad \mu_{C1} - \mu_{C0} = \gamma + \delta_2.$$

The regression model (11.8) is equivalent to a model presented as a "two-way analysis of variance with interactions" in statistical literature. A demonstration of the equivalence of the two models would follow the same lines as in the previously discussed cases, and will not be presented here.

Qualitative and Quantitative Explanatory Variables

In the preceding models all of the included regressors were represented by binary variables. Such models are really not very frequent in economics. More frequently, we encounter models in which *some* regressors are binary and others are not. A traditional example is a consumption function estimated from time-series data that include a major war period. In this model the mean consumption is presumed to depend on income and on whether the period is one of peace or one of war. A simple way of representing this model is

$$(11.9) \qquad C_t = \beta_1 + \beta_2 Y_t + \gamma Z_t + \varepsilon_t,$$

where C represents consumption, Y represents income, and Z is a binary variable such that

$$Z_t = 1 \quad \text{if } t \text{ is a wartime period},$$

$$= 0 \quad \text{otherwise}.$$

Then, we have

$$C_t = (\beta_1 + \gamma) + \beta_2 Y_t + \varepsilon_t \quad \text{(wartime)},$$

$$C_t = \beta_1 + \beta_2 Y_t + \varepsilon_t \qquad \text{(peacetime)}.$$

Thus we are, in fact, postulating that in wartime the intercept of the consumption function changes from β_1 to $\beta_1 + \gamma$. A graphic illustration is given in Figure 11–1.

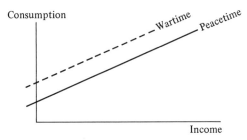

Figure 11–1

If the intercept is viewed as representing the "subsistence level" of consumption, this model implies that the subsistence level changes during the war. Such a change is put forward as a hypothesis to be tested, i.e.,

$$H_0: \quad \gamma = 0,$$

$$H_A: \quad \gamma \neq 0.$$

Statistitical texts show an equivalent formulation of models such as (11.9) under the name of "analysis of covariance."

The effect of war can be brought into the consumption function differently if we postulate that the war conditions affect the slope and not the intercept of the consumption function. According to this theoretical formulation, the regression model is

(11.10) $C_t = \beta_1 + \beta_2 Y_t + \delta Y_t Z_t + \varepsilon_t,$

where the variables are defined as before. In this case we have

$$C_t = \beta_1 + (\beta_2 + \delta) Y_t + \varepsilon_t \quad \text{(wartime)},$$

$$C_t = \beta_1 + \beta_2 Y_t + \varepsilon_t \qquad \text{(peacetime)}.$$

Equation (11.10) implies that the effect of the war is to change the marginal propensity to consume as shown in Figure 11–2. This implication can be checked by testing the hypothesis that δ is zero.

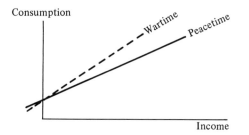

Figure 11–2

The third and final possibility of distinguishing between wartime and peace-time observations is to let *both* the intercept and the slope of the consumption function change in wartime. The regression equation would become

(11.11) $$C_t = \beta_1 + \beta_2 Y_t + \gamma Z_t + \delta Y_t Z_t + \varepsilon_t.$$

Then, we would have

$$C_t = (\beta_1 + \gamma) + (\beta_2 + \delta) Y_t + \varepsilon_t \quad \text{(wartime)},$$

$$C_t = \beta_1 + \beta_2 Y_t + \varepsilon_t \qquad\qquad \text{(peacetime)}.$$

These relations are illustrated in Figure 11–3. The interesting point about (11.11) is that the least squares estimators of the regression coefficients are exactly the same as those that would be obtained from two separate regressions of C_t on Y_t, one estimated from the peacetime observations and the other from the wartime observations. The proof is obtained by a straightforward application of the least squares formulas and will not be presented here. The only difference between the two approaches to estimation concerns σ^2. If, as we normally assume, the variance of ε_t is unchanged throughout the entire period, then its estimate from (11.11) based on *all* observations will be efficient, whereas the two estimates obtained from the two separate subsamples will not be. This is because the estimate of σ^2 based on either subsample does not utilize the information about σ^2 contained in the other subsample.

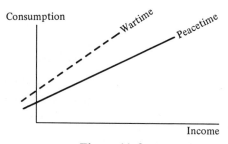

Consumption

Wartime

Peacetime

Income

Figure 11–3

Another use of models with quantitative and qualitative explanatory variables occurs when testing the hypothesis of *asymmetric response*. According to this hypothesis the change in $E(Y_i)$ in response to a unit *increase* of a given explana-tory variable is different in absolute magnitude from the change in response to a unit *decrease* of the same explanatory variable. Behavior of this sort is implied in statements such as "wages are sticky downwards," and in the claim that con-sumers respond more readily to an increase in income than to a decrease. For such behavior the standard formulation of the linear regression equation would be inappropriate. However, asymmetric response of $E(Y_i)$ to changes in an

explanatory variable can be incorporated into the regression equation by introducing a binary variable. Consider a simple regression model,

$$Y_t = \alpha + \beta X_t + \varepsilon_t,$$

for which all of the basic assumptions are satisfied. In this model a unit increase
in X_t leads to a change in $E(Y_t)$ equal to β, and a unit decrease in X_t leads to a
change in $E(Y_t)$ equal to $-\beta$. If we want to make the response of $E(Y_t)$ assym-
metric, we can write

(11.12) $$Y_t = \alpha + \beta X_t + \gamma X_t Z_t + \varepsilon_t$$

where $$Z_t = 1 \quad \text{when } X_t \leq X_{t-1},$$

$$= 0 \quad \text{otherwise.}$$

The test of the asymmetric response hypothesis is equivalent to testing that
$\gamma = 0$. Note that the asymmetric response model can be used not only with time
series but also with cross-section data, providing we have some information
about the value of the relevant explanatory variable in the period preceding the
time of the survey.

Models with quantitative *and* qualitative explanatory variables are used most
frequently in connection with regression models that include seasonal effects.
These models are usually estimated from quarterly or monthly observations.
For instance, consider the following simple regressions:

(11.13) $$Y_t = \alpha_1 + \beta X_t + \varepsilon_t \quad \text{(spring quarter)},$$

$$Y_t = \alpha_2 + \beta X_t + \varepsilon_t \quad \text{(summer quarter)},$$

$$Y_t = \alpha_3 + \beta X_t + \varepsilon_t \quad \text{(fall quarter)},$$

$$Y_t = \alpha_4 + \beta X_t + \varepsilon_t \quad \text{(winter quarter)}.$$

Here the seasonal effects are presumed to shift the intercept of the regression
function. The model can be described by a single regression equation extended
by the introduction of binary regressors representing the seasonal factors:

(11.14) $$Y_t = \alpha + \beta X_t + \gamma_2 Q_{t2} + \gamma_3 Q_{t3} + \gamma_4 Q_{t4} + \varepsilon_t,$$

where $$Q_{t2} = 1 \quad \text{if } t \text{ is a summer quarter},$$

$$= 0 \quad \text{otherwise;}$$

$$Q_{t3} = 1 \quad \text{if } t \text{ is a fall quarter},$$

$$= 0 \quad \text{otherwise;}$$

$$Q_{t4} = 1 \quad \text{if } t \text{ is a winter quarter},$$

$$= 0 \quad \text{otherwise.}$$

Note that the quarterly seasonal effects are represented by three, not four,
binary regressors; otherwise, the least squares estimators of the regression

coefficients would be indeterminate. A comparison of (11.14) and (11.13) reveals that

$$\alpha = \alpha_1,$$
$$\alpha + \gamma_2 = \alpha_2,$$
$$\alpha + \gamma_3 = \alpha_3,$$
$$\alpha + \gamma_4 = \alpha_4.$$

To examine the relevance of the seasonal effects in a regression model such as (11.14), we test the hypothesis that γ_2, γ_3, and γ_4 are jointly zero; that is,

$$H_0: \quad \gamma_2 = \gamma_3 = \gamma_4 = 0,$$
$$H_A: \quad H_0 \text{ is not true.}$$

The appropriate test then is the F test of (10.45).

An alternative way of introducing the seasonal factors into a regression model is

(11.15) $\quad Y_t = \alpha + \beta_1 X_t + \varepsilon_t$ (spring quarter),

$\quad Y_t = \alpha + \beta_2 X_t + \varepsilon_t$ (summer quarter),

$\quad Y_t = \alpha + \beta_3 X_t + \varepsilon_t$ (fall quarter),

$\quad Y_t = \alpha + \beta_4 X_t + \varepsilon_t$ (winter quarter).

In this case, the seasonal factors are supposed to affect the slope of the regression equation but not its intercept. A compact representation of (11.15) is

(11.16) $\quad Y_t = \alpha + \beta X_t + \delta_2 Q_{t2} X_t + \delta_3 Q_{t3} X_t + \delta_4 Q_{t4} X_t + \varepsilon_t,$

where the Q's are defined as in (11.14). By comparing (11.16) with (11.15), we can see that

$$\beta = \beta_1,$$
$$\beta + \delta_2 = \beta_2,$$
$$\beta + \delta_3 = \beta_3,$$
$$\beta + \delta_4 = \beta_4.$$

The relevance of the seasonal effects can be examined by testing the hypothesis that δ_2, δ_3, and δ_4 are jointly zero; i.e.,

$$H_0: \quad \delta_2 = \delta_3 = \delta_4 = 0,$$
$$H_A: \quad H_0 \text{ is not true.}$$

As a final possibility, we could let both the intercept and the slope be affected by the seasonal factors. From the point of view of estimating the regression coefficients, such a formulation is equivalent to splitting the sample into four sub-samples, as discussed earlier in connection with Equation (11.11).

A Note on the Use of Deseasonalized Data

While we are on the subject of seasonal factors in regression equations, we may consider the implications of using "deseasonalized" time-series data in regression analysis. A common practice is to form the regression equation as

$$\tilde{Y}_t = \alpha + \beta \tilde{X}_t + \varepsilon_t,$$

where $\tilde{Y}$ and $\tilde{X}$ are the "deseasonalized" values of X and Y. "Deseasonalizing" means removing regular oscillatory movement of a one-year period from the original time series. This is done either by the statistical agency that makes the data available, or by the econometrician himself. In our discussion we assume that the deseasonalizing has been successful in the sense that the seasonal elements have been completely removed from the series. These elements are usually considered to be additive or multiplicative. In the additive case, we can write

$$Y_t = \tilde{Y}_t + D_{tY},$$

$$X_t = \tilde{X}_t + D_{tX},$$

where D_{tY} and D_{tX} represent seasonal deviations contained in the respective series. Note that for, say, quarterly data,

$$D_{tY} = D_{t+4,\,Y},$$

$$D_{tX} = D_{t+4,\,X},$$

and

$$D_{tY} + D_{t+1,\,Y} + D_{t+2,\,Y} + D_{t+3,\,Y} = 0,$$

$$D_{tX} + D_{t+1,\,X} + D_{t+2,\,X} + D_{t+3,\,X} = 0,$$

for all t. If any series contains no seasonal elements, the corresponding D's would all be zero. The regression equation

$$\tilde{Y}_t = \alpha + \beta \tilde{X}_t + \varepsilon_t$$

then implies that

(11.17) $$(Y_t - D_{tY}) = \alpha + \beta(X_t - D_{tX}) + \varepsilon_t$$

or

(11.17a) $$Y_t = (\alpha + D_{tY} - \beta D_{tX}) + \beta X_t + \varepsilon_t.$$

That is, in this case the seasonal factors are assumed to operate by shifting the intercept of the regression function. This is equivalent to the formulation given by (11.13) or (11.14).

In the case of multiplicative seasonal elements, we can write

$$Y_t = \tilde{Y}_t S_{tY} \quad \text{and} \quad X_t = \tilde{X}_t S_{tX},$$

where S_{tY} and S_{tX} represent seasonal indexes pertaining to the respective series. Note that for, say, quarterly data,

$$S_{tY} = S_{t+4,\,Y} \qquad \text{and} \qquad S_{tX} = S_{t+4,\,X},$$

and
$$S_{tY} \times S_{t+1,\,Y} \times S_{t+2,\,Y} \times S_{t+3,\,Y} = 1,$$

$$S_{tX} \times S_{t+1,\,X} \times S_{t+2,\,X} \times S_{t+3,\,X} = 1$$

for all t. If any series contains no seasonal elements, the corresponding S's would all be equal to unity. The regression equation

$$\tilde{Y}_t = \alpha + \beta \tilde{X}_t + \varepsilon_t$$

in this case implies

(11.18)
$$\frac{Y_t}{S_{tY}} = \alpha + \beta \frac{X_t}{S_{tX}} + \varepsilon_t$$

or

(11.18a)
$$Y_t = \alpha S_{tY} + \beta \frac{S_{tY}}{S_{tX}} X_t + \varepsilon_t^*,$$

where
$$\varepsilon_t^* = S_{tY}\varepsilon_t.$$

Here it is assumed that the seasonal elements affect both the intercept and the slope of the regression equation and that the disturbance is heteroskedastic with variance equal to $\sigma^2 S_{tY}^2$. When a research worker is applying the least squares method to the deseasonalized data while making the usual basic assumptions about the disturbance as in (11.18), then he is implying *something* about the relationship between X and Y in the real, "nondeseasonalized" world. These implications are spelled out by (11.18a). If (11.18a) does not provide a true description of the relationship between X and Y, then the least squares estimators of α and β (based on deseasonalized data) do not, in general, possess the desirable properties that they would otherwise have.

Binary Dependent Variable

At this point we turn our attention to regression models in which the *dependent* variable is binary while the explanatory variables are quantitative. As an example, consider a regression model designed to explain the ownership of a certain appliance—for instance, a dishwasher. Suppose the postulated regression equation is

(11.19)
$$Y_i = \alpha + \beta X_i + \varepsilon_i,$$

where X_i represents the income of the ith family, and Y_i is a binary variable such that

$$Y_i = 1 \quad \text{if the } i\text{th family owns a dishwasher,}$$

$$= 0 \quad \text{otherwise.}$$

The explanatory variable X_i is assumed to be nonstochastic or, if stochastic, independent of ε_i. The disturbance ε_i is a random variable that has a zero mean and is independent of ε_j $(i \neq j)$. Since Y_i can only assume two different values, 0 and 1, we have, by the definition of mathematical expectation given by (3.23),

$$E(Y_i) = 1 \times f_i(1) + 0 \times f_i(0) = f_i(1),$$

where $f_i(1)$ is the probability that a family with income X_i has a dishwasher. Note that since from (11.19)

$$E(Y_i) = \alpha + \beta X_i,$$

the probability $f_i(1)$ is supposed to be different for different income levels. Thus $E(Y_i)$ can be interpreted as measuring the proportion of all families with income X_i who have a dishwasher. This implies that

$$0 \leq \alpha + \beta X_i \leq 1.$$

Let us now consider the disturbance ε_i. Since from (11.19)

$$\varepsilon_i = Y_i - \alpha - \beta X_i,$$

and since Y_i can only be equal to 0 or 1, it follows that for any given income X_i the disturbance can assume only two different values, $(-\alpha - \beta X_i)$ and $(1 - \alpha - \beta X_i)$. This means that ε_i is *not* normally distributed but has a discrete distribution defined as

ε_i	$f(\varepsilon_i)$
$-\alpha - \beta X_i$	f
$1 - \alpha - \beta X_i$	$1 - f$
	1

The probabilities f and $(1 - f)$ can be determined by utilizing the assumption that $E(\varepsilon_i) = 0$. This means that

$$(-\alpha - \beta X_i)f + (1 - \alpha - \beta X_i)(1 - f) = 0,$$

which gives

$$f = 1 - \alpha - \beta X_i.$$

Therefore the variance of ε_i is

(11.20)
$$E(\varepsilon_i^2) = (-\alpha - \beta X_i)^2(1 - \alpha - \beta X_i) + (1 - \alpha - \beta X_i)^2(\alpha + \beta X_i)$$
$$= (\alpha + \beta X_i)(1 - \alpha - \beta X_i) = E(Y_i)[1 - E(Y_i)].$$

This means that ε_i is heteroskedastic, since its variance depends on $E(Y_i)$.

Because of the special nature of the dependent variable in (11.19), there are some problems of estimation and prediction. The first problem is that, because of the heteroskedastic nature of the disturbance, the least squares estimators of α and β, although unbiased, are not efficient. This problem may be overcome, at least for large samples, by using the estimation formulas (8.1) and (8.3), which are designed for heteroskedastic models and involve the variances of ε_i that are unknown. In our case we obtain consistent estimates of the variances by

$$(11.21) \qquad\qquad \hat{\sigma}_i^2 = \hat{Y}_i(1 - \hat{Y}_i),$$

where $\hat{Y}_i$ is the least squares fitted value of Y_i. The second problem concerns the distribution of the estimators of α and β. Because ε_i is not normally distributed, the estimators of α and β also are not normally distributed, and thus the classical tests of significance do not apply. Should we want to test a hypothesis about α or β, we would have to derive the acceptance region from the known distribution of ε_i. However, there is no difficulty about determining the asymptotic means and variances of the estimators of α and β: the asymptotic means are equal to the true values and the asymptotic variances can be derived from formulas (8.2) and (8.4). The third and final problem concerns prediction. Since $E(Y_i)$ is interpreted as a probability, its range is confined to the interval from 0 to 1. However, the predicted value of Y is a point on a straight line and, therefore, its range is from $-\infty$ to $+\infty$ (unless the sample regression line is perfectly horizontal, of course). There are several ways of overcoming this difficulty. Perhaps the simplest is to let the estimates of α and β be $\hat{\alpha}$ and $\hat{\beta}$, and let

$$\hat{Y}_i = \hat{\alpha} + \hat{\beta} X_i.$$

Then we can use as a predictor of the value of Y for a given value of X, say X_0, the value $\overset{\square}{Y}_0$ defined as follows:

$$\overset{\square}{Y}_0 = \hat{Y}_0 \quad \text{if } 0 < \hat{Y}_0 < 1,$$
$$\phantom{\overset{\square}{Y}_0} = 1 \quad \text{if } \hat{Y}_0 \geq 1,$$
$$\phantom{\overset{\square}{Y}_0} = 0 \quad \text{if } \hat{Y}_0 \leq 0,$$

An illustration of this method of prediction is given in Figure 11–4. There are,

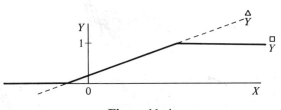

Figure 11–4

of course, difficulties about making exact probability statements concerning Y_0 since the distribution of $\overset{\square}{Y}_0$ is not determined.[2]

Qualitative Dependent and Explanatory Variables

We consider now a model in which both the dependent and the explanatory variables are qualitative. The preceding case of a qualitative dependent variable was discussed with the understanding that the characteristic in question was dichotomous. Here we no longer make such a restriction and allow the dependent characteristic to be polychotomous. However, we confine the analysis to the case in which there is only *one* explanatory characteristic. An example would be a model in which income—classified into some broad groups such as low, medium, and high—is considered to be dependent on the level of education. The sample results for such a model are usually presented in the form of the so-called *contingency table* (see Table 11–3). This is a two-way classification table with the

Table 11–3

		Explanatory Characteristic (X)						
		1	2	...	h	...	H	
Dependent Characteristic (Y)	1	n_{11}	n_{12}	...	n_{1h}	...	n_{1H}	$n_{1.}$
	2	n_{21}	n_{22}	...	n_{2h}	...	n_{2H}	$n_{2.}$
	$\vdots$	$\vdots$	$\vdots$		$\vdots$		$\vdots$	$\vdots$
	g	n_{g1}	n_{g2}	...	n_{gh}	...	n_{gH}	$n_{g.}$
	$\vdots$	$\vdots$	$\vdots$	...	$\vdots$	...	$\vdots$	$\vdots$
	G	n_{G1}	n_{G2}	...	n_{Gh}	...	n_{GH}	$n_{G.}$
		$n_{.1}$	$n_{.2}$	...	$n_{.h}$	...	$n_{.H}$	n

rows representing classifications according to, say, the dependent characteristic, and the columns representing classifications according to the explanatory characteristic. The number shown in each cell is the number of observations corresponding to the particular row and column. The entries in the body of the table represent the number of observations in the cell, and the entries on the margin are the row or column totals.

The motivation behind constructing the contingency table is the belief that there is a relation between the two characteristics. A test of this proposition would involve examining the sample data to see whether they do or do not refute such a proposition. The regression model is not well suited for such a test, but there is a *chi-square contingency table test* which has been designed for this purpose. In this test we use a test statistic that is constructed by comparing the

---

[2] An alternative approach to the problem of having a binary dependent variable is provided by the *probit analysis model*. See, e.g., J. Tobin, "Estimation of relationships for limited dependent variables," *Econometrica*, Vol. 26, January 1958, pp. 24–36.

actual number of observations, or frequencies, in each cell with the number that would occur if there were no relation between X and Y, which is usually called the "theoretical" frequency. The "theoretical" frequencies are determined by reference to "independence in probability," as defined by Theorem 5 of Section 3–3. According to this theorem, if two events are independent, then their joint probability is equal to the product of their respective marginal probabilities. This means that if X and Y are independent, then the probability that an observation drawn at random belongs to the gth row and hth column is

$$P(g \cap h) = P(g)P(h).$$

Here $P(g)$ is the probability that a random observation belongs to the gth row, and $P(h)$ is the probability that a random observation belongs to the hth column. Thus, if we knew $P(g)$ and $P(h)$, we could determine what $P(g \cap h)$ would be under independence between X and Y. Since we do *not* know $P(g)$ and $P(h)$, we estimate them by the respective sample proportions, i.e.,

$$\text{Est. } P(g) = \frac{n_{g\cdot}}{n},$$

$$\text{Est. } P(h) = \frac{n_{\cdot h}}{n}.$$

Now let e_{gh} designate the desired "theoretical" frequency for the cell in the gth row and hth column. Then we can write

(11.22) $\dfrac{e_{gh}}{n} = \text{Est. } P(g \cap h) = \text{Est. } P(g) \times \text{Est. } P(h) = \dfrac{n_{g\cdot}}{n} \times \dfrac{n_{\cdot h}}{n},$

or

(11.22a) $e_{gh} = \dfrac{n_{g\cdot} \times n_{\cdot h}}{n}.$

An intuitive justification for (11.22) can be made as follows. Suppose Y is income and X is education, and suppose the gth row represents a "medium income" group and the hth column a "high school diploma" group. Then if there were no relation between income and education, we would expect the proportion of medium income earners among the high school graduates to be the same as the proportion of medium income earners in the population as a whole. By using sample proportions instead of the population proportions, we have

$$\frac{e_{gh}}{n_{\cdot h}} = \frac{n_{g\cdot}}{n},$$

where $n_{\cdot h}$ in this case stands for the total number of high school graduates and $n_{g\cdot}$ for the total number of medium income earners. This equation is equivalent to (11.22) or (11.22a).

The chi-square contingency table test is a test of the hypothesis that there is *no* relation between X and Y. If this hypothesis is true, then the main reason for the difference between the actual and the "theoretical" frequencies would be the sampling errors. The statistic to be used for testing is

$$\sum_{g=1}^{G} \sum_{h=1}^{H} \frac{(n_{gh} - e_{gh})^2}{e_{gh}}.$$

It can be shown that this statistic has a distribution that, for large samples, can be approximated by the chi-square distribution.[3] In particular, if the sample is large, then

(11.23) $$\sum_{g=1}^{G} \sum_{h=1}^{H} \frac{(n_{gh} - e_{gh})^2}{e_{gh}} \sim \chi^2_{(G-1) \times (H-1)},$$

where the subscript $(G-1) \times (H-1)$ refers to the number of the appropriate degrees of freedom. This number is determined by the fact that with the given row and column totals, only $(G-1) \times (H-1)$ cells can be filled at will; once this is done, the numbers in the remaining cells are automatically determined. With respect to the requirement of a "large" sample size, the criterion used in practice is that none of the "theoretical" frequencies is less than 5. Consequently, it is sometimes necessary to combine cells to bring the number of frequencies up to the required minimum. When the value of the test statistic calculated on the basis of the sample observations exceeds the tabulated value of chi-square for the chosen level of significance, the null hypothesis will be rejected. Note that since the evidence against the null hypothesis can only take the form of a large value of the calculated test statistic, the appropriate test is a *one-tail* test. The chi-square contingency table test is very similar to the chi-square "goodness of fit" test discussed at the end of Section 5–2.

11–2 Models with Restricted Coefficients

Here our problem is how to incorporate into our estimation procedure some prior information about the regression coefficient (or coefficients). Such information can be viewed as providing certain restrictions on one or more given regression coefficients. For instance, if we know a priori that the population regression line passes through the origin, then, if we use this prior knowledge, we are required to restrict the value of the intercept of the sample regression line to zero. The incorporation of this prior knowledge into the estimation procedure has two distinct aspects. First, we do not estimate the intercept, since its value is known; second, we estimate the slope of the regression line in such a way that the estimator has the usual desirable properties *under the condition* that the intercept is zero. The second aspect is quite important because an estimator that has all the desirable properties under general conditions does not necessarily retain these properties when the conditions become special in some way. In our example, "general conditions" mean that the regression line can be anywhere in

---

[3] See, e.g., A. M. Mood and F. A. Graybill, *Introduction to the Theory of Statistics* (New York: McGraw-Hill, 1963), p. 318.

the plane. Once we specify that the regression line *must* pass through the origin, we impose a restriction that reduces the degree of generality.

In this section we consider several types of restrictions, some imposed by prior information about the *value* of the individual regression coefficients and others imposed by the *relations* among the individual regression coefficients.

Fixed-Value Restrictions

To illustrate the case where we have exact information about the value of one of the regression coefficients, we use a regression equation with two explanatory variables,

$$Y_i = \beta_1 + \beta_2 X_{i2} + \beta_3 X_{i3} + \varepsilon_i,$$

but the analysis applies, and can be easily extended, to equations with a larger number of explanatory variables. Suppose now that we know the value of the intercept a priori; in particular, suppose

$$\beta_1 = 0,$$

as is most commonly the case. Then, the regression equation becomes

(11.24) $$Y_i = \beta_2 X_{i2} + \beta_3 X_{i3} + \varepsilon_i.$$

This specification of the regression equation now incorporates our prior knowledge about the value of the intercept as required. The least squares estimators of β_2 and β_3 can be obtained by minimizing the sum of squares S given by

$$S = \sum_i (Y_i - \beta_2 X_{i2} - \beta_3 X_{i3})^2.$$

Differentiating S with respect to β_2 and β_3, we obtain

$$\frac{\partial S}{\partial \beta_2} = -2 \sum_i X_{i2}(Y_i - \beta_2 X_{i2} - \beta_3 X_{i3}),$$

$$\frac{\partial S}{\partial \beta_3} = -2 \sum_i X_{i3}(Y_i - \beta_2 X_{i2} - \beta_3 X_{i3}).$$

Equating each derivative to zero and rearranging terms, we obtain the following least squares normal equations:

$$\sum_i Y_i X_{i2} = \beta_2 \sum_i X_{i2}^2 + \beta_3 \sum_i X_{i2} X_{i3},$$

$$\sum_i Y_i X_{i3} = \beta_2 \sum_i X_{i2} X_{i3} + \beta_3 \sum_i X_{i3}^2.$$

(By comparison with (10.12) and (10.13), these equations are the same as those that would be obtained for the unrestricted least squares estimators if $\bar{Y}$, $\bar{X}_2$, and $\bar{X}_3$ were all zero.) The resulting estimators of β_2 and β_3 are

(11.25) $$\hat{\beta}_2 = \frac{(\sum Y_i X_{i2})(\sum X_{i3}^2) - (\sum Y_i X_{i3})(\sum X_{i2} X_{i3})}{(\sum X_{i2}^2)(\sum X_{i3}^2) - (\sum X_{i2} X_{i3})^2},$$

$$\hat{\beta}_3 = \frac{(\sum Y_i X_{i3})(\sum X_{i2}^2) - (\sum Y_i X_{i2})(\sum X_{i2} X_{i3})}{(\sum X_{i2}^2)(X_{i3}^2) - (\sum X_{i2} X_{i3})^2}.$$

To derive the formulas for the variances of $\hat{\beta}_2$ and $\hat{\beta}_3$, we note that

$$\hat{\beta}_2 = \beta_2 + \frac{(\sum X_{i3}^2)(\sum X_{i2}\varepsilon_i) - (\sum X_{i2}X_{i3})(\sum X_{i3}\varepsilon_i)}{(\sum X_{i2}^2)(\sum X_{i3}^2) - (\sum X_{i2}X_{i3})^2},$$

$$\hat{\beta}_3 = \beta_3 + \frac{(\sum X_{i2}^2)(\sum X_{i3}\varepsilon_i) - (\sum X_{i2}X_{i3})(\sum X_{i2}\varepsilon_i)}{(\sum X_{i2}^2)(\sum X_{i3}^2) - (\sum X_{i2}X_{i3})^2}.$$

Therefore,

$$(11.26)\quad \operatorname{Var}(\hat{\beta}_2) = E(\hat{\beta}_2 - \beta_2)^2 = \frac{\sigma^2 \sum X_{i3}^2}{(\sum X_{i2}^2)(\sum X_{i3}^2) - (\sum X_{i2}X_{i3})^2},$$

$$\operatorname{Var}(\hat{\beta}_3) = E(\hat{\beta}_3 - \beta_3)^2 = \frac{\sigma^2 \sum X_{i2}^2}{(\sum X_{i2}^2)(\sum X_{i3}^2) - (\sum X_{i2}X_{i3})^2},$$

$$\operatorname{Cov}(\hat{\beta}_2,\hat{\beta}_3) = E(\hat{\beta}_2 - \beta_2)(\hat{\beta}_3 - \beta_3) = \frac{-\sigma^2 \sum X_{i2}X_{i3}}{(\sum X_{i2}^2)(\sum X_{i3}^2) - (\sum X_{i2}X_{i3})^2}.$$

It can be shown, by following the steps outlined in the first part of Section 10–1, that $\hat{\beta}_2$ and $\hat{\beta}_3$ have all the desirable properties. The variances of $\hat{\beta}_2$ and $\hat{\beta}_3$ can be estimated by references to (11.26), after we replace σ^2 by its unbiased estimator s^2 defined as

$$(11.27)\qquad s^2 = \frac{1}{n-2}\sum_i (Y_i - \hat{\beta}_2 X_{i2} - \hat{\beta}_3 X_{i3})^2.$$

Note that in (11.27) we divide the sum of the squares of residuals by $(n-2)$—rather than by $(n-3)$, as in (10.34)—since only two regression coefficients are unknown. All of these results can be easily generalized to apply to regression models with more than two explanatory variables.

The preceding case demonstrates the gain achieved by incorporating the prior knowledge about a regression coefficient in the estimation procedure. The gain is essentially twofold. First, we do not have to estimate β_1 since its value is known. Second, the restricted least squares estimators of β_2 and β_3, i.e., those estimators which incorporate the information that $\beta_1 = 0$, have a smaller variance than the ordinary unrestricted least squares estimators. The second type of gain represents a less obvious but very important feature of estimation with restrictions. For example, let $\hat{\beta}_2$ stand for the restricted estimator of β_2 as defined by (11.25), and let $\hat{\beta}_2^{ORD}$ represent the ordinary unrestricted least squares estimator of β_2 as defined by (10.12). The ratio of the variances of the two estimators is

$$(11.28)\quad \frac{\operatorname{Var}(\hat{\beta}_2^{ORD})}{\operatorname{Var}(\hat{\beta}_2)} = \frac{\sigma^2 m_{33}/(m_{22}m_{33} - m_{23}^2)}{\sigma^2 \sum X_{i3}^2/[(\sum X_{i2}^2)(\sum X_{i3}^2) - (\sum X_{i2}X_{i3})^2]}$$

$$= \frac{m_{33}[(m_{22} + n\bar{X}_2^2)(m_{33} + n\bar{X}_3^2) - (m_{23} + n\bar{X}_2\bar{X}_3)^2]}{(m_{33} + n\bar{X}_3^2)(m_{22}m_{33} - m_{23}^2)}$$

$$= 1 + \frac{n(\bar{X}_2 m_{33} - \bar{X}_3 m_{23})^2}{(m_{33} + n\bar{X}_3^2)(m_{22}m_{33} - m_{23}^2)},$$

which is clearly greater than, or at best equal to, one. Thus

$$\text{Var}(\hat{\beta}_2^{ORD}) \geq \text{Var}(\hat{\beta}_2).$$

A similar proof could be presented with respect to β_3. Note, however, that while the restricted estimators of β_2 and β_3 have smaller variances than their unrestricted counterparts, the value of R^2 is higher for the unrestricted sample regression line than for the restricted one. This is because the unrestricted least squares estimation leads to the maximum value of R^2 so that *any* departure from it must result in a decrease.

Suppose now that the prior information about the value of a regression coefficient concerns not the intercept but, say, β_3. Then the regression equation

$$Y_i = \beta_1 + \beta_2 X_{i2} + \beta_3 X_{i3} + \varepsilon_i$$

can be written as

(11.29) $$Y_i^* = \beta_1 + \beta_2 X_{i2} + \varepsilon_i,$$

where Y_i^* is measured by $(Y_i - \beta_3 X_{i3})$. The least squares estimators of β_1 and β_2 of (11.29), to be called $\hat{\beta}_1$ and $\hat{\beta}_2$, have all the desirable properties. Note that in this case the variance of $\hat{\beta}_2$ is

$$\text{Var}(\hat{\beta}_2) = \frac{\sigma^2}{m_{22}},$$

whereas the variance of the unrestricted least squares estimator of β_2 is

$$\text{Var}(\hat{\beta}_2^{ORD}) = \frac{\sigma^2 m_{33}}{m_{22}m_{33} - m_{23}^2}.$$

The ratio of these variances then is

(11.30) $$\frac{\text{Var}(\hat{\beta}_2^{ORD})}{\text{Var}(\hat{\beta}_2)} = \frac{\sigma^2 m_{33}/(m_{22}m_{33} - m_{23}^2)}{\sigma^2/m_{22}} = \frac{m_{22}m_{33}}{m_{22}m_{33} - m_{23}^2}$$

$$= \frac{1}{1 - r_{23}^2},$$

where r_{23}^2 is the sample coefficient of correlation between X_{i2} and X_{i3}. Therefore, unless r_{23}^2 is zero, there is always a gain in efficiency if we use the information about β_3 when estimating β_2. This gain is particularly great if r_{23}^2 is close to unity, i.e., if the two explanatory variables are highly correlated in the sample.

Inequality Constraints

In many cases prior information about a regression coefficient is not given as a definite equality, but instead takes the form of an inequality. For instance, in the case of a linear consumption function, we know a priori that the coefficient attached to income (i.e., the marginal propensity to consume) lies between 0 and 1. In general, suppose the prior information about the regression coefficient β_k is

$$a \leq \beta_k \leq b,$$

where a and b are some known numbers, and $b > a$. Here we have the problem of estimating the coefficients of a regression equation subject to an inequality constraint on one or more of the regression coefficients. This kind of constraint is considerably more awkward to incorporate into our estimation procedure than a definite equality. The simplest way is to obtain a least squares estimator of β_k by ignoring the inequality constraint altogether, and to define the constrained estimator of β_k, say, $\hat{\beta}_k$, as follows:

$$(11.31) \qquad \hat{\beta}_k = \hat{\beta}_k^{ORD} \quad \text{if } a \le \hat{\beta}_k^{ORD} \le b,$$
$$= a \quad \text{if} \quad \hat{\beta}^{ORD} < a,$$
$$= b \quad \text{if} \quad \hat{\beta}^{ORD} > b,$$

where $\hat{\beta}_k^{ORD}$ is the ordinary, unrestricted estimator of β_k. Of course, since $\hat{\beta}_k$ is confined to a limited range, its distribution is no longer normal. However, as the sample size increases, the probability of getting the ordinary, unrestricted estimates outside the interval specified by the inequality becomes small, unless β_k is equal to either a or b. Thus, for large samples, we may regard the normal distribution as a reasonable approximation of the distribution of $\hat{\beta}_k$ of (11.31). Obviously, the closer the true value of β_k is to the center of the interval, the better the approximation will be. This approach to estimating the regression coefficients that are subject to inequality constraints has the disadvantage that the information about β_k is ignored in estimating the remaining regression coefficients. An alternative approach, which is free of this disadvantage, is to obtain estimators of the regression coefficient by maximizing the appropriate likelihood function subject to the inequality constraint (or constraints). This is a problem in quadratic programming, and its solution is complicated.[4]

A still different approach to estimation of the regression coefficients subject to inequality constraints has been suggested by Theil and Goldberger and is known as "mixed estimation."[5] The authors point out that the inequality constraint

$$a \le \beta_k \le b$$

is really a statement by which we assert that we consider it certain that β_k lies between a and b. This can be viewed as if we were making probability statements about β_k, i.e., as if we were saying that the probability of β_k lying outside the interval $a \le \beta_k \le b$ is zero and the probability of β_k lying inside that interval is one. However, if we make such statements when distinguishing between the values of β_k outside and inside the interval $a \le \beta_k \le b$, we may also be willing to make a further probability statement about β_k *within* the interval $a \le \beta_k \le b$. One such statement (which is presumably fairly common) is that we have no idea at all

[4] This approach is developed in G. C. Judge and T. Takayama, "Inequality Restrictions in Regression Analysis," *Journal of the American Statistical Association*, Vol. 61, March 1966, pp. 166–181.

[5] H. Theil and A. S. Goldberger, "On Pure and Mixed Statistical Estimation in Economics," *International Economic Review*, Vol. 2, January 1961, pp. 65–78. The method is called "mixed" because it includes elements of the classical as well as the Bayesian approaches to estimation.

about the location of β_k within the interval. This can be interpreted as meaning that, as far as we know, all values of β_k within the interval are *equally likely*, i.e., that the distribution of β_k within the interval is uniform. In this case, we can write

(11.32) $$\beta_k = \frac{a+b}{2} + u,$$

where u has a continuous uniform distribution with mean

$$E(u) = 0$$

and variance[6]

$$\text{Var}(u) = \frac{(b-a)^2}{12}.$$

This specification can be incorporated into our estimation procedure by using the "mixed" method of Theil and Goldberger.[7]

The main idea behind the "mixed" estimation method is to combine the prior information about one or more of the regression coefficients with the information provided by the sample. This can be achieved by using the inequality restriction as if it were an additional observation, and then applying the least squares method to the "extended" sample. First, we can rewrite (11.32) as

(11.32a) $$\frac{a+b}{2} = \beta_1 \times 0 + \beta_2 \times 0 + \cdots + \beta_k \times 1 + \cdots + \beta_K \times 0 + (-u),$$

which can be viewed as the $(n+1)$th observation on

$$Y_i = \beta_1 X_{i1} + \beta_2 X_{i2} + \cdots + \beta_k X_{ik} + \cdots + \beta_K X_{iK} + \varepsilon_i,$$

with $(-u)$ serving as the disturbance. However, since each of the ε's has a variance equal to σ^2, while the variance of $(-u)$ is $(b-a)^2/12$, the $(n+1)$th observation as stated in (11.32a) would bring in heteroskedasticity. This can be easily remedied by multiplying both sides of (11.32a) by $\sigma\sqrt{12}/(b-a)$ to get

(11.32b)

$$\frac{(b+a)\sigma\sqrt{3}}{b-a} = \beta_1 \times 0 + \beta_2 \times 0 + \cdots + \beta_k \times \left[\frac{\sigma\sqrt{12}}{b-a}\right] + \cdots + \beta_K \times 0 + u^*$$

---

[6] See, e.g., Freund, *op. cit.*, p. 146.

[7] Another specification would be obtained if we believed that the values of β_k in the middle of the interval $a \le \beta_k \le b$ were more likely than the values near the boundaries. Then we might specify the variance of u to be such that

$$\frac{a+b}{2} + 2\sqrt{\text{Var}(u)} = b \quad \text{and} \quad \frac{a+b}{2} - 2\sqrt{\text{Var}(u)} = a,$$

relying on the fact that, for many distributions, the values of the variable outside the range of two standard deviations on either side of the mean occur very rarely. This would give

$$\text{Var}(u) = \frac{(b-a)^2}{16}.$$

This specification is the one used by Theil and Goldberger, *op. cit.*

where

$$u^* = \frac{-u\sigma\sqrt{12}}{b-a},$$

so that

$$\text{Var}(u^*) = \left[\frac{12\sigma^2}{(b-a)^2}\right]\text{Var}(u) = \sigma^2,$$

as desired. Then, the observations in the "extended" sample are:

i	Y_i	X_{i1}	X_{i2}	$\cdots$	X_{ik}	$\cdots$	X_{iK}
1	Y_1	1	X_{12}	$\cdots$	X_{1k}	$\cdots$	X_{1K}
2	Y_2	1	X_{22}	$\cdots$	X_{2k}	$\cdots$	X_{2K}
$\vdots$	$\vdots$	$\vdots$	$\vdots$		$\vdots$		$\vdots$
n	Y_n	1	X_{n2}	$\cdots$	X_{nk}	$\cdots$	X_{nK}
$n+1$	$\dfrac{(b+a)\sigma\sqrt{3}}{b-a}$	0	0	$\cdots$	$\dfrac{\sigma\sqrt{12}}{b-a}$	$\cdots$	0

The value of the $(n+1)$th observation on Y is not known because σ is not known. However, σ can be estimated by s [as defined by (10.34)] from the first n observations. As we have shown, s^2 is an unbiased, consistent, and asymptotically efficient estimator of σ^2. The least squares normal equations for the "mixed" estimators of the regression coefficients then are

(11.33)
$$\sum_i Y_i = \hat\beta_1 n + \hat\beta_2 \sum_i X_{i2} + \cdots + \hat\beta_k \sum_i X_{ik}$$
$$+ \cdots + \hat\beta_K \sum_i X_{iK},$$

$$\sum_i Y_i X_{i2} = \hat\beta_1 \sum_i X_{i2} + \hat\beta_2 \sum_i X_{i2}^2 + \cdots + \hat\beta_k \sum_i X_{i2}X_{ik}$$
$$+ \cdots + \hat\beta_K \sum_i X_{i2}X_{iK},$$

$$\vdots$$

$$\sum_i Y_i X_{ik} + \frac{6s^2(b+a)}{(b-a)^2} = \hat\beta_1 \sum_i X_{ik} + \hat\beta_2 \sum_i X_{i2}X_{ik}$$
$$+ \cdots + \hat\beta_k \left[\sum_i X_{ik}^2 + \frac{12s^2}{(b-a)^2}\right]$$
$$+ \cdots + \hat\beta_K \sum_i X_{ik}X_{iK},$$

$$\vdots$$

$$\sum_i Y_i X_{iK} = \hat\beta_1 \sum_i X_{iK} + \hat\beta_2 \sum_i X_{i2}X_{iK} + \cdots + \hat\beta_k \sum_i X_{ik}X_{iK}$$
$$+ \cdots + \hat\beta_K \sum_i X_{iK}^2,$$

where all summations run from $i = 1$ to $i = n$. In the case of two explanatory variables with the constraint

$$a \leq \beta_2 \leq b,$$

the "mixed" estimators are

(11.34)
$$\hat{\beta}_1 = \bar{Y} - \hat{\beta}_2 \bar{X}_2 - \hat{\beta}_3 \bar{X}_3,$$

$$\hat{\beta}_2 = \frac{m_{Y2}^* m_{33} - m_{Y3} m_{23}}{m_{22}^* m_{33} - m_{23}^2},$$

$$\hat{\beta}_3 = \frac{m_{Y3} m_{22}^* - m_{Y2}^* m_{23}}{m_{22}^* m_{33} - m_{23}^2},$$

where
$$m_{Y2}^* = m_{Y2} + \frac{6s^2(b + a)}{(b - a)^2},$$

$$m_{22}^* = m_{22} + \frac{12s^2}{(b - a)^2}.$$

Except for the obvious modifications, these formulas are the same as those for the ordinary, unrestricted least squares estimators given by (10.11) through (10.13). The variances of the "mixed" estimators can be estimated as follows:

(11.35)
$$\text{Est. Var}(\hat{\beta}_2) = \frac{s^2 m_{33}}{m_{22}^* m_{33} - m_{23}^2}.$$

$$\text{Est. Var}(\hat{\beta}_3) = \frac{s^2 m_{22}^*}{m_{22}^* m_{33} - m_{23}^2}.$$

These results have been obtained by analogy with (10.24) and (10.25). The "mixed" estimators as defined by (11.34) are consistent and asymptotically efficient under the given specification, but unbiasedness is difficult to prove because the formulas involve s^2 in a nonlinear way. Note, though, that we cannot rule out the possibility that the "mixed" estimator of β_2 falls outside the specified interval. If this should happen, it would reflect the fact that, given the maintained hypothesis of the model, the sample is in disagreement with our prior information about β_2.

EXAMPLE   We may illustrate the method of "mixed" estimation by estimating the coefficients of the quarterly consumption function for the United States,

$$C_t = \alpha + \beta Y_t + \varepsilon_t,$$

where C = consumption and Y = income. The prior information concerning β is

$$0 \leq \beta \leq 1.$$

This function has been estimated by Zellner[8] without the inequality constraint with

[8] A. Zellner, "The Short Run Consumption Function," *Econometrica*, Vol. 25, October 1957, pp. 552–567.

the following result:

$$C_t = 38.09 + 0.747\,Y_t + e_t, \qquad \bar{R}^2 = 0.944.$$
$$(0.033)$$

If we wish to impose the inequality restriction on β and use the "mixed" estimation method, we put

$$\beta = \tfrac{1}{2} + u,$$

where $\qquad E(u) = 0 \qquad$ and $\qquad \mathrm{Var}(u) = \dfrac{1}{12}.$

The least squares normal equations then become

$$\sum_i C_i = \hat{\alpha} n + \hat{\beta} \sum_i Y_i,$$

$$\sum_i C_i\,Y_i + 6s^2 = \hat{\alpha} \sum_i Y_i + \hat{\beta}\!\left(\sum_i Y_i^2 + 12s^2\right).$$

By eliminating $\hat{\alpha}$ we obtain

$$\sum (C_i - \bar{C})(Y_i - \bar{Y}) + 6s^2 = \hat{\beta}\!\left[\sum (Y_i - \bar{Y})^2 + 12s^2\right].$$

Now, from Zellner's results, we find that

$$\sum (C_i - \bar{C})(Y_i - \bar{Y}) = 0.747 \times \sum (Y_i - \bar{Y})^2$$

and $\qquad \dfrac{s^2}{\sum (Y_i - \bar{Y})^2} = 0.033^2,$

or $\qquad s^2 = 0.033^2 \times \sum (Y_i - \bar{Y})^2.$

Therefore,

$$0.747 \times \sum (Y_i - \bar{Y})^2 + 6 \times 0.033^2 \times \sum (Y_i - \bar{Y})^2$$
$$= \hat{\beta}\!\left[\sum (Y_i - \bar{Y})^2 + 12 \times 0.033^2 \times \sum (Y_i - \bar{Y})^2\right].$$

This can be solved for $\hat{\beta}$ because the term $\sum (Y_i - \bar{Y})^2$ cancels out. The result is

$$\hat{\beta} = 0.744$$

and $\qquad \hat{\alpha} = \bar{C} - 0.744\,\bar{Y} = (38.09 + 0.747\,\bar{Y}) - 0.744\,\bar{Y}$

$$= 38.09 + 0.003 \times 200.55 = 38.69.$$

Finally,

$$\text{Est. Var}(\hat{\beta}) = \frac{s^2}{\sum (Y_i - \bar{Y})^2 + 12s^2} = \frac{0.033^2 \times \sum (Y_i - \bar{Y})^2}{\sum (Y_i - \bar{Y})^2 + 12 \times 0.033^2 \times \sum (Y_i - \bar{Y})^2}$$

$$= 0.001075.$$

The result of the "mixed" estimation of the consumption function therefore is

$$C_t = 38.69 + 0.744\,Y_t + e_t.$$
$$(0.033)$$

As can be seen, the incorporation of the inequality restriction into the estimation procedure has resulted in only a very slight change in the estimated regression equation in this case.

Linear Restrictions

Frequently, the prior information available is not about the values of the individual regression coefficients, but about the relations among them. For instance, we may know a priori that one coefficient is equal to the sum of two other coefficients, or that certain coefficients form a geometric progression. These restrictions can be divided into two types, depending upon whether the relation between the coefficients is linear or nonlinear. We will discuss the *linear restrictions* first because they are simpler. In either case, we find it convenient to compare the regression equation in which the restrictions are explicitly taken into account with the regression equation in which the restrictions are ignored. The parameters of the former will be called "restricted," and those of the latter "unrestricted." Such a juxtaposition will enable us to introduce the concept of "identification," which plays an important role in many econometric problems. Our discussion will be carried out in terms of examples that illustrate the type of problem and its solution and that can be easily modified to fit other cases.

Consider the problem of estimating a regression model with one explanatory variable and with additive seasonal effects. That is,

$$Y_t = \alpha_1 + \beta X_t + \varepsilon_t \quad \text{(spring quarter)},$$

$$Y_t = \alpha_2 + \beta X_t + \varepsilon_t \quad \text{(summer quarter)},$$

$$Y_t = \alpha_3 + \beta X_t + \varepsilon_t \quad \text{(fall quarter)},$$

$$Y_t = \alpha_4 + \beta X_t + \varepsilon_t \quad \text{(winter quarter)}.$$

By introducing binary variables for the last three quarters, we can rewrite the above compactly:

(11.36) $Y_t = \alpha_1 + \beta X_t + (\alpha_2 - \alpha_1)Q_{t2} + (\alpha_3 - \alpha_1)Q_{t3} + (\alpha_4 - \alpha_1)Q_{t4} + \varepsilon_t,$

where
$$Q_{t2} = 1 \quad \text{if } t \text{ is a summer quarter,}$$
$$= 0 \quad \text{otherwise;}$$
$$Q_{t3} = 1 \quad \text{if } t \text{ is a fall quarter,}$$
$$= 0 \quad \text{otherwise;}$$
$$Q_{t4} = 1 \quad \text{if } t \text{ is a winter quarter,}$$
$$= 0 \quad \text{otherwise.}$$

Here we have five restricted parameters: α_1, α_2, α_3, α_4, and β. The restrictions in this case are that α_2 must be equal to the coefficient of Q_{t2} *plus* the intercept, α_3 to the coefficient of Q_{t3} *plus* the intercept, and α_4 to the coefficient of Q_{t4} *plus* the intercept. The unrestricted form of (11.36) is

(11.36a) $Y_t = \beta_1 + \beta_2 Q_{t2} + \beta_3 Q_{t3} + \beta_4 Q_{t4} + \beta_5 X_t + \varepsilon_t.$

when we compare the unrestricted coefficients of (11.36a) with the restricted parameters of (11.36), we can see that

$$\beta_1 = \alpha_1,$$
$$\beta_2 = \alpha_2 - \alpha_1,$$
$$\beta_3 = \alpha_3 - \alpha_1,$$
$$\beta_4 = \alpha_4 - \alpha_1,$$
$$\beta_5 = \beta.$$

In this case there is a one-to-one correspondence between the restricted parameters in the sense that there is a unique solution for the restricted parameters in terms of the unrestricted parameters. In particular,

$$\alpha_1 = \beta_1,$$
$$\alpha_2 = \beta_2 + \beta_1,$$
$$\alpha_3 = \beta_3 + \beta_1,$$
$$\alpha_4 = \beta_4 + \beta_1,$$
$$\beta = \beta_5.$$

A case like this is called *exact identification* to indicate the fact that the restricted parameters can be uniquely "identified" by reference to the unrestricted coefficients.

The practical importance of exact identification is that we can obtain least squares of estimates of the unrestricted coefficients and use them to obtain estimates of the restricted parameters. Since the estimates of the restricted parameters are all linear functions of the estimates of the unrestricted coefficients, all of the desirable properties of the latter will be carried over to the former. The variances of the estimated restricted parameters can be determined from the variances and covariances of the estimated unrestricted coefficients. In particular,

$$\text{Var}(\hat{\alpha}_1) = \text{Var}(\hat{\beta}_1),$$
$$\text{Var}(\hat{\alpha}_2) = \text{Var}(\hat{\beta}_1) + \text{Var}(\hat{\beta}_2) + 2\,\text{Cov}(\hat{\beta}_1,\hat{\beta}_2),$$
$$\text{Var}(\hat{\alpha}_3) = \text{Var}(\hat{\beta}_1) + \text{Var}(\hat{\beta}_3) + 2\,\text{Cov}(\hat{\beta}_1,\hat{\beta}_3),$$
$$\text{Var}(\hat{\alpha}_4) = \text{Var}(\hat{\beta}_1) + \text{Var}(\hat{\beta}_4) + 2\,\text{Cov}(\hat{\beta}_1,\hat{\beta}_4),$$
$$\text{Var}(\hat{\beta}) = \text{Var}(\hat{\beta}_5).$$

The same relations hold between the respective estimates of the variances. Note that the same results for the estimates of the restricted parameters would be obtained by rewriting (11.36) as

(11.36b) $Y_t = \alpha_1 Q_{t1} + \alpha_2 Q_{t2} + \alpha_3 Q_{t3} + \alpha_4 Q_{t4} + \beta X_t + \varepsilon_t.$

where $Q_{t1} = 1$ if t is a spring quarter,
         $= 0$ otherwise.

Equation (11.36b) is restricted to pass through the origin, and can be estimated by the method of least squares, as described at the outset of this section. The resulting estimates and their variances are precisely the same as those obtained from the unrestricted estimates of (11.36a).

Consider now a different case of linear restrictions, namely, one in which the sum of two or more of the regression coefficients is equal to a given number. A well-known example of such a restriction is the Cobb-Douglas production function characterized by constant returns to scale. Here we require that the sum of the regression slopes be equal to unity. Specifically,

$$(11.37) \qquad Y_i = \alpha_1 + \alpha_2 X_{i2} + (1 - \alpha_2)X_{i3} + \varepsilon_i,$$

where Y_i = log output, X_{i2} = log labor input, and X_{i3} = log capital input. We have two restricted parameters: α_1 and α_2. The unrestricted form of (11.37) is

$$(11.37a) \qquad Y_i = \beta_1 + \beta_2 X_{i2} + \beta_3 X_{i3} + \varepsilon_i.$$

The relationship between the unrestricted and the restricted parameters is

$$\beta_1 = \alpha_1,$$
$$\beta_2 = \alpha_2,$$
$$\beta_3 = 1 - \alpha_2.$$

In this case, the number of unrestricted coefficients exceeds the number of the restricted parameters, and there is no unique solution for α_2. In fact,

$$\alpha_1 = \beta_1,$$
$$\alpha_2 = \beta_2,$$

and
$$\alpha_2 = 1 - \beta_3.$$

This case is called *overidentification*, alluding to the fact that there is more than one solution to "identify" the restricted parameter α_2.

Under the conditions of overidentification, we cannot proceed with estimation (as we can with exact identification) by estimating the unrestricted equation and then translating the results to obtain estimates of the restricted parameters. Rather, we must turn directly to the restricted equation (11.37). The least squares estimators of the restricted parameters can be obtained by minimizing

$$\sum_i [Y_i - \alpha_1 - \alpha_2 X_{i2} - (1 - \alpha_2)X_{i3}]^2$$

with respect to α_1 and α_2. It can be easily shown that the resulting estimates are exactly the same as those obtained by applying the least squares method to

$$(11.37b) \qquad Y_i^* = \alpha_1 + \alpha_2 X_{i2}^* + \varepsilon_i,$$

where Y_i^* is measured by $(Y_i - X_{i3})$ and X_{i2}^* by $(X_{i2} - X_{i3})$. Equation (11.37b) represents just another way of writing (11.37) by rearranging its terms. This possibility is always open whenever we have overidentification and whenever the restrictions are linear.

As a third and final case of linear restrictions, we consider the case where the number of the restricted parameters is larger than the number of unrestricted coefficients. For example, suppose that family expenditure on fruit can be described by the following regression equation:

$$F_i = \alpha_F + \beta_F Y_i + \varepsilon_{iF},$$

where F_i = family expenditure on fruit, and Y_i = family income. Suppose further that family expenditure on vegetables can be described by

$$V_i = \alpha_V + \beta_V Y_i + \varepsilon_{iV},$$

where V_i = family expenditure on vegetables. Now if, as is commonly the case, the sample does not provide separate information on expenditure on fruit and on vegetables but only their total, we have to combine the foregoing regressions to get

(11.38) $$G_i = (\alpha_F + \alpha_V) + (\beta_F + \beta_V) Y_i + \varepsilon_i,$$

where $G_i = F_i + V_i$, and $\varepsilon_i = \varepsilon_{iF} + \varepsilon_{iV}$. The unrestricted version of (11.38) is

(11.38a) $$G_i = \alpha + \beta Y_i + \varepsilon_i.$$

when we compare the coefficients of the two equations, we get

$$\alpha = \alpha_F + \alpha_V \qquad \text{and} \qquad \beta = \beta_F + \beta_V.$$

Here we have four restricted parameters and only two unrestricted coefficients. Clearly, we cannot express the restricted parameters in terms of the unrestricted coefficients. This is known as the case of *underidentification*, in which the restricted parameters cannot be estimated on the basis of the available sample information.

Nonlinear Restrictions

As our first case of nonlinear restrictions we consider *exact identification*. This can be illustrated by a simple version of the so-called "stock adjustment model." Suppose the volume of stock of a commodity that a firm "desires" to hold is equal to a given linear function of sales, i.e.,

$$Y_t^* = \alpha + \beta X_t,$$

where Y_t^* = desired level of stock at the end of period t, and X_t = sales during the period t. Y^* is, in general, not observable. Now suppose further that the adjustment on the part of each firm to the desired level in any one period is not complete, so that

$$Y_t - Y_{t-1} = \gamma(Y_t^* - Y_{t-1}) + \varepsilon_t,$$

where Y_t = actual level of stock at the end of period t. The parameter γ is called the "adjustment coefficient," and its value lies between 0 and 1. A value of γ close to zero indicates that only a small part of the gap between the desired and the actual level of stock is closed during any one period, while a value of γ close to unity indicates that a large part of the gap is closed. The disturbance ε_t is brought in to allow for random influences in carrying out the adjustment. Substituting for Y_t^* and rearranging terms, we obtain

$$(11.39) \qquad Y_t = \alpha\gamma + \beta\gamma X_t + (1 - \gamma)Y_{t-1} + \varepsilon_t.$$

This is an equation that explains investment in stock. All variables in this equation except ε_t are observable. In (11.39) we have three "restricted" parameters: α, β, and γ. The unrestricted counterpart of (11.39) is

$$(11.39a) \qquad Y_t = \beta_1 + \beta_2 X_t + \beta_3 Y_{t-1} + \varepsilon_t.$$

The coefficients of (11.39a) are related to the parameters of (11.39) as follows:

$$\beta_1 = \alpha\gamma,$$
$$\beta_2 = \beta\gamma,$$
$$\beta_3 = 1 - \gamma.$$

In this case, we can obtain a unique solution for the restricted parameters in terms of the unrestricted coefficients; that is, we have *exact identification*. The solution is

$$\alpha = \frac{\beta_1}{1 - \beta_3},$$
$$\beta = \frac{\beta_2}{1 - \beta_3},$$
$$\gamma = 1 - \beta_3.$$

Note that α and β are *nonlinear* functions of the unrestricted β's.

To estimate the parameters of (11.39), we obtain least squares estimates of the unrestricted coefficients of (11.39a), and use the solution for α, β, and γ to obtain the corresponding estimates of these parameters. [The inequality restrictions on γ, and consequently on β_3, can be taken care of by following the rule specified in (11.31).] As for the desirable properties of the resulting estimators, we note that those estimators which are nonlinear functions of the unconstrained coefficients inherit the desirable asymptotic, but *not* small-sample, properties from the unconstrained estimators. The reason is that unbiasedness does not "carry over" *via* nonlinear functions (see Theorem 17 and the subsequent remarks in Section 6–1). In the present case, the unconstrained estimators themselves are not unbiased because of the presence of Y_{t-1} among the explanatory variables, so that *none* of the constrained estimators can be claimed to be unbiased. The variance of the restricted estimator of γ can be determined by reference to the variance of the unrestricted $\hat{\beta}_3$ if we note that

$$\mathrm{Var}(\hat{\gamma}) = \mathrm{Var}(\hat{\beta}_3).$$

The determination of the variances of $\hat{\alpha}$ and $\hat{\beta}$ is somewhat more troublesome because $\hat{\alpha}$ and $\hat{\beta}$ are not linear functions of the unrestricted estimators. However, there is an approximate formula that can be used in this case. The formula refers to the general case where an estimator, say $\hat{\alpha}$, is a function of k other estimators such as, $\hat{\beta}_1, \hat{\beta}_2, \ldots, \hat{\beta}_k$; i.e.,

$$\hat{\alpha} = f(\hat{\beta}_1, \hat{\beta}_2, \ldots, \hat{\beta}_k).$$

Then the large-sample variance of $\hat{\alpha}$ can be approximated[9] as

$$(11.40) \qquad \text{Var}(\hat{\alpha}) \approx \sum_{k} \left[\frac{\partial f}{\partial \hat{\beta}_k}\right]^2 \text{Var}(\hat{\beta}_k) + 2 \sum_{j<k} \left[\frac{\partial f}{\partial \hat{\beta}_j}\right]\left[\frac{\partial f}{\partial \hat{\beta}_k}\right] \text{Cov}(\hat{\beta}_j, \hat{\beta}_k)$$

$$(j, k = 1, 2, \ldots, K; j < k).$$

(The approximation is obtained by using Taylor expansion for $f(\hat{\beta}_1, \hat{\beta}_2, \ldots, \hat{\beta}_k)$ around $\hat{\beta}_1, \hat{\beta}_2, \ldots, \hat{\beta}_k$, dropping terms of the order of two or higher, and then obtaining the variance by the usual formula.) For example, for

$$\hat{\alpha} = \frac{\hat{\beta}_1}{1 - \hat{\beta}_3},$$

we have

$$\text{Var}(\hat{\alpha}) \approx \left[\frac{1}{1 - \hat{\beta}_3}\right]^2 \text{Var}(\hat{\beta}_1) + \left[\frac{\hat{\beta}_1}{(1 - \hat{\beta}_3)^2}\right]^2 \text{Var}(\hat{\beta}_3)$$

$$+ 2 \left[\frac{1}{1 - \hat{\beta}_3}\right]\left[\frac{\hat{\beta}_1}{(1 - \hat{\beta}_3)^2}\right] \text{Cov}(\hat{\beta}_1, \hat{\beta}_3).$$

This formula can be used to approximate the large-sample variance of $\hat{\alpha}$. Since the large-sample variances and covariances of the unrestricted estimators can be readily estimated by the application of the standard formulas, there is no problem in estimating the large-sample variances of the restricted estimators.

An alternative approach to estimating the parameters of (11.39) is to minimize the sum of squares S given by

$$S = \sum_{t=2}^{n} [Y_t - \alpha\gamma - \beta\gamma X_t - (1 - \gamma)Y_{t-1}]^2$$

with respect to α, β, and γ. The resulting estimators of these parameters are called *nonlinear least squares estimators*. It can easily be shown that these estimators are exactly the same as those obtained from the estimated unconstrained coefficients of (11.39a). Further, since the logarithmic likelihood function for $Y_2, Y_3, \ldots, Y_n$ (conditional on Y_1) is

$$L = -\frac{n}{2}\log 2\pi\sigma^2 - \frac{1}{2\sigma^2} \sum_{t=2}^{n} [Y_t - \alpha\gamma - \beta\gamma X_t - (1 - \gamma)Y_{t-1}]^2,$$

minimizing S with respect to α, β, and γ is equivalent to maximizing L with respect to the same parameters. Thus, if the regression disturbance is normally

---

[9] See L. R. Klein, *A Textbook of Econometrics* (Evanston, Illinois: Row, Peterson, 1953), p. 258.

distributed, nonlinear least squares estimators are the same as maximum likelihood estimators. Therefore, we can estimate their asymptotic variances by using the appropriate information matrix.

EXAMPLE   The case of nonlinear restrictions under conditions of exact identification is encountered in connection with one of the consumption function models considered by Zellner.[10] This model is not a "stock adjustment model" in the strict sense, but it has the same basic features. If we use a simple variant of the "permanent income hypothesis," we can postulate the consumption function as

$$C_t = \alpha + k(1 - \lambda)Y_t + \lambda C_{t-1} + u_t$$

where C = real consumption, and Y = real income. The unrestricted counterpart of this equation is

$$C_t = \beta_1 + \beta_2 Y_t + \beta_3 C_{t-1} + u_t.$$

The disturbance term u_t was assumed to be nonautoregressive. Zellner estimated the unrestricted function from 31 quarterly observations for the United States with the following result:

$$C_t = 0.10 + 0.128\,Y_t + 0.870 C_{t-1} + e_t, \quad \bar{R}^2 = 0.978.$$
$$(0.093) \quad\;\; (0.127)$$

Therefore, the estimates of the restricted parameters are

$$\hat{\alpha} = \hat{\beta}_1 = 0.10,$$

$$\hat{k} = \frac{\hat{\beta}_2}{1 - \hat{\beta}_3} = 0.985,$$

$$\hat{\lambda} = \hat{\beta}_3 = 0.870.$$

The estimate of the large-sample standard error of $\hat{\lambda}$ can be obtained directly from the unrestricted result. The estimated large-sample standard error of $\hat{k}$ can be found by using the approximation formula (11.40), i.e., by noting that

$$\text{Var}(\hat{k}) = \left[\frac{1}{1 - \hat{\beta}_3}\right]^2 \text{Var}(\hat{\beta}_2) + \left[\frac{\hat{\beta}_2}{(1 - \hat{\beta}_3)^2}\right]^2 \text{Var}(\hat{\beta}_3)$$

$$+ 2\left[\frac{1}{1 - \hat{\beta}_3}\right]\left[\frac{\hat{\beta}_2}{(1 - \hat{\beta}_3)^2}\right]\text{Cov}(\hat{\beta}_2, \hat{\beta}_3).$$

Estimates of $\text{Var}(\hat{\beta}_2)$ and $\text{Var}(\hat{\beta}_3)$ are directly available from Zellner's results. The estimate of $\text{Cov}(\hat{\beta}_2, \hat{\beta}_3)$ can be obtained by noting that

$$\text{Cov}(\hat{\beta}_2, \hat{\beta}_3) = \frac{-\sigma^2 m_{23}}{m_{22}m_{33} - m_{23}^2} = \frac{-\sigma^2 r_{23}\sqrt{m_{22}}\sqrt{m_{33}}}{m_{22}m_{33} - m_{23}^2} = -r_{23}\sqrt{\text{Var}(\hat{\beta}_2)}\sqrt{\text{Var}(\hat{\beta}_3)},$$

so that the only additional information needed is the value of r_{23}, the sample coefficient of correlation between Y_t and C_{t-1}. This value can be found from the relation

---

[10] *Op. cit.* The theoretical development is not given in Zellner's paper but can be found in A. Zellner, D. S. Huang, and L. C. Chau, "Further Analysis of the Short-Run Consumption Function with Emphasis on the Role of Liquid Assets," *Econometrica*, Vol. 33, July 1965, pp. 571–581.

between the F statistic and the two t statistics. First, since $\bar{R}^2 = 0.978$, it follows from (10.41) that

$$R^2 = 0.9795.$$

Therefore, by reference to (10.43),

$$F = \frac{R^2/(3-1)}{(1-R^2)/(31-3)} = 669.$$

This enables us to utilize (10.44b):

$$669 = \frac{(0.128/0.093)^2 + (0.870/0.127)^2 + 2(0.128/0.093)(0.870/0.127)r_{23}}{2(1-r_{23}^2)}.$$

This is a quadratic equation in r_{23} which has one positive and one negative root. We choose the positive root since the sample correlation between Y_t and C_{t-1} is clearly positive. This gives

$$r_{23} = 0.975,$$

and

$$\text{Est. Cov}(\hat{\beta}_2, \hat{\beta}_3) = -0.975 \times 0.093 \times 0.127 = -0.011515.$$

Therefore,

$$\text{Est. Var}(\hat{k}) = \left[\frac{1}{1-0.870}\right]^2 0.093^2 + \left[\frac{0.128}{(1-0.870)^2}\right]^2 0.127^2$$

$$+ \left[\frac{1}{1-0.870}\right]\left[\frac{0.128}{(1-0.870)^2}\right](-0.011515) = 0.095175.$$

Thus, the estimated large-sample standard errors of the restricted estimators are

$$s_{\hat{\lambda}} = 0.127 \qquad \text{and} \qquad s_{\hat{k}} = 0.308.$$

This means that both $\hat{\lambda}$ and $\hat{k}$ are highly significant.

To illustrate *overidentifying nonlinear restrictions*, we use a simple regression model in which the disturbance follows a first-order autoregressive scheme. In particular, suppose we have

$$Y_t = \alpha + \beta X_t + \varepsilon_t,$$

$$\varepsilon_t = \rho \varepsilon_{t-1} + u_t,$$

where $u_t \sim N(0, \sigma_u^2)$, and $E(u_t \varepsilon_{t-1}) = 0$. As mentioned in Section 8–2, the regression equation can be transformed in such a way that the autoregressive disturbance ε_t is eliminated. By lagging the regression equation by one period, multiplying it by ρ, and deducting the result from the original form of the regression equation, we obtain

$$Y_t - \rho Y_{t-1} = \alpha(1-\rho) + \beta(X_t - \rho X_{t-1}) + u_t.$$

This equation appears as (8.52) in Section 8–2. Alternatively,

(11.41) $$Y_t = \alpha(1-\rho) + \beta X_t - \beta\rho X_{t-1} + \rho Y_{t-1} + u_t,$$

which is a multiple regression equation with parameters α, β, and ρ. The unrestricted counterpart of (11.41) is

(11.41a) $$Y_t = \beta_1 + \beta_2 X_t + \beta_3 X_{t-1} + \beta_4 Y_{t-1} + u_t.$$

By comparing the two versions, we see that

$$\beta_1 = \alpha(1 - \rho),$$

$$\beta_2 = \beta,$$

$$\beta_3 = -\beta\rho,$$

$$\beta_4 = \rho.$$

That is, we have four unrestricted coefficients and only three restricted parameters. Since there is no unique solution for any of the restricted parameters in terms of the unrestricted coefficients, we clearly have a case of *overidentification*. However, there is no great difficulty about estimating the restricted parameters by the nonlinear least squares method; i.e., we can minimize

$$S = \sum_{t=2}^{n} [Y_t - \alpha(1 - \rho) - \beta X_t + \beta\rho X_{t-1} - \rho Y_{t-1}]^2$$

with respect to α, β, and ρ. The resulting estimates are equivalent to the maximum likelihood estimates (conditional on Y_1), and their asymptotic variances can be estimated by reference to the information matrix. A convenient way of carrying out the calculations on a digital computer is described in Section 8–2, where we also discuss several alternative estimation methods designed for this model. The maximum likelihood estimation method is available for any kind of overidentification; but in some cases the computations are highly complicated, and it is not always guaranteed that the maximum of the likelihood function is not a local one rather than a global one.

Finally, we consider *underidentification*. We shall illustrate this in the context of a model in which some parameters are overidentified and some are underidentified. Consider another consumption function model developed and estimated by Zellner, Huang, and Chau:[11]

(11.42) $$C_t = (k - \alpha\eta)(1 - \lambda)Y_t + \alpha L_{t-1} - \alpha\lambda L_{t-2} + \lambda C_{t-1} + u_t,$$

where $$u_t = \varepsilon_t - \lambda\varepsilon_{t-1},$$

and L = actual holdings of liquid assets at the end of the period. Thus we have four parameters—α, λ, k, and η—to estimate. The unrestricted version of (11.42) is

(11.42a) $$C_t = \beta_1 Y_t + \beta_2 L_{t-1} + \beta_3 L_{t-2} + \beta_4 C_{t-1} + u_t.$$

[11] *Ibid.*

There are then four unrestricted coefficients in (11.42a). The relation between the parameters of (11.42) and the coefficients of (11.42a) is

$$\beta_1 = (k - \alpha\eta)(1 - \lambda),$$

$$\beta_2 = \alpha,$$

$$\beta_3 = -\alpha\lambda,$$

$$\beta_4 = \lambda.$$

From this, we can see that

$$\alpha = \beta_2 \quad \text{or} \quad \alpha = -\frac{\beta_3}{\beta_4},$$

and

$$\lambda = \beta_4 \quad \text{or} \quad \alpha = -\frac{\beta_3}{\beta_2}.$$

Thus, α and λ are overidentified, but no solution exists for k and η. This means that k and η are underidentified. The implication of this is that α and λ can be estimated by the nonlinear least squares method, but no estimates of k and η are obtainable from the sample. All that can be done is to get an estimate of $(k - \alpha\eta)$.

EXAMPLE   The estimates of the parameters of (11.42) have been obtained by Zellner, Huang, and Chau from quarterly data for the United States on the assumption that u_t is nonautoregressive. The result of the nonlinear least squares estimation is

$$C_t = 0.475\,Y_t + 0.226L_{t-1} - 0.085L_{t-2} + 0.378C_{t-1} + e_t.$$
$$\quad\;\;(0.085)\quad\;\;(0.045)\qquad\qquad\qquad\quad(0.106)$$

Thus,
$$\hat{\alpha} = 0.226,$$

$$\hat{\lambda} = 0.378,$$

$$\hat{k} - 0.226\hat{\eta} = 0.763.$$

This equation was also estimated by the nonlinear least squares method with the addition of a constant term:

$$C_t = -12.470 + 0.538\,Y_t + 0.376L_{t-1} - 0.091L_{t-2} + 0.242C_{t-1} + e_t.$$
$$\qquad\qquad\quad(0.080)\quad\;\;(0.050)\qquad\qquad\qquad\quad(0.105)$$

The result of the unrestricted least squares estimation of the previous equation is

$$C_t = -1.082 + 0.517\,Y_t + 0.560L_{t-1} - 0.296L_{t-2} + 0.273C_{t-1} + e_t.$$
$$\quad(3.606)\quad(0.085)\quad\;\;(0.172)\qquad\;\;(0.181)\qquad\;\;(0.110)$$

Note that the unrestricted estimates are numerically different from the restricted estimates, but for some coefficients the differences are not overwhelming.

The Effect of Restrictions on R^2 and the Variance of the Forecast Error

In the case where the restricted parameters are exactly identified in terms of the unrestricted coefficients, the restricted estimates lead to the same sample regression equation as the unrestricted estimates. This means that the value of

R^2 and the forecast of the value of the dependent variable are the same for both sets of estimates. However, if the restricted estimation is carried out under conditions of overidentification, then the sample regression line based on the restricted estimates will be different from the sample regression line based on the unrestricted estimates. Since the unrestricted least squares estimates minimize the sum of squares of the residuals, they lead to the maximum attainable value of R^2. This necessarily implies that the value of R^2 for the restricted sample regression equation will be lower than, or equal to, the value of R^2 for the unrestricted sample regression equation. This fact has been used sometimes as an argument for supposing that a forecast of the value of the dependent variable based on the unrestricted estimates is better than one based on the restricted estimates. If we interpret the word "better" as meaning "having a smaller (or equal) variance of the forecast error," then the argument is fallacious. We shall prove this for the case of overidentification under linear restrictions, but the proof could be extended to apply to nonlinear restrictions as well. (In the case of nonlinear restrictions, the proof is complicated by the fact that the restricted estimators are nonlinear functions of the disturbances. However, a proof in terms of asymptotic variances and covariances is quite feasible.)

Consider, for instance, the regression equation (11.37), which we have used to illustrate overidentification with linear restrictions. The equation was presented as

$$Y_i = \alpha_1 + \alpha_2 X_{i2} + (1 - \alpha_2)X_{i3} + \varepsilon_i,$$

with the unrestricted version given by (11.37a) as

$$Y_i = \beta_1 + \beta_2 X_{i2} + \beta_3 X_{i3} + \varepsilon_i.$$

Suppose now that we wish to forecast the value of Y for some given values of the two explanatory variables, say X_{02} and X_{03}. Using the unrestricted regression equation, we would forecast the value of Y by, say, $\hat{Y}_0$, defined as

$$\hat{Y}_0 = \hat{\beta}_1 + \hat{\beta}_2 X_{02} + \hat{\beta}_3 X_{03},$$

where the $\hat{\beta}$'s represent the unrestricted least squares estimates of the β's. Using the formula (10.49), we can determine the variance of the forecast error of $\hat{Y}_0$ as

$$(11.43) \quad E(\hat{Y}_0 - Y_0)^2 = \sigma^2 + \frac{\sigma^2}{u} + (X_{02} - \bar{X}_2)^2 \text{Var}(\hat{\beta}_2) + (X_{03} - \bar{X}_3)^2 \text{Var}(\hat{\beta}_3)$$

$$+ 2(X_{02} - \bar{X}_2)(X_{03} - \bar{X}_3)\text{Cov}(\hat{\beta}_2, \hat{\beta}_3)$$

$$= \sigma^2\left[1 + \frac{1}{n} + \frac{(X_{02} - \bar{X}_2)^2 m_{33} + (X_{03} - \bar{X}_3)^2 m_{22}}{m_{22}m_{33} - m_{23}^2}\right.$$

$$\left. - \frac{2(X_{02} - \bar{X}_2)(X_{03} - \bar{X}_3)m_{23}}{m_{22}m_{33} - m_{23}^2}\right].$$

On the other hand, if we use the restricted regression equation for forecasting the value of Y, we use $\tilde{Y}_0$ defined as

$$\tilde{Y}_0 = \hat{\alpha}_1 + \hat{\alpha}_2 X_{02} + (1 - \hat{\alpha}_2)X_{03},$$

where the $\hat{\alpha}$'s represent the restricted least squares estimates of the α's. The variance of the forecast error in this case is

$$(11.44) \quad E(\tilde{Y}_0 - Y_0)^2 = E[(\tilde{Y}_0 - X_{03}) - (Y_0 - X_{03})]^2$$

$$= \sigma^2 + \frac{\sigma^2}{n} + [(X_{02} - X_{03}) - (\bar{X}_2 - \bar{X}_3)]^2 \mathrm{Var}(\hat{\alpha}_2)$$

$$= \sigma^2 \left[1 + \frac{1}{n} + \frac{(X_{02} - \bar{X}_2)^2 + (X_{03} - \bar{X}_3)^2}{m_{22} + m_{33} - 2m_{23}} \right.$$

$$\left. - \frac{2(X_{02} - \bar{X}_2)(X_{03} - \bar{X}_3)}{m_{22} + m_{33} - 2m_{23}} \right].$$

Let us now compare (11.43) with (11.44). The difference between the two is

$$(11.45)$$

$$E(\hat{Y}_0 - Y_0)^2 - E(\tilde{Y}_0 - Y_0)^2$$

$$= \sigma^2 \left[\frac{(X_{02} - \bar{X}_2)^2 m_{33} + (X_{03} - \bar{X}_3)^2 m_{22} - 2(X_{02} - \bar{X}_2)(X_{03} - \bar{X}_3)m_{23}}{m_{22}m_{33} - m_{23}^2} \right.$$

$$\left. - \frac{(X_{02} - \bar{X}_2)^2 + (X_{03} - \bar{X}_3)^2 - 2(X_{02} - \bar{X}_2)(X_{03} - \bar{X}_3)}{m_{22} + m_{33} - 2m_{23}} \right]$$

$$= \sigma^2 \left\{ \frac{[(X_{02} - \bar{X}_2)(m_{33} - m_{23}) + (X_{03} - \bar{X}_3)(m_{22} - m_{23})]^2}{(m_{22}m_{33} - m_{23}^2)(m_{22} + m_{33} - 2m_{23})} \right\}.$$

This expression is clearly positive (or zero), which indicates that the variance of the forecast error for the unrestricted predictor $\hat{Y}_0$ is larger than, or at best equal to, the variance of the forecast error for the restricted predictor $\tilde{Y}_0$. This means that the restricted regression equation leads to a better forecasting procedure than the unrestricted regression equation.

The Role of Prior Restrictions in Estimation

A useful way of ending this section may be by making a few remarks on the relevance of prior restrictions in estimation. Prior restrictions on the regression coefficients represent information about the population regression equation. If this information is correct, then we may increase the efficiency of our estimators by incorporating this information into our estimation procedure. The extent of this increase in efficiency depends on the type of information (i.e., how *specific* it is) and on the variances of the unconstrained estimators, assuming that these variances exist and that the unconstrained estimators are squared-error consistent. For instance, suppose the prior restriction is in the form of a statement that a given regression coefficient, say, β, is positive. Then, if the variance of the unconstrained estimator of β is small, we may get samples with a negative estimate of β only very rarely. Therefore, the restriction may not, for all practical purposes, be "restrictive" at all. In this case, the value of the prior information may be negligible. This brings up another aspect of prior information—namely, that its value diminishes with the size of the sample. This is because the variances of the unconstrained estimators will, in general, decrease as the sample size increases. This is true regardless of how specific the restrictions are. For example, even such a specific restriction as one that confines β to a given number is not of much value to us if, in fact, the estimates of β are highly concentrated in the near vicinity of the true value of the parameter. In the limit (i.e., when $n \to \infty$), prior information is of no more use. However, if the estimates tend to be highly concentrated around a value different from that specified by the restriction, then either our prior information is false, or the model is misspecified and the claim that the unconstrained estimator is consistent is not justified. Unfortunately, in economics our samples are typically small and generation of additional observations is severely limited, so that prior information is highly valuable. For this reason its use—frequently neglected in applied econometric work—ought to be strongly encouraged.

11–3   Nonlinear Models

The models that we have considered so far have, with a few minor exceptions, all been characterized by linear regression equations. However, this is not as restrictive as it might at first appear for the following reasons. First, all the results for the linear regression models derived in the preceding chapters may apply without any modification to regression models that are nonlinear with respect to the variables but linear with respect to the parameters to be estimated. Second, regression models that are nonlinear with respect to the variables *as well as* with respect to the parameters to be estimated can be analyzed by using many of the basic principles and results derived in connection with purely linear models. Nonlinear regression models can thus be classified into two groups according to whether they are or are not linear with respect to the parameters to be estimated. We may call the first type "models that are intrinsically linear," and the second type "models that are intrinsically nonlinear." We shall discuss each type separately. In addition, we shall also consider the problem of how to test for linearity in the case where the functional form of the regression equation is in doubt.

Intrinsically Linear Models

A nonlinear model that is intrinsically linear is, as indicated, *nonlinear* with respect to the variables but *linear* with respect to the parameters to be estimated. The basic common characteristic of such models is that they can be converted into ordinary linear models by a suitable transformation of the variables. Frequently, such a transformation amounts to nothing more than relabeling one or more of the variables. We have already used some of these models without even having to pause over the fact that some of the variables entered the regression equation in a nonlinear way. Our present intention is to consider intrinsically linear models in a systematic way and with some attention to detail. As the first case, we take a model in which the regressors are represented by a *power series* in X_i:

(11.46) $Y_i = \beta_1 + \beta_2 X_i + \beta_3 X_i^2 + \cdots + \beta_K X_i^{K-1} + \varepsilon_i,$

where X_i is nonstochastic and bounded, and ε_i satisfies all the assumptions of the classical normal linear regression model. For instance, the specification may call first for an increase and then for a decrease in $E(Y_i)$ in response to increases in X_i: as in the relationship between income and age of an individual. In this case, the power series would be given by a parabola

$$Y_i = \beta_1 + \beta_2 X_i + \beta_2 X_i^2 + \varepsilon_i,$$

as illustrated in Figure 11–5. But whatever the degree of the polynomial in (11.46), the equation can be rewritten as

(11.46a) $Y_i = \beta_1 + \beta_2 Z_{i2} + \beta_3 Z_{i3} + \cdots + \beta_K Z_{iK} + \varepsilon_i,$

where $Z_{i2} = X_i, Z_{i3} = X_i^2, \ldots, Z_{iK} = X_i^{K-1}$. Then, if the number of observations exceeds K, the ordinary least squares estimators of the regression coefficients of (11.46a) will have the desirable properties. However, the Z's will often

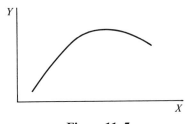

Figure 11–5

be highly correlated, so that the variances of the estimated regression coefficients may be quite large.[12] One nice feature of the power function (11.46) or its equivalent (11.46a) is that we can easily test the hypothesis that the degree of the polynomial is less than $(K - 1)$. For example, we may wish to test the hypothesis that the regression equation is linear against the alternative hypothesis that the regression equation is represented by a polynomial of degree $(K - 1)$. The formulation would be

$$H_0: \quad \beta_3 = \beta_4 = \cdots = \beta_K = 0,$$

$$H_A: \quad H_0 \text{ is not true.}$$

---

[12] If the sample values of X_i are equally spaced, the computations of the least squares estimates can be simplified by the use of the so-called "orthogonal polynomial transformation"; see, e.g., R. L. Anderson and T. A. Bancroft, *Stastitical Theory in Research* (New York: McGraw-Hill, 1952), pp. 207–214. Of course, this does not affect the variances of the least squares estimates of the β's.

The relevant test procedure is described in Section 10–2, with the test statistic given by the formula (10.45).

The preceding discussion is of some relevance not only for the regression models in which the explanatory variable (or variables) enters in the form of a power function, but also for any nonlinear regression model in general. The reason is that any function $f(x)$ that is continuous and has a continuous pth derivative can be written as

$$(11.47)\quad f(x) = f(a) + (x - a)f'(a) + \frac{(x - a)^2}{2!}f''(a) + \frac{(x - a)^3}{3!}f'''(a)$$

$$+ \cdots + \frac{(x - a)^p}{p!}f^{(p)}(a) + R_{p+1},$$

where a is any fixed number in the domain of X and

$$f(a) = f(x)\bigg|_{x=a},$$

$$f'(a) = \frac{df(x)}{dx}\bigg|_{x=a},$$

$$f''(a) = \frac{d^2f(x)}{dx}\bigg|_{x=a}$$

$$\vdots$$

$$R_{p+1} = \text{remainder}.$$

The series given in (11.47) is called the *Taylor's series expansion* of $f(x)$ about the point $x = a$. If p is sufficiently large, the remainder R_{p+1} will be small. Therefore, by disregarding R_{p+1} we obtain an approximation of $f(x)$, which we can make as close as we like by a suitable choice of p.

EXAMPLE 1   Let $f(x) = b_0 + b_1x + b_2x^2 + b_3x^3$, and let $p = 3$. Suppose we expand $f(x)$ around $x = 0$. Then we have

$$f(0) = b_0,$$

$$f'(0) = (b_1 + 2b_2x + 3b_3x^2)_{x=0} = b_1,$$

$$f''(0) = (2b_2 + 6b_3x)_{x=0} = 2b_2,$$

$$f'''(0) = 6b_3,$$

so that

$$f(x) = b_0 + (x - 0)b_1 + \frac{(x - 0)^2}{2}2b_2 + \frac{(x - 0)^3}{6}6b_3$$

$$= b_0 + b_1x + b_2x^2 + b_3x^3,$$

which is exactly correct.

EXAMPLE 2   Let $f(x) = e^{bx}$, $p = 3$, and $a = 0$. Then we have

$$f(0) = 1,$$

$$f'(0) = (be^{bx})_{x=0} = b,$$

$$f''(0) = (b^2 e^{bx})_{x=0} = b^2,$$

$$f'''(0) = (b^3 e^{bx})_{x=0} = b^3,$$

so that

$$f(x) \approx 1 + bx + \left[\frac{b^2}{2}\right]x^2 + \left[\frac{b^3}{6}\right]x^3.$$

If, for instance, $b = 1$, then the approximate values of $f(x)$ for various values of x are

x	Exact $f(x)$	Approximate $f(x)$
0	1.0000	1.0000
0.5	1.6487	1.6458
1	2.7183	2.6667
2	7.3891	6.3333
3	20.0860	13.0000

As shown, the approximation becomes poorer as we move away from the value around which the series is being expanded.

The Taylor's series expansion can be extended to apply to a function of more than one variable. In particular, the expansion for *two* variables is given by

$$(11.48) \quad f(x,z) = f(a,b) + f_x(a,b)(x - a) + f_z(a,b)(z - b)$$

$$+ \frac{1}{2!}[f_{xx}(a,b)(x - a)^2 + 2f_{xz}(a,b)(x - a)(z - b)$$

$$+ f_{zz}(a,b)(z - b)^2] + \cdots,$$

where

$$f_x(a,b) = \left.\frac{\partial f(x,z)}{\partial x}\right|_{\substack{x=a \\ z=b}},$$

$$f_z(a,b) = \left.\frac{\partial f(x,z)}{\partial z}\right|_{\substack{x=a \\ z=b}},$$

$$f_{xx}(a,b) = \left.\frac{\partial^2 f(x,z)}{\partial x^2}\right|_{\substack{x=a \\ z=b}},$$

$$f_{xz}(a,b) = \left.\frac{\partial^2 f(x,z)}{\partial x \partial z}\right|_{\substack{x=a \\ z=b}},$$

$$f_{zz}(a,b) = \left.\frac{\partial^2 f(x,z)}{\partial z^2}\right|_{\substack{x=a \\ z=b}} ,$$

etc. Formula (11.48) has been used to obtain linear approximations of products and ratios of two variables by expanding the series about the sample means of the two variables and retaining only the first three terms of the expansion.[13] Specifically,

$$(11.49) \quad X_i Z_i \approx \bar{X}\bar{Z} + \bar{Z}(X_i - \bar{X}) + \bar{X}(Z_i - \bar{Z}) \approx \bar{Z}X_i + \bar{X}Z_i - \bar{X}\bar{Z},$$

$$(11.50) \qquad \frac{X_i}{Z_i} \approx \frac{\bar{X}}{\bar{Z}} + \frac{1}{\bar{Z}}(X_i - \bar{X}) + \left[-\frac{\bar{X}}{\bar{Z}^2}\right](Z_i - \bar{Z})$$

$$\approx \frac{\bar{X}}{\bar{Z}} + \left[\frac{1}{\bar{Z}}\right]X_i - \left[\frac{\bar{X}}{\bar{Z}^2}\right]Z_i.$$

Consider now a regression equation in which the change in $E(Y_i)$ corresponding to a unit change in X_{ij} depends on the level of X_{ik}. Formally, suppose the mean value of the dependent variable is some function of two nonstochastic explanatory variables X_{i2} and X_{i3}

$$E(Y_i) = f(X_{i2}, X_{i3})$$

such that

$$\frac{\partial E(Y_i)}{\partial X_{i2}} = g(X_{i3})$$

and

$$\frac{\partial E(Y_i)}{\partial X_{i3}} = h(X_{i2}),$$

where $g(X_{i3})$ and $h(X_{i2})$ are some functions whose mathematical form is specified a priori. There are many situations in which such a model is appropriate. For example, in estimations of Engel curves from cross-section data, family expenditure on a given commodity is frequently considered to be dependent on family income and family size. It may be reasonable to expect that families of different sizes respond to a given change in income in a different way, and that families in different income brackets respond differently to a change in family size. The simplest formulation of such a model is obtained by introducing a so-called *interaction term*, defined as a multiple of the product of the two explanatory variables, into the linear regression equation:

$$(11.51) \qquad Y_i = \beta_1 + \beta_2 X_{i2} + \beta_3 X_{i3} + \beta_4 X_{i2} X_{i3} + \varepsilon_i.$$

In this model

$$\frac{\partial E(Y_i)}{\partial X_{i2}} = \beta_2 + \beta_4 X_{i3}$$

and

$$\frac{\partial E(Y_i)}{\partial X_{i3}} = \beta_3 + \beta_4 X_{i2}.$$

[13] See Klein, *op. cit.*, pp. 120–121.

The functions $g(X_{i3})$ and $h(X_{i2})$ are both linear functions of the respective variables and have a common slope equal to β_4. Equation (11.51) is intrinsically linear because we can write $X_{i2}X_{i3} = X_{i4}$.

The presence of the interaction terms in a regression equation has an important implication for the test of the hypothesis that a given explanatory variable is not relevant in the regression model in question, i.e., that it does not influence $E(Y_i)$. When there are interaction terms in the equation, then any given explanatory variable may be represented by not one but several regressors. The hypothesis that this variable does not influence $E(Y_i)$ means that the coefficients of *all* regressors involving this variable are jointly zero. Therefore, the appropriate test of such a hypothesis is the F test described by (10.45). Usually we are also interested in testing the hypothesis that the change in $E(Y_i)$ corresponding to a unit increase in X_{ik} is constant. This is equivalent to testing the hypothesis that the coefficients of the interaction "variables" are equal to zero.

EXAMPLE   The use of the multiple regression model of Section 10–1 was illustrated by estimating the demand for oranges as a linear function of price and the amount spent on advertising. Let us now modify this example by specifying that the regression equation should also include the interaction term. That is, let

$$Y_i = \beta_1 + \beta_2 X_{i2} + \beta_3 X_{i3} + \beta_4 X_{i2} X_{i3} + \varepsilon_i,$$

where Y_i = quantity of oranges sold, X_{i2} = price, and X_{i3} = advertising expenditure. The details for the twelve available sample observations are given in Table 10–1. The results of the basic calculations are

$$m_{22} = 2250,$$

$$m_{23} = -54, \qquad m_{33} = 4.8573,$$

$$m_{24} = 10{,}237.5, \qquad m_{34} = 15.6854, \qquad m_{44} = 66{,}503.85,$$

$$m_{Y2} = -3550, \qquad m_{Y3} = 125.2500, \qquad m_{Y4} = -13{,}542.50,$$

$$m_{YY} = 6300.$$

(The subscript "4" denotes the interaction "variable" $X_{i2}X_{i3}$.) The estimated regression equation then is

$$Y_i = -93.100 + 1.508 X_{i2} + 43.990 X_{i3} - 0.446 X_{i2} X_{i3} + e_i, \qquad R^2 = 0.984.$$
$$ (0.832) \qquad (9.803) \qquad (0.119)$$

These results can be used for testing several interesting hypotheses. First, we shall test the hypothesis that X_{i2} does not influence $E(Y_i)$. Formally,

$$H_0: \quad \beta_2 = \beta_4 = 0,$$

$$H_A: \quad H_0 \text{ is not true.}$$

According to the test described in (10.45), the acceptance region for, say, the 5% level of significance, is

$$\frac{(\text{SSR}_Q - \text{SSR}_K)/(Q - K)}{\text{SSE}_Q/(n - Q)} \le F_{Q-K, \, n-Q, \, 0.05}.$$

In this problem, we have $n = 12$, $Q = 4$, and $K = 2$, so that $F_{2,\,8,\,0.05} = 4.46$, as shown in the table of the F distribution. Now, from our sample we have

$$\text{SSR}_Q = 1.508 \times (-3550) + 43.990 \times 125.25 + (-0.446) \times (-13{,}542.5) = 6198,$$

$$\text{SSE}_Q = 6300 - 6198 = 102.$$

The value of SSR_K is to be obtained by regressing Y_i on X_{i3} alone, i.e., by applying the least squares estimation method to

$$Y_i = \beta_1^* + \beta_3^* X_{i3} + \varepsilon_i^*.$$

Then,

$$\text{SSR}_K = \hat{\beta}_3^* m_{Y3} = \left[\frac{m_{Y3}}{m_{33}}\right] m_{Y3} = \frac{125.25^2}{4.86} = 3228.$$

Therefore,

$$\frac{(\text{SSR}_Q - \text{SSR}_K)/(Q - K)}{\text{SSE}_Q/(n - Q)} = \frac{(6198 - 3228)/(4 - 2)}{102/(12 - 4)} = 116.5,$$

which is considerably greater than the critical value 4.46. Therefore we reject the hypothesis that X_{i2} has no influence on $E(Y_i)$, and we do so even though the t ratio for the coefficient of X_{i2} is less than 2.0. Next, we shall test the same hypothesis with respect to X_{i3}. The acceptance region is exactly the same as for the first test, and so are all the other calculations except for SSR_K. The value of SSR_K will be obtained by regressing Y_i on X_{i2}, that is, by estimating the coefficients of

$$Y_i = \beta_1^{**} + \beta_2^{**} X_{i2} + \varepsilon_i^{**}.$$

Then, we have

$$\text{SSR}_K = \hat{\beta}_2^{**} m_{Y2} = \left[\frac{m_{Y2}}{m_{22}}\right] m_{Y2} = \frac{(-3550)^2}{2250} = 5602.$$

The value of the appropriate test statistic then becomes

$$\frac{(\text{SSR}_Q - \text{SSR}_K)/(Q - K)}{\text{SSE}_Q/(n - Q)} = \frac{(6198 - 5602)/(4 - 2)}{102/(12 - 4)} = 23.4,$$

which again is larger than the critical value, 4.46. Finally, we shall test the hypothesis that the coefficient attached to the interaction "variable" $X_{i2} X_{i3}$ is zero; i.e.,

$$H_0: \ \beta_4 = 0,$$

$$H_A: \ \beta_4 \neq 0.$$

The tabulated t value for a two-sided test at the 5% level of significance and with eight degrees of freedom is 2.306. Therefore, the 5% acceptance region is

$$-2.306 \leq \frac{\hat{\beta}_4}{s_{\hat{\beta}_4}} \leq 2.306.$$

Since in our case

$$\frac{\hat{\beta}_4}{s_{\hat{\beta}_4}} = \frac{-0.446}{0.119} = -3.748,$$

the null hypothesis has to be rejected.

Another intrinsically linear model involves a regression equation that is linear in terms of the logarithms of the variables. This is known as the *multiplicative model* and can be described as

$$(11.52) \qquad Y_i = \alpha X_{i2}^{\beta_2} X_{i3}^{\beta_3} \cdots X_{iK}^{\beta_K} 10^{\varepsilon_i}.$$

A notable feature of this model is the fact that the elasticity of $E(Y_i)$ with respect to any of the explanatory variables is constant, i.e., that

$$\frac{\partial E(Y_i)}{\partial X_{ik}} \frac{X_{ik}}{E(Y_i)} = \beta_k \qquad (k = 2, 3, \ldots, K).$$

An example of such a model is the Cobb-Douglas production function. By taking logarithms (to base 10) of both sides of (11.52), we obtain

$$(11.52a) \quad \log Y_i = \log a + \beta_2 \log X_{i2} + \beta_3 \log X_{i3} + \cdots + \beta_K \log X_{iK} + \varepsilon_i,$$

which can be written as

$$(11.52b) \qquad Y_i^* = \alpha^* + \beta_2 X_{i2}^* + \beta_3 X_{i3}^* + \cdots + \beta_K X_{iK}^* + \varepsilon_i,$$

where the starred symbols represent the logarithms of the unstarred counterparts. Equation (11.52b) is clearly an ordinary linear multiple regression equation, and its estimation can proceed along the usual lines. Two points are worth mentioning, though. First, equation (11.52b) is linear with respect to α^* and the β's, but not with respect to α. Thus, if the assumptions of the classical normal linear regression model are satisfied, the ordinary least squares estimators of $\alpha^*, \beta_2, \beta_3, \ldots, \beta_K$ will have the desirable properties. Since

$$\alpha^* = \log \alpha,$$

the estimator of α will be given by

$$\hat{\alpha} = \text{antilog } \hat{\alpha}^*.$$

While $\hat{\alpha}$ inherits all the desirable asymptotic properties from $\hat{\alpha}^*$, the small-sample properties of $\hat{\alpha}^*$, and in particular its unbiasedness, do not carry over to $\hat{\alpha}$. Second, if we assume that ε_i is normally distributed with zero mean and variance σ^2, then we can write

$$(11.52c) \qquad Y_i = \alpha X_{i2}^{\beta_2} X_{i3}^{\beta_3} \cdots X_{iK}^{\beta_K} \eta_i$$

and assume that the *logarithm* (to base 10) of η_i is normally distributed with mean zero and variance σ^2. The distribution of η_i itself would be called *lognormal*. However, if the regression equation were specified as

$$Y_i = \alpha X_{i2}^{\beta_2} X_{i3}^{\beta_3} \cdots X_{iK}^{\beta_K} + \varepsilon_i,$$

no transformation of the variables could lead to a regression equation that would be linear in the β's, so the equation would have to be classified as intrinsically nonlinear.

There exist many other nonlinear models that can be converted to linear models by a suitable transformation. The following cases have been selected to illustrate the general approach. One frequently applicable nonlinear relation is a *hyperbola*,

(11.53) $$Y_i = \alpha + \beta \frac{1}{X_i} + \varepsilon_i \qquad (\beta < 0),$$

which describes a situation where the mean value of Y_i approaches an upper limit as X_i tends to increase, as illustrated in Figure 11–6. This model might be

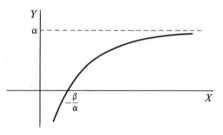

Figure 11–6

applicable, for instance, when one considers the consumption of food as dependent on income. Note that

$$\frac{dE(Y_i)}{dX_i} = -\frac{\beta}{X_i^2},$$

which shows that the change in $E(Y_i)$ corresponding to a change in X_i is inversely related to the square of X_i. Equation (11.53) can be converted into a linear function by simply putting

$$\frac{1}{X_i} = Z_i.$$

In this way, we obtain

(11.53a) $$Y_i = \alpha + \beta Z_i + \varepsilon_i.$$

A relationship similar to (11.53) is represented by a *semilog function*,

(11.54) $$Y_i = \alpha + \beta \log X_i + \varepsilon_i \qquad (\beta > 0).$$

If the base of $\log X_i$ is $e = 2.71828\ldots$, then[14]

$$\frac{dE(Y_i)}{dX_i} = \frac{\beta}{X_i},$$

[14] Note that logarithms to base 10 (i.e., common logarithms) can be converted to logarithms to base e (i.e., natural logarithms) by multiplying the common logarithms by 2.3025850930. Multiplication by 0.4342944819 converts natural logarithms to common logarithms.

which shows that the change in $E(Y_i)$ corresponding to a change in X_i is inversely related to the value of X_i. The main difference between (11.53) and (11.54) is that in (11.54), unlike in (11.53), the value of $E(Y_i)$ can grow without limit. Equation (11.54) can be changed into a linear relationship by putting

$$\log X_i = Z_i.$$

A variation of (11.54) is represented by a function in which the logarithmic operator is attached to the dependent rather than to the explanatory variable, i.e.,

(11.55) $$\log Y_i = \alpha + \beta X_i + \varepsilon_i.$$

If the base of $\log Y_i$ is e, this relationship can be rewritten as

(11.55a) $$Y_i = e^{\alpha + \beta X_i + \varepsilon_i},$$

which is called an *exponential function*. A notable feature of (11.55a) is that, for equally spaced values of X_i, the ratio of each two consecutive values of $E(Y_i)$ is equal to the same constant. For instance, if

$$X_{i+1} - X_i = 1,$$

then $$\frac{E(Y_{i+1})}{E(Y_i)} = \frac{e^{\alpha + \beta X_{i+1}} E(e^{\varepsilon_{i+1}})}{e^{\alpha + \beta X_i} E(e^{\varepsilon_i})} = e^{\beta}.$$

A simple transformation

$$\log Y_i = Y_i^*$$

allows us to express (11.55) as a linear function

(11.55b) $$Y_i^* = \alpha + \beta X_i + \varepsilon_i.$$

In all of the preceding regression models, and in many others, the problem of estimating the regression parameters is simplified by our ability to reduce the models to linearity. The only aspect of the transformation that deserves careful attention concerns the stochastic disturbance. In the cases presented, the stochastic disturbance was always introduced into the relationship in such a way that we could proceed with the linear transformation without any difficulty. However, the specification of the model—including the manner in which the disturbance is introduced—should not be dictated by mathematical or computational convenience. It is important to keep in mind that such a specification represents a commitment on our part concerning our prior knowledge and beliefs about the relationship that is being modeled. Since the stochastic disturbance determines the distribution of the dependent variable for any set of fixed values of the explanatory variables, its role in the regression model is quite crucial. Clearly, we need to be aware of the implications of the particular specification put forward. For instance, in the case of the Cobb-Douglas production function described by (11.52), the particular way in which the disturbance is introduced into the equation implies that the distribution of outputs for any given set of inputs is log-normal, i.e., skewed. This, then, must be our view of the world if we wish to insist on that given specification.

Intrinsically Nonlinear Models

Let us now turn to the *intrinsically nonlinear models*, i.e., models that are nonlinear with respect to the variables as well as with respect to the parameters. There is, of course, a great variety of these models; our discussion will be confined to a few interesting cases. Consider the relationship

$$(11.56) \qquad Y_i = \alpha X_{i2}^{\beta_2} X_{i3}^{\beta_3} + \varepsilon_i$$

which is essentially the same as the multiplicative model (11.52) *except* that the disturbance enters as an additive rather than a multiplicative term. A relationship of this sort could, for instance, describe a demand function for some commodity, with Y_i standing for quantity demanded, X_{i2} for price, and X_{i3} for income. Since

$$\frac{\partial E(Y_i)}{\partial X_{i2}} \frac{X_{i2}}{E(Y_i)} = \beta_2$$

and

$$\frac{\partial E(Y_i)}{\partial X_{i3}} \frac{X_{i3}}{E(Y_i)} = \beta_3,$$

β_2 and β_3 would represent the price and the income elasticity, respectively. Now, as we pointed out earlier, there exists no transformation that would convert (11.56) into a linear relationship with respect to the parameters. However, if X_{i2} and X_{i3} are nonstochastic—or, if stochastic, independent of ε_i—and if ε_i satisfies all the assumptions of the classical normal regression model, we can use the maximum likelihood method of estimation. The likelihood function for a sample of size n is

$$(11.57) \qquad L = -\frac{n}{2}\log 2\pi - \frac{n}{2}\log \sigma^2 - \frac{1}{2\sigma^2}\sum_{i=1}^{n}(Y_i - \alpha X_{i2}^{\beta_2} X_{i3}^{\beta_3})^2.$$

The next step is to differentiate L with respect to α, β_2, β_3, and σ^2 and put the respective derivatives equal to zero. This leads to a system of four equations, which are nonlinear with respect to the four unknowns. An algebraic solution of this system is difficult, but there may be no difficulty about getting a solution with an electronic computer, since programs for nonlinear estimation are now available. These programs are essentially based on a systematic "trial-and-error" approach; i.e., the computer is asked to calculate the value of L for a number of different combinations of the parameter values until the maximum value of L is found. The values of the parameters corresponding to this maximum value of L are the desired maximum likelihood estimates and have the desirable asymptotic properties.

Another interesting intrinsically nonlinear model is the *logistic model*, represented as

$$(11.58) \qquad Y_i = \frac{\gamma}{1 + e^{\alpha + \beta X_i}} + \varepsilon_i \qquad (\gamma > 0, \ \beta < 0),$$

where $e = 2.71828\ldots$. In this case, the population regression line is given by a logistic "growth curve" as shown in Figure 11–7. Note that $E(Y_i)$ is confined to the values between 0 and γ. The values of Y_i are, of course, not restricted. Again, we can obtain the maximum likelihood estimates of the parameters of (11.58) with a computer. The estimation problem becomes seemingly simplified if the specification of the logistic curve is

$$(11.59) \qquad Y_i = \frac{\gamma}{1 + e^{\alpha + \beta X_i + \varepsilon_i}}$$

since in this case we can write

$$(11.59a) \qquad \log\left(\frac{\gamma}{Y_i} - 1\right) = \alpha + \beta X_i + \varepsilon_i.$$

The apparent simplification is because now only one parameter, γ, enters the regression equation in a nonlinear way. However, it should be noted that the

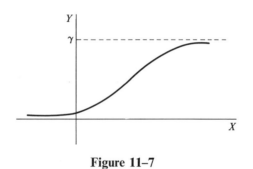

Figure 11–7

model (11.59) is markedly different from that given by (11.58). In particular, in (11.58) the values of Y_i for any given value of X_i can extend from $-\infty$ to $+\infty$, whereas in (11.59) the values of Y_i are confined to the interval from 0 to γ. This implies that, in (11.59), the dependent variable Y_i cannot have a normal distribution. The same complication was encountered in Section 11–1 in the case of a qualitative dependent variable.

As a final illustration of an intrinsically nonlinear model, we consider the so-called CES (constant elasticity of substitution) production function represented as

$$(11.60) \qquad Q_i = \gamma[\delta K_i^{-\rho} + (1 - \delta)L_i^{-\rho}]^{-\nu/\rho}e^{\varepsilon_i}$$

$$(\gamma > 0; 1 > \delta > 0; \nu > 0; \rho \geq -1),$$

where Q_i = output, K_i = capital input, L_i = labor input, and $e = 2.71828\ldots$. The parameter γ is known as the "efficiency parameter," the parameter δ as the "distribution parameter," the parameter ν as the "returns-to-scale parameter," and the parameter ρ as the "substitution parameter," This type of production function has gained a great degree of popularity because it subsumes a number of other more specialized production functions. This degree of generality is achieved through the "substitution parameter" ρ, since the CES production function reduces to the Cobb–Douglas production function for $\rho = 0$, and to the "fixed-proportions" production function for $\rho \to \infty$. By taking logarithms (to base e) of both sides of (11.60), we obtain

$$(11.60a) \qquad \log Q_i = \log \gamma - \frac{\nu}{\rho} \log [\delta K_i^{-\rho} + (1 - \delta)L_i^{-\rho}] + \varepsilon_i.$$

If K_i and L_i are nonstochastic—or, if stochastic, independent of ε_i—we can set up the likelihood function in the usual way and obtain the maximum likelihood estimates of γ, δ, ν, and ρ with a computer.

An alternative and a considerably more simple estimation of the parameters of the CES production function is possible if we replace (11.60a) by its approximation that is linear with respect to ρ. By using Taylor's series formula (11.47), expanding $\log Q_i$ around $\rho = 0$, and dropping the terms involving powers of ρ higher than one, we obtain[15]

$$(11.60b) \qquad \log Q_i = \log \gamma + \nu\delta \log K_i + \nu(1 - \delta) \log L_i$$
$$- \tfrac{1}{2}\rho\nu\delta(1 - \delta)[\log K_i - \log L_i]^2 + \varepsilon_i.$$

Note that the right-hand side of (11.60b) can be conveniently separated into two parts, one corresponding to the Cobb–Douglas production function and one representing a "correction" due to the departure of ρ from zero. The latter part, given by the term $-[\rho\nu\delta(1 - \delta)/2][\log K_i - \log L_i]^2$, will disappear if $\rho = 0$. The estimation of the parameters of (11.60b) is the same as in the case of estimation with nonlinear restrictions under exact identification. The "unrestricted" version of (11.60b) is

$$(11.60c) \quad \log Q_i = \beta_1 + \beta_2 \log K_i + \beta_3 \log L_i + \beta_4[\log K_i - \log L_i]^2 + \varepsilon_i,$$

which represents an intrinsically linear regression model. If the estimate of β_4 is not significantly different from zero, we would reject the CES model in favor of the Cobb–Douglas model. The parameters of (11.60b) are related to the coefficients of (11.60c) as follows:

$$\gamma = \text{antilog } \beta_1,$$

$$\delta = \frac{\beta_2}{\beta_2 + \beta_3},$$

$$\nu = \beta_2 + \beta_3,$$

$$\rho = \frac{-2\beta_4(\beta_2 + \beta_3)}{\beta_2\beta_3}.$$

---

[15] All logarithms are natural logarithms. If common logarithms were to be used, the term involving $[\log K_i - \log L_i]^2$ would have to be multiplied by 2.302585.

Thus we can use ordinary least squares estimates of the β's to obtain estimates of the parameters of (11.60b). The estimated standard errors can be calculated by using the approximation formula (11.40). If (11.60b) is a reasonable approximation of (11.60a), and if the appropriate assumptions about K_i, L_i, and ε_i hold, the estimates of the production function parameters obtained in this way will be very nearly asymptotically efficient.

EXAMPLE   To illustrate the estimation of the CES production function we use the data on inputs and output of 25 firms given in Table 11–4. The maximum likelihood method yields the following estimates of the production function parameters:

Table 11–4

Firm No.	K_i	L_i	Q_i
1	8	23	106.00
2	9	14	81.08
3	4	38	72.80
4	2	97	57.34
5	6	11	66.79
6	6	43	98.23
7	3	93	82.68
8	6	49	99.77
9	8	36	110.00
10	8	43	118.93
11	4	61	95.05
12	8	31	112.83
13	3	57	64.54
14	6	97	137.22
15	4	93	86.17
16	2	72	56.25
17	3	61	81.10
18	3	97	65.23
19	9	89	149.56
20	3	25	65.43
21	1	81	36.06
22	4	11	56.92
23	2	64	49.59
24	3	10	43.21
25	6	71	121.24

$$\log \hat{\gamma} = 1.0564,$$

$$\hat{\delta} = 0.4064,$$

$$\hat{\nu} = 0.8222,$$

$$\hat{\rho} = 0.6042.$$

The estimates of the asymptotic standard errors of the maximum likelihood estimates were not calculated. Using the approximation of the CES production function given by (11.60b), we obtain

$$\log \tilde{\gamma} = 1.2371,$$

$$\tilde{\delta} = 0.4723,$$
$$(0.0291)$$

$$\tilde{\nu} = 0.8245,$$
$$(0.0525)$$

$$\tilde{\rho} = 0.4334.$$
$$(0.1899)$$

The figures in parentheses represent estimates of the asymptotic standard errors. The results show that the sample provides no strong evidence against the CES model.

In general, the parameters of an intrinsically nonlinear model may be estimated by setting up the likelihood function and finding the maximum likelihood estimates. Under the classical assumptions concerning the stochastic disturbance and the explanatory variables, the resulting estimates will have all the desirable asymptotic properties. Of course, the application of the maximum likelihood method is contingent on the assumption that ε_i is normally distributed. If we do not wish to make this assumption, we can obtain our estimates by minimizing the sum of squared deviations of the observed values from the fitted values of Y, i.e., by the least squares method. Since the parameters to be estimated enter in a nonlinear way, this method is usually called the *nonlinear least squares method*. The principal difference between this and the ordinary (linear) least squares method is that in the linear case the estimates can be expressed as linear functions of the disturbances. This is not generally possible in the nonlinear case. The estimates obtained by the nonlinear least squares method are exactly the same as the maximum likelihood estimates whenever the maximization of the likelihood function is achieved by the minimization of the sum of squared deviations of the observed from the fitted values of Y. It can be shown that even without the assumption of normality the *asymptotic* distribution of the nonlinear least squares estimates is then normal and has the same mean and variance as the asymptotic distribution of the maximum likelihood estimates.[16] Thus the assumption of normality of the stochastic disturbance is not always crucial.

The troublesome aspect of the nonlinear estimation is the actual finding of the estimates. As we mentioned earlier, the estimates are obtained with a computer by systematic "trial and error." Essentially, the computer substitutes different values of the parameters into the likelihood function, calculates the value of the function, and repeats this until there can be no further increase in the value of the likelihood function. This works fine if the likelihood function

[16] See E. Malinvaud, *Statistical Methods of Econometrics* (Chicago: Rand McNally, 1966), pp. 290–299.

has only one well-defined peak, but there may be problems if the likelihood function either has more than one peak or is very flat at the top. These possibilities are illustrated in Figure11–8 for the case in which the search is related to a single parameter θ. In Figure 11–8(a) the likelihood function has one well-defined peak and there is no problem about finding $\hat{\theta}$. In Figure 11–8(b) the likelihood function displays two peaks, the lower peak representing a local and the higher peak a global maximum of the function. Here the difficulty arises because if the computer starts its search for the maximizing value of θ in the vicinity of $\hat{\theta}_1$, it will stop at $\hat{\theta}_1$ and present this as the maximum likelihood estimate of θ, while the correct maximum likelihood estimate of θ is really $\hat{\theta}_2$. There is not much that can be done about that, except to require the computer to scan the entire range of possible values of θ. However, if this range is infinite, the computer is faced with a task that it cannot fulfill. However, frequently the range of admissible parameter values is finite, in which case the problem of finding the global maximum may become manageable. A good example is the marginal propensity to consume, which is confined to values between 0 and 1, or the autoregression

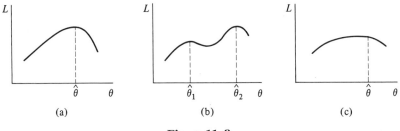

(a)   (b)   (c)

Figure 11–8

parameter ρ, which is confined to values between -1 and $+1$. The case of a relatively flat likelihood function, depicted by Figure 11–8(c), poses yet another problem. The likelihood function in this case is clearly very sensitive to changes in the sample data. This means that even a slight error of measurement or an error of rounding might shift the maximizing value of θ quite markedly, which does not inspire a high degree of confidence in the resulting estimate.

Tests for Linearity

Our discussion, thus far, of estimating the parameters of a nonlinear model has presupposed that the functional form of the population regression equation is known, or assumed, a priori. If this is not the case, we may want to consider the specification of the functional form as a testable rather than a maintained hypothesis. In this context the most interesting hypothesis is that of linearity. That is, frequently we may wish to test the hypothesis that the population regression equation is linear with respect to the variables against some alternative hypothesis. The hypothesis of linearity can be tested in a number of ways, but unfortunately none of the tests is without drawbacks.

The simplest test of linearity is in the case in which the alternative hypothesis is that the regression equation involves a power function of a given degree. This test was already described in connection with (11.46) and (11 46a). Its disadvantage is that we have to commit ourselves to a power function of a specific degree as the alternative to the linear model. Note that the basic idea of this test rests on the fact that a linear function is a special case of a power function, namely, a power function of degree one. If the coefficients attached to the higher powers of the explanatory variable are all zero, the given power function reduces to a simple linear regression. This idea can be exploited by specifying other functional forms, which include linearity as a special case. One such specification [17] is

$$(11.61) \qquad \frac{Y_i^\lambda - 1}{\lambda} = \alpha + \beta \left(\frac{X_i^\lambda - 1}{\lambda} \right) + \varepsilon_i.$$

Let us examine this function for some selected values of λ. First, for $\lambda = 0$, the expressions $(Y_i^\lambda - 1)/\lambda$ and $(X_i^\lambda - 1)/\lambda$ appear to be indeterminate. However, we note that any finite positive number, say, Z, can be written as

$$Z = e^{\log Z},$$

where the base of the logarithm is e, and that $e^{\log Z}$ can be expanded as

$$e^{\log Z} = 1 + \log Z + \frac{1}{2!} (\log Z)^2 + \frac{1}{3!} (\log Z)^3 + \cdots.$$

Therefore, it follows that

$$\frac{Y_i^\lambda - 1}{\lambda} = \frac{1}{\lambda} \left[1 + \lambda \log Y_i + \frac{1}{2!} (\lambda \log Y_i)^2 + \cdots - 1 \right]$$

$$= \log Y_i + \frac{\lambda}{2!} (\log Y_i)^2 + \frac{\lambda^2}{3!} (\log Y_i)^3 + \cdots$$

For $\lambda = 0$,

$$\frac{Y_i^\lambda - 1}{\lambda} = \log Y_i,$$

and, similarly,

$$\frac{X_i^\lambda - 1}{\lambda} = \log X_i.$$

This means that for $\lambda = 0$ (and for X_i and Y_i positive) the regression equation (11.61) reduces to

$$\log Y_i = \alpha + \beta \log X_i + \varepsilon_i.$$

Further, for $\lambda = 1$, we obtain

$$(Y_i - 1) = \alpha + \beta(X_i - 1) + \varepsilon_i$$

---

[17] This specification was proposed in G. E. P. Box and D. R. Cox, "An Analysis of Transformations," *Journal of the Royal Statistical Society, Series B*, Vol. 26, 1964, pp. 211–243.

or
$$Y_i = \alpha^* + \beta X_i + \varepsilon_i,$$

where
$$\alpha^* = \alpha - \beta + 1,$$

which is a simple linear regression model.

In general, different values of λ in (11.61) lead to different functional specifications of the regression equation.[18] This allows us to test the linear hypothesis against the alternative hypothesis that the regression equation is some nonlinear function within the family of functions defined by (11.61). Formally,

$$H_0: \quad \lambda = 1,$$

$$H_A: \quad \lambda \neq 1.$$

To carry out the test, we need an estimate of λ and its standard error. Clearly, λ can be estimated along with the other parameters of (11.61) by the maximum likelihood method. In setting up the likelihood function for $Y_1, Y_2, \ldots, Y_n$, we have to derive the distribution of the Y's from the distribution of the ε's, which is assumed to be normal. By Theorem 18 of Section 7–3 (the "change-of-variable" theorem), we have

$$f(Y_i) = \left| \frac{d\varepsilon_i}{dY_i} \right| f(\varepsilon_i).$$

But
$$\varepsilon_i = \left(\frac{Y_i^\lambda - 1}{\lambda} \right) - \alpha - \beta \left(\frac{X_i^\lambda - 1}{\lambda} \right)$$

so that
$$\frac{d\varepsilon_i}{dY_i} = Y_i^{\lambda - 1}.$$

Therefore, the likelihood function for $Y_1, Y_2, \ldots, Y_n$ is

(11.62) $$L = (\lambda - 1) \sum_i \log Y_i - \frac{n}{2} \log (2\pi) - \frac{n}{2} \log \sigma^2$$

$$- \frac{1}{2\sigma^2} \sum_i \left[\left(\frac{Y_i^\lambda - 1}{\lambda} \right) - \alpha - \beta \left(\frac{X_i^\lambda - 1}{\lambda} \right) \right]^2.$$

The maximizing values of λ, α, β, and σ^2 can be found with an electronic computer, and the respective standard errors can be estimated by reference to the appropriate information matrix. In large samples the maximum likelihood estimates will be distributed normally, or at least approximately so.

The hypothesis that the population regression equation is linear with respect to the variables can also be tested without specifying the alternative functional form or forms. This can be done by considering some of the implications of linearity in a more general way. The rather obvious implication of linearity is

[18] Some attention has to be paid to the restrictions on the values of the dependent variable. Since, under the assumption of normality, the range of ε_i extends from $-\infty$ to $+\infty$, this should also be the range of $(Y_i^\lambda - 1)/\lambda$. However, for some values of λ (e.g., $\lambda = \frac{1}{2}$) this may not be possible, in which case only *approximate* normality can be required. This point was originally raised by J. B. Ramsey.

that the slope and the intercept of the regression equation must remain constant over *all* values of the explanatory variable. What we can do, then, is to divide the sample observations into a number of subsamples, each subsample corresponding to a different and nonoverlapping interval of values of the explanatory variable. We can estimate the slope and the intercept for each subsample and test whether there are any significant differences from one subsample to another.

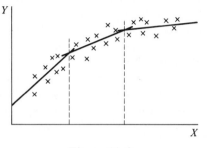

Figure 11–9

This is illustrated in Figure 11–9. To indicate how the test is carried out, we consider a sample of n observations, with the observations being arranged so that

$$X_1 \le X_2 \le X_3 \le \cdots \le X_n.$$

Suppose the sample is divided into three subsamples, with the values of the explanatory variable allocated as follows:

$$\text{Subsample 1:} \quad X_1, X_2, \ldots, X_k,$$

$$\text{Subsample 2:} \quad X_{k+1}, X_{k+2}, \ldots, X_m,$$

$$\text{Subsample 3:} \quad X_{m+1}, X_{m+2}, \ldots, X_n.$$

The regression model can be set up as

$$(11.63) \quad Y_i = \beta_1 + \beta_2 X_i + \gamma_1 Z_{i1} + \gamma_2 X_i Z_{i1} + \gamma_3 Z_{i2} + \gamma_4 X_i Z_{i2} + \varepsilon_i,$$

where
$$\begin{aligned} Z_{i1} &= 1 \quad \text{if } i \text{ belongs to Subsample 1,} \\ &= 0 \quad \text{otherwise;} \\ Z_{i2} &= 1 \quad \text{if } i \text{ belongs to Subsample 2,} \\ &= 0 \quad \text{otherwise.} \end{aligned}$$

The hypothesis of linearity can then be tested by testing

$$H_0: \quad \gamma_1 = \gamma_2 = \gamma_3 = \gamma_4 = 0$$

$$H_A: \quad H_0 \text{ is not true.}$$

The appropriate F test, described in (10.45), has a disadvantage in that its result may depend on the way in which the sample is divided up. If the number of sub-samples is too small, a departure from linearity may remain concealed, and if the number of subsamples is large, we lose many degrees of freedom and thus weaken the power of the test. As a compromise, it has been suggested that in practical applications three or four samples should be sufficient.[19]

Another test of linearity which does not rely on the specification of the alternative functional form is based on the scatter of the residuals around the sample regression line. The idea is to rely on the fact that, under the assumptions of the classical normal linear regression model, the disturbances are *randomly* scattered around the population regression line. If the population regression is *not* linear, the scatter of the disturbances around a straight line will no longer be random. In Figure 11–10 we can see how, because of the nonlinearity of the relation, the deviations from the straight line tend to be at first negative, then positive, and then negative again. This suggests that we can test linearity by determining whether the sequence of the deviations from the regression line is randomly arranged.

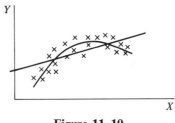

Figure 11–10

An obvious difficulty about carrying out a test of this sort arises because the deviations from the population regression line (i.e., the disturbances) are not observable. All that we have are the deviations from the sample regression line (i.e., the residuals). The trouble is that the residuals are not independent even if the disturbances themselves are. In particular, we have, for $i \neq j$,

$$(11.64) \quad \text{Cov}(e_i, e_j) = E(y_i' - \hat{\beta}x_i')(y_j' - \hat{\beta}x_j')$$

$$= E(\beta x_i' + \varepsilon_i' - \hat{\beta}x_i')(\beta x_j' + \varepsilon_j' - \hat{\beta}x_j')$$

$$= x_i' x_j' E(\hat{\beta} - \beta)^2 - E(\hat{\beta} - \beta)\varepsilon_i' x_j' - E(\hat{\beta} - \beta)\varepsilon_j' x_i' + E(\varepsilon_i' \varepsilon_j')$$

$$= -x_i' x_j' \left[\frac{\sigma^2}{\sum x_i'^2} \right] - \frac{\sigma^2}{n},$$

which is clearly nonzero. This difference between the e's and the ε's has been

[19] Malinvaud, *op. cit.*, p. 270.

taken into account by the Durbin–Watson test described in Section 8–2, which was originally designed for testing the hypothesis that the disturbances are uncorrelated over time against the hypothesis that they follow a first-order autoregressive scheme. If the residuals are arranged according to increasing values of the explanatory variable rather than according to time, this test can be used to check whether the deviations from the population regression line are random. However, the Durbin–Watson test is not without disadvantages. If the ordering of the residuals according to time is similar to their ordering according to increasing values of the explanatory variable, we would be using very much the same test for linearity as for nonautoregression of the disturbances over time. This difficulty is due to the fact that, when the orderings are similar, both non-linearity and autoregression in the disturbances tend to have the same implication with respect to the residuals.

The construction of the Durbin–Watson test has been motivated by the fact that the least squares residuals are not mutually independent even if the disturbances are. This has been shown explicitly in (11.64). However, we note that the expression for the covariance of e_i and e_j $(i \neq j)$ tends to approach zero as the sample size increases to infinity, so that in large samples the residuals will be close to being independent if the disturbances are. Thus, in large samples we can use any general test for "randomness" without risking too large an error. One such test involves examining the peaks and troughs of a series to see whether they may be considered a result of pure chance. We can apply this test to the sequence of residuals arranged in accordance with increasing values of the explanatory variable. A residual e_i is defined as a "peak" if

$$e_{i-1} < e_i > e_{i+1}$$

and as a "trough" if

$$e_{i-1} > e_i < e_{i+1}.$$

If two or more successive residuals have the same value and this value exceeds the neighboring values, we regard them as determining *one* peak, and similarly for troughs. A general name for either a peak or a trough is a "turning point." It can be shown[20] that in a series of n independent values the total number of turning points, say, p, is—for a large n—approximately normally distributed with mean

(11.65) $$E(p) = \frac{2(n-2)}{3}$$

and variance

(11.66) $$\text{Var}(p) = \frac{16n - 29}{90}.$$

[20] G. Udny Yule and M. G. Kendall, *An Introduction to the Theory of Statistics* (London: Charles Griffin, 1950), p. 638.

The test of independence then involves counting the number of turning points in the series of the residuals (arranged according to increasing values of X) and checking whether this number is significantly different from $E(p)$. That is, the hypothesis of independence (and, therefore, presumably of linearity) is

$$H_0: \quad E(p) = \frac{2(n-2)}{3}$$

with a two-sided H_A. The appropriate test statistic for large samples would be

(11.67) $$\frac{p - 2(n-2)/3}{\sqrt{(16n-29)/90}} \sim N(0,1).$$

This test does not require the assumption that the disturbances are normally distributed. Its disadvantage, as in the case of the Durbin–Watson test, is that if the ordering of the residuals according to increasing values of X and according to time is similar, we cannot distinguish between nonlinearity and autoregression of the disturbances over time.

   In addition to the various disadvantages specific to each, all tests of linearity suffer from one particular weakness that detracts from their usefulness: the sample data do not provide any information about the shape of the regression line outside the interval covered by the observed values of the explanatory variable. If the population regression is approximately linear *within* this interval and nonlinear outside, then no test can possibly detect the nonlinearity of the population regression. This situation is illustrated in Figure 11–11. There is nothing

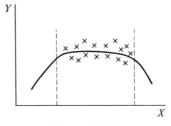

Figure 11–11

that can be done about this with the given sample data. The only possible way to avoid this difficulty is to enlarge the sample and extend the interval encompassed by the observed values of the explanatory variable. Indeed, if the linearity of the population regression is suspect a priori, this would certainly be the recommended procedure. In the past most of the applied work in econometrics has been with linear models only, largely on the grounds of computational simplicity. However, with the spread of electronic computers, this reason has lost some force. There is little excuse for not using nonlinear models when suggested by theory, or for not testing for linearity when its assumption is open to doubt.

11-4   Distributed Lag Models

A simple regression equation designed to explain variations over time in the mean value of the dependent variable is given by

$$Y_t = \alpha + \beta X_t + \varepsilon_t,$$

where ε_t is a random variable with zero mean (conforming to other assumptions as specified), and X_t is either nonstochastic or, if stochastic, independent of ε_t. In setting up the regression equation in this way we are, in fact, assuming that the current value of Y may depend on the current value of X but *not* on any of the past values of X. A more general formulation, which would allow for the current as well as the past values of X to affect Y, would be written as

$$(11.68) \qquad Y_t = \alpha + \beta_0 X_t + \beta_1 X_{t-1} + \beta_2 X_{t-2} + \cdots + \beta_m X_{t-m} + \varepsilon_t.$$

This equation is the basis for the discussion of the present section. For simplicity we shall limit ourselves to the case of a nonstochastic X; a modification to allow for the case in which X is stochastic but independent of ε is quite straightforward.

The regression equation (11.68), extended by the relevant assumptions concerning the behavior of X and ε, is called a *distributed lag model* because the influence of the explanatory variable on $E(Y_t)$ is distributed over a number of lagged values of X. This number, m, may be either finite or infinite. However, we assume that the β's have a finite sum; i.e.,

$$\sum_{i=0}^{m} \beta_i < \infty.$$

This assumption is needed to eliminate the possibility of explosive values of $E(Y_t)$. We also define the *average lag* as the weighted mean of all the lags involved, with weights given by the relative size of the respective β coefficients. Formally,

$$\text{Average lag} = \frac{\sum i\beta_i}{\sum \beta_i},$$

where the summations run from $i = 0$ to $i = m$. Equation (11.68) could (at least in principle) be estimated by the least squares method, or by some other method which leads to estimates with some desirable properties under the given specifications about ε. Of course, if m is large, we may not have enough observations to estimate all the parameters. However, even if we do have enough observations, we are likely to encounter a high degree of multicollinearity, which would have a detrimental effect on the standard errors of the estimated coefficients. As a matter of fact, a distributed lag model has rarely been posited and estimated in as general a form as that specified in (11.68). Most frequently some restrictions are placed on the regression coefficients $\beta_0, \beta_1, \ldots, \beta_m$, so that the number of the regression parameters becomes substantially reduced. In practical applications these restrictions have been of two kinds—one resulting from the requirement that the β's should be declining in a geometric progression, and the other from the requirement that the β's should first be increasing and then decreasing.

Geometric Lag

By far the most popular form of a distributed lag is that of a *geometric lag distribution* characterized as

$$(11.69) \qquad Y_t = \alpha + \beta_0(X_t + \lambda X_{t-1} + \lambda^2 X_{t-2} + \cdots) + \varepsilon_t,$$

where $0 \leq \lambda < 1.$

Here the effect of X on $E(Y_t)$ extends indefinitely into the past (i.e., $m \to \infty$), but the coefficients decline in a fixed proportion so that the effect of the distant values of X eventually becomes negligible. This model has been rationalized in two different ways, each leading to the same description of the population regression equation, but each having a different implication for the behavior of the regression disturbance. The first rationalization is known as the *adaptive expectation model* and is based on the following reasoning. Suppose a simple regression model is modified so that $E(Y_t)$ is a linear function not of X_t but of the "expected" or "permanent" level of X at time t, say, X_t^*. One example would be a demand relationship in which the quantity demanded is a function of expected price, or a consumption function with "permanent income" as the explanatory variable. Then,

$$(11.70) \qquad\qquad\qquad Y_t = \alpha + \beta X_t^* + \varepsilon_t,$$

where, as before, ε_t is a random variable with zero mean. Since X_t^* is not directly observable, we have to state how it is determined. Here, we postulate that

$$(11.71) \qquad\qquad X_t^* - X_{t-1}^* = (1 - \lambda)(X_t - X_{t-1}^*),$$

or equivalently,

$$(11.71a) \qquad\qquad X_t^* = (1 - \lambda)X_t + \lambda X_{t-1}^*,$$

where $0 \leq \lambda < 1.$

This presupposes that the expected or permanent value of X at time t is represented by a weighted average of the current value of X and the value of X expected in the preceding period. Such a formation of expectations is based on the idea that the current expectations are derived by modifying previous expectations in light of the current experience. Thus, for instance, in the case of a demand relationship, X_t may be the price at the beginning of the current period, and X_{t-1}^* may be the average price expected to have prevailed during the preceding period. Or, in the case of a consumption function, the current "permanent" income may be determined by revising the last period's level of the "permanent" income in light of the current income experience. Note that (11.71a) can also be written as

$$(11.71b) \qquad X_t^* = (1 - \lambda)(X_t + \lambda X_{t-1} + \lambda^2 X_{t-2} + \cdots).$$

The equivalence of (11.71a) and (11.71b) can be demonstrated by making use of the so-called "Koyck transformation."[21] By lagging (11.71b) by one period and by multiplying both sides by λ, we obtain

$$\lambda X_{t-1}^* = (1 - \lambda)(\lambda X_{t-1} + \lambda^2 X_{t-2} + \cdots).$$

Deducting this equation from (11.71b) leads to

$$X_t^* - \lambda X_{t-1}^* = (1 - \lambda)X_t,$$

which is the same as (11.71a). Therefore, (11.71a) and (11.71b) are equivalent. The substitution for X_t^* from (11.71b) into (11.70) gives

(11.72) $Y_t = \alpha + \beta(1 - \lambda)(X_t + \lambda X_{t-1} + \lambda^2 X_{t-2} + \cdots) + \varepsilon_t,$

which represents the geometric lag model (11.69) with $\beta_0 = \beta(1 - \lambda)$. The size of the average lag in this case is

$$\frac{\beta(1 - \lambda)(0 + \lambda + 2\lambda^2 + 3\lambda^3 + \cdots)}{\beta(1 - \lambda)(1 + \lambda + \lambda^2 + \lambda^3 + \cdots)} = \frac{\beta(1 - \lambda)[\lambda/(1 - \lambda)^2]}{\beta(1 - \lambda)[1/(1 - \lambda)]} = \frac{\lambda}{1 - \lambda}.$$

Equation (11.72) is clearly awkward from the point of view of estimation because of the infinite number of regressors. It can, however, be simplified by the application of the Koyck transformation. By lagging (11.72) by one period, multiplying through by λ, and subtracting the result from (11.72), we obtain

(11.73) $Y_t = \alpha(1 - \lambda) + \beta(1 - \lambda)X_t + \lambda Y_{t-1} + \eta_t$

where $\eta_t = \varepsilon_t - \lambda\varepsilon_{t-1}.$

The adaptive expectation model is sometimes formulated in a slightly different way. The form of the relationship given by (11.70) is retained, but the formation of the expectations is postulated as

(11.74) $X_t^* - X_{t-1}^* = (1 - \lambda)(X_{t-1} - X_{t-1}^*),$

where again $0 \leq \lambda < 1.$

Equation (11.74) differs from (11.71) in that X_t is replaced by X_{t-1}. Such a formulation would be appropriate where X_t is not known in advance so that expectations have to be revised by comparing X_{t-1}^* with X_{t-1}, the most recent available information on X. Equation (11.74) can be rewritten as

(11.74a) $X_t^* = (1 - \lambda)X_{t-1} + \lambda X_{t-1}^*,$

which, in turn, implies that

(11.74b) $X_t^* = (1 - \lambda)(X_{t-1} + \lambda X_{t-2} + \lambda^2 X_{t-3} + \cdots).$

[21] L. M. Koyck, *Distributed Lags and Investment Analysis* (Amsterdam: North-Holland Publishing Company, 1954).

Substitution for X_t^* from (11.74) into (11.70) and application of the Koyck transformation to the result gives

(11.75) $$Y_t = \alpha(1 - \lambda) + \beta(1 - \lambda)X_{t-1} + \lambda Y_{t-1} + \eta_t,$$

where $\eta_t = \varepsilon_t - \lambda\varepsilon_{t-1}.$

The only difference between (11.73) and (11.75) is that in the latter equation X_t is replaced by X_{t-1}. This does not affect the problem of estimating the regression parameters.

An alternative rationalization of the geometric lag is provided by the so-called *partial adjustment* or *habit persistence* model. Suppose the *desired* level of Y at time t, say, Y_t^*, is given by a linear function of some explanatory variable X_t *plus* a disturbance ε_{t1}; i.e.,

(11.76) $$Y_t^* = \alpha + \beta X_t + \varepsilon_{t1}.$$

For instance, the mean desired level of inventory held by a firm may be a linear function of sales (see the "stock adjustment model" in Section 11–2), or the mean desired level of consumption may be a linear function of wealth. The values of Y^* are not directly observable, but we assume that an attempt is being made to bring the actual level of Y to its desired level, and that such an attempt is only partially successful during any one period. The reasons why a complete adjustment of Y to Y^* is not achieved in a single period may be varied; they may include technological constraints, institutional rigidities, persistence of habit, etc.[22] The relationship between the actual and the desired level of Y may be specified as follows:

(11.77) $$Y_t - Y_{t-1} = \gamma(Y_t^* - Y_{t-1}) + \varepsilon_{t2}$$

where $0 < \gamma \le 1,$

and ε_{t2} is a random disturbance. The coefficient γ is called the "adjustment coefficient" since it indicates the rate of adjustment of Y to Y^*. Solving (11.77) for Y_t^*, we obtain

(11.77a) $$Y_t^* = \frac{1}{\gamma}Y_t + \frac{\gamma - 1}{\gamma}Y_{t-1} - \frac{1}{\gamma}\varepsilon_{t2}.$$

Substitution for Y_t^* from (11.77a) into (11.76) gives

(11.78) $$Y_t = \alpha\gamma + \beta\gamma X_t + (1 - \gamma)Y_{t-1} + \xi_t,$$

where $\xi_t = \gamma\varepsilon_{t1} + \varepsilon_{t2}.$

Equation (11.78) is formally the same as the adaptive expectation model characterized by (11.73) *except* that the disturbance in (11.73), unlike that in (11.78), is generated by events of the preceding as well as the present period.

---

[22] For a more precisely formulated rationale within a particular context, see Z. Griliches, "Distributed Lags: A Survey," *Econometrica*, Vol. 35, January 1967, p. 43.

Note also that (11.78) describes a geometric lag of the form

(11.78a) $Y_t = \alpha + \beta\gamma[X_t + (1 - \gamma)X_{t-1} + (1 - \gamma)^2 X_{t-2} + \cdots] + \zeta_t$,

where $\zeta_t = \xi_t + (1 - \gamma)\xi_{t-1} + (1 - \gamma)^2\xi_{t-2} + \cdots$

As in the case of the adaptive expectation model, the partial adjustment model is also sometimes formulated so that the geometric lag starts with X_{t-1} instead of X_t. This is derived by retaining the specification of the adjustment process exactly as in (11.77), but reformulating the determination of the desired level of Y as

(11.79) $Y_t^* = \alpha + \beta X_{t-1} + \varepsilon_{t1}$.

In this formulation, the current desired level of Y depends on the preceding rather than the current level of X. By substituting for Y_t^* from (11.77a) into (11.79) and rearranging the terms, we obtain

(11.80) $Y_t = \alpha\gamma + \beta\gamma X_{t-1} + (1 - \gamma)Y_{t-1} + \xi_t$

where $\xi_t = \gamma\varepsilon_{t1} + \varepsilon_{t2}$.

Again, (11.80) is formally the same as the alternative version of the adaptive expectation model presented in (11.75), except for the specification of the disturbance. From the point of view of estimating the regression parameters, equation (11.80) involves exactly the same considerations as (11.78).

As a matter of interest, we note that the adaptive expectation and the partial adjustment model can be combined into one *compound geometric lag* model. By comparing equation (11.70) of the adaptive expectation model with equation (11.76) of the partial adjustment model, we can see that each represents a straightforward modification of the simple regression model

$$Y_t = \alpha + \beta X_t + \varepsilon_t.$$

In the adaptive expectation model, X_t is replaced by its "expected" value X_t^*; and in the partial adjustment model, Y_t is replaced by its "desired" value Y_t^*. Combining the two specifications, we have

(11.81) $Y_t^* = \alpha + \beta X_t^* + \varepsilon_{t1}$.

This means that the mean desired value of Y is a linear function of the expected level of X. To complete the model, we have to state how the unobservable X_t^* and Y_t^* are assumed to be determined. We assume that X_t^* is determined by (11.71b) of the adaptive expectation model, and that Y_t^* is determined by (11.77a) of the partial adjustment model. By making the appropriate substitutions in (11.81), we obtain

(11.82) $Y_t = \alpha\gamma + \beta\gamma(1 - \lambda)(X_t + \lambda X_{t-1} + \lambda^2 X_{t-2} + \cdots) + (1 - \gamma)Y_{t-1} + \xi_t$,

where $\xi_t = \gamma\varepsilon_{t1} + \varepsilon_{t2}$.

Equation (11.82) can be simplified by applying the Koyck transformation, so that

(11.83) $Y_t = \alpha\gamma(1-\lambda)+\beta\gamma(1-\lambda)X_t+[(1-\gamma)+\lambda]Y_{t-1}-(1-\gamma)\lambda Y_{t-2}+\omega_t,$

where $\omega_t = \xi_t - \lambda\xi_{t-1}.$

Note that, by analogy with (11.78a), equation (11.83) can be written as

(11.83a) $Y_t = \alpha + \beta\gamma[X_t^* + (1 - \gamma)X_{t-1}^* + (1 - \gamma)^2 X_{t-2}^* + \cdots] + \zeta_t,$

where $\zeta_t = \xi_t + (1 - \gamma)\xi_{t-1} + (1 - \gamma)^2\xi_{t-2} + \cdots$

This shows why the model is called a compound geometric lag model: the regression coefficients of (11.83a) follow a geometric progression while each of X_t^*, X_{t-1}^*, X_{t-2}^*, ..., is a weighted average of the preceding values of X with the weights also following a geometric progression. The model reduces to a pure adaptive expectation model if $\gamma = 1$, to a pure partial adjustment model if $\lambda = 0$, and to a simple regression model if $\gamma = 1$ *and* $\lambda = 0$.

Before turning our attention to the problem of estimating the regression coefficients of the geometric lag models, we should consider the formulation of models in which the distributed lag extends over more than one explanatory variable. In particular, let us take a model in which there are two explanatory variables, X and Z, each exerting its effect on $E(Y_t)$ through its own geometrically distributed lag:

(11.84) $Y_t = \alpha + \beta_0(X_t + \lambda X_{t-1} + \lambda^2 X_{t-2} + \cdots)$

$$+ \delta_0(Z_t + \mu Z_{t-1} + \mu^2 Z_{t-2} + \cdots) + \varepsilon_t,$$

where $0 \le \lambda < 1$ and $0 \le \mu < 1.$

For example, the demand for money may depend on "permanent" income and on an "expected" rate of interest. Equation (11.84) can be reduced to a more manageable form by applying the Koyck transformation twice in succession. First, we lag (11.84) by one period, multiply both sides by λ, and deduct the resulting equation from (11.84). This gives

(11.84a) $Y_t = \alpha(1 - \lambda) + \lambda Y_{t-1} + \delta_0[Z_t + (\mu - \lambda)Z_{t-1} + \mu(\mu - \lambda)Z_{t-2}$

$$+ \mu^2(\mu - \lambda)Z_{t-3} + \cdots] + \beta_0 X_t + \varepsilon_t - \lambda\varepsilon_{t-1}.$$

Next, we lag (11.84a) by one period, multiply both sides by μ, and deduct the resulting equation from (11.84a). The result is

(11.84b) $Y_t = \alpha(1 - \lambda)(1 - \mu) + (\lambda + \mu)Y_{t-1} - \lambda\mu Y_{t-2}$

$$+\beta_0 X_t - \beta_0\mu X_{t-1} + \delta_0 Z_t - \delta_0\lambda Z_{t-1} + \eta_t^*,$$

where $\eta_t^* = \varepsilon_t - (\lambda + \mu)\varepsilon_{t-1} + \lambda\mu\varepsilon_{t-2},$

which is a regression equation with six regressors (in addition to the constant term). It is clear that we could handle models with any number of distributed lags in a similar manner.

Let us now consider the problem of estimating the parameters of a geometrically distributed lag model,

$$Y_t = \alpha + \beta_0(X_t + \lambda X_{t-1} + \lambda^2 X_{t-2} + \cdots) + \varepsilon_t,$$

where ε_t is a random normal variable with mean zero and variance σ^2. Suppose further that the relation is generated by an *adaptive expectation* mechanism, as described by equations (11.70) and (11.71). Estimation of the parameters of this model depends on whether we assume the ε's to be mutually independent or not. We shall start with the case where the ε's are mutually independent; i.e., we assume that the disturbances are normally distributed and

(11.85) $$E(\varepsilon_t \varepsilon_s) = 0 \qquad (t \neq s).$$

The geometric lag model is clearly not suitable for estimation in its original form since it involves an infinite number of regressors. However, by applying the Koyck transformation, we can write

$$Y_t = \alpha(1 - \lambda) + \beta(1 - \lambda)X_t + \lambda Y_{t-1} + \eta_t,$$

or $$Y_t = \alpha_0 + \beta_0 X_t + \lambda Y_{t-1} + \eta_t,$$

where $$\alpha_0 = \alpha(1 - \lambda),$$

$$\beta_0 = \beta(1 - \lambda),$$

and $$\eta_t = \varepsilon_t - \lambda \varepsilon_{t-1}.$$

This equation was presented earlier as (11.73). Its form is relatively simple, but this simplification has not been achieved without cost. The trouble with (11.73) is that the "new" disturbance η_t is correlated with Y_{t-1}, which is now one of the explanatory variables. In particular,

$$E(\eta_t Y_{t-1}) = E(\varepsilon_t - \lambda \varepsilon_{t-1})[\alpha + \beta(X_{t-1} + \lambda X_{t-2} + \cdots) + \varepsilon_{t-1}]$$

$$= -\lambda \sigma^2.$$

This means that the ordinary least squares estimates of the coefficients of (11.73) are *inconsistent* (see Section 8–3), and we have to resort to other estimation methods.

Consistent estimates of the coefficients of (11.73) under the assumption specified in (11.85) can be obtained in several ways. Perhaps the simplest is to use the *method of instrumental variables*, which we have described in connection with the "errors-in-variables" models in Section 9–1. Since equation (11.73) involves two explanatory variables, we have to find two instrumental variables, say, Z_1 and Z_2. These variables should satisfy the following conditions:

1. $\text{plim} \sum_t (Z_{1t} - \bar{Z}_1)\eta_t/n = 0$ and $\text{plim} \sum (Z_{2t} - \bar{Z}_2)\eta_t/n = 0$.
2. $\text{plim} \sum_t (Z_{1t} - \bar{Z}_1)X_t/n$ and $\text{plim} \sum_t (Z_{2t} - \bar{Z})Y_{t-1}/n$ are both finite numbers different from zero.

An additional condition, which is not necessary for consistency but which helps to reduce the asymptotic variance of the instrumental variables estimator, is that the instrumental variables should be highly correlated with the respective regressors. It has been suggested that the following instrumental variables be used:

$$Z_{1t} = X_t, \quad \text{and} \quad Z_{2t} = X_{t-1}.$$

That is, the instrumental variable for the first regressor, X_t, is to be X_t itself, and the instrumental variable for the second regressor, Y_{t-1}, is to be X_{t-1}. Clearly, since X_t is nonstochastic, it serves as an ideal instrumental variable for itself since it satisfies the necessary conditions and is "perfectly correlated" with X_t. The second instrumental variable also satisfies the necessary conditions and is likely to be correlated with Y_{t-1}. The normal equations for the instrumental variables estimates then are

$$\sum_t Y_t = \alpha_0^\dagger(n-1) + \beta_0^\dagger \sum_t X_t + \lambda^\dagger \sum Y_{t-1},$$

$$\sum_t X_t Y_t = \alpha_0^\dagger \sum_t X_t + \beta_0^\dagger \sum_t X_t^2 + \lambda^\dagger \sum X_t Y_{t-1},$$

$$\sum_t X_{t-1} Y_t = \alpha_0^\dagger \sum_t X_{t-1} + \beta_0^\dagger \sum_t X_t X_{t-1} + \lambda^\dagger \sum X_{t-1} Y_{t-1},$$

or, in matrix notation,

$$\mathbf{Z'Y} = (\mathbf{Z'X})\mathbf{b}^\dagger,$$

where

$$\mathbf{Y} = \begin{bmatrix} Y_2 \\ Y_3 \\ \vdots \\ Y_n \end{bmatrix}, \quad \mathbf{Z} = \begin{bmatrix} 1 & X_2 & X_1 \\ 1 & X_3 & X_2 \\ \vdots & \vdots & \vdots \\ 1 & X_n & X_{n-1} \end{bmatrix}, \quad \mathbf{X} = \begin{bmatrix} 1 & X_2 & Y_1 \\ 1 & X_3 & Y_2 \\ \vdots & \vdots & \vdots \\ 1 & X_n & Y_{n-1} \end{bmatrix}, \quad \mathbf{b}^\dagger = \begin{bmatrix} \alpha_0^\dagger \\ \beta_0^\dagger \\ \lambda^\dagger \end{bmatrix}.$$

Note that since the first available observation on Y_t is Y_1, the summation goes from $t = 2$ to $t = n$. The solution of the normal equations is

(11.86) $$\mathbf{b}^\dagger = (\mathbf{Z'X})^{-1}(\mathbf{Z'Y}).$$

The asymptotic variance-covariance matrix of $\mathbf{b}^\dagger$ can be estimated as follows:

(11.87)   Est. Asympt. Var-Cov($\mathbf{b}^\dagger$) $= s^{*2}(\mathbf{Z'X})^{-1}(\mathbf{Z'Z})(\mathbf{X'Z})^{-1}$,

where $$s^{*2} = \frac{1}{n-4} \sum_{t=2}^n (Y_t - \alpha_0^\dagger - \beta_0^\dagger X_t - \lambda^\dagger Y_{t-1})^2.$$

From the consistent estimates of α_0, β_0, and λ, we can easily derive consistent estimates of α and β. Their asymptotic variances can be estimated by (11.40) in conjunction with (11.87).

An alternative approach to estimating the coefficients of (11.73) is based on the *maximum likelihood* principle. The estimators can then be developed as follows.[23] Equation (11.73) can be rewritten as

$$(Y_t - \varepsilon_t) = \alpha(1 - \lambda) + \beta(1 - \lambda)X_t + \lambda(Y_{t-1} - \varepsilon_{t-1}),$$

or $\qquad E(Y_t) = \alpha_0 + \beta_0 X_t + \lambda E(Y_{t-1}).$

However, since

$$E(Y_{t-1}) = \alpha_0 + \beta_0 X_{t-1} + \lambda E(Y_{t-2}),$$

$$E(Y_{t-2}) = \alpha_0 + \beta_0 X_{t-2} + \lambda E(Y_{t-3}),$$

$$\vdots$$

$$E(Y_1) \;\; = \alpha_0 + \beta_0 X_1 + \lambda E(Y_0),$$

we can also write

(11.88) $E(Y_t) = \alpha_0(1 + \lambda + \lambda^2 + \cdots + \lambda^{t-1})$

$$+ \beta_0(X_t + \lambda X_{t-1} + \lambda^2 X_{t-2} + \cdots + \lambda^{t-1} X_1) + \lambda^t E(Y_0).$$

Using the formula for the sum of a geometric progression, and the fact that $\alpha_0 = \alpha(1 - \lambda)$, we can reformulate (11.88) as

(11.88a) $\qquad Y_t = \alpha + \beta_0 W_t^{(\lambda)} + (\theta_0 - \alpha)\lambda^t + \varepsilon_t,$

where $\qquad W_t^{(\lambda)} = X_t + \lambda X_{t-1} + \lambda^2 X_{t-2} + \cdots + \lambda^{t-1} X_1$

and $\qquad \theta_0 = E(Y_0).$

The value of $E(Y_0)$ is the initial mean value of Y and can be regarded as a parameter. Note that if λ were known, equation (11.88a) would be a linear multiple regression equation with two explanatory variables, $W_t^{(\lambda)}$ and λ^t, and could be estimated by the ordinary least squares method. Of course, λ is generally not known and has to be estimated along with α, β_0, and θ_0. The logarithmic likelihood function for $Y_1, Y_2, \ldots, Y_n$ is

(11.89) $L = -\dfrac{n}{2}\log(2\pi\sigma^2) - \dfrac{1}{2\sigma^2}\displaystyle\sum_{t=1}^{n}[Y_t - \alpha - \beta_0 W_t^{(\lambda)} - (\theta_0 - \alpha)\lambda^t]^2.$

Maximizing L with respect to α, β_0, λ, and θ_0 is equivalent to minimizing

$$S^{(\lambda)} = \sum_{t=1}^{n}[Y_t - \alpha - \beta_0 W_t^{(\lambda)} - (\theta_0 - \alpha)\lambda^t]^2$$

---

[23] These estimators have been derived in the appendix of the paper by L. R. Klein, "The Estimation of Distributed Lags," *Econometrica*, Vol. 26, October 1958, pp. 553–565, and operationally developed in P. J. Dhrymes, "Efficient Estimation of Distributed Lags with Autocorrelated Error Terms," *International Economic Review*, Vol. 10, February 1969, pp. 47–67, and in A. Zellner and M. S. Geisel, "Analysis of Distributed Lag Models with Applications to Consumption Function Estimation," manuscript, University of Chicago (January, 1968), forthcoming in *Econometrica*. Our presentation of the method follows closely that of Zellner and Geisel.

with respect to the same parameters. Since we know that $0 \leq \lambda < 1$, we can easily calculate the minimizing values of α, β_0, and θ_0, and the corresponding value of $S^{(\lambda)}$, for different values of λ from 0 to 0.95 or 0.99. Then we select those values of α, β_0, and θ_0, and λ that lead to the smallest value of $S^{(\lambda)}$. These values will be the maximum likelihood estimates of the respective parameters. If we have no information about X other than the sample values of $X_1, X_2, \ldots, X_n$, the maximum likelihood estimates of α, β_0, and λ obtained in this way will be asymptotically efficient. Their asymptotic variances can be estimated by using the appropriate information matrix.

EXAMPLE The preceding method has been applied to estimating the parameters of a consumption function model from United States quarterly observations 1947(I) to 1960(IV).[24] The consumption function is derived from an adaptive expectation model and can be described as

$$C_t = \beta Y_t^* + \varepsilon_t,$$

$$Y_t^* - Y_{t-1}^* = (1 - \lambda)(Y_t - Y_{t-1}^*),$$

where C = measured real consumption, Y^* = "normal" or "permanent" real income, and Y = measured real income. By combining the two equations and eliminating Y^*, we obtain

$$C_t = \beta(1 - \lambda)Y_t + \lambda C_t + \varepsilon_t - \lambda\varepsilon_{t-1}.$$

The coefficients have been estimated from

$$C_t = \beta(1 - \lambda)W_t^{(\lambda)} + \theta_0\lambda^t + \varepsilon_t,$$

where $W_t^{(\lambda)} = Y_t + \lambda Y_{t-1} + \cdots + \lambda^{t-1}Y_1$

and $\theta_0 = E(Y_0).$

The sum of squared residuals (divided by the number of observations) has been calculated for different values of λ between 0 and 1; the results are shown in Figure 11–12. The curve has a local minimum at $\lambda = 0.45$, and a global minimum at $\lambda = 0.963$. The latter is then the maximum likelihood estimate of λ. The corresponding estimates of β and θ_0 are

$$\hat{\beta} = 1.129, \quad \text{and} \quad \hat{\theta}_0 = 191.53.$$

Since β is supposed to measure the marginal propensity to consume out of "normal" income, a value larger than one is unreasonable a priori. Therefore, the results cannot be considered as acceptable. (Zellner and Geisel note that this result may be due to inadequacies of the particular model and/or data. If both the model and the data are thought to be adequate, then we should incorporate the restriction $0 < \beta < 1$ into our estimation procedure.)

[24] See Zellner and Geisel, *op. cit.* The data on personal consumption expenditures and personal disposable income, both series price-deflated and seasonally adjusted, are presented in Z. Griliches *et al.*, "Notes on Estimated Aggregate Quarterly Consumption Function," *Econometrica*, Vol. 30, July 1962, pp. 491–500.

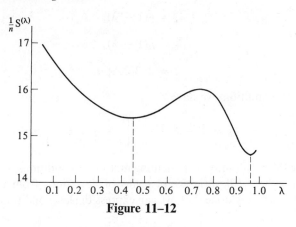

Figure 11–12

A still different approach to estimating the coefficients of (11.73) is possible if we note that

$$(Y_t - \varepsilon_t) = \alpha(1 - \lambda) + \beta(1 - \lambda)X_t + \lambda(Y_{t-1} - \varepsilon_{t-1})$$

is formally similar to an "errors-in-variables" model discussed in Section 9–1. That is, we may view ε_t as an "error" involved in measuring $E(Y_t)$, and ε_{t-1} as an "error" involved in measuring $E(Y_{t-1})$. Since, by assumption, ε is homoskedastic, the variance of ε_t is equal to that of ε_{t-1}. Therefore, we can use the *weighted regression method* by assigning equal weights to each of the errors. In particular, we can minimize

$$(11.90) \quad S = \sum_t \varepsilon_t^2 + \sum_t \varepsilon_{t-1}^2 = \sum_t [Y_t - \alpha(1 - \lambda) - \beta(1 - \lambda)X_t - \lambda\theta_{t-1}]^2$$

$$+ \sum_t [Y_{t-1} - \theta_{t-1}]^2,$$

where
$$\theta_{t-1} = E(Y_{t-1}),$$

with respect to α, β, λ, and each of the θ's. Since the first known value of Y is Y_1, the summation has to run from $t = 2$ to $t = n$. The first-order conditions for minimization are

$$\sum_t (Y_t - \tilde{\alpha}_0 - \tilde{\beta}_0 X_t - \tilde{\lambda}\tilde{\theta}_{t-1}) = 0,$$

$$\sum_t X_t(Y_t - \tilde{\alpha}_0 - \tilde{\beta}_0 X_t - \tilde{\lambda}\tilde{\theta}_{t-1}) = 0,$$

$$\sum_t \tilde{\theta}_{t-1}(Y_t - \tilde{\alpha}_0 - \tilde{\beta}_0 X_t - \tilde{\lambda}\tilde{\theta}_{t-1}) = 0,$$

$$\tilde{\lambda}(Y_t - \tilde{\alpha}_0 - \tilde{\beta}_0 X_t - \tilde{\lambda}\tilde{\theta}_{t-1}) + (Y_{t-1} - \tilde{\theta}_{t-1}) = 0,$$

where
$$\tilde{\alpha}_0 = \tilde{\alpha}(1 - \tilde{\lambda}),$$
$$\tilde{\beta}_0 = \tilde{\beta}(1 - \tilde{\lambda}),$$
$$t = 2, 3, \ldots, n.$$

From the first condition, we have

$$\tilde{\alpha}_0 = \bar{Y} - \tilde{\beta}_0 \bar{X} - \tilde{\lambda}\left[\frac{1}{n-1}\sum_t \tilde{\theta}_{t-1}\right].$$

Substituting this result into the remaining first-order conditions, we can eliminate $\tilde{\alpha}_0$ and then express all variables in terms of deviations from their respective sample means. Having done that, we can express the last condition as

$$\tilde{\theta}'_{t-1} = \frac{\tilde{\lambda}(y'_t - \tilde{\beta}_0 x'_t) + y'_{t-1}}{1 + \tilde{\lambda}^2},$$

where
$$\tilde{\theta}'_{t-1} = \tilde{\theta}_{t-1} - \frac{1}{n-1}\sum_t \tilde{\theta}_{t-1},$$

$$y'_t = Y_t - \bar{Y},$$

$$x'_t = X_t - \bar{X},$$

$$y'_{t-1} = Y_{t-1} - \frac{1}{n-1}\sum_t Y_{t-1}.$$

Substitution for $\tilde{\theta}'_{t-1}$ into the second and third of the first-order conditions and elimination of $\tilde{\beta}_0$ lead to

(11.91)
$$\tilde{\lambda}^2 \left[\frac{\sum x'_t y'_t \sum x'_t y'_{t-1}}{\sum x'^2_t} - \sum y'_t y'_{t-1}\right]$$

$$+ \tilde{\lambda}\left[\frac{(\sum x'_t y'_{t-1})^2 - (\sum x'_t y'_t)^2}{\sum x'^2_t} + \sum y'^2_t - \sum y'^2_{t-1}\right]$$

$$+ \left[\sum y'_t y'_{t-1} - \frac{\sum x'_t y'_t \sum x'_t y'_{t-1}}{\sum x'^2_t}\right] = 0.$$

From the two roots of (11.91), we choose the value of $\tilde{\lambda}$ that minimizes S. Having obtained a solution for $\tilde{\lambda}$, we can easily calculate the estimated values of α, β, and the θ's. These estimates are consistent but not necessarily asymptotically efficient.[25]

Let us now change the specification of the adaptive expectation model by

---

[25] The weighted regression approach to estimating the parameters of a distributed lag model was suggested and developed in Klein (1958), *op. cit.* The relationship between this method and the maximum likelihood method is described in the appendix of the paper. See also T. Amemiya and W. A. Fuller, "A Comparative Study of Alternative Estimators in a Distributed Lag Model," *Econometrica*, Vol. 35, July–October 1967, pp. 509–529.

dropping the assumption of mutual independence of the ε's as implied by (11.85), and replacing it by

(11.92) $$\varepsilon_t = \rho\varepsilon_{t-1} + u_t,$$

with $$E(\varepsilon_{t-1}u_t) = 0,$$

$$u_t \sim N(0, \sigma_u^2),$$

and $$\varepsilon_0 \sim N\left(0, \frac{\sigma_u^2}{1 - \rho^2}\right).$$

First, we note that in the special case in which $\rho = \lambda$, the problem of estimating the coefficients of (11.73) becomes greatly simplified. The reason is that in this case the "transformed" disturbance η_t is now equal to u_t; that is, it is nonautoregressive and uncorrelated with Y_{t-1}. Under these circumstances the ordinary least squares method applied to (11.73) leads to estimates which have all the desirable asymptotic properties. Of course, the assumption that the η's are mutually independent is quite restrictive; it is unfortunate that we cannot test it by using the Durbin–Watson test, but this test is not applicable in this case. Theoretically, the contention that $\rho = \lambda$ is difficult to justify.

The problem of estimating the coefficients of (11.73) subject to the assumption (11.92) when $\lambda \neq \rho$ is more complicated. As in the case of independent ε's, the ordinary least squares estimates are inconsistent, and we must use alternative methods of estimation. Again, the simplest way of getting consistent estimates is by the *method of instrumental variables*. Alternatively, we may rely on the maximum likelihood principle and develop *maximum likelihood estimators* of the parameters of (11.73) and (11.92), in which case we rewrite (11.73) as

$$E(Y_t) = \alpha(1 - \lambda) + \beta(1 - \lambda)X_t + \lambda E(Y_{t-1})$$

and $$\rho E(Y_{t-1}) = \alpha(1 - \lambda)\rho + \beta(1 - \lambda)\rho X_{t-1} + \lambda\rho E(Y_{t-2}).$$

Deducting the second expression from the first, we obtain

$$(11.93) \quad E(Y_t) - \rho E(Y_{t-1}) = \alpha(1 - \lambda)(1 - \rho) + \beta(1 - \lambda)(X_t - \rho X_{t-1})$$

$$+ \lambda[E(Y_{t-1}) - \rho E(Y_{t-2})]$$

$$= \alpha(1 - \lambda)(1 - \rho)(1 + \lambda + \lambda^2 + \cdots + \lambda^{t-1})$$

$$+ \beta(1 - \lambda)[(X_t - \rho X_{t-1}) + \lambda(X_{t-1} - \rho X_{t-2})$$

$$+ \cdots + \lambda^{t-1}(X_1 - \rho X_0)]$$

$$+ \lambda^t[E(Y_0) - \rho E(Y_{-1})].$$

If we now use (11.92) and introduce simplifying notation, we can write (11.93) as

$$(11.93a) \quad (Y_t - \rho Y_{t-1}) = \alpha^* + \beta_0 W_t^{(\lambda, \rho)} + \delta_0\lambda^t + u_t,$$

where

$$W_t^{(\lambda,\rho)} = (X_t - \rho X_{t-1}) + \lambda(X_{t-1} - \rho X_{t-2}) + \cdots + \lambda^{t-2}(X_2 - \rho X_1) + \lambda^{t-1}X_1,$$

$$\alpha^* = \alpha(1 - \rho),$$

$$\beta_0 = \beta(1 - \lambda),$$

$$\delta_0 = E(Y_0) - \rho E(Y_{-1}) - \alpha^* - \frac{\beta_0 \rho X_0}{\lambda}.$$

If λ and ρ were known, (11.93a) would be a linear multiple regression equation with two explanatory variables, $W_t^{(\lambda,\rho)}$ and λ^t. When, as usual, this is not the case, we can set up the likelihood function for $Y_2, Y_3, \ldots, Y_n$ (conditional on Y_1) as

(11.94) $$L = -\frac{n-1}{2} \log (2\pi\sigma_u^2)$$

$$- \frac{1}{2\sigma_u^2} \sum_{t=2}^{n} [Y_t - \rho Y_{t-1} - \alpha^* - \beta_0 W_t^{(\lambda,\rho)} - \delta_0 \lambda^t]^2.$$

Maximizing L with respect to α^*, β_0, δ_0, λ, and ρ is equivalent to minimizing

$$S^{(\lambda,\rho)} = \sum_{t=2}^{n} [Y_t - \rho Y_{t-1} - \alpha^* - \beta_0 W_t^{(\lambda,\rho)} - \delta_0 \lambda^t]^2$$

with respect to the same parameters. Since we know that $0 \le \lambda < 1$ and $-1 < \rho < 1$, we can take different pairs of values of λ and ρ, and for each pair calculate the corresponding estimates of α^*, β_0, and δ_0. Of all the results, we choose that set of values of the parameters which corresponds to the smallest value of $S^{(\lambda,\rho)}$. The estimates of α, β, λ, and ρ will be asymptotically efficient; their asymptotic variances can be determined by reference to the appropriate information matrix.

EXAMPLE   Zellner and Geisel[26] have applied the above method to the consumption model described in the preceding example, using the same set of observations. The results are

$$\hat{\beta} = 0.94,$$
$$(0.46)$$

$$\hat{\lambda} = 0.66,$$
$$(0.085)$$

$$\hat{\rho} = 0.69.$$
$$(0.076)$$

The figures is parentheses are the estimated asymptotic standard errors. The results show that the estimate of λ is very close to that of ρ, which indicates that the assumption $\lambda = \rho$ may not have been too unreasonable in this case.

[26] *Op. cit.*

Let us now consider estimating the parameters of a geometrically distributed lag relation generated by a *partial adjustment* (or *habit persistence*) mechanism. Such a relation was represented by equation (11.78) as

$$Y_t = \alpha\gamma + \beta\gamma X_t + (1 - \gamma)Y_{t-1} + \xi_t,$$

where ξ_t is a normally distributed random variable with mean zero and variance σ^2. The specification of the partial adjustment model does not lead to any further restrictions on ξ_t, which makes estimation much simpler than in the case of the adaptive expectation model. If it can be assumed that $E(\xi_t\xi_s) = 0$ for all $t \neq s$, then we can use the ordinary least squares method and obtain consistent and asymptotically efficient estimates of the parameters of (11.78). On the other hand, if ξ_t follows a first-order autoregression scheme, i.e., if

(11.95) $$\xi_t = \rho\xi_{t-1} + u_t,$$

where $$E(\xi_{t-1}u_t) = 0,$$

$$u_t \sim N(0, \sigma_u^2),$$

and $$\xi_0 \sim N\left(0, \frac{\sigma_u^2}{1 - \rho^2}\right),$$

then the ordinary least squares method applied to (11.78) would lead to inconsistent estimates. In this case, we can use a transformation of (11.78) that eliminates ξ_t and leads to

(11.96) $$(Y_t - \rho Y_{t-1}) = \alpha\gamma(1 - \rho) + \beta\gamma(X_t - \rho X_{t-1})$$
$$+ (1 - \gamma)(Y_{t-1} - \rho Y_{t-2}) + u_t.$$

The maximum likelihood of α, β, γ, and ρ (conditional on Y_1) can then be obtained by maximizing

(11.97) $$L = -\frac{n-1}{2}\log(2\pi\sigma_u^2) - \frac{1}{2\sigma_u^2}\sum_{t=2}^{n}[(Y_t - \rho Y_{t-1}) - \alpha\gamma(1 - \rho)$$
$$- \beta\gamma(X_t - \rho X_{t-1}) - (1 - \gamma)(Y_{t-1} - \rho Y_{t-2})]^2$$

with respect to the unknown parameters. The resulting estimates will have all the desirable asymptotic properties.[27]

Pascal Lag

In some instances, a distributed lag model with the weights declining geometrically from the current period into the past may not be altogether appropriate. For example, in a model relating current capital expenditures to current and past capital appropriations, it is much more reasonable to expect that the weights attached to capital appropriations at times $t, t - 1, t - 2, \ldots$, would

---

[27] See Malinvaud, *op. cit.*, p. 469. For a test of the hypothesis that ξ_t is nonautoregressive, see J. Durbin, "Testing for Serial Correlation in Least-Squares Regression When Some of the Regressors Are Lagged Dependent Variables," *Econometrica*, Vol. 38, May 1970, pp. 410–421.

first rise and then decline instead of declining all the way. Such a distribution of weights may be called an *inverted V-lag distribution*. There are many ways in which such a lag distribution can be formulated. One possibility is to use the so-called *Pascal lag distribution*. This distribution can be described as follows. First rewrite (11.68) as

(11.68a) $Y_t = \alpha + \beta(w_0 X_t + w_1 X_{t-1} + w_2 X_{t-2} + \cdots) + \varepsilon_t,$

where ε_t is a normally distributed disturbance with mean zero and variance σ^2. The weights corresponding to the Pascal lag model then are given as

$$w_i = \binom{i + r - 1}{i}(1 - \lambda)^r \lambda^i = \frac{(i + r - 1)!}{i!(r - 1)!}(1 - \lambda)^r \lambda^i \qquad (i = 0, 1, 2, \ldots),$$

where r is some positive integer and λ a parameter to be estimated. The regression equation then becomes

(11.98) $Y_t = \alpha + \beta(1 - \lambda)^r[X_t + r\lambda X_{t-1} + \dfrac{r(r + 1)}{2!} \lambda^2 X_{t-2} + \cdots] + \varepsilon_t.$

Note that when $r = 1$, we get $w_i = (1 - \lambda)\lambda^i$, which means that the Pascal distribution reduces to a geometric lag distribution. For values of r greater than one, we may get inverted V-lag distributions. Figure 11–13 shows the distribution of weights for $\lambda = 0.6$ and for different values of r.

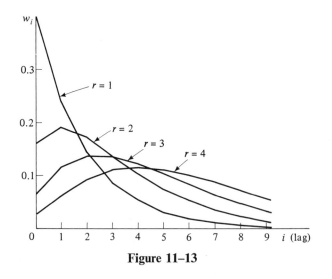

Figure 11–13

The estimation of the parameters in the case of a Pascal lag model is more complicated than with a geometric lag model. Consider, for instance, the case $r = 2$. The Pascal lag relation then is

(11.99) $Y_t = \alpha + \beta(1 - \lambda)^2(X_t + 2\lambda X_{t-1} + 3\lambda^2 X_{t-2} + \cdots) + \varepsilon_t.$

This equation can be simplified by applying the following transformation. First, lag (11.99) by one period and multiply through by -2λ. This gives

(11.99a) $-2\lambda Y_{t-1} = -2\alpha\lambda + \beta(1 - \lambda)^2(-2\lambda X_{t-1} - 4\lambda^2 X_{t-2}$

$$- 6\lambda^3 X_{t-3} - \cdots) - 2\lambda\varepsilon_{t-1}.$$

Next, lag (11.99) by two periods and multiply through by λ^2. The result is

(11.99b) $\lambda^2 Y_{t-2} = \alpha\lambda^2 + \beta(1 - \lambda)^2(\lambda^2 X_{t-2} + 2\lambda^3 X_{t-3}$

$$+ 3\lambda^4 X_{t-4} + \cdots) + \lambda^2\varepsilon_{t-2}.$$

Now add (11.99), (11.99a), and (11.99b) to obtain

(11.100) $Y_t = \alpha(1 - \lambda)^2 + \beta(1 - \lambda)^2 X_t + 2\lambda Y_{t-1} - \lambda^2 Y_{t-2} + \eta_t,$

where $\eta_t = \varepsilon_t - 2\lambda\varepsilon_{t-1} + \lambda^2\varepsilon_{t-2}.$

Unless η_t is nonautoregressive, estimation of (11.100) by the ordinary least squares method leads to inconsistent estimates. To obtain consistent estimates, we can use the *method of instrumental variables*. To allow for the fact that (11.100) is overidentified, we rewrite it as

(11.100a) $Y_t^* = \alpha_0 + \beta_0 X_t + \gamma_0 Y_{t-1}^* + \eta_t,$

where $Y_t^* = Y_t - \lambda Y_{t-1},$

$$Y_{t-1}^* = Y_{t-1} - \lambda Y_{t-2},$$

$$\alpha_0 = \alpha(1 - \lambda)^2,$$

$$\beta_0 = \beta(1 - \lambda)^2,$$

$$\gamma_0 = \lambda.$$

Then we use, as instrumental variables for X_t and Y_{t-1}^*,

$$Z_{1t} = X_t \quad \text{and} \quad Z_{2t} = X_{t-1},$$

and calculate the estimates of α_0, β_0, and γ_0 for different values of λ between 0 and 1. Of all the results, we choose that set of values of α_0, β_0, and γ_0 for which γ_0 is equal to λ, or at least approximately so.

Equation (11.100) could also be estimated by the *maximum likelihood method*. Note that it can also be written as

$$(Y_t - \varepsilon_t) = \alpha(1 - \lambda)^2 + \beta(1 - \lambda)^2 X_t + 2\lambda(Y_{t-1} - \varepsilon_{t-1}) - \lambda^2(Y_{t-2} - \varepsilon_{t-2}),$$

or

$$E(Y_t) = \alpha_0 + \beta_0 X_t + 2\lambda E(Y_{t-1}) - \lambda^2 E(Y_{t-2}).$$

However, since

$$E(Y_{t-1}) = \alpha_0 + \beta_0 X_{t-1} + 2\lambda E(Y_{t-2}) - \lambda^2 E(Y_{t-3}),$$

$$E(Y_{t-2}) = \alpha_0 + \beta_0 X_{t-2} + 2\lambda E(Y_{t-3}) - \lambda^2 E(Y_{t-4}),$$

$$\vdots$$

$$E(Y_1) \ = \alpha_0 + \beta_0 X_1 \ \ + 2\lambda E(Y_0) \ \ - \lambda^2 E(Y_{-1}),$$

we can also write

(11.101) $\quad E(Y_t) = \alpha_0(1 + 2\lambda + 3\lambda^2 + \cdots + t\lambda^{t-1})$

$$+ \beta_0(X_t + 2\lambda X_{t-1} + 3\lambda^2 X_{t-2} + \cdots + t\lambda^{t-1}X_1)$$

$$+ (t + 1)\lambda^t E(Y_0) - t\lambda^{t+1}E(Y_{-1}).$$

Further,

$$\alpha_0(1 + 2\lambda + 3\lambda^2 + \cdots + t\lambda^{t-1}) = \frac{\alpha_0}{1 - \lambda}(1 + \lambda + \lambda^2 + \cdots + \lambda^{t-1} - t\lambda^t)$$

$$= \frac{\alpha_0(1 - \lambda^t)}{(1 - \lambda)^2} - \frac{\alpha_0 t\lambda^t}{(1 - \lambda)}$$

$$= \alpha(1 - \lambda^t) - \alpha(1 - \lambda)t\lambda^t.$$

Thus, (11.101) can be written as

(11.101a) $Y_t = \alpha + \beta_0 W_{2t}^{(\lambda)} + \delta_0\lambda^t + \phi_0 t\lambda^t + \varepsilon_t$

where $W_{2t}^{(\lambda)} = X_t + 2\lambda X_{t-1} + 3\lambda^2 X_{t-2} + \cdots + t\lambda^{t-1}X_1,$

$$\beta_0 = \beta(1 - \lambda)^2,$$

$$\delta_0 = E(Y_0) - \alpha,$$

$$\phi_0 = E(Y_0) - \lambda E(Y_{-1}) - \alpha(1 - \lambda).$$

If λ were known, equation (11.101a) would be a linear regression equation with three regressors: $W_{2t}^{(\lambda)}$, λ^t, and $t\lambda^t$. Of course, in most cases, λ is not known. If it is assumed that the ε's are mutually independent, then we can obtain the maximum likelihood estimates of the unknown parameters by minimizing

$$S^{(\lambda)} = \sum_{t=1}^{n} (Y_t - \alpha - \beta_0 W_{2t}^{(\lambda)} - \delta_0\lambda^t - \phi_0 t\lambda^t)^2$$

with respect to α, β_0, δ_0, and ϕ_0 for different values of λ between 0 and 1. The maximum likelihood estimates of α, β, δ_0, and λ will then be those values which lead to the smallest value of $S^{(\lambda)}$. Under the stated assumptions the estimates of α, β, and λ will have all the desirable asymptotic properties. If the ε's follow a first-order autoregression scheme, we can transform (11.100) into

$$E(Y_t) - \rho E(Y_{t-1}) = \alpha_0(1 - \rho) + \beta_0(X_t - \rho X_{t-1})$$

$$+ 2\lambda[E(Y_{t-1}) - \rho E(Y_{t-2})] - \lambda^2[E(Y_{t-2}) - \rho E(Y_{t-3})] + u_t$$

and then proceed as with (11.93) and (11.93a).

The approach to the problem of estimating the parameters of a Pascal lag model for $r = 3$, 4, etc., could be similar to that for $r = 2$. Of course, the degree of complexity of the estimation problem increases with r. If the value of r cannot be assumed a priori, we have to calculate the value of the likelihood function for each r and then choose the value of r that leads to the maximum value of the likelihood function. While there is no difficulty about such a procedure in principle, its implementation is involved and may not be practicable.

The transformation of the Pascal lag relation presented in (11.100) for $r = 2$ can be extended to any nonnegative integer value of r as follows:

$$(11.102) \qquad Y_t + \binom{r}{1}(-\lambda)^1 Y_{t-1} + \binom{r}{2}(-\lambda)^2 Y_{t-2} + \cdots + \binom{r}{r}(-\lambda)^r Y_{t-r}$$

$$= \alpha(1 - \lambda)^r + \beta(1 - \lambda)^r X_t + \varepsilon_t + \binom{r}{1}(-\lambda)^1 \varepsilon_{t-1} + \cdots + \binom{r}{r}(-\lambda)^r \varepsilon_{t-r}.$$

Note that in (11.102) the coefficients of the current and lagged Y's (and ε's) are all constrained to be equal to specific functions of λ. If we generalize the form of (11.102) by removing these constraints, we obtain

$$(11.103) \quad Y_t + \delta_1 Y_{t-1} + \delta_2 Y_{t-2} + \cdots + \delta_r Y_{t-r}$$

$$= \alpha_0 + \beta_0 X_t + \varepsilon_t + \delta_1 \varepsilon_{t-1} + \cdots + \delta_r \varepsilon_{t-r}.$$

Equation (11.103) describes the so-called *rational distributed lag model* introduced by Jorgenson.[28] The estimation of this model could proceed along the lines similar to those applied to the Pascal lag model.

The complexity of the estimation problem in the case of general inverted V-lag models has led to the search for simpler formulations. One such simplification is available if we are willing to assume that the weights attached to X_t, $X_{t-1}, \ldots$, reach a peak in one of the past $(h - 1)$ periods, and that they decline geometrically after that. The distributed lag relation can then be formulated as

$$(11.104) \qquad Y_t = \alpha + \beta_0 X_t + \beta_1 X_{t-1} + \cdots + \beta_{h-1} X_{t-h+1}$$

$$+ \beta_h(X_{t-h} + \lambda X_{t-h-1} + \lambda^2 X_{t-h-2} + \cdots) + \varepsilon_t.$$

By the application of the Koyck transformation, this becomes

$$(11.104a) \qquad Y_t = \alpha_0 + \beta_0 X_t + \beta_1^* X_{t-1} + \beta_2^* X_{t-2}$$

$$+ \cdots + \beta_h^* X_{t-h} + \lambda Y_{t-1} + \eta_t,$$

where
$$\alpha_0 = \alpha(1 - \lambda),$$
$$\beta_1^* = \beta_1 - \beta_0\lambda,$$
$$\beta_2^* = \beta_2 - \beta_1\lambda,$$
$$\vdots$$
$$\beta_h^* = \beta_h - \beta_{h-1}\lambda,$$
$$\eta_t = \varepsilon_t - \lambda\varepsilon_{t-1}.$$

[28] D. W. Jorgenson, "Rational Distributed Lag Functions," *Econometrica*, Vol. 34, January 1966, pp. 135–149.

The estimation of (11.104a) can be carried out in the same way as that of the conventional geometric lag model discussed earlier.

Polynomial Lag

A different formulation of the inverted V-lag model is possible in a situation in which we can assume that the weights w in

$$Y_t = \alpha + \beta(w_0 X_t + w_1 X_{t-1} + \cdots + w_m X_{t-m}) + \varepsilon_t$$

follow a polynomial of a given degree. Such models are called *polynomial lag models*. To formulate them we have to specify the appropriate degree of the polynomial and state the number of periods before the weights can be assumed to be zero. In the example on capital expenditures and appropriations, we assume that current capital expenditures are influenced neither by capital appropriations made more than m periods ago, nor by those to be made in the future. Thus we wish to fit a polynomial of, say, pth degree to the weights w_{-1}, $w_0, w_1, \ldots, w_m, w_{m+1}$ in such a way that

$$w_{-1} = 0 \qquad \text{and} \qquad w_{m+1} = 0.$$

The weights $w_{-2}, w_{-3}, \ldots$, and $w_{m+2}, w_{m+3}, \ldots$, do not lie on the polynomial but are all assumed to be zero. The estimation problem is quite straightforward. Suppose the degree of the polynomial is chosen to be four. Then to make each of the weights $w_{-1}, w_0, w_1, \ldots, w_{m+1}$ lie along a fourth-degree polynomial curve, we specify

$$(11.105) \quad w_i = \lambda_0 + \lambda_1 i + \lambda_2 i^2 + \lambda_3 i^3 + \lambda_4 i^4, \quad (i = -1, 0, 1, 2, \ldots, m, m+1).$$

Our polynomial lag model then becomes

$$(11.106) \qquad Y_t = \alpha + \beta[\lambda_0 X_t + (\lambda_0 + \lambda_1 + \lambda_2 + \lambda_3 + \lambda_4) X_{t-1}$$
$$+ (\lambda_0 + 2\lambda_1 + 2^2 \lambda_2 + 2^3 \lambda_3 + 2^4 \lambda_4) X_{t-2}$$
$$+ \cdots + (\lambda_0 + m\lambda_1 + m^2 \lambda_2 + m^3 \lambda_3 + m^4 \lambda_4) X_{t-m}] + \varepsilon_t,$$

which can be concentrated as

$$(11.106a) \qquad Y_t = \alpha + \beta\lambda_0 Z_{t0} + \beta\lambda_1 Z_{t1} + \cdots + \beta\lambda_4 Z_{t4} + \varepsilon_t$$

where
$$Z_{t0} = X_t + X_{t-1} + \cdots + X_{t-m},$$
$$Z_{t1} = X_{t-1} + 2X_{t-2} + \cdots + mX_{t-m},$$
$$\vdots$$
$$Z_{t4} = X_{t-1} + 2^4 X_{t-2} + \cdots + m^4 X_{t-m}.$$

Equation (11.106a) involves altogether seven parameters. This number can be reduced by imposing the restrictions that $w_{-1} = 0$ and $w_{m+1} = 0$, i.e., that

$$(11.107) \quad \lambda_0 \qquad - \lambda_1 \qquad + \lambda_2 \qquad - \lambda_3 \qquad + \lambda_4 = 0,$$

$$(11.108) \quad \lambda_0 + (m+1)\lambda_1 + (m+1)^2\lambda_2 + (m+1)^3\lambda_3 + (m+1)^4\lambda_4 = 0.$$

These equations can be solved for, say, λ_0 and λ_1, which leads to

$$\lambda_0 = -(m + 1)\lambda_2 - m(m + 1)\lambda_3 - (m + 1)(m^2 + m + 1)\lambda_4$$

and $\lambda_1 = -m\lambda_2 - (m^2 + m + 1)\lambda_3 - m(m^2 + 2m + 2)\lambda_4.$

Substituting these results into (11.104a) yields

(11.109) $Y_t = \alpha + \beta\lambda_2 W_{t2} + \beta\lambda_3 W_{t3} + \beta\lambda_4 W_{t4} + \varepsilon_t,$

where $W_{t2} = -(m + 1)Z_{t0} - mZ_{t1} + Z_{t2},$

$$W_{t3} = -m(m + 1)Z_{t0} - (m^2 + m + 1)Z_{t1} + Z_{t3},$$

$$W_{t4} = -(m + 1)(m^2 + m + 1)Z_{t0} - m(m^2 + 2m + 2)Z_{t1} + Z_{t4}.$$

For instance, if m is chosen to be 7, the W's are defined as

$$W_{t2} = -8Z_{t0} - 7Z_{t1} + Z_{t2}$$

$$= -8X_t - 14X_{t-1} - 18X_{t-2} - 20X_{t-3} - 20X_{t-4} - 18X_{t-5}$$

$$-14X_{t-6} - 8X_{t-7},$$

$$W_{t3} = -56Z_{t0} - 57Z_{t1} + Z_{t3}$$

$$= -56X_t - 112X_{t-1} - 162X_{t-2} - 200X_{t-3} - 220X_{t-4}$$

$$-216X_{t-5} - 182X_{t-6} - 112X_{t-7},$$

$$W_{t4} = -456Z_{t0} - 455Z_{t1} + Z_{t4}$$

$$= -456X_t - 910X_{t-1} - 1350X_{t-2} - 1740X_{t-3} - 2020X_{t-4}$$

$$-2106X_{t-5} - 1890X_{t-6} - 1240X_{t-7}.$$

Note that the parameter β is still not identified; in practice, its value is usually taken to be unity. The parameters α, λ_2, λ_3, and λ_4 of (11.109) can be estimated by ordinary least squares. If ε_t satisfies all the assumptions of the classical normal regression model, the resulting estimates will have all the desirable properties. In case of autocorrelation, we can use one of the estimation methods described in Section 8–2. The estimated values of the λ's can be substituted into (11.105) to obtain estimates of the weights $w_0, w_1, \ldots, w_m$.[29] If we should require that the weights add up to 1, we would impose a further restriction on the λ's, namely,

$$\lambda_0(m + 1) + \lambda_1 \sum_i i + \lambda_2 \sum_i i^2 + \lambda_3 \sum_i i^3 + \lambda_4 \sum_i i^4 = 1.$$

In this case equation (11.109) would be further reduced to involve only two, rather than three, regressors.

---

[29] In S. Almon, "The Distributed Lag Between Capital Appropriations and Expenditures," *Econometrica*, Vol. 33, January 1965, pp. 178–196, the parameters of the model are estimated with the help of the so-called "Lagrangian interpolation." However, the results should be identical to those obtained by the straightforward application of the ordinary least squares method as described by us.

EXAMPLE   The polynomial lag model was used by Almon[30] to estimate the relationship between current capital expenditures and current and past capital appropriations in the United States manufacturing industries. The degree of the polynomial in each case was 4, but the length of the lag was taken to be different for different industries. The data used for estimation were given by the quarterly observations for the years 1953–1961. The model was specified as

$$Y_t = \alpha_1 S_{t1} + \alpha_2 S_{t2} + \alpha_3 S_{t3} + \alpha_4 S_{t4} + w_0 X_t + w_1 X_{t-1} + \cdots + w_m X_{t-m} + \varepsilon_t,$$

where Y represents capital expenditures, the S's represent seasonal dummy variables, and the X's represent capital appropriations. The parameter α_4 was set to be equal to $(-\alpha_1 - \alpha_2 - \alpha_3)$. The weights were restricted by the conditions that $w_{-1} = 0$ and $w_{m+1} = 0$, but they were not required to add up to unity. The result for "all manufacturing industries" was as follows:

$$Y_t = -283 S_{t1} + 13 S_{t2} - 50 S_{t3} + 320 S_{t4} + 0.048 X_t + 0.099 X_{t-1} + 0.141 X_{t-2}$$
$$\qquad\qquad\qquad\qquad\qquad\qquad (0.023) \qquad (0.016) \qquad\quad (0.013)$$

$$+ 0.165 X_{t-3} + 0.167 X_{t-4} + 0.146 X_{t-5} + 0.105 X_{t-6} + 0.053 X_{t-7} + e_t.$$
$$\ \ (0.023) \qquad\quad (0.023) \qquad\quad (0.013) \qquad\quad (0.016) \qquad\quad (0.024)$$

As can be seen, the chosen length of the lag in this case was 7 periods. The weights add up to 0.922; the difference between 0.922 and 1 can be very nearly accounted for by cancellations. The estimated weights are shown graphically in Figure 11–14.

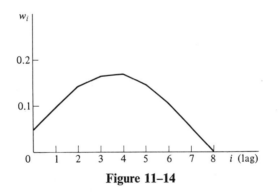

Figure 11–14

The difficulty about using the polynomial lag model is that we have to specify a priori the degree of the polynomial and the length of the lag. Concerning the latter, however, some help may be obtained from the data. One possibility is to keep on extending the length of the lag until the contribution of the additional X's to the regression sum of squares is no longer statistically significant. But if the X's are highly correlated, this criterion may not work very well. Another possibility is to choose that length of the lag which results in the highest value of $\bar{R}^2$, i.e., of the coefficient of determination corrected for the "number of degrees of freedom." However, this also may not always work well since the differences

[30] *Ibid.*

between several values of $\bar{R}^2$ may be very small. Nevertheless, one or the other of these criteria, *plus* other considerations (for example, that all weights should be positive), may help in choosing the "best" lag for the problem at hand.

EXERCISES

11–1. Three salesmen employed by a certain firm had the following weekly earnings in five consecutive days:

Salesman:	A	B	C
Weekly earnings ($):	928	924	793

An analysis-of-variance test of the null hypothesis that the mean earnings of the three salesmen are the same has been carried out, and the value of the F statistic found to be 5.00. Consider this problem as one of regression analysis, with the regression equation given by

$$Y_{ig} = \beta_1 + \beta_2 X_{i2} + \beta_3 X_{i3} + \varepsilon_i,$$

where

$$X_{i2} = 1 \quad \text{if } i \text{ belongs to B,}$$

$$= 0 \quad \text{otherwise;}$$

$$X_{i3} = 1 \quad \text{if } i \text{ belongs to C,}$$

$$= 0 \quad \text{otherwise;}$$

$$i = 1, 2, \ldots, 5;$$

$$g = 1, 2, 3.$$

Find the least squares estimates of the regression coefficients and their estimated standard errors. Also, calculate the value of R^2.

11–2. Demonstrate the equivalence of the regression model (11.8) and a "two-way analysis of variance" model with interactions.

11–3. The least squares estimates of a regression model are:

$$Y_t = 10 + 5X_t + e_t.$$
$$(1) \quad (\sqrt{0.5})$$

The explanatory variable X_t is a binary variable. Suppose that in checking the results it was found that the values of X_t were punched by mistake as 0 and 2 instead of 0 and 1. Make the appropriate corrections.

11–4. The survey records for a sample of twelve families show the weekly consumption expenditures and weekly incomes given in Table 11–5. Families whose income is marked by an asterisk (*) have reported that their income is higher than in the previous year. Test the relevance of the asymmetric response model.

Table 11–5

Family No.	Income	Consumption Expenditure
1	80	70
2	95*	76
3	105	91
4	115	100
5	125*	105
6	135*	113
7	145	122
8	155	120
9	165*	146
10	175*	135
11	185*	147
12	200*	155

11–5. Consider the following consumption function model:

$$C_t = \beta_1 + \beta_2 Y_t + \beta_3 Z_t + \beta_4 Y_t Z_t + \varepsilon_t,$$

where C = consumption, Y = income, and $Z_t = 1$ in wartime and 0 otherwise. Prove that the least squares estimates of the regression coefficient could have been obtained equally well from two separate regressions of C_t on Y_t, one estimated from the peacetime observations and one estimated from the wartime observations.

11–6. A production function model is specified as

$$Y_i = \beta_1 + \beta_2 X_{i2} + \beta_3 X_{i3} + \varepsilon_i,$$

where Y_i = log output, X_{i2} = log labor input, and X_{i3} log capital input. The subscript i refers to the ith firm. There are 23 observations in the sample, and the moment matrices (in terms of deviations from sample means) are

$$(\underline{X'X}) = \begin{bmatrix} 12 & 8 \\ 8 & 12 \end{bmatrix}, \qquad (\underline{X'Y}) = \begin{bmatrix} 10 \\ 8 \end{bmatrix}, \qquad (\underline{Y'Y}) = 10.$$

a. Find the least squares estimates of the regression coefficients β_2 and β_3, and their estimated standard errors. Calculate the value of R^2.

b. Carry out the test for constant returns to scale (i.e., test the hypothesis that $\beta_2 + \beta_3 = 1$).

c. Suppose now that you wish to impose the restriction that $\beta_1 + \beta_2 = 1$ a priori and to estimate the production function in that way. What, then are the least squares estimate of β_2 and its estimated standard error? Also, what is the value of R^2 under this specification?

11–7. Consider the "stock adjustment" model

$$Y_t = \alpha\gamma + \beta\gamma X_t + (1 - \gamma) Y_{t-1} + \varepsilon_t.$$

Give the formula for the nonlinear least squares estimator of α, say, $\hat{\alpha}$. Derive the formula for the estimated variance of $\hat{\alpha}$ by using

a. The approximation formula (11.40).

b. The maximum likelihood information matrix.

11–8. The results of simple least squares regression of Y on X_1 and X_2 are

$$Y_t = 10 + 12X_{1t} + 4X_{2t} + e_t.$$
$$\quad\quad\quad (2) \quad\quad (1)$$

Further, the sample coefficient of correlation between X_1 and X_2 is 0.5. Suppose now that it is suggested that a preferable specification of the model would have been one in which Y were regressed on a weighted average of X_1 and X_2, so that the regression equation would become

$$Y_t = \beta_1 + \beta_2(w_1 X_{1t} + w_2 X_{2t}) + \varepsilon_t,$$

where $w_2 = 1 - w_1$. Find the nonlinear least squares estimates of β_2 and w_1, and their estimated standard errors.

11–9. Using the data on consumption, income, and holdings of liquid assets in the United States presented in Table 11–6, estimate the aggregate consumption function

$$C_t = \beta_1 + \beta_2 Y_t + \beta_3 L_t + \varepsilon_t,$$

subject to the constraint that

$$\tfrac{1}{2} \le \beta_2 \le 1.$$

11–10. Suppose the aggregate consumption function is specified as

$$C_t = \beta_1 + \beta_2 Y_t + \beta_3 L_t + \beta_4 Y_t L_t + \varepsilon_t.$$

Using the data given in Table 11–6:

a. Obtain the least squares estimates of the regression coefficients and their estimated standard errors.

b. Calculate the value of R^2 and test for the existence of a relationship.

c. Test the hypothesis that $\beta_4 = 0$.

11–11. Let $Y_i = Q_i/L_i$ and $X_i = K_i/L_i$, where $Q_i =$ output, $L_i =$ labor input, $K_i =$ capital input, and the subscript i refers to the ith firm. Using the data presented in Table 11–4, estimate the following relationship:

$$\frac{Y_i^\lambda - 1}{\lambda} = \alpha + \beta\left(\frac{X_i^\lambda - 1}{\lambda}\right) + \varepsilon_i.$$

Test the hypothesis that $\lambda = 0$.

11–12. Consider the following distributed lag model:

$$Y_t = \alpha + \beta(w_0 X_t + w_1 X_{t-1} + w_2 X_{t-2} + w_3 X_{t-3}) + \varepsilon_t.$$

Table 11–6*

	C_t	Y_t	L_t
1955 I	248.7	263.0	207.6
II	253.7	271.5	209.4
III	259.9	276.5	211.1
IV	261.8	281.4	213.2
1956 I	263.2	282.0	214.1
II	263.7	286.2	216.5
III	263.4	287.7	217.3
IV	266.9	291.0	217.3
1957 I	268.9	291.1	218.2
II	270.4	294.6	218.5
III	273.4	296.1	219.8
IV	272.1	293.3	219.5
1958 I	268.9	291.3	220.5
II	270.9	292.6	222.7
III	274.4	299.9	225.0
IV	278.7	302.1	229.4
1959 I	283.8	305.9	232.2
II	289.7	312.5	235.2
III	290.8	311.3	237.2
IV	292.8	313.2	237.7
1960 I	295.4	315.4	238.0
II	299.5	320.3	238.4
III	298.6	321.0	240.1
IV	299.6	320.1	243.3
1961 I	297.0	318.4	246.1
II	301.6	324.8	250.0

Source: Z. Griliches *et al.* "Notes on Estimated Aggregate Quarterly Consumption Functions," *Econometrica*, Vol. 30, July 1962, p. 500.
   * All values (in billions of dollars) are price deflated and seasonally adjusted.

The weights w_i ($i = 0, 1, 2, 3$) are assumed to lie along a second-degree polynomial, and they are required to satisfy the following restrictions:

$$w_0 + w_1 + w_2 + w_3 = 1,$$

$$w_{-1} = 0,$$

$$w_4 = 0.$$

Show how you can estimate the coefficients of this model by using ordinary least squares estimation.

12 | Generalized Linear Regression Model and Its Applications

The classical regression model is based on rather restrictive assumptions concerning the behavior of the regression disturbance. An alternative model, known as the "generalized linear regression model," is considerably less restrictive in this respect. This model and its implications for estimating the regression coefficients are discussed in Section 12–1. An interesting application of this model to observations on a number of cross-sectional units over time is described in Section 12–2. Since such observations are now becoming more commonly available, the development of appropriate estimation procedures is very useful. Another and very ingenious application of the generalized linear regression model can be made when estimating a set of regression equations whose disturbances are correlated. The discussion of this application, which also provides a logical bridge between single-equation models and simultaneous equation models (to be discussed in Chapter 13), is presented in Section 12–3.

12–1 Generalized Linear Regression Model

The classical normal linear regression model is characterized by a number of assumptions concerning the stochastic disturbance in the regression equation, including homoskedasticity and nonautocorrelation. Specifically, the disturbance term ε_i in

$$Y_i = \beta_1 + \beta_2 X_{i2} + \beta_3 X_{i3} + \cdots + \beta_K X_{iK} + \varepsilon_i$$

is supposed to satisfy the following requirements:

$$E(\varepsilon_i^2) = \sigma^2 \quad \text{for all } i,$$

$$E(\varepsilon_i \varepsilon_j) = 0 \quad \text{for all } i \neq j.$$

These assumptions are given by (10.4) and (10.5); in the matrix notation they can be described, as in (10.4a–10.5a), by

$$E(\boldsymbol{\varepsilon}\boldsymbol{\varepsilon}') = \sigma^2 \mathbf{I_n},$$

where

$$\boldsymbol{\epsilon} = \begin{bmatrix} \varepsilon_1 \\ \varepsilon_2 \\ \vdots \\ \varepsilon_n \end{bmatrix}$$

and $\mathbf{I_n}$ is an identity matrix of order $(n \times n)$. If we do not make these two assumptions—but retain all the other assumptions of the classical normal linear regression model—we have the so-called *generalized linear regression model*. (Some authors also drop the assumption of normality of ε_i.) The full description of this model is

(12.1) $Y_i = \beta_1 + \beta_2 X_{i2} + \beta_3 X_{i3} + \cdots + \beta_K X_{iK} + \varepsilon_{i\cdot},$

(12.2)   The joint distribution of $\varepsilon_1, \varepsilon_2, \ldots, \varepsilon_n$ is multivariate normal,

(12.3) $E(\varepsilon_i) = 0, \qquad i = 1, 2, \ldots, n.$

(12.4) $E(\varepsilon_i \varepsilon_j) = \sigma_{ij}, \qquad i, j = 1, 2, \ldots, n.$

(12.5)   Each of the explanatory variables is nonstochastic and such that, for any sample size,

$$\frac{1}{n} \sum_{i=1}^{n} (X_{ik} - \bar{X}_k)^2$$

is a finite number different from zero for every $k = 2, 3, \ldots, K$.

(12.6)   The number of observations exceeds the number of explanatory variables *plus* one, i.e., $n > K$.

(12.7)   No exact linear relation exists between any of the explanatory variables.

Note that according to (12.3) and (12.4), σ_{ii} is the variance of ε_i, and σ_{ij} $(i \neq j)$ is the covariance of ε_i and ε_j. If we use matrix notation we can restate (12.1) as

(12.1a) $\mathbf{Y} = \mathbf{X}\boldsymbol{\beta} + \boldsymbol{\epsilon},$

where $\mathbf{Y}$ is an $(n \times 1)$ vector of the sample values of Y, $\mathbf{X}$ is an $(n \times K)$ matrix of the sample values of $X_{i1}, X_{i2}, \ldots, X_{iK}$ (with $X_{i1} = 1$ for all i), $\boldsymbol{\beta}$ is a $(K \times 1)$ vector of the regression coefficients, and $\boldsymbol{\epsilon}$ is an $(n \times 1)$ vector of the sample values of ε. The assumption (12.4) can be written as

(12.4a) $E(\boldsymbol{\epsilon}\boldsymbol{\epsilon}') = \boldsymbol{\Omega},$

where $$\boldsymbol{\Omega} = \begin{bmatrix} \sigma_{11} & \sigma_{12} & \cdots & \sigma_{1n} \\ \sigma_{21} & \sigma_{22} & \cdots & \sigma_{2n} \\ \vdots & \vdots & & \vdots \\ \sigma_{n1} & \sigma_{n2} & \cdots & \sigma_{nn} \end{bmatrix}.$$

This model is called "generalized" because it includes other models as special cases. The classical normal linear regression model is one such special case, in which Ω is a diagonal matrix with σ^2 in place of each of the diagonal elements. Another special case is the heteroskedastic model; here Ω is again diagonal, but the diagonal elements are not necessarily all the same. For the model in which the disturbances follow a first-order autoregressive scheme, the matrix Ω becomes

$$\Omega = \sigma^2 \begin{bmatrix} 1 & \rho & \rho^2 & \cdots & \rho^{n-1} \\ \rho & 1 & \rho & \cdots & \rho^{n-2} \\ \vdots & \vdots & \vdots & & \vdots \\ \rho^{n-1} & \rho^{n-2} & \rho^{n-3} & \cdots & 1 \end{bmatrix}.$$

Let us now turn to the problem of estimating the parameters of the generalized linear regression model. We will assume for the present that the variances and covariances of the disturbances (i.e., the elements of the Ω matrix) are known. First, we note that since the *ordinary least squares estimators* of the regression coefficients are obtained by minimizing

$$\sum_{i=1}^{n} (Y_i - \beta_1 - \beta_2 X_{i2} - \cdots - \beta_K X_{iK})^2,$$

they are exactly the same as the least squares estimators of the classical normal linear regression model; that is,

$$\hat{\beta} = (X'X)^{-1}(X'Y).$$

Note that

$$E(\hat{\beta}) = E(X'X)^{-1}X'[X\beta + \epsilon] = \beta + E(X'X)^{-1}(X'\epsilon) = \beta$$

and

$$\text{plim } \hat{\beta} = \beta + \text{plim} \left[\frac{1}{n} X'X\right]^{-1} \left[\frac{1}{n} X'\epsilon\right] = \beta.$$

This shows the ordinary least squares estimators of β of the generalized linear regression model are unbiased and consistent.

Next, we derive the *best linear unbiased estimators* (BLUE) of the regression coefficients. To find the BLUE of β_1, we put

$$\tilde{\beta}_1 = \sum_{i=1}^{n} a_i Y_i$$

where $a_1, a_2, \ldots, a_n$ are some constants to be determined. In matrix notation we write

$$\tilde{\beta}_1 = Y'a,$$

where
$$\mathbf{a} = \begin{bmatrix} a_1 \\ a_2 \\ \vdots \\ a_n \end{bmatrix}.$$

The mathematical expectation of $\tilde{\beta}_1$ is

$$E(\tilde{\beta}_1) = E\left(\sum_i a_i Y_i\right) = \beta_1 \sum_i a_i + \beta_2 \sum_i a_i X_{i2} + \cdots + \beta_K \sum_i a_i X_{iK}.$$

By the condition of unbiasedness of $\tilde{\beta}_1$, we then require that

$$\sum_i a_i = 1,$$

$$\sum_i a_i X_{i2} = 0,$$

$$\vdots$$

$$\sum_i a_i X_{iK} = 0,$$

or, in matrix notation,

$$\mathbf{X'a} = \mathbf{\iota}_1,$$

where $\mathbf{\iota}_1$ is a $(K \times 1)$ vector defined as

$$\mathbf{\iota}_1 = \begin{bmatrix} 1 \\ 0 \\ \vdots \\ 0 \end{bmatrix}.$$

The variance of $\tilde{\beta}_1$ is

$$\text{Var}(\tilde{\beta}_1) = E\left[\sum_i a_i Y_i - E\left(\sum_i a_i Y_i\right)\right]^2 = E\left(\sum_i a_i \varepsilon_i\right)^2 = \sum_{i=1}^n \sum_{j=1}^n a_i a_j \sigma_{ij},$$

or
$$\text{Var}(\tilde{\beta}_1) = \mathbf{a'\Omega a}.$$

Thus we have to find those values of $a_1, a_2, \ldots, a_n$ which would minimize $\text{Var}(\tilde{\beta}_1)$ subject to $\mathbf{X'a} = \mathbf{\iota}_1$. Using the Lagrange multiplier method, we form

$$H = \sum_{i=1}^n \sum_{j=1}^n a_i a_j \sigma_{ij} - \lambda_1 \left(\sum_{i=1}^n a_i - 1\right) - \lambda_2 \sum_{i=1}^n a_i X_{i2} - \cdots - \lambda_K \sum_{i=1}^n a_i X_{iK}.$$

Differentiating H with respect to $a_1, a_2, \ldots, a_n, \lambda_1, \lambda_2, \ldots, \lambda_K$ and putting each derivative equal to zero, we obtain

$$2(a_1\sigma_{11} + a_2\sigma_{12} + \cdots + a_n\sigma_{1n}) - \lambda_1 - \lambda_2 X_{12} - \cdots - \lambda_K X_{1K} = 0,$$

$$2(a_1\sigma_{21} + a_2\sigma_{22} + \cdots + a_n\sigma_{2n}) - \lambda_1 - \lambda_2 X_{22} - \cdots - \lambda_K X_{2K} = 0,$$

$$\vdots$$

$$2(a_1\sigma_{n1} + a_2\sigma_{n2} + \cdots + a_n\sigma_{nn}) - \lambda_1 - \lambda_2 X_{n2} - \cdots - \lambda_K X_{nK} = 0,$$

$$-\left(\sum_i a_i - 1\right) = 0,$$

$$-\sum_i a_i X_{i2} = 0,$$

$$\vdots$$

$$-\sum_i a_i X_{iK} = 0.$$

In matrix notation this can be written as

(12.8) $$2\boldsymbol{\Omega}\mathbf{a} - \mathbf{X}\boldsymbol{\lambda} = \mathbf{0}$$

(12.9) $$\mathbf{X}'\mathbf{a} = \boldsymbol{\iota}_1,$$

where $$\boldsymbol{\lambda} = \begin{bmatrix} \lambda_1 \\ \lambda_2 \\ \vdots \\ \lambda_K \end{bmatrix}$$

and $\mathbf{0}$ is an $(n \times 1)$ vector of zeros. From (12.8) we obtain

(12.8a) $$\mathbf{a} = \tfrac{1}{2}\boldsymbol{\Omega}^{-1}\mathbf{X}\boldsymbol{\lambda}.$$

Substitution of this expression for $\mathbf{a}$ into (12.9) gives

(12.10) $$\tfrac{1}{2}\mathbf{X}'\boldsymbol{\Omega}^{-1}\mathbf{X}\boldsymbol{\lambda} = \boldsymbol{\iota}_1,$$

or

(12.10a) $$\boldsymbol{\lambda} = 2(\mathbf{X}'\boldsymbol{\Omega}^{-1}\mathbf{X})^{-1}\boldsymbol{\iota}_1.$$

Substituting for $\boldsymbol{\lambda}$ from (12.10a) into (12.8a), we find

(12.11) $$\mathbf{a} = \boldsymbol{\Omega}^{-1}\mathbf{X}(\mathbf{X}'\boldsymbol{\Omega}^{-1}\mathbf{X})^{-1}\boldsymbol{\iota}_1.$$

Therefore,

(12.12) $$\tilde{\beta}_1 = \mathbf{Y}'\mathbf{a} = (\mathbf{Y}'\boldsymbol{\Omega}^{-1}\mathbf{X})(\mathbf{X}'\boldsymbol{\Omega}^{-1}\mathbf{X})^{-1}\boldsymbol{\iota}_1$$

$$= \boldsymbol{\iota}_1'(\mathbf{X}'\boldsymbol{\Omega}^{-1}\mathbf{X})^{-1}(\mathbf{X}'\boldsymbol{\Omega}^{-1}\mathbf{Y}).$$

This then is the BLUE of β_1.[1] Further, since

$$\mathrm{Var}(\tilde{\beta}_1) = \mathbf{a}'\boldsymbol{\Omega}\mathbf{a},$$

---

[1] The proof that this result corresponds to a minimum and not to a maximum variance can be found in J. Johnston, *Econometric Methods* (New York: McGraw-Hill, 1963), pp. 183–184.

we can use (12.11) to determine

$$(12.13) \qquad \text{Var}(\tilde{\beta}_1) = [\iota_1'(X'\Omega^{-1}X)^{-1}X'\Omega^{-1}]\Omega[\Omega^{-1}X(X'\Omega^{-1}X)^{-1}\iota_1]$$

$$= \iota_1'(X'\Omega^{-1}X)^{-1}\iota_1.$$

The procedure for deriving the BLUE of β_1 and its variance can be used also with the other regression coefficients. The results are

$$\tilde{\beta}_2 = \iota_2'(X'\Omega^{-1}X)^{-1}(X'\Omega^{-1}Y),$$

$$\text{Var}(\tilde{\beta}_2) = \iota_2'(X'\Omega^{-1}X)^{-1}\iota_2,$$

$$\vdots$$

$$\tilde{\beta}_K = \iota_K'(X'\Omega^{-1}X)^{-1}(X'\Omega^{-1}Y),$$

$$\text{Var}(\tilde{\beta}_K) = \iota_K'(X'\Omega^{-1}X)^{-1}\iota_K.$$

In general,

$$\tilde{\beta}_k = \iota_k'(X'\Omega^{-1}X)^{-1}(X'\Omega^{-1}Y),$$

$$\text{Var}(\tilde{\beta}_k) = \iota_k'(X'\Omega^{-1}X)^{-1}\iota_k, \qquad (k = 1, 2, \ldots, K),$$

where ι_k is a $(K \times 1)$ vector with the kth element equal to one and each of the remaining elements equal to zero. These results can be summarized by writing

$$(12.14) \qquad\qquad\qquad \tilde{\beta} = (X'\Omega^{-1}X)^{-1}(X'\Omega^{-1}Y),$$

$$(12.15) \qquad\qquad E(\tilde{\beta} - \beta)(\tilde{\beta} - \beta)' = (X'\Omega^{-1}X)^{-1},$$

where

$$\tilde{\beta} = \begin{bmatrix} \tilde{\beta}_1 \\ \tilde{\beta}_2 \\ \vdots \\ \tilde{\beta}_K \end{bmatrix}.$$

The estimator $\tilde{\beta}$ is usually called *Aitken's generalized least squares estimator*.[2] If we denote the elements of the inverse of Ω by appropriate superscripts, that is, if we put

$$\Omega^{-1} = \begin{bmatrix} \sigma^{11} & \sigma^{12} & \cdots & \sigma^{1n} \\ \sigma^{21} & \sigma^{22} & \cdots & \sigma^{2n} \\ \vdots & \vdots & & \vdots \\ \sigma^{n1} & \sigma^{n2} & & \sigma^{nn} \end{bmatrix},$$

[2] A. C. Aitken, "On Least Squares and Linear Combination of Observations," *Proceedings of the Royal Society of Edinburgh*, Vol. 55, 1934–35, pp. 42–48.

then we can describe the elements of $(\mathbf{X'\Omega^{-1}X})$ and $(\mathbf{X'\Omega^{-1}Y})$ and write

$$
\tilde{\boldsymbol{\beta}} =
\begin{bmatrix}
\sum_i \sum_j \sigma^{ij} X_{i1}^2 & \sum_i \sum_j \sigma^{ij} X_{i1} X_{j2} & \cdots & \sum_i \sum_j \sigma^{ij} X_{i1} X_{jK} \\
\sum_i \sum_j \sigma^{ij} X_{i2} X_{i1} & \sum_i \sum_j \sigma^{ij} X_{i2}^2 & \cdots & \sum_i \sum_j \sigma^{ij} X_{i2} X_{jK} \\
\vdots & \vdots & & \vdots \\
\sum_i \sum_j \sigma^{ij} X_{iK} X_{j1} & \sum_i \sum_j \sigma^{ij} X_{iK} X_{j2} & \cdots & \sum_i \sum_j \sigma^{ij} X_{iK}^2
\end{bmatrix}^{-1}
\begin{bmatrix}
\sum_i \sum_j \sigma^{ij} X_{i1} Y_i \\
\sum_i \sum_j \sigma^{ij} X_{i2} Y_i \\
\vdots \\
\sum_i \sum_j \sigma^{ij} X_{iK} Y_i
\end{bmatrix}.
$$

Further, if, as before, we call

$$
\underline{\tilde{\boldsymbol{\beta}}} =
\begin{bmatrix}
\tilde{\beta}_2 \\
\tilde{\beta}_3 \\
\vdots \\
\tilde{\beta}_K
\end{bmatrix}, \qquad
\underline{\mathbf{X}} =
\begin{bmatrix}
(X_{12} - \bar{X}_2) & (X_{13} - \bar{X}_3) & \cdots & (X_{1K} - \bar{X}_K) \\
(X_{22} - \bar{X}_2) & (X_{23} - \bar{X}_3) & \cdots & (X_{2K} - \bar{X}_K) \\
\vdots & \vdots & & \vdots \\
(X_{n2} - \bar{X}_2) & (X_{n3} - \bar{X}_3) & \cdots & (X_{nK} - \bar{X}_K)
\end{bmatrix},
$$

$$
\underline{\mathbf{Y}} =
\begin{bmatrix}
Y_1 - \bar{Y} \\
Y_2 - \bar{Y} \\
\vdots \\
Y_n - \bar{Y}
\end{bmatrix},
$$

then it can be shown that

$$
(12.16) \qquad \underline{\tilde{\boldsymbol{\beta}}} = (\underline{\mathbf{X}}'\mathbf{\Omega}^{-1}\underline{\mathbf{X}})^{-1}(\underline{\mathbf{X}}'\mathbf{\Omega}^{-1}\underline{\mathbf{Y}})
$$

and

$$
(12.17) \qquad E(\underline{\tilde{\boldsymbol{\beta}}} - \underline{\boldsymbol{\beta}})(\underline{\tilde{\boldsymbol{\beta}}} - \underline{\boldsymbol{\beta}})' = (\underline{\mathbf{X}}'\mathbf{\Omega}^{-1}\underline{\mathbf{X}})^{-1}.
$$

The *maximum likelihood estimators* of the regression coefficients can be derived by noting that, under the assumptions of the model, the joint distribution of $\varepsilon_1, \varepsilon_2, \ldots, \varepsilon_n$ is given by[3]

$$
f(\varepsilon_1, \varepsilon_2, \ldots, \varepsilon_n) = (2\pi)^{-(n/2)} |\mathbf{\Omega}|^{-(1/2)} e^{-(1/2)\varepsilon'\mathbf{\Omega}^{-1}\varepsilon},
$$

where $|\mathbf{\Omega}|$ represents the determinant of the matrix $\mathbf{\Omega}$. The logarithmic likelihood function for $Y_1, Y_2, \ldots, Y_n$ is given by[4]

$$
(12.18) \qquad L = -\frac{n}{2} \log(2\pi) - \frac{1}{2}\log|\mathbf{\Omega}| - \frac{1}{2}(\mathbf{Y} - \mathbf{X}\boldsymbol{\beta})'\mathbf{\Omega}^{-1}(\mathbf{Y} - \mathbf{X}\boldsymbol{\beta})
$$

$$
= -\frac{n}{2}\log(2\pi) - \frac{1}{2}\log|\mathbf{\Omega}|
$$

$$
- \frac{1}{2}(\mathbf{Y}'\mathbf{\Omega}^{-1}\mathbf{Y} - 2\mathbf{Y}'\mathbf{\Omega}^{-1}\mathbf{X}\boldsymbol{\beta} + \boldsymbol{\beta}'\mathbf{X}'\mathbf{\Omega}^{-1}\mathbf{X}\boldsymbol{\beta}).
$$

[3] See A. S. Goldberger, *Econometric Theory* (New York: Wiley, 1964), p. 104. If the ε's in the sample are *not* independent of any ε outside the sample, the joint distribution is conditional on the latter.

[4] For the theorem relating to the transformation from the ε's to the Y's, see *ibid.*, p. 106.

By differentiating L with respect to β and putting the result equal to zero, we obtain

$$-\tfrac{1}{2}(-2X'\Omega^{-1}Y + 2X'\Omega^{-1}X\hat{\beta}) = 0,$$

where $\mathbf{0}$ is a $(K \times 1)$ vector of zeros. This gives

$$\hat{\beta} = (X'\Omega^{-1}X)^{-1}(X'\Omega^{-1}Y),$$

which is exactly the same expression as that for Aitken's generalized least squares estimator of β given by (12.14). It can be shown that this estimator has, under fairly general conditions, the desirable properties of consistency, asymptotic efficiency, and asymptotic normality.[5]

Let us now consider some special cases. First, if

$$\Omega = \sigma^2 I_n,$$

that is, if the generalized model reduces to the *classical* model, we have

$$\Omega^{-1} = \frac{1}{\sigma^2} I_n,$$

and Aitken's generalized estimator is the same as the ordinary least squares estimator. Second, if

$$\Omega = \begin{bmatrix} \sigma_{11} & 0 & \cdots & 0 \\ 0 & \sigma_{22} & \cdots & 0 \\ \vdots & \vdots & & \vdots \\ 0 & 0 & \cdots & \sigma_{nn} \end{bmatrix},$$

that is, if the generalized model reduces to a purely *heteroskedastic* model, then

$$\Omega^{-1} = \begin{bmatrix} \dfrac{1}{\sigma_{11}} & 0 & \cdots & 0 \\ 0 & \dfrac{1}{\sigma_{22}} & \cdots & 0 \\ \vdots & \vdots & & \vdots \\ 0 & 0 & \cdots & \dfrac{1}{\sigma_{nn}} \end{bmatrix},$$

and Aitken's generalized estimator is the same as the best linear unbiased estimator developed for the heteroskedastic model (see formulas (8.1) through (8.4)

[5] See A. Zellner, "An Efficient Method of Estimating Seemingly Unrelated Regressions and Tests for Aggregation Bias," *Journal of the American Statistical Association*, Vol. 57, June 1962, pp. 348–368.

and their extension to a multiple regression model in Section 8–1). Finally, if

$$\Omega = \sigma^2 \begin{bmatrix} 1 & \rho & \rho^2 & \cdots & \rho^{n-1} \\ \rho & 1 & \rho & \cdots & \rho^{n-2} \\ \vdots & \vdots & \vdots & & \vdots \\ \rho^{n-1} & \rho^{n-2} & \rho^{n-3} & \cdots & 1 \end{bmatrix},$$

that is, if the disturbance follows a first-order autoregressive scheme, we obtain

$$\Omega^{-1} = \frac{1}{\sigma^2(1-\rho^2)} \begin{bmatrix} 1 & -\rho & 0 & 0 & \cdots & 0 & 0 \\ -\rho & (1+\rho^2) & -\rho & 0 & \cdots & 0 & 0 \\ \vdots & \vdots & \vdots & \vdots & & \vdots & \vdots \\ 0 & 0 & 0 & 0 & \cdots & -\rho & 1 \end{bmatrix}.$$

In this case Aitken's generalized estimator is the same as the best-linear-unbiased estimator derived for the regression model with autoregressive disturbances (see formulas (8.38) through (8.41) and their extension to a multiple regression model in Section 8–2).

The preceding discussion has been carried out on the presumption that Ω, the variance-covariance matrix of the disturbances, is known. In many cases, of course, this is not the case and, therefore, Aitken's generalized least squares estimation procedure is not operational. However, suppose that we can find a *consistent estimator* of Ω, say, $\hat{\Omega}$, and that we substitute $\hat{\Omega}$ for Ω in Aitken's formula to get

(12.19) $$\tilde{\tilde{\beta}} = (X'\hat{\Omega}^{-1}X)^{-1}(X'\hat{\Omega}^{-1}Y).$$

Then, it has been shown,[6] $\tilde{\tilde{\beta}}$ has the same asymptotic properties as Aitken's estimator; i.e., it is consistent, asymptotically efficient, and asymptotically normal. The asymptotic variance-covariance matrix of $\tilde{\tilde{\beta}}$ is given by

(12.20) $$\text{Asympt. Var-Cov}(\tilde{\tilde{\beta}}) = (X'\Omega^{-1}X)^{-1}.$$

Thus the problem is to find a consistent estimator of Ω. If there are no prior restrictions on any of its elements, the Ω matrix involves $n(n + 1)/2$ unknown parameters. It is clear that, with only n observations, estimation under these circumstances becomes impossible. Therefore, we can consider only those models for which we have at least some information—or are willing to make some assumptions—about the elements of Ω. One such model is the heteroskedastic model. However, even here the number of unknown elements of Ω is n, which, together with the K regression coefficients, makes impossible demands on the sample data. In this case consistent estimation becomes possible only if we make

[6] For a proof see *ibid.*

some further restrictions on the parameters (see Section 8–1). Another model in which the elements of Ω are restricted is the regression model with auto-correlated disturbances. If the disturbances are homoskedastic and follow a first-order autoregressive scheme, Ω involves only two unknown parameters, σ^2 and ρ, which can be readily estimated. This model and its estimation was discussed in Section 8–2. We now discuss other restrictions on Ω that arise in other contexts.

12–2   Pooling of Cross-section and Time-Series Data

The question of the appropriate restrictions on Ω is of special interest and significance in connection with *pooling cross-section and time-series observations*, as in the case of observations for a number of households (states, countries, etc.) over several periods of time. Here the behavior of the disturbances over the cross-sectional units (households, states, countries, etc.) is likely to be different from the behavior of the disturbances of a given cross-sectional unit over time. In particular, the relationship between the disturbances of two households at some specific time may differ from the relationship between the disturbances of a specific household at two different periods of time. Clearly, various kinds of prior specifications with respect to the disturbances will lead to various kinds of restrictions on Ω. In general, the regression equation for this type of data can be written as

$$Y_{it} = \beta_1 X_{it,1} + \beta_2 X_{it,2} + \cdots + \beta_K X_{it,K} + \varepsilon_{it} \quad (i = 1, 2, \ldots, N; t = 1, 2, \ldots, T).$$

That is, the sample data are represented by observations on N cross-section units over T periods of time. There are altogether $n = N \times T$ observations. The explanatory variables and the regression disturbance are presumed to satisfy the assumptions of the generalized linear regression model. In most (although not necessarily in all) cases, we will have $X_{it,t} = 1$ for all i and t. In matrix notation the regression equation can be written as

$$\mathbf{Y} = \mathbf{X}\boldsymbol{\beta} + \boldsymbol{\epsilon},$$

where

$$\mathbf{Y} = \begin{bmatrix} Y_{11} \\ Y_{12} \\ \vdots \\ Y_{1T} \\ Y_{21} \\ Y_{22} \\ \vdots \\ Y_{NT} \end{bmatrix}, \quad \mathbf{X} = \begin{bmatrix} X_{11,1} & X_{11,2} & \cdots & X_{11,K} \\ X_{12,1} & X_{12,2} & \cdots & X_{12,K} \\ \vdots & \vdots & & \vdots \\ X_{1T,1} & X_{1T,2} & \cdots & X_{1T,K} \\ X_{21,1} & X_{21,2} & \cdots & X_{21,K} \\ X_{22,1} & X_{22,2} & \cdots & X_{22,K} \\ \vdots & \vdots & & \vdots \\ X_{NT,1} & X_{NT,2} & \cdots & X_{NT,K} \end{bmatrix}, \quad \boldsymbol{\epsilon} = \begin{bmatrix} \varepsilon_{11} \\ \varepsilon_{12} \\ \vdots \\ \varepsilon_{1T} \\ \varepsilon_{21} \\ \varepsilon_{22} \\ \vdots \\ \varepsilon_{NT} \end{bmatrix},$$

and
$$\beta = \begin{bmatrix} \beta_1 \\ \beta_2 \\ \vdots \\ \beta_K \end{bmatrix}.$$

Therefore,

(12.21) $\Omega =$

$$\begin{bmatrix}
E(\varepsilon_{11}^2) & E(\varepsilon_{11}\varepsilon_{12}) & \cdots & E(\varepsilon_{11}\varepsilon_{1T}) & E(\varepsilon_{11}\varepsilon_{21}) & E(\varepsilon_{11}\varepsilon_{22}) & \cdots & E(\varepsilon_{11}\varepsilon_{NT}) \\
E(\varepsilon_{12}\varepsilon_{11}) & E(\varepsilon_{12}^2) & \cdots & E(\varepsilon_{12}\varepsilon_{1T}) & E(\varepsilon_{12}\varepsilon_{21}) & E(\varepsilon_{12}\varepsilon_{22}) & \cdots & E(\varepsilon_{12}\varepsilon_{NT}) \\
\vdots & \vdots & & \vdots & \vdots & \vdots & & \vdots \\
E(\varepsilon_{1T}\varepsilon_{11}) & E(\varepsilon_{1T}\varepsilon_{12}) & \cdots & E(\varepsilon_{1T}^2) & E(\varepsilon_{1T}\varepsilon_{21}) & E(\varepsilon_{1T}\varepsilon_{22}) & \cdots & E(\varepsilon_{1T}\varepsilon_{NT}) \\
E(\varepsilon_{21}\varepsilon_{11}) & E(\varepsilon_{21}\varepsilon_{12}) & \cdots & E(\varepsilon_{21}\varepsilon_{1T}) & E(\varepsilon_{21}^2) & E(\varepsilon_{21}\varepsilon_{22}) & \cdots & E(\varepsilon_{21}\varepsilon_{NT}) \\
E(\varepsilon_{22}\varepsilon_{11}) & E(\varepsilon_{22}\varepsilon_{12}) & \cdots & E(\varepsilon_{22}\varepsilon_{1T}) & E(\varepsilon_{22}\varepsilon_{21}) & E(\varepsilon_{22}^2) & \cdots & E(\varepsilon_{22}\varepsilon_{NT}) \\
\vdots & \vdots & & \vdots & \vdots & \vdots & & \vdots \\
E(\varepsilon_{NT}\varepsilon_{11}) & E(\varepsilon_{NT}\varepsilon_{12}) & \cdots & E(\varepsilon_{NT}\varepsilon_{1T}) & E(\varepsilon_{NT}\varepsilon_{21}) & E(\varepsilon_{NT}\varepsilon_{22}) & \cdots & E(\varepsilon_{NT}^2)
\end{bmatrix}.$$

This specification provides a general framework for the discussion of different models designed to deal with pooled cross-section and time-series observations.

A Cross-sectionally Heteroskedastic and Time-wise Autoregressive Model

One approach to the specification of the behavior of the disturbances when we deal with cross-section and time-series data is to combine the assumptions that we frequently make about cross-sectional observations with those that are usually made when dealing with time series. As for the cross-sectional observations—for example, observations on individual households at a point (or period) of time—it is frequently assumed that the regression disturbances are mutually independent but heteroskedastic.[7] Concerning the time-series data, one usually suspects that the disturbances are autoregressive though not necessarily heteroskedastic. When dealing with pooled cross-section and time-series observations, we may combine these assumptions and adopt a *cross-sectionally heteroskedastic and time-wise autoregressive model*. The particular characterization of this model is as follows:

(12.22) $E(\varepsilon_{it}^2) = \sigma_i^2$ (heteroskedasticity)

(12.23) $E(\varepsilon_{it}\varepsilon_{jt}) = 0 \quad (i \neq j)$ (cross-sectional independence)

(12.24) $\varepsilon_{it} = \rho_i\varepsilon_{i,t-1} + u_{it}$ (autoregression)

---

[7] See, e.g., S. J. Prais and H. S. Houthakker, *The Analysis of Family Budgets* (Cambridge, England: The University Press, 1955). The assumption of mutual independence of the cross-sectional units will be relaxed later.

where $$u_{it} \sim N(0, \sigma_{ui}^2),$$

$$\varepsilon_{i0} \sim N\left(0, \frac{\sigma_{ui}^2}{1 - \rho_i^2}\right),$$

and $$E(\varepsilon_{i, t-1} u_{jt}) = 0 \quad \text{for all } i, j.$$

Note that in this model we allow the value of the parameter ρ to vary from one cross-sectional unit to another. From these specifications we deduce:

$$E(\varepsilon_{it}\varepsilon_{is}) = \rho^{t-s}\sigma_i^2 \qquad (t \geq s),$$

$$E(\varepsilon_{it}\varepsilon_{js}) = 0 \qquad (i \neq j).$$

By making the appropriate substitution into (12.21), we find that for this model

(12.25)
$$\Omega = \begin{bmatrix} \sigma_1^2 \mathbf{P_1} & 0 & \cdots & 0 \\ 0 & \sigma_2^2 \mathbf{P_2} & \cdots & 0 \\ \vdots & \vdots & & \vdots \\ 0 & 0 & \cdots & \sigma_N^2 \mathbf{P_N} \end{bmatrix},$$

where
$$\mathbf{P_i} = \begin{bmatrix} 1 & \rho_i & \rho_i^2 & \cdots & \rho_i^{T-1} \\ \rho_i & 1 & \rho_i & \cdots & \rho_i^{T-2} \\ \vdots & \vdots & \vdots & & \vdots \\ \rho_i^{T-1} & \rho_i^{T-2} & \rho_i^{T-3} & \cdots & 1 \end{bmatrix},$$

and each of the $\mathbf{0}$'s represents a $(T \times T)$ matrix of zeros.

To find consistent estimates of the elements of (12.25), we can proceed in the following way. First, we apply the ordinary least squares method to all $N \times T$ observations. The resulting estimates of the regression coefficients are unbiased and consistent, and can be used to calculate the regression residuals e_{it}. From these residuals, we can obtain estimates of ρ_i, say, $\hat{\rho}_i$, by

(12.26)
$$\hat{\rho}_i = \frac{\sum e_{it} e_{i, t-1}}{\sum e_{i, t-1}^2} \qquad (t = 2, 3, \ldots, T).$$

As pointed out in Section 8–2, $\hat{\rho}_i$ is a consistent estimator of ρ_i. Next, we use the $\hat{\rho}_i$'s to transform the observations in accordance with (8.52); that is, we form

(12.27)
$$Y_{it}^* = \beta_1 X_{it, 1}^* + \beta_2 X_{it, 2}^* + \cdots + \beta_K X_{it, K}^* + u_{it}^*,$$

where
$$Y_{it}^* = Y_{it} - \hat{\rho}_i Y_{i, t-1},$$

$$X_{it, k}^* = X_{it, k} - \hat{\rho}_i X_{i, t-1, k} \qquad (k = 1, 2, \ldots, K),$$

$$u_{it}^* = \varepsilon_{it} - \hat{\rho}_i \varepsilon_{i, t-1},$$

$$t = 2, 3, \ldots, T,$$

$$i = 1, 2, \ldots, N.$$

The purpose here is to estimate σ_i^2 from observations that are, at least asymptotically, nonautoregressive. To this end, we can apply the ordinary least squares method to (12.27) for which we have $N(T - 1)$ observations. The resulting regression residuals, say, $\hat{u}_{it}^*$, can be used to estimate the variances of u_{it} (i.e., σ_{ui}^2) by

(12.28)
$$s_{ui}^2 = \frac{1}{T - K - 1} \sum_{t=2}^{T} \hat{u}_{it}^{*2}.$$

Since
$$\sigma_{ui}^2 = \sigma_i^2(1 - \rho_i^2),$$

it follows that σ_i^2 can be estimated by

(12.29)
$$s_i^2 = \frac{s_{ui}^2}{1 - \hat{\rho}_i^2},$$

Since $\hat{\rho}_i$ is a consistent estimator of ρ_i and s_{ui}^2 is a consistent estimator of σ_{ui}^2, s_i^2 is a consistent estimator of σ_i^2.

Having obtained consistent estimators of ρ_i and σ_i^2, we have completed the task of deriving consistent estimators of the elements of $\mathbf{\Omega}$. By substituting for $\hat{\mathbf{\Omega}}$ into (12.19) and replacing $\mathbf{\Omega}$ by $\hat{\mathbf{\Omega}}$ in (12.20), we obtain the desired estimates of the regression coefficients and their variances. Since the evaluation of (12.19) and (12.20) is quite burdensome computationally, we may choose a slightly different procedure, which leads to almost identical results and is computationally less demanding. The idea is to subject the observations to a double transformation—one transformation designed to remove autoregression and the other to remove heteroskedasticity—and then use the ordinary least squares method on the transformed data. The autoregressive transformation is described by (12.27), so that we only have to worry about the transformation to remove heteroskedasticity. This transformation can be carried out by dividing both sides of (12.27) by s_{ui} obtained from (12.28), which leads to

(12.30)
$$Y_i^{**} = \beta_1 X_{it,\,1}^{**} + \beta_2 X_{it,\,2}^{**} + \cdots + \beta_K X_{it,\,K}^{**} + u_{it}^{**},$$

where
$$Y_{it}^{**} = \frac{Y_i^*}{s_{ui}},$$

$$X_{it,\,k}^{**} = \frac{X_{it,\,k}^*}{s_{ui}} \qquad (k = 1, 2, \ldots, K),$$

$$u_{it}^{**} = \frac{u_{it}^*}{s_{ui}},$$

$$t = 2, 3, \ldots, T,$$

$$i = 1, 2, \ldots, N.$$

The disturbance u_{it}^{**} is asymptotically nonautoregressive and homoskedastic. The equation (12.30) can then be estimated by the ordinary least squares method, utilizing all of the $N(T - 1)$ pooled observations.[8]

---

[8] The difference between the estimation results obtained by using the modified Aitken's formula (12.19) and those obtained by the ordinary least squares method applied to (12.30) is due to the fact that, in the latter case, we drop one observation for each cross-sectional unit. This difference is described in detail in, e.g., Johnston, *op. cit.*, pp. 185–186.

A somewhat different version of the cross-sectionally heteroskedastic and time-wise autoregressive model is obtained when we assume that the parameter ρ has the same value for all cross-sectional units; i.e., when

$$\rho_i = \rho_j = \rho \quad \text{for all } i, j = 1, 2, \ldots, N.$$

In this case, the matrix Ω becomes

$$(12.31) \qquad \Omega = \begin{bmatrix} \sigma_1^2 P & 0 & \cdots & 0 \\ 0 & \sigma_2^2 P & \cdots & 0 \\ \vdots & \vdots & & \vdots \\ 0 & 0 & \cdots & \sigma_N^2 P \end{bmatrix},$$

where

$$P = \begin{bmatrix} 1 & \rho & \rho^2 & \cdots & \rho^{T-1} \\ \rho & 1 & \rho & \cdots & \rho^{T-2} \\ \vdots & \vdots & \vdots & & \vdots \\ \rho^{T-1} & \rho^{T-2} & \rho^{T-3} & \cdots & 1 \end{bmatrix}.$$

The estimation of the regression coefficients can proceed in exactly the same way as in the previous case, except that formula (12.26) for $\hat{\rho}_i$ is replaced by

$$(12.32) \quad \hat{\rho} = \frac{\sum_i \sum_t e_{it} e_{i,t-1}}{\sum_i \sum_t e_{i,t-1}^2} \qquad (i = 1, 2, \ldots, N; t = 2, 3, \ldots, T),$$

and the variables in (12.27) are transformed by using $\hat{\rho}$ instead of $\hat{\rho}_i$. The remaining steps in the estimation procedure are unchanged.

A Cross-sectionally Correlated and Time-wise Autoregressive Model

In many circumstances the most questionable assumption of the preceding model is that the cross-sectional units are mutually independent. For instance, when the cross-sectional units are geographical regions with arbitrarily drawn boundaries—such as the states of the United States—we would not expect this assumption to be well satisfied. If we then generalize the preceding model by dropping the assumption of mutual independence, we have what may be termed a *cross-sectionally correlated and time-wise autoregressive model*. The specification of the behavior of the disturbances in this model is as follows:

$$(12.33) \qquad E(\varepsilon_{it}^2) = \sigma_{ii} \qquad \text{(heteroskedasticity)},$$

$$(12.34) \qquad E(\varepsilon_{it}\varepsilon_{jt}) = \sigma_{ij} \qquad \text{(mutual correlation)},$$

$$(12.35) \qquad \varepsilon_{it} = \rho_i \varepsilon_{i,t-1} + u_{it} \quad \text{(autoregression)},$$

where

$$u_{it} \sim N(0, \phi_{ii}),$$

$$E(\varepsilon_{i,t-1} u_{jt}) = 0,$$

$$E(u_{it} u_{jt}) = \phi_{ij},$$

$$E(u_{it} u_{js}) = 0 \qquad (t \neq s),$$

$$i, j = 1, 2, \ldots, N.$$

The initial value of ε is assumed to have the following properties:

$$\varepsilon_{i0} \sim N\left(0, \frac{\phi_{ii}}{1 - \rho_i^2}\right),$$

$$E(\varepsilon_{i0}\varepsilon_{j0}) = \frac{\phi_{ij}}{1 - \rho_i\rho_j}.$$

Note that the variances of the u's have now been denoted by the symbol ϕ rather than by σ_u^2, as in the preceding, simpler model. The matrix Ω for the present model is

(12.36)
$$\Omega = \begin{bmatrix} \sigma_{11}\mathbf{P}_{11} & \sigma_{12}\mathbf{P}_{12} & \cdots & \sigma_{1N}\mathbf{P}_{1N} \\ \sigma_{21}\mathbf{P}_{21} & \sigma_{22}\mathbf{P}_{22} & \cdots & \sigma_{2N}\mathbf{P}_{2N} \\ \vdots & \vdots & & \vdots \\ \sigma_{N1}\mathbf{P}_{N1} & \sigma_{N2}\mathbf{P}_{N2} & \cdots & \sigma_{NN}\mathbf{P}_{NN} \end{bmatrix},$$

where
$$\mathbf{P}_{ij} = \begin{bmatrix} 1 & \rho_j & \rho_j^2 & \cdots & \rho_j^{T-1} \\ \rho_i & 1 & \rho_j & \cdots & \rho_j^{T-2} \\ \rho_i^2 & \rho_i & 1 & \cdots & \rho_j^{T-3} \\ \vdots & \vdots & \vdots & & \vdots \\ \rho_i^{T-1} & \rho_i^{T-2} & \rho_i^{T-3} & \cdots & 1 \end{bmatrix}.$$

To obtain consistent estimates of the elements of Ω, we first apply the ordinary least squares method to all of the pooled observations, and calculate the corresponding residuals e_{it}. These residuals are used for obtaining ρ_i by application of the formula (12.26). With the help of $\hat{\rho}_i$, we transform the variables and form (12.27). To this equation we again apply the ordinary least squares method and calculate the residuals $\hat{u}_{it}^*$. The variances and covariances of the ε's (i.e., σ_{ij}) can then be estimated by

(12.37)
$$s_{ij} = \frac{\hat{\phi}_{ij}}{1 - \hat{\rho}_i\hat{\rho}_j},$$

where
$$\hat{\phi}_{ij} = \frac{1}{T - K - 1} \sum_{t=2}^{T} \hat{u}_{it}^*\hat{u}_{jt}^*.$$

In this way we obtain consistent estimates of ρ_i and σ_{ij} and, therefore, of Ω. This enables us to use the formulas (12.19) and (12.20), and thus to obtain asymptotically efficient estimates of the regression coefficients and of their variances.

This procedure can be simplified by applying the modified Aitken's estimation formulas (12.19) and (12.20) to the *transformed* variables, that is, by using an estimator of β

(12.38)
$$\tilde{\tilde{\beta}} = (\mathbf{X}^{*\prime}\hat{\phi}^{-1}\mathbf{X}^*)^{-1}(\mathbf{X}^{*\prime}\hat{\phi}^{-1}\mathbf{Y}^*)$$

with

(12.39)   Asympt. Var-Cov$(\tilde{\tilde{\beta}}) = (\mathbf{X}^{*\prime} \boldsymbol{\phi}^{-1} \mathbf{X}^*)^{-1}$.

Here $\mathbf{Y}^*$ is an $N(T-1) \times 1$ vector of the transformed observations of $Y_{it}^* = Y_{it} - \hat{\rho}_i Y_{i,t-1}$, and $\mathbf{X}^*$ is an $N(T-1) \times K$ matrix of the transformed observations $X_{it,k}^* = X_{it,k} - \hat{\rho}_i X_{i,t-1,k}$ $(t = 2, 3, \ldots, T; i = 1, 2, \ldots, N; k = 1, 2, \ldots, K)$. The matrix $\hat{\boldsymbol{\Phi}}$ is the estimated variance-covariance matrix of the u's, and it is of the order $N(T-1) \times N(T-1)$. Its full description is

(12.40)
$$
\hat{\boldsymbol{\Phi}} = \begin{bmatrix} \hat{\phi}_{11}\mathbf{I}_{\mathbf{T}-\mathbf{1}} & \hat{\phi}_{12}\mathbf{I}_{\mathbf{T}-\mathbf{1}} & \cdots & \hat{\phi}_{1N}\mathbf{I}_{\mathbf{T}-\mathbf{1}} \\ \hat{\phi}_{21}\mathbf{I}_{\mathbf{T}-\mathbf{1}} & \hat{\phi}_{22}\mathbf{I}_{\mathbf{T}-\mathbf{1}} & \cdots & \hat{\phi}_{2N}\mathbf{I}_{\mathbf{T}-\mathbf{1}} \\ \vdots & \vdots & & \vdots \\ \hat{\phi}_{N1}\mathbf{I}_{\mathbf{T}-\mathbf{1}} & \hat{\phi}_{N2}\mathbf{I}_{\mathbf{T}-\mathbf{1}} & \cdots & \hat{\phi}_{NN}\mathbf{I}_{\mathbf{T}-\mathbf{1}} \end{bmatrix},
$$

where the $\hat{\phi}_{ij}$'s are as defined in (12.37), and $\mathbf{I}_{\mathbf{T}-\mathbf{1}}$ is an identity matrix of order $(T-1) \times (T-1)$. In general, the value of the estimator in (12.38) will be different from that obtained by using (12.19), but the asymptotic properties of the two estimators are the same.

An Error Components Model

A different approach to the specification of the behavior of the disturbances when combining cross-section and time-series data has been adopted by the proponents of the so-called *error components model*. The basic assumption here is that the regression disturbance is composed of three independent components —one component associated with time, another associated with the cross-sectional units, and the third varying in both dimensions. Specifically,

(12.41) $\varepsilon_{it} = u_i + v_t + w_{it}$ $(i = 1, 2, \ldots, N; t = 1, 2, \ldots, T)$,

where $u_i \sim N(0, \sigma_u^2)$,

$$v_t \sim N(0, \sigma_v^2),$$

$$w_{it} \sim N(0, \sigma_w^2),$$

and the components u_i, v_t, and w_{it} satisfy the following conditions:

$$E(u_i v_t) = E(u_i w_{it}) = E(v_i w_{it}) = 0,$$

$$E(u_i u_j) = 0 \quad (i \neq j),$$

$$E(v_t v_s) = 0 \quad (t \neq s),$$

$$E(w_{it} w_{is}) = E(w_{it} w_{jt}) = E(w_{it} w_{js}) = 0 \qquad (i \neq j; t \neq s).$$

Note that this implies that ε_{it} is *homoskedastic* with variance given by

$$\text{Var}(\varepsilon_{it}) = \sigma^2 = \sigma_u^2 + \sigma_v^2 + \sigma_w^2.$$

The coefficient of correlation between ε_{it} and ε_{jt} $(i \neq j)$—i.e., between the disturbances of two different cross-sectional units at a given point of time—is

$$\frac{\text{Cov}(\varepsilon_{it}, \varepsilon_{jt})}{\sqrt{\text{Var}(\varepsilon_{it})\text{Var}(\varepsilon_{jt})}} = \frac{\sigma_v^2}{\sigma_u^2 + \sigma_v^2 + \sigma_w^2} \qquad (i \neq j).$$

The coefficient of correlation between ε_{it} and ε_{is} $(i \neq s)$—i.e., between the disturbances of a given cross-sectional unit at two different points of time—is

$$\frac{\text{Cov}(\varepsilon_{it}, \varepsilon_{is})}{\sqrt{\text{Var}(\varepsilon_{it})\text{Var}(\varepsilon_{is})}} = \frac{\sigma_u^2}{\sigma_u^2 + \sigma_v^2 + \sigma_w^2} \qquad (t \neq s).$$

This last feature of the error components model means that, for each cross-sectional unit, the correlation of the disturbances over time remains *unchanged* no matter how far apart in time the disturbances are. This contrasts sharply with the usual assumption of first-order autoregression, which implies that the degree of correlation declines geometrically with the time distance involved. Finally, the coefficient of correlation between ε_{it} and ε_{js} is

$$\frac{\text{Cov}(\varepsilon_{it}, \varepsilon_{js})}{\sqrt{\text{Var}(\varepsilon_{it})\text{Var}(\varepsilon_{js})}} = 0 \qquad (i \neq j; \, t \neq s).$$

By substituting these results into (12.21), we find that the matrix $\boldsymbol{\Omega}$ for the error components model is

$$(12.42) \qquad \boldsymbol{\Omega} = \begin{bmatrix} \sigma_u^2 \mathbf{A_T} & \sigma_v^2 \mathbf{I_T} & \cdots & \sigma_v^2 \mathbf{I_T} \\ \sigma_v^2 \mathbf{I_T} & \sigma_u^2 \mathbf{A_T} & \cdots & \sigma_v^2 \mathbf{I_T} \\ \vdots & \vdots & & \vdots \\ \sigma_v^2 \mathbf{I_T} & \sigma_v^2 \mathbf{I_T} & \cdots & \sigma_u^2 \mathbf{A_T} \end{bmatrix},$$

where $\mathbf{A_T}$ is a $(T \times T)$ matrix defined as

$$\mathbf{A_T} = \begin{bmatrix} \dfrac{\sigma^2}{\sigma_u^2} & 1 & \cdots & 1 \\ 1 & \dfrac{\sigma^2}{\sigma_u^2} & \cdots & 1 \\ \vdots & \vdots & & \vdots \\ 1 & 1 & \cdots & \dfrac{\sigma^2}{\sigma_u^2} \end{bmatrix}$$

and $\mathbf{I_T}$ is an identity matrix of order $T \times T$. The elements of the $\boldsymbol{\Omega}$ matrix can be estimated as follows:[9]

[9] See T. D. Wallace and A. Hussain, "The Use of Error Components Models in Combining Cross-Section with Time-Series Data," *Econometrica*, Vol. 37, January 1969, pp. 55–72.

$$(12.43) \quad \hat{\sigma}_w^2 = \frac{1}{(N-1)(T-1)} \sum_{i=1}^{N} \sum_{t=1}^{T} \left[e_{it} - \frac{1}{T} \sum_{t=1}^{T} e_{it} - \frac{1}{N} \sum_{i=1}^{N} e_{it} \right]^2,$$

$$\hat{\sigma}_u^2 = \frac{1}{T} \left\{ \frac{1}{(N-1)T} \sum_{i=1}^{N} \left[\sum_{t=1}^{T} e_{it} \right]^2 - \hat{\sigma}_w^2 \right\},$$

$$\hat{\sigma}_v^2 = \frac{1}{N} \left\{ \frac{1}{N(T-1)} \sum_{t=1}^{T} \left[\sum_{t=1}^{N} e_{it} \right]^2 - \hat{\sigma}_w^2 \right\},$$

where e_{it} represents residuals obtained by applying the ordinary least squares method to the pooled data. Using these estimates and the formulas (12.19) and (12.20), we obtain estimates of the regression coefficients that have the same properties as Aitken's generalized least squares estimator.[10]

A Covariance Model

Another model that is commonly used when dealing with pooled cross-section and time-series observations is the so-called *covariance model*. We mention this as a postscript to the present section because the covariance model is generally treated within the framework of the classical regression model rather than as a generalized regression model. The idea behind the covariance model is the supposition that each cross-sectional unit and each time period are characterized by their own special intercept. This feature is incorporated into the regression equation by the introduction of binary variables. The regression equation then becomes

$$(12.44) \quad Y_{it} = \beta_1 + \beta_2 X_{it,2} + \cdots + \beta_K X_{it,K} + \gamma_2 Z_{2t} + \gamma_3 Z_{3t} + \cdots + \gamma_N Z_{Nt}$$
$$+ \delta_2 W_{i2} + \delta_3 W_{i3} + \cdots + \delta_T W_{iT} + \varepsilon_{it},$$

where
$$Z_{it} = 1 \quad \text{for the } i\text{th cross-sectional unit,}$$
$$= 0 \quad \text{otherwise} \quad (i = 2, 3, \ldots, N);$$
$$W_{it} = 1 \quad \text{for the } t\text{th time period,}$$
$$= 0 \quad \text{otherwise} \quad (t = 2, 3, \ldots, T).$$

The disturbance ε_{it} is supposed to satisfy the assumptions of the classical normal linear regression model. (We could, of course, allow ε_{it} to be autoregressive or heteroskedastic and then choose an appropriate estimation method.) Note that with the foregoing specification of the regression equation, we have

$$Y_{11} = \beta_1 + \beta_2 X_{11,2} + \cdots + \beta_K X_{11,K} + \varepsilon_{11},$$
$$Y_{12} = (\beta_1 + \delta_2) + \beta_2 X_{12,2} + \cdots + \beta_K X_{12,K} + \varepsilon_{12},$$
$$\vdots$$
$$Y_{1T} = (\beta_1 + \delta_T) + \beta_2 X_{1T,2} + \cdots + \beta_K X_{1T,K} + \varepsilon_{1T},$$
$$Y_{21} = (\beta_1 + \gamma_2) + \beta_2 X_{21,2} + \cdots + \beta_K X_{21,K} + \varepsilon_{21},$$
$$Y_{22} = (\beta_1 + \gamma_2 + \delta_2) + \beta_2 X_{22,2} + \cdots + \beta_K X_{22,K} + \varepsilon_{22},$$
$$\vdots$$
$$Y_{NT} = (\beta_1 + \gamma_N + \delta_T) + \beta_2 X_{NT,2} + \cdots + \beta_K X_{NT,K} + \varepsilon_{NT}.$$

[10] For a proof, see *ibid.*

Equation (12.44) contains $K + (N - 1) + (T - 1)$ regression coefficients to be estimated from $N \times T$ observations. If the model is correctly specified and the classical assumptions are satisfied, the ordinary least squares estimates of the regression coefficients will be unbiased and efficient.

12–3   Seemingly Unrelated Regressions

Under the assumptions of the classical normal linear regression model, the least squares estimators of the regression coefficients were found to be unbiased and efficient. This result was derived on the understanding that the specification of the model represents *all* there is to know about the regression equation and the variables involved. If there exists some other piece of information that has not been taken into account, then the result concerning the properties of the least squares estimators can no longer be considered established. One such additional piece of information would be the knowledge that the disturbance in the regression equation under consideration could be correlated with the disturbance in some other regression equation (see fn. 2, page 202). In the present section we shall consider such a situation and examine the implications for estimation of the regression coefficients.

Suppose we are concerned with the problem of estimating the coefficients of any one or all of the following M regression equations:

$$(12.45) \qquad Y_{1t} = \beta_{11} X_{1t,1} + \beta_{12} X_{1t,2} + \cdots + \beta_{1K_1} X_{1t,K_1} + \varepsilon_{1t},$$

$$Y_{2t} = \beta_{21} X_{2t,1} + \beta_{22} X_{2t,2} + \cdots + \beta_{2K_2} X_{2t,K_2} + \varepsilon_{2t},$$

$$\vdots$$

$$Y_{Mt} = \beta_{M1} X_{Mt,1} + \beta_{M2} X_{Mt,2} + \cdots + \beta_{MK_M} X_{Mt,K_M} + \varepsilon_{Mt},$$

$$t = 1, 2, \ldots, T.$$

Using matrix notation, we can write

$$(12.45a) \qquad \mathbf{Y_1} = \mathbf{X_1 \beta_1} + \mathbf{\epsilon_1},$$

$$\mathbf{Y_2} = \mathbf{X_2 \beta_2} + \mathbf{\epsilon_2},$$

$$\vdots$$

$$\mathbf{Y_M} = \mathbf{X_M \beta_M} + \mathbf{\epsilon_M},$$

or

$$(12.45b) \qquad \mathbf{Y_m} = \mathbf{X_m \beta_m} + \mathbf{\epsilon_m} \qquad (m = 1, 2, \ldots, M),$$

where $\mathbf{Y_m}$ is a $(T \times 1)$ vector of the sample values of the dependent variable, $\mathbf{X_m}$ is a $(T \times K_m)$ matrix of the sample values of the explanatory variables, $\mathbf{\beta_m}$ is a $(K_m \times 1)$ vector of the regression coefficients, and $\mathbf{\epsilon_m}$ is a $(T \times 1)$ vector of the sample values of the disturbances. We assume that $\mathbf{\epsilon_m}$ is normally distributed with mean

$$(12.46) \qquad E(\varepsilon_{mt}) = 0 \qquad (t = 1, 2, \ldots, T)$$

and that its variance-covariance matrix is given by

$$(12.47) \qquad E(\boldsymbol{\epsilon}_m \boldsymbol{\epsilon}_m') = \sigma_{mm} \mathbf{I_T},$$

where $\mathbf{I_T}$ is an identity matrix of order $(T \times T)$. The explanatory variables are taken to be nonstochastic and such that $(\mathbf{X'X})/T$ is nonsingular and its limit (for $T \to \infty$) exists. This means that each of the equations is expected to satisfy the assumptions of the classical normal linear regression model. Now, suppose further that we cannot rule out the possibility that the regression disturbances in different equations are *mutually correlated*. In this case we have

$$(12.48) \qquad E(\boldsymbol{\epsilon}_m \boldsymbol{\epsilon}_p') = \sigma_{mp} \mathbf{I_T} \qquad (m, p = 1, 2, \ldots, M).$$

Thus σ_{mp} is the covariance of the disturbances of the mth and the pth equation, which is assumed to be constant over all observations. This covariance represents the *only* link between the mth and the pth equation. Because this link is rather subtle, the system of M equations is called a system of *seemingly unrelated regression equations*. Examples of such regressions would be demand functions for various commodities or production functions for different industries, with observations made over time (or over some cross-sectional units). The disturbance in the demand equation for commodity A is likely to be correlated with the disturbance in the demand equations for commodities B, C, etc. Similarly, the disturbance in the production function for one industry may be correlated with the disturbances in the production functions for other industries. Note that if the regression equations (12.45) are such that the regression coefficients in each equation are the *same* as the regression coefficients in any other equation, the whole system would reduce to a single equation, and the observations would represent pooled cross-section and time-series data.

Estimation When the Variance-Covariance Matrix Is Known

Let us now turn to the problem of estimating the coefficients of the seemingly unrelated regression equations. One possible approach is to apply the ordinary least squares method to each equation separately. This would give

$$\hat{\boldsymbol{\beta}}_m = (\mathbf{X}_m' \mathbf{X}_m)^{-1} (\mathbf{X}_m' \mathbf{Y}_m)$$

and $\qquad E(\hat{\boldsymbol{\beta}}_m - \boldsymbol{\beta}_m)(\hat{\boldsymbol{\beta}}_m - \boldsymbol{\beta}_m)' = \sigma_{mm} (\mathbf{X}_m' \mathbf{X}_m)^{-1}.$

Note that

$$E(\hat{\boldsymbol{\beta}}_m) = \boldsymbol{\beta}_m + E(\mathbf{X}_m' \mathbf{X}_m)^{-1} (\mathbf{X}_m' \boldsymbol{\epsilon}_m) = \boldsymbol{\beta}_m$$

and $\qquad \text{plim } \hat{\boldsymbol{\beta}}_m = \boldsymbol{\beta}_m + \text{plim} \left[\frac{1}{T} \mathbf{X}_m' \mathbf{X}_m \right]^{-1} \left[\frac{1}{T} \mathbf{X}_m' \boldsymbol{\epsilon}_m \right] = \boldsymbol{\beta}_m,$

which means that the ordinary least squares estimators of the regression coefficients are unbiased and consistent. Thus the major question is that of efficiency. By estimating each equation separately and independently, we are disregarding the information about the mutual correlation of the disturbances, and the efficiency of the estimators becomes questionable.

To take into account the correlation of the disturbances across equations, we compress (12.45) into one big equation. This can be done by noting that each equation of the system can be written as

(12.49) $\mathbf{Y_m} = \mathbf{X_1^{(m)}\beta_1} + \mathbf{X_2^{(m)}\beta_2} + \cdots + \mathbf{X_M^{(m)}\beta_M} + \boldsymbol{\epsilon}_m$ $(m = 1, 2, \ldots, M)$,

where $\mathbf{X_p^{(m)}} = \mathbf{X_p}$ if $m = p$,

$= \mathbf{0}$ if $m \neq p$,

with $\mathbf{0}$ representing a $(T \times K_p)$ matrix of zeros. By redefining the explanatory variables in this way, we obtain a set of regression equations in which each equation contains exactly the same regression coefficients as any other. Thus, we are formally in the same situation as when we are dealing with pooled cross-section and time-series observations on a single equation. Equations (12.49) can also be represented as

(12.49a)
$$\begin{bmatrix} \mathbf{Y_1} \\ \mathbf{Y_2} \\ \vdots \\ \mathbf{Y_M} \end{bmatrix} = \begin{bmatrix} \mathbf{X_1^{(1)}} & \mathbf{X_2^{(1)}} & \cdots & \mathbf{X_M^{(1)}} \\ \mathbf{X_1^{(2)}} & \mathbf{X_2^{(2)}} & \cdots & \mathbf{X_M^{(2)}} \\ \vdots & \vdots & & \vdots \\ \mathbf{X_1^{(M)}} & \mathbf{X_2^{(M)}} & \cdots & \mathbf{X_M^{(M)}} \end{bmatrix} \begin{bmatrix} \boldsymbol{\beta}_1 \\ \boldsymbol{\beta}_2 \\ \vdots \\ \boldsymbol{\beta}_M \end{bmatrix} + \begin{bmatrix} \boldsymbol{\epsilon}_1 \\ \boldsymbol{\epsilon}_2 \\ \vdots \\ \boldsymbol{\epsilon}_M \end{bmatrix},$$

or

(12.49b)
$$\begin{bmatrix} \mathbf{Y_1} \\ \mathbf{Y_2} \\ \vdots \\ \mathbf{Y_M} \end{bmatrix} = \begin{bmatrix} \mathbf{X_1} & \mathbf{0} & \cdots & \mathbf{0} \\ \mathbf{0} & \mathbf{X_2} & \cdots & \mathbf{0} \\ \vdots & \vdots & & \vdots \\ \mathbf{0} & \mathbf{0} & \cdots & \mathbf{X_M} \end{bmatrix} \begin{bmatrix} \boldsymbol{\beta}_1 \\ \boldsymbol{\beta}_2 \\ \vdots \\ \boldsymbol{\beta}_M \end{bmatrix} + \begin{bmatrix} \boldsymbol{\epsilon}_1 \\ \boldsymbol{\epsilon}_2 \\ \vdots \\ \boldsymbol{\epsilon}_M \end{bmatrix}.$$

This can be written more compactly as

(12.49c) $\mathbf{Y} = \mathbf{X}\boldsymbol{\beta} + \boldsymbol{\epsilon}$,

where $\mathbf{Y}$ is a $(MT \times 1)$ vector, $\mathbf{X}$ is a $(MT \times \sum_{m=1}^{M} K_m)$ matrix, $\boldsymbol{\beta}$ is a $(\sum_{m=1}^{M} K_m \times 1)$ matrix, and the dimension of $\boldsymbol{\epsilon}$ is $(MT \times 1)$. Note that, by the assumptions (12.46) through (12.48), the variance-covariance matrix of $\boldsymbol{\epsilon}$ is

(12.50) $\boldsymbol{\Omega} = E(\boldsymbol{\epsilon}\boldsymbol{\epsilon}')$

$$= \begin{bmatrix} E(\boldsymbol{\epsilon}_1\boldsymbol{\epsilon}_1') & E(\boldsymbol{\epsilon}_1\boldsymbol{\epsilon}_2') & \cdots & E(\boldsymbol{\epsilon}_1\boldsymbol{\epsilon}_M') \\ E(\boldsymbol{\epsilon}_2\boldsymbol{\epsilon}_1') & E(\boldsymbol{\epsilon}_2\boldsymbol{\epsilon}_2') & \cdots & E(\boldsymbol{\epsilon}_2\boldsymbol{\epsilon}_M') \\ \vdots & \vdots & & \vdots \\ E(\boldsymbol{\epsilon}_M\boldsymbol{\epsilon}_1') & E(\boldsymbol{\epsilon}_M\boldsymbol{\epsilon}_2') & \cdots & E(\boldsymbol{\epsilon}_M\boldsymbol{\epsilon}_M') \end{bmatrix} = \begin{bmatrix} \sigma_{11}\mathbf{I_T} & \sigma_{12}\mathbf{I_T} & \cdots & \sigma_{1M}\mathbf{I_T} \\ \sigma_{21}\mathbf{I_T} & \sigma_{22}\mathbf{I_T} & \cdots & \sigma_{2M}\mathbf{I_T} \\ \vdots & \vdots & & \vdots \\ \sigma_{M1}\mathbf{I_T} & \sigma_{M2}\mathbf{I_T} & \cdots & \sigma_{MM}\mathbf{I_T} \end{bmatrix},$$

where, as before, $\mathbf{I_T}$ is an identity matrix of order $(T \times T)$. The information about the correlation of the disturbances across equations is then contained in the description of the $\boldsymbol{\Omega}$ matrix, and it can be taken into account in that form.

The equation (12.49c), together with the assumptions about $\mathbf{X}$ and $\boldsymbol{\epsilon}$, can be viewed as a generalized linear regression model (discussed in Section 12–1). The best linear unbiased estimator of β for this model is given by Aitken's generalized least squares formula as

$$(12.51) \qquad \tilde{\beta} = (X'\Omega^{-1}X)^{-1}(X'\Omega^{-1}Y).$$

In the context of the seemingly unrelated regressions, this becomes

$$(12.51a) \quad \tilde{\beta} = \begin{bmatrix} \sigma^{11}(X_1'X_1) & \sigma^{12}(X_1'X_2) & \cdots & \sigma^{1M}(X_1'X_M) \\[2mm] \sigma^{21}(X_2'X_1) & \sigma^{22}(X_2'X_2) & \cdots & \sigma^{2M}(X_2'X_M) \\[2mm] \vdots & \vdots & & \vdots \\[2mm] \sigma^{M1}(X_M'X_1) & \sigma^{M2}(X_M'X_2) & \cdots & \sigma^{MM}(X_M'X_M) \end{bmatrix}^{-1} \begin{bmatrix} \sum\limits_{m=1}^{M} \sigma^{1m}(X_1'Y_m) \\[2mm] \sum\limits_{m=1}^{M} \sigma^{2m}(X_2'Y_m) \\[2mm] \vdots \\[2mm] \sum\limits_{m=1}^{M} \sigma^{Mm}(X_m'Y_m) \end{bmatrix},$$

where σ^{mp} represents the element that appears in the mth row and pth column of the inverse of the matrix

$$\begin{bmatrix} \sigma_{11} & \sigma_{12} & \cdots & \sigma_{1M} \\ \sigma_{21} & \sigma_{22} & \cdots & \sigma_{2M} \\ \vdots & \vdots & & \vdots \\ \sigma_{M1} & \sigma_{M2} & \cdots & \sigma_{MM} \end{bmatrix}.$$

Further, the variance-covariance matrix of $\tilde{\beta}$ is given by

$$(12.52) \qquad E(\tilde{\beta} - \beta)(\tilde{\beta} - \beta)' = (X'\Omega^{-1}X)^{-1}.$$

Under the assumption of normality, $\tilde{\beta}$ also represents the maximum likelihood estimator of β. Since the ordinary least squares estimator of β is

$$\hat{\beta} = (X'X)^{-1}(X'Y),$$

which is, in general, different from $\tilde{\beta}$, ordinary least squares estimation of the seemingly unrelated regressions is *not efficient*.

An interesting question concerning the application of Aitken's generalized estimator to seemingly unrelated regressions relates to the special conditions under which this estimator is, in fact, equivalent to the ordinary least squares estimator. One such obvious case exists when the equations are not seemingly but *actually* unrelated; that is, when

$$\sigma_{mp} = 0$$

for all $m \neq p$. In this case $\tilde{\beta}$ becomes

$$\tilde{\beta} = \begin{bmatrix} \sigma^{11}(X_1'X_1) & 0 & \cdots & 0 \\[2mm] 0 & \sigma^{22}(X_2'X_2) & \cdots & 0 \\[2mm] \vdots & \vdots & & \vdots \\[2mm] 0 & 0 & \cdots & \sigma^{MM}(X_M'X_M) \end{bmatrix}^{-1} \begin{bmatrix} \sigma^{11}(X_1'Y_1) \\[2mm] \sigma^{22}(X_2'Y_2) \\[2mm] \vdots \\[2mm] \sigma^{MM}(X_M'Y_M) \end{bmatrix}$$

$$= (X'X)^{-1}(X'Y),$$

which is the formula for the least squares estimator. The two estimators are also equivalent when each of the seemingly unrelated regressions involves exactly the *same* explanatory variables; that is, when

$$\mathbf{X_m} = \mathbf{X_p}$$

for all m and p. We shall prove the equivalence of Aitken's and ordinary least squares formulas in this case for a set of two equations, but the proof can be extended to any number of equations. (The proof could also be extended to where $\mathbf{X_m}$ and $\mathbf{X_p}$ are not exactly the same but $\mathbf{X_m}$ is a linear combination of $\mathbf{X_p}$.) Now, for $M = 2$ and $\mathbf{X_1} = \mathbf{X_2}$, Aitken's generalized estimator is

$$\begin{bmatrix} \tilde{\beta}_1 \\ \tilde{\beta}_2 \end{bmatrix} = \begin{bmatrix} \sigma^{11}(\mathbf{X_1'X_1}) & \sigma^{12}(\mathbf{X_1'X_1}) \\ \sigma^{21}(\mathbf{X_1'X_1}) & \sigma^{22}(\mathbf{X_1'X_1}) \end{bmatrix}^{-1} \begin{bmatrix} \sigma^{11}(\mathbf{X_1'Y_1}) + \sigma^{12}(\mathbf{X_1'Y_2}) \\ \sigma^{21}(\mathbf{X_1'Y_1}) + \sigma^{22}(\mathbf{X_1'Y_2}) \end{bmatrix},$$

or

$$\begin{bmatrix} \sigma^{11}(\mathbf{X_1'X_1})\tilde{\beta}_1 + \sigma^{12}(\mathbf{X_1'X_1})\tilde{\beta}_2 \\ \sigma^{21}(\mathbf{X_1'X_1})\tilde{\beta}_1 + \sigma^{22}(\mathbf{X_1'X_1})\tilde{\beta}_2 \end{bmatrix} = \begin{bmatrix} \sigma^{11}(\mathbf{X_1'Y_1}) + \sigma^{12}(\mathbf{X_1'Y_2}) \\ \sigma^{21}(\mathbf{X_1'Y_1}) + \sigma^{22}(\mathbf{X_1'Y_2}) \end{bmatrix}.$$

But

$$\begin{bmatrix} \sigma^{11} & \sigma^{12} \\ \sigma^{21} & \sigma^{22} \end{bmatrix} = \begin{bmatrix} \sigma_{11} & \sigma_{12} \\ \sigma_{12} & \sigma_{22} \end{bmatrix}^{-1} = \frac{1}{\sigma_{11}\sigma_{22} - \sigma_{12}^2} \begin{bmatrix} \sigma_{22} & -\sigma_{12} \\ -\sigma_{12} & \sigma_{11} \end{bmatrix},$$

so that we have

$$\sigma_{22}(\mathbf{X_1'X_1})\tilde{\beta}_1 - \sigma_{12}(\mathbf{X_1'X_1})\tilde{\beta}_2 = \sigma_{22}(\mathbf{X_1'Y_1}) - \sigma_{12}(\mathbf{X_1'Y_2}),$$

$$-\sigma_{12}(\mathbf{X_1'X_1})\tilde{\beta}_1 + \sigma_{11}(\mathbf{X_1'X_1})\tilde{\beta}_2 = -\sigma_{12}(\mathbf{X_1'Y_1}) + \sigma_{11}(\mathbf{X_1'Y_2}).$$

The solution for $\tilde{\beta}_1$ and $\tilde{\beta}_2$ is then

$$\tilde{\beta}_1 = (\mathbf{X_1'X_1})^{-1}(\mathbf{X_1'Y_1}) \quad \text{and} \quad \tilde{\beta}_2 = (\mathbf{X_2'X_2})^{-1}(\mathbf{X_2'Y_2}),$$

which is the same as the ordinary least squares results.

To illustrate the difference between Aitken's and the ordinary least squares estimators of the coefficients of seemingly unrelated regressions, we consider a simple system of two equations. Suppose we have

(12.53) $$Y_{1t} = \beta_{11} + \beta_{12}X_{1t} + \varepsilon_{1t},$$

$$Y_{2t} = \beta_{21} + \beta_{22}X_{2t} + \varepsilon_{2t},$$

or

(12.53a) $$\mathbf{Y_1} = \mathbf{X_1}\boldsymbol{\beta}_1 + \boldsymbol{\epsilon}_1 \quad \text{and} \quad \mathbf{Y_2} = \mathbf{X_2}\boldsymbol{\beta}_2 + \boldsymbol{\epsilon}_2,$$

where $$\mathbf{X_r} = \begin{bmatrix} 1 & X_{r1} \\ 1 & X_{r2} \\ \vdots & \vdots \\ 1 & X_{rT} \end{bmatrix}, \quad \boldsymbol{\beta}_r = \begin{bmatrix} \beta_{r1} \\ \beta_{r2} \end{bmatrix} \quad (r = 1, 2).$$

In this case,

$$\Omega^{-1} = \frac{1}{\sigma_{11}\sigma_{22} - \sigma_{12}^2}\begin{bmatrix} \sigma_{22}\mathbf{I_T} & -\sigma_{12}\mathbf{I_T} \\ -\sigma_{12}\mathbf{I_T} & \sigma_{11}\mathbf{I_T} \end{bmatrix}.$$

Aitken's generalized estimator of the regression coefficients then is

$$\begin{bmatrix} \tilde{\boldsymbol{\beta}}_1 \\ \tilde{\boldsymbol{\beta}}_2 \end{bmatrix} = \begin{bmatrix} \sigma_{22}(\mathbf{X}_1'\mathbf{X}_1) & -\sigma_{12}(\mathbf{X}_1'\mathbf{X}_2) \\ -\sigma_{12}(\mathbf{X}_2'\mathbf{X}_1) & \sigma_{11}(\mathbf{X}_2'\mathbf{X}_2) \end{bmatrix}^{-1}\begin{bmatrix} \sigma_{22}(\mathbf{X}_1'\mathbf{Y}_1) & -\sigma_{12}(\mathbf{X}_1'\mathbf{Y}_2) \\ -\sigma_{12}(\mathbf{X}_2'\mathbf{Y}_1) & +\sigma_{11}(\mathbf{X}_2'\mathbf{Y}_2) \end{bmatrix}.$$

This leads to the following system of "Aitken's generalized least squares normal equations":

$$\sigma_{22}\sum_t (Y_{1t} - \tilde{\beta}_{11} - \tilde{\beta}_{12}X_{1t}) - \sigma_{12}\sum_t (Y_{2t} - \tilde{\beta}_{21} - \tilde{\beta}_{22}X_{2t}) = 0,$$

$$\sigma_{22}\sum_t X_{1t}(Y_{1t} - \tilde{\beta}_{11} - \tilde{\beta}_{12}X_{1t}) - \sigma_{12}\sum_t X_{1t}(Y_{2t} - \tilde{\beta}_{21} - \tilde{\beta}_{22}X_{2t}) = 0,$$

$$-\sigma_{12}\sum_t (Y_{1t} - \tilde{\beta}_{11} - \tilde{\beta}_{12}X_{1t}) + \sigma_{11}\sum_t (Y_{2t} - \tilde{\beta}_{21} - \tilde{\beta}_{22}X_{2t}) = 0,$$

$$-\sigma_{12}\sum_t X_{2t}(Y_{1t} - \tilde{\beta}_{11} - \tilde{\beta}_{12}X_{1t}) + \sigma_{11}\sum_t X_{2t}(Y_{2t} - \tilde{\beta}_{21} - \tilde{\beta}_{22}X_{2t}) = 0.$$

The first and third of these equations can be solved for $\tilde{\beta}_{11}$ and $\tilde{\beta}_{21}$ to give

(12.54)
$$\tilde{\beta}_{11} = \bar{Y}_1 - \tilde{\beta}_{12}\bar{X}_1,$$
$$\tilde{\beta}_{21} = \bar{Y}_2 - \tilde{\beta}_{22}\bar{X}_2.$$

Substituting these results into the remaining equations and solving for $\tilde{\beta}_{12}$ and $\tilde{\beta}_{22}$, we obtain

(12.55)

$$\tilde{\beta}_{12} = \frac{\sigma_{11}m_{X_2X_2}(\sigma_{22}m_{X_1Y_1} - \sigma_{12}m_{X_1Y_2}) + \sigma_{12}m_{X_1X_2}(\sigma_{11}m_{X_2Y_2} - \sigma_{12}m_{X_2Y_1})}{\sigma_{11}\sigma_{22}m_{X_1X_1}m_{X_2X_2} - \sigma_{12}^2 m_{X_1X_2}^2},$$

$$\tilde{\beta}_{22} = \frac{\sigma_{12}m_{X_1X_2}(\sigma_{22}m_{X_1Y_1} - \sigma_{12}m_{X_1Y_2}) + \sigma_{22}m_{X_1X_1}(\sigma_{11}m_{X_2Y_2} - \sigma_{12}m_{X_2Y_1})}{\sigma_{11}\sigma_{22}m_{X_1X_1}m_{X_2X_2} - \sigma_{12}^2 m_{X_1X_2}^2},$$

where
$$m_{X_rX_s} = \sum_t (X_{rt} - \bar{X}_r)(X_{st} - \bar{X}_s),$$

$$m_{X_rY_s} = \sum_t (X_{rt} - \bar{X}_r)(Y_{st} - \bar{Y}_s),$$

$$r, s = 1, 2.$$

Note that if ε_{1t} and ε_{2t} are uncorrelated (i.e., if $\sigma_{12} = 0$), the formulas for $\tilde{\beta}_{12}$ and $\tilde{\beta}_{22}$ become

$$\tilde{\beta}_{12} = \frac{\sigma_{11}\sigma_{22}m_{X_2X_2}m_{X_1Y_1}}{\sigma_{11}\sigma_{22}m_{X_1X_1}m_{X_2X_2}} = \frac{m_{X_1Y_1}}{m_{X_1X_1}},$$

$$\tilde{\beta}_{22} = \frac{\sigma_{11}\sigma_{22}m_{X_1X_1}m_{X_2Y_2}}{\sigma_{11}\sigma_{22}m_{X_1X_1}m_{X_2X_2}} = \frac{m_{X_2Y_2}}{m_{X_2Y_2}},$$

which is the same result as that for the ordinary least squares estimators. Similarly, if $X_{1t} = X_{2t}$ (i.e., if both equations involve the same explanatory variable), we obtain

$$\tilde{\beta}_{12} = \frac{\sigma_{11}m_{X_1X_1}(\sigma_{22}m_{X_1Y_1} - \sigma_{12}m_{X_1Y_2}) + \sigma_{12}m_{X_1X_1}(\sigma_{11}m_{X_1Y_2} - \sigma_{12}m_{X_1Y_1})}{\sigma_{11}\sigma_{22}m_{X_1X_1}^2 - \sigma_{12}^2 m_{X_1X_1}^2}$$

$$= \frac{(\sigma_{11}\sigma_{22} - \sigma_{12}^2)m_{X_1X_1}m_{X_1Y_1}}{(\sigma_{11}\sigma_{22} - \sigma_{12}^2)m_{X_1X_1}^2} = \frac{m_{X_1Y_1}}{m_{X_1X_1}},$$

$$\tilde{\beta}_{22} = \frac{\sigma_{12}m_{X_1X_1}(\sigma_{22}m_{X_1Y_1} - \sigma_{12}m_{X_1Y_2}) + \sigma_{22}m_{X_1X_1}(\sigma_{11}m_{X_1Y_2} - \sigma_{12}m_{X_1Y_1})}{\sigma_{11}\sigma_{22}m_{X_1X_1}^2 - \sigma_{12}^2 m_{X_1X_1}^2}$$

$$= \frac{(\sigma_{11}\sigma_{22} - \sigma_{12}^2)m_{X_1X_1}m_{X_1Y_2}}{(\sigma_{11}\sigma_{22} - \sigma_{12}^2)m_{X_1X_1}^2} = \frac{m_{X_1Y_2}}{m_{X_1X_1}},$$

which again corresponds to the ordinary least squares formulas.

Because the generalized least squares estimator is BLUE, its variance is smaller than, or at best equal to, the variance of the ordinary least squares estimator. It is appropriate then to ask what the difference between variances is and on what it depends. We shall answer by reference to the simple system of two seemingly unrelated regressions we have just described. First, we note that the variance-covariance matrix of the generalized least squares estimators of β_{12} and β_{22} is

$$E(\tilde{\underline{\beta}} - \underline{\beta})(\tilde{\underline{\beta}} - \underline{\beta}) = (\underline{X}'\Omega^{-1}\underline{X})^{-1}.$$

In this case

$$(\tilde{\underline{\beta}} - \underline{\beta}) = \begin{bmatrix} \tilde{\beta}_{12} - \beta_{12} \\ \tilde{\beta}_{22} - \beta_{22} \end{bmatrix} \quad \text{and} \quad \underline{X} = \begin{bmatrix} (X_{11} - \bar{X}_1) & 0 \\ (X_{12} - \bar{X}_1) & 0 \\ \vdots & \vdots \\ (X_{1T} - \bar{X}_1) & 0 \\ 0 & (X_{21} - \bar{X}_2) \\ 0 & (X_{22} - \bar{X}_2) \\ \vdots & \vdots \\ 0 & (X_{2T} - \bar{X}_2) \end{bmatrix}$$

This means that

$$\begin{bmatrix} \text{Var}(\tilde{\beta}_{12}) & \text{Cov}(\tilde{\beta}_{12},\tilde{\beta}_{22}) \\ \text{Cov}(\tilde{\beta}_{12},\tilde{\beta}_{22}) & \text{Var}(\tilde{\beta}_{22}) \end{bmatrix} = (\sigma_{11}\sigma_{22} - \sigma_{12}^2)\begin{bmatrix} \sigma_{22}m_{X_1X_1} & -\sigma_{12}m_{X_1X_2} \\ -\sigma_{12}m_{X_1X_2} & \sigma_{11}m_{X_2X_2} \end{bmatrix}^{-1}$$

In particular, the variance of the generalized least squares estimator of β_{12} is

$$(12.56) \qquad \text{Var}(\tilde{\beta}_{12}) = \frac{(\sigma_{11}\sigma_{22} - \sigma_{12}^2)\sigma_{11}m_{X_2X_2}}{\sigma_{11}\sigma_{22}m_{X_1X_1}m_{X_2X_2} - \sigma_{12}^2 m_{X_1X_2}^2}.$$

If we let

$$\rho_{12} = \frac{\sigma_{12}}{\sqrt{\sigma_{11}\sigma_{22}}}$$

represent the coefficient of correlation between ε_{1t} and ε_{2t}, and if we let

$$r_{12} = \frac{m_{X_1 X_2}}{\sqrt{m_{X_1 X_1} m_{X_2 X_2}}}$$

represent the sample coefficient of correlation between X_{1t} and X_{2t}, then we can write

$$\text{Var}(\tilde{\beta}_{12}) = \frac{\sigma_{11}\sigma_{22}(1 - \rho_{12}^2)\sigma_{11} m_{X_2 X_2}}{\sigma_{11}\sigma_{22}(1 - \rho_{12}^2 r_{12}^2) m_{X_1 X_1} m_{X_2 X_2}} = \frac{\sigma_{11}}{m_{X_1 X_1}} \frac{1 - \rho_{12}^2}{1 - \rho_{12}^2 r_{12}^2}.$$

On the other hand, the variance of the ordinary least squares estimator of β_{12}, say, $\hat{\beta}_{12}$, is

$$\text{Var}(\hat{\beta}_{12}) = \frac{\sigma_{11}}{m_{X_1 X_1}}.$$

Therefore, the ratio of the two variances is

(12.57) $$\frac{\text{Var}(\tilde{\beta}_{12})}{\text{Var}(\hat{\beta}_{12})} = \frac{1 - \rho_{12}^2}{1 - \rho_{12}^2 r_{12}^2} \leq 1.$$

This ratio is a decreasing function of ρ_{12}^2 and an increasing function of r_{12}^2. This means that the gain in efficiency of the generalized least squares estimator over the ordinary squares estimator is greatest when the disturbances in the two equations are highly correlated and, at the same time, the explanatory variables are uncorrelated. Table 12–1 gives the values of the ratio $\text{Var}(\tilde{\beta}_{12})/\text{Var}(\hat{\beta}_{12})$ for different values of ρ_{12}^2 and r_{12}^2. Clearly, the gain in efficiency is in many cases very substantial. These results could be extended to a more complex system of seemingly unrelated regressions as well.

Table 12–1

r_{12}^2	ρ_{12}^2					
	0	0.1	0.3	0.5	0.7	0.9
0	1.000	0.900	0.700	0.500	0.300	0.100
0.1	1.000	0.909	0.722	0.526	0.323	0.110
0.3	1.000	0.928	0.769	0.588	0.380	0.137
0.5	1.000	0.947	0.823	0.667	0.461	0.182
0.7	1.000	0.967	0.886	0.769	0.588	0.270
0.9	1.000	0.989	0.959	0.909	0.811	0.526
1.0	1.000	1.000	1.000	1.000	1.000	1.000

Estimation When the Variance-Covariance Matrix Is Unknown

In the preceding discussion we assumed that the elements of the Ω matrix (i.e., the variances and covariances of the regression disturbances) are known. However, if they are not known, as is generally the case, we can replace Ω by a consistent estimator of Ω. As pointed out in Section 12–1, the resulting estimator of

β has the same asymptotic properties as Aitken's generalized least squares estimator. Our problem, then, is to find consistent estimators of the variances and covariances of the regression disturbances. One possibility is to estimate these variances and covariances from ordinary least squares residuals (which we call e_{mt}) as suggested by Zellner in his path-breaking paper.[11] For this, we may use

$$(12.58) \qquad \hat{\Omega} = \begin{bmatrix} s_{11}\mathbf{I_T} & s_{12}\mathbf{I_T} & \dots & s_{1M}\mathbf{I_T} \\ s_{21}\mathbf{I_T} & s_{22}\mathbf{I_T} & \dots & s_{2M}\mathbf{I_T} \\ \vdots & \vdots & & \vdots \\ s_{M1}\mathbf{I_T} & s_{M2}\mathbf{I_T} & \dots & s_{MM}\mathbf{I_T} \end{bmatrix},$$

where
$$s_{mp} = \frac{1}{T - K_m} \sum_{t=1}^{T} e_{mt}e_{pt},$$

$$K_m \geq K_p,$$

$$m, p = 1, 2, \dots, M.$$

It is well known that s_{mm} is an unbiased and consistent estimator of σ_{mm}, and it can be shown that s_{mp} $(m \neq p)$ is a consistent estimator of σ_{mp}. (Since we are only concerned with consistency, we could use T instead of $(T - K_m)$ in calculating the estimates of σ_{mp} without affecting the asymptotic properties of the estimator of β.) The resulting estimator of β

$$(12.59) \qquad \tilde{\tilde{\beta}} = (\mathbf{X'}\hat{\Omega}^{-1}\mathbf{X})^{-1}(\mathbf{X'}\hat{\Omega}^{-1}\mathbf{Y})$$

with

$$(12.60) \qquad \text{Asympt. Var-Cov}(\tilde{\tilde{\beta}}) = (\mathbf{X'}\Omega^{-1}\mathbf{X})^{-1}$$

is called a *two-stage Aitken estimator* because its value is calculated in two stages. First, we obtain the ordinary least squares estimates for each equation and use the resulting residuals to estimate the variances and covariances of the disturbances. This enables us to construct $\hat{\Omega}$. The second stage involves substituting $\hat{\Omega}$ into (12.59) and calculating the values of the elements of $\tilde{\tilde{\beta}}$. (A computer program for this estimation method is called EFFEST.) The two-stage Aitken estimator of β is asymptotically equivalent to Aitken's generalized least squares estimator and, therefore, to the maximum likelihood estimator of β. Thus this estimator is asymptotically efficient and its asymptotic distribution is normal. With respect to the small sample properties of the two-stage Aitken estimator, we have some theoretical and some experimental results indicating that this estimator is unbiased and efficient relative to the ordinary least squares estimator.[12]

[11] Zellner, *op. cit.*

[12] See A. Zellner, "Estimators of Seemingly Unrelated Regressions: Some Exact Finite Sample Results," *Journal of the American Statistical Association*, Vol. 58, December 1963, pp. 977–992; N. C. Kakwani, "The Unbiasedness of Zellner's Seemingly Unrelated Regression Equations Estimators," *Journal of the American Statistical Association*, Vol. 62, March 1967, pp. 141–142; J. Kmenta and R. F. Gilbert, "Small Sample Properties of Alternative Estimators of Seemingly Unrelated Regressions," *Journal of the American Statistical Association*, Vol. 63, December 1968, pp. 1180–1200.

An alternative approach to the problem of estimating the elements of Ω is to use the maximum likelihood method. In accordance with (12.18), the likelihood function for $\mathbf{Y}$ in the context of seemingly unrelated regressions is

$$(12.61) \quad L = -\frac{MT}{2} \log (2\pi) - \tfrac{1}{2} \log |\Omega| - \tfrac{1}{2}(\mathbf{Y} - \mathbf{X}\boldsymbol{\beta})'\Omega^{-1}(\mathbf{Y} - \mathbf{X}\boldsymbol{\beta}).$$

We can differentiate L with respect to the elements of $\boldsymbol{\beta}$ *and* Ω, set the resulting derivatives equal to zero, and then solve for the values of the unknown parameters. For the system of two seemingly unrelated regressions described by (12.53), we have

$$
\begin{aligned}
L = &-\frac{2T}{2} \log (2\pi) - \frac{T}{2} \log (\sigma_{11}\sigma_{22} - \sigma_{12}^2) \\
&- \frac{1}{2(\sigma_{11}\sigma_{22} - \sigma_{12}^2)} \Big[\sigma_{22} \sum_t (Y_{1t} - \beta_{11} - \beta_{12}X_{1t})^2 \\
&+ \sigma_{11} \sum_t (Y_{2t} - \beta_{21} - \beta_{22}X_{2t})^2 \\
&- 2\sigma_{12} \sum_t (Y_{1t} - \beta_{11} - \beta_{12}X_{1t})(Y_{2t} - \beta_{21} - \beta_{22}X_{2t}) \Big].
\end{aligned}
$$

The first-order conditions for maximizing L with respect to the β's and the σ's are

$$\hat{\sigma}_{22} \sum_t (Y_{1t} - \hat{\beta}_{11} - \hat{\beta}_{12}X_{1t}) - \hat{\sigma}_{12} \sum_t (Y_{2t} - \hat{\beta}_{21} - \hat{\beta}_{22}X_{2t}) = 0,$$

$$\hat{\sigma}_{22} \sum_t X_{1t}(Y_{1t} - \hat{\beta}_{11} - \hat{\beta}_{12}X_{1t}) - \hat{\sigma}_{12} \sum_t X_{1t}(Y_{2t} - \hat{\beta}_{21} - \hat{\beta}_{22}X_{2t}) = 0,$$

$$-\hat{\sigma}_{12} \sum_t (Y_{1t} - \hat{\beta}_{11} - \hat{\beta}_{12}X_{1t}) + \hat{\sigma}_{11} \sum_t (Y_{2t} - \hat{\beta}_{21} - \hat{\beta}_{22}X_{2t}) = 0,$$

$$-\hat{\sigma}_{12} \sum_t X_{2t}(Y_{1t} - \hat{\beta}_{11} - \hat{\beta}_{12}X_{1t}) + \hat{\sigma}_{11} \sum_t X_{2t}(Y_{2t} - \hat{\beta}_{21} - \hat{\beta}_{22}X_{2t}) = 0,$$

$$\hat{\sigma}_{11} = \frac{1}{T} \sum_t (Y_{1t} - \hat{\beta}_{11} - \hat{\beta}_{12}X_{1t})^2,$$

$$\hat{\sigma}_{22} = \frac{1}{T} \sum_t (Y_{2t} - \hat{\beta}_{21} - \hat{\beta}_{22}X_{2t})^2,$$

$$\hat{\sigma}_{12} = \frac{1}{T} \sum_t (Y_{1t} - \hat{\beta}_{11} - \hat{\beta}_{12}X_{1t})(Y_{2t} - \hat{\beta}_{21} - \hat{\beta}_{22}X_{2t}).$$

Note that the first four equations are essentially the same as "Aitken's generalized least squares normal equations" derived earlier; the only difference is that the σ's are replaced by $\hat{\sigma}$'s. In the case of the two-stage Aitken estimator, the $\hat{\sigma}$'s in the first four equations are replaced by the estimates obtained from the ordinary least squares residuals and, thus, the last three equations are not used. In the case of the maximum likelihood estimator, however, the σ's are to be estimated *jointly* with the β's, using all seven equations.

The first-order conditions for maximizing L for a more complex system of seemingly unrelated regressions can be determined by a simple generalization of the case of two equations. In the first place, we have the equations corresponding to "Aitken's generalized least squares normal equations"; in the second place, we have the expressions for the estimated variances and covariances of the disturbances. Thus the maximum likelihood estimators for the general case, are given by

$$(12.62) \qquad \hat{\boldsymbol{\beta}} = (X'\hat{\Omega}^{-1}X)^{-1}(X'\hat{\Omega}^{-1}Y),$$

$$\hat{\Omega} = \begin{bmatrix} \hat{\sigma}_{11}I_T & \hat{\sigma}_{12}I_T & \cdots & \hat{\sigma}_{1M}I_T \\ \hat{\sigma}_{21}I_T & \hat{\sigma}_{22}I_T & \cdots & \hat{\sigma}_{2M}I_T \\ \vdots & \vdots & & \vdots \\ \hat{\sigma}_{M1}I_T & \hat{\sigma}_{M2}I_T & \cdots & \hat{\sigma}_{MM}I_T \end{bmatrix},$$

where
$$\hat{\sigma}_{mp} = \frac{1}{T}(Y_m - X_m\hat{\beta}_m)'(Y_p - X_p\hat{\beta}_p),$$

$$m, p = 1, 2, \ldots, M.$$

The analytical solution of (12.62) is quite complicated since the equations are nonlinear in the unknowns, but it can be obtained with the help of an electronic computer. The resulting estimator $\hat{\boldsymbol{\beta}}$ has the same asymptotic properties as the two-stage Aitken estimator. There is also some evidence that the small sample properties of these two estimators are fairly similar.[13]

EXAMPLE   As an example of seemingly unrelated regressions, consider the following set of investment functions for individual firms:

$$I_t = \beta_{m1} + \beta_{m2}C_{t-1} + \beta_{m3}F_{t-1} + \varepsilon_{mt}$$

where I = gross investment, C = end-of-period capital stock, and F = end-of-period value of outstanding shares. The following estimates for two firms, General Electric and Westinghouse, were based on annual data for 1935–1954:[14]

General Electric

OLS $I_t = -9.9563 + 0.1517C_{t-1} + 0.0266F_{t-1} + e_t,$
        $(31.3742) \quad (0.0257) \qquad (0.0156)$

EFFEST $I_t = -27.7193 + 0.1390C_{t-1} + 0.0383F_{t-1} + e_t,$
        $(29.3212) \quad (0.0250) \qquad (0.0145)$

ML $I_t = -30.7485 + 0.1359C_{t-1} + 0.0405F_{t-1} + e_t;$
        $(29.6608) \quad (0.0255) \qquad (0.0145)$

[13] See Kmenta and Gilbert, *op. cit.*

[14] From *ibid.* The results are based on the data given in J. C. G. Boot and G. M. deWitt, "Investment Demand: An Empirical Contribution to the Aggregation Problem," *International Economic Review*, Vol. 1, January 1960, pp. 3–30.

Westinghouse

OLS $I_t = -0.5094 + 0.0924C_{t-1} + 0.0529F_{t-1} + e_t,$
               (8.0153)   (0.0561)   (0.0157)

EFFEST $I_t = -1.2520 + 0.0576C_{t-1} + 0.0640F_{t-1} + e_t,$
               (7.5452)   (0.0530)   (0.0145)

ML $I_t = -1.7016 + 0.0593C_{t-1} + 0.0557F_{t-1} + e_t.$
               (7.5149)   (0.0529)   (0.0144)

As can be seen, there appears to be some—though by no means a great—gain in efficiency by going from ordinary least squares to two-stage Aitken or maximum likelihood estimation. The reason for this relatively low gain in efficiency is, at least in part, the high degree of correlation between the explanatory variables in the two equations.

Estimation of Seemingly Unrelated Regressions with Autoregressive Disturbances

As the final point connected with the problem of estimating seemingly unrelated regressions, we consider the case where the disturbances in each equation are not independent *over time*, but follow a first-order autoregressive scheme as described in Section 8–2. In this case the assumptions (12.47) and (12.48) stated at the outset of the present section are replaced by

$$(12.63) \qquad E(\epsilon_m \epsilon_m') = \sigma_{mm} \begin{bmatrix} 1 & \rho_m & \cdots & \rho_m^{T-1} \\ \rho_m & 1 & \cdots & \rho_m^{T-2} \\ \vdots & \vdots & & \vdots \\ \rho_m^{T-1} & \rho_m^{T-2} & \cdots & 1 \end{bmatrix},$$

$$(12.64) \qquad E(\epsilon_m \epsilon_p') = \sigma_{mp} \begin{bmatrix} 1 & \rho_p & \cdots & \rho_p^{T-1} \\ \rho_m & 1 & \cdots & \rho_p^{T-2} \\ \vdots & \vdots & & \vdots \\ \rho_m^{T-1} & \rho_m^{T-2} & \cdots & 1 \end{bmatrix},$$

$$m, p = 1, 2, \ldots, M,$$

where ρ_m is the coefficient of autocorrelation in the mth equation. Here, we can estimate ρ_m separately for each equation, using one of the consistent methods described in Section 8–2. Suppose the resulting estimates are called $\hat{\rho}_m$. They can be used to transform the original observations so that the system of seemingly unrelated regressions now becomes

$$(12.65) \quad (Y_{mt} - \hat{\rho}_m Y_{m,t-1}) = \beta_{m1}(X_{it,1} - \hat{\rho}_m X_{1,t-1,1})$$

$$+ \beta_{m2}(X_{1t,2} - \hat{\rho}_m X_{1,t-1,2})$$

$$+ \cdots + \beta_{mK_m}(X_{mt,K_m} - \hat{\rho}_m X_{m,t-1,K_m}) + u_{mt},$$

$$m = 1, 2, \ldots, M.$$

The regressions in (12.65) can be estimated by the two-stage Aitken method in the usual way. The resulting estimates of the regression coefficients have the same asymptotic properties as Aitken's generalized least squares estimates.[15]

EXERCISES

12–1. Prove the validity of equations (12.16) and (12.17).

12–2. Consider a regression equation to be estimated from observations on N households for 2 consecutive periods of time. Assume that the regression disturbances are cross-sectionally uncorrelated but time-wise autoregressive with $\rho_i = \rho_j$ for all i, j.

a. Determine the elements of Ω (the variance-covariance matrix of the regression disturbances).

b. Devise an estimation procedure that would lead to a consistent estimator of Ω.

c. Devise a transformation of the observations that would enable us to use the ordinary least squares method to get asymptotically efficient estimates of the regression coefficients.

12–3. A regression model to be estimated from pooled cross-section and time-series data is given by

$$Y_{it} = \beta X_{it} + \varepsilon_{it} \qquad (t = 1, 2, \ldots, 21; \, i = 1, 2).$$

Alternatively, we may write

$$\begin{bmatrix} \mathbf{Y}_1 \\ \mathbf{Y}_2 \end{bmatrix} = \begin{bmatrix} \mathbf{X}_1 \\ \mathbf{X}_2 \end{bmatrix} \beta + \begin{bmatrix} \boldsymbol{\epsilon}_1 \\ \boldsymbol{\epsilon}_2 \end{bmatrix},$$

where $\mathbf{Y}_i \to (21 \times 1)$, $\mathbf{X}_i \to (21 \times 1)$, $\boldsymbol{\epsilon}_i \to (21 \times 1)$, and β is a scalar. Assume that the X's are nonstochastic and bounded, and that

$$E(\varepsilon_{it}) = 0,$$

$$E(\varepsilon_{it}\varepsilon_{is}) = 0 \qquad (t \neq s),$$

$$E(\varepsilon_{it}\varepsilon_{jt}) = \sigma_{ij}.$$

The sample data are given as follows:

$\mathbf{X}_1'\mathbf{X}_1 = 10,$	$\mathbf{X}_1'\mathbf{Y}_1 = 10,$	$\mathbf{Y}_1'\mathbf{Y}_1 = 13.90,$
$\mathbf{X}_1'\mathbf{X}_2 = 8,$	$\mathbf{X}_1'\mathbf{Y}_2 = 8,$	$\mathbf{Y}_1'\mathbf{Y}_2 = 11.92,$
$\mathbf{X}_2'\mathbf{X}_2 = 10,$	$\mathbf{X}_2'\mathbf{Y}_1 = 8,$	$\mathbf{Y}_2'\mathbf{Y}_2 = 12.30.$
	$\mathbf{X}_2'\mathbf{Y}_2 = 8,$	

Obtain an asymptotically efficient estimate of β and its estimated standard error.

[15] See R. W. Parks, "Efficient Estimation of a System of Regression Equations when Disturbances are Both Serially and Contemporaneously Correlated," *Journal of the American Statistical Association*, Vol. 62, June 1967, pp. 500–509; J. Kmenta and R. F. Gilbert, "Estimation of Seemingly Unrelated Regressions With Autoregressive Disturbances," *Journal of the American Statistical Association*, Vol. 65, March 1970, pp. 186–197.

12–4. Consider the following two regression equations:

$$Y_{1t} = \beta_1 X_{1t} + \varepsilon_{1t}$$
$$Y_{2t} = \beta_2 X_{2t} + \varepsilon_{2t} \qquad (t = 1, 2, \ldots, 21).$$

Assume that the X's are nonstochastic and bounded, and that

$$\varepsilon_{it} \sim N(0, \sigma_{ii}) \qquad (i = 1, 2),$$
$$E(\varepsilon_{it}\varepsilon_{is}) = 0 \qquad (t \neq s),$$
$$E(\varepsilon_{it}\varepsilon_{jt}) = \sigma_{ij} \qquad (i, j = 1, 2).$$

The sample results are

$$\sum X_{1t}^2 = 10, \qquad \sum X_{1t} Y_{1t} = 10, \qquad \sum Y_{1t}^2 = 12.0,$$
$$\sum X_{2t}^2 = 10, \qquad \sum X_{1t} Y_{2.} = 8, \qquad \sum Y_{2t}^2 = 12.4,$$
$$\sum X_{1t} X_{2t} = 8, \qquad \sum X_{2t} Y_{1t} = 8, \qquad \sum Y_{1t} Y_{2t} = 10.0.$$
$$\sum X_{2t} Y_{2t} = 8,$$

Find asymptotically efficient estimates of the regression coefficients and their estimated standard errors by using

a. Zellner's two-stage Aitken method.

b. The maximum likelihood method.

12–5. A set of three seemingly unrelated regression equations is specified as

$$Y_{i1} = \alpha_1 + \beta_1 X_{i1} + \varepsilon_{i1},$$
$$Y_{i2} = \alpha_2 + \beta_2 X_{i2} + \varepsilon_{i2},$$
$$Y_{i3} = \alpha_3 + \beta_3 X_{i3} + \varepsilon_{i3},$$

The variance-covariance matrix of the disturbances is assumed to be known. Consider two estimators of β_1, the first obtained by applying Aitken's generalized least squares estimation to all three equations, and the second by applying this method only to the first two equations. Examine the efficiency of the first estimator relative to the second.

12–6. Consider the following set of demand equations for different commodities to be estimated from time-series data:

$$V_{it} = \alpha_i + \beta_i P_{it} + \gamma_i V_t + \varepsilon_{it}$$

where V_{it} = expenditure on the ith commodity, P_{it} = price of the ith commodity, and V_t = total expenditure on all commodities. Since

$$\sum_i V_{it} = V_t,$$

the following restrictions are in effect:

$$\sum_i \alpha_i = 0, \qquad \sum_i \beta_i = 0, \qquad \sum_i \gamma_i = 1, \qquad \sum_i \varepsilon_{it} = 0.$$

Describe an estimation procedure that would yield asymptotically efficient estimates of the regression coefficients.

13 | Simultaneous Equation Systems

Economic models frequently involve a *set* of relationships designed to explain the behavior of certain variables. For instance, a simple model of the market for a given commodity may involve a supply and a demand function, and may explain the equilibrium price and quantity of the commodity exchanged in the market. Similarly, a model of aggregate income may explain the determination of various income components by means of appropriately specified relationships. In such models the problem of estimating the parameters has special features that are not present when a model involves only a single relation. In particular, when a relation is a part of a system, some regressors are typically stochastic and correlated with the regression disturbance. In this case the ordinary least squares estimators of the regression coefficients are inconsistent and other methods must be devised to provide consistent estimates.

This chapter is concerned with the problem of estimating equations that belong to a system of relations, and with the analysis and interpretation of such systems. Section 13–1 contains a general description of simultaneous equation systems and introduces some basic concepts. Section 13–2 deals with the problem of identification, which is crucially important for estimation. The discussion represents a logical extension of the identification problem from the single-equation models of Section 11–2 to the multiequation models of this chapter. In Section 13–3 we describe several methods of estimating a single equation that is embedded in a simultaneous equation system, while the methods presented in Section 13–4 are designed to provide estimates for *all* equations of the system. Section 13–5 is concerned with comparing different methods of estimation and also deals with certain special problems. Finally, Section 13–6 provides an analysis and interpretation of dynamic economic systems.

13–1 Description of Simultaneous Equation Systems

The basic requirement an economic model must satisfy is that the number of the variables whose values are to be explained must be equal to the number of independent relationships in the model—i.e., to the number of different pieces of relevant information—otherwise the values of these variables would not be determinate. In addition to the variables whose values are to be explained a model may, and usually does, contain variables whose values are not immediately affected by the mechanism described by the model. The relevance of these variables lies in their role as explanatory factors. This leads to a distinction between those variables whose values are to be explained by the model and those that contribute to providing such an explanation; the former are called *endogenous* and the latter *predetermined*. Predetermined variables can be subdivided into *exogenous* and *lagged endogenous* variables. The values of the exogenous variables are completely determined outside the system under consideration, whereas the values of the lagged endogenous variables are represented by the past values of the endogenous variables of the model. Models having no lagged endogenous variables are not uncommon, but models without any predetermined variables are rather rare. For example, a model of the market for a given commodity may involve a supply and a demand relation, with current equilibrium price and quantity exchanged as the endogenous variables, and the factors that account for systematic shifts of the supply and the demand functions as the predetermined variables. *A model is said to constitute a system of simultaneous equations if all of the relationships involved are needed for determining the value of at least one of the endogenous variables included in the model.* This implies that at least one of the relationships includes more than one endogenous variable.

The definition of a simultaneous equation system can be given a more rigorous interpretation when an economic model has been specifically formulated as a set of well-defined stochastic relationships, that is, when it has been turned into what is generally called an *econometric model*. Typically, economic theory tells us which relations make up the model, which variables are to be included in each of the relations, and what is the sign of some of the partial derivatives. As a rule, economic theory has very little to say about the functional form of the relations, the time lags involved, and the values of the parameters. Also, the relations are deterministic, so that no allowance is made for the presence of stochastic disturbances. In order to put an economic model into the form of a testable proposition, it is necessary to specify the functional form of the relations, the timing of the variables, and the stochastic characterization of the system. The end result is an econometric model that is ready for estimation or testing. This model represents a summary of the prior knowledge of the investigator concerning the phenomenon in question. Given the current state of economics, this prior knowledge is derived in part from economic theory, and in part from ad hoc reasoning or guessing. For example, consider the following simplified supply-demand model for a commodity:

$$Q = f_1(P, Y) \quad \text{(demand)},$$

$$Q = f_2(P) \quad \text{(supply)},$$

$$\frac{\partial f_1}{\partial P} \leq 0, \qquad \frac{\partial f_1}{\partial Y} \geq 0, \qquad \frac{\partial f_2}{\partial P} \geq 0,$$

where Q = equilibrium quantity exchanged on the market, P = equilibrium price, and Y = income of the consumers. The variables Q and P are endogenous, and Y is exogenous. Note that both relations are needed for determining the values of the two endogenous variables, so that the system is one of simultaneous equations. An econometric model representing these relations might look as follows:

$$(13.1) \qquad Q_t = \alpha_1 + \alpha_2 P_t + \alpha_3 Y_t + \varepsilon_{1t} \quad \text{(demand)},$$

$$Q_t = \beta_1 + \beta_2 P_t + \varepsilon_{2t} \qquad \text{(supply)},$$

$$\alpha_2 \le 0, \qquad \alpha_3 \ge 0, \qquad \beta_2 \ge 0,$$

where α's and β's are parameters, ε's are random disturbances, and t represents a specific period of time. Each disturbance is characterized by the assumptions of the classical normal linear regression model. The variances and the covariance of the disturbances are

$$E(\varepsilon_{1t}^2) = \sigma_{11},$$

$$E(\varepsilon_{2t}^2) = \sigma_{22},$$

$$E(\varepsilon_{1t}\varepsilon_{2t}) = \sigma_{12}.$$

Equations (13.1) are called the *structural form* of the model under study. This form is derived from economic theory. The structural equations can be solved for the endogenous variables to give

$$(13.2) \qquad Q_t = \left(\frac{\alpha_2\beta_1 - \alpha_1\beta_2}{\alpha_2 - \beta_2}\right) - \left(\frac{\alpha_3\beta_2}{\alpha_2 - \beta_2}\right)Y_t + \left(\frac{-\beta_2\varepsilon_{1t} + \alpha_2\varepsilon_{2t}}{\alpha_2 - \beta_2}\right)$$

$$P_t = \left(\frac{-\alpha_1 + \beta_1}{\alpha_2 - \beta_2}\right) - \left(\frac{\alpha_3}{\alpha_2 - \beta_2}\right)Y_t + \left(\frac{-\varepsilon_{1t} + \varepsilon_{2t}}{\alpha_2 - \beta_2}\right).$$

The solution given by (13.2) is called the *reduced form* of the model. The reduced form equations show explicitly how the endogenous variables are *jointly dependent* on the predetermined variables and the disturbances of the system. In the case of (13.2), we can see that the values of Q_t and P_t are fully determined by Y_t, ε_{1t}, and ε_{2t}. The value of Y_t, on the other hand, is believed to be determined outside of the market in question and to be in no way influenced by P_t or Q_t. If Y_t is random, it is assumed to be distributed independently of ε_{1t} and ε_{2t}.

From the point of view of statistical inference, the single relevant characteristic of the simultaneous equation systems—and one that requires special consideration—is the appearance of endogenous variables among the explanatory variables of at least some of the structural equations. This leads to problems because the endogenous variables are, in general, correlated with the disturbance of the equation in which they appear. Consider the supply-demand model of (13.1). In both equations the endogenous P_t appears as an explanatory variable. But from (13.2) we can see that

$$E(P_t\varepsilon_{1t}) = \frac{-\sigma_{11} + \sigma_{12}}{\alpha_2 - \beta_2}$$

and
$$E(P_t \varepsilon_{2t}) = \frac{-\sigma_{12} + \sigma_{22}}{\alpha_2 - \beta_2},$$

which shows that P_t is correlated with both disturbances. As pointed out in Section 8-3, the existence of correlation between an explanatory variable and the disturbance leads to inconsistency of the ordinary least squares estimator of the regression coefficients. It appears, then, that the crucial aspect of the predetermined variables in a system is that they are not contemporaneously correlated with the disturbances.

In general, the structural form of a simultaneous equation system can be described as follows:

$$(13.3) \quad \beta_{11} y_{1t} + \beta_{12} y_{2t} + \cdots + \beta_{1G} y_{Gt} + \gamma_{11} x_{1t} + \gamma_{12} x_{2t} + \cdots + \gamma_{1K} x_{Kt} = u_{1t}$$

$$\beta_{21} y_{1t} + \beta_{22} y_{2t} + \cdots + \beta_{2G} y_{Gt} + \gamma_{21} x_{1t} + \gamma_{22} x_{2t} + \cdots + \gamma_{2K} x_{Kt} = u_{2t}$$

$$\vdots$$

$$\beta_{G1} y_{1t} + \beta_{G2} y_{2t} + \cdots + \beta_{GG} y_{Gt} + \gamma_{G1} x_{1t} + \gamma_{G2} x_{2t} + \cdots + \gamma_{GK} x_{K1} = u_{Gt}.$$

where the y's are endogenous variables, the x's are predetermined variables, the u's are stochastic disturbances, and $t = 1, 2, \ldots, T$. The β's and the γ's are known as the structural coefficients. There are G endogenous and K predetermined variables in the system. Generally, of course, not all endogenous and predetermined variables will appear in every equation since some of the β's and γ's will be known to be zero. Further, in each equation one of the β's is taken to be unity, thus indicating that one of the endogenous variables serves as the "dependent" variable when the equation is written out as a standard regression equation. It should also be noted that some of the equations may actually be identities, which means that all their coefficients are known and that they contain no stochastic disturbances. The whole system of equations may be written in matrix form as

$$(13.3a) \qquad\qquad\qquad \mathbf{B}\mathbf{y}_t + \boldsymbol{\Gamma}\mathbf{x}_t = \mathbf{u}_t,$$

where

$$\mathbf{y}_t = \begin{bmatrix} y_{1t} \\ y_{2t} \\ \vdots \\ y_{Gt} \end{bmatrix}, \qquad \mathbf{x}_t = \begin{bmatrix} x_{1t} \\ x_{2t} \\ \vdots \\ x_{Kt} \end{bmatrix}, \qquad \mathbf{u}_t = \begin{bmatrix} u_{1t} \\ u_{2t} \\ \vdots \\ u_{Gt} \end{bmatrix},$$

$$(G \times 1) \qquad\qquad (K \times 1) \qquad\qquad (G \times 1)$$

$$\mathbf{B} = \begin{bmatrix} \beta_{11} & \beta_{12} & \cdots & \beta_{1G} \\ \beta_{21} & \beta_{22} & \cdots & \beta_{2G} \\ \vdots & \vdots & & \vdots \\ \beta_{G1} & \beta_{G2} & \cdots & \beta_{GG} \end{bmatrix}, \qquad \boldsymbol{\Gamma} = \begin{bmatrix} \gamma_{11} & \gamma_{12} & \cdots & \gamma_{1K} \\ \gamma_{21} & \gamma_{22} & \cdots & \gamma_{2K} \\ \vdots & \vdots & & \vdots \\ \gamma_{G1} & \gamma_{G2} & \cdots & \gamma_{GK} \end{bmatrix}.$$

$$(G \times G) \qquad\qquad\qquad (G \times K)$$

If there are constant terms in any of the equations, one of the x's will be equal to unity for all $t = 1, 2, \ldots, T$. With respect to the stochastic disturbances, we stipulate that each disturbance satisfies the assumptions of the classical normal linear regression model, i.e., that

$$u_{gt} \sim N(0, \sigma_{gg}), \qquad g = 1, 2, \ldots, G;$$
$$E(u_{gt}u_{gs}) = 0, \qquad t, s = 1, 2, \ldots, T;$$
$$t \neq s.$$

However, we do not rule out the possibility that the disturbances are correlated across equations, i.e., that

$$E(u_{gt}u_{ht}) = \sigma_{gh} \qquad (g, h = 1, 2, \ldots, G).$$

In matrix notation these assumptions become

(13.4) $$\mathbf{u}_t = N(0, \boldsymbol{\Phi}),$$

(13.5) $$E(\mathbf{u}_t \mathbf{u}_s') = 0,$$

where
$$\boldsymbol{\Phi} = \begin{bmatrix} \sigma_{11} & \sigma_{12} & \cdots & \sigma_{1G} \\ \sigma_{21} & \sigma_{22} & \cdots & \sigma_{2G} \\ \vdots & \vdots & & \vdots \\ \sigma_{G1} & \sigma_{G2} & \cdots & \sigma_{GG} \end{bmatrix}.$$
$$(G \times G)$$

The matrix $\boldsymbol{\Phi}$ is known as the variance-covariance matrix of the structural disturbances. If there are any identities present, $\boldsymbol{\Phi}$ refers only to the equations that are not identities, and its dimension is appropriately reduced.

The reduced form of the system is obtained by solving the structural form equations for the values of the endogenous variables, that is, by expressing the y's in terms of the x's and the u's. The result may be written as

(13.6) $$y_{1t} = \pi_{11}x_{1t} + \pi_{12}x_{2t} + \cdots + \pi_{1K}x_{Kt} + v_{1t},$$
$$y_{2t} = \pi_{21}x_{1t} + \pi_{22}x_{2t} + \cdots + \pi_{2K}x_{Kt} + v_{2t},$$
$$\vdots$$
$$y_{Gt} = \pi_{G1}x_{1t} + \pi_{G2}x_{2t} + \cdots + \pi_{GK}x_{Kt} + v_{Gt}.$$

The π's represent the reduced form coefficients and the v's the reduced form disturbances. In general, each reduced form disturbance is a linear function of *all* structural disturbances. Using matrix notation, we may write (13.6) as

(13.6a) $$\mathbf{y}_t = \boldsymbol{\Pi}\mathbf{x}_t + \mathbf{v}_t,$$

where
$$\boldsymbol{\Pi} = \begin{bmatrix} \pi_{11} & \pi_{12} & \cdots & \pi_{1K} \\ \pi_{21} & \pi_{22} & \cdots & \pi_{2K} \\ \vdots & \vdots & & \vdots \\ \pi_{G1} & \pi_{G2} & \cdots & \pi_{GK} \end{bmatrix}, \qquad \mathbf{v}_t = \begin{bmatrix} v_{1t} \\ v_{2t} \\ \vdots \\ v_{Gt} \end{bmatrix}.$$
$$(G \times K) \qquad\qquad\qquad (G \times 1)$$

The relation between the structural form and the reduced form can be derived explicitly by solving (13.3a) for y_t. This gives

(13.6b)
$$\mathbf{y_t} = -\mathbf{B}^{-1}\mathbf{\Gamma}\mathbf{x_t} + \mathbf{B}^{-1}\mathbf{u_t}.$$

Comparing this result with the reduced form (13.6a), we can see that

(13.7)
$$\mathbf{\Pi} = -\mathbf{B}^{-1}\mathbf{\Gamma}$$

and

(13.8)
$$\mathbf{v_t} = \mathbf{B}^{-1}\mathbf{u_t}.$$

The variance-covariance matrix of the reduced form disturbances, $\mathbf{\Psi}$, is

(13.9)
$$\mathbf{\Psi} = E(\mathbf{v_t v_t'}) = E[\mathbf{B}^{-1}\mathbf{u_t u_t'}(\mathbf{B}^{-1})'] = \mathbf{B}^{-1}\mathbf{\Phi}(\mathbf{B}^{-1})'.$$

EXAMPLE 1   The supply-demand model described by (13.1) is

$$Q_t - \alpha_1 - \alpha_2 P_t - \alpha_3 Y_t = \varepsilon_{1t},$$
$$Q_t - \beta_1 - \beta_2 P_t \qquad\quad = \varepsilon_{2t}.$$

This can be written in the pattern of (13.3a) as

$$\begin{bmatrix} 1 & -\alpha_2 \\ 1 & -\beta_2 \end{bmatrix} \begin{bmatrix} Q_t \\ P_t \end{bmatrix} + \begin{bmatrix} -\alpha_1 & -\alpha_3 \\ -\beta_1 & 0 \end{bmatrix} \begin{bmatrix} 1 \\ Y_t \end{bmatrix} = \begin{bmatrix} \varepsilon_{1t} \\ \varepsilon_{2t} \end{bmatrix}.$$

The reduced form of the system is

$$\begin{bmatrix} Q_t \\ P_t \end{bmatrix} = \begin{bmatrix} \pi_{11} & \pi_{12} \\ \pi_{21} & \pi_{22} \end{bmatrix} \begin{bmatrix} 1 \\ Y_t \end{bmatrix} + \begin{bmatrix} v_{1t} \\ v_{2t} \end{bmatrix},$$

where

$$\begin{bmatrix} \pi_{11} & \pi_{12} \\ \pi_{21} & \pi_{22} \end{bmatrix} = -\mathbf{B}^{-1}\mathbf{\Gamma} = \begin{bmatrix} 1 & -\alpha_2 \\ 1 & -\beta_2 \end{bmatrix}^{-1} \begin{bmatrix} -\alpha_1 & -\alpha_3 \\ -\beta_1 & 0 \end{bmatrix}$$

$$= -\left[\frac{1}{\alpha_2 - \beta_2} \right] \begin{bmatrix} -\beta_2 & \alpha_2 \\ -1 & 1 \end{bmatrix} \begin{bmatrix} -\alpha_1 & -\alpha_3 \\ -\beta_1 & 0 \end{bmatrix}$$

$$= -\left[\frac{1}{\alpha_2 - \beta_2} \right] \begin{bmatrix} (\alpha_1\beta_2 - \alpha_2\beta_1) & \alpha_3\beta_2 \\ (\alpha_1 - \beta_1) & \alpha_3 \end{bmatrix}$$

and

$$\begin{bmatrix} v_{1t} \\ v_{2t} \end{bmatrix} = \mathbf{B}^{-1} \begin{bmatrix} \varepsilon_{1t} \\ \varepsilon_{2t} \end{bmatrix} = \left[\frac{1}{\alpha_2 - \beta_2} \right] \begin{bmatrix} -\beta_2 & \alpha_2 \\ -1 & 1 \end{bmatrix} \begin{bmatrix} \varepsilon_{1t} \\ \varepsilon_{2t} \end{bmatrix} = \left[\frac{1}{\alpha_2 - \beta_2} \right] \begin{bmatrix} -\beta_2\varepsilon_{1t} + \alpha_2\varepsilon_{2t} \\ -\varepsilon_{1t} + \varepsilon_{2t} \end{bmatrix}.$$

Of course, these results are the same as those given by (13.2).

EXAMPLE 2   The following represents a highly simplified model of the economy:

$$C_t = \alpha_0 + \alpha_1 Y_t + \alpha_2 C_{t-1} + u_{1t} \quad \text{(consumption)},$$
$$I_t = \beta_0 + \beta_1 r_t + \beta_2 I_{t-1} + u_{2t} \quad \text{(investment)},$$
$$r_t = \gamma_0 + \gamma_1 Y_t + \gamma_2 M_t + u_{3t} \quad \text{(money market)},$$
$$Y_t = C_t + I_t + G_t \qquad\qquad\quad \text{(income identity)}.$$

where C = consumption, Y = income, I = investment, r = rate of interest, M = money supply, and G = government expenditure. The variables C_t, I_t, Y_t, and r_t are endogenous; the remaining variables are predetermined. We can describe the model as

$$
\begin{bmatrix} 1 & 0 & -\alpha_1 & 0 \\ 0 & 1 & 0 & -\beta_1 \\ 0 & 0 & -\gamma_1 & 1 \\ -1 & -1 & 1 & 0 \end{bmatrix}
\begin{bmatrix} C_t \\ I_t \\ Y_t \\ r_t \end{bmatrix}
+
\begin{bmatrix} -\alpha_0 & -\alpha_2 & 0 & 0 & 0 \\ -\beta_0 & 0 & -\beta_2 & 0 & 0 \\ -\gamma_0 & 0 & 0 & -\gamma_2 & 0 \\ 0 & 0 & 0 & 0 & -1 \end{bmatrix}
\begin{bmatrix} 1 \\ C_{t-1} \\ I_{t-1} \\ M_t \\ G_t \end{bmatrix}
=
\begin{bmatrix} u_{1t} \\ u_{2t} \\ u_{3t} \\ 0 \end{bmatrix}.
$$

The reduced form of this system is

$$
\begin{bmatrix} C_t \\ I_t \\ Y_t \\ r_t \end{bmatrix}
= \frac{1}{\Delta}
\begin{bmatrix}
\alpha_0(1 - \beta_1\gamma_1) + \alpha_1(\beta_0 + \beta_1\gamma_0) & \alpha_1\alpha_2 & \alpha_1\beta_2 & \alpha_1\beta_1\gamma_2 & \alpha_1 \\
\alpha_0\beta_1\gamma_1 + (1 - \alpha_1)(\beta_0 + \beta_1\gamma_0) & \alpha_2\beta_1\gamma_1 & (1 - \alpha_1)\beta_2 & (1 - \alpha_1)\beta_1\gamma_1 & \beta_1\gamma_1 \\
\alpha_0 + \beta_0 + \beta_1\gamma_0 & \alpha_2 & \beta_2 & \beta_1\gamma_2 & 1 \\
(\alpha_0 + \beta_0)\gamma_1 + (1 - \alpha_1)\gamma_0 & \alpha_2\gamma_1 & \beta_2\gamma_1 & (1 - \alpha_1)\gamma_2 & \gamma_1
\end{bmatrix}
\begin{bmatrix} 1 \\ C_{t-1} \\ I_{t-1} \\ M_t \\ G_t \end{bmatrix}
$$

$$
+ \frac{1}{\Delta}
\begin{bmatrix}
1 - \beta_1\gamma_1 & \alpha_1 & \alpha_1\beta_1 \\
\beta_1\gamma_1 & (1 - \alpha_1) & (1 - \alpha_1)\beta_1 \\
1 & 1 & \beta_1 \\
\gamma_1 & \gamma_1 & (1 - \alpha_1)
\end{bmatrix}
\begin{bmatrix} u_{1t} \\ u_{2t} \\ u_{3t} \end{bmatrix},
$$

where $\Delta = 1 - \alpha_1 - \beta_1\gamma_1$.

Types of Structural Models

The position of the zero elements in the **B** matrix indicates which endogenous variables do not appear in different structural equations. This is used as a criterion for distinguishing between various types of structures.

(a) If **B** is *diagonal*, i.e., if

$$
\mathbf{B} =
\begin{bmatrix}
\beta_{11} & 0 & \cdots & 0 \\
0 & \beta_{22} & \cdots & 0 \\
\vdots & \vdots & & \\
0 & 0 & \cdots & \beta_{GG}
\end{bmatrix},
$$

only one endogenous variable appears in each equation. This means that the equations are not simultaneous but *seemingly unrelated*. This case has been discussed in Section 12–3.

(b) If **B** is *block-diagonal*, i.e., if

$$
\mathbf{B} =
\begin{bmatrix}
\mathbf{B_1} & 0 & \cdots & 0 \\
0 & \mathbf{B_2} & \cdots & 0 \\
\vdots & \vdots & & \vdots \\
0 & 0 & \cdots & \mathbf{B_R}
\end{bmatrix},
$$

where $\mathbf{B}_1, \mathbf{B}_2, \ldots, \mathbf{B}_R$ are square matrices and the **0**'s represent zero-matrices of appropriate dimensions, then each block contains its own set of endogenous variables. In this case we have not one but R systems of simultaneous equations. Each block constitutes a separate system since, in the derivation of the reduced form solutions, we utilize only the structural equations of the same block. This can be clearly seen if we partition the structural equations in the following way:

$$
\begin{bmatrix}
\mathbf{B}_1 & \mathbf{0} & \cdots & \mathbf{0} \\
\mathbf{0} & \mathbf{B}_2 & \cdots & \mathbf{0} \\
\vdots & \vdots & & \vdots \\
\mathbf{0} & \mathbf{0} & \cdots & \mathbf{B}_R
\end{bmatrix}
\begin{bmatrix}
\mathbf{y}_t^{(1)} \\
\mathbf{y}_t^{(2)} \\
\vdots \\
\mathbf{y}_t^{(R)}
\end{bmatrix}
+
\begin{bmatrix}
\mathbf{\Gamma}_1 \\
\mathbf{\Gamma}_2 \\
\vdots \\
\mathbf{\Gamma}_R
\end{bmatrix}
\mathbf{x}_t
=
\begin{bmatrix}
\mathbf{u}_t^{(1)} \\
\mathbf{u}_t^{(2)} \\
\vdots \\
\mathbf{u}_t^{(R)}
\end{bmatrix},
$$

where $\mathbf{y}_t^{(r)}$ is a $(G_r \times 1)$ vector of the endogenous variables appearing in the rth block, $\mathbf{u}_t^{(r)}$ is a $(G_r \times 1)$ vector of the corresponding structural disturbances, and $\mathbf{\Gamma}_r$ is a $(G_r \times K)$ matrix of the γ coefficients in the structural equations of the rth block ($r = 1, 2, \ldots, R$). The reduced form solution for $\mathbf{y}_t^{(r)}$ is

$$
\mathbf{y}_t^{(r)} = -\mathbf{B}_r^{-1}\mathbf{\Gamma}_r\mathbf{x}_t + \mathbf{B}_r^{-1}\mathbf{u}_t^{(r)} \qquad (r = 1, 2, \ldots, R).
$$

In this result there is no reference to any equation outside of the rth block. When the **B** matrix is block-diagonal, we speak of a *nonintegrated structure*. If the variance-covariance matrix of the structural disturbances is also block-diagonal in the same way as the **B** matrix, then each block can be treated as a separate system when it comes to estimation. However, if the variance-covariance matrix of the structural disturbances is not block-diagonal, then the blocks are only "seemingly" unrelated. We may add that there is also another, stricter kind of nonintegration known as *dynamic nonintegration*. This condition prevails when the structural equations in any one block do not involve current *as well as* lagged endogenous variables from any other block. This kind of nonintegration implies that not only the current value but also the path through time of an endogenous variable are determined entirely by reference to the equations of the block in which the variable in question appears. We shall comment further on this in Section 13-6.

(c) If **B** is triangular, i.e., if

$$
\mathbf{B} =
\begin{bmatrix}
\beta_{11} & 0 & \cdots & 0 \\
\beta_{21} & \beta_{22} & \cdots & 0 \\
\vdots & & & \vdots \\
\beta_{G1} & \beta_{G2} & \cdots & \beta_{GG}
\end{bmatrix},
$$

the system is known as *recursive*. In this case the solution for the gth endogenous variable involves only the first g structural equations. This means that all G structural equations are needed for the solution only in the case of the last endogenous variable y_{Gt}. The first structural equation involves only one endogenous variable so that it coincides with the first reduced form equation.

(d) If **B** is *block-triangular*, i.e., if

$$\mathbf{B} = \begin{bmatrix} \mathbf{B}_{11} & 0 & \cdots & 0 \\ \mathbf{B}_{21} & \mathbf{B}_{22} & \cdots & 0 \\ \vdots & & & \\ \mathbf{B}_{R1} & \mathbf{B}_{R2} & \cdots & \mathbf{B}_{RR} \end{bmatrix},$$

where the **B**'s are matrices of given dimensions, the system is called *block-recursive*. This system has the same characteristics as the recursive system just described, except that reference is made to blocks of equations rather than to individual equations themselves.

(e) If **B** is neither diagonal nor triangular (block or otherwise), we speak of an *integrated structure*. Such structures have commanded the greatest attention of econometricians and provide the main subject for our discussion of simultaneous equation systems. A system of equations characterized by an integrated structure is sometimes called a *general interdependent system*.

13-2   The Identification Problem

Because there are endogenous variables among the explanatory variables in simultaneous equations, ordinary least squares estimators of the structural coefficients are not consistent, at least in general. However, in the reduced form equations the explanatory variables are represented by the predetermined variables of the system so that ordinary least squares estimators of the reduced form coefficients are consistent. This suggests that we may try to estimate the structural coefficients via the reduced form. The question then is whether we can derive estimates of the structural coefficients from the consistent estimates of the reduced form coefficients. Obviously, we can do this providing we can express the structural coefficients—the β's and the γ's—in terms of the reduced form coefficients—the π's. Thus the problem is one of *identification*, as was discussed in the context of a single equation model in Section 11-2. At present we face the same problem with a system of equations. The reduced form equations described by (13.6a) as

$$\mathbf{y}_t = \mathbf{\Pi}\mathbf{x}_t + \mathbf{v}_t$$

represent the unrestricted version of these equations, while the form (13.6b) given by

$$\mathbf{y}_t = -\mathbf{B}^{-1}\mathbf{\Gamma}\mathbf{x}_t + \mathbf{B}^{-1}\mathbf{u}_t$$

represents the restricted version. As with a single equation model, when there is a one-to-one correspondence between the restricted and the unrestricted parameters (in the sense that there is a unique solution for the restricted parameters in terms of the unrestricted coefficients) we have *exact identification*. On the other hand, when the number of the unrestricted coefficients exceeds the number of the restricted parameters and there is no unique solution, we have *overidentification*. Finally, if the number of unrestricted coefficients is insufficient for the solution, we have *underidentification*. An equation is said to be identified if it is either exactly identified or overidentified.

We may illustrate the identification problem by reference to the supply-demand model (13.1):

$$Q_t = \alpha_1 + \alpha_2 P_t + \alpha_3 Y_t + \varepsilon_{1t} \quad \text{(demand)},$$

$$Q_t = \beta_1 + \beta_2 P_t + \varepsilon_{2t} \qquad\qquad \text{(supply)},$$

and its reduced form (13.2):

$$Q_t = \pi_{11} + \pi_{12} Y_t + v_{1t},$$

$$P_t = \pi_{21} + \pi_{22} Y_t + v_{2t}.$$

The simplest way of finding out whether it is possible to express the α's and the β's in terms of the π's is to substitute for Q_t and P_t from the reduced form (13.2) into the structural form (13.1). This gives

$$(\pi_{11} + \pi_{12} Y_t + v_{1t}) = \alpha_1 + \alpha_2(\pi_{21} + \pi_{22} Y_t + v_{2t}) + \alpha_3 Y_t + \varepsilon_{1t} \quad \text{(demand)},$$

$$(\pi_{11} + \pi_{12} Y_t + v_{1t}) = \beta_1 + \beta_2(\pi_{21} + \pi_{22} Y_t + v_{2t}) + \varepsilon_{2t} \qquad\qquad \text{(supply)}.$$

In light of the definition of v_{1t} and v_{2t} given earlier, the stochastic disturbances in each equation cancel out, and we are left with

$$\pi_{11} + \pi_{12} Y_t = (\alpha_1 + \alpha_2 \pi_{21}) + (\alpha_2 \pi_{22} + \alpha_3) Y_t \quad \text{(demand)},$$

$$\pi_{11} + \pi_{12} Y_t = (\beta_1 + \beta_2 \pi_{21}) + \beta_2 \pi_{22} Y_t \qquad\qquad \text{(supply)}.$$

The equalities implied by the demand equation are

$$\pi_{11} = \alpha_1 + \alpha_2 \pi_{21} \qquad \text{and} \qquad \pi_{12} = \alpha_2 \pi_{22} + \alpha_3.$$

Since there are only two equalities, we cannot solve for the three unknowns represented by α_1, α_2, and α_3. The equalities for the supply equation are

$$\pi_{11} = \beta_1 + \beta_2 \pi_{21} \qquad \text{and} \qquad \pi_{12} = \beta_2 \pi_{22}.$$

This leads to

$$\beta_1 = \pi_{11} - \frac{\pi_{12}\pi_{21}}{\pi_{22}},$$

$$\beta_2 = \frac{\pi_{12}}{\pi_{22}}.$$

Thus the demand equation is underidentified, and the supply equation is exactly identified.

Clearly, it would be desirable to have some general rule for determining the identification status of any given structural equation. Such a rule can be derived in the following way. The structural equations are

$$\mathbf{By_t} + \mathbf{\Gamma x_t} = \mathbf{u_t},$$

while the reduced form equations are

$$\mathbf{y_t} = \mathbf{\Pi x_t} + \mathbf{v_t}.$$

By substituting for $\mathbf{y_t}$ from the reduced form expression into the structural form, we obtain

$$\mathbf{B\Pi x_t} + \mathbf{Bv_t} + \mathbf{\Gamma x_t} = \mathbf{u_t}.$$

But since

$$\mathbf{v_t} = \mathbf{B^{-1}u_t},$$

we can write

$$\mathbf{B\Pi x_t} = -\mathbf{\Gamma x_t}$$

or

$$\mathbf{B\Pi} = -\mathbf{\Gamma}.$$

This is the relation used in determining the identification status of the demand and the supply equations. We shall now try to use this relation for deriving a general identification criterion for each structural equation. Writing out the matrices in full, we have

$$\begin{bmatrix} \beta_{11} & \beta_{12} & \cdots & \beta_{1G} \\ \beta_{21} & \beta_{22} & \cdots & \beta_{2G} \\ \vdots & \vdots & & \vdots \\ \beta_{G1} & \beta_{G2} & \cdots & \beta_{GG} \end{bmatrix} \begin{bmatrix} \pi_{11} & \pi_{12} & \cdots & \pi_{1K} \\ \pi_{21} & \pi_{22} & \cdots & \pi_{2K} \\ \vdots & \vdots & & \vdots \\ \pi_{G1} & \pi_{G2} & \cdots & \pi_{GK} \end{bmatrix} = - \begin{bmatrix} \gamma_{11} & \gamma_{12} & \cdots & \gamma_{1K} \\ \gamma_{21} & \gamma_{22} & \cdots & \gamma_{2K} \\ \vdots & \vdots & & \vdots \\ \gamma_{G1} & \gamma_{G2} & \cdots & \gamma_{GK} \end{bmatrix}.$$

For a single equation of the system, say, the gth, this becomes

$$(13.10) \quad [\beta_{g1} \ \ \beta_{g2} \ \ \cdots \ \ \beta_{gG}] \begin{bmatrix} \pi_{11} & \pi_{12} & \cdots & \pi_{1K} \\ \pi_{21} & \pi_{22} & \cdots & \pi_{2K} \\ \vdots & \vdots & & \vdots \\ \pi_{G1} & \pi_{G2} & \cdots & \pi_{GK} \end{bmatrix} = -[\gamma_{g1} \ \ \gamma_{g2} \ \ \cdots \ \ \gamma_{gK}]$$

or

$$(13.10a) \qquad\qquad \mathbf{\beta_g \Pi} = -\mathbf{\gamma_g},$$

where

$$\mathbf{\beta_g} = [\beta_{g1} \ \ \beta_{g2} \ \ \cdots \ \ \beta_{gG}],$$

$$\mathbf{\gamma_g} = [\gamma_{g1} \ \ \gamma_{g2} \ \ \cdots \ \ \gamma_{gK}].$$

If all of the endogenous and the predetermined variables of the system do not appear in the gth equation, some of the β's and some of the γ's will be equal to zero.

Let G^Δ = number of endogenous variables which appear in the gth equation
        (i.e., number of the nonzero elements in β_g);

$G^{\Delta\Delta} = G - G^\Delta$;

K^* = number of predetermined variables which appear in the gth equation
        (i.e., number of the nonzero elements in γ_g);

$K^{**} = K - K^*$.

Without a loss of generality, we assume that the elements of β_g and γ_g are
arranged in such a way that the nonzero elements appear first, being followed
by the zero elements. Then we can partition β_g and γ_g as

(13.11) $\beta_g = [\beta_\Delta \quad 0_{\Delta\Delta}],$

                            $\gamma_g = [\gamma_* \quad 0_{**}],$

where $\beta_\Delta = [\beta_{g1} \quad \beta_{g2} \quad \ldots \quad \beta_{gG^\Delta}] \to 1 \times G^\Delta,$

                $0_{\Delta\Delta} = [0 \quad\quad 0 \quad\quad \ldots \quad\quad 0] \to 1 \times G^{\Delta\Delta},$

                $\gamma_* = [\gamma_{g1} \quad \gamma_{g2} \quad \ldots \quad \gamma_{gK^*}] \to 1 \times K^*,$

                $0_{**} = [0 \quad\quad 0 \quad\quad \ldots \quad\quad 0] \to 1 \times K^{**}.$

The matrix Π can be partitioned in a corresponding way:

(13.12) $\Pi = \begin{bmatrix} \Pi_{\Delta*} & \Pi_{\Delta**} \\ \Pi_{\Delta\Delta*} & \Pi_{\Delta\Delta**} \end{bmatrix},$

where $\Pi_{\Delta*} \to (G^\Delta \times K^*),$

                $\Pi_{\Delta**} \to (G^\Delta \times K^{**}),$

                $\Pi_{\Delta\Delta*} \to (G^{\Delta\Delta} \times K^*),$

                $\Pi_{\Delta\Delta**} \to (G^{\Delta\Delta} \times K^{**}).$

By using (13.11) and (13.12), we can rewrite (13.10a) as

(13.13) $[\beta_\Delta \quad 0_{\Delta\Delta}]\begin{bmatrix} \Pi_{\Delta*} & \Pi_{\Delta**} \\ \Pi_{\Delta\Delta*} & \Pi_{\Delta\Delta**} \end{bmatrix} = -[\gamma_* \quad 0_{**}].$

This leads to the following equalities:

(13.14) $\beta_\Delta \Pi_{\Delta*} \quad\quad = \quad -\gamma_* \;,$
                    $(1 \times G^\Delta)(G^\Delta \times K^*) \quad (1 \times K^*)$

(13.15) $\beta_\Delta \Pi_{\Delta**} \quad\quad = \quad 0_{**} \;.$
                    $(1 \times G^\Delta)(G^\Delta \times K^{**}) \quad (1 \times K^{**})$

Since one of the β's in each structural equation equals unity, the equalities
(13.14) and (13.15) involve $(G^\Delta - 1)$ unknown β's and K^* unknown γ's. The
equality (13.15) is particularly important since it does not involve any γ's. If

we can solve (13.15) for $\boldsymbol{\beta}_\Delta$, we can solve for $\boldsymbol{\gamma}_*$ easily from (13.14). Now, equality (13.15) contains altogether K^{**} equations, one for each element of the $(1 \times K^{**})$ vector. Clearly, if we want to obtain a solution for the $(G^\Delta - 1)$ unknown elements of $\boldsymbol{\beta}_\Delta$, we need at least $(G^\Delta - 1)$ equations. That means that we require that

$$(13.16) \qquad\qquad K^{**} \geq G^\Delta - 1.$$

This is known as the *order condition* for identifiability. This condition, in fact, states that a necessary condition for identification of a given structural equation is that the number of predetermined variables excluded from the given equation is at least as large as the number of endogenous variables included in the equation less one. Note that this is only a *necessary* and not a sufficient condition for identification since the K^{**} equations in (13.15) may not be independent. That is, it may happen that the equations in (13.15) contain fewer than $G^\Delta - 1$ different pieces of information about the relation between the β's and the π's. Thus a necessary *and* sufficient condition for identification is that the number of independent equations in (13.15) is $G^\Delta - 1$. This will be the case if and only if the order of the largest non-zero determinant that can be formed from all square submatrices of $\boldsymbol{\Pi}_{\Delta**}$ is $G^\Delta - 1$, i.e., if and only if

$$(13.17) \qquad\qquad \text{rank } (\boldsymbol{\Pi}_{\Delta**}) = G^\Delta - 1.$$

This is known as the *rank condition* for identifiability.

A convenient way of determining the rank of $\boldsymbol{\Pi}_{\Delta**}$ involves partitioning the matrices of the structural coefficients as follows:

$$\mathbf{B} = \begin{bmatrix} \boldsymbol{\beta}_\Delta & \mathbf{0}_{\Delta\Delta} \\ \mathbf{B}_\Delta & \mathbf{B}_{\Delta\Delta} \end{bmatrix}, \qquad \boldsymbol{\Gamma} = \begin{bmatrix} \boldsymbol{\gamma}_* & \mathbf{0}_{**} \\ \boldsymbol{\Gamma}_* & \boldsymbol{\Gamma}_{**} \end{bmatrix},$$

where $\boldsymbol{\beta}_\Delta$, $\boldsymbol{\gamma}_*$, $\mathbf{0}_{\Delta\Delta}$, and $\mathbf{0}_{**}$ are row vectors defined as in (13.11), and

$$\mathbf{B}_\Delta \to (G-1) \times G^\Delta,$$

$$\mathbf{B}_{\Delta\Delta} \to (G-1) \times G^{\Delta\Delta},$$

$$\boldsymbol{\Gamma}_* \to (G-1) \times K^*,$$

$$\boldsymbol{\Gamma}_{**} \to (G-1) \times K^{**}.$$

Note that $\mathbf{B}_{\Delta\Delta}$ and $\boldsymbol{\Gamma}_{**}$ are matrices of the structural coefficients for the variables omitted from the gth equation but included in other structural equations. If we now form a new matrix $\boldsymbol{\Delta}$ defined as

$$\boldsymbol{\Delta} = [\mathbf{B}_{\Delta\Delta} \quad \boldsymbol{\Gamma}_{**}],$$

then

$$(13.17a) \qquad\qquad \text{rank } (\boldsymbol{\Pi}_{\Delta**}) = \text{rank } (\boldsymbol{\Delta}) - G^{\Delta\Delta}.$$

This can be proved as follows. Let $\boldsymbol{\Delta}_*$ be defined as

$$\boldsymbol{\Delta}_* = \begin{bmatrix} \mathbf{0}_{**} & \mathbf{0}_{\Delta\Delta} \\ \boldsymbol{\Gamma}_{**} & \mathbf{B}_{\Delta\Delta} \end{bmatrix}.$$

Clearly, the rank of Δ_* is the same as that of Δ since the rank of a matrix is not affected by enlarging the matrix by a row of zeros, or by switching any columns. Now, Δ_* can be written as

$$\Delta_* = \begin{bmatrix} \beta_\Delta & 0_{\Delta\Delta} \\ B_\Delta & B_{\Delta\Delta} \end{bmatrix} \begin{bmatrix} -\Pi_{\Delta**} & 0_{\Delta,\Delta\Delta} \\ -\Pi_{\Delta\Delta**} & I_{\Delta\Delta} \end{bmatrix},$$

where $0_{\Delta,\Delta\Delta}$ is $G^\Delta \times G^{\Delta\Delta}$ matrix of zeros, and $I_{\Delta\Delta}$ is an identity matrix of order $G^{\Delta\Delta} \times G^{\Delta\Delta}$. To see that, we carry out the multiplication indicated in the above equality to obtain

$$\Delta_* = \begin{bmatrix} -\beta_\Delta\Pi_{\Delta**} & 0_{\Delta\Delta} \\ (-B_\Delta\Pi_{\Delta**} - B_{\Delta\Delta}\Pi_{\Delta\Delta**}) & B_{\Delta\Delta} \end{bmatrix}.$$

But by (13.15)

$$-\beta_\Delta\Pi_{\Delta**} = 0_{**},$$

and from the equality $B\Pi = -\Gamma$ it follows that

$$-B_\Delta\Pi_{\Delta**} - B_{\Delta\Delta}\Pi_{\Delta\Delta**} = \Gamma_{**}.$$

Utilizing the theorem[1] that if a matrix A is multiplied by a nonsingular matrix, the product has the same rank as A, we can write

$$\text{rank}(\Delta_*) = \text{rank}(B^{-1}\Delta_*)$$

$$= \text{rank}\begin{bmatrix} -\Pi_{\Delta**} & 0_{\Delta,\Delta\Delta} \\ -\Pi_{\Delta\Delta**} & I_{\Delta\Delta} \end{bmatrix}$$

$$= \text{rank}\begin{bmatrix} -\Pi_{\Delta**} & 0_{\Delta,\Delta\Delta} \\ -\Pi_{\Delta\Delta**} & I_{\Delta\Delta} \end{bmatrix} \begin{bmatrix} I_{**} & 0_{**,\Delta\Delta} \\ \Pi_{\Delta\Delta**} & I_{\Delta\Delta} \end{bmatrix}$$

$$= \text{rank}\begin{bmatrix} -\Pi_{\Delta**} & 0_{\Delta,\Delta\Delta} \\ 0_{\Delta\Delta,**} & I_{\Delta\Delta} \end{bmatrix}$$

$$= \text{rank}(\Pi_{\Delta**}) + G^{\Delta\Delta},$$

where $0_{**,\Delta\Delta}$ and $0_{\Delta\Delta,**}$ are zero matrices of order $K^{**} \times G^{\Delta\Delta}$ and $G^{\Delta\Delta} \times K^{**}$, respectively, and I_{**} is an identity matrix of order $K^{**} \times K^{**}$. This completes the proof of (13.17a). It is clearly much easier to determine the rank of $\Pi_{\Delta**}$ from (13.17a) than from the direct solution for $\Pi_{\Delta**}$ in terms of the structural coefficients.

The order and rank conditions enable us to set up the following general rule for determining the identification status of a structural equation.

    1. If $K^{**} > G^\Delta - 1$ and $\text{rank}(\Pi_{\Delta**}) = G^\Delta - 1$, we have overidentification.

---

[1] See, e.g., J. Johnston, *Econometric Methods* (New York: McGraw-Hill, 1963), p. 92.

2. If $K^{**} = G^\Delta - 1$ and $\operatorname{rank}(\Pi_{\Delta**}) = G^\Delta - 1$, we have exact identification.

3. If $K^{**} \geq G^\Delta - 1$ and $\operatorname{rank}(\Pi_{\Delta**}) < G^\Delta - 1$, the structural equation is underidentified.

4. If $K^{**} < G^\Delta - 1$, the structural equation is underidentified.

EXAMPLE 1   The supply-demand model described by (13.1) is

$$Q_t = \alpha_1 + \alpha_2 P_t + \alpha_3 Y_t + \varepsilon_{1t} \quad \text{(demand)},$$

$$Q_t = \beta_1 + \beta_2 P_t + \varepsilon_{2t} \qquad \text{(supply)},$$

Consider the identification status of the demand equation first. There are two included endogenous variables, Q_t and P_t, so that

$$G^\Delta - 1 = 1.$$

Since no predetermined variables of the system are excluded from the demand equation, we have

$$K^{**} = 0.$$

Therefore,

$$K^{**} < G^\Delta - 1,$$

which means that the order condition is not satisfied, and, therefore, the demand equation is *underidentified*.

Turning now to the supply equation, we note that there are again two included endogenous variables, Q_t and P_t, i.e., that

$$G^\Delta - 1 = 1,$$

but there is now one predetermined variable, Y_t, which appears in the system but not in the supply equation. Thus, in this case we have

$$K^{**} = 1,$$

so that the order condition is satisfied. With respect to the rank condition, we have

$$\operatorname{rank}(\Delta) = \operatorname{rank}[-\alpha_3] = 1.$$

Then, by (13.17a),

$$\operatorname{rank}(\Pi_{\Delta**}) = 1 - 0 = 1,$$

and the rank condition is also satisfied. Note that equality (13.15) for the supply equation of our model is

$$[1 \quad -\beta_2]\begin{bmatrix} \pi_{QY} \\ \pi_{PY} \end{bmatrix} = 0,$$

which involves one equation and one unknown; i.e., the supply function is *exactly* identified.

EXAMPLE 2   An aggregate model of the economy has been given as follows:

$$C_t = \alpha_0 + \alpha_1 Y_t + \alpha_2 C_{t-1} + u_t \quad \text{(consumption)},$$

$$I_t = \beta_0 + \beta_1 r_t + \beta_2 I_{t-1} + u_{2t} \quad \text{(investment)},$$

$$r_t = \gamma_0 + \gamma_1 Y_t + \gamma_2 M_t + u_{3t} \quad \text{(money market)},$$

$$Y_t = C_t + I_t + G_t \qquad\qquad\qquad \text{(income identity)}.$$

For each of the first three structural equations, we have

$$G^\Delta - 1 = 1,$$

$$K^{**} = 3,$$

so that the order condition is satisfied in every case. As for the rank condition, the rank of Δ for the *consumption function* is

$$\text{rank}(\Delta) = \text{rank} \begin{bmatrix} 1 & -\beta_1 & -\beta_2 & 0 & 0 \\ 0 & 1 & 0 & -\gamma_2 & 0 \\ -1 & 0 & 0 & 0 & 1 \end{bmatrix} = 3.$$

Therefore, $$\text{rank}(\Pi_{\Delta**}) = 3 - 2 = 1,$$

so that the rank condition is satisfied. This means that the consumption function is *identified*. Note that the equality (13.15) in the case of our consumption function becomes

$$[1 - \alpha_1] \begin{bmatrix} \pi_{CI_{-1}} & \pi_{CM} & \pi_{CG} \\ \pi_{YI_{-1}} & \pi_{YM} & \pi_{YG} \end{bmatrix} = [0 \quad 0 \quad 0].$$

That is, there are three equations to determine one unknown; i.e., the consumption function is *overidentified*. The derivation of the rank condition for the remaining two structural equations would follow along the same lines.

The above order and rank conditions for identifiability have been stated in terms of population parameters on the assumption that none of the structural parameters is equal to zero. However, we do not know what the values of these parameters really are and, in fact, may want to test the hypothesis that they *are* equal to zero. If this hypothesis were not rejected in every case, some variables would be considered irrelevant and, therefore, should not be counted. For instance, to determine whether a given structural equation satisfies the order condition for identifiability, we count the number of predetermined variables excluded from the equation. But if some of these variables are irrelevant, they should not be counted. This means that a structural equation that appears to satisfy the order condition a priori may not, in fact, satisfy this condition when the irrelevant variables have been discarded. Therefore, we may want to consider the identifiability of an equation as a hypothesis to be tested instead of relying on prior specification. A description of a suggested test procedure can be found in the literature.[2]

[2] R. L. Basmann, "On Finite Sample Distributions of Generalized Classical Linear Identifiability Test Statistics," *Journal of the American Statistical Association*, Vol. 55, December 1960, pp. 650–659.

Identification Through Restrictions on
the Disturbance Variance-Covariance Matrix

The preceding examination of the identifiability conditions has been confined to the specification of the structural equation and no reference has been made to the variance-covariance matrix of the disturbances. We have shown that a structural equation can be identified by specifying that some of the variables appearing in the system are omitted from the equation in question. Since omitting a variable from a linear equation is equivalent to specifying that the corresponding β or γ coefficient is equal to zero, it can be said that identification of an equation is achieved by *zero restrictions* on some of the coefficients. (Of course, identification could also be achieved by *nonzero* restrictions on the structural coefficients, e.g., by specifying that some coefficients are equal to given numbers that are not necessarily zero, or by specifying the ratio or ratios between coefficients in a linear equation.) But if this is the case, it should also be possible to achieve identification by prior restrictions on some of the elements of the variance-covariance matrix of the regression disturbances. We shall illustrate this by reference to the supply-demand model (13.1). In examining the identification status of the structural equations we concluded that, given the zero restrictions on the structural coefficients, the demand equation is underidentified while the supply equation is exactly identified. Let us now add a further restriction by specifying that the disturbances in the two equations are mutually independent, i.e., that

$$E(\varepsilon_{1t}\varepsilon_{2t}) = 0$$

for all t. Our previous results, obtained by utilizing the zero restrictions on the structural coefficients, have led to the following relations between the structural and the reduced form coefficients:

$$\pi_{11} = \alpha_1 + \alpha_2\pi_{21}, \qquad \pi_{11} = \beta_1 + \beta_2\pi_{21},$$

$$\pi_{12} = \alpha_2\pi_{22} + \alpha_3, \qquad \pi_{12} = \beta_2\pi_{22}.$$

As noted earlier, we can solve these equations for the β's but not for the α's. However, now we may add another relation that follows from the zero restriction on the covariance of the two disturbances. First, we note that the reduced form disturbances are given by

$$v_{1t} = \frac{-\beta_2\varepsilon_{1t} + \alpha_2\varepsilon_{2t}}{\alpha_2 - \beta_2},$$

$$v_{2t} = \frac{-\varepsilon_{1t} + \varepsilon_{2t}}{\alpha_2 - \beta_2}.$$

Therefore we can write

$$\varepsilon_{1t} = v_{1t} - \alpha_2 v_{2t},$$

$$\varepsilon_{2t} = v_{1t} - \beta_2 v_{2t}.$$

Thus the restriction

$$E(\varepsilon_{1t}\varepsilon_{2t}) = 0$$

implies that

$$E(v_{1t} - \alpha_2 v_{2t})(v_{1t} - \beta_2 v_{2t}) = 0$$

or

(13.18) $$\psi_{11} - \alpha_2\psi_{12} - \beta_2\psi_{12} + \alpha_2\beta_2\psi_{22} = 0,$$

where the ψ's represent the elements of the variance-covariance matrix of the reduced form disturbances. Since we know that

$$\beta_2 = \frac{\pi_{12}}{\pi_{22}},$$

we can solve (13.18) for α_2 to obtain

$$\alpha_2 = \frac{\pi_{12}\psi_{12} - \pi_{22}\psi_{11}}{\pi_{12}\psi_{22} - \pi_{22}\psi_{12}}.$$

Also, since

$$\alpha_1 = \pi_{11} - \alpha_2\pi_{21}$$

and $$\alpha_3 = \pi_{12} - \alpha_2\pi_{22},$$

we can solve for α_1 and α_3. Thus, with the added restriction on the covariance of the structural disturbances, the previously underidentified demand equation becomes identified.

Underidentification

The question of identification is important because of its implications for estimation and hypothesis testing. If a structural equation is identified, we can obtain consistent estimators of its coefficients. In the case of underidentification, however, it is not possible to derive consistent estimators of the structural coefficients. Of course, we can estimate the coefficients of an underidentified structural equation by the method of ordinary least squares, but the resulting estimates are inconsistent. The fact that consistent estimation of the coefficients of an underidentified structural equation breaks down can be illustrated by reference to the supply-demand model (13.1). We found that—in the absence of any prior information about the variance-covariance matrix of the disturbances—the demand equation of the system is underidentified. This equation was given as

$$Q_t = \alpha_1 + \alpha_2 P_t + \alpha_3 Y_t + \varepsilon_{1t}.$$

Suppose we try to estimate the coefficients of this equation by the method of instrumental variables, which leads to consistent estimates. This method was described in connection with estimating regression models with errors in variables in Section 9–1, and in connection with distributed lag models in Section

11–4. It involves pairing each explanatory variable of the equation to be estimated with an instrumental variable. The latter is supposed to be uncorrelated
with the regression disturbance, but correlated with the explanatory variable
with which it is paired. In the case of our demand equation, the explanatory
variables are Q_t and P_t. Since Y_t is uncorrelated with ε_{1t} by assumption, it can
serve as its own instrumental variable, so that we need only to find an instrumental variable for P_t. Let this variable be called Z_t. Then the "instrumental
variables normal equations" are

$$\sum_t Q_t = \alpha_1^\dagger T + \alpha_2^\dagger \sum_t P_t + \alpha_3^\dagger \sum_t Y_t,$$

$$\sum_t Q_t Z_t = \alpha_1^\dagger \sum_t Z_t + \alpha_2^\dagger \sum_t P_t Z_t + \alpha_3^\dagger \sum_t Y_t Z_t,$$

$$\sum_t Q_t Y_t = \alpha_1^\dagger \sum_t Y_t + \alpha_2^\dagger \sum_t P_t Y_t + \alpha_3^\dagger \sum_t Y_t^2,$$

where $\alpha_1^\dagger$, $\alpha_2^\dagger$, and $\alpha_3^\dagger$ are the instrumental variables estimators of the respective
coefficients. The solution for, say, $\alpha_2^\dagger$, is

$$\alpha_2^\dagger = \frac{m_{QZ} m_{YY} - m_{QY} m_{YZ}}{m_{PZ} m_{YY} - m_{PY} m_{YZ}},$$

where
$$m_{QZ} = \sum_t (Q_t - \bar{Q})(Z_t - \bar{Z}),$$

$$m_{YY} = \sum_t (Y_t - \bar{Y})^2,$$

etc. Since from the reduced form solution we have

$$(Q_t - \bar{Q}) = \left(\frac{-\alpha_3 \beta_2}{\alpha_2 - \beta_2}\right)(Y_t - \bar{Y}) + (v_{1t} - \bar{v}_1),$$

$$(P_t - \bar{P}) = \left(\frac{-\alpha_3}{\alpha_2 - \beta_2}\right)(Y_t - \bar{Y}) + (v_{2t} - \bar{v}_2),$$

it follows that

$$\operatorname{plim} \frac{1}{T} m_{QZ} = \left(\frac{-\alpha_3 \beta_2}{\alpha_2 - \beta_2}\right) \operatorname{plim} \frac{1}{T} m_{YZ},$$

$$\operatorname{plim} \frac{1}{T} m_{QY} = \left(\frac{-\alpha_3 \beta_2}{\alpha_2 - \beta_2}\right) \operatorname{plim} \frac{1}{T} m_{YY},$$

$$\operatorname{plim} \frac{1}{T} m_{PZ} = \left(\frac{-\alpha_3}{\alpha_2 - \beta_2}\right) \operatorname{plim} \frac{1}{T} m_{YZ},$$

$$\operatorname{plim} \frac{1}{T} m_{PY} = \left(\frac{-\alpha_3}{\alpha_2 - \beta_2}\right) \operatorname{plim} \frac{1}{T} m_{YY}.$$

Therefore,

$$\text{plim } \alpha_2^\dagger = \frac{\left(\dfrac{-\alpha_3\beta_2}{\alpha_2-\beta_2}\right)\text{plim}\dfrac{m_{YZ}}{T}\cdot\text{plim}\dfrac{m_{YY}}{T}-\left(\dfrac{-\alpha_3\beta_2}{\alpha_2-\beta_2}\right)\text{plim}\dfrac{m_{YY}}{T}\cdot\text{plim}\dfrac{m_{YZ}}{T}}{\left(\dfrac{-\alpha_3}{\alpha_2-\beta_2}\right)\text{plim}\dfrac{m_{YZ}}{T}\cdot\text{plim}\dfrac{m_{YY}}{T}-\left(\dfrac{-\alpha_3}{\alpha_2-\beta_2}\right)\text{plim}\dfrac{m_{YY}}{T}\cdot\text{plim}\dfrac{m_{YZ}}{T}}=\frac{0}{0},$$

i.e., plim $\alpha_2^\dagger$ is indeterminate. Similar results can be obtained for $\alpha_1^\dagger$ and $\alpha_3^\dagger$. Thus the instrumental variables method breaks down as claimed.

Our inability to obtain consistent estimates of the structural coefficients of an underidentified equation can also be explained in a more intuitive way. In the supply-demand model (13.1), we note that the identification of the supply equation is due to the presence of the exogenous income variable in the demand function. If this variable did not appear in the demand function, both equations of the model would be underidentified. In that case all observations on price and quantity would be scattered around the single point of intersection of the mean price and the mean quantity. An increase in the number of observations in the sample would only increase the denseness of the points without providing any more information about the two lines to be estimated. With the income variable present, however, the demand function shifts with changes in income; and in this way, we observe points that are scattered around the supply function. The more points we observe, the more accurate are the estimates of the coefficients of the supply function. Since there is no exogenous variable in the supply equation, we cannot trace out the demand function in a similar way. However, if the disturbances of the two functions are mutually independent, their covariance is zero, and this additional information enables us to identify the parameters of the demand function as well. Note that since the parameters of underidentified equations cannot be consistently estimated, the hypotheses about their values cannot be refuted by sample observations. This means that the underlying theory is, from scientific viewpoint, incomplete.

13–3   Single-Equation Methods of Estimation

In Section 13–1 we emphasized that the ordinary least squares method of estimation applied to the structural equations of a simultaneous equation system in general leads to inconsistent estimates. Therefore we have to develop other methods to obtain consistent estimates of the structural coefficients. As stated, this is not possible when a structural equation is underidentified.

Our concern here is with structural equations that are identified and for which consistent methods of estimation are available. We have two categories of methods of estimating structural equations: (1) methods designed to estimate a single structural equation with only a limited reference to the rest of the system and (2) methods by which all equations of the system are estimated simultaneously. This section deals with methods belonging to the first category.

Estimation of an Exactly Identified Equation

Consider the problem of estimating an *exactly identified* structural equation belonging to a general interdependent system of simultaneous equations with no restrictions on the variance-covariance matrix of the disturbances. In this case there exists a unique solution for the structural coefficients in terms of the reduced form coefficients. The reduced form equations are given by (13.6a) as

$$\mathbf{y_t} = \mathbf{\Pi x_t} + \mathbf{v_t},$$

where $\mathbf{y_t}$ is a $(G \times 1)$ vector of the endogenous variables, $\mathbf{\Pi}$ is a $(G \times K)$ matrix of the reduced form coefficients, $\mathbf{x_t}$ is a $(K \times 1)$ vector of the predetermined variables, and $\mathbf{v_t}$ is a $(G \times 1)$ vector of the reduced form disturbances. Since the reduced form disturbances are represented by linear combinations of the structural disturbances, they satisfy all the assumptions of the classical normal linear regression model. The predetermined variables, which serve as explanatory variables in the reduced form equations, are either nonstochastic or, if stochastic, independent of the current disturbances. We shall also assume that they have finite variances and covariances as $T \to \infty$, and that there exists no exact linear relation between them. If the predetermined variables include lagged endogenous variables, we assume that the initial values of these variables are fixed. Under these assumptions, the application of the ordinary (unrestricted) least squares method to each reduced form equation leads to consistent estimates of the π's. If *all* structural equations are exactly identified, these estimates will be equivalent to the maximum likelihood estimates and will, in addition to consistency, also possess the properties of asymptotic efficiency and asymptotic normality. The ordinary least squares estimates of the reduced form coefficients can be used to determine the corresponding estimates of the structural coefficients as specified by (13.14) and (13.15). The latter are called *indirect least squares estimates.* They are, in general, given as nonlinear functions of the reduced form estimates and inherit all their asymptotic properties.

EXAMPLE   To illustrate the use of the indirect least squares method, we use the supply-demand model described by (13.1):

$$Q_t = \alpha_1 + \alpha_2 P_t + \alpha_3 Y_t + \varepsilon_{1t} \quad \text{(demand)},$$

$$Q_t = \beta_1 + \beta_2 P_t + \varepsilon_{2t} \qquad \text{(supply)},$$

where Q_t and P_t are endogenous and Y_t is exogenous. Without any restrictions on the variance-covariance matrix of the disturbances, the demand equation is under-identified, but the supply equation is exactly identified. The reduced form equations are

$$Q_t = \pi_{11} + \pi_{12} Y_t + v_{1t},$$

$$P_t = \pi_{21} + \pi_{22} Y_t + v_{2t}.$$

Substituting the reduced form expression for Q_t and P_t into the supply equation, we obtain

$$\pi_{11} + \pi_{12}Y_t + v_{1t} = \beta_1 + \beta_2(\pi_{21} + \pi_{22}Y_t + v_{2t}) + \varepsilon_{2t}.$$

Therefore,

$$\pi_{11} = \beta_1 + \beta_2\pi_{21},$$

$$\pi_{12} = \beta_2\pi_{22},$$

or

$$\beta_2 = \frac{\pi_{12}}{\pi_{22}},$$

$$\beta_1 = \pi_{11} - \frac{\pi_{12}\pi_{21}}{\pi_{22}}.$$

Now the ordinary least squares estimators of the reduced form coefficients are

$$\hat{\pi}_{12} = \frac{m_{QY}}{m_{YY}},$$

$$\hat{\pi}_{11} = \bar{Q} - \left(\frac{m_{QY}}{m_{YY}}\right)\bar{Y},$$

$$\hat{\pi}_{22} = \frac{m_{PY}}{m_{YY}},$$

$$\hat{\pi}_{21} = \bar{P} - \left(\frac{m_{PY}}{m_{YY}}\right)\bar{Y},$$

where

$$m_{QY} = \sum_t (Q_t - \bar{Q})(Y_t - \bar{Y}),$$

$$m_{PY} = \sum_t (P_t - \bar{P})(Y_t - \bar{Y}),$$

$$m_{YY} = \sum_t (Y_t - \bar{Y})^2.$$

Hence the indirect least squares estimators of β_1 and β_2 are

$$\tilde{\beta}_2 = \frac{m_{QY}}{m_{PY}},$$

$$\tilde{\beta}_1 = \bar{Q} - \left(\frac{m_{QY}}{m_{PY}}\right)\bar{P}.$$

The problem of estimating the coefficients of a structural equation can also be approached by resorting to the *instrumental variables method*. Suppose the structural equation that we wish to estimate is the first equation of the system, i.e.,

(13.19) $\beta_{11}y_{1t} + \beta_{12}y_{2t} + \cdots + \beta_{1G}y_{Gt} + \gamma_{11}x_{1t} + \gamma_{12}x_{2t} + \cdots + \gamma_{1K}x_{Kt} = u_{1t}.$

This involves no loss of generality since the structural equations can be written in any order we like. Let us suppose further that β_{11} is equal to unity, and that the

included endogenous and predetermined variables are $y_{1t}, y_{2t}, \ldots, y_{G^\Delta t}, x_{1t},$
$x_{2t}, \ldots, x_{K^* t}$. Then (13.19) can be written as

(13.19a) $y_{1t} = -\beta_{12} y_{2t} - \beta_{13} y_{3t} - \cdots - \beta_{1G^\Delta} y_{G^\Delta t} - \gamma_{11} x_{1t} - \gamma_{12} x_{2t}$

$$- \cdots - \gamma_{1K^*} x_{K^* t} + u_{1t}.$$

In matrix notation, Equation (13.19a) can be expressed as

(13.20) $\mathbf{y_1} = \mathbf{Y_1} \boldsymbol{\beta}_1 + \mathbf{X_1} \boldsymbol{\gamma}_1 + \mathbf{u_1},$

where

$$\mathbf{y_1} = \begin{bmatrix} y_{11} \\ y_{12} \\ \vdots \\ y_{1T} \end{bmatrix}, \quad \mathbf{Y_1} = \begin{bmatrix} y_{21} & y_{31} & \cdots & y_{G^\Delta 1} \\ y_{22} & y_{32} & \cdots & y_{G^\Delta 2} \\ \vdots & \vdots & & \vdots \\ y_{2T} & y_{3T} & \cdots & y_{G^\Delta T} \end{bmatrix}, \quad \mathbf{X_1} = \begin{bmatrix} x_{11} & x_{21} & \cdots & x_{K^* 1} \\ x_{12} & x_{22} & \cdots & x_{K^* 2} \\ \vdots & \vdots & & \vdots \\ x_{1T} & x_{2T} & \cdots & x_{K^* T} \end{bmatrix},$$

$$(T \times 1) \qquad\qquad (T \times \overline{G^\Delta - 1}) \qquad\qquad (T \times K^*)$$

$$\boldsymbol{\beta}_1 = \begin{bmatrix} -\beta_{12} \\ -\beta_{13} \\ \vdots \\ -\beta_{1G^\Delta} \end{bmatrix}, \quad \boldsymbol{\gamma}_1 = \begin{bmatrix} -\gamma_{11} \\ -\gamma_{12} \\ \vdots \\ -\gamma_{1K^*} \end{bmatrix}.$$

$$(\overline{G^\Delta - 1} \times 1) \qquad\qquad (K^* \times 1)$$

An alternative way of writing (13.20) is

(13.20a) $\mathbf{y_1} = \mathbf{Z_1} \boldsymbol{\alpha}_1 + \mathbf{u_1},$

where $\mathbf{Z_1} = [\mathbf{Y_1} \quad \mathbf{X_1}]$ and $\boldsymbol{\alpha}_1 = \begin{bmatrix} \boldsymbol{\beta}_1 \\ \boldsymbol{\gamma}_1 \end{bmatrix}.$

An instrumental variables estimator of the structural coefficients is

(13.21) $\boldsymbol{\alpha}^\dagger = (\mathbf{W_1'Z_1})^{-1}(\mathbf{W_1'y_1}),$

and its asymptotic variance-covariance matrix is

(13.22)   Asympt. Var-Cov $(\boldsymbol{\alpha}^\dagger) = \sigma_{11}(\mathbf{W_1'Z_1})^{-1}(\mathbf{W_1'W_1})(\mathbf{Z_1'W_1})^{-1},$

where $\mathbf{W_1}$ is a $T \times (G^\Delta - 1 + K^*)$ matrix of the observed values of the chosen
instrumental variables. (The formulas for the instrumental variables estimator
and its variance are given by (11.86) and (11.87) of Section 11–4.) The parameter
σ_{11} can be consistently estimated by

(13.23) $s_{11} = \dfrac{(\mathbf{y_1} - \mathbf{Z_1}\boldsymbol{\alpha}_1^\dagger)'(\mathbf{y_1} - \mathbf{Z_1}\boldsymbol{\alpha}_1^\dagger)}{(T - G^\Delta + 1 - K^*)}$

(The consistency of the estimator will not be changed if we use any denominator D in place of $(T - G^\Delta + 1 - K^*)$ *providing* plim $(D/T) = 1$.) As for the choice of appropriate instrumental variables, the problem is confined to the $(G^\Delta - 1)$ included endogenous variables, since the predetermined variables included in the equation can serve as their own instrumental variables. Natural candidates for the "outside" instrumental variables would be the predetermined variables that appear in the system but not in the equation to be estimated. The number of these is K^{**}, which, in the case of an *exactly identified* structural equation, is just equal to $(G^\Delta - 1)$. Let $\underline{X}_1$ be the matrix of the observed values of the excluded predetermined variables, i.e., let

$$(13.24) \qquad \underline{X}_1 = \begin{bmatrix} x_{K^*+1,1} & x_{K^*+2,1} & \cdots & x_{K1} \\ x_{K^*+1,2} & x_{K^*+2,2} & \cdots & x_{K2} \\ \vdots & \vdots & & \vdots \\ x_{K^*+1,T} & x_{K^*+2,T} & \cdots & x_{KT} \end{bmatrix}.$$

The order in which these variables are arranged is immaterial. Then the instrumental variables for our structural equation can be taken as

$$(13.25) \qquad W_1 = [\underline{X}_1 \quad X_1].$$

Therefore,

$$W_1'Z_1 = \begin{bmatrix} \underline{X}_1' \\ X_1' \end{bmatrix} [Y_1 \quad X_1] = \begin{bmatrix} \underline{X}_1'Y_1 & \underline{X}_1'X_1 \\ X_1'Y_1 & X_1'X_1 \end{bmatrix},$$

and

$$W_1'y_1 = \begin{bmatrix} \underline{X}_1'y_1 \\ X_1'y_1 \end{bmatrix}.$$

Hence the instrumental variables estimator of the structural coefficients in the exactly identified case is

$$(13.26) \qquad \alpha_1^\dagger = \begin{bmatrix} \beta_1^\dagger \\ \gamma_1^\dagger \end{bmatrix} = \begin{bmatrix} \underline{X}_1'Y_1 & \underline{X}_1'X_1 \\ X_1'Y_1 & X_1'X_1 \end{bmatrix}^{-1} \begin{bmatrix} \underline{X}_1'y_1 \\ X_1'y_1 \end{bmatrix}.$$

Further, following (13.22) and (13.23) we define a consistent estimator of the variance-covariance matrix of $\alpha^\dagger$ as

$$(13.27) \quad \text{Est. Var-Cov}(\alpha^\dagger) = s_{11} \begin{bmatrix} \underline{X}_1'Y_1 & \underline{X}_1'X_1 \\ X_1'Y_1 & X_1'X_1 \end{bmatrix}^{-1} \begin{bmatrix} \underline{X}_1'\underline{X}_1 & \underline{X}_1'X_1 \\ X_1'\underline{X}_1 & X_1'X_1 \end{bmatrix} \begin{bmatrix} Y_1'\underline{X}_1 & Y_1'X_1 \\ X_1'\underline{X}_1 & X_1'X_1 \end{bmatrix}^{-1},$$

where s_{11} is determined as in (13.23).

The instrumental variables estimator (13.26) is, in fact, *exactly the same* as the indirect least squares estimator described earlier. We shall not give a general proof of this proposition, but we will demonstrate its validity with reference to the supply equation of the supply-demand model (13.1). This equation,

$$Q_t = \beta_1 + \beta_2 P_t + \varepsilon_{2t},$$

is exactly identified, with Y_t being the excluded predetermined variable. In terms of the notation used for instrumental variables estimation, we have

$$\mathbf{Z_1} = [\mathbf{P} \quad \iota],$$

$$\mathbf{W_1} = [\mathbf{Y} \quad \iota],$$

$$\mathbf{y_1} = [\mathbf{Q}],$$

where

$$\mathbf{Q} = \begin{bmatrix} Q_1 \\ Q_2 \\ \vdots \\ Q_T \end{bmatrix}, \quad \mathbf{P} = \begin{bmatrix} P_1 \\ P_2 \\ \vdots \\ P_T \end{bmatrix}, \quad \mathbf{Y} = \begin{bmatrix} Y_1 \\ Y_2 \\ \vdots \\ Y_T \end{bmatrix}, \quad \iota = \begin{bmatrix} 1 \\ 1 \\ \vdots \\ 1 \end{bmatrix}.$$

$$\quad (T \times 1) \qquad\qquad (T \times 1) \qquad\qquad (T \times 1) \qquad\qquad (T \times 1)$$

Then

$$\mathbf{W_1'Z_1} = \begin{bmatrix} \mathbf{Y'} \\ \iota' \end{bmatrix} [\mathbf{P} \quad \iota] = \begin{bmatrix} \sum_t P_t Y_t & \sum_t Y_t \\ \sum_t P_t & T \end{bmatrix},$$

and

$$\mathbf{W_1'y_1} = \begin{bmatrix} \mathbf{Y'} \\ \iota' \end{bmatrix} [\mathbf{Q}] = \begin{bmatrix} \sum_t Q_t Y_t \\ \sum_t Q_t \end{bmatrix}.$$

Therefore, by (13.21) we have

$$(13.28) \qquad \begin{bmatrix} \beta_2^\dagger \\ \beta_1^\dagger \end{bmatrix} = \frac{1}{T \sum P_t Y_t - (\sum P_t)(\sum Y_t)} \begin{bmatrix} T & -\sum_t Y_t \\ -\sum_t P_t & \sum_t P_t Y_t \end{bmatrix} \begin{bmatrix} \sum_t Q_t Y_t \\ \sum_t Q_t \end{bmatrix}$$

$$= \begin{bmatrix} \dfrac{m_{QY}}{m_{PY}} \\ \bar{Q} - \left(\dfrac{m_{QY}}{m_{PY}}\right)\bar{P} \end{bmatrix}.$$

Clearly, these formulas are exactly the same as the indirect least squares formulas.

The equivalence of the indirect least squares and the instrumental variables estimator enables us to use the instrumental variables formula for the asymptotic variance-covariance matrix of the estimated coefficients. This is very useful since the derivation of the asymptotic variance-covariance matrix of the indirect least squares estimator is otherwise awkward. For example, consider estimating the variance-covariance matrix of the estimated coefficients of the supply equation discussed in (13.1). By appropriate substitution into (13.27) we obtain

(13.29)   Est. Var-Cov $\begin{bmatrix} \beta_2^\dagger \\ \beta_1^\dagger \end{bmatrix}$

$$= s_{22} \begin{bmatrix} \sum_t P_t Y_t & \sum_t Y_t \\ \sum_t P_t & T \end{bmatrix}^{-1} \begin{bmatrix} \sum_t Y_t^2 & \sum_t Y_t \\ \sum_t Y_t & T \end{bmatrix} \begin{bmatrix} \sum_t P_t Y_t & \sum_t P_t \\ \sum_t Y_t & T \end{bmatrix}^{-1}$$

$$= \frac{s_{22}}{(Tm_{PY})^2} \begin{bmatrix} T^2 m_{YY} & -T(\sum P_t)m_{YY} \\ -T(\sum P_t)m_{YY} & (\sum P_t)^2 m_{YY} + Tm_{PY}^2 \end{bmatrix}$$

$$= s_{22} \begin{bmatrix} \left(\dfrac{m_{YY}}{m_{PY}^2}\right) & \left(\dfrac{-\bar{P}m_{YY}}{m_{PY}^2}\right) \\ \left(\dfrac{-\bar{P}m_{YY}}{m_{PY}^2}\right) & \left(\dfrac{\bar{P}^2 m_{YY}}{m_{PY}^2} + \dfrac{1}{T}\right) \end{bmatrix},$$

where

(13.30) $$s_{22} = \frac{1}{T-2} \sum_t (Q_t - \beta_1^\dagger - \beta_2^\dagger P_t)^2$$

$$= \frac{1}{T-2} \left(\frac{m_{QQ}m_{PY}^2 - 2m_{QY}m_{QP}m_{PY} + m_{PP}m_{QY}^2}{m_{PY}^2} \right).$$

EXAMPLE   The supply equation in (13.1) can be estimated from the annual data on the American meat market for the period 1919–1941.[3]

Q_t = per capita consumption of meat (pounds);

P_t = retail prices of meat (index, 1935–39 = 100);

Y_t = per capita disposable real income (dollars).

The sample means of these variables are

$$\bar{Q} = 166.1913,$$

$$\bar{P} = \ \ 92.3391,$$

$$\bar{Y} = 495.5652;$$

the sums of squares and cross-products of the deviations from sample means are

$m_{QQ} = 1{,}369.53826,$	$m_{PP} = \ \ 1{,}581.49478,$
$m_{QP} = -352.55217,$	$m_{PY} = \ \ 8{,}354.59130,$
$m_{QY} = 3{,}671.91304,$	$m_{YY} = 83{,}433.65217.$

[3] From G. Tintner, *Econometrics* (New York: Wiley, 1965), p. 169.

The indirect least squares estimates of the structural coefficients of the supply equation are as follows:

$$\tilde{\beta}_2 = \frac{3,671.91304}{8,354.59130} = 0.43951,$$

$$\tilde{\beta}_1 = 166.1913 - 0.43951 \times 92.3391 = 125.60749.$$

The estimate of the variance of the structural disturbance, calculated according to (13.30), is

$$s_{22} = \frac{1,984.9311}{21} = 94.5205.$$

The estimated variances of the indirect least squares estimates are then obtained from (13.29) as follows:

$$\text{Est. Var}(\tilde{\beta}_2) = 94.5205\left(\frac{83,433.65217}{8,354.59130^2}\right) = 0.11298318,$$

$$\text{Est. Var}(\tilde{\beta}_1) = 94.5205\left(\frac{92.3391^2 \times 83,433.65217}{8,354.59130^2} + \frac{1}{23}\right) = 10.23547072.$$

Thus the final result of indirect least squares estimation is

$$Q_t = 125.60749 + 0.43951P_t + \hat{\varepsilon}_{2t}.$$
$$\quad\quad (3.19929) \quad (0.33613)$$

For comparison we also present the (inconsistent) ordinary least squares estimates of the supply equation:

$$Q_t = 145.60676 - 0.22292P_t + e_{2t}.$$

The estimation of an *exactly identified* structural equation when identification is achieved by *restrictions on the variance-covariance matrix* of the structural disturbances, can also be examined in the context of the supply-demand model (13.1). The demand equation

$$Q_t = \alpha_1 + \alpha_2 P_t + \alpha_3 Y_t + \varepsilon_{1t}$$

—which, in the case of no restrictions on the variance-covariance matrix of the disturbances, is underidentified—becomes exactly identified if we assume that ε_{1t} and ε_{2t} are uncorrelated, as discussed in Section 13–2. The identifying relations between the structural coefficients and the reduced form parameters are as follows. First, by substituting the reduced form expressions for Q_t and P_t into the demand equation, we obtain

(13.31) $\pi_{11} = \alpha_1 + \alpha_2 \pi_{21},$

(13.32) $\pi_{12} = \alpha_2 \pi_{22} + \alpha_3.$

Next, from (13.18) we know that

$$\psi_{11} - \alpha_2 \psi_{12} - \beta_2 \psi_{12} + \alpha_2 \beta_2 \psi_{22} = 0,$$

where the ψ's are the elements of the variance-covariance matrix of the reduced form disturbances and β_2 is a structural coefficient of the supply equation. Since from the results for the supply equation we get

$$\beta_2 = \frac{\pi_{12}}{\pi_{22}},$$

we can write

(13.33)
$$\alpha_2 = \frac{\pi_{12}\psi_{12} - \pi_{21}\psi_{11}}{\pi_{12}\psi_{22} - \pi_{22}\psi_{12}}.$$

Equations (13.31), (13.32), and (13.33) enable us to express the structural coefficients α_1, α_2, and α_3 in terms of the π's and ψ's of the reduced form equations. The reduced form parameters can be estimated by application of the ordinary least squares formulas. From the estimates of the reduced form parameters we can determine the corresponding estimates of the α's. Since both equations are now exactly identified, these estimates are maximum likelihood estimates, and their asymptotic variance-covariance matrix can be determined by reference to the information matrix for the appropriate likelihood function. Note that the likelihood function for the sample observations on Q_t and P_t of our supply-demand model is

$$L = -T \log (2\pi) - \frac{T}{2} \log (\sigma_{11}\sigma_{22}) + T \log |\alpha_2 - \beta_2|$$

$$- \frac{\sum_t (Q_t - \alpha_1 - \alpha_2 P_t - \alpha_3 Y_t)^2}{2\sigma_{11}} - \frac{\sum_t (Q_t - \beta_1 - \beta_2 P_t)^2}{2\sigma_{22}}.$$

EXAMPLE We will estimate the demand equation of (13.1) on the assumption of zero covariance between ε_{1t} and ε_{2t} from the data on the American meat market given in the preceding example. First, note that the ordinary least squares estimators of the reduced form coefficients are

$$\hat{\pi}_{12} = \frac{m_{QY}}{m_{YY}},$$

$$\hat{\pi}_{11} = \bar{Q} - \hat{\pi}_{12}\bar{Y},$$

$$\hat{\pi}_{22} = \frac{m_{PY}}{m_{YY}},$$

$$\hat{\pi}_{21} = \bar{P} - \hat{\pi}_{22}\bar{Y}.$$

The variances and the covariance of the reduced form disturbances are estimated as follows:

$$\hat{\psi}_{11} = \frac{m_{QQ} - \hat{\pi}_{12}m_{QY}}{T} = \frac{m_{QQ}m_{YY} - m_{QY}^2}{Tm_{YY}},$$

$$\hat{\psi}_{22} = \frac{m_{PP} - \hat{\pi}_{22}m_{PY}}{T} = \frac{m_{PP}m_{YY} - m_{PY}^2}{Tm_{YY}},$$

$$\hat{\psi}_{12} = \frac{m_{QP} - \hat{\pi}_{12}m_{PY} - \hat{\pi}_{22}m_{QY} + \hat{\pi}_{12}\hat{\pi}_{22}m_{YY}}{T} = \frac{m_{QP}m_{YY} - m_{QY}m_{PY}}{Tm_{YY}}.$$

By substituting these results into (13.33) we find, after some simplifications,

$$\tilde{\alpha}_2 = \frac{m_{QY}m_{QP} - m_{QQ}m_{PY}}{m_{QY}m_{PP} - m_{QP}m_{PY}}$$

$$= \frac{3{,}671.91304 \times (-352.55217) - 1{,}369.53826 \times 8{,}354.59130}{3{,}671.91304 \times 1{,}581.49478 - (-352.55217) \times 8{,}354.59130} = -1.4551.$$

Further, from (13.31), we have

$$\tilde{\alpha}_1 = \hat{\pi}_{11} - \tilde{\alpha}_2\hat{\pi}_{21} = 206.5374,$$

and from (13.32),

$$\tilde{\alpha}_3 = \hat{\pi}_{12} - \tilde{\alpha}_2\hat{\pi}_{22} = 0.1897.$$

Therefore, the estimated demand equation is

$$Q_t = 206.5374 - 1.4551P_t + 0.1897Y_t + \hat{\varepsilon}_{1t}.$$

Under the assumptions of the model, these estimates are consistent and asymptotically efficient. For comparison we also present the ordinary least squares estimates, which are not consistent:

$$Q_t = 185.8452 - 0.9739P_t + 0.1418Y_t + e_{1t}.$$

Two-Stage Least Squares Estimation

In estimating an *overidentified* structural equation belonging to a general interdependent system of equations, there are several methods leading to consistent estimation that can be used. Probably the best-known single equation method is that of *two-stage least squares.* Suppose the overidentified structural equation is the first equation of the system:

$$(13.34) \qquad\qquad \mathbf{y}_1 = \mathbf{Y}_1\boldsymbol{\beta}_1 + \mathbf{X}_1\boldsymbol{\gamma}_1 + \mathbf{u}_1,$$

where $\mathbf{y}_1$ is a $(T \times 1)$ vector of the endogenous variable whose coefficient in the first equation is one, $\mathbf{Y}_1$ is a $T \times (G^\Delta - 1)$ matrix of the remaining endogenous variables in the first equation, $\mathbf{X}_1$ is a $(T \times K^*)$ matrix of the predetermined variables in the first equation, and $\mathbf{u}_1$ is a $(T \times 1)$ vector of the disturbances in this equation. An alternative way of writing (13.34) is

$$(13.34a) \qquad\qquad \mathbf{y}_1 = \mathbf{Z}_1\boldsymbol{\alpha}_1 + \mathbf{u}_1,$$

where $\qquad\qquad \mathbf{Z}_1 = [\mathbf{Y}_1 \quad \mathbf{X}_1] \quad$ and $\quad \boldsymbol{\alpha}_1 = \begin{bmatrix} \boldsymbol{\beta}_1 \\ \boldsymbol{\gamma}_1 \end{bmatrix}.$

The matrix $\mathbf{Y}_1$ can be partitioned to give

$$\mathbf{Y}_1 = [\mathbf{y}_2 \quad \mathbf{y}_3 \quad \cdots \quad \mathbf{y}_{G^\Delta}],$$

where each of the $\mathbf{y}$'s is a vector of order $T \times 1$. The reduced form equations for these variables are

$$\mathbf{y}_2 = \mathbf{X}\boldsymbol{\pi}_2 + \mathbf{v}_2,$$

$$\mathbf{y}_3 = \mathbf{X}\boldsymbol{\pi}_3 + \mathbf{v}_3,$$

$$\vdots$$

$$\mathbf{y}_{G^\Delta} = \mathbf{X}\boldsymbol{\pi}_{G^\Delta} + \mathbf{v}_{G^\Delta},$$

where $\mathbf{X}$ is a $(T \times K)$ matrix of *all* predetermined variables in the system, each of the $\boldsymbol{\pi}$'s represents a $(K \times 1)$ vector of the corresponding reduced form coefficients, and each of the $\mathbf{v}$'s is a $(T \times 1)$ vector of the corresponding reduced form disturbances. Let

$$\mathbf{V}_1 = [\mathbf{v}_2 \quad \mathbf{v}_3 \quad \cdots \quad \mathbf{v}_{G^\Delta}]$$

and

$$\mathbf{Y}_1 - \mathbf{V}_1 = [\mathbf{X}\boldsymbol{\pi}_2 \quad \mathbf{X}\boldsymbol{\pi}_3 \quad \cdots \quad \mathbf{X}\boldsymbol{\pi}_{G^\Delta}].$$

Therefore (13.34) can be written as

(13.35) $$\mathbf{y}_1 = (\mathbf{Y}_1 - \mathbf{V}_1)\boldsymbol{\beta}_1 + \mathbf{X}_1\boldsymbol{\gamma}_1 + (\mathbf{u}_1 + \mathbf{V}_1\boldsymbol{\beta}_1).$$

Since $(\mathbf{Y}_1 - \mathbf{V}_1)$ depends only on $\mathbf{X}$ and does not involve any disturbance, it is uncorrelated with $(\mathbf{u}_1 + \mathbf{V}_1\boldsymbol{\beta}_1)$. Thus applying the ordinary least squares method to (13.35) would lead to consistent estimates of $\boldsymbol{\beta}_1$ and $\boldsymbol{\gamma}_1$. The difficulty is that $\mathbf{V}_1$—and therefore $(\mathbf{Y}_1 - \mathbf{V}_1)$—is not observable. However, we can replace $\mathbf{V}_1$ by the corresponding reduced form least squares residuals and use

$$\mathbf{Y}_1 - \hat{\mathbf{V}}_1 = \hat{\mathbf{Y}}_1 = [\mathbf{X}\hat{\boldsymbol{\pi}}_2 \quad \mathbf{X}\hat{\boldsymbol{\pi}}_3 \quad \cdots \quad \mathbf{X}\hat{\boldsymbol{\pi}}_{G^\Delta}].$$

Clearly,

$$\text{plim}\,(\mathbf{Y}_1 - \hat{\mathbf{V}}_1) = [\mathbf{X}\boldsymbol{\pi}_2 \quad \mathbf{X}\boldsymbol{\pi}_3 \quad \cdots \quad \mathbf{X}\boldsymbol{\pi}_{G^\Delta}] = \mathbf{Y}_1 - \mathbf{V}_1,$$

so that $(\mathbf{Y}_1 - \hat{\mathbf{V}}_1)$ and $(\mathbf{u}_1 + \hat{\mathbf{V}}_1\boldsymbol{\beta}_1)$ are *asymptotically uncorrelated*. Therefore, if we apply the ordinary least squares method to

(13.36) $$\mathbf{y}_1 = \hat{\mathbf{Y}}_1\boldsymbol{\beta}_1 + \mathbf{X}_1\boldsymbol{\gamma}_1 + \mathbf{u}_1^*,$$

where $$\mathbf{u}_1^* = \mathbf{u}_1 + \hat{\mathbf{V}}_1\boldsymbol{\beta}_1,$$

we obtain consistent estimates of $\boldsymbol{\beta}_1$ and $\boldsymbol{\gamma}_1$. These estimates are called "two-stage least squares" because the estimation process may be viewed as consisting of two successive applications of the ordinary least squares method. In the first stage we estimate the reduced form equations for $\mathbf{y}_2, \mathbf{y}_3, \ldots, \mathbf{y}_{G^\Delta}$ and calculate the fitted values of these variables. In the second stage we apply the least squares method to (13.36) where the fitted values of $\mathbf{y}_2, \mathbf{y}_3, \ldots, \mathbf{y}_{G^\Delta}$ are used as explanatory variables.

By analogy with (13.34a), equation (13.36) could also be written as

(13.36a) $$\mathbf{y}_1 = \hat{\mathbf{Z}}_1\boldsymbol{\alpha}_1 + \mathbf{u}_1^*,$$

where $$\hat{\mathbf{Z}}_1 = [\hat{\mathbf{Y}}_1 \quad \mathbf{X}_1].$$

The application of the least squares method to (13.36a) leads to

$$(13.37) \qquad \tilde{\alpha}_1 = \begin{bmatrix} \tilde{\beta}_1 \\ \tilde{\gamma}_1 \end{bmatrix} = (\hat{Z}'\hat{Z})^{-1}(\hat{Z}y_1) = \begin{bmatrix} \hat{Y}_1'\hat{Y}_1 & \hat{Y}_1'X_1 \\ X_1'\hat{Y}_1 & X_1'X_1 \end{bmatrix}^{-1} \begin{bmatrix} \hat{Y}_1'y_1 \\ X_1'y_1 \end{bmatrix}.$$

(In what follows we make use of the fact that ordinary least squares residuals are orthogonal to the fitted value of the dependent variable and to each explanatory variable. This implies that $\hat{V}_1'\hat{Y}_1 = 0$ and $\hat{V}_1'X_1 = 0$.) Since

$$\hat{Y}_1'\hat{Y}_1 = (Y_1 - \hat{V}_1)'(Y_1 - \hat{V}_1) = Y_1'Y_1 - \hat{V}_1'Y_1 - Y_1'\hat{V}_1 + \hat{V}_1'\hat{V}_1$$

$$= Y_1'Y_1 + \hat{V}_1'(\hat{Y}_1 + \hat{V}_1) - (\hat{Y}_1 + \hat{V}_1)'\hat{V}_1 + \hat{V}_1'\hat{V}_1$$

$$= Y_1'Y_1 - \hat{V}_1'\hat{V}_1 - \hat{V}_1'\hat{V}_1 + \hat{V}_1'\hat{V}_1 = Y_1'Y_1 - \hat{V}_1'\hat{V}_1,$$

$$\hat{Y}_1'X_1 = (Y_1 - \hat{V}_1)'X_1 = Y_1'X_1,$$

$$X_1'\hat{Y}_1 = X_1'(Y_1 - \hat{V}_1) = X_1'Y_1,$$

and $\qquad \hat{Y}_1'y_1 = (Y_1 - \hat{V}_1)'y_1 = Y_1'y_1 - \hat{V}'y_1,$

equation (13.37) can be written as

$$(13.38) \qquad \tilde{\alpha}_1 = \begin{bmatrix} \tilde{\beta}_1 \\ \tilde{\gamma}_1 \end{bmatrix} = \begin{bmatrix} Y_1'Y_1 - \hat{V}_1'\hat{V}_1 & Y_1'X_1 \\ X_1'Y_1 & X_1'X_1 \end{bmatrix}^{-1} \begin{bmatrix} Y_1'y_1 - \hat{V}_1'y_1 \\ X_1'y_1 \end{bmatrix}.$$

This is the form in which the formula for the two-stage least squares estimator is usually presented because it shows clearly how this estimator differs from the (inconsistent) ordinary least squares estimator, which is given as

$$(13.39) \qquad \hat{\alpha}_1 = \begin{bmatrix} \hat{\beta}_1 \\ \tilde{\gamma}_1 \end{bmatrix} = \begin{bmatrix} Y_1'Y_1 & Y_1'X_1 \\ X_1'Y_1 & X_1'X_1 \end{bmatrix}^{-1} \begin{bmatrix} Y_1'y_1 \\ X_1'y_1 \end{bmatrix}.$$

The two-stage least squares estimator can also be presented as an *instrumental variables estimator*, with $\hat{Y}_1$ serving as an instrument for Y_1, and X_1 serving as its own instrument. This can be shown as follows. According to (13.21), an instrumental variables estimator of the coefficients of the first structural equation is

$$\alpha_1^\dagger = (W_1'Z_1)^{-1}(W_1'y_1),$$

where W_1 is a matrix of the instrumental variables. By putting

$$W_1 = [\hat{Y}_1 \quad X_1]$$

we obtain

$$W_1'Z_1 = \begin{bmatrix} \hat{Y}_1' \\ X_1' \end{bmatrix} [Y_1 \quad X_1] = \begin{bmatrix} \hat{Y}_1'Y_1 & \hat{Y}_1'X_1 \\ X_1'Y_1 & X_1'X_1 \end{bmatrix},$$

and $\qquad W_1'y_1 = \begin{bmatrix} \hat{Y}_1'y_1 \\ X_1'y_1 \end{bmatrix}.$

But

$$\hat{Y}'Y_1 = (Y_1 - \hat{V}_1)'Y_1 = Y_1'Y_1 - \hat{V}_1'(\hat{Y}_1 + \hat{V}_1) = Y_1'Y_1 - \hat{V}_1'\hat{V}_1,$$

and, from previous results,

$$\hat{Y}_1'X_1 = Y_1'X_1,$$

$$\hat{Y}_1'y_1 = Y_1'y_1 - \hat{V}_1'y_1.$$

Therefore,

$$(13.40) \qquad \alpha_1^\dagger = \begin{bmatrix} Y_1'Y_1 - \hat{V}_1'\hat{V}_1 & Y_1'X_1 \\ X_1'Y_1 & X_1'X_1 \end{bmatrix}^{-1} \begin{bmatrix} Y_1'y_1 - \hat{V}_1'y_1 \\ X_1'y_1 \end{bmatrix},$$

which is precisely the same formula as that for $\tilde{\alpha}_1$ given by (13.38). Because of the equivalence of $\alpha_1^\dagger$ and $\tilde{\alpha}_1$, we can use formula (13.22) to determine the asymptotic variance-covariance matrix of the two-stage least squares estimator. This gives

$$(13.41) \quad \text{Asympt. Var-Cov}(\tilde{\alpha}_1) = \sigma_{11}(W_1'Z_1)^{-1}(W_1'W_1)(Z_1'W_1)^{-1} = \sigma_{11}(W_1'Z_1)^{-1}$$

$$= \sigma_{11} \begin{bmatrix} Y_1'Y_1 - \hat{V}_1'\hat{V}_1 & Y_1'X_1 \\ X_1'Y_1 & X_1'X_1 \end{bmatrix}^{-1},$$

where $\sigma_{11} = \text{Var}(u_{1t})$. A consistent estimator of σ_{11} is, according to (13.23),

$$(13.42) \qquad s_{11} = \frac{(y_1 - Y_1\tilde{\beta}_1 - X_1\tilde{\gamma}_1)'(y_1 - Y_1\tilde{\beta}_1 - X_1\tilde{\gamma}_1)}{T - G^\Delta + 1 - K^*}.$$

The two-stage least squares estimator, although consistent, is in general not asymptotically efficient because it does not take into account the correlation of the structural disturbances across equations. However, its construction does not require a complete knowledge of the whole system; all that is needed is a listing of all predetermined variables and their sample values.

When the two-stage least squares method is applied to an exactly identified equation, the resulting estimates are the same as those obtained by the indirect least squares method. This can be proved as follows. The two-stage least squares estimator can be presented as

$$\tilde{\alpha}_1 = (W_1'Z_1)^{-1}(W_1'y_1),$$

where $\qquad W_1 = [\hat{Y}_1 \quad X_1] \qquad$ and $\qquad Z_1 = [Y_1 \quad X_1].$

Now, we can write

$$(13.43) \qquad\qquad\qquad \hat{Y}_1 = \underline{X}_1 A,$$

where $\underline{X}_1$ is a $(T \times K^{**})$ matrix of the excluded predetermined variables as defined by (13.24), and A is a $(K^{**} \times K^{**})$ matrix defined as

$$A = (\underline{X}_1'\underline{X}_1)^{-1}(\underline{X}_1'Y_1).$$

Of course, the equation to be estimated has to be exactly identified; i.e., it is required that $K^{**} = G^\Delta - 1$, otherwise the dimension of $(\mathbf{X_1 A})$ would not be the same as that of $\mathbf{\hat{Y}_1}$. The legitimacy of (13.43) can be established by substituting for $\mathbf{A}$ and premultiplying both sides by $\mathbf{\underline{X}_1'}$:

$$\mathbf{\underline{X}_1'\hat{Y}_1} = \mathbf{\underline{X}_1'X_1(\underline{X}_1'\underline{X}_1)^{-1}(\underline{X}_1'Y)} = \mathbf{\underline{X}_1'Y_1} = \mathbf{\underline{X}_1'(\hat{Y}_1 + \hat{V}_1)} = \mathbf{\underline{X}_1'\hat{Y}_1}.$$

By substituting for $\mathbf{\hat{Y}_1}$ from (13.43) into the formula for $\mathbf{\tilde{\alpha}_1}$, we obtain

$$(13.44) \qquad \mathbf{\tilde{\alpha}_1} = \mathbf{(W_1'Z_1)^{-1}(W_1'y_1)} = \begin{bmatrix} \mathbf{A'\underline{X}_1'Y_1} & \mathbf{A'\underline{X}_1'X_1} \\ \mathbf{X_1'Y_1} & \mathbf{X_1'X_1} \end{bmatrix}^{-1} \begin{bmatrix} \mathbf{A'\underline{X}_1'y_1} \\ \mathbf{X_1'y_1} \end{bmatrix}$$

$$= \left\{ \begin{bmatrix} \mathbf{A'} & \mathbf{0} \\ \mathbf{0} & \mathbf{I_{K^*}} \end{bmatrix} \begin{bmatrix} \mathbf{\underline{X}_1'Y_1} & \mathbf{\underline{X}_1'X_1} \\ \mathbf{X_1'Y_1} & \mathbf{X_1'X_1} \end{bmatrix} \right\}^{-1} \begin{bmatrix} \mathbf{A'} & \mathbf{0} \\ \mathbf{0} & \mathbf{I_{K^*}} \end{bmatrix} \begin{bmatrix} \mathbf{\underline{X}_1'y_1} \\ \mathbf{X_1'y_1} \end{bmatrix}$$

$$= \begin{bmatrix} \mathbf{\underline{X}_1'Y_1} & \mathbf{\underline{X}_1'X_1} \\ \mathbf{X_1'Y_1} & \mathbf{X_1'X_1} \end{bmatrix}^{-1} \begin{bmatrix} \mathbf{\underline{X}_1'y_1} \\ \mathbf{X_1'y_1} \end{bmatrix}.$$

This expression for $\mathbf{\tilde{\alpha}_1}$ is precisely the same as that for the indirect least squares estimator given by (13.26).

EXAMPLE   Following is a simplified model designed to explain variations in the consumption and prices of food:

$$(13.45) \qquad Q_t = \alpha_1 + \alpha_2 P_t + \alpha_3 D_t + u_{1t} \qquad \text{(demand)},$$

$$Q_t = \beta_1 + \beta_2 P_t + \beta_3 F_t + \beta_4 A_t + u_{2t} \quad \text{(supply)}.$$

Here $Q_t =$ food consumption per head, $P_t =$ ratio of food prices to general consumer prices, $D_t =$ disposable income in constant prices, $F_t =$ ratio of preceding year's prices received by farmers for products to general consumer prices, and $A_t =$ time in years. The variables Q_t and P_t are endogenous, while D_t, F_t, and A_t are predetermined. The demand equation is overidentified; the supply equation is exactly identified. Instead of estimating this model from actual data, we will *simulate* the sample observations on prices and quantities by presetting the values of the parameters, specifying the sample values of the predetermined variables, and drawing the values of the disturbances at random from a normal population. Using such an artificial sample, we may try various methods to compare the estimates of the parameters with their true values. Specifically, let the true model be

$$(13.45a) \qquad Q_t = 96.5 - 0.25P_t + 0.30D_t + u_{1t} \qquad \text{(demand)},$$

$$Q_t = 62.5 + 0.15P_t + 0.20F_t + 0.36A_t + u_{2t} \quad \text{(supply)}.$$

The true reduced form for this model is

$$(13.46) \qquad Q_t = 75.25 + 0.1125D_t + 0.125F_t + 0.225A_t + v_{1t},$$

$$P_t = 85.00 + 0.75D_t - 0.50F_t - 0.90A_t + v_{2t}.$$

Suppose now that we draw two sets of 20 values of random $N(0,1)$ deviates from the table in Appendix D. Let us call the values belonging to the first set ε_{1t} and those belonging to the second set ε_{2t} $(t = 1, 2, \ldots, 20)$. The values of the reduced form disturbances are then constructed as

$$v_{1t} = 2\varepsilon_{1t},$$

$$v_{2t} = -0.5\, v_{1t} + \varepsilon_{2t}.$$

This implies the following variance-covariance matrix of the reduced form disturbances:

$$\Psi = \begin{bmatrix} 4 & -2 \\ -2 & 2 \end{bmatrix}.$$

Since for our model

$$u_{1t} = v_{1t} + 0.25 v_{2t},$$

$$u_{2t} = v_{1t} - 0.15 v_{2t},$$

the variance-covariance matrix of the structural disturbances is

$$\Phi = \begin{bmatrix} 3.125 & 3.725 \\ 3.725 & 4.645 \end{bmatrix}.$$

The choice of the values of the elements of Ψ is, of course, arbitrary. The sample values of D_t and F_t are taken from a paper by Girschick and Haavelmo.[4] They represent actual values for the United States economy for the years 1922–1941, expressed in terms of index numbers with the average for 1935–39 = 100. The values of Q_t and P_t are calculated according to (13.46). The resulting sample data are given in Table 13–1. The ordinary least squares estimates of the reduced form equations are

$$Q_t = 72.2778 + 0.1126 D_t + 0.1646 F_t + 0.1648 A_t + \hat{v}_{1t}, \qquad R^2 = 0.7076,$$

$$P_t = 87.3149 + 0.7020 D_t - 0.5206 F_t - 0.5209 A_t + \hat{v}_{2t}, \qquad R^2 = 0.8719.$$

These may be compared with the true reduced form equations given by (13.46). Applying the two-stage least squares method to the structural equations in (13.45), we obtain

$$Q_t = 94.6333 - 0.2436 P_t + 0.3140 D_t + \tilde{u}_{1t} \qquad \text{(demand)},$$
$$(7.9208) \quad\; (0.0965) \quad\;\; (0.0469)$$

$$Q_t = 49.5324 + 0.2401 P_t + 0.2556 F_t + 0.2529 A_t + \tilde{u}_{2t} \quad \text{(supply)}.$$
$$(12.0105) \quad (0.0999) \quad\;\, (0.0472) \quad\;\;\; (0.0996)$$

The figures in parentheses are the estimated standard errors. These results may be compared with the true structural equations (13.45a). It is also interesting to show the (inconsistent) ordinary least squares estimates of the two structural equations:

$$Q_t = 99.8954 - 0.3163 P_t + 0.3346 D_t + \hat{u}_{1t} \qquad \text{(demand)},$$
$$R^2 = 0.7638,$$

$$Q_t = 58.2754 + 0.1604 P_t + 0.2481 F_t + 0.2483 A_t + \hat{u}_{2t} \quad \text{(supply)},$$
$$R^2 = 0.6548.$$

[4] M. A. Girschick and T. Haavelmo, "Statistical Analysis of the Demand for Food: Examples of Simultaneous Estimation of Structural Equations," *Econometrica*, Vol. 15, April 1947, pp. 79–110; reprinted in W. C. Hood and T. C. Koopmans (eds.), *Studies in Econometric Method* (New York: Wiley, 1953).

Table 13–1

Q_t	P_t	D_t	F_t	A_t
98.485	100.323	87.4	98.0	1
99.187	104.264	97.6	99.1	2
102.163	103.435	96.7	99.1	3
101.504	104.506	98.2	98.1	4
104.240	98.001	99.8	110.8	5
103.243	99.456	100.5	108.2	6
103.993	101.066	103.2	105.6	7
99.900	104.763	107.8	109.8	8
100.350	96.446	96.6	108.7	9
102.820	91.228	88.9	100.6	10
95.435	93.085	75.1	81.0	11
92.424	98.801	76.9	68.6	12
94.535	102.908	84.6	70.9	13
98.757	98.756	90.6	81.4	14
105.797	95.119	103.1	102.3	15
100.225	98.451	105.1	105.0	16
103.522	86.498	96.4	110.5	17
99.929	104.016	104.4	92.5	18
105.223	105.769	110.7	89.3	19
106.232	113.490	127.1	93.0	20

k-Class Estimators

The formula for the two-stage least squares estimator as given by (13.38) can be generalized to cover a whole class of different estimators. These estimators, known as *k-class estimators*, are defined as

$$(13.47) \quad \tilde{\alpha}_1^{(k)} = \begin{bmatrix} \tilde{\beta}_1^{(k)} \\ \gamma_1^{(k)} \end{bmatrix} = \begin{bmatrix} Y_1'Y_1 - k\hat{V}_1'\hat{V}_1 & Y_1'X_1 \\ X'Y_1 & X_1'X_1 \end{bmatrix}^{-1} \begin{bmatrix} Y_1'y_1 - k\hat{V}_1'y_1 \\ X_1'y_1 \end{bmatrix}.$$

This formula differs from (13.38) only because $\hat{V}_1'\hat{V}_1$ and $\hat{V}_1'y_1$ are multiplied by a scalar k. This scalar can be set a priori to be equal to some number, or its value can be determined from the sample observations according to some rule. We have already encountered two k-class estimators; namely the two-stage least squares estimator for which $k = 1$, and the ordinary least squares estimator [given by (13.39)] for which $k = 0$. The fact that the ordinary least squares estimator belongs to the k-class indicates that not all k-class estimators are consistent. To find which values of k lead to consistent estimates, we first note that (13.47) can be formally expressed as a formula for an *instrumental variables estimator*. This can be shown as follows. An instrumental variables estimator of the first structural equation is, according to (13.21), defined as

$$\alpha_1^\dagger = (W_1'Z_1)^{-1}(W_1'y_1),$$

where
$$Z_1 = [Y_1 \quad X_1],$$

as before. By choosing the instrumental variables as

$$\mathbf{W}_1 = [(\mathbf{Y}_1 - k\hat{\mathbf{V}}_1) \quad \mathbf{X}_1],$$

we have

$$\boldsymbol{\alpha}_1^\dagger = \begin{bmatrix} (\mathbf{Y}_1 - k\hat{\mathbf{V}}_1)'\mathbf{Y}_1 & (\mathbf{Y}_1 - k\hat{\mathbf{V}}_1)'\mathbf{X}_1 \\ \mathbf{X}_1'\mathbf{Y}_1 & \mathbf{X}_1'\mathbf{X}_1 \end{bmatrix}^{-1} \begin{bmatrix} (\mathbf{Y}_1 - k\hat{\mathbf{V}}_1)'\mathbf{y}_1 \\ \mathbf{X}_1'\mathbf{y}_1 \end{bmatrix}.$$

However,

$$(\mathbf{Y}_1 - k\hat{\mathbf{V}}_1)'\mathbf{Y}_1 = \mathbf{Y}_1'\mathbf{Y}_1 - k\hat{\mathbf{V}}_1'(\hat{\mathbf{Y}}_1 + \hat{\mathbf{V}}_1) = \mathbf{Y}_1'\mathbf{Y}_1 - k\hat{\mathbf{V}}_1'\hat{\mathbf{V}}_1$$

$$(\mathbf{Y}_1 - k\hat{\mathbf{V}}_1)'\mathbf{X}_1 = \mathbf{Y}_1'\mathbf{X}_1 - k\hat{\mathbf{V}}_1'\mathbf{X}_1 = \mathbf{Y}_1'\mathbf{X}_1,$$

$$(\mathbf{Y}_1 - k\hat{\mathbf{V}}_1)'\mathbf{y}_1 = \mathbf{Y}_1'\mathbf{y}_1 - k\hat{\mathbf{V}}_1'\mathbf{y}_1;$$

therefore,

$$(13.48) \qquad \boldsymbol{\alpha}_1^\dagger = \begin{bmatrix} \mathbf{Y}_1'\mathbf{Y}_1 - k\hat{\mathbf{V}}_1'\hat{\mathbf{V}}_1 & \mathbf{Y}_1'\mathbf{X}_1 \\ \mathbf{X}_1'\mathbf{Y}_1 & \mathbf{X}_1'\mathbf{X}_1 \end{bmatrix}^{-1} \begin{bmatrix} \mathbf{Y}_1'\mathbf{y}_1 - k\hat{\mathbf{V}}_1'\mathbf{y}_1 \\ \mathbf{X}_1'\mathbf{y}_1 \end{bmatrix},$$

which is precisely the same as $\tilde{\boldsymbol{\alpha}}^{(k)}$ in (13.47). However, $\mathbf{W}_1$ does not qualify as a set of instrumental variables *unless* these variables are asymptotically uncorrelated with the structural disturbance $\mathbf{u}_1$, i.e., unless

$$\operatorname{plim} \frac{1}{T}\, \mathbf{W}_1'\mathbf{u}_1 = \mathbf{0}.$$

That is, we require

$$(13.49) \qquad\qquad \operatorname{plim} \frac{1}{T}\, (\mathbf{Y}_1 - k\hat{\mathbf{V}}_1)'\mathbf{u}_1 = \mathbf{0},$$

$$(13.50) \qquad\qquad \operatorname{plim} \frac{1}{T}\, \mathbf{X}_1'\mathbf{u}_1 = \mathbf{0}.$$

Now (13.50) is always satisfied, since all predetermined variables are uncorrelated with the structural disturbances by definition. As for (13.49), we have

$$(13.49a) \quad \operatorname{plim} \frac{1}{T}\, (\mathbf{Y}_1 - k\hat{\mathbf{V}}_1)'\mathbf{u}_1 = \operatorname{plim} \frac{1}{T}\, \mathbf{Y}_1'\mathbf{u}_1 - \operatorname{plim} k \cdot \operatorname{plim} \hat{\mathbf{V}}_1'\mathbf{u}_1$$

$$= \operatorname{plim} \frac{1}{T}\, (\hat{\mathbf{Y}}_1 + \hat{\mathbf{V}}_1)'\mathbf{u}_1 - \operatorname{plim} k \cdot \operatorname{plim} \hat{\mathbf{V}}_1'\mathbf{u}_1$$

$$= \operatorname{plim} \frac{1}{T}\, \hat{\mathbf{V}}_1'\mathbf{u}_1 - \operatorname{plim} k \cdot \operatorname{plim} \hat{\mathbf{V}}_1'\mathbf{u}_1.$$

Since $\operatorname{plim} (\hat{\mathbf{V}}_1'\mathbf{u}_1)/T$ is a finite number different from zero, it follows that

$$\operatorname{plim} \frac{1}{T}\, (\mathbf{Y}_1 - k\hat{\mathbf{V}}_1)'\mathbf{u}_1 = 0$$

if and only if

$$(13.51) \qquad\qquad \operatorname{plim} k = 1.$$

This condition is automatically fulfilled in the case of two-stage least squares estimation in which k is *always* equal to one. Further, it can be shown that the asymptotic variance-covariance matrix of all k-class estimators for which

$$(13.52) \qquad \text{plim } \sqrt{T}(k - 1) = 0$$

reduces to (13.41).[5] This means that all of these estimators must have the same asymptotic variance-covariance matrix as the two-stage least squares estimator. This matrix is usually estimated as follows:

$$(13.53) \qquad \text{Est. Var-Cov}(\tilde{\alpha}^{(k)}) = s_{11}\begin{bmatrix} \mathbf{Y}_1'\mathbf{Y}_1 - k\hat{\mathbf{V}}_1'\hat{\mathbf{V}}_1 & \mathbf{Y}_1'\mathbf{X}_1 \\ \mathbf{X}_1'\mathbf{Y}_1 & \mathbf{X}_1'\mathbf{X}_1 \end{bmatrix}^{-1}$$

where

$$(13.54) \qquad s_{11} = \frac{(\mathbf{y}_1 - \mathbf{Z}_1\tilde{\alpha}_1^{(k)})'(\mathbf{y}_1 - \mathbf{Z}_1\tilde{\alpha}_1^{(k)})}{T - G^{\Delta} + 1 - K^*}.$$

This, of course, is asymptotically equivalent to (13.41).

Limited Information Maximum Likelihood Estimation

Another single equation estimator, which is known as the *limited information maximum likelihood estimator*, also belongs to the k-class family and is consistent. It is derived by maximizing the likelihood function for the observations on the endogenous variables included in the equation to be estimated. The phrase "limited information" means that, in setting up the likelihood function, we limit ourselves to those endogenous variables that appear in the equation under investigation and disregard the identifying restrictions on the remaining structural equations. Suppose this equation is again the first one of the system as described by (13.34):

$$\mathbf{y}_1 = \mathbf{Y}_1\boldsymbol{\beta}_1 + \mathbf{X}_1\boldsymbol{\gamma}_1 + \mathbf{u}_1,$$

where
$$\mathbf{Y}_1 = [\mathbf{y}_2 \quad \mathbf{y}_3 \quad \cdots \quad \mathbf{y}_{G^{\Delta}}].$$

Thus the included endogenous variables are $y_{1t}, y_{2t}, \ldots, y_{G^{\Delta}t}$. The reduced form equations for these variables are

$$y_{1t} = \pi_{11}x_{1t} + \pi_{12}x_{2t} + \cdots + \pi_{1K}x_{Kt} + v_{1t},$$

$$y_{2t} = \pi_{21}x_{1t} + \pi_{22}x_{2t} + \cdots + \pi_{2K}x_{Kt} + v_{2t},$$

$$\vdots$$

$$y_{G^{\Delta}t} = \pi_{G^{\Delta}1}x_{1t} + \pi_{G^{\Delta}2}x_{2t} + \cdots + \pi_{G^{\Delta}K}x_{Kt} + v_{G^{\Delta}t}.$$

[5] See H. Theil, *Economic Forecasts and Policy*, 2nd ed. (Amsterdam: North-Holland Publishing Company, 1961), p. 232.

Since $v_{1t}, v_{2t}, \ldots, v_{G^\Delta t}$ are normally distributed stochastic disturbances, their joint distribution is[6]

$$f(v_{1t}, v_{2t}, \ldots, v_{G^\Delta t}) = (2\pi)^{-(G^\Delta/2)} |\boldsymbol{\Psi}_\Delta|^{-(1/2)} e^{-(1/2)\mathbf{v}'_{\Delta t}\boldsymbol{\Psi}_\Delta^{-1}\mathbf{v}_{\Delta t}}$$

where

$$\mathbf{v}_{\Delta t} = \begin{bmatrix} v_{1t} \\ v_{2t} \\ \vdots \\ v_{G^\Delta t} \end{bmatrix} \quad \text{and} \quad \boldsymbol{\Psi}_\Delta = E(\mathbf{v}_\Delta \mathbf{v}'_\Delta) = \begin{bmatrix} \psi_{11} & \psi_{12} & \cdots & \psi_{1G^\Delta} \\ \psi_{21} & \psi_{22} & \cdots & \psi_{2G^\Delta} \\ \vdots & \vdots & & \\ \psi_{G^\Delta 1} & \psi_{G^\Delta 2} & \cdots & \psi_{G^\Delta G^\Delta} \end{bmatrix}.$$

Under the classical assumptions concerning disturbances, the joint distribution of $v_{1t}, v_{2t}, \ldots, v_{G^\Delta t}$ for all sample observations is

$$(13.55) \quad f(v_{11}, v_{12}, \ldots, v_{1T}, v_{21}, v_{22}, \ldots, v_{G^\Delta T}) = (2\pi)^{-(TG^\Delta/2)} |\boldsymbol{\Psi}_\Delta|^{-(T/2)} e^{-\sum_t \mathbf{v}'_{\Delta t}\boldsymbol{\Psi}_\Delta^{-1}\mathbf{v}_{\Delta t}}.$$

We are interested in the likelihood function for the sample observations on the G^Δ endogenous variables included in the first structural equation. This so-called *limited information likelihood function* is obtained from (13.55) by expressing the elements of $\mathbf{v}_{\Delta t}$ in terms of the y's. Furthermore, we know that the y's are linearly connected by the structural equation that is being estimated. This fact is taken into account by maximizing the limited information likelihood function *subject* to the identifying restrictions for this equation. These restrictions, which are derived from (13.10), are

$$(13.56) \qquad \pi_{11} = -\beta_{12}\pi_{21} - \beta_{13}\pi_{31} - \cdots - \beta_{1G^\Delta}\pi_{G^\Delta 1} - \gamma_{11},$$

$$\pi_{12} = -\beta_{12}\pi_{22} - \beta_{13}\pi_{32} - \cdots - \beta_{1G^\Delta}\pi_{G^\Delta 2} - \gamma_{12},$$

$$\vdots$$

$$\pi_{1K*} = -\beta_{12}\pi_{2K*} - \beta_{13}\pi_{3K*} - \cdots - \beta_{1G^\Delta}\pi_{G^\Delta K*} - \gamma_{1K*},$$

$$\pi_{1, K*+1} = -\beta_{12}\pi_{2, K*+1} - \beta_{13}\pi_{3, K*+1} - \cdots - \beta_{1G^\Delta}\pi_{G^\Delta, K*+1},$$

$$\vdots$$

$$\pi_{1K} = -\beta_{12}\pi_{2K} - \beta_{13}\pi_{3K} - \cdots - \beta_{1G^\Delta}\pi_{G^\Delta K}.$$

These restrictions can be introduced into the limited information likelihood function by putting

$$v_{1t} = y_{1t} - \pi_{11}x_{1t} - \ldots - \pi_{1K}x_{Kt},$$

$$v_{2t} = y_{2t} - \pi_{21}x_{1t} - \cdots - \pi_{2K}x_{Kt},$$

$$\vdots$$

$$v_{G^\Delta T} = y_{G^\Delta t} - \pi_{G^\Delta 1}x_{1t} - \cdots - \pi_{G^\Delta K}x_{Kt},$$

and then replacing $\pi_{11}, \pi_{12}, \ldots, \pi_{1K}$ with the expressions on the right-hand side of (13.56). The resulting function then can be maximized with respect to the unknown parameters that include the structural coefficients.

[6] A. S. Goldberger, *Econometric Theory* (New York: Wiley, 1964), p. 104. If the x's are stochastic, the joint distribution of the v's should be viewed as being conditional on the sample values of the x's.

To derive the limited information maximum likelihood estimator by maximizing the restricted likelihood function is quite complicated. However, the same results can also be obtained by utilizing the so-called *least variance ratio principle*. The equivalence of the two approaches is well known and will not be proved here.[7] The least variance ratio estimates are derived as follows. The first structural equation,

$$\mathbf{y}_1 = \mathbf{Y}_1\boldsymbol{\beta}_1 + \mathbf{X}_1\boldsymbol{\gamma}_1 + \mathbf{u}_1$$

can be written as

(13.57) $$\tilde{\mathbf{y}}_1 = \mathbf{X}_1\boldsymbol{\gamma}_1 + \mathbf{u}_1,$$

where $$\tilde{\mathbf{y}}_1 = \mathbf{y}_1 - \mathbf{Y}_1\boldsymbol{\beta}_1.$$

The "composite" variable $\tilde{\mathbf{y}}_1$ represents a linear combination of the endogenous variables included in the first structural equation. If its values could be observed, we could estimate $\boldsymbol{\gamma}_1$ by the ordinary least squares method. This would lead to

$$\hat{\boldsymbol{\gamma}}_1 = (\mathbf{X}_1'\mathbf{X}_1)^{-1}\mathbf{X}_1'\tilde{\mathbf{y}}_1,$$

and the sum of the squared residuals would be

$$\mathrm{SSE}_1 = (\tilde{\mathbf{y}}_1 - \mathbf{X}_1\hat{\boldsymbol{\gamma}}_1)'(\tilde{\mathbf{y}}_1 - \mathbf{X}_1\boldsymbol{\gamma}_1) = \tilde{\mathbf{y}}_1'\tilde{\mathbf{y}}_1 - \tilde{\mathbf{y}}_1'\mathbf{X}_1(\mathbf{X}_1'\mathbf{X}_1)^{-1}\mathbf{X}_1'\tilde{\mathbf{y}}_1.$$

Note that in (13.57) the explanatory variables consist of the predetermined variables included in the first structural equation. If this set were extended to include *all* the predetermined variables of the system, we would have

(13.58) $$\tilde{\mathbf{y}}_1 = \mathbf{X}\boldsymbol{\gamma} + \mathbf{u}_1,$$

where $\mathbf{X}$ is a $(T \times K)$ matrix of all predetermined variables and

$$\boldsymbol{\gamma} = \begin{bmatrix} \boldsymbol{\gamma}_1 \\ \mathbf{0}_{**} \end{bmatrix}.$$
$$(K \times 1)$$

If we applied the ordinary least squares method to (13.58)—ignoring the fact that the true value of some of the γ coefficients is zero—we would get

$$\hat{\boldsymbol{\gamma}} = (\mathbf{X}'\mathbf{X})^{-1}(\mathbf{X}'\tilde{\mathbf{y}}_1),$$

and the sum of the squared residuals would be

$$\mathrm{SSE} = (\tilde{\mathbf{y}}_1 - \mathbf{X}\boldsymbol{\gamma})'(\tilde{\mathbf{y}}_1 - \mathbf{X}\boldsymbol{\gamma}) = \tilde{\mathbf{y}}_1'\tilde{\mathbf{y}}_1 - \tilde{\mathbf{y}}_1'\mathbf{X}(\mathbf{X}'\mathbf{X})^{-1}\mathbf{X}'\tilde{\mathbf{y}}_1.$$

Since the addition of further explanatory variables can never increase the residual sum of squares, the ratio

(13.59) $$\ell = \frac{\mathrm{SSE}_1}{\mathrm{SSE}} = \frac{\tilde{\mathbf{y}}_1'\tilde{\mathbf{y}}_1 - \tilde{\mathbf{y}}_1'\mathbf{X}_1(\mathbf{X}_1'\mathbf{X}_1)^{-1}\mathbf{X}_1'\tilde{\mathbf{y}}_1}{\tilde{\mathbf{y}}_1'\tilde{\mathbf{y}}_1 - \tilde{\mathbf{y}}_1'\mathbf{X}(\mathbf{X}'\mathbf{X})^{-1}\mathbf{X}'\tilde{\mathbf{y}}_1}$$

can never be smaller than unity.

[7] See T. C. Koopmans and W. C. Hood, "The Estimation of Simultaneous Linear Economic Relationships," in Hood and Koopmans, *op. cit.*, pp. 166–177.

The problem now is to estimate the elements of β_1. Let us write

(13.60) $$\tilde{y}_1 = Y_{1\Delta}\beta_{1\Delta},$$

where $\qquad Y_{1\Delta} = [y_1 \quad y_2 \quad \cdots \quad y_{G^\Delta}] \qquad$ and $\qquad \beta_{1\Delta} = \begin{bmatrix} 1 \\ \beta_{12} \\ \vdots \\ \beta_{1G^\Delta} \end{bmatrix}.$

Therefore, (13.59) can be written as

(13.59a) $$\ell = \frac{\beta'_{1\Delta}W_{1*}\beta_{1\Delta}}{\beta'_{1\Delta}W_1\beta_{1\Delta}}$$

where $$W_{1*} = Y'_{1\Delta}Y_{1\Delta} - (Y'_{1\Delta}X_1)(X'_1X_1)^{-1}X'_1Y_{1\Delta},$$

$$W_1 = Y'_{1\Delta}Y_{1\Delta} - (Y'_{1\Delta}X)(X'X)^{-1}X'Y_{1\Delta}.$$

The least variance ratio estimator of $\beta_{1\Delta}$ is given by those values of the β coefficients that lead to the smallest value of ℓ. Thus we have to minimize ℓ with respect to $\beta_{1\Delta}$. Taking the first derivative of ℓ, we get

(13.61) $$\frac{\partial \ell}{\partial \beta_{1\Delta}} = \frac{2(W_{1*}\beta_{1\Delta})(\beta'_{1\Delta}W_1\beta_{1\Delta}) - 2(\beta'_{1\Delta}W_{1*}\beta_{1\Delta})(W_1\beta_{1\Delta})}{(\beta'_{1\Delta}W_1\beta_{1\Delta})^2}.$$

By setting this equal to zero, we obtain

(13.62) $$W_{1*}\tilde{\tilde{\beta}}_{1\Delta} - \left[\frac{\beta'_{1\Delta}W_{1*}\beta_{1\Delta}}{\beta'_{1\Delta}W_1\beta_{1\Delta}}\right]W_1\tilde{\tilde{\beta}}_{1\Delta} = 0$$

or

(13.62a) $$(W_{1*} - \ell W_1)\tilde{\tilde{\beta}}_{1\Delta} = 0.$$

Now, for $\tilde{\tilde{\beta}}_{1\Delta} \neq 0$ we must have

(13.63) $$\text{Det}(W_{1*} - \ell W_1) = 0;$$

that is, the determinant of the matrix $(W_{1*} - \ell W_1)$—whose dimension is $(G^\Delta \times G^\Delta)$—must equal zero. Since all elements of W_{1*} and W_1 can be determined from the sample observations, equation (13.63) becomes a polynomial of G^Δ degree in ℓ. As noted, we want ℓ to be as close to unity as possible, and thus the appropriate root of (13.63) is the smallest one, say, ℓ_1. By using ℓ_1 in place of ℓ in (13.62a), we can obtain a solution for the $(G^\Delta - 1)$ unknown elements of $\tilde{\tilde{\beta}}_{1\Delta}$. The elements of γ_1 are then estimated by

(13.64) $$\tilde{\tilde{\gamma}}_1 = (X'_1X_1)^{-1}(X'_1\tilde{y}_1) = (X'_1X_1)^{-1}(X'_1Y_{1\Delta})\tilde{\tilde{\beta}}_1.$$

These are the limited information maximum likelihood estimates.

When the limited information maximum likelihood estimator was introduced, we mentioned that it belongs to the k-class family. We can now elaborate by stating that, for this estimator,

$$k = \ell_1$$

and that

$$\text{plim } \ell_1 = 1,$$

$$\text{plim } \sqrt{T}(\ell_1 - 1) = 0.$$

The proof of these propositions can be found elsewhere.[8] Their implications are that the limited information maximum likelihood estimator is consistent and that it has the same asymptotic variance-covariance matrix as the two-stage least squares estimator. One difference between these two estimators is that the limited information maximum likelihood estimator is *invariant* with respect to the choice of the endogenous variable whose structural coefficient is to be equal to one, whereas the two-stage least squares estimator is not invariant in this respect. Consider the first structural equation written as

$$\beta_{11}y_{1t} + \beta_{12}y_{2t} + \cdots + \beta_{1G^\Delta}y_{G^\Delta t} + \gamma_{11}x_{1t} + \cdots + \gamma_{1K*}x_{K*t} = u_{1t}.$$

In deriving the two-stage least squares estimator and the limited information maximum likelihood estimator, we have taken the value of β_{11} to be equal to one. This means that the structural equation may be written as

$$y_{1t} = -\beta_{12}y_{2t} - \cdots - \beta_{1G^\Delta}y_{G^\Delta t} - \gamma_{11}x_{1t} - \cdots - \gamma_{1K*}x_{K*t} + u_{1t}.$$

In our notation the two-stage least squares estimate of β_{12} is $\tilde{\beta}_{12}$ and the limited information maximum likelihood estimate is $\tilde{\tilde{\beta}}_{12}$. Now suppose we change our specification and take β_{12}, rather than β_{11}, to be equal to one. Then the structural equation would be written as

$$y_{2t} = -\beta_{11}y_{1t} - \cdots - \beta_{1G^\Delta}y_{G^\Delta t} - \gamma_{11}x_{1t} - \cdots - \gamma_{1K*}x_{K*t} + u_{1t}.$$

The two-stage least squares estimate of β_{11} is $\tilde{\beta}_{11}$, and the limited information maximum likelihood estimate is $\tilde{\tilde{\beta}}_{11}$. Then

$$\tilde{\beta}_{11} \neq \frac{1}{\tilde{\beta}_{12}},$$

but

$$\tilde{\tilde{\beta}}_{11} = \frac{1}{\tilde{\tilde{\beta}}_{12}}.$$

This is what is meant by "invariance" of the limited information maximum likelihood estimator. In this respect it is unique among all members of the k-class family.[9] Invariance may be useful whenever economic theory offers no guidance concerning the choice of endogenous variable for which the structural coefficient is to be unity. Finally, it may be noted that when the structural equation is exactly identified, the limited information maximum likelihood method leads to the same result as the indirect least squares method.

---

[8] See Goldberger, *op. cit.*, pp. 341–344.

[9] See A. S. Goldberger, "An Instrumental Variable Interpretation of k-Class Estimation," *Indian Economic Journal*, Vol. 13, No. 3, 1965, pp. 424–431.

EXAMPLE   We can illustrate the construction of the limited information maximum likelihood estimates by reference to the food market model (13.45). The two-equation model given by (13.45) is

$$Q_t = \alpha_1 + \alpha_2 P_t + \alpha_3 D_t + u_{1t} \qquad \text{(demand)},$$

$$Q_t = \beta_1 + \beta_2 P_t + \beta_3 F_t + \beta_4 A_t + u_{2t} \quad \text{(supply)}.$$

The sample observations ($T = 20$) are given in Table 13–1. For the demand equation, which is overidentified, we have

$$\mathbf{Y}_{1\Delta} = \begin{bmatrix} Q_1 & P_1 \\ Q_2 & P_2 \\ \vdots & \vdots \\ Q_{20} & P_{20} \end{bmatrix}, \quad \mathbf{X}_1 = \begin{bmatrix} 1 & D_1 \\ 1 & D_2 \\ \vdots & \vdots \\ 1 & D_{20} \end{bmatrix}, \quad \mathbf{X} = \begin{bmatrix} 1 & D_1 & F_1 & A_1 \\ 1 & D_2 & F_2 & A_2 \\ \vdots & \vdots & \vdots & \vdots \\ 1 & D_{20} & F_{20} & A_{20} \end{bmatrix},$$

$$\boldsymbol{\beta}_{1\Delta} = \begin{bmatrix} 1 \\ -\alpha_2 \end{bmatrix}, \quad \boldsymbol{\gamma}_1 = \begin{bmatrix} \alpha_1 \\ \alpha_3 \end{bmatrix}.$$

Then,

$$\mathbf{W}_{1*} = \begin{bmatrix} \sum Q_t^2 & \sum Q_t P_t \\ \sum Q_t P_t & \sum P_t^2 \end{bmatrix} - \begin{bmatrix} \sum Q_t & \sum Q_t D_t \\ \sum P_t & \sum P_t D_t \end{bmatrix} \begin{bmatrix} T & \sum D_t \\ \sum D_t & \sum D_t^2 \end{bmatrix}^{-1} \begin{bmatrix} \sum Q_t & \sum P_t \\ \sum Q_t D_t & \sum P_t D_t \end{bmatrix}$$

and

$$\mathbf{W}_1 = \begin{bmatrix} \sum Q_t^2 & \sum Q_t P_t \\ \sum Q_t P_t & \sum P_t^2 \end{bmatrix} - \begin{bmatrix} \sum Q_t & \sum Q_t D_t & \sum Q_t F_t & \sum Q_t A_t \\ \sum P_t & \sum P_t D_t & \sum P_t F_t & \sum P_t A_t \end{bmatrix}$$

$$\times \begin{bmatrix} T & \sum D_t & \sum F_t & \sum A_t \\ \sum D_t & \sum D_t^2 & \sum D_t F_t & \sum D_t A_t \\ \sum F_t & \sum F_t D_t & \sum F_t^2 & \sum F_t A_t \\ \sum A_t & \sum A_t D_t & \sum A_t F_t & \sum A_t^2 \end{bmatrix}^{-1} \begin{bmatrix} \sum Q_t & \sum P_t \\ \sum Q_t D_t & \sum P_t D_t \\ \sum Q_t F_t & \sum P_t F_t \\ \sum Q_t A_t & \sum P_t A_t \end{bmatrix}.$$

Thus the determinant of $(\mathbf{W}_{1*} - \ell\mathbf{W}_1)$ is a second-degree polynomial in ℓ. Its two roots are

$$\ell_1 = 1.1739 \qquad \text{and} \qquad \ell_2 = 12.0031.$$

Therefore, (13.62a) becomes

(13.65) $$[\mathbf{W}_{1*} - 1.1739\,\mathbf{W}_1] \begin{bmatrix} 1 \\ -\tilde{\alpha}_2 \end{bmatrix} = \begin{bmatrix} 0 \\ 0 \end{bmatrix}.$$

The two equations in (13.65) lead to the same value of $\tilde{\alpha}_2$:

$$\tilde{\alpha}_2 = -0.2295.$$

The solution for $\tilde{\tilde{\gamma}}_1$ is obtained from (13.64) as

$$\tilde{\tilde{\gamma}}_1 = \begin{bmatrix} \tilde{\alpha}_1 \\ \tilde{\alpha}_3 \end{bmatrix} = \begin{bmatrix} T & \sum D_t \\ \sum D_t & \sum D_t^2 \end{bmatrix}^{-1} \begin{bmatrix} \sum Q_t & \sum P_t \\ \sum Q_t D_t & \sum P_t D_t \end{bmatrix} \begin{bmatrix} 1 \\ 0.2295 \end{bmatrix} = \begin{bmatrix} 93.6192 \\ 0.3100 \end{bmatrix}.$$

The estimated standard errors of these estimates are calculated in accordance with (13.53) and (13.54). The results for both equations of the model are

$$Q_t = 93.6192 - 0.2295P_t + 0.3100D_t + \tilde{\tilde{u}}_{1t} \qquad \text{(demand)},$$
$$\quad\;\; (8.0312) \quad (0.0980) \quad\;\; (0.0474)$$

$$Q_t = 49.5324 + 0.2401P_t + 0.2556F_t + 0.2529A_t + \tilde{\tilde{u}}_{2t} \quad \text{(supply)}.$$
$$\quad (12.0105) \quad (0.0999) \quad\;\; (0.0472) \quad\;\; (0.0996)$$

The estimated demand equation may be compared with the true demand equation in (13.45a) as well as with the result obtained for the two-stage least squares method in the preceding example. The results for the supply equation—which is exactly identified—are precisely the same as those obtained by the two-stage least squares method.

13–4   System Methods of Estimation

The single equation estimation methods lead to estimates that are consistent but, in general, not asymptotically efficient. The reason for the lack of asymptotic efficiency is the disregard of the correlation of the disturbances across equations. (An alternative explanation for the lack of asymptotic efficiency is that single equation estimators do not take into account prior restrictions on other equations in the model.) This parallels the situation in which a regression equation belonging to a set of seemingly unrelated regressions is estimated by the ordinary least squares method (see Section 12–3). If we do not take into account the correlation between the disturbances of different structural equations, we are not using all the available information about each equation and, therefore, do not attain asymptotic efficiency. This deficiency can be overcome—as in the case of seemingly unrelated regressions—by estimating all equations of the system simultaneously. For this purpose we can use one of the so-called *system methods* described in this section.

Three-Stage Least Squares Estimation

The simplest system method is that of *three-stage least squares*, which involves a straightforward application of Aitken's generalized estimation to the system of structural equations written, in accordance with (13.36), as

(13.66)
$$\mathbf{y}_1 = \hat{\mathbf{Y}}_1\boldsymbol{\beta}_1 + \mathbf{X}_1\boldsymbol{\gamma}_1 + \mathbf{u}_1^*,$$
$$\mathbf{y}_2 = \hat{\mathbf{Y}}_2\boldsymbol{\beta}_2 + \mathbf{X}_2\boldsymbol{\gamma}_2 + \mathbf{u}_2^*,$$
$$\vdots$$
$$\mathbf{y}_G = \hat{\mathbf{Y}}_G\boldsymbol{\beta}_G + \mathbf{X}_G\boldsymbol{\gamma}_G + \mathbf{u}_G^*.$$

where
$$\mathbf{y}_g \to T \times 1,$$
$$\hat{\mathbf{Y}}_g \to T \times (G_g - 1),$$
$$\mathbf{X}_g \to T \times K_g,$$
$$\boldsymbol{\beta}_g \to (G_g - 1) \times 1,$$
$$\boldsymbol{\gamma}_g \to K_g \times 1,$$
$$\mathbf{u}_g^* \to T \times 1.$$

Note that G_g = number of endogenous variables included in the gth equation;

K_g = number of predetermined variables included in the gth equation;

$g = 1, 2, \ldots, G.$

If there are any identities in the system, they are simply omitted from (13.66). Alternatively, we may describe the system as

(13.66a)
$$y_1 = \hat{Z}_1\alpha_1 + u_1^*,$$
$$y_2 = \hat{Z}_2\alpha_2 + u_2^*,$$
$$\vdots$$
$$y_G = \hat{Z}_G\alpha_G + u_G^*,$$

where
$$\hat{Z}_g = [\hat{Y}_g \quad X_g],$$
$$\alpha_g = \begin{bmatrix} \beta_g \\ \gamma_g \end{bmatrix}.$$

A compact way of writing (13.66a) is

(13.66b)
$$\begin{bmatrix} y_1 \\ y_2 \\ \vdots \\ y_G \end{bmatrix} = \begin{bmatrix} \hat{Z}_1 & 0 & \cdots & 0 \\ 0 & \hat{Z}_2 & \cdots & 0 \\ \vdots & \vdots & & \vdots \\ 0 & 0 & \cdots & \hat{Z}_G \end{bmatrix} \begin{bmatrix} \alpha_1 \\ \alpha_2 \\ \vdots \\ \alpha_G \end{bmatrix} + \begin{bmatrix} u_1^* \\ u_2^* \\ \vdots \\ u_G^* \end{bmatrix},$$

or

(13.66c) $$y = \hat{Z}\alpha + u^*$$

where
$$y \to GT \times 1,$$
$$\hat{Z} \to GT \times \sum_{g=1}^{G} (G_g - 1 + K_g),$$
$$\alpha \to \sum_{g=1}^{G} (G_g - 1 + K_g) \times 1,$$
$$u^* \to GT \times 1.$$

Describing the system of equations in the form (13.66c) enables us to apply Aitken's generalized least squares formula as given by (12.50). This leads to

(13.67) $$\bar{\bar{\alpha}} = (\hat{Z}'\Omega^{-1}\hat{Z})^{-1}(\hat{Z}'\Omega^{-1}y)$$

where $$\Omega = E(u^*u^{*\prime}).$$

The three-stage least squares estimator of $\boldsymbol{\alpha}$ is obtained by replacing $\boldsymbol{\Omega}$, whose elements are unknown, by $\hat{\boldsymbol{\Omega}}$, which is defined as

(13.68)
$$
\hat{\boldsymbol{\Omega}} = \begin{bmatrix} \hat{\psi}_{11}\mathbf{I_T} & \hat{\psi}_{12}\mathbf{I_T} & \cdots & \hat{\psi}_{1G}\mathbf{I_T} \\ \hat{\psi}_{21}\mathbf{I_T} & \hat{\psi}_{22}\mathbf{I_T} & \cdots & \hat{\psi}_{2G}\mathbf{I_T} \\ \vdots & \vdots & & \vdots \\ \hat{\psi}_{G1}\mathbf{I_T} & \hat{\psi}_{G2}\mathbf{I_T} & \cdots & \hat{\psi}_{GG}\mathbf{I_T} \end{bmatrix},
$$

where

(13.69)
$$
\hat{\psi}_{gh} = \frac{(\mathbf{y_g} - \hat{\mathbf{Y}}_\mathbf{g}\tilde{\boldsymbol{\beta}}_\mathbf{g} - \mathbf{X_g}\tilde{\boldsymbol{\gamma}}_\mathbf{g})'(\mathbf{y_h} - \hat{\mathbf{Y}}_\mathbf{h}\tilde{\boldsymbol{\beta}}_\mathbf{h} - \mathbf{X_h}\tilde{\boldsymbol{\gamma}}_\mathbf{h})}{(T - G_g + 1 - K_g)},
$$

$$
G_g + K_g \geq G_h + K_h,
$$

$$
g, h = 1, 2, \ldots, G,
$$

and $\tilde{\boldsymbol{\beta}}$ and $\tilde{\boldsymbol{\gamma}}$ represent the two-stage least squares estimates of the respective coefficients. (Some authors prefer using T instead of $(T - G_g + 1 - K_g)$ in the denominator of $\hat{\psi}_{gh}$; this makes no difference to the asymptotic properties of the three-stage least squares estimator. Note, however, that $\hat{\boldsymbol{\Omega}}$ will be singular if the number of equations exceeds the number of observations.) The three-stage least squares estimator of the structural coefficients then is

(13.70) $\tilde{\tilde{\boldsymbol{\alpha}}} = (\hat{\mathbf{Z}}'\hat{\boldsymbol{\Omega}}^{-1}\hat{\mathbf{Z}})^{-1}(\hat{\mathbf{Z}}'\hat{\boldsymbol{\Omega}}^{-1}\mathbf{y})$

$$
= \begin{bmatrix} \hat{\psi}^{11}(\hat{\mathbf{Z}}_1'\hat{\mathbf{Z}}_1) & \hat{\psi}^{12}(\hat{\mathbf{Z}}_1'\hat{\mathbf{Z}}_2) & \cdots & \hat{\psi}^{1G}(\hat{\mathbf{Z}}_1'\hat{\mathbf{Z}}_\mathbf{G}) \\ \hat{\psi}^{21}(\hat{\mathbf{Z}}_2'\hat{\mathbf{Z}}_1) & \hat{\psi}^{22}(\hat{\mathbf{Z}}_2'\hat{\mathbf{Z}}_2) & \cdots & \hat{\psi}^{2G}(\hat{\mathbf{Z}}_2'\hat{\mathbf{Z}}_\mathbf{G}) \\ \vdots & \vdots & & \vdots \\ \hat{\psi}^{G1}(\hat{\mathbf{Z}}_\mathbf{G}'\hat{\mathbf{Z}}_1) & \hat{\psi}^{G2}(\hat{\mathbf{Z}}_\mathbf{G}'\hat{\mathbf{Z}}_2) & \cdots & \hat{\psi}^{GG}(\hat{\mathbf{Z}}_\mathbf{G}'\hat{\mathbf{Z}}_\mathbf{G}) \end{bmatrix}^{-1} \begin{bmatrix} \sum_g \hat{\psi}^{1g}(\hat{\mathbf{Z}}_1'\mathbf{y_g}) \\ \sum_g \hat{\psi}^{2g}(\hat{\mathbf{Z}}_2'\mathbf{y_g}) \\ \vdots \\ \sum_g \hat{\psi}^{Gg}(\hat{\mathbf{Z}}_\mathbf{G}'\mathbf{y_g}) \end{bmatrix},
$$

where $\hat{\psi}^{gh}$ represents the corresponding element of the *inverse* of $\hat{\boldsymbol{\Omega}}$. As in the two-stage Aitken estimator of Section 12–3, the variance-covariance matrix of the three-stage least squares estimator can be estimated by

(13.71)   Est. Var-Cov$(\tilde{\tilde{\boldsymbol{\alpha}}}) = (\hat{\mathbf{Z}}'\hat{\boldsymbol{\Omega}}^{-1}\hat{\mathbf{Z}})^{-1}$.

An alternative way of deriving the three-stage least squares estimation formula can also be presented. The structural equations of the system can be written as

(13.72) $\mathbf{y_1} = \mathbf{Z_1}\boldsymbol{\alpha}_1 + \mathbf{u_1}$,

$\mathbf{y_2} = \mathbf{Z_2}\boldsymbol{\alpha}_2 + \mathbf{u_2}$,

$\vdots$

$\mathbf{y_G} = \mathbf{Z_G}\boldsymbol{\alpha}_G + \mathbf{u_G}$,

where $\mathbf{Z_g} = [\mathbf{Y_g} \quad \mathbf{X_g}]$,

$$
\boldsymbol{\alpha}_\mathbf{g} = \begin{bmatrix} \boldsymbol{\beta}_\mathbf{g} \\ \boldsymbol{\gamma}_\mathbf{g} \end{bmatrix}.
$$

Premultiplying each equation of (13.72) by X' gives

(13.73)
$$X'y_1 = X'Z_1\alpha_1 + X'u_1,$$
$$X'y_2 = X'Z_2\alpha_2 + X'u_2,$$
$$\vdots$$
$$X'y_G = X'Z_G\alpha_G + X'u_G.$$

This can be written as

(13.73a)
$$
\begin{bmatrix} X'y_1 \\ X'y_2 \\ \vdots \\ X'y_G \end{bmatrix}
=
\begin{bmatrix}
X'Z_1 & 0 & \cdots & 0 \\
0 & X'Z_2 & \cdots & 0 \\
\vdots & \vdots & & \vdots \\
0 & 0 & \cdots & X'Z_G
\end{bmatrix}
\begin{bmatrix} \alpha_1 \\ \alpha_2 \\ \vdots \\ \alpha_G \end{bmatrix}
+
\begin{bmatrix} X'u_1 \\ X'u_2 \\ \vdots \\ X'u_G \end{bmatrix},
$$

or

(13.73b)
$$\bar{y} = \bar{Z}\alpha + \bar{u},$$

where
$$\bar{y} \to KG \times 1,$$

$$\bar{Z} \to KG \times \sum_{g=1}^{G} (G_g - 1 + K_g),$$

$$\alpha \to \sum_{g=1}^{G} (G_g - 1 + K_g) \times 1,$$

$$\bar{u} \to KG \times 1.$$

We note that

$$
E(\bar{u}\bar{u}') =
\begin{bmatrix}
\sigma_{11}(X'X) & \sigma_{12}(X'X) & \cdots & \sigma_{1G}(X'X) \\
\sigma_{21}(X'X) & \sigma_{22}(X'X) & \cdots & \sigma_{2G}(X'X) \\
\vdots & \vdots & & \vdots \\
\sigma_{G1}(X'X) & \sigma_{G2}(X'X) & \cdots & \sigma_{GG}(X'X)
\end{bmatrix},
$$

where the σ's represent variances and covariances of the structural disturbances. The application of Aitken's generalized least squares formula to (13.73b) leads to

(13.74)
$$\bar{\bar{\alpha}} = (\bar{Z}'\Theta^{-1}\bar{Z})^{-1}(\bar{Z}'\Theta^{-1}\bar{y}),$$

where
$$\Theta = E(\bar{u}\bar{u}').$$

Consistent estimates of the variances and covariances of the structural disturbances can be obtained by using the two-stage least squares residuals. That is, we can obtain consistent estimates of σ_{gh} by utilizing

(13.75)
$$s_{gh} = \frac{(y_g - Y_g\tilde{\beta}_g - X_g\tilde{\gamma}_g)'(y_h - Y_h\tilde{\beta}_h - X_h\tilde{\gamma}_h)}{(T - G_g + 1 - K_g)},$$

$$G_g + K_g \geq G_h + K_h,$$

$$g, h = 1, 2, \ldots, G.$$

Then α can be estimated by

(13.76)

$$\hat{\hat{\alpha}} = (\bar{Z}'\hat{\Theta}^{-1}\bar{Z})^{-1}(\bar{Z}'\hat{\Theta}^{-1}\bar{y})$$

$$= \begin{bmatrix} s^{11}Z_1'X(X'X)^{-1}X'Z_1 & s^{12}Z_1'X(X'X)^{-1}X'Z_2 & \cdots & s^{1G}Z_1'X(X'X)^{-1}X'Z_G \\ s^{21}Z_2'X(X'X)^{-1}X'Z_1 & s^{22}Z_2'X(X'X)^{-1}X'Z_2 & \cdots & s^{2G}Z_2'X(X'X)^{-1}X'Z_G \\ \vdots & \vdots & & \vdots \\ s^{G1}Z_G'X(X'X)^{-1}X'Z_1 & s^{G2}Z_G'X(X'X)^{-1}X'Z_2 & \cdots & s^{GG}Z_G'X(X'X)^{-1}X'Z_G \end{bmatrix}^{-1}$$

$$\times \begin{bmatrix} \sum_g s^{1g}Z_1'X(X'X)^{-1}X'y_g \\ \sum_g s^{2g}Z_2'X(X'X)^{-1}X'y_g \\ \vdots \\ \sum_g s^{Gg}Z_G'X(X'X)^{-1}X'y_g \end{bmatrix},$$

where s^{gh} represents the corresponding element of the *inverse* of $\hat{\Theta}$. The expression (13.76) is equivalent to (13.70). Further,

(13.77) $\text{Est. Var-Cov}(\hat{\hat{\alpha}}) = (\bar{Z}'\hat{\Theta}^{-1}\bar{Z})^{-1},$

which is equivalent to (13.71). Under the assumptions stated at the outset of this chapter, the three-stage least squares estimates of the structural coefficients are consistent and asymptotically efficient. (If the predetermined variables in the system include lagged endogenous variables, their initial values are assumed to be fixed.) In models in which it can be assumed that the structural disturbances are uncorrelated across equations, Θ will be diagonal, and the three-stage least squares estimates will be the same as the two-stage least squares estimates. We also note that the three-stage least squares estimator, like the two-stage estimator, is *not invariant* with respect to the choice of the endogenous variable whose structural coefficient is to be unity. A final point worth mentioning is that in applying the three-stage least squares method, the omission of exactly identified equations will not affect the three-stage least squares estimates of the coefficients of the remaining equations.[10] This means that exactly identified equations add no information that is relevant for estimation of the overidentified equations of the system. The reverse, however, is not true.

EXAMPLE   Continuing with the food market example, we use the results from the application of the two-stage least squares method to estimate the variance-covariance matrix of the structural disturbances. By (13.75) this is

$$\tilde{\Phi} = \begin{bmatrix} s_{11} & s_{12} \\ s_{21} & s_{22} \end{bmatrix} = \begin{bmatrix} 3.8664 & 4.3574 \\ 4.3574 & 6.0396 \end{bmatrix}.$$

---

[10] See A. Zellner and H. Theil, "Three-Stage Least Squares: Simultaneous Estimation of Simultaneous Equations," *Econometrica*, Vol. 30, January, 1962, pp. 63–68.

The three-stage least squares estimates of the structural coefficients then are

$$Q_t = 94.6333 - 0.2436P_t + 0.3140D_t + \tilde{\tilde{u}}_{1t} \qquad \text{(demand)},$$
$$(7.9208) \quad\;\; (0.0965) \quad\;\;\; (0.0469)$$

$$Q_t = 52.1176 + 0.2289P_t + 0.2290F_t + 0.3579A_t + \tilde{\tilde{u}}_{2t} \quad \text{(supply)}.$$
$$(11.8934) \quad\; (0.0997) \quad\;\;\; (0.0440) \quad\;\;\; (0.0729)$$

The supply equation is exactly identified and, therefore, adds no information for estimating the overidentified demand equation. Thus the three-stage least squares estimates of the demand equation are the same as those obtained by the two-stage least squares method. However, the three-stage least squares results for the supply equation are different from those obtained by the two-stage least squares method.

It may be noted that the residuals from the estimated three-stage least squares equations can be used to obtain new estimates of the variances and covariances of the structural disturbances. These can then replace the previous estimates in the three-stage least squares formula, thus leading to new estimates of the structural coefficients. The process could be repeated until there is no change in the estimated structural coefficients. The resulting estimates, known as *iterative three-stage least squares estimates*, have the same asymptotic properties as the ordinary three-stage least squares estimates.[11] For our food market example, the estimated coefficients converged at the tenth decimal place after nine iterations. The final estimates of the variance-covariance matrix of the structural disturbances are

$$\tilde{\tilde{\Phi}} = \begin{bmatrix} 3.8664 & 5.0907 \\ 5.0907 & 6.9564 \end{bmatrix}.$$

As a result, the converged iterative three-stage least squares are

$$Q_t = 94.6333 - 0.2436P_t + 0.3140D_t + \bar{\bar{u}}_{1t} \qquad \text{(demand)},$$
$$(7.9208) \quad\;\; (0.0965) \quad\;\;\; (0.0469)$$

$$Q_t = 52.5527 + 0.2271P_t + 0.2245F_t + 0.3756A_t + \bar{\bar{u}}_{2t} \quad \text{(supply)}.$$
$$(12.7408) \quad\; (0.1069) \quad\;\;\; (0.0465) \quad\;\;\; (0.0717)$$

Full Information Maximum Likelihood Estimation

Another system method designed for estimating the structural coefficients of a simultaneous equation system is the *full information maximum likelihood method*. It involves the usual application of the maximum likelihood principle to all stochastic equations of the system simultaneously. Consider the complete system

$$\mathbf{B}\mathbf{y}_t + \mathbf{\Gamma}\mathbf{x}_t = \mathbf{u}_t$$

specified in (13.3a), and the corresponding variance-covariance matrix of the disturbances

$$\mathbf{\Phi} = E(\mathbf{u}_t\mathbf{u}_t').$$

[11] See A. Madansky, "On the Efficiency of Three-Stage Least Squares Estimation," *Econometrica*, Vol. 32, January–April 1964, p. 55.

On the assumptions previously specified, the joint distribution of the elements of u_t is

$$f(\mathbf{u}_t) = (2\pi)^{-(G/2)} |\boldsymbol{\Phi}|^{-(1/2)} e^{-(\mathbf{u}_t'\boldsymbol{\Phi}^{-1}\mathbf{u}_t)/2}.$$

The probability transformation from the unobservable $\mathbf{u}_t$ to the observable $\mathbf{y}_t$ is

$$f(\mathbf{y}_t \mid \mathbf{x}_t) = f(\mathbf{u}_t) \left| \frac{\partial \mathbf{u}_t}{\partial \mathbf{y}_t} \right| = f(\mathbf{u}_t) \left| \frac{\partial (\mathbf{B}\mathbf{y}_t + \boldsymbol{\Gamma}\mathbf{x}_t)}{\partial \mathbf{y}_t} \right| = f(\mathbf{u}_t)|\mathbf{B}|,$$

where $|\mathbf{B}|$ is the Jacobian, given by the absolute value of the determinant of the matrix $\mathbf{B}$. Then the logarithmic likelihood function for the T observations on $\mathbf{y}_t$ conditional on the values of $\mathbf{x}_t$ is

(13.78)
$$L = -\frac{GT}{2} \log (2\pi) - \frac{T}{2} \log |\boldsymbol{\Phi}| + T \log |\mathbf{B}|$$

$$-\frac{1}{2} \sum_{t=1}^{T} (\mathbf{B}\mathbf{y}_t + \boldsymbol{\Gamma}\mathbf{x}_t)' \boldsymbol{\Phi}^{-1} (\mathbf{B}\mathbf{y}_t + \boldsymbol{\Gamma}\mathbf{x}_t).$$

The maximum likelihood estimators of $\mathbf{B}$, $\boldsymbol{\Gamma}$, and $\boldsymbol{\Phi}$ are then obtained by maximizing (13.78) with respect to these parameters. These estimators are consistent, asymptotically efficient, and their asymptotic distribution is normal. This means that they have the same asymptotic properties—and the same asymptotic variance-covariance matrix—as the three-stage least squares estimators. The asymptotic variance-covariance matrix of the full information maximum likelihood estimators can be estimated in the usual way by reference to the appropriate information matrix. The full information maximum likelihood estimators are equivalent to the so-called *least generalized residual variance estimators*, which are obtained by minimizing the determinant of the variance-covariance matrix of the reduced form residuals.[12]

EXAMPLE   To illustrate the construction of the logarithmic likelihood function (13.78), we use the food market model (13.45):

$$Q_t = \alpha_1 + \alpha_2 P_t + \alpha_3 D_t + u_{1t} \qquad \text{(demand)},$$

$$Q_t = \beta_1 + \beta_2 P_t + \beta_3 F_t + {}_4A_t + u_{2t} \quad \text{(supply)}.$$

Here,

$$\mathbf{y}_t' = [Q_t \quad P_t], \qquad \mathbf{x}_t' = [1 \quad D_t \quad F_t \quad A_t]$$

and

$$\mathbf{B} = \begin{bmatrix} 1 & -\alpha_2 \\ 1 & -\beta_2 \end{bmatrix}, \qquad \boldsymbol{\Gamma} = \begin{bmatrix} -\alpha_1 & -\alpha_3 & 0 & 0 \\ -\beta_1 & 0 & -\beta_3 & -\beta_4 \end{bmatrix}, \qquad \boldsymbol{\Phi} = \begin{bmatrix} \sigma_{11} & \sigma_{12} \\ \sigma_{12} & \sigma_{22} \end{bmatrix}.$$

---

[12] See Goldberger (1964), *op. cit.*, pp. 352–356. A somewhat different interpretation of interdependent systems and an iterative method of estimation known as "fix-point" are described in H. Wold and E. J. Mosbaek, *Interdependent Systems, Structure and Estimation* (Amsterdam: North-Holland Publishing Company, 1970).

Then,

$$|\boldsymbol{\Phi}| = \sigma_{11}\sigma_{22} - \sigma_{12}^2,$$

$$|\mathbf{B}| = -\beta_2 + \alpha_2,$$

and

$$(\mathbf{By_t} + \boldsymbol{\Gamma x_t})'\boldsymbol{\Phi}^{-1}(\mathbf{By_t} + \boldsymbol{\Gamma x_t})$$

$$= [u_{1t} \quad u_{2t}] \frac{1}{|\boldsymbol{\Phi}|} \begin{bmatrix} \sigma_{22} & -\sigma_{12} \\ -\sigma_{12} & \sigma_{11} \end{bmatrix} \begin{bmatrix} u_{1t} \\ u_{2t} \end{bmatrix} = \frac{1}{|\boldsymbol{\Phi}|}(\sigma_{22}u_{1t}^2 + \sigma_{11}u_{2t}^2 - 2\sigma_{12}u_{1t}u_{2t}),$$

where
$$u_{1t} = Q_t - \alpha_1 - \alpha_2 P_t - \alpha_3 D_t,$$
$$u_{2t} = Q_t - \beta_1 - \beta_2 P_t - \beta_3 F_t - \beta_4 A_t.$$

Therefore, the logarithmic likelihood function (13.78) becomes

$$(13.79) \quad L = -\frac{GT}{2}\log(2\pi) - \frac{T}{2}\log(\sigma_{11}\sigma_{22} - \sigma_{12}^2) + T\log|\alpha_2 - \beta_2|$$

$$- \frac{1}{2(\sigma_{11}\sigma_{22} - \sigma_{12}^2)}\left\{\sigma_{22}\sum_{t=1}^{T}(Q_t - \alpha_1 - \alpha_2 P_t - \alpha_3 D_t)^2\right.$$

$$+ \sigma_{11}\sum_{t=1}^{T}(Q_t - \beta_1 - \beta_2 P_t - \beta_3 F_t - \beta_4 A_t)^2$$

$$\left. - 2\sigma_{12}\sum_{t=1}^{T}(Q_t - \alpha_1 - \alpha_2 P_t - \alpha_3 D_t)(Q_t - \beta_1 - \beta_2 P_t - \beta_3 F_t - \beta_4 A_t)\right\}$$

where $|\alpha_2 - \beta_2|$ stands for the absolute value of $(\alpha_2 - \beta_2)$.

In the preceding exposition we did not consider the possibility that the system might include identities as well as stochastic equations. If that is the case, the variance-covariance matrix of the structural disturbances will be singular so that its inverse will not exist. One way of dealing with this problem is to eliminate all identities (and the corresponding endogenous variables) by substitution before setting up the likelihood function. For instance, consider the following model:

$$C_t = \alpha_0 + \alpha_1 Y_t + \alpha_2 C_{t-1} + u_{1t} \quad \text{(consumption)},$$
$$I_t = \beta_0 + \beta_1 r_t + \beta_2 I_{t-1} + u_{2t} \quad \text{(investment)},$$
$$r_t = \gamma_0 + \gamma_1 Y_t + \gamma_2 M_t + u_{3t} \quad \text{(money market)},$$
$$Y_t = C_t + I_t + G_t \quad\quad\quad\quad\quad \text{(income identity)},$$

where C = consumption, Y = income, I = investment, r = rate of interest, M = money supply, and G = government expenditure. The variables C_t, Y_t, I_t, and r_t are endogenous; the remaining variables are predetermined. The income identity can be eliminated by substituting for Y_t into the rest of the system. The system then becomes

$$C_t = \left(\frac{\alpha_0}{1-\alpha_1}\right) + \left(\frac{\alpha_1}{1-\alpha_1}\right)I_t + \left(\frac{\alpha_1}{1-\alpha_1}\right)G_t + \left(\frac{\alpha_2}{1-\alpha_1}\right)C_{t-1} + \left(\frac{1}{1-\alpha_1}\right)u_{1t},$$

$$I_t = \beta_0 + \beta_1 r_t + \beta_2 I_{t-1} + u_{2t},$$

$$r_t = \gamma_0 + \gamma_1 C_t + \gamma_1 I_t + \gamma_1 G_t + \gamma_2 M_t + u_{3t},$$

which involves only stochastic equations. Of course, the variance-covariance matrix Φ of the structural disturbances must now be changed to Φ^*, which is defined as

$$
\Phi^* = \begin{bmatrix}
\dfrac{\sigma_{11}}{(1-\alpha_1)^2} & \dfrac{\sigma_{12}}{(1-\alpha_1)} & \dfrac{\sigma_{13}}{(1-\alpha_1)} \\[2ex]
\dfrac{\sigma_{12}}{(1-\alpha_1)} & \sigma_{22} & \sigma_{23} \\[2ex]
\dfrac{\sigma_{13}}{(1-\alpha_1)} & \sigma_{23} & \sigma_{33}
\end{bmatrix}.
$$

The disadvantage of this approach is that it introduces nonzero restrictions into the structural equations and thus makes the derivation of the maximum likelihood estimates more complicated. An alternative way of dealing with identities without making a direct substitution is also available.[13]

EXAMPLE   The full information maximum likelihood estimates of the structural equations of the food market model are:

$$
Q_t = 93.6192 - 0.2295 P_t + 0.3100 D_t + \hat{u}_{1t} \qquad \text{(demand)},
$$
$$
(8.0312) \quad (0.0980) \qquad (0.0474)
$$

$$
Q_t = 51.9445 + 0.2373 P_t + 0.2208 F_t + 0.3697 A_t + \hat{u}_{2t} \quad \text{(supply)}.
$$
$$
(12.7460) \quad (0.1078) \qquad (0.0457) \qquad (0.0765)
$$

We note that the estimates of the coefficients of the demand equation are identical with the limited information maximum likelihood estimates given earlier. Again, this is the result of the fact that the supply equation is exactly identified and, therefore, provides no information about the demand equation.

13–5   Comparison of Alternative Methods of Estimation and Special Problems

In discussing the methods of estimating structural equations of a general interdependent system, we have been using the food market model for which the true values of the parameters are known. Therefore, it might be interesting to compare the results obtained for this model by the different estimation methods. In making the comparison, however, we should keep in mind that we have only one sample on which to base the comparisons. In this case comparing various estimators is like comparing different guns on the basis of one shot from each. The summary of the results is shown in Table 13–2, which also includes the OLS estimates. The latter are inconsistent, but they are nevertheless sometimes used in applied work, mainly because they are simple to compute. In our particular

---

[13] A detailed description can be found in W. L. Ruble, "Improving the Computation of Simultaneous Stochastic Linear Equations Estimates," *Agricultural Economics Report No. 116*, Department of Agricultural Economics, Michigan State University, East Lansing, 1968, pp. 163–171.

Table 13-2

Method*	Demand			Supply			
	Constant	P_t	D_t	Constant	P_t	F_t	A_t
True values of coefficients	96.5	−0.25	0.30	62.5	0.15	0.20	0.36

ESTIMATES

OLS	99.8954	−0.3163	0.3346	58.2754	0.1604	0.2481	0.2483
	(7.5194)	(0.0907)	(0.0454)	(11.4629)	(0.0949)	(0.0462)	(0.0975)
2SLS	94.6333	−0.2436	0.3140	49.5324	0.2401	0.2556	0.2529
	(7.9208)	(0.0965)	(0.0469)	(12.0105)	(0.0999)	(0.0472)	(0.0996)
LIML	93.6192	−0.2295	0.3100	49.5324	0.2401	0.2556	0.2529
	(8.0312)	(0.0980)	(0.0474)	(12.0105)	(0.0999)	(0.0472)	(0.0996)
3SLS	94.6333	−0.2436	0.3140	52.1176	0.2289	0.2290	0.3579
	(7.9208)	(0.0965)	(0.0469)	(11.8934)	(0.0997)	(0.0440)	(0.0729)
I3SLS	94.6333	−0.2436	0.3140	55.5527	0.2271	0.2245	0.3756
	(7.9208)	(0.0965)	(0.0469)	(12.7408)	(0.1069)	(0.0465)	(0.0717)
FIML	93.6192	−0.2295	0.3100	51.9445	0.2373	0.2208	0.3697
	(8.0312)	(0.0980)	(0.0474)	(12.7460)	(0.1078)	(0.0457)	(0.0765)

SAMPLING ERRORS

OLS	3.3954	−0.0663	0.0346	−4.2246	0.0104	0.0481	−0.1117
2SLS	−1.8667	0.0064	0.0140	−12.9676	0.0901	0.0556	−0.1071
LIML	−2.8808	0.0205	0.0100	−12.9676	0.0901	0.0556	−0.1071
3SLS	−1.8667	0.0064	0.0140	−10.3824	0.0789	0.0290	−0.0021
I3SLS	−1.8667	0.0064	0.0140	−6.9473	0.0771	0.0245	0.0156
FIML	−2.8808	0.0205	0.0100	−10.5555	0.0873	0.0208	0.0097

* Notation: OLS ordinary least squares
               2SLS two-stage least squares
               LIML limited information maximum likelihood
               3SLS three-stage least squares
               I3SLS iterative three-stage least squares
               FIML full information maximum likelihood

example, their performance in estimating the supply equation compares quite well with that of the 2SLS and LIML estimators. With respect to the consistent methods, we can distinguish between the results for the overidentified demand equation and those for the exactly identified supply equation. In the case of the *demand equation*, we obtain identical results for 2SLS, 3SLS, and I3SLS, on one hand, and for LIML and FIML on the other. The reasons for this were given in the text. (However, note that, if the model contained—in addition to the exactly identified equation—*more than one* overidentified equation, the results for the system methods would differ from those for the single equation methods.) In the present case there is therefore no gain in going from the single equation methods (2SLS or LIML) to the system methods (3SLS, I3SLS, or FIML). Furthermore, the results for 2SLS and LIML do not appear to be markedly different. As for the *supply equation*, we obtain identical results for the 2SLS and LIML methods. Comparing the system methods with the single equation methods, we see that the former clearly performed better than the latter. There is, however, no clear-cut answer to the question as to *which* of the system methods performed best. On the grounds of computational effort the 3SLS is, of course, the one to be preferred. In assessing the general performance of the consistent methods, we note that *in each case* the true values of the coefficients are covered by the conventionally calculated 95% confidence intervals. This result would be expected for a large sample since the estimated standard errors are justified on asymptotic grounds, but it is gratifying to see it happen also in a sample of only 20 observations.

All simultaneous equation estimation methods discussed in this section have some desirable asymptotic properties. These properties become effective in large samples, but since our samples are mostly small, we would be more interested in knowing the *small sample properties* of these estimators. Unfortunately, our knowledge in this respect is far from complete. The results from the food market example presented in Table 13–2 relate to a single set of values of the various estimators, but they give no information about the characteristics of their sampling distributions. Ideally, we would like to know the mathematical description of the distributions of each of the estimators. Such knowledge is available only for a small number of special cases.[14] From this we can conclude that the small sample distribution of the 2SLS estimator has a finite mean, but that its variance is, at least in some cases, infinite. The shape of the distribution appears to be similar to that of the normal distribution, but its peak is taller and its tails thicker than in the case of the normal distribution. Most of the evidence on the small sample properties of the simultaneous equation estimators comes from sampling (or Monte Carlo) experiments similar to those described in Chapter 2 and in the concluding part of Section 8–2 (our food example, for instance, could serve as the first sample of a Monte Carlo experiment). Since a survey of these experiments can be found elsewhere,[15] only the main results will be reported here. For the most part, the experimenters have presented some of the basic characteristics of the sampling distributions rather than their full description. Typically, these characteristics were the mean, the variance, and the mean square error. Of course, when an estimator has no finite variance, the value of the variance or of the mean square error of an experimental sampling distribution has no meaning,

---

[14] See especially R. L. Basmann, "A Note on the Exact Finite Sample Frequency Functions of Generalized Classical Linear Estimators in Two Leading Over-Identified Cases," *Journal of the American Statistical Association*, Vol. 56, September 1961, pp. 619–636, and "A Note on the Exact Finite Sample Frequency Functions of Generalized Classical Linear Estimators in a Leading Three-Equation Case," *Journal of the American Statistical Association*, Vol. 58, March 1963, pp. 161–171.

[15] See Johnston, *op. cit.*, Chapter 10, and C. F. Christ, *Econometric Models and Methods* (New York: Wiley, 1966), pp. 474–481.

since it tends to increase without limit as the number of samples increases. Nevertheless, these values may serve as a basis for comparison of alternative estimators in relation to the same samples whose number is fixed. In all of the experiments the predetermined variables included only exogenous variables, but it can be conjectured that the presence of lagged endogenous variables would not alter the essence of the results obtained. While the results of different experiments do not appear to be in complete agreement in all respects, some common features have been confirmed repeatedly. In particular, the OLS estimator tends to have a larger bias but a smaller variance than 2SLS or LIML. If the mean square error is used as a criterion in comparing the single equation estimators, the results are somewhat mixed. In some cases the OLS estimator performs better than 2SLS or LIML, in others worse, and sometimes about the same. When 2SLS is compared with LIML, it appears that the former usually leads to smaller mean square errors than the latter, particularly when the exogenous variables are highly intercorrelated. As for the system estimators, the experimental results are much less numerous than those for the single equation estimators. From the available evidence it appears that the asymptotic advantage of the system methods over the single equation methods persists also in small samples, although not in an equally pronounced way. However, the FIML method appears to be more sensitive to errors of specification (such as omitting a relevant explanatory variable) than 2SLS.

In assessing various estimation methods, we are frequently concerned not only with the properties of the estimators, but also with the performance of the methods when it comes to *hypothesis testing*. In this context the most important quantity is the ratio of the estimated coefficient to its estimated standard error. This test statistic is frequently referred to as the "*t* ratio" in spite of the fact that the *t* distribution is not necessarily appropriate. When consistent simultaneous equation estimation methods are used, the asymptotic distribution of this statistic is normal. In small samples the desired acceptance regions or confidence intervals are usually determined by reference to the tabulated *t* distribution. This procedure is clearly not exactly valid, since the test statistic does *not* have a *t* distribution. The question, then, is whether the *t* distribution can serve as a tolerable approximation of the true distribution so that the results of the tests and of interval estimation are not seriously distorted. The available Monte Carlo evidence suggests that the distortion is usually (although not always) reasonably small. For instance, Cragg, who has conducted a large number of experiments, concludes on this point as follows:

> Usually use of the standard errors of the consistent methods would lead to reliable inferences, but this was not always the case. The standard errors of DLS were not useful for making inference about the true values of the coefficients.[16]

---

[16] J. G. Cragg, "On the Relative Small-Sample Properties of Several Structural-Equation Estimators," *Econometrica*, Vol. 35, January 1967, p. 109. The term "DLS" refers to the OLS estimator.

A very similar conclusion was reached by Summers.[17] This suggests that, at least from the point of view of hypothesis testing or interval estimation, the OLS method is inferior to the consistent methods of estimation.

Another relevant criterion for judging various estimators is their ability to *forecast*. In simultaneous equations the values of the endogenous variables can be predicted by reference to the reduced form equations. Suppose the $(K \times 1)$ vector of the values of the predetermined variables for the period of the forecast is $\mathbf{x}_0$. Then the forecast values of the G endogenous variables are

$$\hat{\mathbf{y}}_0 = \hat{\mathbf{\Pi}}\mathbf{x}_0,$$

where $\hat{\mathbf{\Pi}}$ is a $(G \times K)$ matrix of the reduced form coefficients estimated from the sample observations. Now, consistent estimates of $\mathbf{\Pi}$ can be obtained either by a direct application of the OLS method to the reduced form equations, or by using consistent estimates of the structural coefficients, say, $\tilde{\mathbf{B}}$ and $\tilde{\mathbf{\Gamma}}$, and setting

$$(13.80) \qquad\qquad \tilde{\mathbf{\Pi}} = -\tilde{\mathbf{B}}\tilde{\mathbf{\Gamma}}$$

in accordance with (13.7). If the estimated reduced form coefficients are obtained by a direct application of OLS, they are called "unrestricted"; otherwise, they are called "derived." Unless all structural equations are exactly identified, the unrestricted and the derived reduced form coefficients will not coincide. Since the unrestricted least squares estimator of $\mathbf{\Pi}$ does not, in general, incorporate the prior restrictions imposed by the relation

$$\mathbf{\Pi} = -\mathbf{B}^{-1}\mathbf{\Gamma},$$

it will be asymptotically less efficient than the derived estimator $\tilde{\mathbf{\Pi}}$. Furthermore, since the FIML and 3SLS methods lead to asymptotically efficient estimates of $\mathbf{B}$ and $\mathbf{\Gamma}$, and since this property carries over to any single-valued functions of $\mathbf{B}$ and $\mathbf{\Gamma}$, it follows that the derived estimator of $\mathbf{\Pi}$ based on FIML or 3SLS estimates of the structural coefficients is itself asymptotically efficient. This implies that an estimator of $\mathbf{\Pi}$ derived from FIML or 3SLS leads to a smaller asymptotic variance of the forecast error than an estimator derived from 2SLS or LIML. On the basis of Monte Carlo experiments there is some evidence that these results tend to hold in small samples as well, although such ranking is to be regarded as very tentative.[18]

Recursive Systems

We have dealt so far with the estimation problem for a general interdependent system of equations. We shall now briefly consider the estimation problem in the case where the system is *recursive*. As stated in Section 13–1, a system

$$\mathbf{B}\mathbf{y}_t + \mathbf{\Gamma}\mathbf{x}_t = \mathbf{u}_t$$

[17] R. M. Summers, "A Capital Intensive Approach to the Small Sample Properties of Various Simultaneous Equation Estimators," *Econometrica*, Vol. 33, January 1965, pp. 1–41.

[18] *Ibid.*, pp. 31–22

is called recursive if the matrix **B** is triangular. A well-known example of a recursive system is the so-called "cobweb model," which may be exemplified as follows:

(13.81) $$Q_t = \alpha_1 + \alpha_2 P_{t-1} + u_{1t} \qquad \text{(supply)},$$

$$P_t = \beta_1 + \beta_2 Q_t + \beta_3 Y_t + u_{2t} \quad \text{(demand)},$$

where $Q = $ equilibrium quantity, $P = $ equilibrium price, and $Y = $ income (exogenous). Here

$$\mathbf{B} = \begin{bmatrix} 1 & 0 \\ -\beta_2 & 1 \end{bmatrix} \quad \text{and} \quad \mathbf{\Gamma} = \begin{bmatrix} -\alpha_1 & -\alpha_2 & 0 \\ -\beta_1 & 0 & -\beta_3 \end{bmatrix}.$$

Note that the supply equation involves only one endogenous variable and, therefore, using ordinary least squares would lead to consistent estimates. These estimates would not be asymptotically efficient, though, because they disregard the implied correlation between the disturbances of the two equations. The demand equation could be consistently estimated by ILS. Alternatively, both equations could be estimated by one of the system methods, in which case the estimates would be not only consistent but also asymptotically efficient. The notable feature of the recursive models such as (13.81) is that the calculation of the FIML estimates is greatly simplified by the fact that the Jacobian (i.e., the determinant of **B**) is equal to unity. (The foregoing presupposes that each diagonal element of **B** is unity; if this is not so, we can divide each structural equation by the appropriate coefficient β_{gg}.)

If the system

$$\mathbf{B}\mathbf{y}_t + \mathbf{\Gamma}\mathbf{x}_t = \mathbf{u}_t$$

is *diagonally recursive*—that is, if **B** is triangular and the variance-covariance matrix of the structural disturbances, **Φ**, is diagonal—the estimation problem becomes really simple. The reason is that the endogenous variables, which serve as explanatory factors in the structural equations, are *not* correlated with the disturbance of the equation in which they appear. For instance, in the demand equation of (13.81) the explanatory variables include the endogenous variable Q_t. However, if u_{1t} and u_{2t} are independent and nonautoregressive, then

$$E(Q_t u_{2t}) = E[(\alpha_1 + \alpha_2 P_{t-1} + u_{1t})u_{2t}] = 0.$$

This means that *the application of the OLS method to each of the structural equations leads to consistent and asymptotically efficient estimates.* (In the absence of lagged endogenous variables, the OLS estimates are also *unbiased.*) It should be emphasized that this is true only if the system is *diagonally* recursive, not otherwise. Finally, we note that if **B** is block-triangular and the **Φ** matrix is correspondingly block-diagonal, then the equations corresponding to each diagonal block of **Φ** can be treated as belonging to separate systems. Of course, this also simplifies estimation considerably.

Autoregressive Disturbances

As the final point connected with the problem of estimating the coefficients of structural equations in a simultaneous equation system, we consider the case in which the structural disturbances are not independent over time. In particular, suppose the structural disturbances follow a first-order *autoregressive* scheme of the type described in Section 8–2. In this case we have

$$u_{1t} = \rho_1 u_{1,t-1} + \varepsilon_{1t},$$

$$u_{2t} = \rho_2 u_{2,t-1} + \varepsilon_{2t},$$

$$\vdots$$

$$u_{Gt} = \rho_G u_{G,t-1} + \varepsilon_{Gt}.$$

The ε's are *not* assumed to be independent across equations. Consider the problem of estimating the first structural equation of the system as described by (13.34):

$$\mathbf{y}_1 = \mathbf{Y}_1\boldsymbol{\beta}_1 + \mathbf{X}_1\boldsymbol{\gamma}_1 + \mathbf{u}_1.$$

The tth observation is then represented as

$$(13.82) \quad y_{1t} = -\beta_{12}y_{2t} - \cdots - \beta_{1G^\Delta}y_{G^\Delta t} - \gamma_{11}x_{1t} - \cdots - \gamma_{1K^*}x_{K^*t} + u_{1t}.$$

For the time being we shall confine ourselves to the case in which *the predetermined variables of the system do not include any lagged endogenous variables.* In this case the OLS estimates of the reduced form coefficients are consistent. Therefore, the straightforward application of the 2SLS method leads to consistent estimates of the structural coefficients, but the estimates of the variance-covariance matrix are inconsistent. However, we can easily modify the 2SLS method to account for the autoregressive nature of u_{1t}. First, we apply the transformation described in (8.52) to (13.82) to obtain

$$(13.83) \quad y_{1t} - \rho_1 y_{1,t-1} = -\beta_{12}(y_{2t} - \rho_1 y_{2,t-1}) - \beta_{13}(y_{3t} - \rho_1 y_{3,t-1})$$

$$- \cdots - \beta_{1G^\Delta}(y_{G^\Delta t} - \rho_1 y_{G^\Delta,t-1})$$

$$- \gamma_{11}(x_{1t} - \rho_1 x_{1,t-1}) - \gamma_{12}(x_{2t} - \rho_1 x_{2,t-1})$$

$$- \cdots - \gamma_{1K^*}(x_{K^*t} - \rho_1 x_{K^*,t-1}) + \varepsilon_{1t}.$$

Now, a similar transformation can be applied to each structural equation. This leads to the replacement of the autoregressive u's by the nonautoregressive ε's. The resulting system can then be solved for the current values of the endogenous variables in terms of the lagged values of the endogenous variables and current and lagged values of the exogenous variables. The equations thus obtained may be called "augmented reduced form equations" because they contain an augmented set of explanatory variables as compared to the ordinary reduced form equations. With respect to (13.83) the relevant augmented reduced form equations are those for $y_{2t}, y_{3t}, \ldots, y_{G^\Delta t}$. The coefficients of these equations can be estimated by application of the ordinary (unrestricted) least squares method.

Let us denote the resulting fitted values of the y's by $\hat{y}_{2t}, \hat{y}_{3t}, \ldots, \hat{y}_{G^{\Delta}t}$. Then we form

$$(13.84) \quad y_{1t} - \rho_1 y_{1,t-1} = -\beta_{12}(\hat{y}_{2t} - \rho_1 \hat{y}_{2,t-1}) - \beta_{13}(\hat{y}_{3t} - \rho_1 \hat{y}_{3,t-1})$$

$$- \cdots - \beta_{1G^{\Delta}}(\hat{y}_{G^{\Delta}t} - \rho_1 \hat{y}_{G^{\Delta},t-1})$$

$$- \gamma_{11}(x_{1t} - \rho_1 x_{1,t-1}) - \gamma_{12}(x_{2t} - \rho_1 x_{2,t-1})$$

$$- \cdots - \gamma_{1K^*}(x_{K^*t} - \rho_1 x_{K^*,t-1}) + \varepsilon_{1t}^*$$

or

$$(13.84a) \qquad\qquad \mathbf{y}_1^* = \hat{\mathbf{Y}}_1^* \boldsymbol{\beta}_1 + \mathbf{X}_1^* \boldsymbol{\gamma}_1 + \boldsymbol{\epsilon}_1^*,$$

where

$$\mathbf{y}_1^* = \begin{bmatrix} y_{12} - \rho_1 y_{11} \\ y_{13} - \rho_1 y_{12} \\ \vdots \\ y_{1T} - \rho_1 y_{1,T-1} \end{bmatrix},$$

$$\hat{\mathbf{Y}}_1^* = \begin{bmatrix} (\hat{y}_{22} - \rho_1 \hat{y}_{21}) & (\hat{y}_{32} - \rho_1 \hat{y}_{31}) & \cdots & (\hat{y}_{G^{\Delta}2} - \rho_1 \hat{y}_{G^{\Delta}1}) \\ (\hat{y}_{23} - \rho_1 \hat{y}_{22}) & (\hat{y}_{33} - \rho_1 \hat{y}_{32}) & \cdots & (\hat{y}_{G^{\Delta}3} - \rho_1 \hat{y}_{G^{\Delta}2}) \\ \vdots & \vdots & & \vdots \\ (\hat{y}_{2T} - \rho_1 \hat{y}_{2,T-1}) & (\hat{y}_{3T} - \rho_1 \hat{y}_{3,T-1}) & \cdots & (\hat{y}_{G^{\Delta}T} - \rho_1 \hat{y}_{G^{\Delta},T-1}) \end{bmatrix},$$

and

$$\mathbf{X}_1^* = \begin{bmatrix} (x_{12} - \rho_1 x_{11}) & (x_{22} - \rho_1 x_{21}) & \cdots & (x_{K^*2} - \rho_1 x_{K^*1}) \\ (x_{13} - \rho_1 x_{12}) & (x_{23} - \rho_1 x_{22}) & \cdots & (x_{K^*3} - \rho_1 x_{K^*2}) \\ \vdots & \vdots & & \vdots \\ (x_{1T} - \rho_1 x_{1,T-1}) & (x_{2T} - \rho_1 x_{2,T-1}) & \cdots & (x_{K^*T} - \rho_1 x_{K^*,T-1}) \end{bmatrix},$$

The coefficients ρ_1, $\boldsymbol{\beta}_1$, and $\boldsymbol{\gamma}_1$ can then be estimated by applying the restricted least squares method to (13.84) as described in Section 8–2.

The 3SLS method can also be easily modified to take into account the autoregressive character of the structural disturbances. By applying the modified 2SLS method to each structural equation, we obtain consistent estimates of $\rho_1, \rho_2, \ldots, \rho_G$. These can be used to transform the variables so that the system can be written as

$$(13.85) \qquad\qquad \mathbf{y}_1^{**} = \hat{\mathbf{Y}}_1^{**} \boldsymbol{\beta}_1 + \mathbf{X}_1^{**} \boldsymbol{\gamma}_1 + \boldsymbol{\epsilon}_1^{**},$$

$$\mathbf{y}_2^{**} = \hat{\mathbf{Y}}_2^{**} \boldsymbol{\beta}_2 + \mathbf{X}_2^{**} \boldsymbol{\gamma}_2 + \boldsymbol{\epsilon}_2^{**},$$

$$\vdots$$

$$\mathbf{y}_G^{**} = \hat{\mathbf{Y}}_G^{**} \boldsymbol{\beta}_G + \mathbf{X}_G^{**} \boldsymbol{\gamma}_G + \boldsymbol{\epsilon}_G^{**},$$

where the double asterisk indicates that the ρ's have been replaced by their consistent estimates; otherwise the notation in (13.85) conforms to that in (13.84a). The coefficients of (13.85) can then be estimated by two-stage Aitken's estimation method as in the case of the ordinary 3SLS method. It would also be possible to set up a joint distribution function for the ε's and use it to derive the FIML estimates for the autoregressive case, but this would be quite complicated.

The preceding discussion has been restricted to simultaneous equation systems in which the predetermined variables do not include any lagged endogenous variables. If this is not the case, the estimation problem under autoregressive disturbances becomes rather difficult. The source of this difficulty is the fact that, under these circumstances, the predetermined variables are no longer uncorrelated with the structural disturbances. One consequence is that the OLS estimates of the reduced form coefficients are inconsistent, which creates serious complications. A way out of this difficulty would be to use the method of instrumental variables. Another approach, similar to that adopted in the context of distributed lag models, has been proposed by Fisher.[19]

13–6   Analysis of Dynamic Econometric Models[20]

A simultaneous equation model represents a set of relations between the endogenous and the predetermined variables of a system. If the predetermined variables are all purely exogenous, then the model specifies how the exogenous variables, together with the stochastic disturbances, generate the values of the endogenous variables at a given point (or period) of time. This was illustrated in detail in the food market example of Section 13–2. However, if the predetermined variables also include lagged endogenous variables, then the model specifies not only how the predetermined variables (together with the disturbances) generate the current values of the endogenous variables, but also how the time paths of the exogenous variables and the disturbances determine the time paths of the endogenous variables. This is implicit in the structure of the model, but it is of some interest to have such a dynamic dependence formulated explicitly. Further questions of interest concern the stability of the system, and the influence of the past values of the exogenous variables on the current values

[19] See F. M. Fisher, *The Identification Problem in Econometrics* (New York: McGraw-Hill, 1966), pp. 168–175. The instrumental variables approach is described in R. C. Fair, "The Estimation of Simultaneous Equation Models with Lagged Endogenous Variables and First Order Serially Correlated Errors," *Econometrica*, Vol. 38, May 1970, pp. 507–516.

[20] In our exposition we present only the very basic elements of dynamic analysis applicable to simple linear systems. Considerably more sophisticated methods involving simulation, policy analysis, and nonlinear dynamic multipliers are now becoming known and may be studied. See, e.g., L. R. Klein, M. K. Evans, and M. Hartley, *Econometric Gaming* (New York: Macmillan, 1969); Gary Fromm and Paul Taubman, *Policy Simulations with an Econometric Model* (Washington: Brookings Institution, 1968); or M. K. Evans and L. R. Klein, *The Wharton Econometric Forecasting Model* (Philadelphia: University of Pennsylvania Press, 1967).

of the endogenous variables. The purpose of this section is to examine these
questions, since providing the answers represents a natural and important part of
the work of an econometrician. Our approach will be to illustrate the problems
and their solution by reference to a specific model; in this way the special concepts of dynamic analysis will acquire a concrete meaning. However, the basic
procedures can easily be adapted to other models as well.

Consider the following simple model of the economy:

$$C_t = \alpha_0 + \alpha_1 Y_t + \alpha_2 C_{t-1} + u_{1t} \quad \text{(consumption)},$$

$$I_t = \beta_0 + \beta_1 r_t + \beta_2 I_{t-1} + u_{2t} \quad \text{(investment)},$$

$$r_t = \gamma_0 + \gamma_1 Y_t + \gamma_2 M_t + u_{3t} \quad \text{(money market)},$$

$$Y_t = C_t + I_t + G_t \quad \text{(income identity)},$$

where C = consumption, Y = income, I = investment, r = rate of interest,
M = money supply, and G = government expenditure. C, Y, I, and r are endogenous; M and G are exogenous. The latter may be viewed as policy variables
that can be, and have been, manipulated at will by the policymakers. The reduced form of this system is

(13.86) $C_t = \pi_{11} + \pi_{12} C_{t-1} + \pi_{13} I_{t-1} + \pi_{14} M_t + \pi_{15} G_t + v_{1t},$

(13.87) $I_t = \pi_{21} + \pi_{22} C_{t-1} + \pi_{23} I_{t-1} + \pi_{24} M_t + \pi_{25} G_t + v_{2t},$

(13.88) $Y_t = \pi_{31} + \pi_{32} C_{t-1} + \pi_{33} I_{t-1} + \pi_{34} M_t + \pi_{35} G_t + v_{3t},$

(13.89) $r_t = \pi_{41} + \pi_{42} C_{t-1} + \pi_{43} I_{t-1} + \pi_{44} M_t + \pi_{45} G_t + v_{4t}.$

The reduced form coefficients can, of course, be expressed in terms of the structural coefficients. In the language of dynamic analysis, the reduced form coefficients are called *impact multipliers*, since they measure the immediate response
of the endogenous variables to changes in the predetermined variables. For
instance, π_{15} measures the change in the mean value of current consumption due
to a unit change in current government expenditure, given the current value of
the money supply and given the level of consumption and investment in the preceding period.

The reduced form equations are useful mainly for short-term forecasting. We
can forecast the next period's values of the endogenous variables on the basis of
our knowledge of the current values of I and C and of the forthcoming values of
the policy variables. However, we cannot use the reduced form equations to
determine how the system operates under continuous impact of the exogenous
variables. For instance, the reduced form equation for consumption shows that
the current value of consumption depends not only on the current values of G
and M but also on the previous values of consumption and investment. This is
not greatly illuminating because it pushes part of the responsibility for explaining
the current level of consumption onto its own immediate history. To understand the mechanism of the determination of consumption and of other endogenous variables, we need a solution that would determine the level of these

variables *without* reference to their immediate past. Such a solution can be obtained by manipulating the reduced form equations so that all lagged endogenous variables are eliminated. This elimination can proceed in two steps. First we reformulate the reduced form equations so that each equation contains only one endogenous variable, whether current or lagged. Then we remove the lagged endogenous variables as intended.

Let us take the reduced form equation for consumption. Here the only "foreign" lagged endogenous variable is I_{t-1}. Now, from (13.87) we have

$$(13.90) \qquad I_t - \pi_{23}I_{t-1} = \pi_{21} + \pi_{22}C_{t-1} + \pi_{24}M_t + \pi_{25}G_t + v_{2t}$$

or

$$(13.90a) \quad I_{t-1} - \pi_{23}I_{t-2} = \pi_{21} + \pi_{22}C_{t-2} + \pi_{24}M_{t-1} + \pi_{25}G_{t-1} + v_{2,t-1}.$$

Further, lagging (13.86) by one period and multiplying by $-\pi_{23}$ gives

$$(13.91) \quad -\pi_{23}C_{t-1} = -\pi_{11}\pi_{23} - \pi_{12}\pi_{23}C_{t-2} - \pi_{13}\pi_{23}I_{t-2} - \pi_{14}\pi_{23}M_{t-1}$$
$$-\pi_{15}\pi_{23}G_{t-1} - \pi_{23}v_{1,t-1}.$$

By adding (13.86) and (13.91), we obtain

$$(13.92) \qquad C_t = \pi_{11}(1 - \pi_{23}) + (\pi_{12} + \pi_{23})C_{t-1} - \pi_{12}\pi_{23}C_{t-2}$$
$$+ \pi_{13}(I_{t-1} - \pi_{23}I_{t-2}) + \pi_{14}M_t - \pi_{14}\pi_{23}M_{t-1}$$
$$+ \pi_{15}G_t - \pi_{15}\pi_{23}G_{t-1} + v_{1t} - \pi_{23}v_{1,t-1}.$$

Substitution for $(I_{t-1} - \pi_{23}I_{t-2})$ from (13.90a) into (13.92) then leads to

$$(13.93) \quad C_t = [\pi_{11}(1 - \pi_{23}) + \pi_{13}\pi_{21}] + (\pi_{12} + \pi_{23})C_{t-1}$$
$$+ (\pi_{13}\pi_{22} - \pi_{12}\pi_{23})C_{t-2} + \pi_{14}M_t + (\pi_{13}\pi_{24} - \pi_{14}\pi_{23})M_{t-1}$$
$$+ \pi_{15}G_t + (\pi_{13}\pi_{25} - \pi_{15}\pi_{23})G_{t-1} + v_{1t} - \pi_{23}v_{1,t-1}$$
$$+ \pi_{13}v_{2,t-1},$$

or, in obvious notation,

$$(13.93a) \quad C_t = \delta + \mu_1 C_{t-1} + \mu_2 C_{t-2} + \kappa_0 M_t + \kappa_1 M_{t-1} + v_0 G_t + v_1 G_{t-1} + \varepsilon_t.$$

Equation (13.93), or its equivalent (13.93a), is called the *fundamental dynamic equation* for the consumption variable. Similar equations could be derived for the remaining endogenous variables of the system. Since it can be shown that in a general interdependent linear system each variable satisfies the same final autoregressive equation,[21] we will refer to consumption alone. The fundamental dynamic equation has special importance in determining the stability of the system, and we shall return to it. Our present aim is to express current consumption in terms of current and past values of the exogenous variables and

[21] See A. S. Goldberger, *Impact Multipliers and Dynamic Properties of the Klein-Goldberger Model* (Amsterdam: North-Holland Publishing Company, 1959), pp. 106–108.

disturbances, which can be done by a series of successive substitutions. First, note that by (13.93a) the expression for C_t at $t = 1$ is

$$(13.94) \qquad C_1 = \delta + \mu_1 C_0 + \mu_2 C_{-1} + \kappa_0 M_1 + \kappa_1 M_0 + \nu_0 G_1 + \nu_1 G_0 + \varepsilon_1.$$

The values of C_0 and C_{-1} have been determined prior to the beginning of the series, and are called the *initial conditions*. For the purpose of dynamic analysis we shall assume them to be given. The values of M_0 and G_0 are of no special interest to us and can be merged with the constant term, so that (13.94) can be written as

$$(13.94a) \qquad C_1 = \eta + \mu_1 C_0 + \mu_2 C_{-1} + \kappa_0 M_1 + \nu_0 G_1 + \varepsilon_1.$$

Next, the expression for C_t at $t = 2$ is

$$(13.95) \quad C_2 = \delta + \mu_1 C_1 + \mu_2 C_0 + \kappa_0 M_2 + \kappa_1 M_1 + \nu_0 G_2 + \nu_1 G_1 + \varepsilon_2.$$

Since C_0 is taken as given, we have only to eliminate C_1 from (13.95), by substituting from (13.94a), which gives

$$(13.96) \quad C_2 = (\delta + \mu_1 \eta) + (\mu_1^2 + \mu_2)C_0 + \mu_1 \mu_2 C_{-1}$$
$$+ \kappa_0 M_2 + (\kappa_1 + \kappa_0 \mu_1)M_1 + \nu_0 G_2 + (\nu_1 + \nu_0 \mu_1)G_1 + \varepsilon_2 + \mu_1 \varepsilon_1.$$

In a similar way we can obtain a solution for C_3, C_4, etc. The outcome is a general expression for C_t, which is

$$(13.97) \quad C_t = \eta_t + \eta_1 C_0 + \eta_2 C_{-1} + \zeta_0 M_t + \zeta_1 M_{t-1} + \cdots + \zeta_{t-1} M_1$$
$$+ \xi_0 G_t + \xi_1 G_{t-1} + \cdots + \xi_{t-1} G_1 + \varepsilon_t + \theta_1 \varepsilon_{t-1} + \cdots + \theta_{t-1} \varepsilon_1.$$

Thus C_t is—for a set of given initial conditions—expressed purely in terms of current and lagged exogenous variables and disturbances. (If the system is stable, η_t becomes a constant for large t.) Similar expressions could be derived for the other endogenous variables. These equations are called the *final form* of the equation system. They show how the time paths of the exogenous variables determine the time path of each endogenous variable. The coefficients attached to the exogenous variables are here called the *dynamic multipliers*. Note that equations such as (13.97) can also be used to answer questions concerning the influence of some past policy action on the current level of the endogenous variables, or the extent of corrective measures necessary to bring about some desired changes in the endogenous variables over any number of future periods.

Stability Conditions and Dynamic Analysis

Let us now turn to the question of the stability of a system. In general, we say that a system is stable if, in a situation where the values of the exogenous variables are held constant through time, the mean values of the endogenous variable settle down to some constant levels. (The actual values of the endogenous variables will, of course, fluctuate because of the effect of the stochastic disturbances. We will consider only cases where the probability is very small that an otherwise stable system could turn unstable because of random disturbances.)

This means that a system is considered unstable if, for constant values of the exogenous variables, the mean values of the endogenous variables either explode or display a regular oscillatory movement. One way of determining whether a system is stable or not is to refer to the final form equations. Clearly, if the system is to settle down when the levels of the exogenous variables are unchanged, the sums of each set of dynamic multipliers must be finite. That is, the requirement for stability is that the sums

$$\sum_{i=0}^{\infty} \zeta_i \quad \text{and} \quad \sum_{i=0}^{\infty} \xi_i$$

are finite. These sums represent the *long-run* or *equilibrium multipliers* for consumption with respect to money supply and to government expenditure. Another way of finding out whether a system is stable or not is to examine the fundamental dynamic equation. If the exogenous variables are held constant (and the disturbances are disregarded), this equation becomes an ordinary linear nonhomogeneous difference equation and can be solved as such.[22] In our case we have from (13.93a)

$$(13.98) \qquad C_t - \mu_1 C_{t-1} - \mu_2 C_{t-2} = \text{constant}.$$

The characteristic equation for (13.98) is

$$(13.99) \qquad \lambda^2 - \mu_1 \lambda - \mu_2 = 0$$

with roots

$$\lambda_{1,2} = \frac{\mu_1 \pm \sqrt{\mu_1^2 + 4\mu_2}}{2}.$$

The system is stable if and only if the absolute value of the largest root (or modulus) of (13.99) is smaller than one. If this is the case, we can determine the equilibrium mean value of consumption from (13.93a) as

$$(13.100) \qquad C_E = \frac{\delta + \kappa_0 M_t + \kappa_1 M_{t-1} + \nu_0 G_t + \nu_1 G_{t-1}}{1 - \mu_1 - \mu_2}.$$

The stability condition is clearly important from the economic point of view. It should also be realized that the existence of stability (or, at worst, of a regular oscillatory pattern) is, in fact, assumed in the process of estimation. The assumption that the predetermined variables of the system have finite variances as $t \to \infty$ applies also to the lagged endogenous variables, and this assumption would be violated if the endogenous variables were to grow or decline without limit. If this assumption were not made, there would be difficulties in proving the asymptotic properties of estimators.

The dynamic solution given by the final form equations answers questions concerning the influence of hypothetical changes in the exogenous variables of

---

[22] See, e.g., R. G. D. Allen, *Mathematical Economics* (London: Macmillan, 1956), pp. 176–195.

the system. If we are interested in the effect of changes in the values of exogenous variables that actually did take place during the period under observation, we may trace these more conveniently by using first differences. In our model we have, by reference to (13.97),

$$(13.101) \quad C_t - C_{t-1} = (\eta_t - \eta_{t-1}) + \zeta_0(M_t - M_{t-1}) + \zeta_1(M_{t-1} - M_{t-2})$$
$$+ \cdots + \zeta_{t-2}(M_2 - M_1) + \zeta_{t-1}M_1 + \xi_0(G_t - G_{t-1})$$
$$+ \xi_1(G_{t-1} - G_{t-2}) + \cdots + \xi_{t-2}(G_2 - G_1)$$
$$+ \xi_{t-1}G_1 + \omega_t.$$

The first term on the right-hand side indicates the influence of the initial conditions and of the dynamics of the system operating in absence of any changes in the exogenous variables. For systems that are stable the value of this term will diminish as the system moves from the initial position, and will eventually approach zero. The terms $\zeta_{t-1}M_1$ and $\xi_{t-1}G_1$ measure the influence of the starting levels of the exogenous variables. The term ω_t summarizes the influence of the random disturbances. By substituting the actual values of the exogenous variables for the period under investigation into (13.101), we can determine the part that any policy measure played in affecting the observed change in the level of consumption.

The preceding discussion has been carried out in terms of the population parameters, which are, of course, not known and must be replaced by sample estimates. Therefore, it would be desirable to accompany each estimate with its standard error. Formulas for estimating the standard errors are available for the impact multipliers of the reduced form equations, but not for the dynamic multipliers of the final form equations. As for the characteristic roots that are crucial for the determination of the stability condition of a system, a formula for the asymptotic variance of the largest root has been derived by Theil and Boot.[23] In general, however, dynamic analysis in econometrics has not yet been well developed from the viewpoint of statistical inference.

EXAMPLE   A model of the United States economy for the period 1921–1941, known as Klein's Model I, has been estimated as follows:[24]

Consumption: $C_t = 16.555 + 0.017P_t + 0.216P_{t-1} + 0.810W_t + \tilde{u}_{1t};$

Investment: $I_t = 20.278 + 0.150P_t + 0.616P_{t-1} - 0.158K_{t-1} + \tilde{u}_{2t};$

Private wages: $W_t^* = 1.500 + 0.439E_t + 0.147E_{t-1} + 0.130A_t + \tilde{u}_{3t};$

Product: $Y_t + T_t = C_t + I_t + G_t;$

Income: $Y_t = P_t + W_t;$

---

[23] H. Theil and J. C. G. Boot, "The Final Form of Econometric Equation Systems," *Review of the International Statistical Institute*, Vol. 30, 1962, pp. 136–152.

[24] The model is presented in L. R. Klein, *Economic Fluctuations in the United States 1921–1941* (New York: Wiley, 1950), pp. 65–68. The estimates of the coefficients are two-stage least squares estimates given in A. S. Goldberger, *op. cit.* (1964), p. 365.

Capital: $K_t = K_{t-1} + I_t;$

Wages: $W_t = W_t^* + W_t^{**};$

Private product: $E_t = Y_t + T_t - W_t^{**}.$

Endogenous variables:

C	consumption	Y	national income
I	investment	K	end-of-year capital stock
W^*	private wage bill	W	total wage bill
P	profits	E	private product.

Exogenous variables:

W^{**} government wage bill

T indirect taxes

A time in years $(1931 = 1)$

All variables except time are measured in billions of constant (1934) dollars. We are especially interested in the income variable. The estimated fundamental dynamic equation for this variable is

$$Y_t - 1.726\, Y_{t-1} + 1.029\, Y_{t-2} - 0.183\, Y_{t-3}$$

$$= 4.880 + 1.773 G_t - 1.493 G_{t-1} + 0.154 A_t - 0.294 A_{t-1} + 0.162 A_{t-2}$$

$$- 1.254 T_t + 0.673 T_{t-1} + 0.213 T_{t-2} + 0.183 T_{t-3} + 0.663 W_t^{**}$$

$$- 1.443 W_{t-1}^{**} + 1.029 W_{t-2}^{**} - 0.183 W_{t-3}^{**} + \tilde{\omega}_t.$$

The characteristic equation

$$\lambda^3 - 1.726\, \lambda^2 + 1.029\, \lambda - 0.183 = 0$$

has as its roots

$$\lambda_1 = 0.310 \quad \text{and} \quad \lambda_{2,3} = 0.708 \pm 0.298i.$$

The modulus of the complex roots is $\sqrt{0.708^2 + 0.298^2} = 0.768$, which is smaller than unity. Thus, according to our estimates, the system appears stable. Table 13–3 shows the dynamic multipliers of government expenditure on income (Y) or net national product $(Y + T)$. Finally, we are interested in how government expenditure affected the changes in the net national product during the period 1921–1941. Table 13–4 shows the actual changes in $(Y + T)$ as well as those estimated to be due to current and past changes in government expenditure. The latter were calculated in accordance with (13.101) as

$$\xi_0(G_t - G_{t-1}) + \xi_1(G_{t-1} - G_{t-2}) + \cdots + \xi_{t-2}(G_2 - G_1).$$

Table 13–4 may be used to examine the extent of anticyclical fiscal policy effects during the period.

Table 13–3 Dynamic Multipliers of G on $(Y + T)$

Lag	Multiplier
0	1.773
1	1.567
2	0.881
3	0.232
4	−0.219
5	−0.456
6	−0.519
7	−0.466
8	−0.355
9	−0.227
10	−0.112
11	−0.025
12	0.031
13	0.058
14	0.064
15	0.057
16	0.042
17	0.027
18	0.013
19	0.002
20	−0.004
Total	2.071

Table 13–4 Changes in $(Y + T)$ Accounted by Past and Current Changes in G

Year	$\Delta(Y + T)$	Due to changes in G
1922	4.7	−0.9
1923	7.1	−1.4
1924	0.1	0.5
1925	4.0	0.8
1926	3.1	0.8
1927	0.7	2.4
1928	0.2	2.4
1929	2.8	1.8
1930	−5.6	3.0
1931	−7.2	4.2
1932	−8.6	1.6
1933	1.1	−1.8
1934	5.0	−1.4
1935	4.8	−0.5
1936	9.6	−0.8
1937	1.6	0.4
1938	−3.1	3.9
1939	8.7	5.7
1940	6.4	5.6
1941	13.2	15.2

Concluding Remarks

In conclusion, we may draw the attention of the reader to some of the main gaps that have yet to be filled. Most of the work on estimation of simultaneous equation models has relied upon the basic assumptions of the classical linear regression model. Clearly, there is a need to consider the estimation problem under circumstances in which these assumptions do not hold. Other than the problem of autoregression in the disturbances, which we noted at the end of Section 13–5, we have to develop estimators for simultaneous equation models with nonlinear equations, and with equations containing distributed lags. But perhaps the most important problems relate to errors of measurement and specification. Unfortunately, these problems have not yet been entirely satisfactorily resolved even in the simpler context of single-equation models, much less in the relatively complex framework of simultaneous equations.

EXERCISES

13–1. A highly simplified Keynesian model of the economy is

$$C_t = \alpha + \beta Y_t + \varepsilon_t,$$
$$Y_t = C_t + I_t,$$

where Y = income, C = consumption, and I = exogenous investment. Show that the ILS, 2SLS, LIML, and FIML methods of estimation lead to identical results.

13–2. Consider the following simultaneous equation model:

$$Y_{1t} = \beta_{12} Y_{2t} + \gamma_{11} + u_{1t},$$

$$Y_{2t} = \gamma_{21} + \gamma_{22} X_t + u_{2t},$$

where X is a nonstochastic exogenous variable. The disturbances are assumed to have zero means and constant variances, and to be nonautoregressive over time. Further, u_{1t} and u_{2t} are mutually independent. Compare the variances of the ordinary least squares and the indirect least squares estimator of β_{12}.

13–3. Tintner's model of the American meat market is

$$Y_{1t} = a_0 + a_1 Y_{2t} + a_2 X_{1t} + u_{1t} \qquad \text{(demand)},$$

$$Y_{1t} = b_0 + b_1 Y_{2t} + b_2 X_{2t} + b_3 X_{3t} + u_{2t} \quad \text{(supply)},$$

where u_{1t} and u_{2t} are disturbance terms, Y_{1t} and Y_{2t} are endogenous variables, and X_{1t}, X_{2t}, and X_{3t} are predetermined variables. These variables are defined as follows:

Y_1 per capita meat consumption;
Y_2 index of meat prices;
X_1 per capita disposable income;
X_2 index of meat processing costs;
X_3 index of agricultural production costs.

The $T \times 1$ disturbance vectors, $\mathbf{u_1}$ and $\mathbf{u_2}$, are assumed to have the following covariance matrix:

$$E \begin{bmatrix} \mathbf{u_1} \\ \mathbf{u_2} \end{bmatrix} [\mathbf{u_1'} \quad \mathbf{u_2'}] = \begin{bmatrix} \sigma_{11}\mathbf{I_T} & \sigma_{12}\mathbf{I_T} \\ \sigma_{11}\mathbf{I_T} & \sigma_{22}\mathbf{I_T} \end{bmatrix}.$$

a. Discuss the identification of the two equations.

b. Suppose that it is known a priori that $b_2/b_3 = K$, where K is a known number. Discuss the identification properties of the model after adding this specification.

c. Suppose instead that the term $a_3 X_{4t}$ is added to the demand equation, where X_4 is an index of prices of nonanimal proteins and fats. How does this alter the identification of the model?

13–4. Assume the following aggregate model for the economy:

$$C_t = \alpha_1 + \alpha_2 D_t + u_{1t},$$

$$I_t = \beta_1 + \beta_2 Y_t + \beta_3 Y_{t-1} + u_{2t},$$

$$Y_t = D_t + T_t,$$

$$Y_t = C_t + I_t + G_t,$$

where C = consumption, D = net national income, I = investment, Y = net national product, T = indirect taxes, and G = autonomous expenditures. The variables C, D, I, and Y are endogenous; T and G are exogenous.

a. Examine the conditions of identification of the first two equations of the model.

b. Obtain consistent estimates of the consumption and investment equations using data in Table 13–5 for the United States economy, 1921–1941.

Table 13–5*

1920	C	D	Y	I
1920	—	—	47.1	—
1921	41.9	40.6	48.3	−0.2
1922	45.0	49.1	53.0	1.9
1923	49.2	55.4	60.1	5.2
1924	50.6	56.4	60.2	3.0
1925	52.6	58.7	64.2	5.1
1926	55.1	60.3	67.3	5.6
1927	56.2	61.3	68.0	4.2
1928	57.3	64.0	68.2	3.0
1929	57.8	67.0	71.0	5.1
1930	55.0	57.7	65.4	1.0
1931	50.9	50.7	58.2	−3.4
1932	45.6	41.3	49.6	−6.2
1933	46.5	45.3	50.7	−5.1
1934	48.7	48.9	55.7	−3.0
1935	51.3	53.3	60.5	−1.3
1936	57.7	61.8	70.1	2.1
1937	58.7	65.0	71.7	2.0
1938	57.5	61.2	68.6	−1.9
1939	61.6	68.4	77.3	1.3
1940	65.0	74.1	83.7	3.3
1941	69.7	85.3	96.9	4.9

Source: L. R. Klein, *Economic Fluctuations in the United States 1921–1941* (New York: Wiley, 1950), p. 135.

* All variables measured in billions of 1934 dollars.

13–5. Using the results from Exercise 13–4:

a. Derive the fundamental dynamic equation and use it to determine whether the system is stable or not.

b. Calculate the dynamic multipliers of Y with respect to G.

c. Find the value of the long-run (equilibrium) multiplier of Y with respect to G.

13–6. Consider the following dynamic model of the market for a certain commodity:

$$S_t = \alpha_0 + \alpha_1 P_t + u_{1t},$$

$$D_t = \beta_0 + \beta_1 P_t + u_{2t},$$

$$P_t - P_{t-1} = m(Q_{t-1} - Q_{t-2}) + u_{3t},$$

$$S_t - D_t = Q_t - Q_{t-1},$$

where S_t = production, D_t = sales, P_t = price, and Q_t = end-of-period level of stock. Note that

$$\alpha_1 > 0,$$
$$\beta_1 < 0,$$
$$\alpha_0 < \beta_0,$$
$$m < 0.$$

a. Determine the identification status of the first three equations.

b. Show that the time path of Q_t is determined by a second-order homogeneous difference equation, and that the time path of P_t is determined by a first-order non-homogeneous difference equation.

c. Derive the conditions for the existence of equilibrium in this market.

d. Disregarding the stochastic disturbances, find the value of m for which the time path of P_t is one of regular oscillations.

Appendix

A. Algebra of Summations

Expressions involving sums are widely used in statistics. They are usually abbreviated with the help of the so-called "$\sum$ notation." The basic definition relating to this notation states that if m and n are integers and $m \leq n$, then

$$\sum_{i=m}^{n} x_i = x_m + x_{m+1} + x_{m+2} + \cdots + x_n.$$

This notation is used most frequently with sums of observations on a given variable or variables, with the subscript designating the numbering of the observations. When this notation is used, the following rules are useful:

(A.1)
$$\sum_{i=1}^{n} kx_i = k \sum_{i=1}^{n} x_i.$$

Proof:

$$\sum_{i=1}^{n} kx_i = kx_1 + kx_2 + \cdots + kx_n = k(x_1 + x_2 + \cdots + x_n) = k \sum_{i=1}^{n} x_i.$$

(A.2)
$$\sum_{i=1}^{n} k = nk.$$

Proof:

$$\sum_{i=1}^{n} k = k + k + \cdots + k = nk.$$

(A.3)
$$\sum_{i=1}^{n} (x_i + y_i) = \sum_{i=1}^{n} x_i + \sum_{i=1}^{n} y_i.$$

Proof:

$$\sum_{i=1}^{n} (x_i + y_i) = (x_1 + y_1) + (x_2 + y_2) + \cdots + (x_n + y_n)$$

$$= (x_1 + x_2 + \cdots + x_n) + (y_1 + y_2 + \cdots + y_n) = \sum_{i=1}^{n} x_i + \sum_{i=1}^{n} y_i.$$

Useful formulas are established by considering the sum of the first n positive integers and the sums of their powers. The results, given without proof, are

(A.4) $\displaystyle\sum_{i=1}^{n} i = 1 + 2 + \cdots + n = \frac{1}{2}[n(n+1)] = \frac{1}{2}[(n+1)^2 - (n+1)],$

(A.5) $\displaystyle\sum_{i=1}^{n} i^2 = 1^2 + 2^2 + \cdots + n^2 = \frac{1}{6}[n(n+1)(2n+1)]$

$$= \frac{1}{3}[(n+1)^3 - \frac{3}{2}(n+1)^2 + \frac{1}{2}(n+1)],$$

(A.6) $\displaystyle\sum_{i=1}^{n} i^3 = 1^3 + 2^3 + \cdots + n^3 = \frac{1}{4}[n^2(n+1)^2]$

$$= \frac{1}{4}[(n+1)^4 - 2(n+1)^3 + (n+1)^2],$$

(A.7) $\displaystyle\sum_{i=1}^{n} i^4 = 1^4 + 2^4 + \cdots + n^4 = \frac{1}{30}[n(n+1)(2n+1)(3n^2 + 3n - 1)]$

$$= \frac{1}{5}[(n+1)^5 - \frac{5}{2}(n+1)^4 + \frac{5}{3}(n+1)^3 - \frac{1}{6}(n+1)].$$

The Σ notation can also be extended to multiple sums. For instance, a double summation is defined as

$$\sum_{i=1}^{n}\sum_{j=1}^{m} x_{ij} = \sum_{i=1}^{n} (x_{i1} + x_{i2} + \cdots + x_{im})$$

$$= (x_{11} + x_{21} + \cdots + x_{n1}) + (x_{12} + x_{22} + \cdots + x_{n2})$$

$$+ \cdots + (x_{1m} + x_{2m} + \cdots + x_{nm}).$$

The following double-summation rules are of special interest:

(A.8) $\displaystyle\sum_{i=1}^{n}\sum_{j=1}^{m} (x_{ij} + y_{ij}) = \sum_{i=1}^{n}\sum_{j=1}^{m} x_{ij} + \sum_{i=1}^{n}\sum_{j=1}^{m} y_{ij}.$

Proof:

$$\sum_{i=1}^{n}\sum_{j=1}^{m} (x_{ij} + y_{ij}) = \sum_{j=1}^{m} (x_{1j} + y_{1j}) + \sum_{j=1}^{m} (x_{2j} + y_{2j}) + \cdots + \sum_{j=1}^{m} (x_{nj} + y_{nj})$$

$$= \sum_{j=1}^{m} (x_{1j} + x_{2j} + \cdots + x_{nj}) + \sum_{j=1}^{m} (y_{1j} + y_{2j} + \cdots + y_{nj})$$

$$= \sum_{i=1}^{n}\sum_{j=1}^{m} x_{ij} + \sum_{i=1}^{n}\sum_{j=1}^{m} y_{ij}.$$

(A.9) $\displaystyle\sum_{i=1}^{n}\sum_{j=1}^{m} x_i = m \sum_{i=1}^{n} x_i.$

Proof:

$$\sum_{i=1}^{n}\sum_{j=1}^{m} x_i = \sum_{j=1}^{m} \left[\sum_{i=1}^{n} x_i\right] = m \sum_{i=1}^{n} x_i.$$

(A.10) $\displaystyle\sum_{i=1}^{n}\sum_{j=1}^{m} x_i y_j = \left[\sum_{i=1}^{n} x_i\right]\left[\sum_{j=1}^{m} y_j\right].$

Proof:

$$\sum_{i=1}^{n}\sum_{j=1}^{m} x_i y_j = \sum_{i=1}^{n}(x_i y_1 + x_i y_2 + \cdots + x_i y_m)$$

$$= y_1 \sum_{i=1}^{n} x_i + y_2 \sum_{i=1}^{n} x_i + \cdots + y_m \sum_{i=1}^{n} x_i = \left[\sum_{i=1}^{n} x_i\right]\left[\sum_{j=1}^{m} y_j\right].$$

(A.11)
$$\sum_{i=1}^{n}\sum_{j=1}^{m} x_i y_{ij} = \sum_{i=1}^{n} x_i \sum_{j=1}^{m} y_{ij}.$$

Proof:

$$\sum_{i=1}^{n}\sum_{j=1}^{m} x_i y_{ij} = \sum_{i=1}^{n}(x_i y_{i1} + x_i y_{i2} + \cdots + x_i y_{im}) = \sum_{i=1}^{n} x_i(y_{i1} + y_{i2} + \cdots + y_{im})$$

$$= \sum_{i=1}^{n} x_i \sum_{j=1}^{m} y_{ij}.$$

(A.12)
$$\left[\sum_{i=1}^{n} x_i\right]^2 = \sum_{i=1}^{n} x_i^2 + 2\sum_{i=1}^{n-1}\sum_{j=i+1}^{n} x_i x_j = \sum_{i=1}^{n} x_i^2 + 2\sum_{i<j} x_i x_j.$$

Proof:

$$\left[\sum_{i=1}^{n} x_i\right]^2 = (x_1 + x_2 + \cdots + x_n)^2$$

$$= x_1^2 + x_2^2 + \cdots + x_n^2 + 2(x_1 x_2 + x_1 x_3 + \cdots + x_1 x_n$$

$$+ x_2 x_3 + x_2 x_4 + \cdots + x_{n-1} x_n) = \sum_{i=1}^{n} x_i^2 + 2\sum_{i<j} x_i x_j.$$

A special case of (A.12) is

(A.13)
$$\sum_{i=1}^{n}(x_i - \bar{x})^2 = -2\sum_{i<j}(x_i - \bar{x})(x_j - \bar{x}).$$

Proof: Since

$$\sum_{i=1}^{n}(x_i - \bar{x}) = 0,$$

we have

$$\left[\sum_{i=1}^{n}(x_i - \bar{x})\right]^2 = \sum_{i=1}^{n}(x_i - \bar{x})^2 + 2\sum_{i<j}(x_i - \bar{x})(x_j - \bar{x}) = 0,$$

or
$$\sum_{i=1}^{n}(x_i - \bar{x})^2 = -2\sum_{i<j}(x_i - \bar{x})(x_j - \bar{x}).$$

B.   Elements of Matrix Algebra

Definitions

An $(M \times N)$ matrix is defined as a rectangular array of real numbers arranged in M rows and N columns as in

(B.1)
$$\mathbf{A} = \begin{bmatrix} a_{11} & a_{12} & \cdots & a_{1N} \\ a_{21} & a_{22} & \cdots & a_{2N} \\ \vdots & \vdots & & \vdots \\ a_{M1} & a_{M2} & \cdots & a_{MN} \end{bmatrix}.$$

The numbers a_{ij} ($i = 1, 2, \ldots, M; j = 1, 2, \ldots, N$) are the *elements* of $\mathbf{A}$; the term a_{ij} itself is frequently used to designate a typical element of $\mathbf{A}$. The number of rows and columns—in the case of (B.1) given as $M \times N$—is referred to as the *order* or the *dimension* of the matrix. A matrix of order 1×1 is a *scalar*, a matrix of order $M \times 1$ is called a *column vector*, and a matrix of order $1 \times N$ is called a *row vector*. A matrix with an equal number of rows and columns is a *square matrix*. The sum of the diagonal elements of a square matrix is called the *trace* of the matrix. A *diagonal matrix* is a square matrix such that each element that does not lie along the principal diagonal is equal to zero; i.e.,

$$\mathbf{A} = \begin{bmatrix} a_{11} & 0 & \cdots & 0 \\ 0 & a_{22} & \cdots & 0 \\ \vdots & \vdots & & \vdots \\ 0 & 0 & \cdots & a_{MM} \end{bmatrix}.$$

An *identity* or a *unit matrix* is a diagonal matrix whose diagonal elements are all equal to one; i.e.,

$$\mathbf{I} = \begin{bmatrix} 1 & 0 & \cdots & 0 \\ 0 & 1 & \cdots & 0 \\ \vdots & \vdots & & \vdots \\ 0 & 0 & \cdots & 1 \end{bmatrix}.$$

Sometimes we use a subscript to indicate the order of the identity matrix in question, e.g., $\mathbf{I_M}$. Finally, a *zero matrix* is any matrix whose elements are all zero.

Basic Operations with Matrices

(B.2)   **Equality of matrices** $\mathbf{A} = \mathbf{B}$ *if and only if* $\mathbf{A}$ *and* $\mathbf{B}$ *are of the same order and* $a_{ij} = b_{ij}$ *for all* i, j.

(B.3)   **Addition of matrices** $\mathbf{A} + \mathbf{B} = \mathbf{C}$ *if and only if* $\mathbf{A}$, $\mathbf{B}$, *and* $\mathbf{C}$ *are of the same order and* $a_{ij} + b_{ij} = c_{ij}$ *for all* i, j.

EXAMPLE

$$\begin{bmatrix} 5 & 0 \\ 2 & -4 \end{bmatrix} + \begin{bmatrix} -1 & 3 \\ 3 & 5 \end{bmatrix} = \begin{bmatrix} 4 & 3 \\ 5 & 1 \end{bmatrix}.$$

(B.4) Scalar multiplication *If k is a scalar, then $k\mathbf{A} = [ka_{ij}]$.*

This means that if we want to multiply a matrix $\mathbf{A}$ by a scalar, we have to multiply each element of $\mathbf{A}$.

(B.5) Matrix multiplication *If $\mathbf{A}$ is of order $M \times N$ and $\mathbf{B}$ is of order $N \times P$, then the product of the two matrices is given as*

$$\mathbf{AB} = \mathbf{C},$$

where $\mathbf{C}$ is a matrix of order $M \times P$ whose element in the ith row and the jth column is given by

$$c_{ij} = \sum_{k=1}^{N} a_{ik}b_{kj}.$$

That is, the element c_{11} is obtained by multiplying the elements of the first row of $\mathbf{A}$ by the elements of the first column of $\mathbf{B}$ and then summing over all terms; the element c_{12} is obtained by performing the same operation with the elements of the first row of $\mathbf{A}$ and the second column of $\mathbf{B}$, and so on.

EXAMPLE 1

$$\begin{bmatrix} a_{11} & a_{12} \\ a_{21} & a_{22} \\ a_{31} & a_{32} \end{bmatrix} \begin{bmatrix} b_{11} & b_{12} \\ b_{21} & b_{22} \end{bmatrix} = \begin{bmatrix} (a_{11}b_{11} + a_{12}b_{21}) & (a_{11}b_{12} + a_{12}b_{22}) \\ (a_{21}b_{11} + a_{22}b_{21}) & (a_{21}b_{12} + a_{22}b_{22}) \\ (a_{31}b_{11} + a_{32}b_{21}) & (a_{31}b_{12} + a_{32}b_{22}) \end{bmatrix}$$

EXAMPLE 2

$$\begin{bmatrix} 1 & 2 & 3 \\ 4 & 5 & 6 \end{bmatrix} \begin{bmatrix} 7 & 10 \\ 8 & 11 \\ 11 & 12 \end{bmatrix} = \begin{bmatrix} (1 \times 7 + 2 \times 8 + 3 \times 9) & (1 \times 10 + 2 \times 11 + 3 \times 12) \\ (4 \times 7 + 5 \times 8 + 6 \times 9) & (4 \times 10 + 5 \times 11 + 6 \times 12) \end{bmatrix}$$

$$= \begin{bmatrix} 50 & 68 \\ 122 & 167 \end{bmatrix}.$$

Note that, in general,

$$\mathbf{AB} \neq \mathbf{BA}.$$

This inequality implies that we must distinguish between pre- and postmultiplication by a matrix.

Transposition

(B.6) *If $\mathbf{A}$ is an $(M \times N)$ matrix, then the* transpose *of $\mathbf{A}$, denoted by $\mathbf{A}'$, is an $(N \times M)$ matrix obtained by interchanging the rows with the columns in $\mathbf{A}$; i.e.,*

$$\mathbf{A}' = \begin{bmatrix} a_{11} & a_{21} & \cdots & a_{M1} \\ a_{12} & a_{22} & \cdots & a_{M2} \\ \vdots & \vdots & & \vdots \\ a_{1N} & a_{2N} & \cdots & a_{MN} \end{bmatrix}.$$

EXAMPLE

$$A = \begin{bmatrix} 2 & 5 \\ 3 & 6 \\ 4 & 7 \end{bmatrix}, \qquad A' = \begin{bmatrix} 2 & 3 & 4 \\ 5 & 6 & 7 \end{bmatrix}.$$

The following theorems apply to transposed matrices:

(B.7) $(A')' = A,$

(B.8) $(A + B)' = A' + B',$

(B.9) $(AB)' = B'A'.$

The proofs follow directly from the definition of matrix operations.

(B.10)   *If* A *is a square matrix and* A = A′, *then* A *is symmetric.*

A well-known expression involving a transpose of a vector is known as *quadratic form.* Suppose **x** is an $(M \times 1)$ nonzero vector and A is a square and symmetric matrix of order $M \times M$. Then the quadratic form of **x** is a scalar defined as

(B.11) $$x'Ax = \sum_{i=1}^{M} \sum_{j=1}^{M} a_{ij}x_i x_j.$$

EXAMPLE   If

$$x = \begin{bmatrix} x_1 \\ x_2 \end{bmatrix} \quad \text{and} \quad A = \begin{bmatrix} a_{11} & a_{12} \\ a_{21} & a_{22} \end{bmatrix},$$

then

$$x'Ax = [x_1 \ x_2] \begin{bmatrix} a_{11} & a_{12} \\ a_{21} & a_{22} \end{bmatrix} \begin{bmatrix} x_1 \\ x_2 \end{bmatrix} = [x_1 \ x_2] \begin{bmatrix} a_{11}x_1 + a_{12}x_2 \\ a_{21}x_1 + a_{22}x_2 \end{bmatrix}$$

$$= a_{11}x_1^2 + a_{12}x_1x_2 + a_{21}x_1x_2 + a_{22}x_2^2 = a_{11}x_1^2 + 2a_{12}x_1x_2 + a_{22}x_2^2.$$

A symmetric matrix A is called *positive definite* if $x'Ax > 0$, and *positive semidefinite* if $x'Ax \geq 0$. Similarly, A is *negative definite* if $x'Ax < 0$, and *negative semidefinite* if $x'Ax \leq 0$. Note that all variance-covariance matrices are positive definite.

Partitioned Matrices

Frequently it is convenient to *partition* a matrix into submatrices. In this case the submatrices are treated as scalar elements except that care has to be taken to insure that the rules of matrix multiplication are preserved. In particular, if

$$A = \begin{bmatrix} P_{11} & P_{12} \\ P_{21} & P_{22} \end{bmatrix} \quad \text{and} \quad B = \begin{bmatrix} Q_{11} & Q_{12} \\ Q_{21} & Q_{22} \end{bmatrix},$$

where the dimensions of the submatrices are

$$P_{11} \rightarrow (M_1 \times N_1), \qquad Q_{11} \rightarrow (N_1 \times R_1),$$
$$P_{12} \rightarrow (M_1 \times N_2), \qquad Q_{12} \rightarrow (N_1 \times R_2),$$
$$P_{21} \rightarrow (M_2 \times N_1), \qquad Q_{21} \rightarrow (N_2 \times R_1),$$
$$P_{22} \rightarrow (M_2 \times N_2), \qquad Q_{22} \rightarrow (N_2 \times R_2),$$

then

(B.12)
$$A' = \begin{bmatrix} P'_{11} & P'_{21} \\ P'_{12} & P'_{22} \end{bmatrix}$$

and

(B.13)
$$AB = \begin{bmatrix} P_{11}Q_{11} + P_{12}Q_{21} & P_{11}Q_{12} + P_{12}Q_{22} \\ P_{21}Q_{11} + P_{22}Q_{21} & P_{21}Q_{12} + P_{22}Q_{22} \end{bmatrix}.$$

Determinants

A determinant is a scalar whose value is calculated by a certain rule from a square matrix. The determinant of matrix A is denoted by $\det A$ or $|A|$. The rules for calculating determinants are as follows. For a (2×2) matrix

$$A = \begin{bmatrix} a_{11} & a_{12} \\ a_{21} & a_{22} \end{bmatrix},$$

the determinant is given by

(B.14)
$$\det A = a_{11}a_{22} - a_{12}a_{21}.$$

Note that the value of $\det A$ has been obtained by multiplying certain elements of A by certain other elements, and then by assigning a positive or a negative sign to the resulting product. If we use solid lines to designate products with a positive sign, and dashed lines to designate products with a negative sign, then the rule for calculating the determinant of a (2×2) matrix can be represented schematically as in Figure B–1(a).

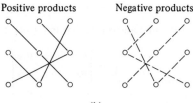

(a)   (b)

Figure B–1

For a (3×3) matrix

$$A = \begin{bmatrix} a_{11} & a_{12} & a_{13} \\ a_{21} & a_{22} & a_{23} \\ a_{31} & a_{32} & a_{33} \end{bmatrix}$$

the determinant is

(B.15) $\det A = a_{11}a_{22}a_{33} + a_{12}a_{23}a_{31} + a_{13}a_{32}a_{21}$

$$- a_{13}a_{22}a_{31} - a_{23}a_{32}a_{11} - a_{33}a_{21}a_{12},$$

and the schematic representation is shown in Figure B–1(b).

For square matrices of higher order, the schematic rules for calculating determinants become messy and are rarely used. Instead we use a general rule for calculating determinants of matrices of *any* order. This rule involves the use of *minors* and *cofactors*. Suppose we take a matrix A of order $M \times M$ and eliminate the ith row and the jth column, i.e., eliminate the row and the column corresponding to the element a_{ij}. Then the determinant of the resulting $(M-1) \times (M-1)$ matrix is called a *minor* of a_{ij}. A *cofactor* of a_{ij} is simply the minor of a_{ij} multiplied by $(-1)^{i+j}$. A common term to designate a cofactor of a_{ij} is A_{ij}. The general rule for evaluating the determinant of A is to take *any* row or *any* column of A, multiply each element by the corresponding cofactor, and then add the results. Thus the determinant of an $(M \times M)$ matrix A can be calculated as

(B.16) $$\det A = a_{11}A_{11} + a_{12}A_{12} + \cdots + a_{1M}A_{1M}.$$

In formula (B.16) we use the first row as the basis for calculations, but any other row, or any column, would do equally well. The importance of the "cofactor formula" (B.16) is that it enables us to reduce a determinant of any order to a linear combination of determinants of lower order. Of course, this formula also applies to the cases of $M = 2$ and $M = 3$, for which we gave special formulas in (B.14) and (B.15). For $M = 2$ we have

$$A = \begin{bmatrix} a_{11} & a_{12} \\ a_{21} & a_{22} \end{bmatrix},$$

$$A_{11} = a_{22},$$

$$A_{12} = -a_{21},$$

so that, by (B.16),

$$\det A = a_{11}(a_{22}) + a_{12}(-a_{21}) = a_{11}a_{22} - a_{12}a_{21},$$

which is the same answer as that in (B.14). Further, for $M = 3$ we have

$$A = \begin{bmatrix} a_{11} & a_{12} & a_{13} \\ a_{21} & a_{22} & a_{23} \\ a_{31} & a_{32} & a_{33} \end{bmatrix},$$

$$A_{11} = \det \begin{bmatrix} a_{22} & a_{23} \\ a_{32} & a_{33} \end{bmatrix} = a_{22}a_{33} - a_{23}a_{32},$$

$$A_{12} = -\det \begin{bmatrix} a_{21} & a_{23} \\ a_{31} & a_{33} \end{bmatrix} = -a_{21}a_{33} + a_{23}a_{31},$$

$$A_{13} = \det \begin{bmatrix} a_{21} & a_{22} \\ a_{31} & a_{32} \end{bmatrix} = a_{21}a_{32} - a_{22}a_{31},$$

so that, by (B.16),

$$\det A = a_{11}(a_{22}a_{33} - a_{23}a_{32}) + a_{12}(-a_{21}a_{33} + a_{23}a_{31}) + a_{13}(a_{21}a_{32} - a_{22}a_{31})$$

$$= a_{11}a_{22}a_{33} - a_{11}a_{23}a_{32} - a_{12}a_{21}a_{33} + a_{12}a_{23}a_{31} + a_{13}a_{21}a_{32} - a_{13}a_{22}a_{31},$$

which is the same expression as that in (B.15).

B. Elements of Matrix Algebra

Some interesting and useful properties of determinants are

(B.17) Interchanging any two rows or any two columns of **A** changes the sign of det **A**.

(B.18) If every element of a row, or of a column, of **A** is multiplied by a scalar, then det **A** is multiplied by the same scalar.

(B.19) If any row (column) of **A** is extended by the addition of a multiple of any other row (column), the value of det **A** is unaltered.

(B.20) The value of the determinant of a matrix in which two rows (or two columns) are identical is zero.

(B.21) det **A** = det **A'**.

(B.22) det **AB** = (det **A**)(det **B**).

Determinants are also used to describe certain properties of matrices. In particular, if det **A** = 0, then **A** is called *singular*, and if det **A** ≠ 0, then **A** is called *nonsingular*. Further, the order of the largest determinant contained in an $(M \times N)$ matrix is called the *rank* of the matrix.

EXAMPLE 1 If

$$A = \begin{bmatrix} 1 & 2 & 3 \\ 4 & 5 & 6 \\ 7 & 8 & 9 \end{bmatrix},$$

this should be to be consistent, 10 with rest of discussion

then

$$\det A = 1 \times 5 \times 10 + 2 \times 6 \times 7 + 3 \times 8 \times 4 - 3 \times 5 \times 7 - 6 \times 8 \times 1 - 10 \times 4 \times 2 = -3.$$

The same result could have been obtained by the "cofactor formula" (B.16):

$$\det A = 1 \times \det \begin{bmatrix} 5 & 6 \\ 8 & 10 \end{bmatrix} + 2 \times (-1) \det \begin{bmatrix} 4 & 6 \\ 7 & 10 \end{bmatrix} + 3 \times \det \begin{bmatrix} 4 & 5 \\ 7 & 8 \end{bmatrix}$$

$$= 1 \times 2 + 2 \times 2 + 3 \times (-3) = -3.$$

Note also that

$$A' = \begin{bmatrix} 1 & 4 & 7 \\ 2 & 5 & 8 \\ 3 & 6 & 10 \end{bmatrix} \quad \text{and} \quad \det A' = -3.$$

Suppose we change **A** by (a) multiplying the first row by 4 and deducting the result from the second row, and (b) multiplying the first row by 7 and deducting the result from the third row. The resulting matrix, say, **A***, is

$$A^* = \begin{bmatrix} 1 & 2 & 3 \\ (4-4) & (5-8) & (6-12) \\ (7-7) & (8-14) & (10-21) \end{bmatrix} = \begin{bmatrix} 1 & 2 & 3 \\ 0 & -3 & -6 \\ 0 & -6 & -11 \end{bmatrix}$$

and

$$\det A^* = 1 \det \begin{bmatrix} -3 & -6 \\ -6 & -11 \end{bmatrix} = -3 = \det A.$$

Example 2 Let

$$A = \begin{bmatrix} 1 & 2 \\ 3 & 4 \end{bmatrix} \quad \text{and} \quad B = \begin{bmatrix} 5 & 6 \\ 7 & 8 \end{bmatrix}.$$

Then

$$\det A = 1 \times 4 - 2 \times 3 = -2,$$

$$\det B = 5 \times 8 - 6 \times 7 = -2.$$

Now, define

$$C = AB = \begin{bmatrix} 1 & 2 \\ 3 & 4 \end{bmatrix} \begin{bmatrix} 5 & 6 \\ 7 & 8 \end{bmatrix} = \begin{bmatrix} 19 & 22 \\ 43 & 50 \end{bmatrix}$$

and note that

$$\det C = 950 - 946 = 4 = (\det A)(\det B)$$

Matrix Inversion

The *inverse* of a square matrix A is a matrix that, when premultiplied or post-multiplied by A, yields the identity matrix. The inverse of A is denoted by A^{-1}. Thus we define

(B.23) $B = A^{-1}$ *if and only if* $BA = AB = I$.

Not all matrices have an inverse. The following theorem establishes the conditions under which an inverse exists:

(B.24)   *The matrix A has an inverse if and only if $\det A \neq 0$, that is, if and only if A is a nonsingular matrix.*

The calculation of an inverse involves the formation of the so-called *adjoint*. The adjoint of a square matrix A is defined as a matrix that is formed from A by replacing each element of A by the corresponding cofactor, and by transposing the result. If we denote the adjoint of A by adj A, then we have

$$(B.25) \quad \text{adj } A = \begin{bmatrix} A_{11} & A_{12} & \cdots & A_{1M} \\ A_{21} & A_{22} & \cdots & A_{2M} \\ \vdots & \vdots & & \vdots \\ A_{M1} & A_{M2} & \cdots & A_{MM} \end{bmatrix}' = \begin{bmatrix} A_{11} & A_{21} & \cdots & A_{M1} \\ A_{12} & A_{22} & \cdots & A_{M2} \\ \vdots & \vdots & & \vdots \\ A_{1M} & A_{2M} & \cdots & A_{MM} \end{bmatrix}.$$

The inverse of A is then obtained as follows:

$$(B.26) \qquad\qquad A^{-1} = \frac{1}{\det A} \text{ adj } A.$$

It can be shown[1] that

$$(B.27) \qquad\qquad (AB)^{-1} = B^{-1}A^{-1},$$

$$(B.28) \qquad\qquad (A^{-1})' = (A')^{-1}.$$

Note that the result in (B.28) implies that if A is symmetric (and nonsingular), then A^{-1} is also symmetric.

---

[1] See, e.g., J. Johnston, *Econometric Methods* (New York: McGraw-Hill, 1963), pp. 85–86.

EXAMPLE 1   If

$$A = \begin{bmatrix} a_{11} & a_{12} \\ a_{21} & a_{22} \end{bmatrix},$$

then

$$A_{11} = a_{22},$$
$$A_{12} = -a_{21},$$
$$A_{21} = -a_{12},$$
$$A_{22} = a_{11},$$

and

$$\text{adj } A = \begin{bmatrix} a_{22} & -a_{21} \\ -a_{12} & a_{11} \end{bmatrix}' = \begin{bmatrix} a_{22} & -a_{12} \\ -a_{21} & a_{11} \end{bmatrix}.$$

Therefore,

$$A^{-1} = \frac{1}{a_{11}a_{22} - a_{12}a_{21}} \begin{bmatrix} a_{22} & -a_{12} \\ -a_{21} & a_{11} \end{bmatrix}.$$

EXAMPLE 2   If

$$A = \begin{bmatrix} 1 & 2 & 3 \\ 4 & 5 & 6 \\ 7 & 8 & 10 \end{bmatrix},$$

then

$A_{11} = 2,$	$A_{21} = 4,$	$A_{31} = -3,$
$A_{12} = 2,$	$A_{22} = -11,$	$A_{32} = 6,$
$A_{13} = -3,$	$A_{23} = 6,$	$A_{33} = -3,$

and

$$\det A = -3.$$

Therefore,

$$\text{adj } A = \begin{bmatrix} 2 & 2 & -3 \\ 4 & -11 & 6 \\ -3 & 6 & -3 \end{bmatrix}' = \begin{bmatrix} 2 & 4 & -3 \\ 2 & -11 & 6 \\ -3 & 6 & -3 \end{bmatrix},$$

and

$$A^{-1} = \frac{1}{-3} \begin{bmatrix} 2 & 4 & -3 \\ 2 & -11 & 6 \\ -3 & 6 & -3 \end{bmatrix} = \begin{bmatrix} -\frac{2}{3} & -\frac{4}{3} & 1 \\ -\frac{2}{3} & \frac{11}{3} & -2 \\ 1 & -2 & 1 \end{bmatrix}.$$

To check this result we multiply

$$A^{-1}A = \begin{bmatrix} -\frac{2}{3} & -\frac{4}{3} & 1 \\ -\frac{2}{3} & \frac{11}{3} & -2 \\ 1 & -2 & 1 \end{bmatrix} \begin{bmatrix} 1 & 2 & 3 \\ 4 & 5 & 6 \\ 7 & 8 & 10 \end{bmatrix}$$

$$= \begin{bmatrix} (-\frac{2}{3} - \frac{16}{3} + 7) & (-\frac{4}{3} - \frac{20}{3} + 8) & (-\frac{6}{3} - \frac{24}{3} + 10) \\ (-\frac{2}{3} + \frac{44}{3} - 14) & (-\frac{4}{3} + \frac{55}{3} - 16) & (-\frac{6}{3} + \frac{66}{3} + 20) \\ (1 - 8 + 7) & (2 - 10 + 8) & (3 - 12 + 10) \end{bmatrix} = \begin{bmatrix} 1 & 0 & 0 \\ 0 & 1 & 0 \\ 0 & 0 & 1 \end{bmatrix}.$$

Partitioned Inversion

Sometimes we may be interested in obtaining the inverse of a matrix in partitioned form. Suppose $\mathbf{A}$ is partitioned as

$$\mathbf{A} = \begin{bmatrix} \mathbf{P}_{11} & \mathbf{P}_{12} \\ \mathbf{P}_{21} & \mathbf{P}_{22} \end{bmatrix},$$

where the dimensions of the submatrices are

$$\mathbf{P}_{11} \to M_1 \times M_1,$$

$$\mathbf{P}_{12} \to M_1 \times M_2,$$

$$\mathbf{P}_{21} \to M_2 \times M_1,$$

$$\mathbf{P}_{22} \to M_2 \times M_2.$$

Then[2]

$$\mathbf{A}^{-1} = \begin{bmatrix} \mathbf{P}_{11}^{-1} + \mathbf{P}_{11}^{-1}\mathbf{P}_{12}\mathbf{Q}_{22}^{-1}\mathbf{P}_{21}\mathbf{P}_{11}^{-1} & -\mathbf{P}_{11}^{-1}\mathbf{P}_{12}\mathbf{Q}_{22}^{-1} \\ -\mathbf{Q}_{22}^{-1}\mathbf{P}_{21}\mathbf{P}_{11}^{-1} & \mathbf{Q}_{22}^{-1} \end{bmatrix}$$

where

$$\mathbf{Q}_{22} = \mathbf{P}_{22} - \mathbf{P}_{21}\mathbf{P}_{11}^{-1}\mathbf{P}_{12}.$$

Note that the inverse of a block-diagonal matrix is also block-diagonal. Specifically,

(B.29) If $\mathbf{A} = \begin{bmatrix} \mathbf{P}_{11} & 0 \\ 0 & \mathbf{P}_{22} \end{bmatrix}$, then $\mathbf{A}^{-1} = \begin{bmatrix} \mathbf{P}_{11}^{-1} & 0 \\ 0 & \mathbf{P}_{22}^{-1} \end{bmatrix}$.

Differentiation in Matrix Notation

Let $y = f(x_1, x_2, \ldots, x_M)$ be a scalar, and let $\mathbf{x}$ be a column vector defined as

$$\mathbf{x} = \begin{bmatrix} x_1 \\ x_2 \\ \vdots \\ x_M \end{bmatrix}.$$

Then, the first partial derivative of y with respect to each element of $\mathbf{x}$ is defined as

(B.30)

$$\frac{\partial y}{\partial \mathbf{x}} = \begin{bmatrix} \dfrac{\partial y}{\partial x_1} \\ \dfrac{\partial y}{\partial x_2} \\ \vdots \\ \dfrac{\partial y}{\partial x_M} \end{bmatrix},$$

[2] See A. S. Goldberger, *Econometric Theory* (New York: Wiley, 1964), p. 27.

and the second partial derivative as

(B.31)
$$\frac{\partial^2 y}{\partial \mathbf{x}^2} = \begin{bmatrix} \dfrac{\partial^2 y}{\partial x_1^2} & \dfrac{\partial^2 y}{\partial x_1 \partial x_2} & \cdots & \dfrac{\partial^2 y}{\partial x_1 \partial x_M} \\[2ex] \dfrac{\partial^2 y}{\partial x_2 \partial x_1} & \dfrac{\partial^2 y}{\partial x_2^2} & \cdots & \dfrac{\partial^2 y}{\partial x_2 \partial x_M} \\[1ex] \vdots & \vdots & & \vdots \\[1ex] \dfrac{\partial^2 y}{\partial x_M \partial x_1} & \dfrac{\partial^2 y}{\partial x_M \partial x_2} & \cdots & \dfrac{\partial^2 y}{\partial x_M^2} \end{bmatrix}.$$

These basic rules can be applied to some frequently encountered cases. First, if

$$\mathbf{a} = \begin{bmatrix} a_1 \\ a_2 \\ \vdots \\ a_M \end{bmatrix}$$

where a_i $(i = 1, 2, \ldots, M)$ are constants, then

(B.32)
$$\frac{\partial(\mathbf{a}'\mathbf{x})}{\partial \mathbf{x}} = \mathbf{a}.$$

This can be easily demonstrated by noting that

$$\mathbf{a}'\mathbf{x} = \sum_{i=1}^{M} a_i x_i,$$

and by using the rule (B.30). Second, if $\mathbf{A}$ is a symmetric matrix of order $M \times M$ whose typical element is a constant a_{ij}, then

(B.33)
$$\frac{\partial(\mathbf{x}'\mathbf{A}\mathbf{x})}{\partial \mathbf{x}} = 2\mathbf{A}\mathbf{x}.$$

This follows from the fact that

$$\mathbf{x}'\mathbf{A}\mathbf{x} = \sum_{i=1}^{M} \sum_{j=1}^{M} a_{ij} x_i x_j,$$

and from the application of the rule of differentiation in (B.30). Finally, if $\mathbf{A}$ and $\mathbf{B}$ are two symmetric matrices whose elements are constants and whose order is $M \times M$, then

(B.34)
$$\frac{\partial\left(\dfrac{\mathbf{x}'\mathbf{A}\mathbf{x}}{\mathbf{x}'\mathbf{B}\mathbf{x}}\right)}{\partial \mathbf{x}} = \frac{2(\mathbf{A}\mathbf{x})(\mathbf{x}'\mathbf{B}\mathbf{x}) - 2(\mathbf{x}'\mathbf{A}\mathbf{x})(\mathbf{B}\mathbf{x})}{(\mathbf{x}'\mathbf{B}\mathbf{x})^2}.$$

This can be proven in the same way as (B.33).

C.   Computational Design for Least Squares Estimation

C–1   Simple Linear Regression Model

The following computational scheme is designed for obtaining simple least squares estimates of the regression parameters for the model,

$$Y_i = \alpha + \beta X_i + \varepsilon_i.$$

The procedure has been designed to achieve a high degree of computational accuracy.

Basic Calculations

First, we calculate the sums of squares and cross-products of X and Y. These are usually referred to as "sample moments about zero." A tabular presentation is

	1	X	Y
1	n	$\sum X_i$	$\sum Y_i$
X		$\sum X_i^2$	$\sum X_i Y_i$
Y			$\sum Y_i^2$

As a check, we construct n observations on an artificial variable S defined as

$$S_i = X_i + Y_i.$$

Then we must have

$$\sum S_i^2 = \sum X_i^2 + \sum Y_i^2 + 2 \sum X_i Y_i.$$

Next, we compute the values of the so-called "augmented sample moments about the means," which are defined as follows:

$$M_{XX} = n \sum X_i^2 - \left(\sum X_i \right)^2,$$

$$M_{XY} = n \sum X_i Y_i - \left(\sum X_i \right)\left(\sum Y_i \right),$$

$$M_{YY} = n \sum Y_i^2 - \left(\sum Y_i \right)^2,$$

$$M_{SS} = n \sum S_i^2 - \left(\sum S_i \right)^2.$$

These can be arranged as

	X	Y
X	M_{XX}	M_{XY}
Y		M_{YY}

To check our calculations, we note whether the following equality is preserved:

$$M_{SS} = M_{XX} + M_{YY} + 2M_{XY}.$$

Estimates of the Regression Coefficients

The least squares estimates of the regression coefficients are calculated as follows:

$$\hat{\beta} = \frac{M_{XY}}{M_{XX}},$$

$$\hat{\alpha} = \frac{\left(\sum Y_i - \hat{\beta} \sum X_i \right)}{n}.$$

Further,

$$n\text{SSR} = \hat{\beta} M_{XY},$$

$$n\text{SST} = M_{YY},$$

$$n\text{SSE} = n\text{SST} - n\text{SSR},$$

which leads to

$$R^2 = \frac{n\text{SSR}}{n\text{SST}},$$

$$ns^2 = \frac{n\text{SSE}}{n-2},$$

$$s_\beta^2 = \frac{ns^2}{M_{XX}},$$

$$s_\hat{\alpha}^2 = \frac{(ns^2)(\sum X_i^2)}{nM_{XX}}.$$

The final result is

$$Y_i = \hat{\alpha} + \hat{\beta}X_i + e_i, \qquad R^2 = \cdots.$$
$$\quad (s_\hat{\alpha}) \quad (s_\hat{\beta})$$

C–2 *Multiple Linear Regression Model*

Here we present a computational scheme for the model

$$Y_i = \beta_1 + \beta_2 X_{i2} + \beta_3 X_{i3} + \beta_4 X_{i4} + \beta_5 X_{i5} + \varepsilon_i.$$

However, the procedure can be easily modified to apply to models with a smaller number of explanatory variables. The computational design is aimed at providing a reasonably high degree of accuracy combined with computational efficiency.

Computation of Augmented Moments

Let

$$M_{rs} = n\sum_i X_{ir}X_{is} - \left(\sum_i X_{ir}\right)\left(\sum_i X_{is}\right),$$

$$M_{rY} = n\sum_i X_{ir}Y_i - \left(\sum_i X_{ir}\right)\left(\sum_i Y_i\right),$$

$$M_{YY} = n\sum_i Y_i^2 - \left(\sum_i Y_i\right)^2,$$

$$M_{SS} = n\sum_i S_i^2 - \left(\sum_i S_i\right)^2,$$

$$r, s = 2, 3, 4, \text{ and } 5;$$

$$S_i = X_{i2} + X_{i3} + X_{i4} + X_{i5} + Y_i.$$

These moments may be presented as

	X_2	X_3	X_4	X_5	Y
X_2	M_{22}	M_{23}	M_{24}	M_{25}	M_{2Y}
X_3		M_{33}	M_{34}	M_{35}	M_{3Y}
X_4			M_{44}	M_{45}	M_{4Y}
X_5				M_{55}	M_{5Y}
Y					M_{YY}

If all calculations are correct, we must have

$$M_{SS} = M_{22} + M_{33} + M_{44} + M_{55} + M_{YY}$$

$$+ 2(M_{23} + M_{24} + M_{25} + M_{2Y} + M_{34} + M_{35} + M_{3Y} + M_{45} + M_{4Y} + M_{5Y}).$$

Scaling of Variables

It will contribute to the accuracy of the solution if all the moments are of approximately the same order of magnitude. Therefore, we change the units in which the variables are measured by multiplying each variable by an appropriate power of 10, so that the values of the diagonal moments lie between 0.1 and 10.0. Of course, this will lead to an adjustment of the off-diagonal moments, also. For many practical purposes it may be sufficient if all scaled moments are enumerated up to six decimal places. The scaled variables and their moments will be denoted by starred symbols.

EXAMPLE   Suppose

$$M_{22} = 6560.3575, \qquad M_{YY} = \quad 0.0604,$$

$$M_{33} = \quad 320.12, \qquad M_{2Y} = \quad 76.2344,$$

$$M_{23} = \quad 21.066, \qquad M_{3Y} = \quad 1.177.$$

Then, we adopt the following scaling:

$$X_{i2}^* = 10^{-2} X_{i2},$$

$$X_{i3}^* = 10^{-1} X_{i3},$$

$$Y_i^* = 10^1 Y_i.$$

Consequently,

$$M_{22}^* = 0.656036 \qquad M_{YY}^* = 6.040000$$

$$M_{33}^* = 3.201200 \qquad M_{2Y}^* = 7.623440$$

$$M_{23}^* = 0.021066 \qquad M_{3Y}^* = 1.177000$$

Basic Solution of Least Squares Normal Equations

To obtain the solution of the least squares normal equations, we use the Gauss-Doolittle method, which represents a systematic way of solving symmetric linear equations.[3] First, we present the augmented scaled moments in the following form:

Row		(1)	(2)	(3)	(4)	(5)	(6)	(7)	(8)	(9)	(10)
					Column						
(1)	R_1:	M_{22}^*	M_{23}^*	M_{24}^*	M_{25}^*	M_{2Y}^*	1	0	0	0	S_1
(2)	R_2:	M_{32}^*	M_{33}^*	M_{34}^*	M_{35}^*	M_{3Y}^*	0	1	0	0	S_2
(3)	R_3:	M_{42}^*	M_{43}^*	M_{44}^*	M_{45}^*	M_{4Y}^*	0	0	1	0	S_3
(4)	R_4:	M_{52}^*	M_{53}^*	M_{54}^*	M_{55}^*	M_{5Y}^*	0	0	0	1	S_4

[3] See P. S. Dwyer, *Linear Computations* (New York: Wiley, 1951).

Column (10) is a checking column and its elements are equal to row totals. The successive rows of the worksheet are obtained by the following rules:

(5) $A_{1j} = R_{1j}$ (i.e., reproduce row (1) here in the fifth row).

(6) $B_{1j} = A_{1j}/A_{11}$ (i.e., divide row (4) by its leading element).

(7) $A_{2j} = R_{2j} - A_{12}B_{1j}$.

(8) $B_{2j} = A_{2j}/A_{22}$.

(9) $A_{3j} = R_{3j} - A_{13}B_{1j} - A_{23}B_{2j}$.

(10) $B_{3j} = A_{3j}/A_{33}$.

(11) $A_{4j} = R_{4j} - A_{14}B_{1j} - A_{24}B_{2j} - A_{34}B_{3j}$.

(12) $B_{4j} = A_{4j}/A_{44}$.

The worksheet now includes the following entries below row (4):

Row		(1)	(2)	(3)	(4)	(5)	(6)	(7)	(8)	(9)	(10)
(5)	A_1:	A_{11}	A_{12}	A_{13}	A_{14}	A_{15}	1	0	0	0	S_4
(6)	B_1:	1	B_{12}	B_{13}	B_{14}	B_{15}	B_{16}	0	0	0	S_5
(7)	A_2:	0	A_{22}	A_{23}	A_{24}	A_{25}	A_{26}	1	0	0	S_6
(8)	B_2:	0	1	B_{23}	B_{24}	B_{25}	B_{26}	B_{27}	0	0	S_7
(9)	A_3:	0	0	A_{33}	A_{34}	A_{35}	A_{36}	A_{37}	1	0	S_8
(10)	B_3:	0	0	1	B_{34}	B_{35}	B_{36}	B_{37}	B_{38}	0	S_9
(11)	A_4:	0	0	0	A_{44}	A_{45}	A_{46}	A_{47}	A_{48}	1	S_{10}
(12)	B_4:	0	0	0	1	B_{45}	B_{46}	B_{47}	B_{48}	B_{49}	S_{11}

Continuing, the rules are

(13) $C_{4j} = B_{4j}$.

(14) $C_{3j} = B_{3j} - B_{34}C_{4j}$.

(15) $C_{2j} = B_{2j} - B_{23}C_{3j} - B_{24}C_{4j}$.

(16) $C_{1j} = B_{1j} - B_{12}C_{2j} - B_{13}C_{3j} - B_{14}C_{4j}$.

These rows are entered on the worksheet in *reverse order:*

Row		(1)	(2)	(3)	(4)	(5)	(6)	(7)	(8)	(9)	(10)
(16)	C_1:	1	0	0	0	C_{15}	C_{16}	C_{17}	C_{18}	C_{19}	S_{15}
(15)	C_2:	0	1	0	0	C_{25}	C_{26}	C_{27}	C_{28}	C_{29}	S_{14}
(14)	C_3:	0	0	1	0	C_{35}	C_{36}	C_{37}	C_{38}	C_{39}	S_{13}
(13)	C_4:	0	0	0	1	C_{45}	C_{46}	C_{47}	C_{48}	C_{49}	S_{12}

In completing the worksheet there is no need to calculate the entries that are shown to be equal to 0 or 1. Check each row *as it is produced* by using the check-sum column. That is, the entry in column (10) of each row should be equal to the sum of all the other entries in the row, or else an error has been made in computing that row. Of course, rounding errors (in sixth or fifth decimal place) may be tolerable. If the model includes only three, rather than four, explanatory variables, then columns (4) and (9) and rows (4), (11), (12), and (13) are not applicable, and rows (14), (15), and (16) have to be appropriately reduced.

Results

The least squares estimates of the regression coefficients appear in the last four rows of the worksheet. Specifically,

$$\hat{\beta}_2^* = C_{15},$$

$$\hat{\beta}_3^* = C_{25},$$

$$\hat{\beta}_4^* = C_{35},$$

$$\hat{\beta}_5^* = C_{45},$$

and

$$\hat{\beta}_1^* = \bar{Y} - \hat{\beta}_2^* \bar{X}_2^* - \hat{\beta}_3^* \bar{X}_3^* - \hat{\beta}_4^* \bar{X}_4^* - \hat{\beta}_5^* \bar{X}_5^*.$$

Furthermore,

$$n\text{SSR}^* = \sum_{n=2}^{5} \hat{\beta}_r^* M_{rY}^*,$$

$$n\text{SST}^* = M_{YY}^*,$$

$$n\text{SSE}^* = n\text{SST}^* - n\text{SSR}^*,$$

which leads to

$$R^2 = \frac{n\text{SSR}^*}{n\text{SST}^*}$$

and

$$ns^{*2} = \frac{n\text{SSE}^*}{n - 5}.$$

The estimated variances of the regression coefficients are obtained as follows:

$$s_{\hat{\beta}_2^*}^{*2} = (ns^{*2})C_{16},$$

$$s_{\hat{\beta}_3^*}^{*2} = (ns^{*2})C_{27},$$

$$s_{\hat{\beta}_4^*}^{*2} = (ns^{*2})C_{38},$$

$$s_{\hat{\beta}_5^*}^{*2} = (ns^{*2})C_{49}.$$

The estimated variance of $\hat{\beta}_1^*$ can be calculated by reference to formula (10.32) of the text. The F statistic for testing the hypothesis that no relationship exists can be calculated as

$$\frac{n\text{SSR}^*/4}{ns^{*2}} \sim F_{4,\,n-5}.$$

To return to the original, unstarred variables, we substitute for Y_i^* and for the X_i^*'s into

$$Y_i^* = \hat{\beta}_1^* + \hat{\beta}_2^* X_{i2}^* + \hat{\beta}_3^* X_{i3}^* + \hat{\beta}_4^* X_{i4}^* + \hat{\beta}_5^* X_{i5}^* + e_i^*$$

to get

$$(10^{a_Y}) Y_i = \hat{\beta}_1^* + \hat{\beta}_2^*(10^{a_2}) X_{i2} + \hat{\beta}_3^*(10^{a_3}) X_{i3} + \hat{\beta}_4^*(10^{a_4}) X_{i4} + \hat{\beta}_5^*(10^{a_5}) X_{i5} + e_i^*,$$

where $a_Y, a_2, \ldots, a_5$ represent the appropriate powers of 10 that were used for scaling the original variables. Then

$$\hat{\beta}_1 = (10^{-a_Y})\hat{\beta}_1^*,$$
$$\hat{\beta}_2 = (10^{a_2 - a_Y})\hat{\beta}_2^*,$$
$$\hat{\beta}_3 = (10^{a_3 - a_Y})\hat{\beta}_3^*,$$
$$\hat{\beta}_4 = (10^{a_4 - a_Y})\hat{\beta}_4^*,$$
$$\hat{\beta}_5 = (10^{a_5 - a_Y})\hat{\beta}_5^*.$$

Note that the estimated standard errors of the regression coefficients will be changed by the same factor as the regression coefficients themselves, and that R^2 and the F statistic remain unchanged.

D. Statistical Tables

Table D–1   Areas Under the Normal Distribution

z	.00	.01	.02	.03	.04	.05	.06	.07	.08	.09
0.0	.0000	.0040	.0080	.0120	.0160	.0199	.0239	.0279	.0319	.0359
0.1	.0398	.0438	.0478	.0517	.0557	.0596	.0636	.0675	.0714	.0753
0.2	.0793	.0832	.0871	.0910	.0948	.0987	.1026	.1064	.1103	.1141
0.3	.1179	.1217	.1255	.1293	.1331	.1368	.1406	.1443	.1480	.1517
0.4	.1554	.1591	.1628	.1664	.1700	.1736	.1772	.1808	.1844	.1879
0.5	.1915	.1950	.1985	.2019	.2054	.2088	.2123	.2157	.2190	.2224
0.6	.2257	.2291	.2324	.2357	.2389	.2422	.2454	.2486	.2517	.2549
0.7	.2580	.2611	.2642	.2673	.2704	.2734	.2764	.2794	.2823	.2852
0.8	.2881	.2910	.2939	.2967	.2995	.3023	.3051	.3078	.3106	.3133
0.9	.3159	.3186	.3212	.3238	.3264	.3289	.3315	.3340	.3365	.3389
1.0	.3413	.3438	.3461	.3485	.3508	.3531	.3554	.3577	.3599	.3621
1.1	.3643	.3665	.3686	.3708	.3729	.3749	.3770	.3790	.3810	.3830
1.2	.3849	.3869	.3888	.3907	.3925	.3944	.3962	.3980	.3997	.4015
1.3	.4032	.4049	.4066	.4082	.4099	.4115	.4131	.4147	.4162	.4177
1.4	.4192	.4207	.4222	.4236	.4251	.4265	.4279	.4292	.4306	.4319
1.5	.4332	.4345	.4357	.4370	.4382	.4394	.4406	.4418	.4429	.4441
1.6	.4452	.4463	.4474	.4484	.4495	.4505	.4515	.4525	.4535	.4545
1.7	.4554	.4564	.4573	.4582	.4591	.4599	.4608	.4616	.4625	.4633
1.8	.4641	.4649	.4656	.4664	.4671	.4678	.4686	.4693	.4699	.4706
1.9	.4713	.4719	.4726	.4732	.4738	.4744	.4750	.4756	.4761	.4767
2.0	.4772	.4778	.4783	.4788	.4793	.4798	.4803	.4808	.4812	.4817
2.1	.4821	.4826	.4830	.4834	.4838	.4842	.4846	.4850	.4854	.4857
2.2	.4861	.4864	.4868	.4871	.4875	.4878	.4881	.4884	.4887	.4890
2.3	.4893	.4896	.4898	.4901	.4904	.4906	.4909	.4911	.4913	.4916
2.4	.4918	.4920	.4922	.4925	.4927	.4929	.4931	.4932	.4934	.4936
2.5	.4938	.4940	.4941	.4943	.4945	.4946	.4948	.4949	.4951	.4952
2.6	.4953	.4955	.4956	.4957	.4959	.4960	.4961	.4962	.4963	.4964
2.7	.4965	.4966	.4967	.4968	.4969	.4970	.4971	.4972	.4973	.4974
2.8	.4974	.4975	.4976	.4977	.4977	.4978	.4979	.4979	.4980	.4981
2.9	.4981	.4982	.4982	.4983	.4984	.4984	.4985	.4985	.4986	.4986
3.0	.4987	.4987	.4987	.4988	.4988	.4989	.4989	.4989	.4990	.4990

Table D–2   Values of $t_{\alpha, \nu}$

ν	$\alpha = 0.10$	$\alpha = 0.05$	$\alpha = 0.025$	$\alpha = 0.01$	$\alpha = 0.005$	ν
1	3.078	6.314	12.706	31.821	63.657	1
2	1.886	2.920	4.303	6.965	9.925	2
3	1.638	2.353	3.182	4.541	5.841	3
4	1.533	2.132	2.776	3.747	4.604	4
5	1.476	2.015	2.571	3.365	4.032	5
6	1.440	1.943	2.447	3.143	3.707	6
7	1.415	1.895	2.365	2.998	3.499	7
8	1.397	1.860	2.306	2.896	3.355	8
9	1.383	1.833	2.262	2.821	3.250	9
10	1.372	1.812	2.228	2.764	3.169	10
11	1.363	1.796	2.201	2.718	3.106	11
12	1.356	1.782	2.179	2.681	3.055	12
13	1.350	1.771	2.160	2.650	3.012	13
14	1.345	1.761	2.145	2.624	2.977	14
15	1.341	1.753	2.131	2.602	2.947	15
16	1.337	1.746	2.120	2.583	2.921	16
17	1.333	1.740	2.110	2.567	2.898	17
18	1.330	1.734	2.101	2.552	2.878	18
19	1.328	1.729	2.093	2.539	2.861	19
20	1.325	1.725	2.086	2.528	2.845	20
21	1.323	1.721	2.080	2.518	2.831	21
22	1.321	1.717	2.074	2.508	2.819	22
23	1.319	1.714	2.069	2.500	2.807	23
24	1.318	1.711	2.064	2.492	2.797	24
25	1.316	1.708	2.060	2.485	2.787	25
26	1.315	1.706	2.056	2.479	2.779	26
27	1.314	1.703	2.052	2.473	2.771	27
28	1.313	1.701	2.048	2.467	2.763	28
29	1.311	1.699	2.045	2.462	2.756	29
inf.	1.282	1.645	1.960	2.326	2.576	inf.

This table is abridged from Table IV of R. A. Fisher, *Statistical Methods for Research Workers*, published by Oliver and Boyd Ltd., Edinburgh, by permission of the author and publishers.

Table D-3   Values of $\chi^2_{\alpha, \nu}$

ν	$\alpha = 0.995$	$\alpha = 0.99$	$\alpha = 0.975$	$\alpha = 0.95$	$\alpha = 0.05$	$\alpha = 0.025$	$\alpha = 0.01$	$\alpha = 0.005$	ν
1	0.0000393	0.000157	0.000982	0.00393	3.841	5.024	6.635	7.879	1
2	0.0100	0.0201	0.0506	0.103	5.991	7.378	9.210	10.597	2
3	0.0717	0.115	0.216	0.352	7.815	9.348	11.345	12.838	3
4	0.207	0.297	0.484	0.711	9.488	11.143	13.277	14.860	4
5	0.412	0.554	0.831	1.145	11.070	12.832	15.086	16.750	5
6	0.676	0.872	1.237	1.635	12.592	14.449	16.812	18.548	6
7	0.989	1.239	1.690	2.167	14.067	16.013	18.475	20.278	7
8	1.344	1.646	2.180	2.733	15.507	17.535	20.090	21.955	8
9	1.735	2.088	2.700	3.325	16.919	19.023	21.666	23.589	9
10	2.156	2.558	3.247	3.940	18.307	20.483	23.209	25.188	10
11	2.603	3.053	3.816	4.575	19.675	21.920	24.725	26.757	11
12	3.074	3.571	4.404	5.226	21.026	23.337	26.217	28.300	12
13	3.565	4.107	5.009	5.892	22.362	24.736	27.688	29.819	13
14	4.075	4.660	5.629	6.571	23.685	26.119	29.141	31.319	14
15	4.601	5.229	6.262	7.261	24.996	27.488	30.578	32.801	15
16	5.142	5.812	6.908	7.962	26.296	28.845	32.000	34.267	16
17	5.697	6.408	7.564	8.672	27.587	30.191	33.409	35.718	17
18	6.265	7.015	8.231	9.390	28.869	31.526	34.805	37.156	18
19	6.844	7.633	8.907	10.117	30.144	32.852	36.191	38.582	19
20	7.434	8.260	9.591	10.851	31.410	34.170	37.566	39.997	20
21	8.034	8.897	10.283	11.591	32.671	35.479	38.932	41.401	21
22	8.643	9.542	10.982	12.338	33.924	36.781	40.289	42.796	22
23	9.260	10.196	11.689	13.091	35.172	38.076	41.638	44.181	23
24	9.886	10.856	12.401	13.848	36.415	39.364	42.980	45.558	24
25	10.520	11.524	13.120	14.611	37.652	40.646	44.314	46.928	25
26	11.160	12.198	13.844	15.379	38.885	41.923	45.642	48.290	26
27	11.808	12.879	14.573	16.151	40.113	43.194	46.963	49.645	27
28	12.461	13.565	15.308	16.928	41.337	44.461	48.278	50.993	28
29	13.121	14.256	16.047	17.708	42.557	45.722	49.588	52.336	29
30	13.787	14.953	16.791	18.493	43.773	46.979	50.892	53.672	30

Based on Table 8 of *Biometrika Tables for Statisticians, Volume I.* By permission of the *Biometrika* trustees.

Table D-4A Values of $F_{0.05, \nu_1, \nu_2}$

ν_1 = degrees of freedom for numerator

ν_2	1	2	3	4	5	6	7	8	9	10	12	15	20	24	30	40	60	120	∞
1	161	200	216	225	230	234	237	239	241	242	244	246	248	249	250	251	252	253	254
2	18.5	19.0	19.2	19.2	19.3	19.3	19.4	19.4	19.4	19.4	19.4	19.4	19.4	19.5	19.5	19.5	19.5	19.5	19.5
3	10.1	9.55	9.28	9.12	9.01	8.94	8.89	8.85	8.81	8.79	8.74	8.70	8.66	8.64	8.62	8.59	8.57	8.55	8.53
4	7.71	6.94	6.59	6.39	6.26	6.16	6.09	6.04	6.00	5.96	5.91	5.86	5.80	5.77	5.75	5.72	5.69	5.66	5.63
5	6.61	5.79	5.41	5.19	5.05	4.95	4.88	4.82	4.77	4.74	4.68	4.62	4.56	4.53	4.50	4.46	4.43	4.40	4.37
6	5.99	5.14	4.76	4.53	4.39	4.28	4.21	4.15	4.10	4.06	4.00	3.94	3.87	3.84	3.81	3.77	3.74	3.70	3.67
7	5.59	4.74	4.35	4.12	3.97	3.87	3.79	3.73	3.68	3.64	3.57	3.51	3.44	3.41	3.38	3.34	3.30	3.27	3.23
8	5.32	4.46	4.07	3.84	3.69	3.58	3.50	3.44	3.39	3.35	3.28	3.22	3.15	3.12	3.08	3.04	3.01	2.97	2.93
9	5.12	4.26	3.86	3.63	3.48	3.37	3.29	3.23	3.18	3.14	3.07	3.01	2.94	2.90	2.86	2.83	2.79	2.75	2.71
10	4.96	4.10	3.71	3.48	3.33	3.22	3.14	3.07	3.02	2.98	2.91	2.85	2.77	2.74	2.70	2.66	2.62	2.58	2.54
11	4.84	3.98	3.59	3.36	3.20	3.09	3.01	2.95	2.90	2.85	2.79	2.72	2.65	2.61	2.57	2.53	2.49	2.45	2.40
12	4.75	3.89	3.49	3.26	3.11	3.00	2.91	2.85	2.80	2.75	2.69	2.62	2.54	2.51	2.47	2.43	2.38	2.34	2.30
13	4.67	3.81	3.41	3.18	3.03	2.92	2.83	2.77	2.71	2.67	2.60	2.53	2.46	2.42	2.38	2.34	2.30	2.25	2.21
14	4.60	3.74	3.34	3.11	2.96	2.85	2.76	2.70	2.65	2.60	2.53	2.46	2.39	2.35	2.31	2.27	2.22	2.18	2.13
15	4.54	3.68	3.29	3.06	2.90	2.79	2.71	2.64	2.59	2.54	2.48	2.40	2.33	2.29	2.25	2.20	2.16	2.11	2.07
16	4.49	3.63	3.24	3.01	2.85	2.74	2.66	2.59	2.54	2.49	2.42	2.35	2.28	2.24	2.19	2.15	2.11	2.06	2.01
17	4.45	3.59	3.20	2.96	2.81	2.70	2.61	2.55	2.49	2.45	2.38	2.31	2.23	2.19	2.15	2.10	2.06	2.01	1.96
18	4.41	3.55	3.16	2.93	2.77	2.66	2.58	2.51	2.46	2.41	2.34	2.27	2.19	2.15	2.11	2.06	2.02	1.97	1.92
19	4.38	3.52	3.13	2.90	2.74	2.63	2.54	2.48	2.42	2.38	2.31	2.23	2.16	2.11	2.07	2.03	1.98	1.93	1.88
20	4.35	3.49	3.10	2.87	2.71	2.60	2.51	2.45	2.39	2.35	2.28	2.20	2.12	2.08	2.04	1.99	1.95	1.90	1.84
21	4.32	3.47	3.07	2.84	2.68	2.57	2.49	2.42	2.37	2.32	2.25	2.18	2.10	2.05	2.01	1.96	1.92	1.87	1.81
22	4.30	3.44	3.05	2.82	2.66	2.55	2.46	2.40	2.34	2.30	2.23	2.15	2.07	2.03	1.98	1.94	1.89	1.84	1.78
23	4.28	3.42	3.03	2.80	2.64	2.53	2.44	2.37	2.32	2.27	2.20	2.13	2.05	2.01	1.96	1.91	1.86	1.81	1.76
24	4.26	3.40	3.01	2.78	2.62	2.51	2.42	2.36	2.30	2.25	2.18	2.11	2.03	1.98	1.94	1.89	1.84	1.79	1.73
25	4.24	3.39	2.99	2.76	2.60	2.49	2.40	2.34	2.28	2.24	2.16	2.09	2.01	1.96	1.92	1.87	1.82	1.77	1.71
30	4.17	3.32	2.92	2.69	2.53	2.42	2.33	2.27	2.21	2.16	2.09	2.01	1.93	1.89	1.84	1.79	1.74	1.68	1.62
40	4.08	3.23	2.84	2.61	2.45	2.34	2.25	2.18	2.12	2.08	2.00	1.92	1.84	1.79	1.74	1.69	1.64	1.58	1.51
60	4.00	3.15	2.76	2.53	2.37	2.25	2.17	2.10	2.04	1.99	1.92	1.84	1.75	1.70	1.65	1.59	1.53	1.47	1.39
120	3.92	3.07	2.68	2.45	2.29	2.18	2.09	2.02	1.96	1.91	1.83	1.75	1.66	1.61	1.55	1.50	1.43	1.35	1.25
∞	3.84	3.00	2.60	2.37	2.21	2.10	2.01	1.94	1.88	1.83	1.75	1.67	1.57	1.52	1.46	1.39	1.32	1.22	1.00

ν_2 = degrees of freedom for denominator

Abridged from M. Merrington and C. M. Thompson, "Tables of percentage points of the inverted beta (F) distribution," *Biometrika*, Vol. 33, 1943, p. 73. By permission of the *Biometrika* trustees.

Table D–4B Values of $F_{0.01, v_1, v_2}$

v_1 = degrees of freedom for numerator

v_2	1	2	3	4	5	6	7	8	9	10	12	15	20	24	30	40	60	120	∞
1	4052	5000	5403	5625	5764	5859	5928	5982	6023	6056	6106	6157	6209	6235	6261	6287	6313	6339	6366
2	98.5	99.0	99.2	99.2	99.3	99.3	99.4	99.4	99.4	99.4	99.4	99.4	99.4	99.5	99.5	99.5	99.5	99.5	99.5
3	34.1	30.8	29.5	28.7	28.2	27.9	27.7	27.5	27.3	27.2	27.1	26.9	26.7	26.6	26.5	26.4	26.3	26.2	26.1
4	21.2	18.0	16.7	16.0	15.5	15.2	15.0	14.8	14.7	14.5	14.4	14.2	14.0	13.9	13.8	13.7	13.7	13.6	13.5
5	16.3	13.3	12.1	11.4	11.0	10.7	10.5	10.3	10.2	10.1	9.89	9.72	9.55	9.47	9.38	9.29	9.20	9.11	9.02
6	13.7	10.9	9.78	9.15	8.75	8.47	8.26	8.10	7.98	7.87	7.72	7.56	7.40	7.31	7.23	7.14	7.06	6.97	6.88
7	12.2	9.55	8.45	7.85	7.46	7.19	6.99	6.84	6.72	6.62	6.47	6.31	6.16	6.07	5.99	5.91	5.82	5.74	5.65
8	11.3	8.65	7.59	7.01	6.63	6.37	6.18	6.03	5.91	5.81	5.67	5.52	5.36	5.28	5.20	5.12	5.03	4.95	4.86
9	10.6	8.02	6.99	6.42	6.06	5.80	5.61	5.47	5.35	5.26	5.11	4.96	4.81	4.73	4.65	4.57	4.48	4.40	4.31
10	10.0	7.56	6.55	5.99	5.64	5.39	5.20	5.06	4.94	4.85	4.71	4.56	4.41	4.33	4.25	4.17	4.08	4.00	3.91
11	9.65	7.21	6.22	5.67	5.32	5.07	4.89	4.74	4.63	4.54	4.40	4.25	4.10	4.02	3.94	3.86	3.78	3.69	3.60
12	9.33	6.93	5.95	5.41	5.06	4.82	4.64	4.50	4.39	4.30	4.16	4.01	3.86	3.78	3.70	3.62	3.54	3.45	3.36
13	9.07	6.70	5.74	5.21	4.86	4.62	4.44	4.30	4.19	4.10	3.96	3.82	3.66	3.59	3.51	3.43	3.34	3.25	3.17
14	8.86	6.51	5.56	5.04	4.70	4.46	4.28	4.14	4.03	3.94	3.80	3.66	3.51	3.43	3.35	3.27	3.18	3.09	3.00
15	8.68	6.36	5.42	4.89	4.56	4.32	4.14	4.00	3.89	3.80	3.67	3.52	3.37	3.29	3.21	3.13	3.05	2.96	2.87
16	8.53	6.23	5.29	4.77	4.44	4.20	4.03	3.89	3.78	3.69	3.55	3.41	3.26	3.18	3.10	3.02	2.93	2.84	2.75
17	8.40	6.11	5.19	4.67	4.34	4.10	3.93	3.79	3.68	3.59	3.46	3.31	3.16	3.08	3.00	2.92	2.83	2.75	2.65
18	8.29	6.01	5.09	4.58	4.25	4.01	3.84	3.71	3.60	3.51	3.37	3.23	3.08	3.00	2.92	2.84	2.75	2.66	2.57
19	8.19	5.93	5.01	4.50	4.17	3.94	3.77	3.63	3.52	3.43	3.30	3.15	3.00	2.92	2.84	2.76	2.67	2.58	2.49
20	8.10	5.85	4.94	4.43	4.10	3.87	3.70	3.56	3.46	3.37	3.23	3.09	2.94	2.86	2.78	2.69	2.61	2.52	2.42
21	8.02	5.78	4.87	4.37	4.04	3.81	3.64	3.51	3.40	3.31	3.17	3.03	2.88	2.80	2.72	2.64	2.55	2.46	2.36
22	7.95	5.72	4.82	4.31	3.99	3.76	3.59	3.45	3.35	3.26	3.12	2.98	2.83	2.75	2.67	2.58	2.50	2.40	2.31
23	7.88	5.66	4.76	4.26	3.94	3.71	3.54	3.41	3.30	3.21	3.07	2.93	2.78	2.70	2.62	2.54	2.45	2.35	2.26
24	7.82	5.61	4.72	4.22	3.90	3.67	3.50	3.36	3.26	3.17	3.03	2.89	2.74	2.66	2.58	2.49	2.40	2.31	2.21
25	7.77	5.57	4.68	4.18	3.86	3.63	3.46	3.32	3.22	3.13	2.99	2.85	2.70	2.62	2.53	2.45	2.36	2.27	2.17
30	7.56	5.39	4.51	4.02	3.70	3.47	3.30	3.17	3.07	2.98	2.84	2.70	2.55	2.47	2.39	2.30	2.21	2.11	2.01
40	7.31	5.18	4.31	3.83	3.51	3.29	3.12	2.99	2.89	2.80	2.66	2.52	2.37	2.29	2.20	2.11	2.02	1.92	1.80
60	7.08	4.98	4.13	3.65	3.34	3.12	2.95	2.82	2.72	2.63	2.50	2.35	2.20	2.12	2.03	1.94	1.84	1.73	1.60
120	6.85	4.79	3.95	3.48	3.17	2.96	2.79	2.66	2.56	2.47	2.34	2.19	2.03	1.95	1.86	1.76	1.66	1.53	1.38
∞	6.63	4.61	3.78	3.32	3.02	2.80	2.64	2.51	2.41	2.32	2.18	2.04	1.88	1.79	1.70	1.59	1.47	1.32	1.00

v_2 = degrees of freedom for denominator

Abridged from M. Merrington and C. M. Thompson, "Tables of percentage points of the inverted beta (F) distribution," *Biometrika*, Vol. 33, 1943, p. 73. By permission of the *Biometrika* trustees.

Table D–5A   Significance Points of d_L and d_U: 5%

n	$k'=1$		$k'=2$		$k'=3$		$k'=4$		$k'=5$	
	d_L	d_U	d_L	d_U	d_L	d_U	d_L	d_U	d_L	d_U
15	1.08	1.36	0.95	1.54	0.82	1.75	0.69	1.97	0.56	2.21
16	1.10	1.37	0.98	1.54	0.86	1.73	0.74	1.93	0.62	2.15
17	1.13	1.38	1.02	1.54	0.90	1.71	0.78	1.90	0.67	2.10
18	1.16	1.39	1.05	1.53	0.93	1.69	0.82	1.87	0.71	2.06
19	1.18	1.40	1.08	1.53	0.97	1.68	0.86	1.85	0.75	2.02
20	1.20	1.41	1.10	1.54	1.00	1.68	0.90	1.83	0.79	1.99
21	1.22	1.42	1.13	1.54	1.03	1.67	0.93	1.81	0.83	1.96
22	1.24	1.43	1.15	1.54	1.05	1.66	0.96	1.80	0.86	1.94
23	1.26	1.44	1.17	1.54	1.08	1.66	0.99	1.79	0.90	1.92
24	1.27	1.45	1.19	1.55	1.10	1.66	1.01	1.78	0.93	1.90
25	1.29	1.45	1.21	1.55	1.12	1.66	1.04	1.77	0.95	1.89
26	1.30	1.46	1.22	1.55	1.14	1.65	1.06	1.76	0.98	1.88
27	1.32	1.47	1.24	1.56	1.16	1.65	1.08	1.76	1.01	1.86
28	1.33	1.48	1.26	1.56	1.18	1.65	1.10	1.75	1.03	1.85
29	1.34	1.48	1.27	1.56	1.20	1.65	1.12	1.74	1.05	1.84
30	1.35	1.49	1.28	1.57	1.21	1.65	1.14	1.74	1.07	1.83
31	1.36	1.50	1.30	1.57	1.23	1.65	1.16	1.74	1.09	1.83
32	1.37	1.50	1.31	1.57	1.24	1.65	1.18	1.73	1.11	1.82
33	1.38	1.51	1.32	1.58	1.26	1.65	1.19	1.73	1.13	1.81
34	1.39	1.51	1.33	1.58	1.27	1.65	1.21	1.73	1.15	1.81
35	1.40	1.52	1.34	1.58	1.28	1.65	1.22	1.73	1.16	1.80
36	1.41	1.52	1.35	1.59	1.29	1.65	1.24	1.73	1.18	1.80
37	1.42	1.53	1.36	1.59	1.31	1.66	1.25	1.72	1.19	1.80
38	1.43	1.54	1.37	1.59	1.32	1.66	1.26	1.72	1.21	1.79
39	1.43	1.54	1.38	1.60	1.33	1.66	1.27	1.72	1.22	1.79
40	1.44	1.54	1.39	1.60	1.34	1.66	1.29	1.72	1.23	1.79
45	1.48	1.57	1.43	1.62	1.38	1.67	1.34	1.72	1.29	1.78
50	1.50	1.59	1.46	1.63	1.42	1.67	1.38	1.72	1.34	1.77
55	1.53	1.60	1.49	1.64	1.45	1.68	1.41	1.72	1.38	1.77
60	1.55	1.62	1.51	1.65	1.48	1.69	1.44	1.73	1.41	1.77
65	1.57	1.63	1.54	1.66	1.50	1.70	1.47	1.73	1.44	1.77
70	1.58	1.64	1.55	1.67	1.52	1.70	1.49	1.74	1.46	1.77
75	1.60	1.65	1.57	1.68	1.54	1.71	1.51	1.74	1.49	1.77
80	1.61	1.66	1.59	1.69	1.56	1.72	1.53	1.74	1.51	1.77
85	1.62	1.67	1.60	1.70	1.57	1.72	1.55	1.75	1.52	1.77
90	1.63	1.68	1.61	1.70	1.59	1.73	1.57	1.75	1.54	1.78
95	1.64	1.69	1.62	1.71	1.60	1.73	1.58	1.75	1.56	1.78
100	1.65	1.69	1.63	1.72	1.61	1.74	1.59	1.76	1.57	1.78

Note: k' = number of explanatory variables excluding the constant term.

Source: J. Durbin and G. S. Watson, "Testing for Serial Correlation in Least Squares Regression," *Biometrika*, Vol. 38, 1951, pp. 159–177. Reprinted with the permission of the authors and the *Biometrika* trustees.

Table D–5B Significance Points of d_L and d_U: 2.5%

n	$k' = 1$		$k' = 2$		$k' = 3$		$k' = 4$		$k' = 5$	
	d_L	d_U	d_L	d_U	d_L	d_U	d_L	d_U	d_L	d_U
15	0.95	1.23	0.83	1.40	0.71	1.61	0.59	1.84	0.48	2.09
16	0.98	1.24	0.86	1.40	0.75	1.59	0.64	1.80	0.53	2.03
17	1.01	1.25	0.90	1.40	0.79	1.58	0.68	1.77	0.57	1.98
18	1.03	1.26	0.93	1.40	0.82	1.56	0.72	1.74	0.62	1.93
19	1.06	1.28	0.96	1.41	0.86	1.55	0.76	1.72	0.66	1.90
20	1.08	1.28	0.99	1.41	0.89	1.55	0.79	1.70	0.70	1.87
21	1.10	1.30	1.01	1.41	0.92	1.54	0.83	1.69	0.73	1.84
22	1.12	1.31	1.04	1.42	0.95	1.54	0.86	1.68	0.77	1.82
23	1.14	1.32	1.06	1.42	0.97	1.54	0.89	1.67	0.80	1.80
24	1.16	1.33	1.08	1.43	1.00	1.54	0.91	1.66	0.83	1.79
25	1.18	1.34	1.10	1.43	1.02	1.54	0.94	1.65	0.86	1.77
26	1.19	1.35	1.12	1.44	1.04	1.54	0.96	1.65	0.88	1.76
27	1.21	1.36	1.13	1.44	1.06	1.54	0.99	1.64	0.91	1.75
28	1.22	1.37	1.15	1.45	1.08	1.54	1.01	1.64	0.93	1.74
29	1.24	1.38	1.17	1.45	1.10	1.54	1.03	1.63	0.96	1.73
30	1.25	1.38	1.18	1.46	1.12	1.54	1.05	1.63	0.98	1.73
31	1.26	1.39	1.20	1.47	1.13	1.55	1.07	1.63	1.00	1.72
32	1.27	1.40	1.21	1.47	1.15	1.55	1.08	1.63	1.02	1.71
33	1.28	1.41	1.22	1.48	1.16	1.55	1.10	1.63	1.04	1.71
34	1.29	1.41	1.24	1.48	1.17	1.55	1.12	1.63	1.06	1.70
35	1.30	1.42	1.25	1.48	1.19	1.55	1.13	1.63	1.07	1.70
36	1.31	1.43	1.26	1.49	1.20	1.56	1.15	1.63	1.09	1.70
37	1.32	1.43	1.27	1.49	1.21	1.56	1.16	1.62	1.10	1.70
38	1.33	1.44	1.28	1.50	1.23	1.56	1.17	1.62	1.12	1.70
39	1.34	1.44	1.29	1.50	1.24	1.56	1.19	1.63	1.13	1.69
40	1.35	1.45	1.30	1.51	1.25	1.57	1.20	1.63	1.15	1.69
45	1.39	1.48	1.34	1.53	1.30	1.58	1.25	1.63	1.21	1.69
50	1.42	1.50	1.38	1.54	1.34	1.59	1.30	1.64	1.26	1.69
55	1.45	1.52	1.41	1.56	1.37	1.60	1.33	1.64	1.30	1.69
60	1.47	1.54	1.44	1.57	1.40	1.61	1.37	1.65	1.33	1.69
65	1.49	1.55	1.46	1.59	1.43	1.62	1.40	1.66	1.36	1.69
70	1.51	1.57	1.48	1.60	1.45	1.63	1.42	1.66	1.39	1.70
75	1.53	1.58	1.50	1.61	1.47	1.64	1.45	1.67	1.42	1.70
80	1.54	1.59	1.52	1.62	1.49	1.65	1.47	1.67	1.44	1.70
85	1.56	1.60	1.53	1.63	1.51	1.65	1.49	1.68	1.46	1.71
90	1.57	1.61	1.55	1.64	1.53	1.66	1.50	1.69	1.48	1.71
95	1.58	1.62	1.56	1.65	1.54	1.67	1.52	1.69	1.50	1.71
100	1.59	1.63	1.57	1.65	1.55	1.67	1.53	1.70	1.51	1.72

Note: k' = number of explanatory variables excluding the constant term.

Source: J. Durbin and G. S. Watson, "Testing for Serial Correlation in Least Squares Regression," *Biometrika*, Vol. 38, 1951, pp. 159–177. Reprinted with the permission of the authors and the *Biometrika* trustees.

Table D–5C   Significance Points of d_L and d_U: 1%

n	$k' = 1$		$k' = 2$		$k' = 3$		$k' = 4$		$k' = 5$	
	d_L	d_U	d_L	d_U	d_L	d_U	d_L	d_U	d_L	d_U
15	0.81	1.07	0.70	1.25	0.59	1.46	0.49	1.70	0.39	1.96
16	0.84	1.09	0.74	1.25	0.63	1.44	0.53	1.66	0.44	1.90
17	0.87	1.10	0.77	1.25	0.67	1.43	0.57	1.63	0.48	1.85
18	0.90	1.12	0.80	1.26	0.71	1.42	0.61	1.60	0.52	1.80
19	0.93	1.13	0.83	1.26	0.74	1.41	0.65	1.58	0.56	1.77
20	0.95	1.15	0.86	1.27	0.77	1.41	0.68	1.57	0.60	1.74
21	0.97	1.16	0.89	1.27	0.80	1.41	0.72	1.55	0.63	1.71
22	1.00	1.17	0.91	1.28	0.83	1.40	0.75	1.54	0.66	1.69
23	1.02	1.19	0.94	1.29	0.86	1.40	0.77	1.53	0.70	1.67
24	1.04	1.20	0.96	1.30	0.88	1.41	0.80	1.53	0.72	1.66
25	1.05	1.21	0.98	1.30	0.90	1.41	0.83	1.52	0.75	1.65
26	1.07	1.22	1.00	1.31	0.93	1.41	0.85	1.52	0.78	1.64
27	1.09	1.23	1.02	1.32	0.95	1.41	0.88	1.51	0.81	1.63
28	1.10	1.24	1.04	1.32	0.97	1.41	0.90	1.51	0.83	1.62
29	1.12	1.25	1.05	1.33	0.99	1.42	0.92	1.51	0.85	1.61
30	1.13	1.26	1.07	1.34	1.01	1.42	0.94	1.51	0.88	1.61
31	1.15	1.27	1.08	1.34	1.02	1.42	0.96	1.51	0.90	1.60
32	1.16	1.28	1.10	1.35	1.04	1.43	0.98	1.51	0.92	1.60
33	1.17	1.29	1.11	1.36	1.05	1.43	1.00	1.51	0.94	1.59
34	1.18	1.30	1.13	1.36	1.07	1.43	1.01	1.51	0.95	1.59
35	1.19	1.31	1.14	1.37	1.08	1.44	1.03	1.51	0.97	1.59
36	1.21	1.32	1.15	1.38	1.10	1.44	1.04	1.51	0.99	1.59
37	1.22	1.32	1.16	1.38	1.11	1.45	1.06	1.51	1.00	1.59
38	1.23	1.33	1.18	1.39	1.12	1.45	1.07	1.52	1.02	1.58
39	1.24	1.34	1.19	1.39	1.14	1.45	1.09	1.52	1.03	1.58
40	1.25	1.34	1.20	1.40	1.15	1.46	1.10	1.52	1.05	1.58
45	1.29	1.38	1.24	1.42	1.20	1.48	1.16	1.53	1.11	1.58
50	1.32	1.40	1.28	1.45	1.24	1.49	1.20	1.54	1.16	1.59
55	1.36	1.43	1.32	1.47	1.28	1.51	1.25	1.55	1.21	1.59
60	1.38	1.45	1.35	1.48	1.32	1.52	1.28	1.56	1.25	1.60
65	1.41	1.47	1.38	1.50	1.35	1.53	1.31	1.57	1.28	1.61
70	1.43	1.49	1.40	1.52	1.37	1.55	1.34	1.58	1.31	1.61
75	1.45	1.50	1.42	1.53	1.39	1.56	1.37	1.59	1.34	1.62
80	1.47	1.52	1.44	1.54	1.42	1.57	1.39	1.60	1.36	1.62
85	1.48	1.53	1.46	1.55	1.43	1.58	1.41	1.60	1.39	1.63
90	1.50	1.54	1.47	1.56	1.45	1.59	1.43	1.61	1.41	1.64
95	1.51	1.55	1.49	1.57	1.47	1.60	1.45	1.62	1.42	1.64
100	1.52	1.56	1.50	1.58	1.48	1.60	1.46	1.63	1.44	1.65

Note: k' = number of explanatory variables excluding the constant term.

Source: J. Durbin and G. S. Watson, "Testing for Serial Correlation in Least Squares Regression," *Biometrika*, Vol. 38, 1951, pp. 159–177. Reprinted with the permission of the authors and the *Biometrika* trustees.

Table D-6 Random Normal Numbers, $\mu = 0$, $\sigma = 1$

01	02	03	04	05	06	07	08	09	10
0.464	0.137	2.455	−0.323	−0.068	0.296	−0.288	1.298	0.241	−0.957
0.060	−2.526	−0.531	−0.194	−0.543	−1.558	0.187	−1.190	0.022	0.525
1.486	−0.354	−0.634	0.697	0.926	1.375	0.785	−0.963	−0.853	−1.865
1.022	−0.472	1.279	3.521	0.571	−1.851	0.194	1.192	−0.501	−0.273
1.394	−0.555	0.046	0.321	2.945	1.974	−0.258	0.412	0.439	−0.035
0.906	−0.513	−0.525	0.595	0.881	−0.934	1.579	0.161	−1.885	0.371
1.179	−1.055	0.007	0.769	0.971	0.712	1.090	−0.631	−0.255	−0.702
−1.501	−0.488	−0.162	−0.136	1.033	0.203	0.448	0.748	−0.423	−0.432
−0.690	0.756	−1.618	−0.345	−0.511	−2.051	−0.457	−0.218	0.857	−0.465
1.372	0.225	0.378	0.761	0.181	−0.736	0.960	−1.530	−0.260	0.120
−0.482	1.678	−0.057	−1.229	−0.486	0.856	−0.491	−1.983	−2.830	−0.238
−1.376	−0.150	1.356	−0.561	−0.256	−0.212	0.219	0.779	0.953	−0.869
−1.010	0.598	−0.918	1.598	0.065	0.415	−0.169	0.313	−0.973	−1.016
−0.005	−0.899	0.012	−0.725	1.147	−0.121	1.096	0.481	−1.691	0.417
1.393	−1.163	−0.911	1.231	−0.199	−0.246	1.239	−2.574	−0.558	0.056
−1.787	−0.261	1.237	1.046	−0.508	−1.630	−0.146	−0.392	−0.627	0.561
−0.105	−0.357	−1.384	0.360	−0.992	−0.116	−1.698	−2.832	−1.108	−2.357
−1.339	1.827	−0.959	0.424	0.969	−1.141	−1.041	0.362	−1.726	1.956
1.041	0.535	0.731	1.377	0.983	−1.330	1.620	−1.040	0.524	−0.281
0.279	−2.056	0.717	−0.873	−1.096	−1.396	1.047	0.089	−0.573	0.932
−1.805	−2.008	−1.633	0.542	0.250	−0.166	0.032	0.079	0.471	−1.029
−1.186	1.180	1.114	0.882	1.265	−0.202	0.151	−0.376	−0.310	0.479
0.658	−1.141	1.151	−1.210	−0.927	0.425	0.290	−0.902	0.610	2.709
−0.439	0.358	−1.939	0.891	−0.227	0.602	0.873	−0.437	−0.220	−0.057
−1.399	−0.230	0.385	−0.649	−0.577	0.237	−0.289	0.513	0.738	−0.300
0.199	0.208	−1.083	−0.219	−0.291	1.221	1.119	0.004	−2.015	−0.594
0.159	0.272	−0.313	0.084	−2.828	−0.439	−0.792	−1.275	−0.623	−1.047
2.273	0.606	0.606	−0.747	0.247	1.291	0.063	−1.793	−0.699	−1.347
0.041	−0.307	0.121	0.790	−0.584	0.541	0.484	−0.986	0.481	0.996
−1.132	−2.098	0.921	0.145	0.446	−1.661	1.045	−1.363	−0.586	−1.023
0.768	0.079	−1.473	0.034	−2.127	0.665	0.084	−0.880	−0.579	0.551
0.375	−1.658	−1.851	0.234	−0.656	0.340	−0.086	−0.158	−0.120	0.418
−0.513	−0.344	0.210	−0.736	1.041	0.008	0.427	−0.831	0.191	0.074
0.292	−0.521	1.266	−1.206	−0.899	0.110	−0.528	−0.813	0.071	0.524
1.026	2.990	−0.574	−0.491	−1.114	1.297	−1.433	−1.345	−3.001	0.479
−1.334	1.278	−0.568	−0.109	−0.515	−0.566	2.923	0.500	0.359	0.326
−0.287	−0.144	−0.254	0.574	−0.451	−1.181	−1.190	−0.318	−0.094	1.114
0.161	−0.886	−0.921	−0.509	1.410	−0.518	0.192	−0.432	1.501	1.068
−1.346	0.193	−1.202	0.394	−1.045	0.843	0.942	1.045	0.031	0.772
1.250	−0.199	−0.288	1.810	1.378	0.584	0.216	0.733	0.402	0.226
0.630	−0.537	0.782	0.060	0.499	−0.431	1.705	1.164	0.884	−0.298
0.375	−1.941	0.247	−0.491	0.665	−0.135	−0.145	−0.498	0.457	1.064
−1.420	0.489	−1.711	−1.186	0.754	−0.732	−0.066	1.006	−0.798	0.162
−0.151	−0.243	−0.430	−0.762	0.298	1.049	1.810	2.885	−0.768	−0.129
−0.309	0.531	0.416	−1.541	1.456	2.040	−0.124	0.196	0.023	−1.204
0.424	−0.444	0.593	0.993	−0.106	0.116	0.484	−1.272	1.066	1.097
0.593	0.658	−1.127	−1.407	−1.579	−1.616	1.458	1.262	0.736	−0.916
0.862	−0.885	−0.142	−0.504	0.532	1.381	0.022	−0.281	−0.342	1.222
0.235	−0.628	−0.023	−0.463	−0.899	−0.394	−0.538	1.707	−0.188	−1.153
−0.853	0.402	0.777	0.833	0.410	−0.349	−1.094	0.580	1.395	1.298

Source: *A Million Random Digits and One Hundred Thousand Deviates* (Santa Monica: Rand Corporation, 1950). Reproduced with the permission of the publishers.

Table D–6 (*cont.*) Random Normal Numbers, $\mu = 0$, $\sigma = 1$

11	12	13	14	15	16	17	18	19	20
−1.329	−0.238	−0.828	−0.988	−0.445	−0.964	−0.266	−0.322	−1.726	−2.252
1.284	−0.229	1.058	0.090	0.050	0.523	0.016	0.277	1.639	0.554
0.619	0.628	0.005	0.973	−0.058	0.150	−0.635	−0.917	0.313	−1.203
0.699	−0.269	0.722	−0.994	−0.807	−1.203	1.163	1.244	1.306	−1.210
0.101	0.202	−0.150	0.731	0.420	0.116	−0.496	−0.037	−2.466	0.794
−1.381	0.301	0.522	0.233	0.791	−1.017	−0.182	0.926	−1.096	1.001
−0.574	1.366	−1.843	0.746	0.890	0.824	−1.249	−0.806	−0.240	0.217
0.096	0.210	1.091	0.990	0.900	−0.837	−1.097	−1.238	0.030	−0.311
1.389	−0.236	0.094	3.282	0.295	−0.416	0.313	0.720	0.007	0.354
1.249	0.706	1.453	0.366	−2.654	−1.400	0.212	0.307	−1.145	0.639
0.756	−0.397	−1.772	−0.257	1.120	1.188	−0.527	0.709	0.479	0.317
−0.860	0.412	−0.327	0.178	0.524	−0.672	−0.831	0.758	0.131	0.771
−0.778	−0.979	0.236	−1.033	1.497	−0.661	0.906	1.169	−1.582	1.303
0.037	0.062	0.426	1.220	0.471	0.784	−0.719	0.465	1.559	−1.326
2.619	−0.440	0.477	1.063	0.320	1.406	0.701	−0.128	0.518	−0.676
−0.420	−0.287	−0.050	−0.481	1.521	−1.367	0.609	0.292	0.048	0.592
1.048	0.220	1.121	−1.789	−1.211	−0.871	−0.740	0.513	−0.558	−0.395
1.000	−0.638	1.261	0.510	−0.150	0.034	0.054	−0.055	0.639	−0.825
1.170	−1.131	−0.985	0.102	−0.939	−1.457	1.766	1.087	−1.275	2.362
0.389	−0.435	0.171	0.891	1.158	1.041	1.048	−0.324	−0.404	1.060
−0.305	0.838	−2.019	−0.540	0.905	1.195	−1.190	0.106	0.571	0.298
−0.321	−0.039	1.799	−1.032	−2.225	−0.148	0.758	−0.862	0.158	−0.726
1.900	1.572	−0.244	−1.721	1.130	0.495	0.484	0.014	−0.778	−1.483
−0.778	−0.288	−0.224	−1.324	−0.072	0.890	−0.410	0.752	0.376	−0.224
0.617	−1.718	−0.183	−0.100	1.719	0.696	−1.339	−0.614	1.071	−0.386
−1.430	−0.953	0.770	−0.007	−1.872	1.075	−0.913	−1.168	1.775	0.238
0.267	−0.048	0.972	0.734	−1.408	−1.955	−0.848	2.002	0.232	−1.273
0.978	−0.520	−0.368	1.690	−1.479	0.985	1.475	−0.098	−1.633	2.399
−1.235	−1.168	0.325	1.421	2.652	−0.486	−1.253	0.270	−1.103	0.118
−0.258	0.638	2.309	0.741	−0.161	−0.679	0.336	1.973	0.370	−2.277
0.243	0.629	−1.516	−0.157	0.693	1.710	0.800	−0.265	1.218	0.655
−0.292	−1.455	−1.451	1.492	−0.713	0.821	−0.031	−0.780	1.330	0.977
−0.505	0.389	0.544	−0.042	1.615	−1.440	−0.989	−0.580	0.156	0.052
0.397	−0.287	1.712	0.289	−0.904	0.259	−0.600	−1.635	−0.009	−0.799
−0.605	−0.470	0.007	0.721	−1.117	0.635	0.592	−1.362	−1.441	0.672
1.360	0.182	−1.476	−0.599	−0.875	0.292	−0.700	0.058	−0.340	−0.639
0.480	−0.699	1.615	−0.225	1.014	−1.370	−1.097	0.294	0.309	−1.389
−0.027	−0.487	−1.000	−0.015	0.119	−1.990	−0.687	−1.964	−0.366	1.759
−1.482	−0.815	−0.121	1.884	−0.185	0.601	0.793	0.430	−1.181	0.426
−1.256	−0.567	−0.994	1.011	−1.071	−0.623	−0.420	−0.309	1.362	0.863
−1.132	2.039	1.934	−0.222	0.386	1.100	0.284	1.597	−1.718	−0.560
−0.780	−0.239	−0.497	−0.434	−0.284	−0.241	−0.333	1.348	−0.478	−0.169
−0.859	−0.215	0.241	1.471	0.389	−0.952	0.245	0.781	1.093	−0.240
0.447	1.479	0.067	0.426	−0.370	−0.675	−0.972	0.225	0.815	0.389
0.269	0.735	−0.066	−0.271	−1.439	1.036	−0.306	−1.439	−0.122	−0.336
0.097	−1.883	−0.218	0.202	−0.357	0.019	1.631	1.400	0.223	−0.793
−0.686	1.596	−0.286	0.722	0.655	−0.275	1.245	−1.504	0.066	−1.280
0.957	0.057	−1.153	0.701	−0.280	1.747	−0.745	1.338	−1.421	0.386
−0.976	−1.789	−0.696	−1.799	−0.354	0.071	2.355	0.135	−0.598	1.883
0.274	0.226	−0.909	−0.572	0.181	1.115	0.406	0.453	−1.218	−0.115

Table D–6 (*cont.*)   Random Normal Numbers, $\mu = 0$, $\sigma = 1$

21	22	23	24	25	26	27	28	29	30
−1.752	−0.329	−1.256	0.318	1.531	0.349	−0.958	−0.059	0.415	−1.084
−0.291	0.085	1.701	−1.087	−0.443	−0.292	0.248	−0.539	−1.382	0.318
−0.933	0.130	0.634	0.899	1.409	−0.883	−0.095	0.229	0.129	0.367
−0.450	−0.244	0.072	1.028	1.730	−0.056	−1.488	−0.078	−2.361	−0.992
0.512	−0.882	0.490	−1.304	−0.266	0.757	−0.361	0.194	−1.078	0.529
−0.702	0.472	0.429	−0.664	−0.592	1.443	−1.515	−1.209	−1.043	0.278
0.284	0.039	−0.518	1.351	1.473	0.889	0.300	0.339	−0.206	1.392
−0.509	1.420	−0.782	−0.429	−1.266	0.627	−1.165	0.819	−0.261	0.409
−1.776	−1.033	1.977	0.014	0.702	−0.435	−0.816	1.131	0.656	0.061
−0.044	1.807	0.342	−2.510	1.071	−1.220	−0.060	−0.764	0.079	−0.964
0.263	−0.578	1.612	−0.148	−0.383	−1.007	−0.414	0.638	−0.186	0.507
0.986	0.439	−0.192	−0.132	0.167	0.883	−0.400	−1.440	−0.385	−1.414
−0.441	−0.852	−1.446	−0.605	−0.348	1.018	0.963	−0.004	2.504	−0.847
−0.866	0.489	0.097	0.379	0.192	−0.842	0.065	1.420	0.426	−1.191
−1.215	0.675	1.621	0.394	−1.447	2.199	−0.321	−0.540	−0.037	0.185
−0.475	−1.210	0.183	0.526	0.495	1.297	−1.613	1.241	−1.016	−0.090
1.200	0.131	2.502	0.344	−1.060	−0.909	−1.695	−0.666	−0.838	−0.866
−0.498	−1.202	−0.057	−1.354	−1.441	−1.590	0.987	0.441	0.637	−1.116
−0.743	0.894	−0.028	1.119	−0.598	0.279	2.241	0.830	0.267	−0.156
0.779	−0.780	−0.954	0.705	−0.361	−0.734	1.365	1.297	−0.142	−1.387
−0.206	−0.195	1.017	−1.167	−0.079	−0.452	0.058	−1.068	−0.394	−0.406
−0.092	−0.927	−0.439	0.256	0.503	0.338	1.511	−0.465	−0.118	−0.454
−1.222	−1.582	1.786	−0.517	−1.080	−0.409	−0.474	−1.890	0.247	0.575
0.068	0.075	−1.383	−0.084	0.159	1.276	1.141	0.186	−0.973	−0.266
0.183	1.600	−0.335	1.553	0.889	0.896	−0.035	0.461	0.486	1.246
−0.811	−2.904	0.618	0.588	0.533	0.803	−0.696	0.690	0.820	0.557
−1.010	1.149	1.033	0.336	1.306	0.835	1.523	0.296	−0.426	0.004
1.453	1.210	−0.043	0.220	−0.256	−1.161	−2.030	−0.046	0.243	1.082
0.759	−0.838	−0.877	−0.177	1.183	−0.218	−3.154	−0.963	−0.822	−1.114
0.287	0.278	−0.454	0.897	−0.122	0.013	0.346	0.921	0.238	−0.586
−0.669	0.035	−2.077	1.077	0.525	−0.154	−1.036	0.015	−0.220	0.882
0.392	0.106	−1.430	−0.204	−0.326	0.825	−0.432	−0.094	−1.566	0.679
−0.337	0.199	−0.160	0.625	−0.891	−1.464	−0.318	1.297	0.932	−0.032
0.369	−1.990	−1.190	0.666	−1.614	0.082	0.922	−0.139	−0.833	0.091
−1.694	0.710	−0.655	−0.546	1.654	0.134	0.466	0.033	−0.039	0.838
0.985	0.340	0.276	0.911	−0.170	−0.551	1.000	−0.838	0.275	−0.304
−1.063	−0.594	−1.526	−0.787	0.873	−0.405	−1.324	0.162	−0.163	−2.716
0.033	−1.527	1.422	0.308	0.845	−0.151	0.741	0.064	1.212	0.823
0.597	0.362	−3.760	1.159	0.874	−0.794	−0.915	1.215	1.627	−1.248
−1.601	−0.570	0.133	−0.660	1.485	0.682	−0.898	0.686	0.658	0.346
−0.266	−1.309	0.597	0.989	0.934	1.079	−0.656	−0.999	−0.036	−0.537
0.901	1.531	−0.889	−1.019	0.084	1.531	−0.144	−1.920	0.678	−0.402
−1.433	−1.008	−0.990	0.090	0.940	0.207	−0.745	0.638	1.469	1.214
1.327	0.763	−1.724	−0.709	−1.100	−1.346	−0.946	−0.157	0.522	−1.264
−0.248	0.788	−0.577	0.122	−0.536	0.293	1.207	−2.243	1.642	1.353
−0.401	−0.679	0.921	0.476	1.121	−0.864	0.128	−0.551	−0.872	1.511
0.344	−0.324	0.686	−1.487	−0.126	0.803	−0.961	0.183	−0.358	−0.184
0.441	−0.372	−1.336	0.062	1.506	−0.315	−0.112	−0.452	1.594	−0.264
0.824	0.040	−1.734	0.251	0.054	−0.379	1.298	−0.126	0.104	−0.529
1.385	1.320	−0.509	−0.381	−1.671	−0.524	−0.805	1.348	0.676	0.799

Table D–6 (*cont.*)   Random Normal Numbers, $\mu = 0$, $\sigma = 1$

31	32	33	34	35	36	37	38	39	40
1.556	0.119	−0.078	0.164	−0.455	0.077	−0.043	−0.299	0.249	−0.182
0.647	1.029	1.186	0.887	1.204	−0.657	0.644	−0.410	−0.652	−0.165
0.329	0.407	1.169	−2.072	1.661	0.891	0.233	−1.628	−0.762	−0.717
−1.188	1.171	−1.170	−0.291	0.863	−0.045	−0.205	0.574	−0.926	1.407
−0.917	−0.616	−1.589	1.184	0.266	0.559	−1.833	−0.572	−0.648	−1.090
0.414	0.469	−0.182	0.397	1.649	1.198	0.067	−1.526	−0.081	−0.192
0.107	−0.187	1.343	0.472	−0.112	1.182	0.548	2.748	0.249	0.154
−0.497	1.907	0.191	0.136	−0.475	0.458	0.183	−1.640	−0.058	1.278
0.501	0.083	−0.321	1.133	1.126	−0.299	1.299	1.617	1.581	2.455
−1.382	−0.738	1.225	1.564	−0.363	−0.548	1.070	0.390	−1.398	0.524
−0.590	0.699	−0.162	−0.011	1.049	−0.689	1.225	0.339	−0.539	−0.445
−1.125	1.111	−1.065	0.534	0.102	0.425	−1.026	0.695	−0.057	0.795
0.849	0.169	−0.351	0.584	2.177	0.009	−0.696	−0.426	−0.692	−1.638
−1.233	−0.585	0.306	0.773	1.304	−1.304	0.282	−1.705	0.187	−0.880
0.104	−0.468	0.185	0.498	−0.624	−0.322	−0.875	1.478	−0.691	−0.281
0.261	−1.883	−0.181	1.675	−0.324	−1.029	−0.185	0.004	−0.101	−1.187
−0.007	1.280	0.568	−1.270	1.405	1.731	2.072	1.686	0.728	−0.417
0.794	−0.111	0.040	−0.536	−0.976	2.192	1.609	−0.190	−0.279	−1.611
0.431	−2.300	−1.081	−1.370	2.943	0.653	−2.523	0.756	0.886	−0.983
−0.149	1.294	−0.580	0.482	−1.449	−1.067	1.996	−0.274	0.721	0.490
−0.216	−1.647	1.043	0.481	−0.011	−0.587	−0.916	−1.016	−1.040	−1.117
1.604	−0.851	−0.317	−0.686	−0.008	1.939	0.078	−0.465	0.533	0.652
−0.212	0.005	0.535	0.837	0.362	1.103	0.219	0.488	1.332	−0.200
0.007	−0.076	1.484	0.455	−0.207	−0.554	1.120	0.913	−0.681	1.751
−0.217	0.937	0.860	0.323	1.321	−0.492	−1.386	−0.003	−0.230	0.539
−0.649	0.300	−0.698	0.900	0.569	0.842	0.804	1.025	0.603	−1.546
−1.541	0.193	2.047	−0.552	1.190	−0.087	2.062	−2.173	−0.791	−0.520
0.274	−0.530	0.112	0.385	0.656	0.436	0.882	0.312	−2.265	−0.218
0.876	−1.498	−0.128	−0.387	−1.259	−0.856	−0.353	0.714	0.863	1.169
−0.859	−1.083	1.288	−0.078	−0.081	0.210	0.572	1.194	−1.118	−1.543
−0.015	−0.567	0.113	2.127	−0.719	3.256	−0.721	−0.663	−0.779	−0.930
−1.529	−0.231	1.223	0.300	−0.995	−0.651	0.504	0.138	−0.064	1.341
0.278	−0.058	−2.740	−0.296	−1.180	0.574	1.452	0.846	−0.243	−1.208
1.428	0.322	2.302	−0.852	0.782	−1.322	−0.092	−0.546	0.560	−1.430
0.770	−1.874	0.347	0.994	−0.485	−1.179	0.048	−1.324	1.061	0.449
−0.303	−0.629	0.764	0.013	−1.192	−0.475	−1.085	−0.880	1.738	−1.225
−0.263	−2.105	0.509	−0.645	1.362	1.504	−0.755	1.274	1.448	0.604
0.997	−1.187	−0.242	0.121	2.510	−1.935	0.350	0.073	0.458	−0.446
−0.063	−0.475	−1.802	−0.476	0.193	−1.199	0.339	0.364	−0.684	1.353
−0.168	1.904	−0.485	−0.032	−0.554	0.056	−0.710	−0.778	0.722	−0.024
0.366	−0.491	0.301	−0.008	−0.894	−0.945	0.384	−1.748	−1.118	0.394
0.436	−0.464	0.539	0.942	−0.458	0.445	−1.883	1.228	1.113	−0.218
0.597	−1.471	−0.434	0.705	−0.788	0.575	0.086	0.504	1.445	−0.513
−0.805	−0.624	1.344	0.649	−1.124	0.680	−0.986	1.845	−1.152	−0.393
1.681	−1.910	0.440	0.067	−1.502	−0.755	−0.989	−0.054	−2.320	0.474
−0.007	−0.459	1.940	0.220	−1.259	−1.729	0.137	−0.520	−0.412	2.847
0.209	−0.633	0.299	0.174	1.975	−0.271	0.119	−0.199	0.007	2.315
1.254	1.672	−1.186	−1.310	0.474	0.878	−0.725	−0.191	0.642	−1.212
−1.016	−0.697	0.017	−0.263	−0.047	−1.294	−0.339	2.257	−0.078	−0.049
−1.169	−0.355	1.086	−0.199	0.031	0.396	−0.143	1.572	0.276	0.027

Table D–6 (*cont.*)   Random Normal Numbers, $\mu = 0$, $\sigma = 1$

41	42	43	44	45	46	47	48	49	50
−0.856	−0.063	0.787	−2.052	−1.192	−0.831	1.623	1.135	0.759	−0.189
−0.276	−1.110	0.752	−1.378	−0.583	0.360	0.365	1.587	0.621	1.344
0.379	−0.440	0.858	1.453	−1.356	0.503	−1.134	1.950	−1.816	−0.283
1.468	0.131	0.047	0.355	0.162	−1.491	−0.739	−1.182	−0.533	−0.497
−1.805	−0.772	1.286	−0.636	−1.312	−1.045	1.559	−0.871	−0.102	−0.123
2.285	0.554	0.418	−0.577	−1.489	−1.255	0.092	−0.597	−1.051	−0.980
−0.602	0.399	1.121	−1.026	0.087	1.018	−1.437	0.661	0.091	−0.637
0.229	−0.584	0.705	0.124	0.341	1.320	−0.824	−1.541	−0.163	2.329
1.382	−1.454	1.537	−1.299	0.363	−0.356	−0.025	0.294	2.194	−0.395
0.978	0.109	1.434	−1.094	−0.265	−0.857	−1.421	−1.773	0.570	−0.053
−0.678	−2.335	1.202	−1.697	0.547	−0.201	−0.373	−1.363	−0.081	0.958
−0.366	−1.084	−0.626	0.798	1.706	−1.160	−0.838	1.462	0.636	0.570
−1.074	−1.379	0.086	−0.331	−0.288	−0.309	−1.527	−0.408	0.183	0.856
−0.600	−0.096	0.696	0.446	1.417	−2.140	0.599	−0.157	1.485	1.387
0.918	1.163	−1.445	0.759	0.878	−1.781	−0.056	−2.141	−0.234	0.975
−0.791	−0.528	0.946	1.673	−0.680	−0.784	1.494	−0.086	−1.071	−1.196
0.598	−0.352	0.719	−0.341	0.056	−1.041	1.429	0.235	0.314	−1.693
0.567	−1.156	−0.125	−0.534	0.711	−0.511	0.187	−0.644	−1.090	−1.281
0.963	0.052	0.037	0.637	−1.335	0.055	0.010	−0.860	−0.621	0.713
0.489	−0.209	1.659	0.054	1.635	0.169	0.794	−1.550	1.845	−0.388
−1.627	−0.017	0.699	0.661	−0.073	0.188	1.183	−1.054	−1.615	−0.765
−1.096	1.215	0.320	0.738	1.865	−1.169	−0.667	−0.674	−0.062	1.378
−2.532	1.031	−0.799	1.665	−2.756	−0.151	−0.704	0.602	−0.672	1.264
0.024	−1.183	−0.927	−0.629	0.204	−0.825	0.496	2.543	0.262	−0.785
0.192	0.125	0.373	−0.931	−0.079	0.186	−0.306	0.621	−0.292	1.131
−1.324	−1.229	−0.648	−0.430	0.811	0.868	0.787	1.845	−0.374	−0.651
−0.726	−0.746	1.572	−1.420	1.509	−0.361	−0.310	−3.117	1.637	0.642
−1.618	1.082	−0.319	0.300	1.524	−0.418	−1.712	0.358	−1.032	0.537
1.695	0.843	2.049	0.388	−0.297	1.077	−0.462	0.655	0.940	−0.354
0.790	0.605	−3.077	1.009	−0.906	−1.004	0.693	−1.098	1.300	0.549
1.792	−0.895	−0.136	−1.765	1.077	0.418	−0.150	0.808	0.697	0.435
0.771	−0.741	−0.492	−0.770	−0.458	−0.021	1.385	−1.225	−0.066	−1.471
−1.438	0.423	−1.211	0.723	−0.731	0.883	−2.109	−2.455	−0.210	1.644
−0.294	1.266	−1.994	−0.730	0.545	0.397	1.069	−0.383	−0.097	−0.985
−1.966	0.909	0.400	0.685	−0.800	1.759	0.268	1.387	−0.414	1.615
−0.999	1.587	1.423	0.937	−0.943	0.090	1.185	−1.204	0.300	−1.354
0.581	0.481	−2.400	0.000	0.231	0.079	−2.842	−0.846	−0.508	−0.516
0.370	−1.452	−0.580	−1.462	−0.972	1.116	−0.994	0.374	−3.336	−0.058
0.834	−1.227	−0.709	−1.039	−0.014	−0.383	−0.512	−0.347	0.881	−0.638
−0.376	−0.813	0.660	−1.029	−0.137	0.371	0.376	0.968	1.338	−0.786
−1.621	0.815	−0.544	−0.376	−0.852	0.436	1.562	0.815	−1.048	0.188
0.163	−0.161	2.501	−0.265	−0.285	1.934	1.070	0.215	−0.876	0.073
1.786	−0.538	−0.437	0.324	0.105	−0.421	−0.410	−0.947	0.700	−1.006
2.140	1.218	−0.351	−0.068	0.254	0.448	−1.461	0.784	0.317	1.013
0.064	0.410	0.368	0.419	−0.982	1.371	0.100	−0.505	0.856	0.890
0.789	−0.131	1.330	0.506	−0.645	−1.414	2.426	1.389	−0.169	−0.194
−0.011	−0.372	−0.699	2.382	−1.395	−0.467	1.256	−0.585	−1.359	−1.804
−0.463	0.003	−1.470	−1.493	0.960	0.364	−1.267	−0.007	0.616	0.624
−1.210	−0.669	0.009	1.284	−0.617	0.355	−0.589	−0.243	−0.015	−0.712
−1.157	0.481	0.560	1.287	1.129	−0.126	0.006	1.532	1.328	0.980

Table D–6 (*cont.*) Random Normal Numbers, $\mu = 0$, $\sigma = 1$

51	52	53	54	55	56	57	58	59	60
0.240	1.774	0.210	−1.471	1.167	−1.114	0.182	−0.485	−0.318	1.156
0.627	−0.758	−0.930	1.641	0.162	−0.874	−0.235	0.203	−0.724	−0.155
−0.594	0.098	0.158	−0.722	1.385	−0.985	−1.707	0.175	0.449	0.654
1.082	−0.753	−1.944	−1.964	−2.131	−2.796	−1.286	0.807	−0.122	0.527
0.060	−0.014	1.577	−0.814	−0.633	0.275	−0.087	0.517	0.474	−1.432
−0.013	0.402	−0.086	−0.394	0.292	−2.862	−1.660	−1.658	1.610	−2.205
1.586	−0.833	1.444	−0.615	−1.157	−0.220	−0.517	−1.668	−2.036	−0.850
−0.405	−1.315	−1.355	−1.331	1.394	−0.381	−0.729	−0.447	−0.906	0.622
−0.329	1.701	0.427	0.627	−0.271	−0.971	−1.010	1.182	−0.143	0.844
0.992	0.708	−0.115	−1.630	0.596	0.499	−0.862	0.508	0.474	−0.974
0.296	−0.390	2.047	−0.363	0.724	0.788	−0.089	0.930	−0.497	0.058
−2.069	−1.422	−0.948	−1.742	−1.173	0.215	0.661	0.842	−0.984	−0.577
−0.211	−1.727	−0.277	1.592	−0.707	0.327	−0.527	0.912	0.571	−0.525
−0.467	1.848	−0.263	−0.862	0.706	−0.533	0.626	−0.200	−2.221	0.368
1.284	0.412	1.512	0.328	0.203	−1.231	−1.480	−0.400	−0.491	0.913
0.821	−1.503	−1.066	1.624	1.345	0.440	−1.416	0.301	−0.355	0.106
1.056	1.224	0.281	−0.098	1.868	−0.395	0.610	−1.173	−1.449	1.171
1.090	−0.790	0.882	1.687	−0.009	−2.053	−0.030	−0.421	1.253	−0.081
0.574	0.129	1.203	0.280	1.438	−2.052	−0.443	0.522	0.468	−1.211
−0.531	2.155	0.334	0.898	−1.114	0.243	1.026	0.391	−0.011	−0.024
0.896	0.181	−0.941	−0.511	0.648	−0.710	−0.181	−1.417	−0.585	0.087
0.042	0.579	−0.316	0.394	1.133	−0.305	−0.863	−1.318	−0.050	0.993
2.328	−0.243	0.534	0.241	0.275	0.060	0.727	−1.459	0.174	−1.072
0.486	−0.558	0.426	0.728	−0.360	−0.068	0.058	1.471	−0.051	0.337
−0.304	−0.309	0.646	0.309	−1.320	0.311	−1.407	−0.011	0.387	0.128
−2.319	−0.129	0.866	−0.424	−0.236	0.419	−1.359	−1.088	−0.045	1.096
1.098	−0.875	0.659	−1.086	−0.424	−1.462	0.743	−0.787	1.472	1.677
−0.038	−0.118	−1.285	−0.545	−0.140	1.244	−1.104	0.146	0.058	1.245
−0.207	−0.746	1.681	0.137	0.104	−0.491	−0.935	0.671	−0.448	−0.129
0.333	−1.386	1.840	1.089	0.837	−1.642	−0.273	−0.798	0.067	0.334
1.190	−0.547	−1.016	0.540	−0.993	0.443	−0.190	1.019	−1.021	−1.276
−1.416	−0.749	0.325	0.846	2.417	−0.479	−0.655	−1.326	−1.952	1.234
0.622	0.661	0.028	1.302	−0.032	−0.157	1.470	−0.766	0.697	−0.303
−1.134	0.499	0.538	0.564	−2.392	−1.398	0.010	1.874	1.386	0.000
0.725	−0.242	0.281	1.355	−0.036	0.204	−0.345	0.395	−0.753	1.645
−0.210	0.611	−0.219	0.450	0.308	0.993	−0.146	0.225	−1.496	0.246
0.219	0.302	0.000	−0.437	−2.127	0.883	−0.599	−1.516	0.826	1.242
−1.098	−0.252	−2.480	−0.973	0.712	−1.430	−0.167	−1.237	0.750	−0.763
0.144	0.489	−0.637	1.990	0.411	−0.563	0.027	1.278	2.105	−1.130
−1.738	−1.295	0.431	−0.503	2.327	−0.007	−1.293	−1.206	−0.066	1.370
−0.487	−0.097	−1.361	−0.340	0.204	0.938	−0.148	−1.099	−0.252	−0.384
−0.636	−0.626	1.967	1.677	−0.331	−0.440	−1.440	1.281	1.070	−1.167
−1.464	−1.493	0.945	0.180	−0.672	−0.035	−0.293	−0.905	0.196	−1.122
0.561	−0.375	−0.657	1.304	0.833	−1.159	1.501	1.265	0.438	−0.437
−0.525	−0.017	1.815	0.789	−1.908	−0.353	1.383	−1.208	−1.135	1.082
0.980	−0.111	−0.804	−1.078	−1.930	0.171	−1.318	2.377	−0.303	1.062
0.501	0.835	−0.518	−1.034	−1.493	0.712	0.421	−1.165	0.782	−1.484
1.081	−1.176	−0.542	0.321	0.688	0.670	−0.771	−0.090	−0.611	−0.813
−0.148	−1.203	−1.553	1.244	0.826	0.077	0.128	−0.772	1.683	0.318
0.096	−0.286	0.362	0.888	0.551	1.782	0.335	2.083	0.350	0.260

Table D–6 (*cont.*)   Random Normal Numbers, $\mu = 0$, $\sigma = 1$

61	62	63	64	65	66	67	68	69	70
0.052	1.504	−1.350	−1.124	−0.521	0.515	0.839	0.778	0.438	−0.550
−0.315	−0.865	0.851	0.127	−0.379	1.640	−0.441	0.717	0.670	−0.301
0.938	−0.055	0.947	1.275	1.557	−1.484	−1.137	0.398	1.333	1.988
0.497	0.502	0.385	−0.467	2.468	−1.810	−1.438	0.283	1.740	0.420
2.308	−0.399	−1.798	0.018	0.780	1.030	0.806	−0.408	−0.547	−0.280
1.815	0.101	−0.561	0.236	0.166	0.227	−0.309	0.056	0.610	0.732
−0.421	0.432	0.586	1.059	0.278	−1.672	1.859	1.433	−0.919	−1.770
0.008	0.555	−1.310	−1.440	−0.142	−0.295	−0.630	−0.911	0.133	−0.308
1.191	−0.114	1.039	1.083	0.185	−0.492	0.419	−0.433	−1.019	−2.260
1.299	1.918	0.318	1.348	0.935	1.250	−0.175	−0.828	−0.336	0.726
0.012	−0.739	−1.181	−0.645	−0.736	1.801	−0.209	−0.389	0.867	−0.555
−0.586	−0.044	−0.983	0.332	0.371	−0.072	−1.212	1.047	−1.930	0.812
−0.122	1.515	0.338	−1.040	−0.008	0.467	−0.600	0.923	1.126	−0.752
0.879	0.516	−0.920	2.121	0.674	1.481	0.660	−0.986	1.644	−2.159
0.435	1.149	−0.065	1.391	0.707	0.548	−0.490	−1.139	0.249	−0.933
0.645	0.878	−0.904	0.896	−1.284	0.237	−0.378	−0.510	−1.123	−0.129
−0.514	−1.017	0.529	0.973	−1.202	0.005	−0.644	−0.167	−0.664	0.167
0.242	−0.427	−0.727	−1.150	−1.092	−0.736	0.925	−0.050	−0.200	−0.770
0.443	0.445	−1.287	−1.463	−0.650	−0.412	−2.714	−0.903	−0.341	0.957
0.273	0.203	0.423	1.423	0.508	1.058	−0.828	0.143	−1.059	0.345
0.255	1.036	1.471	0.476	0.592	−0.658	0.677	0.155	1.068	−0.759
0.858	−0.370	0.522	−1.890	−0.389	0.609	1.210	0.489	−0.006	0.834
0.097	−1.709	1.790	−0.929	0.405	0.024	−0.036	0.580	−0.642	−1.121
0.520	0.889	−0.540	0.266	−0.354	0.524	−0.788	−0.497	−0.973	1.481
−0.311	−1.772	−0.496	1.275	−0.904	0.147	1.497	0.657	−0.469	−0.783
−0.604	0.857	−0.695	0.397	0.296	−0.285	0.191	0.158	1.672	1.190
−0.001	0.287	−0.868	−0.013	−1.576	−0.168	0.047	0.159	0.086	−1.077
1.160	0.989	0.205	0.937	−0.099	−1.281	−0.276	0.845	0.752	0.663
1.579	−0.303	−1.174	−0.960	−0.470	−0.556	−0.689	1.535	−0.711	−0.743
−0.615	−0.154	0.008	1.353	−0.381	1.137	0.022	0.175	0.586	2.841
1.578	1.529	−0.294	−1.301	0.614	0.099	−0.700	−0.003	1.052	1.643
0.626	−0.447	−1.261	−2.029	0.182	−1.176	0.083	1.868	0.872	0.965
−0.493	−0.020	0.920	1.473	1.873	−0.289	0.410	0.394	0.881	0.054
−0.217	0.342	1.423	0.364	−0.119	0.509	−2.266	0.189	0.149	1.041
−0.792	0.347	−1.367	−0.632	−1.238	−0.136	−0.352	−0.157	−1.163	1.305
0.568	−0.226	0.391	−0.074	−0.312	0.400	1.583	0.481	−1.048	0.759
0.051	0.549	−2.192	1.257	−1.460	0.363	0.127	−1.020	−1.192	0.449
−0.891	0.490	0.279	0.372	−0.578	−0.836	2.285	−0.448	0.720	0.510
0.622	−0.126	−0.637	1.255	−0.354	0.032	−1.076	0.352	0.103	−0.496
0.623	0.819	−0.489	0.354	−0.943	−0.694	0.248	0.092	−0.673	−1.428
−1.208	−1.038	0.140	−0.762	−0.854	−0.249	2.431	0.067	−0.317	−0.874
−0.487	−2.117	0.195	2.154	1.041	−1.314	−0.785	−0.414	−0.695	2.310
0.522	0.314	−1.003	0.134	−1.748	−0.107	0.459	1.550	1.118	−1.004
0.838	0.613	0.227	0.308	−0.757	0.912	2.272	0.556	−0.041	0.008
−1.534	−0.407	1.202	1.251	−0.891	−1.588	−2.380	0.059	0.682	−0.878
−0.099	2.391	1.067	−2.060	−0.464	−0.103	3.486	1.121	0.632	−1.626
0.070	1.465	−0.080	−0.526	−1.090	−1.002	0.132	1.504	0.050	−0.393
0.115	−0.601	1.751	1.956	−0.196	0.400	−0.522	0.571	−0.101	−2.160
0.252	−0.329	−0.586	−0.118	−0.242	−0.521	0.818	−0.167	−0.469	0.430
0.017	0.185	0.377	1.883	−0.443	−0.039	−1.244	−0.820	−1.171	0.104

Table D–6 (cont.)   Random Normal Numbers, $\mu = 0$, $\sigma = 1$

71	72	73	74	75	76	77	78	79	80
2.988	0.423	−1.261	−1.893	0.187	−0.412	−0.228	0.002	−1.384	−1.032
0.760	0.995	−0.256	−0.505	0.750	−0.654	0.647	0.613	0.086	−0.118
−0.650	−0.927	−1.071	−0.796	1.130	−1.042	−0.181	−1.020	1.648	−1.327
−0.394	−0.452	0.893	1.410	1.133	0.319	0.537	−0.789	0.078	−0.062
−1.168	1.902	0.206	0.303	1.413	2.012	0.278	−0.566	−0.900	0.200
1.343	−0.377	−0.131	−0.585	0.053	0.137	−1.371	−0.175	−0.878	0.118
−0.733	−1.921	0.471	−1.394	−0.885	−0.523	0.553	0.344	−0.775	1.545
−0.172	−0.575	0.066	−0.310	1.795	−1.148	0.772	−1.063	0.818	0.302
1.457	0.862	1.677	−0.507	−1.691	−0.034	0.270	0.075	−0.554	1.420
−0.087	0.744	1.829	1.203	−0.436	−0.618	−0.200	−1.134	−1.352	−0.098
−0.092	1.043	−0.255	0.189	0.270	−1.034	−0.571	−0.336	−0.742	2.141
0.441	−0.379	−1.757	0.608	0.527	−0.338	−1.995	0.573	−0.034	−0.056
0.073	−0.250	0.531	−0.695	1.402	−0.462	−0.938	1.130	1.453	−0.106
0.637	0.276	−0.013	1.968	−0.205	0.486	0.727	1.416	0.963	1.349
−0.792	−1.778	1.284	−0.452	0.602	0.668	0.516	−0.210	0.040	−0.103
−1.223	1.561	−2.099	1.419	0.223	−0.482	1.098	0.513	0.418	−1.686
−0.407	1.587	0.335	−2.475	−0.284	1.567	−0.248	−0.759	1.792	−2.319
−0.462	−0.193	−0.012	−1.208	2.151	1.336	−1.968	−1.767	−0.374	0.783
1.457	0.883	1.001	−0.169	0.836	−1.236	1.632	−0.142	−0.222	0.340
−1.918	−1.246	−0.209	0.780	−0.330	−2.953	−0.447	−0.094	1.344	−0.196
−0.126	1.094	−1.206	−1.426	1.474	−1.080	0.000	0.764	1.476	−0.016
−0.306	−0.847	0.639	−0.262	−0.427	0.391	−1.298	−1.013	2.024	−0.539
0.477	1.595	−0.762	0.424	0.799	0.312	1.151	−1.095	1.199	−0.765
0.369	−0.709	1.283	−0.007	−1.440	−0.782	0.061	1.427	1.656	0.974
−0.579	0.606	−0.866	−0.715	−0.301	−0.180	0.188	0.668	−1.091	1.476
−0.418	−0.588	0.919	−0.083	1.084	0.944	0.253	−1.833	1.305	0.171
0.128	−0.834	0.009	0.742	0.539	−0.948	−1.055	−0.689	−0.338	1.091
−0.291	0.235	−0.971	−1.696	1.119	0.272	0.635	−0.792	−1.355	1.291
−1.024	1.212	−1.100	−0.348	1.741	0.035	1.268	0.192	0.729	−0.467
−0.378	1.026	0.093	0.468	−0.967	0.675	0.807	−2.109	−1.214	0.559
1.232	−0.815	0.608	1.429	−0.748	0.201	0.400	−1.230	−0.398	−0.674
1.793	−0.581	−1.076	0.512	−0.442	−1.488	−0.580	0.172	−0.891	0.311
0.766	0.310	−0.070	0.624	−0.389	1.035	−0.101	−0.926	0.816	−1.048
−0.606	−1.224	1.465	0.012	1.061	0.491	−1.023	1.948	0.866	−0.737
0.106	−2.715	0.363	0.343	−0.159	2.672	1.119	0.731	−1.012	−0.889
−0.060	0.444	1.596	−0.630	0.362	−0.306	1.163	−0.974	0.486	−0.373
2.081	1.161	−1.167	0.021	0.053	−0.094	0.381	−0.628	−2.581	−1.243
−1.727	−1.266	0.088	0.936	0.368	0.648	−0.799	1.115	−0.968	−2.588
0.091	1.364	1.677	0.644	1.505	0.440	−0.329	0.498	0.869	−0.965
−1.114	−0.239	−0.409	−0.334	−0.605	0.501	−1.921	−0.470	2.354	−0.660
0.189	−0.547	−1.758	−0.295	−0.279	−0.515	−1.053	0.553	−0.297	0.496
−0.065	−0.023	−0.267	−0.247	1.318	0.904	−0.712	−1.152	−0.543	0.176
−1.742	−0.599	0.430	−0.615	1.165	0.084	2.017	−1.207	2.614	1.490
0.732	0.188	2.343	0.526	−0.812	0.389	1.036	−0.023	0.229	−2.262
−1.490	0.014	0.167	1.422	0.015	0.069	0.133	0.897	−1.678	0.323
1.507	−0.571	−0.724	1.741	−0.152	−0.147	−0.158	−0.076	0.652	0.447
0.513	0.168	−0.076	−0.171	0.428	0.205	−0.865	0.107	1.023	0.077
−0.834	−1.121	1.441	0.492	0.559	1.724	−1.659	0.245	1.354	−0.041
0.258	1.880	−0.536	1.246	−0.188	−0.746	1.097	0.258	1.547	1.238
−0.818	0.273	0.159	−0.765	0.526	1.281	1.154	−0.687	−0.793	0.795

Table D-6 (*cont.*)   Random Normal Numbers, $\mu = 0$, $\sigma = 1$

81	82	83	84	85	86	87	88	89	90
−0.713	−0.541	−0.571	−0.807	−1.560	1.000	0.140	−0.549	0.887	2.237
−0.117	0.530	−1.599	−1.602	0.412	−1.450	−1.217	1.074	−1.021	−0.424
1.187	−1.523	1.437	0.051	1.237	−0.798	1.616	−0.823	−1.207	1.258
−0.182	−0.186	0.517	1.438	0.831	−1.319	−0.539	−0.192	0.150	2.127
1.964	−0.629	−0.944	−0.028	0.948	1.005	0.242	−0.432	−0.329	0.113
0.230	1.523	1.658	0.753	0.724	0.183	−0.147	0.505	0.448	−0.053
0.839	−0.849	−0.145	−1.843	−1.276	0.481	−0.142	−0.534	0.403	0.370
−0.801	0.343	−1.822	0.447	−0.931	−0.824	−0.484	0.864	−1.069	0.860
−0.124	0.727	1.654	−0.182	−1.381	−1.146	−0.572	0.159	0.186	1.221
−0.088	0.032	−0.564	0.654	1.141	−0.056	−0.343	0.067	−0.267	−0.219
0.912	−1.114	−1.035	−1.070	−0.297	1.195	0.030	0.022	0.406	−0.414
1.397	−0.473	0.433	0.023	−1.204	1.254	0.551	−1.012	−0.789	0.906
−0.652	−0.029	0.064	0.511	1.117	−0.465	0.523	−0.083	0.386	0.259
1.236	−0.457	−1.354	−0.898	−0.270	−1.837	1.641	−0.657	−0.753	−1.686
−0.498	1.302	0.816	−0.936	1.404	0.555	2.450	−0.789	−0.120	0.505
−0.005	2.174	1.893	−1.361	−0.991	0.508	−0.823	0.918	0.524	0.488
0.115	−1.373	−0.900	−1.010	0.624	0.946	0.312	−1.384	0.224	2.343
0.167	0.254	1.219	1.153	−0.510	−0.007	−0.285	−0.631	−0.356	0.254
0.976	1.158	−0.469	1.099	0.509	−1.324	−0.102	−0.296	−0.907	0.449
0.653	−0.366	0.450	−2.653	−0.592	−0.510	0.983	0.023	−0.881	0.876
−0.150	−0.088	0.457	−0.448	0.605	0.668	−0.613	0.261	0.023	−0.050
0.060	0.276	0.229	−1.527	−0.316	−0.834	−1.652	−0.387	0.632	0.895
−0.678	0.547	0.243	−2.183	−0.368	1.158	−0.996	−0.705	−0.314	1.464
2.139	0.395	−0.376	−0.175	0.406	0.309	−1.021	−0.460	−0.217	0.307
0.091	1.793	0.822	0.054	0.573	−0.729	−0.517	0.589	1.927	0.940
−0.003	0.344	1.242	−1.105	0.234	−1.222	−0.474	1.831	0.124	−0.840
−0.965	0.268	−1.543	0.690	0.917	2.017	−0.297	1.087	0.371	1.495
−0.076	−0.495	−0.103	0.646	2.427	−2.172	0.660	−1.541	−0.852	0.583
−0.365	−3.305	0.805	−0.418	−1.201	0.623	−0.223	0.109	0.205	−0.663
0.578	0.145	−1.438	1.122	−1.406	1.172	0.272	−2.245	1.207	1.227
−0.398	−0.304	0.529	−0.514	−0.681	−0.366	0.338	0.801	−0.301	−0.790
−0.951	−1.483	−0.613	−0.171	−0.459	1.231	−1.232	−0.497	−0.779	0.247
1.025	−0.039	−0.721	0.813	1.203	0.245	0.402	1.541	0.691	−1.420
−0.958	0.791	0.948	0.222	−0.704	−0.375	−0.246	−0.862	−0.871	0.056
1.097	−1.428	1.402	−1.425	−0.877	0.536	0.988	2.529	0.768	−1.321
0.377	2.240	0.854	−1.158	0.066	−1.222	0.821	−1.602	−0.760	−0.871
1.729	0.073	1.022	0.891	0.659	−1.040	0.251	−0.710	−1.734	−0.038
−1.329	−0.381	−0.515	1.484	−0.430	−0.466	−0.167	−0.788	−0.660	0.003
−0.132	0.391	2.205	−1.165	0.200	0.415	−0.765	0.239	−1.182	1.135
0.336	0.657	−0.805	0.150	−0.938	1.057	−1.090	1.604	−0.598	−0.760
0.124	−1.812	1.750	0.270	−0.114	0.517	−0.226	0.127	0.129	−0.751
−0.036	0.365	0.766	0.877	−0.804	−0.140	0.182	−0.483	−0.376	−0.564
−0.609	−0.019	−0.992	−1.193	−0.516	0.517	1.677	0.839	−1.134	0.675
−0.894	0.318	0.607	−0.865	0.526	−0.971	1.365	0.319	1.804	1.740
−0.357	−0.802	0.635	−0.491	−1.110	0.785	−0.042	−1.042	−0.572	0.243
−0.258	−0.383	−1.013	0.001	−1.673	0.561	−1.054	−0.106	−0.760	−1.009
2.245	−0.431	−0.496	0.796	0.193	1.202	−0.429	−0.217	0.333	−0.643
1.956	0.477	0.812	−0.117	0.606	−0.330	0.425	−0.232	0.802	0.656
1.358	0.139	0.199	−0.475	−0.120	0.184	−0.020	−1.326	0.517	−1.708
0.656	1.081	0.180	0.145	0.376	−1.363	−0.491	0.352	−1.477	1.280

Table D–6 (cont.)   Random Normal Numbers, $\mu = 0$, $\sigma = 1$

91	92	93	94	95	96	97	98	99	100
−0.181	0.583	−1.478	−0.181	0.281	−0.559	1.985	−1.122	−1.106	1.441
1.549	−1.183	−2.089	−1.997	−0.343	1.275	0.676	−0.212	1.252	0.163
0.978	−1.067	−2.640	0.134	0.328	−0.052	−0.030	−0.273	−0.570	1.026
−0.596	−0.420	−0.318	−0.057	−0.695	−1.148	0.333	−0.531	−2.037	−1.587
−0.440	0.032	0.163	1.029	0.079	1.148	0.762	−1.961	−0.674	−0.486
0.443	−1.100	0.728	−2.397	−0.543	0.872	−0.568	0.980	−0.174	0.728
−2.401	−1.375	−1.332	−2.177	−2.064	−0.245	−0.039	0.585	1.344	1.386
0.311	0.322	−0.158	0.359	0.103	0.371	0.735	0.011	2.091	0.490
−1.209	0.241	−1.488	−0.667	−1.772	−0.197	0.741	−1.303	−1.149	2.251
0.575	−1.227	−1.674	1.400	0.289	0.005	0.185	−1.072	0.431	−1.096
−0.190	0.272	1.216	0.227	1.358	0.215	−2.306	−1.301	−0.597	−1.401
−0.817	−0.769	−0.470	−0.633	0.187	−0.517	−0.888	−1.712	1.774	−0.162
0.265	−0.676	0.244	1.897	−0.629	−0.206	−1.419	1.049	0.266	−0.438
−0.221	0.678	2.149	1.486	−1.361	1.402	−0.028	0.493	0.744	0.195
−0.436	0.358	−0.602	0.107	0.085	0.573	0.529	1.577	0.239	1.898
−0.010	0.475	0.655	0.659	−0.029	−0.029	0.126	−1.335	−1.261	2.036
−0.244	1.654	1.335	−0.610	0.617	0.642	0.371	0.241	0.001	−1.799
−0.932	−1.275	−1.134	−1.246	−1.508	0.949	1.743	−0.271	−1.333	−1.875
−0.199	−1.285	−0.387	0.191	0.726	−0.151	0.064	−0.803	−0.062	0.780
−0.251	−0.431	−0.831	0.036	−0.464	−1.089	−0.284	−0.451	1.693	1.004
1.074	−1.323	−1.659	−0.186	−0.612	1.612	−2.159	−1.210	0.596	−1.421
1.518	2.101	0.397	0.516	−1.169	−1.821	1.346	2.435	1.165	−0.428
0.935	−0.206	1.117	−0.241	−0.963	−0.099	0.412	−1.344	0.411	0.583
1.360	−0.380	0.031	1.066	0.893	0.431	−0.081	0.099	0.500	−2.441
0.115	−0.211	1.471	0.332	0.750	0.652	−0.812	1.383	−0.355	−0.638
0.082	−0.309	−0.355	−0.402	0.774	0.150	0.015	2.539	−0.756	−1.049
−1.492	0.259	0.323	0.697	−0.509	0.968	−0.053	1.033	−0.220	−2.322
−0.203	0.548	1.494	1.185	0.083	−1.196	−0.749	−1.105	1.324	0.689
1.857	−0.167	−1.531	1.551	0.848	0.120	0.415	−0.317	1.446	1.002
0.669	−1.017	−2.437	−0.558	−0.657	0.940	0.985	0.483	−0.361	0.095
0.128	1.463	−0.436	−0.239	−1.443	0.732	0.168	−0.144	−0.392	0.989
1.879	−2.456	0.029	0.429	0.618	−1.683	−2.262	0.034	−0.002	1.914
0.680	0.252	0.130	1.658	−1.023	0.407	−0.235	−0.224	−0.434	0.253
−0.631	0.225	−0.951	1.072	−0.285	−1.731	−0.427	−1.446	−0.873	0.619
−1.273	0.723	0.201	0.505	−0.370	−0.421	−0.015	−0.463	0.288	1.734
−0.643	−1.485	0.403	0.003	−0.243	0.000	0.964	−0.703	0.844	−0.686
−0.435	−2.162	−0.169	−1.311	−1.639	0.193	2.692	−1.994	0.326	0.562
−1.706	0.119	−1.566	0.637	−1.948	−1.068	0.935	0.738	0.650	0.491
−0.498	1.640	0.384	−0.945	−1.272	0.945	−1.013	−0.913	−0.469	2.250
−0.065	−0.005	0.618	−0.523	−0.055	1.071	0.758	−0.736	−0.959	0.598
0.190	−1.020	−1.104	0.936	−0.029	−1.004	−0.657	1.270	−0.060	−0.809
0.879	−0.642	1.155	−0.523	−0.757	−1.027	0.985	−1.222	1.078	0.163
0.559	1.094	1.587	−0.384	−1.701	0.418	0.327	0.669	0.019	0.782
−0.261	1.234	−0.505	−0.664	−0.446	−0.747	0.427	−0.369	0.089	−1.302
3.136	1.120	−0.591	2.515	−2.853	1.375	2.421	0.672	1.817	−0.067
−1.307	−0.586	−0.311	−0.026	1.633	−1.340	−1.209	0.110	−0.126	−0.288
1.455	1.099	−1.225	−0.817	0.667	−0.212	0.684	0.349	−1.161	−2.432
−0.443	−0.415	−0.660	0.098	0.435	−0.846	−0.375	−0.410	−1.747	−0.790
−0.326	0.798	0.349	0.524	0.690	−0.520	−0.522	0.602	−0.193	−0.535
−1.027	−1.459	−0.840	−1.637	−0.462	0.607	−0.760	1.342	−1.916	0.424

Suggested Further Readings

Entries are generally given in order of importance and relevance to the material presented in the text of each chapter.

Chapter 1   Introduction to Statistical Inference

W. A. WALLIS and H. V. ROBERTS, *The Nature of Statistics* (New York: The Free Press, 1956).

G. U. YULE and M. G. KENDALL, *An Introduction to the Theory of Statistics* (London: Charles Griffin, 1950), Chapter 16.

IAN HOCKING, *Logic of Statistical Inference* (New York: Cambridge University Press, 1965).

H. JEFFREYS, *Theory of Probability* (New York: Oxford University Press, 1961), Chapter 1.

C. L. LASTRUCCI, *The Scientific Approach* (Cambridge, Mass.: Schenkman, 1963).

Chapter 2   Experimental Derivation of Sampling Distributions

W. J. DIXON and F. J. MASSEY, *Introduction to Statistical Analysis* (New York: McGraw-Hill, 1957), Chapter 4.

J. M. HAMMERSLEY and D. C. HANDSCOMB, *Monte Carlo Methods* (New York: Wiley, 1964).

Chapter 3   Probability and Probability Distributions

S. H. HYMANS, *Probability Theory* (Englewood Cliffs, N.J.: Prentice-Hall, 1967), Chapters 1-4.

F. MOSTELLER, R. E. K. ROURKE, and G. B. THOMAS, *Probability with Statistical Applications* (Reading, Mass.: Addison-Wesley, 1961), Chapters 1-5.

J. E. Freund, *Mathematical Statistics* (Englewood Cliffs, N.J.: Prentice-Hall, 1962), Chapters 1-6.

A. M. MOOD and F. A. GRAYBILL, *Introduction to the Theory of Statistics*, 2nd ed. (New York: McGraw-Hill, 1963), Chapters 1-5.

E. PARZEN, *Modern Probability Theory and Its Applications* (New York: Wiley, 1960).

Chapter 4   Theoretical Derivation of Sampling Distributions

S. S. WILKS, *Elementary Statistical Analysis* (Princeton, N.J.: Princeton University Press, 1958), Chapter 9.

S. H. HYMANS, *Probability Theory* (Englewood Cliffs, N.J.: Prentice-Hall, 1967), Chapters 5 and 6.

W. A. WALLIS and H. V. ROBERTS, *Statistics: A New Approach* (London: Methuen, 1957), Chapter 11.

C. R. RAO, *Linear Statistical Inference and Its Applications* (New York: Wiley, 1965), Chapter 3.

M. G. KENDALL and A. STUART, *The Advanced Theory of Statistics*, Vol. I, 2nd ed. (New York: Hafner, 1963), Chapters 11–13.

Chapter 5   Tests of Hypotheses

W. A. WALLIS, and H. V. ROBERTS, *Statistics: A New Approach* (London: Methuen, 1957), Chapters 12 and 13.

J. E. FREUND, *Mathematical Statistics* (Englewood Cliffs, N.J.: Prentice-Hall, 1962), Chapters 11 and 12.

A. M. MOOD and F. A. GRAYBILL, *Introduction to the Theory of Statistics*, 2nd ed. (New York: McGraw-Hill, 1963), Chapter 12.

R. L. ANDERSON and T. A. BANCROFT, *Statistical Theory in Research* (New York: McGraw-Hill, 1952), Chapters 11 and 12.

E. L. LEHMANN, *Testing Statistical Hypotheses* (New York: Wiley, 1959).

Chapter 6   Estimation

S. H. HYMANS, *Probability Theory* (Englewood Cliffs, N.J.: Prentice-Hall, 1967), Chapter 7.

B. W. LINDGREN, *Statistical Theory* (New York: Macmillan, 1968), Chapter 5.

A. S. Goldberger, *Econometric Theory* (New York: Wiley, 1964), Chapter 3.

P. J. DHRYMES, *Econometrics*, (New York: Harper & Row, 1970), Chapter 3.

R. DEUTSCH, *Estimation Theory* (Englewood Cliffs, N.J.: Prentice-Hall, 1965).

Chapter 7   Simple Regression

J. JOHNSTON, *Econometric Methods* (New York: McGraw-Hill, 1963), Chapter 1.

A. S. Goldberger, *Topics in Regression Analysis* (New York: Macmillan, 1968), Chapters 1 and 2.

R. L. ANDERSON and T. A. BANCROFT, *Statistical Theory in Research* (New York: McGraw-Hill, 1952), Chapter 13.

A. M. MOOD and F. A. GRAYBILL, *Introduction to the Theory of Statistics*, 2nd ed. (New York: McGraw-Hill, 1963), Chapter 13.

E. MALINVAUD, *Statistical Methods of Econometrics* (Chicago: Rand McNally, 1966), Chapter 3.

Chapter 8   Violations of Basic Assumptions

8–1   Heteroskedasticity

J. JOHNSTON, *Econometric Methods* (New York: McGraw-Hill, 1963), Chapter 8, section 2.

E. J. KANE, *Economic Statistics and Econometrics* (New York: Harper & Row, 1968), Chapter 14.

H. C. RUTEMILLER and D. A. BOWERS, "Estimation in a Heteroskedastic Regression Model," *Journal of the American Statistical Association*, Vol. 63, June 1968, pp. 552–557.

S. M. GOLDFELD and R. F. QUANDT, "Some Tests for Homoscedasticity," *Journal of the American Statistical Association*, Vol. 60, September 1965, pp. 539–547.

8–2   Autoregressive Disturbances

J. JOHNSTON, *Econometric Methods* (New York: McGraw-Hill, 1963), Chapter 7.

E. MALINVAUD, *Statistical Methods of Econometrics* (Chicago: Rand McNally, 1966), Chapter 13.

C. F. CHRIST, *Econometric Models and Methods* (New York: Wiley, 1966), Chapter 9, section 13, and Chapter 10, section 4.

8–3   Stochastic Explanatory Variable

A. S. GOLDBERGER, *Econometric Theory* (New York: Wiley, 1964), Chapter 6.

Chapter 9   Estimation with Deficient Data

9–1   Errors of Measurement

J. JOHNSTON, *Econometric Methods* (New York: McGraw-Hill, 1963), Chapter 6.

E. MALINVAUD, *Statistical Methods of Econometrics* (Chicago: Rand McNally, 1966), Chapter 10.

M. G. KENDALL and A. STUART, *The Advanced Theory of Statistics*, Vol. II (London: Charles Griffin, 1961), Chapter 29.

M. HALPERIN, "Fitting of Straight Lines and Prediction When Both Variables Are Subject to Error," *Journal of the American Statistical Association*, Vol. 56, September 1961, pp. 657–669.

9–2   Estimation from Grouped Data

E. MALINVAUD, *Statistical Methods of Econometrics* (Chicago: Rand McNally, 1966), Chapter 8, section 2.

J. S. CRAMER, "Efficient Grouping, Regression and Correlation in Engel Curve Analysis," *Journal of the American Statistical Association*, Vol. 59, March 1964, pp. 233–250.

9-3   Estimation When Some Observations Are Missing

A. A. AFIFI and R. M. ELASHOFF, "Missing Observations in Multivariate Statistics II. Point Estimation in Simple Linear Regression," *Journal of the American Statistical Association*, Vol. 62, March 1967, pp. 10–29.

A. A. AFIFI and R. M. ELASHOFF, "Missing Observations in Multivariate Statistics III. Large Sample Analysis of Simple Linear Regression," *Journal of the American Statistical Association*, Vol. 64, March 1969, pp. 337–358.

A. A. AFIFI and R. M. ELASHOFF, "Missing Observations in Multivariate Statistics IV. A Note on Simple Linear Regression," *Journal of the American Statistical Association*, Vol. 64, March 1969, pp. 359–365.

Chapter 10   Multiple Regression

J. JOHNSTON, *Econometric Methods* (New York: McGraw-Hill, 1963), Chapters 2 and 4.

K. A. FOX, *Intermediate Economic Statistics* (New York: Wiley, 1968), Chapters 7 and 13.

A. S. GOLDBERGER, *Econometric Theory* (New York: Wiley, 1964), Chapter 4.

E. MALINVAUD, *Statistical Methods of Econometrics* (Chicago: Rand McNally, 1966), Chapter 6 and Chapter 8, section 5.

J. B. RAMSEY, "Tests for Specification Errors in Classical Linear Least-squares Regresssion Analysis," *Journal of the Royal Statistical Society*, Series B, Vol. 31, 1969, pp. 350–371.

Chapter 11   Formulation and Estimation of Special Models

11-1   Models with Binary Variables

J. JOHNSON, *Econometric Methods* (New York: McGraw-Hill, 1963), Chapter 8, section 4.

A. S. GOLDBERGER, *Econometric Theory* (New York: Wiley, 1964), Chapter 5, sections 2 and 3.

H. SCHEFFE, *The Analysis of Variance* (New York: Wiley, 1959).

11-2   Models with Restricted Coefficients

A. S. GOLDBERGER, *Econometric Theory* (New York: Wiley, 1964), Chapter 5, section 6.

L. G. JUDGE and T. TAKAYAMA, "Inequality Restrictions in Regression Analysis," *Journal of the American Statistical Association*, Vol. 61, March 1966, pp. 166–181.

H. THEIL and A. S. GOLDBERGER, "On Pure and Mixed Statistical Estimation in Econometrics," *International Econometric Review*, Vol. 2, January 1961, pp. 65–78.

11–3   Nonlinear Models

E. MALINVAUD, *Statistical Methods of Econometrics* (Chicago: Rand McNally, 1966), Chapter 9.

G. E. P. BOX and D. R. COX, "An Analysis of Transformations," *Journal of the Royal Statistical Society*, Series B, Vol. 26, 1964, pp. 211–243.

11–4   Distributed Lag Models

E. MALINVAUD, *Statistical Methods of Econometrics* (Chicago: Rand McNally, 1966), Chapter 15.

Z. GRILICHES, "Distributed Lags: A Survey," *Econometrica*, Vol. 35, January 1967, pp. 16–49.

A. ZELLNER and M. S. GEISEL, "Analysis of Distributed Lag Models with Applications to Consumption Function Estimation," paper presented to the European Meeting of the Econometric Society, Amsterdam, September 1968 (forthcoming in *Econometrica*).

Chapter 12   Generalized Linear Regression Model and Its Applications

12–1   Generalized Linear Regression Model

A. S. GOLDBERGER, *Econometric Theory* (New York: Wiley, 1964), Chapter 5, section 4.

J. JOHNSTON, *Econometric Methods* (New York: McGraw-Hill, 1963), Chapter 7, section 3.

12–2   Pooling of Cross-section and Time-Series Data

T. D. WALLACE and A. HUSSAIN, "The Use of Error Components Models in Combining Cross-Section with Time-Series Data," *Econometrica*, Vol. 37, January 1969, pp. 55–72.

P. BALESTRA and M. NERLOVE, "Pooling Cross-Section and Time-Series Data in the Estimation of a Dynamic Model: The Demand for Natural Gas," *Econometrica*, Vol. 34, July 1966, pp. 585–612.

12–3   Seemingly Unrelated Regressions

A. ZELLNER, "An Efficient Method of Estimating Seemingly Unrelated Regressions and Tests for Aggregation Bias," *Journal of the American Statistical Association*, Vol. 57, June 1962, pp. 348–368.

L. G. TELSER, "Iterative Estimation of a Set of Linear Regression Equations," *Journal of the American Statistical Association*, Vol. 59, September 1964, pp. 842–862.

J. KMENTA and R. F. GILBERT, "Small Sample Properties of Alternative Estimators of Seemingly Unrelated Regressions," *Journal of the American Statistical Association*, Vol. 63, December 1968, pp. 1180–1200.

R. W. PARKS, "Efficient Estimation of a System of Regression Equations When Distributions Are Both Serially and Contemporaneously Correlated," *Journal of the American Statistical Association*, Vol. 62, June 1967, pp. 500–509.

Chapter 13   Simultaneous Equation Systems

E. MALINVAUD, *Statistical Methods of Econometrics* (Chicago: Rand McNally, 1966), Chapters 16–18.

C. F. CHRIST, *Econometric Models and Methods* (New York: Wiley, 1966), Chapters 8 and 9.

F. M. FISHER, *The Identification Problem in Econometrics* (New York: McGraw-Hill, 1966).

A. S. GOLDBERGER, *Econometric Theory* (New York: Wiley, 1964), Chapter 7.

J. JOHNSTON, *Econometric Methods* (New York: McGraw-Hill, 1963), Chapters 9 and 10.

P. R. FISK, *Stochastically Dependent Equations* (New York: Hafner, 1967).

P. J. DHRYMES, *Econometrics* (New York: Harper & Row, 1970), Chapters 4 and 6–8.

13–6   Analysis of Dynamic Econometric Models

A. S. GOLDBERGER, *Impact Multipliers and Dynamic Properties of the Klein-Goldberger Model* (Amsterdam: North-Holland, 1959).

I. ADELMAN and F. L. ADELMAN, "The Dynamic Properties of the Klein-Goldberger Model," *Econometrica*, Vol. 27, October 1959, pp. 597–625.

L. R. KLEIN, M. K. Evans, and M. HARTLEY, *Econometric Gaming* (New York: Macmillan, 1969).

M. K. EVANS and L. R. KLEIN, *The Wharton Econometric Forecasting Model* (Philadelphia: University of Pennsylvania Press, 1967).

G. FROMM and P. TAUBMAN, *Policy Simulations with an Econometric Model* (Washington: The Brookings Institution, 1968).

H. THEIL and J. C. G. BOOT, "The Final Form of Econometric Equation Systems," *Review of the International Statistical Institute*, Vol. 30, 1962, pp. 136–152.

Appendix

B   Elements of Matrix Algebra

J. JOHNSTON, *Econometric Methods* (New York: McGraw-Hill, 1963), Chapter 3.

A. S. GOLDBERGER, *Econometric Theory* (New York: Wiley, 1964), Chapter 2.

G. Hadley, *Linear Algebra* (Reading, Mass.: Addison-Wesley, 1961).

C   Computational Design for Least Squares Estimation

R. L. ANDERSON and R. A. BANCROFT, *Statistical Theory in Research* (New York: McGraw-Hill, 1952), Chapter 15.

L. R. Klein, *Textbook of Econometrics* (Evanston, Ill.: Row, Peterson, 1953), Chapter 4.

P. S. DWYER, *Linear Computations* (New York: Wiley, 1951).

Index

Acceptance region, 116, 131–132

Adaptive expectation model, 474–476, 479–486

  see also Compound geometric lag

Addition theorem, 42

Adjustment coefficient, 476

Aitken's generalized least squares estimator, 504, 573–574, 576

Analysis of covariance, 420

Analysis of variance

  one-way, 413–415

  two-way, 416–418

  two-way with interactions, 419

Approximation formula

  for nonlinear functions, *see* Taylor expansion

  for variance of a nonlinear estimator, 444

Associative law, 33

Asymmetric response, 421–422

Asymptotic distribution, 162–164

Asymptotic efficiency, 167

Asymptotic mean, 164

Asymptotic unbiasedness, 164

Asymptotic variance, 164

  estimator of, 182

Attribute, 5

Augmented moments, 614, 615

Autocorrelated disturbances, *see* Autoregressive disturbances

Autocorrelation coefficient, 273

  maximum likelihood estimator, 284–285

  variance of maximum likelihood estimator, 285

Autoregressive disturbances, 269–297, 380, 501, 507

  best linear unbiased estimation of regression coefficients, 275, 282–283

  distributed lag models, 485–486, 487, 490–491

  Durbin's estimation method, 289

  first difference estimation method, 289–292

  generation of, 271–273

  iterative estimation method, 287–288

  maximum likelihood estimation, 284–285

  properties of least squares estimators, 273–282

  small sample properties of alternative estimators, 292–294

  tests for nonautoregression, 294–297

  two-stage estimation method, 288

  variances of least squares estimators, 276–278

  see also Simultaneous equation systems, estimation of equations with autoregressive disturbances

647

she looks in her last two chapters at legislation and at the observations of prominent Americans and travelers. A lengthy bibliography is included.

513   Berg, Barbara J. **The Remembered Gate: Origins of American Feminism: The Woman and the City, 1800-1860.** New York: Oxford University Press, 1978. 334p. bibliog. index. $14.95. ISBN 0195022807. LC 76-51709.

Berg argues that historians have failed to understand the true origins of American feminism, largely because of their tendency to equate "feminism" with "women's rights," and with suffrage in particular. This equation has generated the familiar account of the rise of the nineteenth-century women's movement out of abolition-ism: women active in the fight against slavery came to compare their own lack of rights with the oppressed status of black people. Defining feminism in much broader terms than women's rights (for example, as "the freedom to decide her own destiny"), Berg finds the origins of American feminism in the female volun-tary associations that flourished in urban areas after 1800 and in the experiences and consciousness of the women active in these associations. Feminist awareness is thus seen as an outgrowth of the change in women's status that accompanied the transition from a rural, colonial America to an increasingly urban and industrial society. Berg bases her thesis on such materials as diaries, public records, songs, novels, and sermons, in addition to more conventional sources.

514   Bloomer, Dexter C., 1820-1900. **Life and Writings of Amelia Bloomer.** New York: Schocken Books, 1975. 387p. bibliog. $3.95. ISBN 0805204830. LC 74-26848.

Originally published in 1895, "the book reprinted here, *The Life and Writings of Amelia Bloomer*, written after her death by her husband, Dexter C. Bloomer, reflects the concerns and origins of the antebellum reformers" (from S. J. Kleinberg's introduction). Editor of *The Lily*, a forum for women writing on the issues of temperance, women's rights, fashion reform, and abolition, Bloomer defended the Bloomer costume, which consisted of Turkish pantaloons and a knee length dress. Considering that in the 1850s women wore voluminous skirts and petticoats weighing up to fifteen pounds, it is no wonder that the dress reform issue received much attention, especially in the West and Northwest, where women did much active work. Kleinberg says in her introduction: "the significance of the *Life and Writings of Amelia Bloomer* lies both in the nature of Bloomer's participation in the reform movements of her day and in her typicality.... Bloomer publicized the thoughts of her more famous co-workers as well as her own feelings on reform issues." Amelia Bloomer could be rather forceful in her editorializing concerning the necessity of women to participate actively in the great moral and social issues of the day: "We deny that it is woman's duty to love and obey her husband unless he prove himself worthy of her love and unless his requirements are just and reasonable." She spoke out for prohibition of liquor, bloomers, women mechanics, sewing machines, and women typesetters, against bigoted clergymen and women drunkards, and gave her opinions on a host of other issues related to the emancipation of women and temperance.

515   Blumenthal, Walter Hart, 1883-1969. **Brides from Bridewell: Female Felons Sent to Colonial America.** Rutland, VT: Charles E. Tuttle, 1962; repr. Westport, CT: Greenwood Press, 1973. 139p. bibliog. $9.25. ISBN 0837169240. LC 73-7307.

" . . . from the first sending of female felons to the trans-Atlantic colonies in 1619, to the end of the last shipment to Australia in 1868, more than 33,000 women prisoners were expelled by Great Britain." Blumenthal's intention is to fill in this little-known history of one way in which the "New World" was colonized. Men and women both were deported (often as a mitigation of the death sentence) for minor crimes (e.g., forgery or shoplifting) or merely for the crime of dissent, poverty, or being of "objectionable character." Others were kidnapped, while large numbers of Irish men and women were shipped under the duress of political, economic, and religious oppression. Conditions during the voyages would appear almost to have rivaled those prevailing on the earlier slave ships from Africa, mortality being high and arrival promising only various forms of bondage. Blumenthal writes in a readable, if rather quaint, style.

516   Blumenthal, Walter Hart, 1883-1969. **Women Camp Followers of the American Revolution.** Philadelphia, PA: G. S. MacManus, 1952; repr. New York: Arno Press, 1974. 104p. bibliog. $9.50. ISBN 0405060777. LC 74-3931.

"What of the women behind the men at Valley Forge? Walter H. Blumenthal has combed through records of orderlies, expense and ration accounts, and other primary sources preserved from the time of the American Revolution. He has gathered together the bits of information, the revealing written notes, the entries in diaries and bulletins that together create a picture that touches the heart and reprimands history. There were women on both sides of the conflict that followed the men into bloody battle lines and bitter winter weather. Some were drawn by love, others by hunger . . . " ("A Note about This Volume," A. K. Baxter and L. Stein, eds.).

517   Boulding, Elise. **The Underside of History: A View of Women through Time.** Boulder, CO: Westview Press, 1976. 829p. bibliog. index. $24.75. ISBN 0891580093. LC 75-30558.

Boulding brings a unique feel for history to this enormous undertaking. Her introduction is instructive and compelling for its attention to the problems that all women's studies scholars face in selecting and ordering facts and names out of what appears to be a tangled jungle of sources in order to be able to write a macrohistory. The approach in this massive work is to examine the "underlife" concepts inherent in the roles of women: "since differentiation between men's and women's spaces are found in all societies, the underlife concept becomes crucial to an analysis of women's roles." Boulding gives us what she calls "my personal 'sociological' walk through history and accounts of the activities of the women I have seen there," beginning with the Paleolithic period and pre-history, moving into "Women as Civilizers" (from 2000 to 200 B.C.), and concluding with "The Emergence of Women from the Renaissance: 1450 to 1900." Her tables, including such diverse information as "Types of Scholarly and Literary Publications by Years of Christine de Pisan" to "Number of Women on the Professional Staff of the United Nations and Related Agencies," along with chapter bibliographies, make this an essential beginning point for students looking for an overview of women's history.

518 Boyer, Paul S., and Stephen Nissenbaum. **Salem Possessed: The Social Origins of Witchcraft.** Cambridge, MA: Harvard University Press, 1974. 231p. bibliog. index. $14.00. ISBN 0677785258. LC 73-84399.

Boyer and Nissenbaum approach the Salem witch trials by examining the social realities of late seventeenth-century Western culture—vying men eager for real estate and power, which caused great psychological slashings in the fabric of Salem society. They see the social struggle in terms of a peasant-based economy's being overturned by a capitalist mercantile economy, so their analysis is understandably caught up in the examination of real estate transactions, wills and estate settlements, genealogies, house and property locations of witnesses, and networks of special interest groups. In this analysis, women, who were the accused and the passive victims, are mainly left out, except as they figure into kinship patterns and marriage ties. As creative as the approach is in this study of cause and effect, it never addresses the Puritan belief system, which singled out women as the target for persecution in this war among male property and mercantile interests. The maps, charts, and genealogies are fascinating.

519 Bridenthal, Renate, and Claudia Koonz, eds. **Becoming Visible: Women in European History.** Boston: Houghton Mifflin, 1977. 510p. bibliog. index. $6.95. ISBN 0395244773. LC 76-11978.

Geared to a college audience, this collection of articles comes out of the important and innovative work currently being done by feminist historians with the aim not just of filling in the gaps in historical data on women, but of exploring how feminist perspectives in history alter those basic historical conceptions and categories long taken for granted. The collection has a very broad historical and geographical scope and is organized chronologically. A basic unifying theme is the hope shared by the authors "to destroy simplistic notions about women's passivity or activity, progress or regress. Women must be seen within the complexity of their specific cultural contexts." Among the articles are: "Women in Egalitarian Societies," by Eleanor Leacock; "Did Women Have a Renaissance?," by Joan Kelly-Gadol; "Loaves and Liberty: Women in the French Revolution," by Ruth Graham; "The Long Road Home: Women's Work and Industrialization," by Theresa M. McBride; and "Mothers in the Fatherland: Women in Nazi Germany," by Claudia Koonz.

520 Brown, Dee Alexander. **The Gentle Tamers: Women of the Old Wild West.** New York: Bantam Books, 1974. 295p. bibliog. index. $1.25. ISBN 0553103164.

This history of pioneer women is full of anecdotes about the difficult conditions in the West and the strong women who ventured out there. Brown discusses the arduous situations that awaited them, the shortage of women and consequent prostitution and importation of women, the various kinds of work that women did, and the struggles of frontier women for equality. Slight drawbacks to the book are its "cute" tone and Brown's dubious thesis that it was women rather than history that "tamed" the "Wild West."

521* Buhle, Mari Jo, 1943- . **Feminism and Socialism in the United States,
1820-1920.** Madison: University of Wisconsin, Ph.D. dissertation,
1974; Ann Arbor, MI: University Microfilms, 1974. 407p. 1 reel.
bibliog.

Mari Jo Buhle is well respected as one of the important feminist historians to
come out of the contemporary women's movement. Best known for her contribution to *Women in American Society* (1972; written with Ann D. Gordon and
Nancy E. Schrom) and her article, "Women and the Socialist Party of America,
1901-1914" (in E. Altbach, *From Feminism to Liberation,* 1971), Buhle brings
the perspective and material of these writings and more together in her thesis
on feminism and socialism in the U.S. from 1820 to 1920. Chapter headings
are as follows: Prologue: Utopian Socialism and Woman's Equality; Woman's
Rights and the First International in America; Feminism and Socialism in
Transition, 1880's and 1890's; Women's Organization: Socialist Party of America,
1901-1908; The Woman's National Committee; Conversion and Education: The
Feminist Message of Socialism; The Politics of Woman Suffrage; The Politics
of Sexual Liberation; The Demise of the Woman's National Committee and the
End of Women's Organization.

522 Bullough, Vern L. **Sexual Variance in Society and History.** New York:
Wiley, 1976. 715p. bibliog. index. $26.50. ISBN 0471120804. LC
75-38911.

Bullough attempts to construct "a history of attitudes toward sex and their
relationship to certain forms of stigmatized sexual behavior, primarily homosexuality. . . . " Also discussed in less detail are masturbation, transvestism,
transsexualism, bestiality, celibacy, incest, rape, adultery, eunuchism, pornography, phallicism, sadism, masochism, and fetishism. As was the case with
his 1973 book, *The Subordinate Sex,* Bullough's approach here is so ambitious—
looking as he does to the whole of "Western Culture," with comparative glances
at Islamic, Indian and Chinese culture—that the treatment must necessarily be
superficial. Nonetheless, given the scant treatment of the subject of sexuality
by most historians, this survey will be of some value. Readers might also want
to consult Jonathan Katz's *Gay American History* (1976), which works at
developing a history of homosexuality (specifically in the United States),
primarily from the viewpoint of homosexuals themselves.

523 Bullough, Vern L. **The Subordinate Sex: A History of Attitudes Toward
Women.** Urbana: University of Illinois Press, 1973. 375p. bibliog.
$10.95. ISBN 0252003209. LC 72-91079.

As a history of (primarily men's) attitudes toward women the world over and
throughout the ages, this book is necessarily superficial, and depressing as well.
Beginning with the Judeo-Christian roots of Western attitudes, Bullough moves
on to discuss ancient Rome, Byzantium, Islamic culture, China, India and the
contemporary United States. Also included are a final chapter by Bonnie Bullough
("Some Questions about the Past and the Future") and a guide to further reading.

524 Bullough, Vern L., and Bonnie L. Bullough. **Prostitution: An Illustrated Social History.** New York: Crown, 1978. 352p. bibliog. index.
$14.95. ISBN 0517529572. LC 78-1842.

Prostitution is receiving greater scholarly attention as it becomes recognized as a major societal paradigm of male dominance (male prostitution is negligible historically and contemporarily). The Bulloughs demonstrate encyclopedic knowledge of their subject (see also their *Bibliography of Prostitution*; Garland, 1977); they maneuver dazzlingly through the history of prostitution as it has operated for many reasons in diverse cultures, under its many names and variations. Thoroughly conversant with the legal, medical, social, and religious aspects, the Bulloughs have not missed "a trick" from the Tigris-Euphrates valley to Las Vegas, Nevada. And they provide an extraordinarily rich bibliography, thick with esoteric sources. Only one problem: in knowing their material so well, they become skillful raconteurs of colorful prostitution vignettes, polished peddlers of tall tales of sexual excess. In this stockpiling of sexual anecdotes, even given their acknowledgement of the double-standard in the creation and control of prostitution, one senses that the Bulloughs occasionally lose perspective, even miss the point. Still, the comprehensiveness of their volume makes it essential for all types of libraries.

525   Butler, Elizabeth Beardsley. **Women and the Trades.** New York: Arno Press, 1969. (Repr. of 1909 ed.). 440p. bibliog. index. $18.00. ISBN 0405021089. LC 70-89757.

Women and the Trades was originally published in 1909 as volume 1 of *The Pittsburgh Survey*, intended to be a "fairly comprehensive study of the conditions under which working people live and labor in a great industrial city." Butler's work describes the conditions in the manufacturing and mercantile industries in which the majority of the employees were women: food production (canning, cracker, and confectionary industries); the stogy industry (cigar-making); the needle trades; the cleaning industries; metals, lamps, and glass; the commercial trades (printing, telephone and telegraph, mercantile houses); and miscellaneous trades (broom, brush, and paper box making; caskets, cork, paint, soap, trunks). In addition, there is a chapter on the social life of working women in and outside the factories and another that summarizes industrial conditions (wages, hours, and health). Connie Pohl writes in a review of the study (in *American Labor History: Women in the Working Class*), "what emerges is a uniformly appalling picture of women's work: long, exhausting hours spent performing painfully monotonous tasks in crowded, dirty workrooms for subsistence wages." Of particular interest is the evidence Butler presents on hierarchical divisions within and between the trades along lines of race, nationality, and sex—divisions particularly sharp in this period of successive waves of immigration.

526   Campbell, Helen (Stuart), 1839-1918. **Women Wage-Earners.** New York: Arno Press, 1972. (Repr. of 1893 ed.). 313p. bibliog. index. $15.00. ISBN 0405044518. LC 72-2594.

This study, first published in 1893, of women's wage labor in England, Europe, and the United States from the emergence of the factory system to the late nineteenth century was written by Helen Stuart Campbell, author of children's and popular fiction and studies in home economics, and respected authority on life in the slums. *Women Wage-Earners* discusses women's work in the colonial period and during the early days of the factory system, the rise and growth of trades through the nineteenth century, labor bureaus and their work in relation to women, wage rates in the U.S. at the time of Campbell's writing, general conditions for women workers in England, Europe, and the U.S. (with particular attention to the western states), abuses in factory life and in general trades, and remedies and suggestions. The appendix includes the Factory Inspection Law of 1886 of New York State, a bibliography of Campbell's sources for this book, and a bibliography of German, French, and English-language sources on woman's labor and "the woman question." Responsibly researched, *Women Wage-Earners* also appears to be well written and to reflect the sensitivity of a woman acutely aware of the oppression of workers, and of women workers in particular. Interested readers may also want to look at Campbell's earlier work, *Prisoners of Poverty*, a study of conditions of women workers in the needle trades and department stores of New York City (1887; repr. Greenwood Press, 1970).

527   Cantor, Milton, and Bruce Laurie, eds. **Class, Sex, and the Woman Worker.** Westport, CT: Greenwood Press, 1977. 253p. bibliog. index. $14.95. ISBN 0837190320. LC 76-15304.

This is a group of significant essays in women's history, almost all of which were originally prepared as papers for various conferences but are now made more easily accessible in book form: Introduction, by Caroline F. Ware; "The Systematic Study of Urban Women," by Susan J. Kleinberg; "Women, Work, and Protest in the Early Lowell Mills," by Thomas Dublin; "Hearts to Feel and Tongues to Speak: New England Mill Women in the Early Nineteenth Century," by Lise Vogel; " 'She Earns as a Child; She Pays as a Man': Women Workers in a Mid-Nineteenth-Century New York City Community," by Carol Groneman; "Italian Women and Work," by Virginia Yans-McLaughlin; "Italian-American Women in New York City, 1900-1950: Work and School," by Miriam Cohen; "Organizing the Unorganizable: Three Jewish Women and Their Union," by Alice Kessler-Harris; "Imperfect Unions: Class and Gender in Cripple Creek, 1894-1904," by Elizabeth Jameson; "The Women's Trade Union League and American Feminism," by Robin Miller Jacoby; "Creating a Feminist Alliance: Sisterhood and Class Conflict in the New York Women's Trade Union League, 1903-1914," by Nancy Schrom Dye.

528   Carroll, Berenice A., ed. **Liberating Women's History: Theoretical and Critical Essays.** Urbana: University of Illinois Press, 1976. 434p. bibliog. $14.95. ISBN 0252004418. LC 75-45451.

"The essays in this volume fall broadly into two categories: essays of critical historiography which raise general questions of theory and conceptualization in the field; and case studies or surveys which are primarily empirical in character, but in which the authors suggest, explore, or illustrate some theoretical questions or models" (from the preface). Part 1, "On the Historiography of Women," engages for the most part in a critique of past work in women's history, while in part 4, "Toward a Future Human Past," the authors are concerned with current questions of theory and new approaches to research. The empirical studies in part 2, "On Ideology, Sex, and History," tend to emphasize the influence of ideology, attitudes, tradition, or consciousness on the position of women; while in part 3, "On Class, Sex, and Social Change," the emphasis is on questions of class structure and relations. Among the contributors represented here are Linda Gordon, Mari Jo Buhle, Robin Miller Jacoby, Ann M. Pescatello, Joyce A. Ladner, Sarah B. Pomeroy, Renate Bridenthal and Claudia Koonz (editors of another anthology of women's history articles, *Becoming Visible*), Alice Kessler-Harris, Gerda Lerner and Juliet Mitchell. This represents a valuable contribution to the new field of women's history.

529   Chafe, William Henry. **The American Woman: Her Changing Social, Economic, and Political Roles, 1920-1970.** New York: Oxford University Press, 1974. 351p. bibliog. index. $3.95. ISBN 0195017854. LC 74-161886.

Chafe is interested in the frequently advanced argument of contemporary feminists that the achievement of woman suffrage was not the achievement of women's liberation and that little has, in fact, changed since 1920. His aim is to test this argument against an examination of the historical evidence for the period, and to explore the nature of the changes that did actually take place in sexual relations. A key focus is the sexual division of labor, which he takes as the structural basis of sexual inequality; within this framework, women's paid labor receives particular attention. This is based on the author's Ph.D. dissertation at Columbia University.

530   Chafe, William Henry. **Women and Equality: Changing Patterns in American Culture.** New York: Oxford University Press, 1977. 207p. bibliog. index. $8.95. ISBN 0195021584. LC 76-42639.

Chafe tells us in his preface that, "women's history can provide a unique angle of vision on how society functions and how various groups within it succeed or fail to achieve control over their own lives." The introductory essay, "Women's History: Problems of Definition and Approach," is important for its identification of the significant problems and issues that emerge in a historical analysis of women's experience. Other chapters grow out of this essay: An Historical Overview; Sex and Race: The Analogy of Social Control; Sex and Race: The Analogy of Social Change; Feminism in the 1970's: An Historical Perspective; and Where Do We Go from Here? Reflections on Equality Between the Sexes.

531   Clark, Alice. **Working Life of Women in the Seventeenth Century.** New York: A. M. Kelley, 1968. (Repr. of 1919 ed.). 328p. bibliog. index. $12.50. ISBN 0678050392. LC 67-31558.

Contemporary feminist historians acknowledge a profound debt to Alice Clark's study, first published in 1919, *Working Life of Women in the Seventeenth Century*. Clark chose to focus on seventeenth-century England because this was a period of transition in the pattern of production—from domestic industry (exclusively for family use) to family industry (for exchange) to capitalist industry and wage labor. She examines these changes to learn what impact they had on women's participation in production, women's status, and family organization. Her analysis provides a foundation for understanding the historicity of women's oppression as we know it today—in particular, how the usurpation of production (which had traditionally occurred in the home) by the factory system created a geographic and economic split between work and home that led to the deterioration of women's productive roles and to their narrow identification with family.

532   Conrad, Susan Phinney. **Perish the Thought: Intellectual Women in Romantic America, 1830-1860.** New York: Oxford University Press, 1976. 292p. bibliog. index. $12.95. ISBN 0195019954. LC 75-25463.

This volume concentrates only on women who made important contributions to American social thought during the nineteenth-century romantic revolution, which emphasized new and unique forms of personal and cultural identity and a quest after knowledge for its own sake. Conrad defines intellectual women between 1830 and 1860 as a distinct group, drawn from the daughters of professional men, who emulated the intellectual efforts of their fathers while being denied entry into their fathers' professions. Catharine Beecher, Sarah Hale, Harriet Martineau, Elizabeth Oakes Smith, Margaret Fuller, and Sarah Moore Grimké figure priminently among the women discussed here.

533   Cott, Nancy F. **The Bonds of Womanhood: "Woman's Sphere" in New England, 1780-1835.** New Haven: Yale University Press, 1977. 225p. bibliog. index. $12.50. ISBN 0300020236. LC 76-49728.

Cott began her research for this book hoping to gain an understanding of "how a certain congeries of social attitudes that has been called the 'cult of true womanhood' and the 'cult of domesticity,' and first became conspicuous in the early nineteenth century, related to women's actual circumstances, experiences, and consciousness. . . . It made sense, then, to look at the years before 1830, to find out what had happened that might clarify the reception of or the need for a 'cult' of domesticity." With these goals in mind, Cott turned to women's personal documents (letters and diaries) in preference to prescriptive works, eventually concentrating on 100 New England women of middle-class or upper-middle-class background. She discusses work, domesticity, education, religion, sisterhood, and the relation between "woman's sphere" and feminism. With regard to the last, Cott is particularly interested in the contradictory nature of "woman's sphere"–as a sphere of confinement and oppression, as an ideological construct utilized by feminists themselves to argue their cause, and as the concrete basis for a subculture and sisterhood among women.

534   Cott, Nancy F., comp. **Root of Bitterness: Documents of the Social History of American Women.** New York: E. P. Dutton, 1972. 373p. bibliog. $5.45. ISBN 0525473289. LC 72-194870.

This is an important collection of primary-source documents on the history of American women from colonial times to the beginning of the twentieth century. The materials include women's autobiographical narratives, diaries and letters, court transcripts, industrial and institutional reports, tracts, sermons, stories, and so on. The unifying theme is "the consciousness and self-consciousness of American women." Nancy Cott (the compiler) has written a helpful introduction, gives brief comments on each selection, and provides a bibliography for further reading. The reader might also want to consult the more recent collection of primary-source material, *America's Working Women* (edited by R. Baxandall, et al.); the Baxandall collection concentrates primarily on women's work experiences and will help fill out the section in the Cott reader, "Industrialization and Women's Work."

535*   Crow, Duncan. **The Victorian Woman.** New York: Stein and Day,
        1972. 351p. bibliog. index. ISBN 0812814479. LC 74-185885.
Crow profiles the Victorian period (1837-1901) with specific reference to women
both in Britain and the United States, deliberately avoiding generalizations
about *all* Victorian women by looking at a broad sweep of women's lives.
Governesses, seamstresses, nail-makers and mill-girls were characteristic Victorian
types, but so were individual women of the ilk of Florence Nightengale, Elizabeth
Blackwell, and Beatrice Webb.

536   Davis, Rebecca (Harding), 1831-1910. **Life in the Iron Mills: Or, The
        Korl Woman.** Old Westbury, NY: Feminist Press, 1972. 174p. $3.25.
        ISBN 0912670053. LC 72-8880.
Life in the Iron Mills was first published in the *Atlantic Monthly*, April 1861.
This edition offers a biographical interpretation by Tillie Olsen, who sketches
the life of the thirty-year-old Rebecca Harding, who wrote *Life* and was unwittingly
"a social historian invaluable for an understanding access to her time." Though
Harding lived a privileged life in Wheeling, West Virginia, she identified strongly
with the inhuman conditions that mill workers experienced and wrote penetratingly of this world in which she could not have participated. What emerges is
neither fiction, nor journalism, nor poetry, but a synthesis of all of these filtered
through her powers of observation, intellect, and imagination.

537   Demos, John. **A Little Commonwealth: Family Life in Plymouth Colony.**
        New York: Oxford University Press, 1970. 201p. bibliog. index. $7.95.
        ISBN 0195005287. LC 75-83040.
This case-study in the social history of early American family life attempts to
reconstruct the existence of the "average" family in Plymouth Colony from the
paltry available data—physical artifacts, wills and inventories, official records,
and literary materials. The discussion is organized topically: housing, clothing,
furnishings, membership in the houshold, husbands and wives, parents and children,
masters and servants, infancy and childhood, aging, and a concluding section on
the family in comparative perspective. Demos touches upon a number of questions about male/female relations in marriage, including authority, relative status,
property rights, parenthood, economic roles, sexual relations and adultery, and
divorce.

538   De Pauw, Linda Grant, and Conover Hunt. **Remember the Ladies:
        Women in America 1750-1815.** New York: Viking Press, 1976. 168p.
        bibliog. $16.95. ISBN 0670593621. LC 76-14477.
This book is largely based on an exhibition documenting the lives and achievements of women in the era of the American Revolution. It is a period of particular interest for women's history not just because it coincides with the Revolutionary War, but because of the contrast it provides to the more familiar period
of industrialization. Among the topics discussed in this book are love and
marriage, motherhood, work, war, slavery, and art. The volume is beautifully
illustrated throughout with photographs, paintings, and graphics. It should
be noted that the book is more a catalog of an exhibition than an indepth
historical analysis.

539   Dexter, Elisabeth Williams (Anthony), 1887- . **Career Women of America, 1776-1840.** Clifton, NJ: A. M. Kelley, 1972. (Repr. of 1950 ed.). 262p. bibliog. index. $12.50. ISBN 0678035687. LC 77-153179.

This study (originally published in 1950) continues the history of women and work in America begun by Dexter in her *Colonial Women of Affairs* (originally 1931; reprint 1972). In addition to a continuation of her discussions of specific occupations—among them, teaching, midwifery, writing, tavern keeping, store keeping, and sewing—Dexter presents observations on changes in attitudes toward women's labor from the eighteenth to the nineteenth centuries: the nineteenth century found a larger proportion of women working outside the home than in colonial times, but—paradoxically—a social climate of increasing disapproval for these activities and a steadily developing ideology of "woman's place."

540   Dexter, Elisabeth Williams (Anthony), 1887- . **Colonial Women of Affairs: Women in Business and the Professions in America Before 1776.** Boston: Houghton Mifflin, 1931; repr. New York: A. M. Kelley, 1972. 223p. bibliog. $12.50. ISBN 0678035695. LC 71-153180.

Dexter refutes the notion that colonial women were not businesswomen. Her method is to mine newspaper sources of the mid-1770s for advertisements and articles giving evidence of the socially accepted business roles that women played in colonial America. Chief among the business interests of women were tavern keeping, teaching, midwifery, land management, writing and printing, and merchandising. She has some very interesting insights into Anne Bradstreet's work in her chapter "With Tongue, Pen, and Printer's Ink." Her conclusion points to the fact that, on the whole, colonial men accorded women of the day honor and respect for their endeavors. The references to eighteenth and early nineteenth-century sources on colonial women and their place in America's economic history will be particularly useful. Readers will want to consult Dexter's *Career Women of America, 1776-1840*, which continues the history begun in her *Colonial Women*.

541   Duniway, Abigail (Scott), 1834-1915. **Path Breaking: An Autobiographical History of the Equal Suffrage Movement in Pacific Coast States.** (2nd ed.). New York: Schocken Books, 1971. 297p. $4.50. ISBN 0805203222. LC 79-162285.

Modesty is not a strong suit of Abigail Duniway, a leading suffragist of her time, and as she proclaims, "the original advocate and leader of the Equal Suffrage Movement in the Pacific Northwest." But then Duniway did not attempt modest tasks. A pioneer conditioned by childhood to the endless drudgery of woman's life on the farm, farmwife, founder and mistress of a school, businesswoman, public speaker, newspaper editor—Abigail Duniway displayed enormous energy and audacity in all of her projects. Her brisk narration of the events leading up to Oregon's vote for women's suffrage is consistently interesting. A savvy political strategist, Duniway recognized early on the problems that blurring the prohibition issue with the suffrage issue would cause in women's winning the right to vote. Duniway's story is fascinating reading for its history of suffrage, and also for the details that the author has selected about life on the farm, the general lot of women in the Pacific Northwest, and the stamina and will of a woman who championed individual liberty.

542   Eisler, Benita, ed. **The Lowell Offering: Writings by New England Mill Women (1840-1845).** Philadelphia, PA: Lippincott, 1977. 233p. bibliog. $12.95. ISBN 039701225X. LC 77-24986.

The women factory workers of the textile mills in Lowell, Massachusetts, have been a frequent focus for historical investigation for a variety of reasons. First, the history of their recruitment and integration into factory work provides a case study in how an industrial labor force was created out of a rural population in the United States. Second, the Lowell factories were touted as "model" workplaces, featuring attractive and airy mills, decent boarding facilities, religious facilities, etc. (though the women were working twelve to fourteen hours a day). Third, the women somehow found time to produce remarkable writings for their literary magazine, the *Lowell Offering*, which attracted international acclaim. Finally, the mill workforce was more than three-fourths women, at a time when factory work for women was considered controversial. It is of course this last factor that has made the Lowell factories an important topic for the new women's history, and the renewed interest has resulted in the publication of new studies on the topic as well as the reissuing of works long out of print. Eisler has done the great service of bringing together in accessible book form a collection of representative writings from the *Lowell Offering*, together with her own introduction and commentary, all of it illustrated with a series of interesting graphics. The letters, stories, essays, and sketches address the following topics: Mill and Boarding House: The New Community; Continuing Education: "A Glimpse of Something Grand Before Us"; Looking Back: Nature, Family, and Childhood; Choice and Conflict: The Cost of Independence; Caste and Class: Mill Job or Marriage; and Changes: Reform, Regret, and a Vision of the Future. A complete reprint of the *Lowell Offering* is also available from Greenwood Press, both in print and microfiche editions. Readers will also want to be aware of the recently reprinted editions of Lucy Larcom's *A New England Girlhood* (1889; reprint Peter Smith, 1973) and Harriet Robinson's *Loom and Spindle* (1898; reprint Press Pacifica, 1976). Finally, Philip Foner's recent anthology, *The Factory Girls* (1977), is of particular relevance, as it brings together little-known writings by militant factory women who saw the *Lowell Offering* as a company organ and the women who wrote for it as "the genteel factory girls."

543   Ferrero, Guglielmo, 1871- . **The Women of the Caesars.** Albuquerque, NM: American Classical College Press, 1977. $22.50. ISBN 0892660376.

Originally published in 1915, this study begins with a discussion of the legal and economic independence of Roman women during the last century of the Republic. Ferrero attempts to disentangle certain romantic legends that adhere to the names of these Roman women. The author takes a moderate view of history, seeking to find rational causes for the sometimes shocking behavior of these Roman women. He attempts to demythologize at every point. The illustrations are particularly fine. Chapters center on the marital role of women in ancient Rome.

544   Filene, Peter Gabriel. **Him/Her/Self: Sex Roles in Modern America.**
New York: Harcourt Brace Jovanovich, 1975. 351p. bibliog. index.
$10.00. ISBN 0151402701. LC 74-23153.

Filene has set out to answer three major questions concerning the evolution in
sex roles in modern America (1890-1974): "How have middle-class men and
women defined themselves during the eighty-five years from the late Victorian
era to the present? Why have these definitions changed? What psychological
and intellectual dilemmas have people undergone, and perhaps resolved, as they
try to find satisfactory roles?" Filene's book is a long and graceful essay that
relies heavily on theoretical premises of post-Freudians such as Kenneth Keniston,
Gordon Allport, and Robert W. White. People seek definition by controlling
their environment, by becoming "competent," asserts Filene. In modern American
culture, "competence" for women meant home and family; for man, job or
career. The notion of separate spheres of "competence" needs to be altered.
Major sections of this essay are: The End of the Victorian Era (1890-1910),
The Modern Era (1920-1974). One specific feature, which separates this book
from other general historical studies of American sex roles, is Filene's thorough
"Essay on Research," in which he explains his search through quantities of
materials: periodicals and newspapers; public opinion polls; personal histories;
fictional histories; general histories of men, women, education, employment,
sexuality, and the family; and social psychology. His notes are very detailed as
well.

545   Flexner, Eleanor, 1908- . **Century of Struggle: The Woman's Rights
Movement in the United States.** (rev. ed.). Cambridge, MA: Belknap
Press of Harvard University Press, 1975. 405p. bibliog. index. $15.00.
ISBN 0674106512. LC 74-34542.

This book was originally published in 1959, when, as Flexner writes in her
preface to the new edition, "there was almost no interest in the past history
of women or their current situation." A decade later came the "new wave"
of feminism; Flexner's classic history of the "first wave" was rediscovered, and
today it continues to be a key source on the nineteenth-century woman's
movement. Apart from Flexner's meticulous research and documentation, the
chief merit of the book is the way it situates the history of the suffrage movement within a broader framework of the social history of the period. Thus,
she discusses not only the fight for the vote, but also the connections and the
tensions between this struggle and other reform movements (abolitionism, the
labor movement, the struggle for women's education, and general social currents
of the time). Her next-to-last chapter, "Who Opposed Woman Suffrage?,"
is especially valuable for the way in which it lifts anti-feminism out of the realm
of the psychological, analyzing the social and economic forces that made (and
continue to make) opposition to women's demands a formidable obstacle.

546   Foner, Philip Sheldon, 1910- , ed. **The Factory Girls: A Collection of
Writings on Life and Struggles in the New England Factories of the
1840's.** By the factory girls themselves, and the story, in their own
words, of the first trade unions of women workers in the United
States. Urbana: University of Illinois Press, 1977. 360p. bibliog. index.
$10.00. ISBN 0252004221. LC 77-22410.

The women factory workers of the textile mills in Lowell, Massachusetts, have
been a frequent focus for historical investigation for a variety of reasons. (See
the annotation for Eisler, Benita, in this section.) However, as Foner points
out in his preface, the recent reprints (e.g., Eisler's the *Lowell Offering*, 1977;
Lucy Larcom's *A New England Girlhood*, 1889, reprint Peter Smith, 1973; and
Harriet Robinson's *Loom and Spindle*, 1898, reprint Press Pacifica, 1976) all
emphasize the experimental and progressive aspects of Lowell history and the
Lowell Offering, neglecting the history of conflict and the increasingly oppressive
conditions which emerged in the mills. Foner seeks to balance the prevailing
perspective with this anthology of little-known writings by more militant factory
workers who repudiated the *Lowell Offering* as a company organ, saw its
contributors as "the genteel factory girls," and produced their own magazines
and periodicals in which to express their discontent.

547   Friedman, Jean E., and William G. Shade, comps. **Our American Sisters:
       Women in American Life and Thought.** (2nd ed.). Boston: Allyn and
       Bacon, 1976. 446p. bibliog. $8.50. ISBN 0205055788. LC 76-21252.
With the purpose of providing a wide range of materials written by noted
scholars on woman's place in American life, Friedman has chosen articles "both
for their historic merit and their general readability." Among the essays: Gerda
Lerner, "The Lady and the Mill Girl: Changes in the Status of Women in the
Age of Jackson"; Barbara Welter, "The Cult of True Womanhood: 1820-1860";
Christopher Lasch, "Woman as Alien"; Carl N. Degler, "Charlotte Perkins Gilman
on the Theory and Practice of Feminism"; Aileen S. Kraditor, "Women Suffrage
in Perspective"; Pauli Murray, "The Liberation of Black Women."

548*   Fryer, Peter. **The Birth Controllers.** New York: Stein and Day, 1966.
       384p. bibliog. index. LC 66-17152.
Fryer writes an account of those he considers to be the chief pioneers of birth
control—their activities, their conception of birth control, the contraceptive
methods they taught, and the opposition they faced. Part I, "The Prehistory
of Birth Control," tells of pioneers pre-dating the 1823 handbill campaign of
Francis Place, "Britain's first birth control propagandist" ("these were the
teachers of primitive techniques mingling magic and science . . . "). Part II,
"The Tailor and the Tinsmith," discusses Place and Richard Carlile and their
birth control propaganda in the 1820s. Part III, "The Rise of Neo-Malthusianism,"
gives accounts of Robert Dale Owen (Robert Owen's son) and Charles Knowlton
in the United States and Charles Bradlaugh, Annie Besant, and the Malthusian
League in England. Part IV, "Fighters Against Comstockery," looks to Margaret
Sanger's famous career and the work of her predecessors. The concluding section,
"From Neo-Malthusianism to Family Planning," discusses Marie Stopes and the
immediate precursors of the Family Planning Association. Readers may want
to compare Linda Gordon's *Woman's Body, Woman's Right: A Social History
of Birth Control in America* (1976).

549   **Generations: Women in the South.** Chapel Hill, NC: Southern Exposure;
       distr. Old Westbury, NY: Feminist Press, 1977. 120p. $3.00.
A special issue of the quarterly, *Southern Exposure*, dealing with the lives of
southern women. Included are: "Second Letter to Southern White Women,"

by civil rights activist Ann Braden (an analysis of the connections between sexism and racism); "In Search of Our Mothers' Gardens," by Alice Walker (a tribute to black women whose life conditions prevented the expression of their creativity in any permanent form); interviews with grassroots organizers Sallie Mae Hadnott and Anna Mae Dickson; "Magnolias Grow in the Dirt," by folklorist Rayna Green (on the humor of southern women); "Women and Lynching," by historian Jacquelyn Dowd; and a substantial bibliography on women in the South.

550   Genovese, Eugene D., 1930- . **Roll, Jordan, Roll: The World The Slaves Made.** New York: Pantheon Books, 1974. 823p. bibliog. index. $17.50. ISBN 0394491319. LC 74-4760.

Along with Herbert Aptheker's *A Documentary History of the Negro People in the United States* (3 volumes, 1951-1974) and Herbert Gutman's *The Black Family in Slavery and Freedom, 1750-1925* (1976), *Roll, Jordan, Roll* represents essential background on black experience in white America. While none of these three works is concerned specifically with black women's experience, they provide a point of departure valuable by any criteria, but indispensable in view of the paucity of research on black women. Genovese's aim in *Roll, Jordan, Roll* is to bring to life "the world the slaves made." As is clear from the title, the emphasis is more on the active and creative survival of the slave community than on their passive victimization, although exploitation and oppression, of course, set the brutal context within which the drama takes place.

551   George, Carol V. R., ed. **"Remember the Ladies": New Perspectives on Women in American History; Essays in Honor of Nelson Manfred Blake.** Syracuse, NY: Syracuse University Press, 1975. 201p. bibliog. index. $10.00. ISBN 0815601107. LC 75-12295.

This collection of original articles in American women's history was dedicated by his friends, former students and colleagues to Nelson Manfred Blake, whose "interest in social history has always included concern for the part that women have played in it." The editor, Carol George, has written a general introduction as well as brief introductions to each of the three sections, The Growth of American Feminist Thought, The "Cult of True Womanhood," and The "New Woman" and Social Change. Among the articles: "Anne Hutchinson and the 'Revolution Which Never Happened' " (Carol George); "Eighteenth-Century Theorists of Women's Liberation" (Marguerite Fisher); "The Puritan Ethic in the Revolutionary Era: Abigail Adams and Thomas Jefferson" (Ralph Ketcham); "Women and the Nativist Movement" (David H. Bennett); "Man-Midwifery and the Delicacy of the Sexes" (Jane B. Donegan); "The Meaning of Harriet Tubman" (Otey Scruggs); "Divorce as a Moral Issue" (William L. O'Neill); and "Ume Tsuda and Motoko Hani: Echoes of American Cultural Feminism in Japan" (Noriko Shimada, Hiroko Takamura, Masako Iino, and Hisako Ito).

552   Gies, Frances, and Joseph Gies. **Women in the Middle Ages.** New York: Thomas Y. Crowell, 1978. 264p. bibliog. index. $10.95. ISBN 0690017243. LC 77-25832.

The authors note at the outset that a focus on women in the Middle Ages is problematic. First, it is difficult to assess the value of available sources, which tend to be prescriptive in nature (e.g., writings of Church Fathers, theologians, preachers). Second, the "Middle Ages" encompass a time period spanning 1,000 years and a sequence of momentous upheavals, which call into question the validity of generalizations about the period as a whole. Furthermore, they note, "the first and most important consideration in evaluating the quality of life in the Middle Ages applies equally to men and women: the technological and economic level of a low-energy but expanding society, influencing work, housing, food, clothing, health, security, comfort, and self-fulfillment." Having stated these qualifications, the Gies proceed with their project. In the first section, they outline the conditions of women's lives and the character of attitudes toward women during and after the period known as the Dark Ages. In part 2, they examine the lives of a series of women who lived between 1100 and 1500 (the high Middle Ages), drawing upon chronicles, tax roles, legal and manorial records, private account books, diaries and letters. An abbess, a queen, Piers Plowman's wife, a city working woman, an Italian merchant's wife, and a fifteenth-century gentlewoman are represented here.

553   Glanz, Rudolf. **The Jewish Woman in America: Two Female Immigrant Generations, 1820-1929.** New York: Ktav, 1976- . v.1. **The Eastern European Jewish Woman.** bibliog. index. $15.00. ISBN 0870684620. LC 75-29350.

This important work on the Eastern European Jewish women who arrived in the U.S. with the New Immigration (1881-1924) is to be followed by a second volume on the German Jewish women who came with the Old Immigration (1820-1880). Chapters in this first volume are: The Character of the Immigration of Jewish Women; Status of Jewish Women in Russia; Immigrant Mothers and Working Girls; The Jewish Community Meets the Working Girl; Unionizing and Strikes; The Structure of the Russian-Jewish Immigrant Family; The Feminine Sphere; The Fight for Women's Rights; The Social Life of the Immigrant Woman; Cultural Activities in Yiddish (theater and literature); and The Image of the Russian-Jewish Woman in Print. While the treatment of any one of these topics is somewhat brief, the notes are voluminous.

554   Gordon, Ann D., et al. **Women in American Society: An Historical Contribution.** Cambridge, MA: Radical America, 1972. 71p. bibliog.

This pamphlet by Ann D. Gordon, Mari Jo Buhle, and Nancy E. Schrom (originally published in *Radical America* 5 [July/August 1971]), is an important early attempt to develop a feminist social history from available sources. In part 1, the authors explicate the problems inherent in this task, some of which are common to all attempts to write social history, some of which are peculiar to historical explorations of women's lives ("the work of reconstructing the history of the inarticulate has just begun, and women make up the largest and probably the most silent of society's inarticulate groups"). Part 2 is a sketch of the historical evolution from colonial times, through industrialization and into the twentieth century, of the conditions of women's lives and of ideologies of "woman's place."

555   Gordon, Michael, comp. **The American Family in Social-Historical Perspective.** New York: St. Martin's Press, 1973. 428p. bibliog. index. $12.95. ISBN 0312022751. LC 72-95836.

Gordon has compiled an excellent collection of articles in the social history of
the family, with emphasis on the American experience. Included are: "The
Comparative History of Household and Family" (Peter Laslett); "Family,
Household, and the Industrial Revolution" (Michael Anderson); "Family and
Community Structure: Salem in 1800" (Bernard Farber); "Middle-Class Families
and Urban Violence: The Experience of a Chicago Community in the Nineteenth
Century" (Richard Sennett); "Patterns of Work and Family Organization:
Buffalo's Italians" (Virginia Yans McLaughlin); "The Two-Parent Household:
Black Family Structure in Late Nineteenth-Century Boston" (Elizabeth H.
Pleck); "Infancy and Childhood in the Plymouth Colony" (John Demos);
"Adolescence in Historical Perspective" (John and Virginia Demos); "The Cult
of True Womanhood: 1820-1860" (Barbara Welter); "Divorce in the Progressive
Era" (Richard Jensen); "The Puritans and Sex" (Edmund S. Morgan); "Illegiti-
macy, Sexual Revolution, and Social Change" (Edward Shorter); "The Spermatic
Economy: A Nineteenth-Century View of Sexuality" (Ben Barker-Benfield);
and "The Demographic History of Colonial New England" (Daniel Scott Smith).
Gordon, has also written an introduction to the volume, plus short blurbs on
each piece.

556   Greenbie, Marjorie Latta Barstow, 1891- . **My Dear Lady: The Story of
        Anna Ella Carroll, the "Great Unrecognized Member of Lincoln's
        Cabinet."** New York: Whittlesey House, 1940; repr. New York:
        Arno Press, 1974. 316p. bibliog. index. $20.00. ISBN 0405061013.
        LC 74-3953.
"Anna Ella Carroll (1815-1893) began her controversial career in the decade
before the Civil War when she lectured and wrote pamphlets on behalf of the
Know Nothing Party. The cry of secession rallied her to the Union cause, and
she put her talents to use at the highest level of government. While her claim
to formulating the plans for the Tennessee River campaign has been challenged,
'it seems incredible,' Lyman Beecher Stowe wrote in *The New York Times*,
'that the amazing story should have been known to a handful of historians only
until the publication of this book. In Lincoln's Kitchen Cabinet was a dashing
and brilliant Southern lady of the oldest aristocracy who, although not a lawyer,
gave President Lincoln indispensable legal advice on his war powers and, although
not a soldier, gave him the plan for the Tennessee River campaign by which
the Civil War was finally won. . . .' " ("A Note about This Volume," L. Stein
and A. K. Baxter, eds.).

557*   Grimes, Alan Pendleton, 1919- . **The Puritan Ethic and Woman Suffrage.**
        New York: Oxford University Press, 1967. 159p. bibliog. index.
        LC 67-15460.
"In part, my interest in the background of woman suffrage in America arose
out of an effort to explain a paradox: in 1869 the modern woman suffrage
movement was formally launched in the East with the establishment of the
National Woman Suffrage Association and the American Woman Suffrage Association; yet it was in that year in remote, primitive Wyoming Territory that woman
suffrage was first enacted into law, followed three months later by a similar
enactment in the Mormon Territory of Utah. Why did the actuality of woman
suffrage come out of the West when the ideology of the movement came out

of the East?" (from the introduction). This is the central question of Grimes's
book, in which he comes to the conclusion that, "the evidence indicates that to
a large extent, at least in the West, the constituency granting woman suffrage
was composed of those who also supported prohibition and immigration restriction and felt woman suffrage would further their enactment." This is a basic
study, routinely cited, on the social forces leading to the achievement of woman
suffrage in the United States.

558   Groves, Ernest Rutherford, 1878-1946. **The American Woman: The
       Feminine Side of a Masculine Civilization.** New York: Arno Press,
       1972. (Repr. of 1944 ed.). 465p. bibliog. index. $20.00. ISBN
       0405044607. LC 72-2605.
Chapters in this discussion of "woman's advance in status in a setting of mascu-
line dominance" include: The Cultural Background of the American Woman;
The Colonial Woman; The Frontier Woman; The Woman of the North from the
Revolution to the Civil War; The Woman of the South from the Revolution to
the Civil War; The Woman of the Middle West and Great Plains; Woman, North
and South, During and After the Civil War; Woman's Political and Social Advance;
Woman's Industrial and Educational Advance; The American Woman in the
Twentieth Century; The American Woman and Her Changing Status; Near
Equality with Men. Though the conclusions of the author about woman's
status in this country are perhaps more sanguine than is justified (especially
keeping in mind the 1944 imprint), Groves does provide a number of pertinent
background sources and is worth looking at.

559   Gutman, Herbert George, 1928- . **The Black Family in Slavery and
       Freedom, 1750-1925.** New York: Pantheon Books, 1976. 664p. bibliog.
       index. $15.95. ISBN 0394471164. LC 76-7550.
Gutman's monumental study of the black family attracted immediate critical
attention and praise. His decade-long research was originally set in motion by
the controversy surrounding the (in)famous "Moynihan Report" (*The Negro
Family in America: The Case for National Action*, 1965), in which Daniel P.
Moynihan attributed contemporary problems faced by blacks to the "tangle
of pathology" engendered by the "destruction" of the black family in slavery.
What he identified as pathological was the pattern of a mother-child family,
with father either unknown, absent, or lacking influence—a "matriarchal" family.
In this volume, Gutman reconstructs the history of black family and extended
kin patterns before and after emancipation. What he found directly contradicts
the Moynihan analysis. The typical pattern was one of double-headed families
and powerful, enduring kinship ties. While Gutman grounded his analysis in an
awesome amount of quantitative research, he made liberal use of "qualitative"
data as well (the voluminous Freedman's Bureau records, literary records, etc.)
in the attempt to bring this history to life. The result is a well-written, readable
account, replete with anecdotes, excerpts from slave narratives and oral histories,
and quotations from literature. The reader is referred to the appendices for
much of the statistical data.

560   Hahn, Emily, 1905- . **Once upon a Pedestal.** New York: Thomas Y. Crowell, 1974. 279p. bibliog. index. $6.95. ISBN 0690005075. LC 74-5354.

Emily Hahn is a popularizer. Her eighteen books to date, though not necessarily scholarly, have been interesting. Though this is a rather superficial treatment of "great" women (among them Frances Wright, The Tennessee commune leader of the 1820s; Angelina and Sarah Grimké; Victoria Woodhull, presidential candidate of the 1870s; Margaret Sanger, birth control pioneer of the early twentieth century; and other women of this extraordinary stature) and Hahn's emphases can be easily questioned, still she writes an engrossing strain of history. Libraries should probably have this kind of popular social history available.

561   Hahner, June E., ed. **Women in Latin American History: Their Lives and Views.** Los Angeles: UCLA Latin American Center Publications, University of California, 1976. 181p. bibliog. $5.00. ISBN 0879030348. LC 75-620131.

An important and valuable group of materials, these readings on Latin American women "endeavor to let Latin American women speak for themselves" through letters, diaries, poetry, interviews and autobiographies. The editor notes the historical misrepresentation of Latin American women—a generalized stereotype of her place in a *machismo* tradition. Such an interpretation does not allow for class differences, political variances, or diverse marital situations or status. Five major sections include glimpses of the Latin American woman from the colonial period to the twentieth century. Selections range from "Indian Revolt in Peru" to "A Prostitute in San Juan, Puerto Rico." It is good to see materials surfacing in this neglected historical area. The bibliographic essay at the end of the volume will direct readers to sources on women in the Iberian peninsula, Indian women of the preconquest period, nuns in colonial Latin America, colonial women, general studies on race relations and marriage, the Mexican suffrage movement, economic status of Latin American women, images of Latin American women, revolutionary participation, and writings of Latin American feminists and educators.

562   Harley, Sharon, and Rosalyn Terborg-Penn, eds. **The Afro-American Woman: Struggles and Images.** Port Washington, NY: National University Publications, 1978. index. $12.95. ISBN 0804692092. LC 78-9821.

This is a collection of nine essays on the history of Afro-American women, collected by black historians Sharon Harley and Rosalyn Terborg-Penn. Among the topics explored here are the labor history of black women in the early days of the republic, the role of black women and the racism of white women in the Woman Suffrage Movement, the history of education for black women, and black women poets and blues artists.

563   Holcombe, Lee. **Victorian Ladies at Work: Middle-Class Working Women In England and Wales, 1850-1914.** Hamden, CT: Archon Books, 1973. 253p. bibliog. index. $12.00. ISBN 0208013407. LC 73-3357.

Carefully researched and documented, this study looks at middle-class working women in Victorian England. In the 1850s, working implied that a woman was *not* a lady, the author points out. Getting married was the conventional way of avoiding the stigma that came from working outside the house. The entire educational system directed these women toward cultivating the "womanly" arts so that they could occupy an ornamental niche in the home. John Stuart Mill's essay, *The Subjection of Women* (1869), was a classic indictment of the absurdity of woman's position as ornament, prevented from exercising anything like control over her own life. Holcombe documents the evolution of the position of working women from that of a rejected, neglected group in the 1850s to a much-changed, "respected and self-respecting group" by 1914, when women became recognized as essential to England's labor force. The women's movement, teaching, nursing, shop work, clerical work, and civil service are the major topics covered.

564   Janeway, Elizabeth, ed. **Women: Their Changing Roles.** New York: New York Times, 1973. 556p. bibliog. index. $35.00. ISBN 0405041640. LC 72-5020.

"American women are not the only people in the world who manage to lose track of themselves, but we do seem to mislay the past in a singularly absent-minded fashion." Thus Janeway opens her introduction to this fascinating collection of clippings from the *New York Times* of the last 110 years—including news items, essays, reports and advertisements. Janeway's discriminating selection from voluminous material creates a lively and vivid social history of American women and popular attitudes toward them in the last century. Organized into nine chapters—Social Feminism; The Twenties; The Thirties; World War II; The Postwar Period; Women in the Arts; Sexual Emancipation; Radical Feminism; and Challenge and Change—the clippings cover a wide variety of events, topics, and people. Some sample headlines: "Emma Goldman, Anarchist—Disillusioned by Soviets" (May 14, 1940); "Feminism" by Ellen Glasgow (Nov. 30, 1913); "The Nestle Permanent Hair Wave" (Dec. 3, 1916); "Crisis in the Suffrage Movement," by Carrie Chapman Catt (Sept. 3, 1916); "New Women of Russia Test Lenin's Theories" (March 20, 1927); "Mother Jones Dies; Led Mine Workers" (Dec. 1, 1930); "Shall Wives Work?" (July 23, 1939); " 'Occupation Housewife'— No Amateur Job" (June 13, 1943); "Will Success Spoil American Women?" (Nov. 10, 1957); "Homogenized Children of New Suburbs" (Sept. 19, 1954); "What the Black Woman Thinks About Women's Lib," by Toni Morrison (Aug. 22, 1971). Subject and byline indexes are provided.

565   Josephson, Hannah (Geffen). **The Golden Threads: New England's Mill Girls and Magnates.** New York: Duell, Sloan, and Pearce, 1949; repr. New York: Russell and Russell, 1967. 325p. bibliog. index. $10.00. ISBN 0846208733. LC 66-27109.

The women factory workers of the textile mills in Lowell, Massachusetts, have been a frequent focus for historical investigation for a variety of reasons, as the annotation for Eisler in this section shows. Josephson's *The Golden Threads* (originally 1949) analyzes the emergence of the industry and the characteristics of its owners and workers. She discusses the original vision of the factories and the actual gradual emergence of more oppressive working conditions as pressures of competition and economic depression prevailed. Oppressive conditions produced spontaneous rebellion among the factory women, who were as a result rapidly replaced by Irish immigrant women. Unfortunately, it is at this point in the history that Josephson's account concludes, leaving unexamined the subsequent history of protest by the Irish and their replacement, in turn, by new immigrant groups. Readers will also want to be aware of the following recently published or reprinted books: Harriet Robinson's *Loom and Spindle* (1898, reprint Press Pacifica, 1976); Lucy Larcom's *A New England Girlhood* (1889, reprint Peter Smith, 1973); Eisler's *The Lowell Offering* (1977); and Philip Foner's *The Factory Girls* (1977).

566   Katz, Jonathan. **Gay American History: Lesbians and Gay Men in the U.S.A.: A Documentary.** New York: Thomas Y. Crowell, 1976. 690p. bibliog. index. $15.00. ISBN 0690011644. LC 76-2039.

"I will be pleased if this book helps to revolutionize the traditional concept of homosexuality. This concept is so profoundly ahistorical that the very existence of Gay history may be met with disbelief. The common image of the homosexual has been a figure divorced from any temporal-social context. The concept of homosexuality must be historicized." This is a landmark book. Katz has collected documents spanning over four centuries in his attempt to begin filling in the outlines of a Gay American history. A first attempt, it is bound to be incomplete, but Katz's intention was never to write an exhaustive account. Rather, by bringing together documents by or about ordinary homosexuals over the last 400 years, he creates a historical background for the experiences and struggles of Gay people today. The materials are organized into six chronologically-arranged topical sections: 1) "Trouble: 1566-1966" includes materials reflective of the experience of homosexual oppression and self-oppression; 2) "Treatment: 1884-1974" contains materials about the (mis)treatment of homosexuals by psychiatrists and psychologists; 3) "Passing Women: 1782-1920" reprints accounts of women who dressed, lived and worked as men, and pursued intimate relation-ships with women; 4) "Native Americans/Gay Americans: 1528-1976" presents observations on forms of homosexuality in Native American culture; 5) "Resis-tance: 1859-1972" includes documents on liberation struggles—both isolated acts and organized movements; and 6) "Love: 1779-1932" collects accounts reflective of love relationships between persons of the same sex. Katz has written introductions to each of the six sections and to the individual selections within these. He takes great care to be sensitive to the differences between men's and women's experiences as homosexuals in a heterosexist society. Katz is also author of *Coming Out: A Documentary Play about Gay Life and Liberation in the U.S.A.* (Arno Press, 1975), which speaks to both lesbian and male homosexual experiences.

567   Lavrin, Asuncion, ed. **Latin American Women: Historical Perspectives.** Westport, CT: Greenwood Press, 1978. index. $22.50. ISBN 0313203091. LC 77-94758.

This collection of scholarly essays illuminates the common and different experi-ences of pre-twentieth century Latin American women. It distinguishes their shared history (as a rule, a common heritage of undereducation and non-participa-tion in public affairs) from the history of Latin American men, while highlighting the important differences among women along lines of class and race. Predictably, the social roles of the white elite receive prominent examination; yet there is surprisingly rich information about Indian and black women, too. The sources are varied: for example, nunneries of Spanish America for insight into both colonial and Indian women's choices and professional options, and nineteenth-century periodical literature for documentation of liberalized male attitudes toward female education. The diverse patterns of family roles and sex polarization, trends in the feminist movement, and women's political participation are among the important themes in these essays. Lavrin's useful introductory essay centers the volume and points the way to further research. Extensive chapter notes identify significant clusters of primary and secondary sources.

568   Lemons, J. Stanley. **The Woman Citizen: Social Feminism in the 1920's.**
       Urbana: University of Illinois Press, 1973. 266p. bibliog. index. $9.50.
       ISBN 0252002679. LC 72-75488.

Lemons borrows William O'Neill's distinction between "social feminism," which incorporated women's rights goals within a broad concern for social reform, and "hard core" or "extreme feminism," which put women's rights before all else. Lemon's interest in social feminism grew out of a prior interest in the progressive era and, in particular, in the debate on the extent of continuity between progressivism and New Deal liberalism. The twenties have been popularly stereotyped as an era of excess and reaction, marked by the receding of progressivism and also of the Woman Movement after the suffrage victory. Lemons argues that, on the contrary, "the social feminists constituted an important link in the chain from the progressive era to the New Deal." Social feminists "were the woman citizens of the 1920's, who wanted to use their newly won citizenship to advance the reform effort" in the areas of education, health, labor, and social welfare. Among the people and organizations discussed by Lemons are Jane Addams, Anna Howard Shaw, Mary Anderson, Mary Dreier Robins, Carrie Chapman Catt, Alice Paul, Maud Wood Park, the National American Woman Suffrage Association, the National Woman's Party, the National League of Women Voters, the National Women's Trade Union League, and the Women's International League for Peace and Freedom. Lemons offers an extended essay on sources at the end, including personal papers, archives, periodical literature, official proceedings, unpublished manuscripts, biographical materials, and secondary works.

569   Lerner, Gerda, 1920- , comp. **Black Women in White America: A**
       Documentary History. New York: Pantheon Books, 1972. 630p.
       bibliog. $17.50. ISBN 0394475402. LC 72-8643.

This is a fine collection of primary-source material on black women's history, written by black women. The limitations of the anthology reflect for the most part the limitations of the available documentary record, limitations indicative of the low priority that has historically been placed on the collection and preservation of sources and records about black women. Within these limitations, Lerner has chosen to emphasize the family and work experiences of black women—both well-known and anonymous—primarily in the nineteenth and early twentieth centuries. She gives less emphasis to cultural figures and to the civil rights struggles of the '50s and '60s because sources on these are more readily accessible. Documents are included on the following topics: slavery; education; sexual oppression; domestic, service and factory work; the struggle for survival of the family; government work and political life; racism and resistance struggles; and black women's views on womanhood and women's liberation. Lerner gives brief introductions to each section and the selections within these. Her approach is reflective of her longtime interest in the history of both racism and the oppression of women, and is sensitive to the tensions that exist between movements for black liberation and women's liberation. For further reading and research, Lerner recommends Herbert Aptheker's *A Documentary History of the Negro People in the United States* (Citadel Press, 1951-1974, 3 volumes), which—she says—"remains an indispendable collection of documentary sources . . . remarkably rich in materials pertaining to women."

570   Lerner, Gerda, 1920- , ed. **The Female Experience: An American Documentary.** Indianapolis, IN: Bobbs-Merrill, 1977. bibliog. index. $12.50. ISBN 0672515555. LC 76-40258.

In studying women's history, much depends on keying in to difficult-to-access sources. It is not so much a matter of reading about the experiences of spectacularly successful or recognized women as to come to an understanding of ordinary, forgotten women. The sources woven together in this important book of readings are enlightening for their relative obscurity and draw on the experience of American women from birth to death. A mother's advice to a daughter (1855), an experience of a difficult childbirth (1869), a chronicle of life on an Illinois farm (1905), counsel for domestics (1846): these are among the readings taken from documentary sources of lesser known women. Louisa May Alcott, Sojourner Truth, and Elizabeth Blackwell are here, too. The reader interested in such primary-source material on women's history in the U.S. might also want to consult the collection by Baxandall, et al., *America's Working Women* (1976). Lerner herself has written a brief overview of the history of women in the U.S. entitled *The Woman in American History* (Addison-Wesley, 1971). She has also produced a *Bibliography in the History of American Women* (Sarah Lawrence College, 2nd rev. ed. 1975), which may prove somewhat hard to get hold of.

571   Levine, David, 1946- . **Family Formation in an Age of Nascent Capitalism.** New York: Academic Press, 1977. 194p. bibliog. index. $14.50. ISBN 0124450504. LC 76-50398.

"The controversy over the growth of population during the English Industrial Revolution provided the starting point for this study, but in the course of my research I found myself, as it were, moving backward in time. This study deals with the impact of early capitalism on the strategies of family formation among four sets of English villagers in the period before the wholesale switch-over to factory industry. Although this era, roughly speaking from 1550 to 1850, has been variously described as 'traditional,' 'preindustrial,' and more recently, 'protoindustrial,' I prefer to see it as a stage in the transition from feudalism to capitalism—a halfway house" (from the introduction). Levine purposefully chose four representatively different socioeconomic communities on which to build his theory of English socioeconomic development in an era of nascent capitalism: Shepshed, Leicestershire; Bottesford, Leicestershire; Terling, Essex; Colyton, Devon. The work of family reconstitution is painstaking and slow, thus Levine's concentration on only four communities in order "to explain the interplay between socioeconomic change and demographic behavior and to test the adequacy of that explanation with reference to empirical data." Though this is important reading for those interested in the relationship between production and reproduction, it is difficult material. Levine provides excellent appendix and bibliographical sources for the primary material he has used in reassembling the family from parochial records from 1600 to 1850.

572   Lewenhak, Sheila. **Women and Trade Unions: An Outline History of Women in the British Trade Union Movement.** New York: St. Martin's Press, 1977. 308p. bibliog. index. $14.95. ISBN 0312887752. LC 77-72772.

Unlike the usual historical accounts, this work documents the important role of British women in the labor movement. However, their lower legal status kept them from organizing as thoroughly as men did. Lewenhak shows the enduring paradox of women's performing the same duties as men from early Anglo-Saxon times, yet being relegated to inferior roles and reward. During the mid-nineteenth century, women formed societies (the Female Foresters and the Ancient Shepherd-esses), seeking to compensate for being excluded from male-established associations. Seminal years for women's unionism, these saw the establishment of the Women's Trade Union League (1871), which "pioneered the technique of long-term political lobbying on behalf of women workers. . . ." "According to the book's subtitle, this volume is intended to be an outline history. Unfortunately, this is its major flaw—too much ground is covered sketchily, and the narrative lacks cohesion. Nevertheless, this account represents a good beginning for the assessment of women laborers" (*Choice* 15 [June 1978], p. 586).

573*   Lutz, Alma. **Crusade for Freedom: Women of the Antislavery Movement.** Boston: Beacon Press, 1968. 338p. bibliog. LC 68-12841.

Lutz, who has written biographies of the two chief first-generation American suffragists, Elizabeth Cady Stanton and Susan B. Anthony, here gives an account of women's part in the Abolition Movement—from Elizabeth Margaret Chandler (1807-1934), one of the earliest American antislavery poets, and Prudence Crandall (1803-1890), who made an unsuccessful attempt to open a boarding school for black women in Connecticut, to the Grimké sisters, Susan B. Anthony, and Elizabeth Cady Stanton. Writing in the late 1960s, Lutz remarked on how the contemporary period was once again revealing the inseparability of women's liberation and black liberation "in the larger struggle for human rights," as a new feminist movement was born of the civil rights struggles of the 1950s and '60s.

574   Mackenzie, Midge, comp. **Shoulder to Shoulder: A Documentary.** New York: Knopf, 1975. 338p. bibliog. index. $15.00. ISBN 0394497341. LC 74-25426.

This pictorial history of the Women's Social and Political Union (WSPU), founded by Emmeline Pankhurst and her daughters, Christabel and Sylvia, represents the material the author used for the BBC television series "Shoulder to Shoulder." The WSPU, active from 1903 to 1914, was the first and largest of England's militant suffrage groups. Depicted in this volume are the many endeavors and hardships of the WSPU: speechmaking, peaceful agitation efforts, forcible feedings, imprisonment. The text for the volume is culled from the WSPU women's diaries, memoirs, the suffragette magazines *Votes for Women* and *The Suffragette*, as well as from the British national press of the day. Important reading for understanding the British Women's Suffrage Movement.

575   Martinez, Elizabeth Sutherland, 1925- , and Enriqueta Longeaux Y
        Vasquez. **Viva La Raza! The Struggle of the Mexican-American People.**
        Garden City, NY: Doubleday, 1974. 353p. index. $4.95. ISBN
        0385092636. LC 72-89816.

" 'La Raza' means in Spanish 'the race' and stands for the blending of predominantly Indian and Spanish peoples who were our ancestors—the blend that we
are today. The essence of La Raza is that we are a mestizo people, a mixed
people, a blend of races and culture." Two Chicana women active in the Chicano
movement try here to bring into focus the censored and submerged history
of La Raza in America. They write, "The biggest lie, the root of all the other
lies, is that the Anglo belongs here and we are the immigrants. . . . " Though
the focus in this history is La Raza as a whole and not specifically Chicanas,
it remains essential background for an understanding of the lives of Chicana
women today. The authors begin with the true first settlers in America (long
before Columbus's "discovery"), move on to the colonization by Spain and
United States expansion, propose an alternative view of "how the West was
really won," give an account of the Mexican Revolution and its defeat, tell
the story of the farmworkers, analyze "the big brainwash" (the perpetuation of
degrading stereotypes about Chicanos), and finally tell something of the different
facets of the current Chicano movement.

576   Martinez-Alier, Verena. **Marriage, Class and Colour in Nineteenth-
        Century Cuba: A Study of Racial Attitudes and Sexual Values in a
        Slave Society.** New York: Cambridge University Press, 1974. 202p.
        bibliog. index. $14.95. ISBN 0521204127. LC 73-82463.

In nineteenth-century Cuba, the majority of the very large black population was
held in slavery. *Marriage, Class and Colour* is a case-study of the ways in which
racism and sexual values both reflect and buttress a social structure built on
inequality and repression. These relationships are examined through a careful
investigation of nineteenth-century cases of parental opposition to a marriage,
of elopement, and of interracial marriage.

577   Marzolf, Marion. **Up from the Footnote: A History of Women Journalists.**
        New York: Hastings House, 1977. 310p. bibliog. index. $12.95. ISBN
        0803875029. LC 77-5398.

This book could be faulted for its brevity in dealing with major journalistic
figures and its omission of still other notable women journalistic luminaries
and policy makers. Nonetheless, Marzolf has managed to dredge up many previously invisible, lost, and forgotten names and achievements that reflect the
contributions of women to American journalism. She has extracted information
about women journalists from their own writings, from scholarly and popular
studies, from tapes, clippings, interviews, memorabilia, and letters. She has
attempted to graph the development of women in journalism from their beginnings as printers in colonial America, to their roles as sob sisters, war corres-
pondents, and spokespersons for the women's movement, and, most recently
as "serious" writers and journalists. On the way, Marzolf looks at organizational
roles—women as anchor people, news directors, and management executives.
Her comprehensive evaluation and description of women who shape the media
spends some time on feminist presses and journalism educators. The last chapter,

"View from Europe," sizes up the European journalistic scene as it relates to women, noting the parallel growth of the women's movement in America and in Europe with its increased attention to the status of women journalists both at home and abroad during the '70s. Ambitious in scope, this book points the way to future research and offers a state-of-the-art report on the topic. Sources noted at the end of each chapter offer many fine suggestions for additional reading on women journalists.

578   Meyer, Annie (Nathan), 1867-1951, ed. **Woman's Work in America.**
       New York: Arno Press, 1972. (Repr. of 1891 ed.). 457p. bibliog.
       index. $20.00. ISBN 0405044690. LC 72-2615.
Though the material here is, of course, nearly a century out of date, this collection of articles bears so much resemblance to contemporary surveys of women's status in the labor force that it makes for potentially rich historical comparisons. Annie Nathan Meyer, the editor and a prime mover behind the founding of Barnard College, brought together in this volume writings on the following topics: the education of women in the eastern, western and southern states, and women in literature, journalism, medicine, the ministry, law, industry, and "philanthropy" (i.e., what we would call volunteer work today), including charity, nursing, work with criminals, work with Native Americans, abolitionism, the Women's Christian Temperance Union, and the Red Cross. Among the more familiar authors represented here are Julia Ward Howe, Helen Grey Cone, Mary Putnam Jacobi, Mary A. Livermore, Frances E. Willard, and Clara Barton.

579   Middleton, Lucy, ed. **Women in the Labor Movement: The British
       Experience.** London: Croom Helm; Totowa, NJ: Rowman and Little-
       field, 1977. 221p. bibliog. index. $13.50. ISBN 0874719429. LC
       76-54160.
Collected here are a series of articles on women's labor struggles in Britain since 1900, the year in which the British Labor Party was founded. Part 1, The Early Years, includes: Lucy Middleton's "Women in Labour Politics"; Sheila Ferguson's "Labour Women and the Social Services"; Margherita Rendel's "The Contribution of the Women's Labour League to the Winning of the Franchise"; Mary Walker's "Labour Women and Internationalism"; Anne Godwin's "Early Years in the Trade Unions"; and Jean Gaffin's "Women and Cooperation." Part 2, The Movement Today, includes: Oonagh McDonald's "Women in the Labour Party"; Margaret McCarthy's "Women in the Trade Unions"; and Maeve Denby's "Women in Parliament and Government." Nine appendices offer, for example, a table showing women candidates in general elections since 1918, a list of Labour women members of Parliament, women members of the General Council of the Trades Union Congress, etc.

580   Mohr, James C. **Abortion in America: The Origins and Evolution of
       National Policy, 1800-1900.** New York: Oxford University Press,
       1978. 331p. bibliog. index. $12.50. ISBN 0195022491. LC 77-9430.
"In 1800 no jurisdiction in the United States had enacted any statutes whatsoever on the subject of abortion. . . . Yet by 1900 virtually every jurisdiction in the United States had laws upon its books that proscribed the practice sharply and declared most abortions to be criminal offenses" (preface). Mohr sets out

to trace the history of this remarkable transformation of American public policy. To begin with, the nineteenth century saw a dramatic drop in U.S. birthrates due to increased usage of both contraception and abortion. What is more, the public became aware that this usage was not-as previously supposed—restricted to the desperate and pitiable impoverished single woman—but was increasingly common among married WASP middle-class women. However, as Mohr makes clear, it was not the independent force of a nativist, racist, and anti-feminist public opinion that managed to turn abortion legislation upside down. The prime movers in the anti-abortion campaigns of the late 1800s were "regular physicians" associated with the fledgling American Medical Association and its struggle for professionalization and monopoly control of American medicine. Public sentiment was aroused and used by these physicians in their efforts to outlaw abortion. Though Mohr's approach is not particularly feminist, and though some of this ground has been previously covered (see, for example, Linda Gordon's *Woman's Body, Woman's Right*), *Abortion in America* is important for its careful research into the history of a right that women are still struggling to establish.

581   Morgan, David, 1937- . **Suffragists and Democrats: The Politics of Woman Suffrage in America.** East Lansing: Michigan State University Press, 1972. 225p. bibliog. index. $7.50. ISBN 087013163X. LC 76-150079.

Morgan confines his study of woman suffrage in the United States to the final years of the battle, 1916-1920, "when it had become a source of political dispute among the politicians." He is interested in exploring the nature of the economic, social, and legal forces that made possible the suffrage victory of 1920. He also explores the nature of the formidable opposition to suffrage these same forces gave rise to (e.g., the brewing and textile industries). Morgan's contention is that the suffrage struggle and victory shed light "on the nature of the political process in Wilsonian America." A lengthy bibliography of manuscripts, government documents, newspapers, periodical literature, and books is appended. Morgan has followed this study with a second, similar investigation of the suffrage battle in England (*Suffragists and Liberals*, 1975). Together these two works offer rich material for a comparative historical analysis.

582   Morgan, David, 1937- . **Suffragists and Liberals: The Politics of Woman Suffrage in England.** Totowa, NJ: Rowman and Littlefield, 1975. 184p. bibliog. index. $12.50. ISBN 0874715830. LC 74-17334.

This study of a critical period in the suffrage struggle in England makes for a rich comparison with Morgan's earlier study of woman suffrage in the United States, *Suffragists and Democrats* (1972). Whereas that work focused on the victorious culmination of the battle with the ratification of the suffrage amendment in 1920, *Suffragists and Liberals* looks at the English campaign "as it entered its climacteric phase and failed" in the years preceding World War I. Much of the debate around the English history has centered on the question of whether the militance of the suffragists was responsible for their defeat. Morgan suggests that historians have been guilty of treating the politicians involved (principally Asquith) as "a static 'given.' " Perhaps more central to the defeat than the issue of militancy, he implies, was the predicament of "a moribund Liberalism" facing the threat of the rising Labour Party. A lengthy bibliography of printed and unprinted sources is included. Readers may also want to look at the more recent study of the English movement, Jill Liddington and Jill Norris's *One Hand Tied Behind Us: The Rise of the Women's Suffrage Movement* (Virago, 1978).

583   Morgan, Edmund Sears. **The Puritan Family: Religion and Domestic Relations in Seventeenth-Century New England.** (Rev. ed.). New York: Harper and Row, 1966. 196p. bibliog. index. $2.25. ISBN 0061312274. LC 65-25695.

Morgan's is a standard work on the Puritan family that inquires into both the impact of Puritan religious ideas on the family and the impact of the family on the religion. Originally written as a dissertation at Harvard (1942) and first published in book form in 1944, this revised edition has been considerably enlarged. Chapter 2, "Husband and Wife," is likely to be of most interest to the readers with feminist questions in mind. A related work of more recent date is John Demos's *A Little Commonwealth: Family Life in Plymouth Colony* (1970).

584*   Muncy, Raymond Lee. **Sex and Marriage in Utopian Communities: 19th-Century America.** Bloomington: Indiana University Press, 1973. 275p. bibliog. index. ISBN 0253180643. LC 72-85852.

The task that Muncy has set himself is to investigate how nineteenth-century American utopian communities dealt with marital and sexual arrangements and what strategies were developed to cope with the needs of the nuclear family within a communal living situation. Coping strategies included celibacy (Ann Lee and the Shakers), communal care of children (Owenites), abolition of marriage (Fourierism), familism (Amana), polygyny (Mormonism), and male continence and complex marriage (Oneidanism). The problems facing utopian communities were these: free love, polygyny, and complex marriage were not accepted by the larger society; celibacy militated against propagation of the collective within a generation; familial attachments of husband and wife, mother and child, tended to resurface; and monogamy threatened collectivism.

585   Neff, Wanda (Fraiken), 1889- . **Victorian Working Women: An Historical and Literary Study of Women in British Industries and Professions, 1832-1850.** New York: Columbia University Press, 1929; repr. New York: Humanities Press, 1967. 288p. bibliog. index. $8.50. LC 67-13855.

Victorian Working Women, based on Neff's Ph.D. thesis at Columbia University, is one of those classic studies (rediscovered by contemporary feminists) that have served as a foundation for the new emerging women's history. Neff was interested in the history of prevailing social consciousness which considered the employment of women a new and reprehensible practice. Women's participation in production was hardly a new phenomenon in Victorian England; however, "to the Victorians belongs the discovery of the woman worker as an object of pity. . . . " In part, this discovery represents the awakening of consciousness about horrendous working conditions which were the product of industrialization and the very real deterioration of the conditions of working women's lives. In part, it was a product of the developing ideology of woman's place, named by Barbara Welter the "Cult of True Womanhood," which defined women as idle, aesthetic objects too fragile for normal human pursuits. Neff bases her discussion of the textile worker, the non-textile worker, the dressmaker, the governess, and the idle woman (workers who received government investigation during the period 1832-1850) on fiction and verse published 1832-1850, fiction and verse of the next generation that dealt with conditions of the period under consideration, and journalism and parliamentary reports.

586   Noble, Jeanne L. **Beautiful, Also, Are the Souls of My Black Sisters.**
       Englewood Cliffs, NJ: Prentice-Hall, 1978. 346p. bibliog. index.
       $12.50. ISBN 013066555X. LC 77-27408.

Subtitled "A History of the Black Woman in America," Noble's book is an angry, righteous history that draws from many, mainly contemporary, sources— popular, personal experiences, interviews, and scholarly sources. Well-researched as this social history is, Noble admits that records are scant, especially when the investigator is trying to draw on black source materials (as the citations here demonstrate she is attempting to do). Noble's perspective emanates from her identity as a black woman scholar, and the point she returns to again and again is the survival and resilience of black women. Beginning with a discussion of the African heritage of strength and self-reliance as attributes of women, she moves to a discussion of slavery where again her strength and adaptability held the black woman in good stead. The chapter on emancipation sketches portraits of Elizabeth Keckley, a White House servant to Mary Todd Lincoln, and of Sojourner Truth. It is in the black singers, domestics, single mothers and teachers that Noble finds the strength of present models of black woman- hood. Her discussion of the role of the domestic in the chapter "Dishwater Images" is one of the more effective in the volume. Another lengthy essay— this one on black singers—chronicles the "extraordinarily brilliant honor roll of black women who 'spread their moufs' and sing." Although this work has some problems with unevenness, and at times is more a pep talk than an objective study, the dearth of material on the history of Afro-American women written by a black woman makes this study essential.

587   O'Neill, William L. **Divorce in the Progressive Era.** New Haven, CT:
       Yale University Press, 1967. 295p. bibliog. index. $17.50. ISBN
       0300008058. LC 67-24507.

This is based on the author's thesis, *The Divorce Crisis of the Progressive Era*, at the University of California (1963). O'Neill's analysis of divorce in America (late 1880s-1919) is considered the definitive work on this topic. A major thesis is that when the modern family, in its intimate privatized form, came to a position of dominance in the society, divorce became common. O'Neill terms divorce a "safety valve," allowing a socially acceptable form of release for those who can no longer bear the intimate form of domestic life they have chosen. Interestingly, the Puritans, who had a very close-knit family situation that focused on children, made divorce a legal possibility. O'Neill dates modern opposition to divorce from the 1889 Bureau of Labor's report *Marriage and Divorce*, which documented how common divorce had become. Thereafter, a conservative opposition to divorce backed by many divided opposition groups took hold. Divorce was made the center of moral controversy between conservative and liberal groups, which debated this personal question of civil liberty. O'Neill's sources, especially primary government documents and report literature of the Progressive period, are particularly interesting.

588*   O'Sullivan, Judith, and Rosemary Gallick. **Workers and Allies: Female Participation in the American Trade Union Movement, 1824-1976.** Washington: Smithsonian Institution Press, 1975. 96p. bibliog. LC 75-619279.

"This Bicentennial exhibition on the contributions of women to the American labor movement is welcome because it focuses at last on an aspect of our nation's history known only to a very few and known scarcely at all to women. In presenting this fascinating pictorial display, the Smithsonian tells us not only about our past but enriches our understanding of present struggles" (from Bella Abzug's introduction). This is an excellent source for women's participation in the trade union movement because of the many visual representations gathered for the Smithsonian exhibition (1975); the informative overview of the subject provided by O'Sullivan's essay on women's contribution to labor in America; the chronology section, which gives short summaries of female participation in labor, beginning with 1765 and the organization of the first society of working women and continuing to 1974, the date of the founding convention of the Coalition of Labor Union Women (CLUW) in Chicago; the biographies of approximately 175 women, including "past and present workers and allies who have contributed as members of the rank and file, organizers, union officials, educators, journalists, archivists, historians, and benefactresses," each accompanied by a large number of references. A long bibliography of books, articles and papers is given, arranged in chronological order.

589   Pankhurst, Estelle Sylvia, 1882-1960. **The Suffragette Movement.** New York: Kraus Reprint, 1971. (Repr. of 1931 ed.). 631p. $31.00. ISBN 052769570X.

First published in 1931, three years after the passage of a full suffrage act in England, Sylvia Pankhurst's history of the British Woman Suffrage Movement concentrates primarily on the period from the founding of the Women's Social and Political Union (WSPU) in 1903 to the passage of a limited suffrage bill in 1917. This movement history is at the same time (and inevitably) a family history of the Pankhursts: Mrs. (Emmaline) Pankhurst, founder of the WSPU, and her two daughters, Christabel and Sylvia. Many tensions and conflicts beset the suffrage movement relating to its policy on militancy, its relation to the Labour Party, its support for working women, its internal structure, and its position with regard to World War I. These same conflicts were responsible for a painful estrangement between Mrs. Pankhurst and Christabel, on the one side, and Sylvia, on the other. Sylvia was eventually expelled from the WSPU, which her mother and sister continued to run in autocratic fashion. Following this split, Sylvia tells us that "Christabel said that sometimes we should meet, 'not as Suffragettes, but as sisters.' To me the words seemed meaningless; we had no life apart from the movement." Sylvia's story is important as a first-hand account of the British movement. An earlier account by Sylvia (first published in 1911 prior to the family split) is entitled *The Suffragette: The*

History of the Women's Militant Suffrage Movement, 1905-1910 (repr. Source
Book Press, 1970). Readers may also be interested in Mrs. Pankhurst's *My Own
Story* (orig. 1914; repr. Source Book Press, 1970).

590   Papachristou, Judith. **Women Together: A History in Documents of
the Women's Movement in the United States.** New York: Knopf; distr.
New York: Random House, 1976. 273p. bibliog. index. $15.00. ISBN
0394494296. LC 75-37709.
Speeches, letters, resolutions, declarations, reports, and documents of strategy
comprise the text of this reexamination of American history, which tells the
story of the women's movement through documents and represents a good
introduction to primary-source material. Each segment of the original document
is introduced by useful background material. A source for each document is
cited in the bibliography, which in itself is extremely valuable as a reading
list for an American history of women. The twelve chapters reflect major
historical periods during which the women's movement made significant, recognizable strides forward: The Women's Movement is Born: The 1830's; The First
Decade: The 1850's; Defeat, Conflict, and Schism: 1865-1869; Division and
Reunion: 1869-1890; The First Suffrage Drive; Associationism and Reform:
1890-1920; A Brief History of Wage-Earning Women: 1820-1914; The Between
Women—Class, Race, Ethnicity, and the Women's Movement: 1850-1920;
Final Suffrage Drive; Action, Reform, and Quiescence: 1920-1950; Revival
of the Women's Movement: 1960's and 1970's.

591   Paulson, Ross E. **Women's Suffrage and Prohibition: A Comparative
Study of Equality and Social Control.** Glenview, IL: Scott, Foresman,
1973. 212p. bibliog. index. $3.95. ISBN 0673059820. LC 72-92341.
Credited by feminist historian Ellen Dubois (*Feminism and Suffrage*, 1978)
with being one of the major histories of the woman suffrage movement, this
study seeks a comparative understanding of "the interaction of the women's
suffrage and prohibition movements in history." Paulson writes in his preface,
"my contention is that the 'woman question' of the nineteenth and early twentieth centuries was an aspect of the debate on the meaning of equality, and that
the temperance and prohibition movements involved questions concerning
the nature of democracy and the means of social control within society."
Paulson discusses women's rights, suffrage, revolutionary politics, prohibition,
social control, and the question of equality from the 1830s to the 1930s in the
United States, France, Norway, Sweden, England, Australia, New Zealand,
and Finland.

592   Phillips, Margaret, 1891- , and William Shirley Tomkinson, 1885- .
English Women in Life and Letters. New York: Arno Press, 1971.
(Repr. of 1926 ed.). 408p. index. $20.00. LC 72-151974.
A profusely illustrated account of Englishwomen, drawing from historical and
literary sources spanning the fifteenth to the nineteenth centuries, though
primarily concentrating on the seventeenth and eighteenth centuries. The authors
treat the lives of women in England from every station. "Thus Pamela Andrews
and Moll Flanders testify in these pages along with Dorothy Osborne and
Fanny Burney." Chapters are: Two Centuries of English Women;

Seventeenth-century Housekeepers in Country and Town; Fashionable Women
in the Eighteenth Century; Servants of the Seventeenth and Eighteenth Century;
An Eighteenth Century Novelist and her Blue-Stocking Friends; Country Ladies
and Cottage Housewives in the Eighteenth Century; The Woman Criminal;
Women in the Professions: The Nurse and the Governess; Women's Industry
in the Home and the Factory.

593   Pinchbeck, Ivy, 1898- . **Women Workers and the Industrial Revolution,
       1750-1850.** New York: A. M. Kelley, 1969. (Repr. of 1930 ed.).
       342p. bibliog. index. $13.50. ISBN 0678051062. LC 75-96378.
First published in 1930, Pinchbeck's study of the impact of industrialization
on women workers in England is one of those classic works that have formed
the foundation for the new emerging women's history. Taking issue with the
common misconception that "the woman worker was produced by the Industrial Revolution," Pinchbeck provides a detailed picture of the scope of women's
work in agriculture, industry, and trade prior to industrialization. She shows
how the economic dependence and vulnerability of women in the marriage
and household-centered economy laid the basis for their extreme sufferings
under the dislocating and uprooting forces of industrialization. Pinchbeck
focuses on the period of 1750-1850 as that of the most notable transformation
in women's activities and analyzes in particular detail those employments most
dramatically transformed (agriculture, textiles, the mines and metal trades,
crafts, trade, and the professions). Readers will also want to be aware of the
classic work of another "foremother" historian, *Working Life of Women in the
Seventeenth Century*, by Alice Clark (orig. 1919; repr. 1968).

594   Pivar, David J. **Purity Crusade: Sexual Morality and Social Control,
       1868-1900.** Westport, CT: Greenwood Press, 1973. 308p. bibliog.
       $12.50. ISBN 0837163196. LC 70-179650.
Exploring the sexual attitudes of nineteenth-century America, this study focuses
on the sexual morality crusades of such conservative women's organizations as
the Women's Christian Temperance Union and the General Foundation of
Women's Clubs. Chapters are: The Genesis of Purity Reform; Repulsing the
Regulationists; The Emergence of the Social Purity Alliance, 1877-1885;
Becoming a National Movement, 1885-1895; Purity and Urban Moral Awaken-
ing, 1895-1900; Purity Reform in Perspective.

595   Pomeroy, Sarah B. **Goddesses, Whores, Wives, and Slaves: Women in
       Classical Antiquity.** New York: Schocken Books, 1975. 265p. bibliog.
       index. $12.00. ISBN 0805235620. LC 74-8782.
"This book was conceived when I asked myself what women were doing while
men were active in all the areas traditionally emphasized by classical scholars.
The overwhelming ancient and modern preference for political and military
history, in addition to the current fascination with intellectual history, has
obscured the record of those people who were excluded by sex or class from
participation in the political and intellectual life of their societies" (from the
introduction). Pomeroy's highly respected study, intended as "a social history
of women through the centuries in the Greek and Roman worlds" (a period
spanning more than 1,500 years), is the first such work to appear in English.

Geared towards women's history readers as well as classicists, the analysis calls
into question the received views of the "glory of classical Athens" and the
"grandeur of Rome." Pomeroy suggests that, while Roman society does seem
to have been somewhat less constricting to women than the Greek, popular
conceptions of Roman women as liberated need serious qualification. Noting
that ancient history is for the most part "the study of the ruling classes,"
Pomeroy describes the problems she encountered in looking for sources to
recreate a history of all women in classical antiquity. She turned to archeologi-
cal evidence in addition to literary sources, including sculpture, vase painting,
frescoes, mosaics, ornaments, kitchen utensils, looms, and furniture.

596   Putnam, Emily James (Smith), 1865-1944. **The Lady: Studies of Cer-
       tain Significant Phases of Her History.** Chicago: University of Chicago
       Press, 1970. (Repr. of 1910 ed.). 323p. $8.50. ISBN 0226685624.
       LC 70-108990.
A member of Bryn Mawr's first graduating class in 1899, a postgraduate student
at Cambridge, a faculty member of the classics department at the University
of Chicago, in 1894 she became the first dean of Barnard College as Emily
James Smith. When she married publisher George Putnam in 1899 and resigned
her post because of the conservative attitudes toward her career/motherhood
role, Emily Putnam turned to teaching and writing. Her book, *The Lady* (1910),
airs her observations culled from reading and analysis on the "woman question"
in eight historically differentiated periods—The Greek Lady, The Roman Lady,
The Lady Abbess, The Lady of the Castle, The Lady of the Renaissance, The
Lady of the Salon, The Lady of the Blue Stockings, and The Lady of the Slave
States. Putnam, though personally liberated, was an intellectual product of her
times. Her judgments on the societies she writes about are mild, one might
say "ladylike." Yet, Putnam was a careful scholar and a feminist fully in touch
with the complexity of the issues involved in a discussion of societies that
created the position of "the lady."

597   Rabb, Theodore K., and Robert I. Rotberg, eds. **The Family in History:
       Interdisciplinary Essays.** New York: Harper and Row, 1971. 235p.
       bibliog. $3.95. ISBN 0061317578. LC 73-12978.
Rabb and Rotberg collect in this volume a series of essays (previously published
in the *Journal of Interdisciplinary History*, 1970-1972) in the social history
of the family. Among the papers included are: Emily R. Coleman's "Medieval
Marriage Characteristics: A Neglected Factor in the History of Medieval Serf-
dom"; Edward Shorter's "Illegitimacy, Sexual Revolution, and Social Change
in Modern Europe"; Virginia Yans McLaughlin's "Patterns of Work and Family
Organization: Buffalo's Indians"; John Demos's "Developmental Perspectives
on the History of Childhood"; Lois W. Banner's "On Writing Women's History";
David J. Rothman's "Documents in Search of a Historian: Toward a History
of Children and Youth in America"; Tamara K. Hareven's "The History of the
Family as an Interdisciplinary Field"; and C. John Sommerville's "Bibliographic
Note: Toward a History of Childhood and Youth."

598*   Rasmussen, Linda, 1950- , et al. **A Harvest Yet to Reap: A History of Prairie Women.** Toronto: Women's Press, 1975. 240p. bibliog. index. ISBN 0889610304. LC 77-361015.

A visually beautiful book about the history of women on the Canadian prairies in those early years of agricultural settlement, this overview provides a great deal of documentary material in the form of papers and writings of influential women, records from established women's organizations, and government documents related to legal reforms. The authors acknowledge that material on "ordinary" women is difficult to find and seldom is easy to gain access to in archives. Material from non-white, non-English-speaking communities is even more difficult to come by. "This is a serious deficiency in the book, which once again reflects the deficiencies of archive collections. Documents in languages other than English are rare and seldom translated." The organization of the book follows the westward movement of women as farm homemakers; the grueling routines of farm life during that establishment period; women's separate reflections about their legal and social status as farm homemakers during their years of isolation from other women on the prairie farms; the political reform years of community improvement, political reform and legislative changes when such laws affected the home; the woman's suffrage movement and its waning in the '20s. Many capsule biographies and a fine bibliography including films are here.

599   Riencourt, Amaury de. **Sex and Power in History.** New York: Dell, 1975. 469p. bibliog. index. $3.95. ISBN 0440559480.

"Essentially this work is an all-inclusive interpretation of history from end to end, as seen through the interplay of the primary biosocial forces that have shaped it—the yin and yang, the female and male principles that are the warp and woof of an intricate tapestry." De Riencourt's ambitious aims lead him on a whirlwind tour, from a posited early period in human society during which the "Great Mother" was the dominant cultural force, to a partriarchal revolution triggered by men's discovery of the secret of paternity, to the cultural transformation which ensued, replacing feminine cultural symbolism and values (cycles, womb, fertility, nature, Life) with patriarchal values (the linear, brain, abstraction, Idea over Life), through the "first feminist revolt" and the consequent (he claims) fall of Rome, to the birth of Christianity, with its synthesis of the masculine and the feminine, through the Reformation, which expelled the female component of Christianity (the Virgin), and the Renaissance, which repudiated medieval (feminine) symbolic thought and revered classical Greco-Roman thought with its emphasis on the supremacy of the rational and scientific, leading to the development of modern science and the Industrial Revolution, with all their attendant transformations—including the cultural devaluation of women and their "life-creating function." The result?—the current women's liberation movement, whose emphasis on androgyny and "unisexual values" " . . . implies a social and cultural death-wish and the end of the civilization that endorses it." As should be plain, De Riencourt is ultimately committed to the necessity of sexual differentiation and urges a rebirth of cultural identification with the "eternal feminine" as the path to salvation.

600   Rose, Al. **Storyville, New Orleans: Being an Authentic, Illustrated Account of the Notorious Red-Light District**. University: University of Alabama Press, 1974. 225p. bibliog. index. $12.50. ISBN 0817344039. LC 74-491.

This meticulous study of New Orleans's legally established red-light district (1898-1917) has attracted more critical attention since the release of Louis Malle's controversial film (based largely on Rose's book), "Pretty Baby." While *Storyville* is not a feminist account, it is fascinating as a documentary of prostitution. It is also unusual in its lack of conventional moralizing, on the one hand, and pornographic titillation, on the other. After twelve years of research, Rose is convinced that he has tracked down all extant sources—a great accomplishment, given the efforts that were taken after the District was closed down in 1917 to destroy the documentary record and the physical locale. Perhaps of most interest to readers will be chapter 9, "Some Anonymous Survivors of Storyville," which presents reminiscences of four prostitutes who worked in various grade houses, a pimp, and two customers. Rose provides interesting illustrations throughout, including a series of Ernest Bellocq's amazing photographic portraits of Storyville prostitutes. A complete collection of Bellocq's portraits is reproduced in *E. J. Bellocq: Storyville Portraits; Photographs from the New Orleans Red-Light District, circa 1912* (Museum of Modern Art, 1970), edited by John Szarkowski.

601   Rosen, Andrew. **Rise Up, Women! The Militant Campaign of the Women's Social and Political Union, 1903-1914**. Routledge and Kegan Paul, 1974. 312p. bibliog. index. $21.75. ISBN 0710079346. LC 74-81317.

Rosen has written a meticulous, scholarly study of the English Women's Social and Political Union (WSPU) from its founding in 1903 to its abandonment of militancy in the face of the First World War. The WSPU's choice of illegal and violent tactics as a means of attracting public attention to the suffrage cause distinguishes it from most suffrage organizations in the United States. The history of its militancy and of the suffrage struggle in England thus provides crucial comparative material for those trying to understand the American Woman Suffrage Movement. There is much discussion here of the Pankhursts, founders of the WSPU. Rosen has taken advantage of extensive archival sources— never previously used—in the research for this volume.

602   Rosenberg, Charles E., et al., eds. **The Family in History**. Philadelphia: University of Pennsylvania Press, 1975. 207p. bibliog. $10.00. ISBN 0812277033. LC 75-14962.

Terming the analytic approach used here "the new social history," Rosenberg argues that the social historian must rely on non-quantifiable data. "These include every kind of cultural artifact from sermons and theological exegeses to nursery rhymes and child-rearing manuals, engravings, and toys. . . . Personal documents—letters, diaries and journals—constitute still another kind of source, frustratingly erratic in the quality of truth they convey as well as in the very accident of their survival. Social historians have, in general, utilized such documents infrequently and anecdotally; the practice of using personal documents in the elucidation of social phenomena is still in its infancy. But this must inevitably change as we become increasingly concerned with ritual and belief, with the way man throughout history has dealt with the primary social processes" (from the introduction). Essays in this volume include: Lawrence Stone, "The Rise of the Nuclear Family in Early Modern England: The Patriarchal Stage"; Wolfram Eberhard, "The Upper-Class Family in Traditional China"; David Landes, "Bleichröders and Rothschilds: The Problem of Continuity in the Family Firm"; Diane Hughes, "Domestic Ideals and Social Behavior: Evidence from Medieval Genoa"; Joan W. Scott and Louise A. Tilly, "Women's Work and Family in Nineteenth-Century Europe"; and Michael Zuckerman, "Dr. Spock: The Confidence Man." Diverse in approach, all essays wrestle with the intersection of social and economic change and role shifts in the family unit. For more material on this rapidly growing field of family history, several journals are worth consulting for their consistent treatment of the subject: *Family History Newsletter, History of Childhood Quarterly*, and *The Journal of Interdisciplinary History*.

603   Rothman, Sheila M. **Woman's Proper Place: A History of Changing Ideals and Practices, 1870 to the Present.** New York: Basic Books, 1978. 322p. bibliog. index. $12.50. ISBN 0465092039. LC 78-55000.

Rothman contends that every generation has defined its own notion of women's "proper place" and set up social machinery to support the current definition. She isolates four separate shifts from the post-Civil War era to the present in attitudes toward women: "virtuous womanhood" at the close of the nineteenth century; progressivism attended by the cult of "educated motherhood" opening the twentieth century; the "wife-companion" woman of the 1920s, a romantically and sexually defined woman; and finally, the liberated woman of contemporary times, a woman defined as an achieving individual in her own right. Each of these periods ushered in social movements and reforms and technological change. The invention of the typewriter, for example, moved women into the business world. The sexual mores of the 1920s and the emphasis on woman's role as a glamorous companion gave impetus to the birth control movement. The possibility for abortion and the demand for day care have been closely tied to women's liberation, which seeks to free women from roles that restrict them as people. Each of the changes in woman's definition has been characterized by conflict within the woman and some turmoil within the family. Rothman calls for rational recognition of the conflicts in reshaping social policy.

604   Rowbotham, Sheila. **Hidden from History: Rediscovering Women in History from the 17th Century to the Present.** New York: Pantheon Books, 1975. 183p. bibliog. index. $8.95. ISBN 0394494121. LC 74-4772.

This book emerges from the same perspective that produced Sheila Rowbotham's *Women, Resistance and Revolution*, but *Hidden from History* restricts its focus primarily to England. Once again, it is essentially a sketch—more an attempt to create a new way of looking at history than to write an exhaustive account. Rowbotham is particularly interested in the ways in which patriarchy and capitalism together shape women's lives and in the connections and contradictions between feminist and socialist movements. She has written a special introduction to the American edition, tracing her own evolution as a social historian.

605   Ryan, Mary P. **Womanhood in America: From Colonial Times to the Present**. New York: New Viewpoints, 1975. 496p. bibliog. index. $15.00. ISBN 0531053652. LC 74-17318.
"The aim of this volume is to describe the making of the social and cultural category, womanhood, the artificial mold into which history has persistently shaped the female sex. . . . It is to history . . . that we turn to observe the installation of biological woman in that matrix of specialized roles, responsibilities, and characteristics called womanhood. Removed to the plane of historical analysis, the specific origins of female inequality become more concrete" (from the introduction). Ryan explores the creation and recreation of womanhood in America from the time of the colonial subsistence agrarian economy, through industrialization and into the twentieth century. The book can be highly recommended as an overview of American history, researched with feminist questions in mind, and beautifully written.

606   Sanger, William W. **The History of Prostitution**. New York: Arno Press, 1972. (Repr. of 1859 ed.). 685p. index. $32.00. ISBN 0405044771. LC 72-2621.
First published in 1859, this massive volume is the classic early study of prostitution. It was the official report to the Board of Alms-house Governors of the City of New York, compiled under the direction of the resident physician at Blackwell's Island, Dr. William Wallace Sanger. The first 450 pages and 31 chapters provide a vast historical survey, international in scope, of prostitution—its incidence, social conditions, attitudes towards and legislation governing the practice. The remainder of the study focuses on prostitution in New York City, based on a survey of 2,000 prostitutes. There is here a wealth of information documenting the harsh reality of poverty and unemployment that made (and make) women turn to prostitution to survive. Sanger is indignant about the hypocrisy of moralists who "drive a woman to starvation by refusing to give her employment, and then condemn her for maintaining a wretched existence at the price of virtue."

607   Scott, Anne Firor, 1921- . **The Southern Lady: From Pedestal to Politics, 1830-1930**. Chicago: University of Chicago Press, 1970. 247p. bibliog. index. $10.00. ISBN 0226743462. LC 73-123750.
Scott states her fourfold purpose of studying the image of the southern woman before, during, and following the Civil War and Reconstruction as follows: "to describe the culturally defined image of the lady; to trace the effect this definition had on women's behavior; to describe the realities of women's lives which were often at odds with the image; to describe and characterize the struggle of women to free themselves from the confines of cultural expectation and find a way to self-determination." The author relies on letters and diaries in redefining an image of southern womanhood before 1865, and she notes that after 1865, these materials become scarcer as women began to emerge from the domestic sphere and to create a public record. Scott writes a well-researched analysis that undercuts the image of the genteel southern lady and shows that in the South, as everywhere else in the country, the roles of women were broadened as people moved from a simpler notion of society to one more receptive to various patterns and lifestyles. Scott gives the reader a particularly fine

bibliographic essay describing the framework of her analysis: manuscripts, personal documents, biographies, contemporary commentary, some fiction, and particularly relevant scholarly books and articles.

608   Scott, Anne Firor, and Andrew MacKay Scott. **One Half the People: The Fight for Woman Suffrage.** Philadelphia, PA: Lippincott, 1975. 173p. bibliog. $3.25. ISBN 0397473338. LC 74-28032.

The Scotts view Woman Suffrage as a major social movement neglected in traditional approaches to American history and politics. In their introduction, the authors argue for the importance of their topic to the current women's movement; "the woman suffrage movement is likely to be of particular interest to contemporary women in search of liberation. The detailed issues and circumstances have changed, but the cultural conservatism and male prejudice which postponed the vote for women until 1920 remain. An analysis of the dynamics of the earlier movement—its progress, its problems—is therefore illuminating in the light of present concerns." Their study is divided into two parts, the first examining the beginnings of the movement, its leaders, the growth of women's organizations, woman's place, the National Amendment, the election of 1916, and finally ratification. Part two contains documents and excerpts including: an anonymous essay on woman's non-voting status in the seventeenth century; the Seneca Falls "Declaration of Sentiments"; Elizabeth Cady Stanton's speech on the rationale of the Woman Suffrage Amendments; the introduction of the Woman Suffrage Amendment in the Senate on May 28, 1874; and a state-by-state listing of woman suffrage gained by constitutional amendments before the passage of the 19th Amendment. The bibliographic essay in part 3 is a fine one, concisely outlining major reference works, bibliographies, and specific studies on the history of woman suffrage (particular suffragists), important primary sources, and document anthologies on feminism.

609   Sears, Hal D., 1942- . **The Sex Radicals: Free Love in High Victorian America.** Lawrence: Regents Press of Kansas, 1977. 342p. bibliog. index. $15.00. ISBN 0700601481. LC 76-49946.

The "free love" label was a misnomer, because its practitioners—an interesting assortment including Mormons, Christians, freethinkers, Oneidans, and other radicals—believed that the coercion involved in conventional domestic arrangements sullied the meaning of love and sexual relations between men and women. They hardly espoused libertinism. The sex radicals equated racial slavery with sexual slavery and tended, predictably, to be abolitionists. Sears entertainingly presents well-researched material on some of the most notorious of the nineteenth-century social reformers, including Victoria Woodhull, John Humphrey Noyes, Ezra Heywood, and Karl Heinzen. Excellent notes and a bibliographic essay are here also.

610   Smith, Julia E., 1792-1886. **Abby Smith and Her Cows.** New York: Arno Press, 1972. (Repr. of 1877 ed.). 94p. $9.00. ISBN 040504478X. LC 72-2622.

"The spinster Smith sisters, Abby Hadassah (1797-1878) and Julia Evelina (1792-1886) lived a quiet life of learning, good works and husbandry on their farm in Glastonbury, Connecticut, until 1869, when, hit by a double tax, they

raised a cry for representation and joined the fight for suffrage and women's
rights. Another tax in 1872, directed especially at women, caused these sprightly
ancient warriors to make soapbox speeches in town and to take to the courts,
even while their land and their cattle were being confiscated by the town fathers.
They fought and won their case while the whole world watched, laughed and
learned" ("A Note about This Volume," A. K. Baxter and L. Stein, eds.).
While it is only one, obscure incident in the long history of the suffrage struggle
depicted in this scrapbook of newspaper clippings, letters to the editor, and
court transcripts, the materials provided make for a good case-study in the
painfully slow process of social change—and specifically, in the power struggle
between men and women.

611   Smuts, Robert W. **Women and Work in America.** New York: Schocken
       Books, 1971. 176p. bibliog. index. $3.95. ISBN 0805202986. LC
       59-8116.
Smuts has written a slim but useful volume on women's work from 1890-1950,
using an historian's approach rather than that of the social scientist. Though
he takes a hard look at United States census data, he stresses the causes for the
statistics rather than the statistics themselves. His chapter profiling working
women of 1890 is especially fine.

612   Sochen, June, 1937- . **Herstory: A Woman's View of American History.**
       New York: Alfred, 1974. 448p. bibliog. index. $12.50. ISBN
       0882840177. LC 74-80471.
Sochen writes a readable introduction to American women's history from 1600
to 1973. She takes a distinctive approach in focusing attention not just on
women, but also on children, blacks, Native Americans, foreigners, the environment—in other words, on all victims of the developing power structure of what
she terms "WASMs" (white Anglo-Saxon males). She argues that "there are
more similarities than differences between the white male attitude toward women,
Indians, black slaves, forests, and wildlife than historians have realized." Her
account is enlivened by the addition of relevant quotations, song lyrics, and
illustrations. Readers will find her suggestions for further reading helpful.
Sochen has written another. more in-depth historical analysis of a period covered
only briefly in *Herstory—The New Woman: Feminism in Greenwich Village,
1910-1920* (Quadrangle Books, 1972). In this book, Sochen focuses on five
feminists who lived in Greenwich Village during the 1910s: Crystal Eastman,
a radical pacifist and lawyer; Henrietta Rodman, who designed a working women's
cooperative apartment house (never built); Ida Rauh, a Jewish Marxist-feminist;
and Neith Boyce and Susan Glaspell, fiction writers.

613   Sochen, June, 1937- . **Movers and Shakers: American Women Thinkers
       and Activists, 1900-1970.** New York: Quadrangle Books, 1973. 320p.
       bibliog. index. $8.95. ISBN 0812903609. LC 73-76290.
This is a well-known and respected historical study of twentieth-century American
women intellectuals and activists, selected specifically for their efforts to
consciously struggle with the constraints shaping their lives as women. Sochen
looks at some familiar names, such as Emma Goldman and Alice Paul, as well
as at such lesser-known women as Rose Schneiderman and Agnes Nestor (the

former, a candidate for the Senate in 1920 and later an official in Franklin D.
Roosevelt's administration; the latter, a vice-president of the International
Glove Workers Union of America and involved in the Women's Trade Union
League).

614   Sprague, William Forrest. **Women and the West: A Short Social History.**
       New York: Arno Press, 1972. (Repr. of 1940 ed.). 294p. bibliog.
       $13.00. ISBN 0405044801. LC 72-2624.

"The chief purposes of the work are to portray the hardships and accomplishments of the female pioneers in the trans-Alleghany region, and to mention
somewhat more sketchily the important effects of the westward movement
upon the lives of women in the older sections of the nation" (from the preface).
Women and the West further considers "the economic and social aspects of
western life which assisted [the female] sex in its struggle for greater legal and
political rights." Particularly relevant to this last focus are chapters five ("The
Last West Gives Equal Suffrage Its First Chance") and six ("Western Feminism
in the Nineties"). One limitation of Sprague's study is that it is confined to women
of European descent, excluding women of Native American tribes and of Oriental
ancestry. An appendix includes brief accounts by women of diverse backgrounds
about their experiences in the West. The bibliography is quite extensive, though
of course dated (1940).

615   Spruill, Julia Cherry. **Women's Life and Work in the Southern Colonies.**
       New York: Russell and Russell, 1969. (Repr. of 1938 ed.). 426p.
       bibliog. index. $15.00. ISBN 0846213400. LC 71-75468.

Spruill originally undertook this research in the late 1920s, hoping to write a
book about changing attitudes toward women in the South. She soon realized
that she would herself have to lay the necessary groundwork in social history,
and hence came to confine her focus to the life and status of women in the
English colonies of the South. Working primarily from contemporary records,
she explored "the everyday life of women, their function in the settlement of
colonies, their homes and domestic occupations, their social life and recreations,
the aims and methods of their education, their participation in affairs outside
the house, and the manner in which they were regarded by the law and by society
in general." While this is a pioneering and invaluable work, it should be remarked
that the women she is concerned with are white women and that the lives of
black slave women remain incidental to the account.

616   Stone, Lawrence. **The Family, Sex and Marriage in England, 1500-1800.**
       New York: Harper and Row, 1977. 800p. bibliog. index. $30.00.
       ISBN 0060141425. LC 77-50.

Written by the distinguished historian Lawrence Stone (Dodge Professor at
Princeton), *Family, Sex and Marriage* is a work of overwhelming scope: 800
pages depict the history of the family in England over the three centuries from
1500 to 1800. Stone's opus is noteworthy for its unusual wealth of detail and
anecdotes and for its suggested typology of changes in family structure during
the period under investigation. Stone argues that the "open-lineage family"—
a wide kin network placing scant importance on privacy—gave rise to a transitional form he calls the "restricted, patriarchal, nuclear family"—a narrower

domestic circle under the authority of the father—to culminate in the "closed, domesticated, nuclear family"—an even narrower and more private circle, but characterized by warmer and more egalitarian family relations. This last form he identifies as possessing the basic characteristics of the modern family, which, he asserts, was well established by 1750 in the middle and upper classes of England. He attributes these changes in the family to the emergence of "affective individualism." While feminist readers and scholars may or may not find Stone's controversial typology useful, the work merits attention on at least two grounds— its standing in the discipline of history and its rich offering of historical detail.

617   Stuard, Susan Mosher, ed. **Women in Medieval Society**. Philadelphia: University of Pennsylvania Press, 1976. 219p. bibliog. index. $15.00. ISBN 0812277082. LC 75-41617.

A collection of articles in the social history of women in medieval society, this includes: "Land, Family, and Women in Continental Europe, 701-1200," by David Herlihy; "Infanticide in the Early Middle Ages," by Emily Coleman; "Marriage and Divorce in the Frankish Kingdom," by Jo-Ann McNamara and Suzanne F. Wemple; "Widow and Ward: The Feudal Law of Child Custody in Medieval England," by Sue Sheridan Walker; and "Dowries and Kinsmen in Early Renaissance Venice," by Stanley Chojnacki.

618   Summers, Montague, 1880-1948. **The Geography of Witchcraft**. Secaucus, NJ: Citadel Press, 1973. $4.95. ISBN 0806503912.

In this scholarly and wide-ranging study of witchcraft, Summers traces witch-craft and sorcery in Greece and Rome, Scotland, New England, France, Germany, Italy, and Spain. This work is complementary to Summers's *History of Witch-craft and Demonology*.

619   Sumner, Helen L. **History of Women in Industry in the United States**. Washington: Govt. Print. Off., 1910; repr. New York: Arno Press, 1974. 277p. bibliog. index. $15.00. ISBN 0405061242. LC 74-3976.

"Helen Laura Sumner (Woodbury) (1876-1933) was a member of the group of scholars and faculty who under the direction of John R. Commons at the University of Wisconsin produced the foundation studies of American labor history. In later life she did studies for the Children's Bureau but her major work in labor studies was done in the first decade of this century. This volume was published in 1910 as the ninth volume of the massive report on the conditions of women and child wage earners which was sponsored by the United States Bureau of Labor Statistics. It is a thorough summary of the conditions under which women have worked from colonial times until the 20th century. The environment of work, the position relative to men in terms of wages and hours, housework, the fate of children and the family are all documented as women moved from the home to the factory and American enterprise evolved into the corporate structure and mass production" ("A Note about This Volume," L. Stein and A. K. Baxter, eds.). Among Sumner's specific topics are: changes in occupations of women; history of labor conditions; textile industries; clothing and the sewing trades; domestic and personal service; food and kindred products; tobacco and cigar factory operatives; paper and printing industries; trade and transportation (including saleswomen and office workers). A lengthy appendix provides many statistical tables documenting the occupational changes described by Sumner in the text.

620   Thompson, Roger, 1933- . **Women in Stuart England and America: A Comparative Study.** Boston: Routledge and Kegan Paul, 1974. 276p. bibliog. index. $13.25. ISBN 0710078226. LC 73-93638.
Puritanism, legal status and rights, home life, interpersonal relations, and economics are some of the issues with which Thompson deals with here. It would be helpful for the reader to look at Richard Vann's "Toward a New Lifestyle: Women in Pre-industrial Capitalism," in *Becoming Visible: Women in European History*, edited by Bridenthal and Koonz (Boston, Houghton Mifflin, 1977), along with Thompson.

621*   Trofimenkoff, Susan Mann, 1941- , and Alison L. Prentice, eds. **The Neglected Majority: Essays in Canadian Women's History.** Toronto: McClelland and Stewart, 1977. 192p. bibliog. $5.95. ISBN 0771085958. LC 77-365876.
Spanning the historical period of the fur trade to the Second World War, this book of essays outlines the roles and contributions of Canadian women to their history and society. Contents are: Isabel Foulché-Delbosc, "Women of Three Rivers: 1651-63"; Sylvia Van Kirk, "The Impact of White Women on Fur Trade Society"; Alison Prentice, "The Feminization of Teaching"; D. Suzanne Cross, "The Neglected Majority: The Changing Role of Women in 19th Century Montreal"; Veronica Strong-Boag, " 'Setting the Stage': National Organization and the Women's Movement in the Late 19th Century"; Susan Mann Trofimenkoff, "Henri Bourassa and 'the Woman Question' "; Mary Vipond, "The Image of Women in Mass Circulation Magazines in the 1920s"; Ruth Pierson, "Women's Emancipation and the Recruitment of Women into the Labour Force in World War II." The bibliographical essay introduces periodical literature, "state-of-the-art" approaches, bibliographies, general accounts, primary and secondary sources, and approaches dealing in detail with specific periods from the seventeenth to the twentieth century.

622   Vicinus, Martha, ed. **Suffer and Be Still: Women in the Victorian Age.** Bloomington: Indiana University Press, 1972. 239p. index. $10.00. ISBN 0253355729. LC 71-184524.
Concentrating on the "high Victorian" decades of the 1850s and '60s, Vicinus had edited an anthology that barely begins to hoe the neglected ground of women's situation in nineteenth-century British history. Essays are: Martha Vicinus, "The Perfect Victorian Lady"; M. Jeanne Peterson, "The Victorian Governess: Status Incongruence in Family and Society"; Jane W. Stedman, "W. S. Gilbert and Theatrical Transvestism"; Elaine and English Showalter, "Victorian Women and Menstruation"; Helen E. Roberts, "The Painter's View of Women in the First Twenty-Five Years of Victoria's Reign"; Sigsworth and Wyke, "A Study of Victorian Prostitution and Venereal Disease"; Peter N. Stearns, "Working-Class Women in Britain, 1890-1914"; Kate Millett, "The Debate over Women: Ruskin vs. Mill"; Jill Conway, "Stereotypes of Femininity in a Theory of Sexual Evolution"; Peter T. Cominos, "Innocent *Femina Sensualis* in Unconscious Conflict"; and Barbara Kanner, "The Women of England in a

Century of Social Change 1815-1914: A Select Bibliography." Interested readers will also want to look at the follow-up to this anthology, *A Widening Sphere* (Indiana University Press, 1977), also edited by Vicinus.

623   Vicinus, Martha, 1939- , ed. **A Widening Sphere: Changing Roles of Victorian Women.** Bloomington: Indiana University Press, 1977. 326p. index. $15.00. ISBN 0253365406. LC 76-26433.

In this follow-up to her other edited volume, *Suffer and Be Still*, Vicinus explores recent trends in scholarly treatments of Victorian women. Among the essays included: Lee Holcombe, "Victorian Wives and Property"; Judith Walkowitz, "The Making of an Outcast Group: Prostitutes and Working Women in Nineteenth-Century Plymouth and Southampton"; Shelia Ryan Johansson, "Sex and Death in Victorian England: An Examination of Age- and Sex-Specific Death Rates, 1840-1910." Of special interest is Barbara Kanner's "The Women of England in a Century of Social Change, 1815-1914: A Select Bibliography, Part II."

624   Welter, Barbara. **Dimity Convictions: The American Woman in the Nineteenth Century.** Athens: Ohio University Press, 1976. 230p. bibliog. $12.00. ISBN 0821403524. LC 76-8305.

Among the essays Welter gives us are: "The American Girl in the Nineteenth Century"; "The Cult of True Womanhood: 1800-1860"; "Female Complaints: Medical Views of American Women"; "The Feminization of American Religion 1800-1860"; and "Margaret Fuller, a Woman of the Nineteenth Century." Many of these essays have been given as lectures. They are well documented as well as entertaining.

625   Welter, Barbara, comp. **The Woman Question in American History.** Athens: Ohio University Press, 1976. bibliog. $12.00. ISBN 0821403524. LC 76-8305.

Includes Walter O'Meara, "American Indian Women"; William R. Taylor, "Ante-Bellum Southern Women"; Aileen S. Kraditor, "Ideology of the Suffrage Movement"; Eleanor Flexner, "Enemies of Suffrage"; Christopher Lasch, "Woman as Alien"; Kate Millett, "The Politics of Sex." Excellent essays, often taken from longer works, provide a glimpse of "the woman question" using a variety of perspectives and methodological approaches from the conventionally historical to the psychoanalytical.

626   Wertheimer, Barbara M. **We Were There: The Story of Working Women in America.** New York: Pantheon Books, 1977. 427p. bibliog. index. $15.95. ISBN 039449590X. LC 76-9597.

This is an extremely significant book, meticulously researched and well written, which pays attention to all strata of American working women—domestics, American Indian agricultural workers, shop clerks, mill workers, nurses, soldiers. Although Wertheimer relies on conventional historical markers in defining the evolution of social and legal conditions for women workers, she distinguishes herself in providing a great deal of background on black women workers, notably in her chapters "Black Women in Colonial America" and "In Factory and Field: Black Women and Slavery in America, 1808-1860." A particularly excellent and detailed bibliography, this would be useful to read in conjunction with the

Baxandall, et al., *America's Working Women*, a collection of primary historical materials on working women from the same period of American history, and also Gerda Lerner's two collections of primary-source material, *The Female Experience* and *Black Women in White America*. Another important study by Wertheimer, co-authored with Anne H. Nelson, is *Trade Union Women: A Study of Their Participation in New York City Locals* (Praeger, 1975).

627 Wertz, Richard W., and Dorothy C. Wertz. **Lying-in: A History of Childbirth in America.** New York: Free Press, 1977. 260p. bibliog. index. $10.00. ISBN 0029345103. LC 77-72040.

Viewing the threefold nature of childbirth as a creative, biological, and social event, this history of childbirth in America over the last 350 years attempts to chronicle shifting theories and attitudes, which have in turn affected procedures, techniques, and settings for childbirth. Noting the transformation of the art of childbirth to the science of obstetrical practice, the Wertzs observe: "childbirth as a social event aided by the cunning of women becomes a medical event aided by the tools and skills of men. Childbirth as an act of God becomes a medical indicator of the health of the whole society" (introduction). Chapters include: Midwives and Social Childbirth in Colonial America; The New Midwifery; Modesty and Morality; The Wounds of Birth: Birthpain and Puerperal Fever; Birth in the Hospital; Natural Childbirth; and Government Involvement. The authors cover a great diversity of medical and historical sources, which their extensive bibliographical essay outlines. Important complementary reading will be Mary Walsh, *"Doctors Wanted, No Women Need Apply": Sexual Barriers in the Medical Profession 1835-1975* (1977); Suzanne Arms, *Immaculate Deception: A New Look at Women and Childbirth in America* (1975); Judy Barrett Litoff, *American Midwives: 1860 to the Present* (Greenwood Press, 1978); and Jane B. Donegan, *Women and Men Midwives: Medicine, Morality, and Misogyny in Early America* (Greenwood Press, 1978).

628 Wisconsin. State Historical Society. **Women's History: Resources at the State Historical Society of Wisconsin.** (3rd ed., enl.). By James P. Danky and Eleanor McKay. Madison: The Society, 1976. 29p. index. $1.25. ISBN 0870201522. LC 75-14243.

Danky and McKay have accomplished no small feat in outlining and describing the Society's vast resources on women's history. "Since its founding 130 years ago the society has collected printed materials, manuscripts, archival materials, pictures, and museum artifacts that detail the accomplishments and positions of women in North American society" (from the introduction). Under the broad heading "Library Resources," the authors have described specific materials and research strategies to locate catalogs, subject headings, newspapers, periodicals, government documents, and census materials. In addition, they give general orientation information to guide the user of the Society's library. Their approach to archives and manuscripts is similarly thorough. Topics covered under this broad heading include the Draper Collection, Family Life, Religious Organizations, Educational Institutions, Women's Rights, Employment and Professional Activity, The Arts and Mass Communications, Social Action, Women's Clubs, Municipal and State Records, and University of Wisconsin—Madison Resources. Mention is made of particularly rich clusters of materials in iconography and the Museum of the Historical Society (e.g., photographs documenting women's roles and photographs augmenting the manuscript collections in iconography; all manner of art work, costume, and household furnishings in the Museum). Indexing is thorough. The fourth edition of this resource guide will appear in 1979 under the same title, authored by Danky, Youtz, and McKay.

629   Woman's Rights Convention, Seneca Falls, N.Y., 1848. **Woman's Rights Conventions, Seneca Falls and Rochester, 1848.** New York: Arno Press, 1969. 9, 16p. $3.50. ISBN 0405001177. LC 76-79180. This is a reprint of the 1870 edition, which was published under the title: *Proceedings of the Woman's Rights Conventions Held at Seneca Falls and Rochester, N.Y., July & August, 1848.* This work includes *Proceedings of the Woman's Rights Convention, Held at the Unitarian Church, Rochester, N.Y., August 2, 1848,* published in 1848. The Seneca Falls Convention—called by Elizabeth Cady Stanton, Lucretia Mott, and Martha C. Wright—was the first United States woman's rights convention. There a "Declaration of Sentiments" was issued, drafted by Stanton and based on the Declaration of Independence, that proclaimed the equality of men and women and protested existing legal inequities. The convention also adopted a resolution advocating suffrage for women, which marked the initiation of what was to be a 70-year-long struggle to win the franchise. The convention was reconvened two weeks later in Rochester, New York, where it attracted larger numbers of men and women, many of whom signed the "Declaration of Sentiments."

630   **Working Girls of Cincinnati.** New York: Arno Press, 1974. 45, 76, 52p. bibliog. $10.00. ISBN 0405061293. LC 74-3981. Three separate studies of working women in Cincinnati early in the century are collected here: 1) Annette Mann's *Women Workers in Factories*, "a study of working conditions in 275 industrial establishments in Cincinnati and adjoining towns" (originally published in 1918 by the Consumers' League of Cincinnati); 2) Frances Ivins Rich's *Wage-Earning Girls of Cincinnati*, a study of "the wages, employment, housing, food, recreation and education of a sample group" (originally published in 1927 by the Helen S. Trounstine Foundation and the YWCA of Cincinnati); and 3) Frances R. Whitney's *What Girls Live On and How*, "a study of the expenditures of a sample group of girls employed in Cincinnati in 1929" (originally published in 1930 by the Consumers' League of Cincinnati).

631   Zahm, John Augustine [Mozans, H. J.], 1851-1921. **Woman in Science: With an Introductory Chapter on Woman's Long Struggle for Things of the Mind.** New York: Appleton, 1913; repr. Cambridge, MA: MIT Press, 1974. 452p. bibliog. index. $17.50. ISBN 0262131137. LC 74-7889. Writing in the flowery prose style of the turn of the century, Mozans sets out "to review the progress and achievements of woman in science from her earliest efforts in ancient Greece down to the present time. I shall relate how, in every department of natural knowledge, when not inhibited by her environment, she has been the colleague and emulatress, if not the peer, of the most illustrious men who have contributed to the increase and diffusion of human learning." A useful survey of the history of science with an emphasis on contributions by women up to 1913, the book reflects a liberated male viewpoint of the early

nineteenth century, with attention to mathematics, astronomy, physics, chemistry, the natural sciences, medicine and surgery, archaeology, woman inventors, and women inspirers and collaborators. The author concludes with a somewhat romantic forecast of "the Golden Age of Science—the Golden Age of cultured, noble, perfect womanhood."

LANGUAGE AND LINGUISTICS

The sparse material in this chapter reflects the state of the art. Periodical literature surfaces through the identification tool, *Women's Studies Abstracts*. Women's use of language in literature shows up in works of feminist criticism identified in the section, Literature: History and Criticism.

632   Henley, Nancy. **Body Politics: Power, Sex, and Nonverbal Communication.** Englewood Cliffs, NJ: Prentice-Hall, 1977. 214p. bibliog. index. $9.95. ISBN 0130796409. LC 76-53030.

Henley's work on language has had some impact. She is co-compiler of *She Said/He Said*. In *Body Politics*, she is particularly interested in power relations and how power is conveyed through nonverbal communication. She notes that studies have shown women to be more sensitive to nonverbal communication than men, yet nonverbal behavior has often been used against them in the display of sex and class differences. (For example, rape victims have often been blamed for *appearing to be* giving seductive body signals.) Some of Henley's conclusions about body language and women's liberation may seem obvious— e.g., that women need to stop smiling except when they feel it; to give supportive, attentive nonverbal listening cues to other women; to stare people in the eye; and to touch people when it seems right. Henley suggests that men need to start smiling, stop interrupting, value women's speech by listening, and avoid excessive touching and invasion of women's space. The same suggestions apply to the rearing of children. Basic, but when one reads this book it becomes painfully obvious how often women take submissive stances because of their nonverbal communication patterns. Henley suggests new directions for research.

633   Hiatt, Mary P., 1920- . **The Way Women Write.** New York: Teachers College Press, 1977. 152p. bibliog. $4.95. ISBN 0807725420. LC 77-14122.

Noting that often critics' use of impressionistic adjectives to describe an author's writing—e.g., sensitive, masculine, virile, strong, flowery, lyrical—may "be attached more to the critic's concern with or notions about the gender of an author than with any true stylistic description," Hiatt proceeds to analyze over 200,000 words of contemporary prose in 100 recent works, half by men and half by women. Using a computer analysis, Hiatt's is the first objective study of writing style differences in the work of male and female published writers. This synchronic study includes fiction and non-fiction randomly chosen from works published during the 1960s and 1970s in the United States in order to confine the data to one linguistic era. Her data reveal much surprising information. If sentence length is any indication, for example, women write shorter sentences and terser prose. In non-fiction, women tend to use less frequent exclamations and to support their ideas with reasons rather than to announce conclusions. Very little difference in style was found in the fiction writing. Women tend to employ parallelism in their rhetoric more frequently than do male writers and thus achieve more balanced writing. In fiction, Hiatt finds men's use of similes more predictable and clichéd than the more complex use of similes made by women writers. Men and women use approximately the same number of adverbs in writing, though women tend to use adverbs of emotion, and men adverbs of pace. Hiatt concludes, "in many ways, the nature of much criticism of the feminine style is revealed to be unfair and distorted, because most often men have done the judging and based their judgments on the standard of masculine style."

634   Key, Mary Ritchie. **Male/Female Language, With a Comprehensive Bibliography.** Metuchen, NJ: Scarecrow Press, 1975. 200p. bibliog. index. $7.00. ISBN 0810807483. LC 74-19105.
"As I researched the linguistic studies on 'women's language,' it became abundantly clear that men were left out. . . . Often the studies simply reiterated the old saw that women were peculiar and their speech types 'abnormal' or 'cute' or somehow less than normal. Equally balanced studies of female *and* male differences and varieties are needed, in order to understand the whole" (from the preface). Among the topics that Key discusses are dialect differences, styles of speech, labels and descriptors, titles, names and greetings, early education and language ability, nonverbal extra-linguistic messages, and "an androgynous language" of the future. Key illustrates her analysis with a sequence of comic strips that have appeared since the current women's movement. She concludes the volume with an extensive, but unannotated, bibliography.

635   Kroeber, Karl, 1926- . **Styles in Fictional Structure: The Art of Jane Austen, Charlotte Brontë, George Eliot.** Princeton, NJ: Princeton University Press, 1971. 293p. bibliog. index. $15.00. ISBN 0691061912. LC 72-113004.
Kroeber is concerned with the stylistic techniques of Brontë, Eliot, and Austen, and thus has much to say in his study about linguistics and stylistics. Scholars interested in comparing the use of words among novelists will find the appendix material fascinating (e.g., words referring to parts of the body and bodily movement by Austen, Dickens, Brontë, and Eliot).

636   Lakoff, Robin T. **Language and Woman's Place.** New York: Harper and Row, 1975; repr. New York: Octagon Books, 1976. 83p. bibliog. $8.00. ISBN 0374947104. LC 76-27825.
Beginning from the premise that "language uses us as much as we use language," Lakoff (a linguist by training) analyzes some of the implications of the language used by and about women. In part 1, "Language and Woman's Place," Lakoff presents evidence that women's speech patterns differ in observable ways from those of men and that common language treats women as sexual objects, as animals, or solely in relation to men. Lakoff illustrates her discussion with numerous examples (e.g., "Why can't you say: '*John is Mary's widower*'?"). In part 2, "Why Women Are Ladies," Lakoff discusses norms governing politeness in our society and the way in which they often function to silence women. These two essays are only a beginning foray into the sexual politics of language, but they succeed in raising some interesting questions.

637   Miller, Casey, and Kate Swift. **Words and Women.** Garden City, NY:
       Anchor Press, 1976. 197p. bibliog. index. $7.95. ISBN 0385048572.
       LC 75-36601.
Swift and Miller are interested in the complex relationship between language
and social structure. More specifically, they want to understand how it is that
the English language is both product of the prevailing structure of sexual
inequality and bulwark to that structure. Chapters are included on personal
names, on the use of "man" as generic, the history of the English gender system,
positive and negative connotations of male and female descriptive terms, religion
and language, how the English language developed its sexist biases, comparative
male/female patterns of language use, the specter of unisex language, and language and liberation. In an epilog, the authors give brief discussions of specific
language problems or controversies, such as "-ess" endings (e.g., "authoress"),
forms of address, job titles, "-person" compounds (e.g., "salesperson"), and
"they" as a singular pronoun. Interesting examples and historical derivations are
interspersed throughout.

638   Thorne, Barrie, and Nancy Henley, eds. **Language and Sex: Difference
       and Dominance.** Rowley, MA: Newbury House, 1975. 311p. bibliog.
       index. $8.95. ISBN 0883770431. LC 76-379519.
This collection of twelve articles makes a valuable contribution to the emerging
field of feminist linguistics. Contributors from the disciplines of linguistics,
English, sociology, communications, and child development present new empirical
evidence and/or reassess existing data on the complex interrelationship between
language, sex and power. The editors' lead article, entitled "Difference and
Dominance: An Overview of Language, Gender, and Society," considers the
interplay between study of the sexual politics of language and actual linguistic
change in society. The collection of essays is followed by a substantial annotated
bibliography on the topic, also available as a separate publication from Know,
Inc. (*She Said/He Said: An Annotated Bibliography of Sex Differences in Language, Speech, and Nonverbal Communication*; 1975).

Material here tends to be practical and informational in both tone and content, clustering around the topics of ERA, women's marriage and divorce rights under the law in various states, rape, and abortion from a legal rather than sociological perspective. Legal materials also show up in the chapter, Reference: Bibliographies. A good journal covering the law from a women's studies perspective is *Woman's Rights Law Reporter*. The microfilmed "Woman and the Law" collection compiled by the Women's History Research Center in Berkeley contains a massive amount of file information documenting all aspects of women-related legal issues, including women as lawyers, sex discrimination, female offenders, racism, and employment.

639   Alexander, Shana, 1925- . **Shana Alexander's State-by-State Guide to Women's Legal Rights.** Los Angeles: Wollstonecraft, 1975. 224p. $12.95. ISBN 0883810085. LC 74-10169.
Marriage, divorce, property, rape, abortion, custody, and employment are areas of law that are compared in an alphabetically arranged guide to state laws that affect women. Inequities in existing laws and trends in the improvement of laws to end discrimination against women are noted. Caution must be exercised when using reference materials on the law as this is a very dynamic subject area; many changes have accurred since 1975.

640   Anthony, Susan Brownell, 1820-1906, defendant. **An Account of the Proceedings on the Trial of Susan B. Anthony, On the Charge of Illegal Voting, at the Presidential Election in Nov., 1872.** Rochester, NY: Daily Democrat and Chronicle Book Print, 1874; repr. New York: Arno Press, 1974. 212p. $14.00. ISBN 0405060726. LC 74-3923.
This is an account of the trial of Susan B. Anthony for the crime of attempting to vote, along with thirteen other women, in the presidential and congressional elections of 1872. Anthony claimed that the right to vote was hers and all women's, based on the privileges and immunities granted by the Fourteenth Amendment. Needless to say, her claim was denied, a verdict of guilty was pronounced by the court (bypassing the jury), and Anthony was fined $100. Particularly inspiring is the verbatim account of her speech upon receiving her sentence.

641   Babcock, Barbara Allen, et al. **Sex Discrimination and the Law: Causes and Remedies.** Boston: Little, Brown, 1975. 1092p. index. $22.50. ISBN 0316074209. LC 74-21219.
Though this kind of text is out of date before it is printed, nonetheless it is and will undoubtedly continue to be a very valuable and widely used sourcebook on sex discrimination and the law. It provides in one place and in compact form the key materials for a history of the legal status of women in the United States: cases and statutory materials; articles; historical, economic, and sociological materials; practice manuals; and notes by the authors (Barbara Allen Babcock, Ann E. Freedman, Eleanor Holmes Norton, and Susan C. Ross). Major topics

are: Constitutional Law and Feminist History; Employment Discrimination; Sex Role Discrimination in the Law of the Family; Women and the Criminal Law; and Women's Rights to Control Their Reproductive Capacities, Obtain Equal Education, and Gain Equal Access to Places of Public Accommodation. Readers may also wish to consult Kenneth Davidson, et al., *Text, Cases and Materials on Sex-Based Discrimination in Family Law* (1974; 1975 supplement).

642   Baer, Judith A. **The Chains of Protection: The Judicial Response to Women's Labor Legislation.** Westport, CT: Greenwood Press, 1978. 238p. bibliog. index. $16.95. ISBN 0837197856. LC 77-82695.

This study of protective labor legislation for women in the United States is particularly valuable for its historical approach, which seeks the relationship between women's labor history and the labor movement and labor history in general and which distinguishes between the *motives* of labor reformers and the *effects* of the reforms they achieve. Thus, while Baer confirms the discriminatory impact that protective legislation has had historically on women, she also finds that those struggling for the legislation had a multiplicity of aims, many of them in women's interests. After setting the historical context of nineteenth-century industrialization, women's working conditions, and the evolving labor movement, Baer moves into a detailed historical analysis of court decisions on protective legislation. This analysis is broken down into four historical segments: first, the period ending in 1908 with the landmark *Muller v. Oregon* case, which simultaneously legitimized economic regulation of freedom of contract and established a precedent validating protective legislation for women on the basis of sex differences; second, 1908-1937, during which the courts considered expansion of the *Muller* decision to general labor legislation and to other types of special women's labor legislation; third, 1937 to the present, during which the *Muller* precedent has been endlessly elaborated and expanded; and fourth, the period since the Equal Pay Act (1963) and the Civil Rights Act (1964) raised questions about the discriminatory impact of protective legislation. In her final two chapters, Baer turns her attention to the underlying moral issues, in particular the question of the justice of differential treatment of the sexes. A lengthy bibliography, an index of cases, and a subject index are appended.

643   Barnett, Walter. **Sexual Freedom and the Constitution: An Inquiry into the Constitutionality of Repressive Sex Laws.** Albuquerque: University of New Mexico Press, 1973. 333p. bibliog. index. $10.00. ISBN 0826302556. LC 72-94661.

The author, a professor at the University of New Mexico School of Law, is concerned with the way our legal system assumes marriage and heterosexuality as moral norms and consequently discriminates against "deviants" (single people and especially homosexuals). He also considers the constitutionality of laws against heterosexual "deviance"—for example, sodomy laws. Chapters include The Right-of-Privacy Doctrine, Establishment of Religion, The Scientific View of Psychosexual Deviation, The "Sickness Theory" of Homosexuality and the Prospects for "Cure," and Equal Protection of the Laws. A Statutory Appendix is included at the end.

644   Brandeis, Louis Dembitz, 1856-1941, and Josephine Clara Goldmark,
       1877-1950. **Women in Industry.** New York: Arno Press, 1969. (Repr.
       of 1908 ed.). 113p. $10.00. ISBN 0405021062. LC 73-89720.
In this volume are reprinted the decision of the United States Supreme Court
in the case of *Muller v. Oregon* and the famous brief prepared for the state of
Oregon by Louis Brandeis and Josephine Goldmark. *Muller v. Oregon* was the
first decision to uphold "protective laws" for women only in industry, and it
was followed by many more such decisions based on its authority. Prior to the
Muller case, limitations on hours and wages had been held invalid based on the
doctrine of liberty of contract. Brandeis argued that "protective laws" for women
were valid because of the physical differences between men and women and
the threat posed to women's childbearing by bad working conditions and over-
work. The case became one of the most frequently cited authorities for the
view that sex is a valid basis for legislative classification, and it has continued
to serve as an obstacle to the achievement of equal treatment for women under
the law. Readers may be interested in the recent historical analysis of protective
legislation, *The Chains of Protection*, by Judith A. Baer (1978).

645   Brown, Barbara A., et al. **Women's Rights and the Law: The Impact
       of the ERA on State Laws.** New York: Praeger, 1977. 432p. bibliog.
       $30.00. ISBN 0030223164. LC 77-9961.
Endorsed by many advocate groups of the ERA, contents of this book include:
an essay by Hazel Greenberg, "The ERA in Context: Its Impact on Society";
Equal Rights Amendment Theory, including a legislative history of the federal
amendment and state ERA cases; Methodology of State Legislative Reform;
Criminal Law; Domestic Relations; Employment and Employment Related
Benefits; Civil Rights and Public Obligations; Antidiscrimination Laws. This is
a major source book for factual information about the ERA.

646   California. Equal Rights Amendment Project. **Impact ERA: Limitations
       and Possibilities.** Edited by the Equal Rights Amendment Project of
       the California Commission on the Status of Women. Millbrae, CA:
       Les Femmes, 1976. 287p. bibliog. index. $4.95. ISBN 0890879192.
       LC 76-4908.
Brought together here is a collection of articles that consider the political,
economic, social, and psychological impact implicit in the Equal Rights Amendment. Within each of these categories, different authors discuss the probable
limitations and possibilities of such impact. Among the twenty authors represented here are Jo Freeman, Carolyn Shaw Bell, Cynthia Fuchs Epstein, Lenore J.
Weitzman, Marc Feigen Fasteau, Beverly Chiñas, and Naomi Weisstein.

647   Chappell, Duncan, et al., eds. **Forcible Rape: The Crime, the Victim,
       and the Offender.** New York: Columbia University Press, 1977. 393p.
       bibliog. index. $15.00. LC 77-3377.
Edited by Duncan Chappell, Robley Geis, and Gilbert Geis, this is a collection
of articles (many published here for the first time) on the subject of hetero-
sexual forcible rape. Among them are: "Rape: The All-American Crime," by
Susan Griffin; "Rape and Rape Law: Sexism in Society and Law," by Camille E.
Le Grand; "Forcible Rape in the United States: A Statistical Profile," by

Michael J. Hindelang and Bruce L. Davis; "Race, Rape, and the Death Penalty," by Marvin E. Wolfgang and Marc Riedel; "Judicial Attitudes Toward Rape Victims," by Carol Bohmer; "The Hitchhike Victim of Rape: A Research Report," by Steve Nelson and Manachem Amir; "The Psychology of Rapists," by Murray L. Cohen, Ralph Garofalo, Richard B. Boucher, and Theoharis Seghorn; "Rape Trauma Syndrome," by Ann Wolbert Burgess and Lynda Lytle Holmstrom; and "The Philadelphia Rape Victim Project," by Joseph J. Peters. An introduction by Gilbert Geis relates the question of rape and the material presented in this collection to developments in the women's movement, social science, and legal reform. A bibliography for further research is appended. A classic feminist analysis of rape is the New York Radical Feminists' *Rape: The First Sourcebook for Women*, edited by Noreen Connell and Cassandra Wilson (New American Library, 1974).

648*   Davidson, Kenneth M., et al. **Text, Cases and Materials on Sex-Based Discrimination in Family Law.** St. Paul, MN: West, 1974. 1031p. **[1975 Supplement**: West, 1975. 167p.] . bibliog. index. LC 74-4513.
Compiled by Kenneth M. Davidson (associate professor of law, SUNY Buffalo), Ruth Bader Ginsburg (professor of law, Columbia University), and Herma Hill Kay (professor of law, University of California, Berkeley), this casebook on sex-based discrimination in family law would be most profitably used in conjunction with another sourcebook on similar topics, *Sex Discrimination and the Law*, by Barbara Babcock, et al. While the Davidson book limits itself essentially to cases and statutory materials, the Babcock text has, in addition, a great deal of historical, economic, and sociological literature, which helps put the legal history in context. Chapters in Davidson's text are as follows: Constitutional Aspects; Sexual Interaction Within the Family; Women and Employment; Educational Opportunity; and A Glance at Normative Aspects of the Criminal Law in Delineating Sex Roles. A Statutory Appendix and Table of Cases are included. Readers will also want to consult the 1975 supplement to this text.

649   DeCrow, Karen. **Sexist Justice.** New York: Random House, 1974. 329p. bibliog. $7.95. ISBN 0394484037. LC 73-15835.
DeCrow states in chapter 1, "this book is not a summary or a compendium of the laws on women. It is a feminist analysis of the laws, the legislators, the judges, the lawyers and the law professors that make up our legal system. Clearly, the 'hydraulic pressure' at work in virtually all litigation involving women is the misogyny present in legal institutions and in the men who create and run them." DeCrow's writing style tends to be anecdotal, biting, rhetorical. Those who have read her *Young Woman's Guide to Liberation* will recognize her approach, one that puts no stock in male institutions or token efforts toward combatting discrimination. As a lawyer and president of NOW at the time of the book's publication, DeCrow is strident but informed about major legal issues facing women: employment, the Fourteenth Amendment, credit, family law, criminal law, ERA, education, name-change, abortion, and motherhood.

650   Eisler, Riane. **Dissolution: No-Fault Divorce, Marriage, and the Future of Women.** New York: McGraw-Hill, 1977. 279p. bibliog. index. $8.95. ISBN 0070191425. LC 76-41416.

Eisler brings to her subject not just her professional experience as an attorney in the field of family law, but also her personal experience as a woman who went from suburban housewifery to law school to law practice, teaching, lecturing, and writing—via a divorce. *Dissolution* (the word is a new term for divorce) "is an analysis of the new and old family laws and of the social realities and values they reflect. Beyond this, the book is also about the dissolution of the traditional American nuclear family itself, and about the rapidly changing status of women." Divided into three parts, the first compares old divorce laws with the emerging new ones with respect to division of property, alimony, child support, and child custody; part 2 considers the social context of divorce, including the institution of marriage, women's employment, welfare, and illegitimacy and birth control; part 3 considers future alternatives for the changing institutions upon which the family rests. A practical "Divorce Checklist" is appended to guide women facing the upheaval of imminent divorce.

651   Gibson, Gifford Guy, and Mary Jo Risher. **By Her Own Admission:**
        A Lesbian Mother's Fight to Keep Her Son. Garden City, NY: Double-
        day, 1977. 276p. $8.95. ISBN 0385124457. LC 76-50767.
"On December 23, 1975, a Dallas Domestic Relations Court jury of ten men and two women found that a 'material and substantial change' had occurred in the home of thirty-eight-year-old Mary Jo Risher, and awarded custody of nine-year-old Richard Clavin Risher to his father. The 'material and substantial change' in question was a life style—homosexuality" (from the introduction). Gifford Guy Gibson was doing investigative reporting for the Pacific News Service in Texas when the opportunity presented itself to cover the Risher trial for a Dallas weekly, the *Iconoclast.* Following the trial, Gibson felt a need to develop the story beyond what could emerge in a court of law, "to restore human sensibility." *By Her Own Admission* is the product of hundreds of hours of tape-recorded interviews and the full collaboration of Mary Jo Risher and Gibson. It describes the emergence of Mary Jo Risher's relationship with her lover, Ann Foreman, their establishment of a family and house together with Mary Jo's two sons and Ann's daughter, the trial, and the aftermath—the loss of Mary Jo's son and her work with Ann around the issue of lesbian mothers and child custody.

652   Kanowitz, Leo, comp. **Sex Roles in Law and Society: Cases and**
        Materials. Albuquerque: University of New Mexico Press, 1973. (Sup-
        plement, 1974). 706p. bibliog. index. $20.00. ISBN 0826302548.
        LC 72-94656.
A casebook on sex-based discrimination intended for use as a text in law courses, by the author of *Women and the Law: The Unfinished Revolution* (1969). A brief and somewhat unimaginative collection of introductory essays on sex roles is followed by a series of chapters presenting cases on: law's traditional view of sex roles; sex roles with regard to marital status; marriage; employment; the Constitution; public accommodations; education; pornography; the media; sex preferences and appearance; the military; and poverty. Excerpts from cases are for the most part presented without commentary. The reader is urged to also consult the slightly more recent *Sex Discrimination and the Law*

(by Barbara Babcock, et al., 1975), which attempts to set case materials on sex discrimination in historical and sociological context.

653   Kanowitz, Leo. **Women and the Law: The Unfinished Revolution.**
       Albuquerque: University of New Mexico Press, 1969. 312p. bibliog.
       index. $3.95. ISBN 0826301738. LC 70-78551.
Kanowitz's exploration of the many areas of sex-based discrimination in the American legal system has long been considered a classic study of women and the law. Writing in 1969, it is perhaps understandable that Kanowitz has titled his chapter on the legal status of single women "Law and the Single Girl." Other major segments are Law and the Married Woman; Title VII of the 1964 Civil Rights Act and the Equal Pay Act of 1963; The Relationship Between the Equal Pay Act of 1963 and Title VII; Constitutional Aspects of Sex-Based Discrimination in American Law. Kanowitz notes that "almost everywhere the special crimes of statutory rape, seduction and enticement impose different standards of behavior upon females than they do upon males; the criminal abortion laws, while not in legal contemplation a 'cause' of women's fatalities, contribute significantly to the production of those deaths, without having the effect upon males; the definition of prostitution and the enforcement of laws prohibiting prostitution and related crimes express law's partisanship with regard to the conflicting views of the appropriate modes of sexual conduct for males and females; and the 'unwritten law' defense for married men, but not for married women, also leaves no doubt where the 'law' stands on such matters." Kanowitz further observes that even with the improvement of women's legal rights, recent legislation can be undermined by loopholes. This legal essay was written when NOW and other women's movement groups were in the formation stages. Much has changed, but Kanowitz's thesis remains sound reading in this area. Appendices include Title VII of the Civil Rights Act of 1964 and the Equal Employment Opportunity Act text. A case index has been included.

654   Reston, James, 1941- . **The Innocence of Joan Little: A Southern
       Mystery.** New York: Times Books, 1977. 340p. ISBN 0812907140.
       LC 77-79038.
"These are the facts. In the early morning hours of August 27, 1974, a policeman bringing a drunken prisoner to the Beaufort County Jail in Washington, North Carolina, discovered the dead body of the white jailer, Clarence Alligood, lying on the bunk bed of the sole female prisoner in the jail, Miss Joan Little, twenty-one years old and black. Alligood's body was naked from the waist down. Sperm was present on his leg, and a icepick lay loosely cupped in his hand. He had icepick wounds around his temple and his heart. Joan Little was gone." James Reston, freelance journalist, reconstructs the case of Joan Little from accounts obtained from fifteen of its participants, including Little herself; her chief counsel, Jerry Paul; the sheriff; and the prosecutor. The intent is to let the reader "judge the guilt or innocence of Joan Little," who was acquitted of charges of first-degree murder on August 14, 1975, but is still fighting the minor charges that had caused her incarceration in the first place. Her case, like that of Inez Garcia in California, became important within the black and women's movements because of the important issues it raised: the nature of justice in a racist and sexist society; the race, sex, and class oppression suffered

by black women; the question of woman's right to self-defense against sexual assult. The story of Joan Little has already taken on mythic dimensions, immortalized in songs written by feminist bluegrass singers Hazel and Alice and by the black feminist a cappella group, Sweet Honey in the Rock.

655*   Russier, Gabrielle, 1937-1969. **The Affair of Gabrielle Russier.** New York: Knopf; distr. New York: Random House, 1971. 176p. ISBN 0394469240. LC 75-154931.

Gabrielle Russier, a French literature teacher in the Lycée Saint-Exupéry in Marseilles during the 1960s, became involved in a national scandal when it became known that she was sleeping with a seventeen year-old student, Christian. Gabrielle was thirty at the time. The parents of Christian Rossi took their son's teacher to court. Russier was given a suspended sentence of twelve months and a small fine, but the real issue became one of sexism. Following the verdict, realizing that her career was gone, Russier committed suicide. This personal account of the wretched handling of Gabrielle's case includes her letters written from prison and other letters from a convalescent home shortly before her suicide. These letters reveal a compassionate and courageous woman caught in a legal imbroglio gone awry. Russier stands as a tragic figure out of synch with the judgmental society in which she lived and worked, and uncomprehending until the end of the cruelty that this society was capable of meting out to her.

656   Schulder, Diane, and Florynce Kennedy, 1916- . **Abortion Rap.** New York: McGraw-Hill, 1971. 238p. bibliog. $8.95. ISBN 0070557128. LC 75-139561.

Important because of its narrative perspective on the subject, this book allows women to tell their stories of how they handled the traumas of unwanted pregnancies—of searching for an abortionist, of carrying a baby to term and giving the child up for adoption, of being an unwed pregnant woman often in a strange town or household because of parental pressures. Schulder and Kennedy collected and edited the stories that appear here from testimony presented in federal court during a suit pressed by women opposing the anti-abortion laws in New York state. The suit sought to have anti-abortion laws repealed rather than merely liberalized. In addition to the tragic personal histories related by the victims of anti-abortion legislation, experts testified from the fields of theology, health, and population research. Appendix material includes legal papers for the case, including the plaintiffs' brief, which argued that abortion laws discriminated against all women as a class in that control of their own bodies has been denied them. Nancy Stearns, Esq., wrote the brief for the suit.

657   Stannard, Una, 1927- . **Married Women v. Husbands' Names: The Case for Wives Who Keep Their Own Name.** San Francisco, CA: Germainbooks, 1973. 55p. bibliog. index. $4.95. ISBN 0914142003. LC 73-87334.

"*Married Women v. Husbands' Names* is a guide for the relatively few women who want to keep their own name after marriage. Other women are not urged to do likewise. Most women (and men) neither approve nor understand why a few odd wives make such a fuss about a name. 'What's in a name?' they always ask. 'There is a great deal in a name,' answered Elizabeth Cady Stanton, a nineteenth-century feminist, who felt that a name 'often signifies much, and may involve a great principle.' " So opens this useful handbook on the social and legal history and current status of married women's right to use their own names. Stannard discusses the legal treatment in a number of states (Arizona, California, Florida, Minnesota, Alabama, Kentucky, Vermont, Nebraska, Iowa, Louisiana, Massachusetts, New York, Texas, Maryland, and Wisconsin, among others). Other topics she reviews are: English Common Law v. American law; antenuptial contracts and other public notices; court-ordered change of name without a lawyer; passports; surnames of children; women v. fathers' names; and professional names and hyphenated surnames. Much of the information here is undoubtedly out of date, so the reader should regard the handbook as a point of departure.

658   United States. Congress. Senate. Committee on the Judiciary. Sub-committee on Constitutional Amendments. **Women and the "Equal Rights" Amendment; Senate Subcommittee Hearings on the Constitutional Amendment, 91st Congress.** Edited by Catharine Stimpson. New York: Bowker, 1972. 538p. index. $14.95. ISBN 0835205320. LC 77-39745.

Testimony and documents presented at the Seante Subcommittee hearings on the ERA are presented in this volume for the purposes of making this depository material more accessible to the public through commercial publication. Part 1 contains testimony given on May 5-7, 1970, both in support of and in opposition to the ERA. Among the witnesses: Eugene McCarthy, Martha Griffiths, Shirley Chisholm, Charles Goodell, Gloria Steinem, Caroline Bird, Betty Friedan, and John Mack Carter. Part 2, the documents section, contains statements in opposition issued by the National Council of Jewish Women and the National Council of Catholic Women, and also statements in support and in opposition by organized labor. A number of supporting documents submitted by such groups as the Commission on the Status of Women and the National Woman's Party are printed. Much additional material pertinent to the ERA appears, such as reports from the Task Force on Family Law and Policy and the President's Task Force on Women's Rights and Responsibilities.

659*   United States. National Commission on the Observance of International Women's Year, 1975. " ... **To Form a More Perfect Union ... ": Justice for American Women: Report of the National Commission on the Observance of International Women's Year.** Washington: Dept. of State: for sale by the Supt. of Docs., U.S. Govt. Print. Off., 1976. 382p. bibliog. $5.20. LC 76-602322.

Prepared as a report to the president and to the people of the United States, parts 1, 2, and 3 discuss barriers keeping women from full participation in American life: Full Partnership for the Homemaker; Mass Media; ERA; The Creative Woman; Money for Culture and Research; The Power Brokers; Strong Laws—Weak Enforcement; Women in the Work Place; Indian Problems; Reproductive Freedom; Parents and Children; Where Women Are Heading; The Third Century. Part 4 lists the members of the Commission, while part 5 contains the findings and recommendations of its working committees. "These are addressed to the various agencies of government—federal, state, and local—which will be responsible for their implementation. Women and women's organizations are also addressed in a number of the recommendations. Useful reference material and original research, authorized by the Commission, are summarized" in part 6, the appendix (from the "Note to the Reader").

660* Wisconsin. Governor's Commission on the Status of Women. **Wisconsin Women and the Law.** (2nd ed.). Madison: University of Wisconsin-Extension, 1977. 114p. bibliog.
This is a helpful handbook on legal issues of interest to women living in Wisconsin, including: marriage, divorce and separation, parental rights in children, names, employment, child care, education, birth control, taxes and social security, business, criminal law, and legal problems of poor women. A directory of services is appended.

661 Women in Transition, Inc. **Women in Transition: A Feminist Handbook on Separation and Divorce.** New York: Scribner, 1975. 538p. bibliog. index. $12.95. ISBN 0684142589. LC 75-15728.
Developed from *The Women's Survival Manual* (published in 1972), this is written in an informative, readable style and is a good basic source of information on legal, social, and financial aspects of divorce.

LITERATURE
Anthologies

Literature has been divided into sections treating: fiction, poetry, drama, essays, literary history and criticism, and anthologies. Since women's studies literature courses study not only the works of women writers (contemporary and rediscovered) but also the critical treatment they have been accorded and the images of women projected in literature by both men and women, literature becomes a complexly layered bibliographic concern for women's studies. I have handled it here by including works mainly by women writers but also works by men that have been cited frequently in many women's studies course outlines. Literary criticism takes up two major concerns: feminist criticism and other criticism, which while not necessarily feminist, illuminates the work of major writers, especially English-language women writers. As fiction by women novelists, whatever its theme, can be important for the female sensibility it reveals and the values of the era that produced it, some novels written by women appear here even though they may not directly relate to women. Maria Edgeworth's *Castle Rackrent* is such a work. For ongoing assistance in literature selections important to women's studies, users will want to consult feminist review media (e.g., *Signs, Booklegger*) in addition to the traditional review sources. *Choice* has featured several excellent review articles on women's publications including a lengthy review essay on literature anthologies (see Silvia Ruffo-Fiore, in *Choice*, July/August 1978, 645-655). Small press materials appear in the catalogs of Women in Distribution, and review essays and bibliographies about small press literature, in the magazine, *Chrysalis*. Much additional material on women writers and feminist criticism appears in the Reference sections.

662   Bankier, Joanna, et al., eds. **The Other Voice: Twentieth-Century Women's Poetry in Translation.** New York: Norton, 1976. 218p. bibliog. index. $10.00. ISBN 0393044165. LC 76-45349.

Introduced by Adrienne Rich, this anthology is a valuable contribution to the unearthing of diverse poetic traditions and to the identification of women poets in the twentieth century who write in languages *other* than English. "Every woman included here, Western or Third World, poor or middle-class in origin, is a 'special' woman, one of those who somehow found her voice and moved out of the silence or the unwritten verbal tradition of women, into the glare and vulnerability of print." Examples of the intense subjects of this poetry: Farrokhzād's "Mechanical Doll"; Boye's "A Sword"; Ditlevsen's "Divorce"; Backberger's "I'm Taking Off"; Melodowsky's "Women Songs I." In this collection of translations, the imagery comes through powerfully even if the original sound has been lost. Brief biographical sketches identify further works of these women poets.

663   Bernikow, Louise, 1940- , comp. **The World Split Open: Four Centuries of Women Poets in England and America, 1552-1950.** New York:

Vintage Books, 1974. 346p. index. $3.95. ISBN 039471072X. LC
74-8582.

Bernikow states in her introduction that she has "tried in this book to uncover
a lost tradition in English and American poetry." As a feminist interested in
recovering work of poets writing before 1950 that is often not printed, Bernikow
has succeeded admirably. Among the lesser-known poets here: Katherine Philips,
Anne Collins, Aphra Behn, Anne Killigrew, Anne Finch, Lady Mary Wortley
Montagu, Mary Elizabeth Coleridge, Alice Meynell, Rachel Annand Taylor,
Sylvia Pankhurst, Anna Wickham, Charlotte Mew, Dorothy Wellesley, Virginia
Moore, Elizabeth Daryrush, Ruth Pitter, Lilian Bowes Lyon, Alison Boodson,
Lizette Woodworth Reese, Adelaide Crapsey, Lola Ridge, Georgia Douglas
Johnson, Genevieve Taggard, Babette Deutsch, and Josephine Miles. Poems are
selected from blues artists and anonymous worker poets, too. The important
introductory essay, an excellent summary of feminist theory on poetry, examines
the political question of systematic exclusion of women from the literary canon.
Outstanding biographical notes. Ann Stanford has assembled a similar representation of women poets entitled *The Women Poets in English: An Anthology*
(McGraw-Hill, 1972). More comprehensive in coverage (800 A.D. to the present),
her assessments are less feminist in tone. It is a good anthology but a neutral
editorial voice prevails.

664   Cahill, Susan, ed. **Women and Fiction; Short Stories by and about
        Women.** New York: New American Library. 1975. 379p. bibliog.
        $2.25. LC 75-21588.

In this useful collection of stories by important women writers, each story is
accompanied by a biographical note. Included are: Chopin, "The Story of
an Hour"; Wharton, "The Other Two"; Cather, "A Wagner Matinee"; Colette,
"The Secret Woman"; Stein, "Miss Furr and Miss Skeen"; Woolf, "The New
Dress"; Mansfield, "The Garden Party"; Porter, "Rope"; Boyle, "Winter Night";
Welty, "A Worn Path"; Calisher, "The Scream on Fifty-Seventh Street"; Petry,
"Like a Winding Sheet"; Lavin, "In a Cafe"; Olsen, "I Stand Here Ironing";
McCullers, "Wunderkind"; Lessing, "To Room Nineteen"; Paley, "An Interest
in Life"; O'Connor, "Revelation"; Stubbs, "Cousin Lewis"; O'Brien, "A Jour-
ney"; Munro, "The Office"; Oates, "In the Region of Ice"; Drabble, "The Gifts
of War"; Hayden, "Day-Old Baby Rats"; and Walker, "Everyday Use." The
bibliography lists major works and publication dates for each author.

665   Chester, Laura, and Sharon Barba, 1943- , eds. **Rising Tides: Twentieth
        Century American Women Poets.** New York: Washington Square Press,
        1973. 410p. index. $1.95. ISBN 0671487531.

Anaïs Nin says in her introduction, "this is an era of poetry, poetry against the
inarticulate, the stuttering, the muttering wordless suffering which cannot
be shared or heard. The skillful, the clarified expression of our joys and sorrows,
our angers and rebellions, makes them sharable and therefore less destructive. . . .
The fusion here is in the voice of woman. Woman determined to end woman's
mysteries and woman's secrets." These poets are represented by their work,
a short biography, and a photograph: Gertrude Stein, Amy Lowell, Elinor
Wylie, H. D., Marianne Moore, Edna St. Vincent Millay, Babette Deutsch,
Louise Bogan, Lorine Niedecker, Kay Boyle, Helen Wolfert, Rosalie Moore,

Josephine Miles, May Sarton, Muriel Rukeyser, Barbara Howes, Isabella Gardner, May Swenson, Madeline DeFrees, Mona Van Duyn, Ruth Whitman, Denise Levertov, Daisy Aldan, Besmilr Brigham, Barbara Guest, Shirley Kaufman, Lisel Mueller, Vassar Miller, Sonya Dorman, Carolyn Kizer, Leatrice W. Emeruwa, Jeanette Nichols, Maxine Kumin, Carolyn Stoloff, Anne Sexton, Ruth Lisa Schechter, Adrienne Rich, Colette Inez, Barbara Greenberg, Linda Pastan, Sylvia Plath, Lenore Kandel, Joanne Kyger, Grace Butcher, Diane de Prima, Sonia Sanchez, Sandra Hochman, Rochelle Owens, Lucille Clifton, Nancy Willard, Deena Metzger, June Jordan, Marge Piercy, Judy Grahn, Lynn Sukenick, Kathleen Fraser, Daniela Gioseffi, Siv Cedering Fox, Lynn Strongin, Lyn Lifshin, Erica Jong, Summer Brenner, Sharon Barba, Nikki Giovanni, Susan Griffin, Sandra McPherson, Anne Waldman, Miriam Palmer, Anita Barrows, Laura Chester.

666   Edwards, Lee R., and Arlyn Diamond, eds. **American Voices, American Women.** New York: Avon Books, 1973. 432p. $1.95. LC 73-87720.
The works reprinted here capture as a recurrent theme the split between societal realities and the hopes and yearnings of women who come into conflict with society. The anthology draws from a cross-section of regional fiction: Harriet Prescott Spofford (1835-1921), Elizabeth Stuart Phelps (1844-1911), and Mary Wilkins Freeman (1852-1930) represent New England. Works of Kate Chopin (1851-1904), Mary Hunter Austin (1868-1934), Dorothy Canfield Fisher (1879-1958), and Susan Keating Glaspell (1876?-1948) represent the Midwest's perspective, and Jessie Redmon Fauset (1885-1961), that of the East. The introduction finds chords of similarity among these American women writers.

667   Efros, Susan, comp. **This Is Women's Work: An Anthology of Prose and Poetry.** San Francisco, CA: Panjandrum Press, 1974. 147p. $3.95. ISBN 0915572028. LC 74-19118.
Some of the writers in this anthology are familiar names: Tillie Olsen, Marge Piercy, Susan Griffin. But the majority of the writers will not be familiar to most women, though the work presented here is generally first-rate feminist poetry and prose. A sampling of names: Thalia Kitrilakis, Sybil Wood, Julia Vose, Alison Zier, Kathleen Fraser. The book is illustrated by feminist artists Laura Beausoleil, Barbara Rogers, Shoko Titus, Gay Humperton, Karen Breschi, Gloria Boatright, Carmen Ann Estrada, Mary Snowden, Honor Johnson, Ursula Schneider, Agathe Bennich, Marta Hoyos Cuneo, Josie Grant.

668   Exum, Pat Crutchfield, comp. **Keeping the Faith: Writings by Contemporary Black American Women.** Greenwich, CT: Fawcett Publications, 1974. 288p. $1.75. LC 74-20743.
This is an important collection of writings by black women, including poetry, autobiography and fiction. Among the poets are: Jeannette Adams, Barbara Banks, Myrtle Bates, Sister Bernadine, Gwendolyn Brooks, Lucille Clifton, Jayne Cortez, Ann du Cille, Mari Evans, Pat Crutchfield Exum, Julia Fields, Nikki Giovanni, Bernette Golden, Sharon Henderson, Lezli Hope, Mae Jackson, Gayl Jones, Marte Jones, June Jordan, Audrey Lee, Audré Lorde, Elouise Loftin, Pat Nottingham, Sonia Sanchez, Sharyn Jeanne Skeeter, Margaret Walker, and Delores Williams. Autobiographical selections are from: Maya Angelou, Lois-Allison Henry, Anne Moody, and Michele Wallace. Fiction by

Toni Cade Bambara, Barbara Banks, Toni Morrison, Alice Walker, S. A. Williams, and Sarah E. Wright. Also included are an introductory essay by Pat Crutchfield Exum, a panel discussion on "The Negro Woman in American Literature" (by Sarah E. Wright, Abbey Lincoln, Alice Childress, and Paule Marshall), and "The Black Writer and His Role," by Carolyn F. Gerald. Biographical notes on the contributors are appended.

669   Ferguson, Mary Anne, comp. **Images of Women in Literature.** Boston: Houghton Mifflin, 1973. 437p. bibliog. index. $6.75. ISBN 0395139066. LC 72-4394.

These 26 short stories, eight poems, and a playlet organized around female stereotypes and archetypes are intended to provide a central text for an "Images of Women" course. Some may disagree with Ferguson's groupings—the submissive wife and the feminine mystique; the mother; the dominating wife: the bitch; the seductress-goddess; man's prey: the sex object; the old maid; the liberated woman—and with her assignment of stories to these groupings. Among the authors represented: Wharton, Kay Boyle, Hemingway, Keats, Frost, Fitzgerald, Howells, Colette, Welty, Mailer, Blake, Auden, Mansfield, Tillie Olsen, Nin, and Lessing. The introduction will be helpful to students thinking about stereotypes in literature for the first time.

670   Gidlow, Elsa, 1898- . **Sapphic Songs: Seventeen to Seventy.** Baltimore, MD: Diana Press, 1976. 79p. $3.50. ISBN 0884470091. LC 76-22702.

This is an important volume of lesbian erotic verse spanning 56 years of the author's life. The poet's more recent *Moods of Eros* (self-published under the imprint Druid Heights Books) complements the experience presented in the retrospective volume.

671   Gill, Elaine, comp. **Mountain Moving Day: Poems by Women.** Trumansburg, NY: Crossing Press, 1973. 126p. $8.95. ISBN 0912278374. LC 73-77320.

"*Mountain Moving Day* is a collection of poems written by 17 women, 5 from Canada and 12 from the U.S. It is contemporary. I didn't want to give an historical perspective on women poets—I wanted to present the picture now only. *Mountain Moving Day* is a small, fine collection of the best poems I could find." A photograph of the poet along with a brief personal statement precedes her work. Poets are: Alta, Margaret Atwood, Carol Berge, Elizabeth Brewster, Carol Cox, Susan Griffin, Jessica Tarahata Hagedorn, Marie Harris, Erica Jong, Lyn Lifshin, Pat Lowther, Gwendolyn MacEwen, Marge Piercy, Cathleen Quirk, Phyllis Webb, Kathleen Wiegner, and Fran Winant.

672   Goulianos, Joan, comp. **By a Woman Writt: Literature from Six Centuries By and About Women.** Indianapolis, IN: Bobbs-Merrill, 1973. 379p. $14.95. ISBN 0672516160. LC 72-80810.

Goulianos makes accessible six centuries of women's literature in this splendid anthology, choosing deliberately selections from diaries, journals, letters, fiction, and poetry that are often not well-known. From Margery Kempe (1373-?), the writer of the first known extant autobiography in English, she has taken an account of her marriage, childbirth, and temptation to adultery. Alice

Thornton (1627-1707) details her marriage and constant childbearing and sickness in excerpts from her autobiography of life in northern England. The feminist poetry of Anne Finch, Countess of Wichilsea (1661-1720), is represented, as is the passionate poetry of Aphra Behn (ca.1640-1689). Political journalism in the form of satire of Mary Manley (ca. 1663-1724) is represented here, along with the letters of another celebrated literary figure of the eighteenth century, Lady Mary Wortley Montagu. Mary Wollstonecraft (1759-1797) and her daughter, Mary Shelley (1797-1851), appear together in the anthology. The selections from Mary Shelley's journal contain extremely moving accounts of her isolation. Olive Schreiner is represented in a segment of *The Story of an African Farm*. The work of Kate Chopin and Mary E. Wilkins Freeman (1852-1930) each appear in short story form. Goulianos has chosen two selections from *Pilgrimage*, by Dorothy Richardson (1873-1957), and passages from Anaïs Nin's diaries and fiction. Poetry has been chosen from Dilys Lang (1906-1960), a Canadian; from Margaret Walker (1915-), the celebrated black novelist and poet; and from Muriel Rukeyser (1913-). Selections from Sylvia Ashton-Warner's journal, *From Myself*, also appear. Extremely helpful notes about the author and work are given at the head of each selection.

673   Grier, Barbara [Damon, Gene], 1933- , and Coletta Reid, 1943-), eds.
       The Lesbians Home Journal: Stories from the Ladder. Oakland, CA:
       Diana Press, 1976. 326p. $5.75. ISBN 088447013X. LC 76-53825.
Very important for understanding the development of lesbian thought and consciousness, these selections were taken from *The Ladder*, which from 1956 to 1972 was the only journal providing a forum for lesbian thought and life. The writers in this volume are: Jane Rule, Isabel Miller, Carol Moran, Jocelyn Hayward, Jane Alden, Lynn Lonidier, Lynn Michaels, Beverly Lynch, Jeannette Lee, Melinda Brown, Gabrielle Vivian Bertrand, Delores Klaich, Flicka Moore, Helen Rose Hull, and Valerie Taylor. Each of the editors writes an introduction to the volume and, additionally, an essay by Barbara Grier entitled "The Lesbian Paperback" is included.

674   Griswold, Rufus Wilmot, 1815-1857, ed. **The Female Poets of America.**
       New York: MSS Information, 1972. (Repr. of 1873 ed.). $22.50.
       ISBN 0842280634. LC 72-8380.
Perhaps the most interesting feature of this volume of women's poetry is the preface to the original 1848 edition by Griswold in which he lectures the reader "it is less easy to be assured of the genuineness of literary ability in women than in men. The moral nature of women, in its finest and richest development, partakes of some of the qualities of genius; it assumes, at least, the similitude of that which in men is the characteristic or accompaniment of the highest grade of mental inspiration." So saying, he included the writings of Mrs. Maria Brooks, Mrs. Oakes-Smith, Mrs. Osgood, and Mrs. Whitman, suggesting that their poetry was illustrative of "as high and sustained a range of poetic art, as the female genius of any age or country can display." In the 1873 edition, R. H. Stoddard enlarged the 1848 edition, chastizing Griswold for his choice of "singers of spontaneous verse." The volume contains a number of familiar names and a good many forgotten ones: Anne Bradstreet, Mercy Warren, Elizabeth Ferguson, Anne Eliza Bleecker, Phillis Wheatley, Susannah Rowson,

Margaretta Faugeres, Eliza Townsend, Lavinia Stoddard, Hannah Gould, Caroline Gilman, Sarah Josepha Hale, Anna Maria Wells, Maria James, Maria Brooks, Julia Rush Ward, Lydia Huntley Sigourney, Katharine Ware, Jane Gray, Sophia Little, Lydia Maria Child, Louisa J. Hall, Eliza L. Follen, Frances Green, Jessie McCartee, Cynthia Taggart, Francesca Pascalis Canfield, Elizabeth Bogart, Mary Brooks, Margaret St. Leon Loud, Julia Ward Howe, Helen Hunt, and Emma Lazarus.

675   Hamalian, Linda, and Leo Hamalian, eds. **Solo: Women on Woman Alone.** New York: Delacorte Press, 1977. 367p. $10.00. ISBN 0440080681. LC 77-11861.
This is an interesting collection of short stories; however, the editors bring them together in this volume under the dubious premise that a "self-destructive longing for dependency" and fears of being alone are feelings more relevant to women than men. Stories are grouped into three themes: struggle, tragedy, and independence. "The theme of struggle centers on women who, neither independent nor dependent, understand the rewards inherent in autonomy. . . . The theme of tragedy explores the lives of women who are too fragile to fight the temptation to be passive and malleable. . . . Under the theme of independence, there are stories about women who are coping with, even enjoying, the state of singleness" (from the editors' introduction). Included are stories by both well known and lesser known authors, among them: Margaret Lamb, Willa Cather, Joyce Carol Oates, Penelope Gilliatt, Edna O'Brien, Jane Mayhall, Jean Stafford, Wakako Yamauchi, Jean Rhys, Marge Piercy, and Doris Lessing. Biographical notes on each author are included at the end, including listings of their major works.

676   Hermey, Carl, ed. **Contemporary French Women Poets: A Bilingual Critical Anthology.** Van Nuys, CA: Perivale Press; distr. San Rafael, CA: B and H Books, 1977. 207p. bibliog. $5.95. ISBN 0912288086. LC 76-3065.
Andrée Chedid, Thérèse Plantier, Yvonne Caroutch, Marie-Françoise Prager, Denise Grappe, and Annie Salager are the poets whose work appears in this bilingual anthology. The editor put this anthology together noting the lack of critical attention accorded to French-speaking women poets. Though the poetry is worth the effort, it is disconcerting that Hermey did not include a contents page or place the poet's name on the pages of a given writer's work.

677   Howe, Florence, and Ellen Bass, comps. **No More Masks! An Anthology of Poems by Women.** Garden City, NY: Anchor Press, 1973. 396p. $3.95. ISBN 038502553X. LC 72-89675.
Most importantly, anthologies of women poets speak to those life concerns left out of traditional anthologies: of woman's body and woman's love, of woman's alienation and her bitterness, of lives expressed without masks and apologies. Heavy emphasis in this anthology is on living poets publishing in the '60s. Some of the lesser-known poets are: Alta (b. 1942), Sandra McPherson (b. 1943), Jean Tepperman (b. 1945), Miriam Palmer (b. 1946), Ellen Bass (b. 1947), Margo Magid (b. 1947), Beatrice Walter (b. 1948), Peggy Henderson (b. 1949), Margo Taft (b. 1950), Wendy Wieber (b. 1951), and Janice Henderson Crosby

(b. 1952). The title is from Muriel Rukeyser's verse, "No more masks! No more mythologies!" in "The Poem as Mask" (1971).

678   Iverson, Lucille, and Kathryn Ruby, 1947- , eds. **We Become New:
       Poems by Contemporary American Women.** Pittsburgh, PA: Know,
       1974. $2.25. ISBN 0912786310.

Announcing the emergence of a poetic renaissance, Ruby draws the parallel
in her preface between feminist poetry and black verse as populist poetry.
"It has a large, enthusiastic, and diverse audience. No matter how polished,
it is not the poetry of the academy." The work of 43 contemporary poets is
represented and their work addresses a wide range of feminist concerns. Contri-
butors: Marge Piercy, Sonia Sanchez, Daniela Gioseffi, Judith McCombs, Anne
Sexton, Alice Walker, Honor Moore, Ann Darr, Colette Inez, Barbara Holland,
Michele Wallace, Robin Morgan, Morgan Sanders, Jane Mayhall, Jodi Braxton,
Olga Cabral, Martha Shelley, Judith Johnson Sherwin, Audré Lorde, Madeline
Bass, Susan Fromberg Schaeffer, Erica Jong, Elizabeth Sargent, Cynthia Mac-
Donald, Carolyn Kizer, Anne Hazlewood Brady, Fran Winant, Kathleen Fraser,
Lucille Iverson, Maxine Kumin, Judy Grahn, Karen Swenson, Denise Levertov,
Rosemary Daniell, Rochelle Owens, Adrienne Rich, Rita Mae Brown, Ruth
Herschberger, Kathryn Ruby, June Jordan, Muriel Rukeyser, Yvonne, Rochelle
Ratner. *Contemporary Women Poets*, edited by Catharine R. Stimpson, is an
important collection of essays on contemporary women's poetry to appear in
1979 (Spectrum Books).

679   Kaplan, Cora. **Salt and Bitter and Good: Three Centuries of English
       and American Women Poets.** New York: Paddington Press, 1975.
       304p. bibliog. index. $12.95. ISBN 0846700239. LC 73-15027.

Twenty-four women poets appear in this volume: Bradstreet (1612?-1672),
K. Philips (1631-1664), Behn (1640-1689), Anne Finch (1661-1720), C. Smith
(1749-1806), Wheatley (c.1753-1784), F. Hemans (1793-1835), Browning
(1806-1861), Rossetti (1830-1894), Dickinson (1830-1886), Blind (1841-1896),
E. Lazarus (1849-1887), A. Meynell (1847-1922), C. Mew (1869-1928), Lowell
(1874-1925), E. Wylie (1885-1928), H. D. (1886-1961), M. Moore (1887-1972),
Millay (1892-1950), V. Sackville-West (1892-1962), D. Parker (1893-1967),
L. Bogan (1897-1970), S. Smith (1902-1971), and Plath (1932-1963). The biographical profiles accompanied by original portraits are useful for factual detail
and for brief exploration of the poetic philosophy of each artist. The format
is particularly attractive.

680   Katz, Jane B., ed. **I Am the Fire of Time: The Voices of Native Ameri-
       can Women.** New York: E. P. Dutton, 1977. 201p. bibliog. $6.95.
       ISBN 0525474757. LC 77-79801.

This is a landmark anthology because it represents the first collection of writings
by Native American women. The ceremonial songs, prayers, oral histories,
memoirs, poetry, and prose fragments in this volume celebrate the Native
American literary tradition. Katz has divided the collection into two major
segments representing nineteenth- and twentieth-century voices. In part 1,
From the Tribal World, selections cluster around the themes of birth, childhood, and marriage. An Eskimo woman recounts her childhood as a member

of a migrant family living in a harsh environment; a Papago woman describes girlhood in Arizona as the daughter of a chief; a Caribou Eskimo woman records her traditional song, "I'm a Little Woman Who's Happy to Slave." In part 2, Voices of Today, Indian women representing many different fields blend their perceptions of modern life with their spiritual allegiance to the old ways. Examples of these selections are "I Am a Metis," by Yvonne Monkman of Winnipeg, Manitoba; "Beating the Drum for Ourselves," by Grace Thorpe; and "I Have Bowed Before the Sun," by Anna Lee Waters, the Oklahoma poet and painter. Striking photographs of Native American women accompany the text. In her introduction, Katz points to the relative equality of sex roles in Indian life and culture: "in the total culture, there was a blending of male and female roles; harmony was the objective." Much of the literature represented celebrates the essential role of women in the community.

681   Katz, Naomi, 1931- , and Nancy Milton, 1929- , comps. **Fragment from a Lost Diary and Other Stories: Women of Asia, Africa, and Latin America.** New York: Pantheon Books, 1973. 317p. $10.00. ISBN 0394484754. LC 73-7014.
"We agree, as Third World spokesmen have been asserting in recent years, that the primary cultural definitions must come from the 'inside.' " Katz and Milton have collected in this volume a fine series of short stories by both men and women of Asia, Africa, and Latin America whose common theme is women's confrontation with their situations as women. The stories were chosen and arranged to represent different points in this confrontation: the relatively hopeless struggle of women living within oppressive situations, with few or no alternatives; women struggling with conflict posed by alternatives opening up; and women who have chosen new alternatives and are living "in a new relationship to society, and as a consequence, in a changed relationship to men."

682   Kidd, Virginia, ed. **Millenial Women: Tales for Tomorrow.** New York: Delacorte Press, 1978. 300p. $6.95. ISBN 0440055997. LC 77-86299.
This is a collection of four short stories and two short novels by women about women, with an introduction by Virginia Kidd. Stories include C. Felice's "No One Said Forever"; Diana Paxson's "The Song of N'Sardi-El"; E. A. Lynn's "Jubilee's Story"; and Cherry Wilder's "Mab Gallen Recalled." Novels are "Phoenix in the Ashes," by Joan Vinge, and "The Eye of the Heron," by Ursula LeGuin. Biographical notes are included.

683   Lifshin, Lyn, ed. **Tangled Vines: A Collection of Mother and Daughter Poems.** Boston: Beacon Press, 1978. 95p. $9.95. ISBN 0807063665. LC 77-88340.
Thirty-nine women poets contribute their verse to this first anthology devoted to mother-daughter poems. Sylvia Plath and Anne Sexton are the only non-living poets included. Lifshin describes the book's wide-ranging emotional territory as: "poems about inheritance . . . of objects, of physical traits . . . and emotional inheritance . . . poems about rituals; about lust, envy, rivalry; about separation, estrangement, and letting go; about acceptance . . . rejection, and reconciliation . . . about the need for closeness, the fear of closeness."

684*   Livesay, Dorothy, 1909- , comp. **40 Women Poets of Canada.** Montreal:
        Ingluvin Publications, 1971. 141p. ISBN 091952298X. LC 73-155718.
More than sixty women poets in Canada were invited to submit their work to
this strong collection. Some major poets of Canada (e.g., Margaret Avis and
Phyllis Webb) did not submit and consequently, do not appear. Among those
who do surface in this collection are Margaret Atwood, Judith Copithorne,
Dorothy Farmiloe, Gail Fox, Gwendolyn Macewen, and Miriam Waddington.
Although poetry appears here that does speak to a specifically Canadian experi-
ence, the greatest part of this verse deals with inward landscapes.

685   McDowell, Jennifer, and Milton Loventhal, eds. **Contemporary Women
        Poets: An Anthology of California Poets.** San Jose, CA: Merlin Press,
        1977. 178p. $7.95. ISBN 0930142012. LC 76-58797.
In this excellent poetry anthology, the organizing principle is worthy of note.
The project began as an effort to document the work of California poets. Requests
were sent for contributions to bookstores, English departments, public libraries,
periodicals, the women's prison, and other possible centers of women's poetry
throughout the state. The yield was over 6,000 poems representing women from
every type of background. Selected for inclusion were 183 poems reflecting the
work of 126 poets—new poets, well-known local poets, and California poets
of national reputation. Some of the distinguished California poets whose work
appears here are Flora Arnstein, Ellen Bass, Kathleen Fraser, Deena Metzger,
Wendy Rose, and Julia Vinograd. Although some of the poetry speaks to the
California experience (e.g., Wendy Rose's "Remembering a Catholic Girlhood
in El Cerrito," and Jean Pumphrey's "Winter California"), much speaks of the
universal concerns of women—marriage, solitude, womanhood, mother-daughter
relationships, divorce and racism. Biographical blurbs on poets are here also.

686   Mahl, Mary R., and Helene Koon, 1925- , eds. **The Female Spectator:
        English Women Writers Before 1800.** Bloomington: Indiana University
        Press; Old Westbury, NY: Feminist Press, 1977. 310p. bibliog. $15.00.
        ISBN 0253321662. LC 76-26430.
The editors set out to unearth the work of obscure but worthy English women
writers before the nineteenth century. Twenty "good" writers surfaced in their
intensive search through the Huntington Library catalogs and collections. The
materials selected, along with brief and lively biographies about the authors,
suggest a distinct profile of the pre-nineteenth-century woman writer: generally,
a woman of leisure and money who wrote for her own enjoyment on religion,
politics, childrearing, or education, sometimes penning fiction or drama for
the pleasure of friends or family. Included here are Dame Julian of Norwich
(1342-1417?), Dame Margery Kempe (1373-1438?), Queen Catharine Parr
(1513-1548), Queen Elizabeth I (1533-1603), Elizabeth Grymeston (d. 1603),
Mary Sidney Herbert (1561-1621), Aemelia Lanier (1570?-1640?), Elizabeth
Clinton (1574-1630?), Elizabeth Cary (1585-1639), Bathsua Makin (1612?-
1674?), Margaret Cavendish (1623-1673), Katherine Philips (1632-1664),
Aphra Behn (1640?-1689), Mary Delariviere Manley (1667?-1724), Susannah
Centlivre (1667?-1723), Eliza Haywood (1690?-1756), Frances Glanville Bos-
cawen (1719-1805), Anna Laetitia Barbauld (1743-1825), Hannah More
(1745-1833), and Anna Seward (1742-1809).

687*   Miles, Sara, 1952- , et al., eds. **Ordinary Women: An Anthology of Poetry by New York City Women.** New York: Ordinary Women Books, 1978. $3.95. LC 78-848.

The content of the poetry presented in this collection grows directly out of the life experiences of the poets who have contributed to the anthology. They are seventeen mainly single and childless women living in New York City and of Afro-American, Hispanic, European, and Asian descent. Their poetry reflects working-class neighborhoods and speech. All of the poetry has a distinct urban "real life" taste. Obtain from Ordinary Women Books, Box 664, Old Chelsea Station, New York, NY.

688   Murray, Michele, comp. **A House of Good Proportion: Images of Women in Literature.** New York: Simon and Schuster, 1973. 379p. bibliog. $9.95. ISBN 0671214713. LC 72-93509.

Drawing together poems, stories, and excerpts from novels, the point of Murray's anthology is to show a range of images of women in literature. The book can be criticized because of its reliance on major recognized writers who have written, in the main, prose and poetry depicting woman in a positive light and in harmony with her environment. In her introduction, Murray states, "in literature women are not disadvantaged, even if they are scorned, their losses and failures and incompletions are only part of the general drift to loss and mortality that snags all men and the world made from action, ideas, words. All, finally, goes down to night, men have no more staying power than women, a jade cup or a gold brooch will last long beyond either of them." The familiar images organize the excerpts: The Little Girl, The Young Girl, The Virgin, Women in Love, Independent Women, The Wife, The Mother, Scenes from Family Life, Women Lost, The Old Maid, The Old Woman, The Unattainable Other. Writers include William Carlos Williams, Samuel Richardson, Adrienne Rich, H. D., Diane Wakowski, Djuna Barnes, Patrick White, Nathaniel Hawthorne, Michele Murray, and many more.

689   Pachmuss, Temira, ed. **Women Writers in Russian Modernism: An Anthology.** Urbana: University of Illinois Press, 1978. 340p. bibliog. index. ISBN 025200245. LC 78-8957.

Biographical, critical, and bibliographical data accompany these selections from important women writers of the Russian avant-garde. Pachmuss notes the need for such a volume in support of Alexandra Kollontai's charge that, despite the contributions of women writers in working for the aesthetic revolution in the early twentieth century, their names and works are largely unknown. The writers whose poetry and prose appear here along with substantial introductions are: Zinaida Hippius (1869-1945), Mirra Lokhvitskaya (1869-1905), Anastasiya Verbitskaya (1861-1928), Poliksena Solovyova (1867-1924), Lidiya Zinovyeva-Annibal (1866-1907), Cherubina de Gabriak (d. 1928), Nadezhda Teffi (1876-1952), and Adelaida Gertsyk (d. 1925).

690   Parker, Jeri, 1939- , comp. **Uneasy Survivors: Five Women Writers.** Santa Barbara, CA: Peregrine Smith, 1975. 219p. bibliog. $5.95. ISBN 0879050616. LC 75-37705.

Parker brings together selected excerpts from five major American women writers along with an introduction, biographies, and comments about their place in the American literary scene. Their years span the period from 1849 to 1947 and their tradition is that of literary realism. Selections are from: Sarah Orne Jewett, *The Country of the Pointed Firs* and "Going to Shrewsburg"; Mary E. Wilkins Freeman, "A Conquest of Humility" and "A Village Singer"; Willa Cather, *My Antonia* and *O Pioneers*; Ellen Glasgow, "Jordan's End" and *A Sheltered Life*; Edith Wharton, *The Age of Innocence* and "Roman Fever." Parker suggests that all five women writers watched the progressive tides of change in America with some degree of anxiety and skepticism. However, the work of all reaffirms and expresses a belief in a return to the traditional values dethroned by the scientific and technological revolution of the late nineteenth and early twentieth centuries. The bibliography suggests further reading on the period and lists the works of each author along with selected biographical and critical works about these women.

691   Pearson, Carol, 1944- , and Katherine Pope, 1939- , eds. **Who Am I This Time? Female Portraits in British and American Literature.** New York: McGraw-Hill, 1976. 305p. bibliog. $6.95. ISBN 0070490325. LC 75-29130.

Pearson and Pope, two feminist critics, have turned to models constructed by Northrup Frye in *Anatomy of Criticism* and Joseph Campbell in *The Hero with a Thousand Faces* for their discussion of portraits of women in literature. They have chosen to see women portrayed in literature in two antipodal ways. As a "heroine," woman is Virgin, Mistress, or Helpmate who acts in relation to the male hero figure, who encounters her while on *his* quest. As hero herself, woman takes on the traditional heroic role and can be Sage, Artist, or Warrior; in *her* role as hero, she is on her own quest. "The portraits in the six sections represent the major literary achievements of female and male authors in Britain and America. They therefore reflect the myths and literary conventions that have affected women in Western culture from the Anglo-Saxon period in Britain and the colonial period in America to the present. The balance of female and male voices and the chronological arrangement of each section provide an opportunity for comparison and contrast of female and male and of traditional and contemporary viewpoints and literary techniques" (the introduction). There is a tremendous diversity of literature here—from Sir Philip Sidney to William Faulkner (The Virgin); from Anne Boleyn to Muriel Rukeyser (The Mistress); from Chaucer to Alurista (The Helpmate); from Rachel Speght to Dorothy West (The Sage); from Thomas Campion to Denise Levertov (The Artist); and from William Congreve to Jean Tepperman (The Warrior).

692   Reit, Ann, comp. **The World Outside: Collected Short Fiction about Women at Work.** New York: Four Winds Press, 1977. 214p. $6.95. ISBN 0590074849. LC 77-7986.

This collection provides some controversial material about how men see women working and how women see themselves in a work situation. Often the theme emerges as the conflict between love and work. Authors included are: Katherine Mansfield, Jean Rhys, Henry James, O. Henry, Alice Munro, Sara Orne Jewett, Margaret Laurence.

693   Rexroth, Kenneth, 1905- , and Ikuko Atsumi, eds. **The Burning Heart:**
       The Women Poets of Japan. New York: Seabury Press, 1977. 184p.
       bibliog. $8.95. ISBN 0816493189. LC 77-1833.
Rexroth and Atsumi present translations of poems by 76 Japanese women poets
from the seventh century to the present. Included are selections from: the classic
period (seventh-thirteenth century), the Haiku poets of the Tokugawa period
(seventeenth-early nineteenth century), modern Tanka poets (1878-), modern
Haiku poets (1890-), free verse poets (1878-), and anonymous Geisha songs.
The editors provide notes on the individual poets, a table of Japanese historical
periods, and a brief survey of the women poets of Japan. Rexroth is also compiler
of another collection of poetry by Asian women, *The Orchid Boat: Women Poets
of China* (Seabury Press, 1972).

694   Rotter, Pat, comp. **Bitches and Sad Ladies: An Anthology of Fiction**
       by and about Women. New York: Harper's Magazine Press, 1975.
       432p. bibliog. $10.95. ISBN 0061275158. LC 74-3902.
One distinguishing characteristic of this exceptionally fine anthology is Rotter's
lively introduction, in which she contrasts and compares the differences between
"bitches" and "sad ladies." "The bitch takes care of herself, seeks her identity
from within," Rotter writes. "The sad lady needs to be taken care of. She fears
independence almost as much as she fears losing love. She wants to bury herself
in a man, wants him to protect her the way she was protected by her family."
The collection assembled here is a good one—mainly of recognized, contemporary
writers, plus some who are relatively unknown. Among the writers represented:
Gail Godwin, Glenda Adams, Cynthia Ozick, Rosellen Brown, Rebecca Morris,
Jane Mayhall, Andrea Dworkin, Judith Rossner, Anne Sexton, Grace Paley,
Toni Cade Bambara, Ursula Le Guin, and Lynda Schor. No happy ladies here.

695   Schneiderman, Beth Kline, comp. **By and About Women: An Anthology**
       of Short Fiction. New York: Harcourt, Brace and Jovanovich, 1973.
       337p. bibliog. $5.95. ISBN 0155056654. LC 72-96987.
A collection of short fiction reflecting women authors' views of women, arranged
thematically around the central experiences of womanhood (adolescence, mar-
riage, motherhood). Included are selections from Dorothy Parker, Carson
McCullers, Virginia Woolf, Katherine Mansfield, Mary McCarthy, Joyce Carol
Oates, Anaïs Nin, Katherine Anne Porter, Gwendolyn Brooks, Shirley Jackson,
and others. Another similar collection (though of narrower focus) is Stephanie
Spinner's *Feminine Plural: Stories By Women About Growing Up* (Macmillan,
1972). The Spinner collection includes stories by Doris Lessing, Carson McCullers,
Colette, Katherine Anne Porter, Edna O'Brien, Tillie Olsen, Flannery O'Connor,
and others.

696   Showalter, Elaine, comp. **Women's Liberation and Literature.** New
       York: Harcourt Brace Jovanovich, 1971. 338p. bibliog. $5.95. ISBN
       0155961950. LC 79-153750.
This anthology of drama, poetry, fiction, essays on feminist criticism, and
psychology provides many variations on the theme of feminist consciousness
in literature. An essential question is posed by the readings: is there, in fact,
a feminist consciousness in literature or not? Intended for classroom use, the

volume includes discussion questions following each selection, a brief bibliography of works about feminism, and a listing of possible topics for further research and writing assignments. Writers represented are: Mary Wollstonecraft, John Stuart Mill, Henrik Ibsen, Elizabeth Barrett Browning, Anne Sexton, Sylvia Plath, Dorothy Parker, Mary McCarthy, George Henry Lewes, Virginia Woolf, Elizabeth Hardwick, Mary Ellmann, Hortense Calisher, Betty Friedan, Naomi Weisstein, Kate Millett, Earnest Van Den Haag, and Jonathan Yardley.

697   Singer, Frieda. **Daughters in High School: An Anthology of Their Work.**
       Plainfield, VT: Daughters, 1974. 244p. $3.80. ISBN 0913780324.
       LC 74-79917.
Singer describes the history of this anthology written by high school women: "when high school women students around the country were asked last spring by a new publishing house, Daughters Inc., a publisher of books by women, to contribute manuscripts and art work to a high school anthology on any subject of their choice, including work based on their experiences as young women growing up in contemporary American society, neither the publishers nor the editor of this anthology could anticipate the results." The contributions reflect feminist thought and good writing—essays, short stories and poetry—which are grouped around the following themes: The Unknown, Roles, The Male Protagonist, Questioning, Relationships, and Walk Tall Daughter.

698   Slung, Michele B., 1947- , comp. **Crime on Her Mind: Fifteen Stories
       of Female Sleuths from the Victorian Era to the Forties.** New York:
       Pantheon Books, 1975. 380p. bibliog. $10.00. ISBN 039449573X.
       LC 74-26201.
Stories here are by C. L. Pirkis, G. R. Sims, C. Rook, Baroness E. Orczy, H. C. Weir, A. K. Green, and others. Though the sleuths here are women, more of the stories in this anthology are written by men.

699   Spinner, Stephanie. **Motherlove: Stories by Women about Motherhood.**
       New York: Dell, 1978. 256p. $2.25. ISBN 0440356938.
Included here are: Colette's "Bastienne's Child"; Gail Godwin's "Dream Children"; Katherine Mansfield's "At Lehmann's"; Penelope Gilliatt's "Come Back If It Doesn't Get Better"; Alice Walker's "Everyday Use"; Jean Stafford's "Cops and Robbers"; Nadine Gordimer's "A Chip of Glass Ruby"; Joanne Greenberg's "Hunting Season"; Rosellen Brown's "Good Housekeeping"; Maxine Kingston's "Shaman"; Mary Lavin's "Happiness"; Joyce Carol Oates's "The Children"; Edna O'Brien's "Cords"; Merrill Joan Gerber's "Forty Watts"; Tillie Olsen's "I Stand Here Ironing"; and Grace Paley's "Faith in a Tree." Introduction is by Stephanie Spinner.

700   Sullivan, Victoria, and James Vernon Hatch, 1928- , comps. **Plays By
       and About Women: An Anthology.** New York: Vintage Books, 1974.
       425p. $2.95. ISBN 0394718968. LC 73-14734.
This anthology includes "Overtones," by Alice Gerstenberg; "The Children's Hour," by Lillian Hellman; "The Women," by Clare Booth; "Play with a Tiger," by Doris Lessing; "Calm Down Mother," by Megan Terry; "The Advertisement,"

by Natalia Ginzburg; "Rites," by Maureen Duffy; and "Wine in the Wilderness," by Alice Childress. An introduction is provided by the editors.

701   Thurman, Judith, 1946- . **I Became Alone: Five Women Poets—Sappho, Louise Labe, Ann Bradstreet, Juana Ines de la Cruz, Emily Dickinson.** New York: Atheneum, 1975. 140p. bibliog. $6.95. ISBN 0689304870. LC 75-9589.

Thurman explores the lives and work of five women poets—Sappho, Louise Labe, Ann Bradstreet, Juana Ines de la Cruz, and Emily Dickinson—through brief biographies and selections from their poetry.

702   Washington, Mary Helen, ed. **Black-eyed Susans: Classic Stories By and About Black Women.** Garden City, NY: Anchor Books, 1975. 163p. bibliog. $2.95. ISBN 0385090439. LC 75-6169.

In this important collection of fiction by and about Afro-American women, the stories rail against stereotyped images of black women. Many deal with the insensitivity of black males to the humanity of black women and deplore the sexual arrangements in black society. The tone is one of sardonic humor. Washington has written a fine introduction and provided a well-researched bibliography for each author who appears: Jean Wheeler Smith, Toni Morrison, Gwendolyn Brooks, Louise Meriwether, Toni Cade Bambara, Alice Walker, and Paule Marshall.

703   Webber, Jeannette L., and Joan Grumman, eds. **Woman As Writer.** Boston: Houghton Mifflin, 1978. 451p. bibliog. $7.95. ISBN 0395260884. LC 77-74379.

An excellent text for women's studies literature courses offering a general introduction to the work of women writers, this anthology has been organized into two sections: 1, Woman On Writing, in which well-known women writers describe the creative process using poetry, diary, journal and interview forms, (e.g., Carson McCullers, "How I Learned to Write," and Joan Didion, "On Keeping a Notebook") and 2, Woman Writing, with representative samples of creative writing. All told, there are over 100 selections here, ranging from well-known to lesser-known contemporary writers, from working-class writers to black writers. A rather full biographical sketch accompanies each writer's work, and there is a copious selection of further readings divided by genre: Journals, Autobiographies and Letters; Novels; Short Stories; Poetry; Drama; Essays and Criticism. A few of the writers represented are: Carolyn Kizer, Cynthia Ozick, Adrienne Kennedy, Joanna Russ, Myrna Lamb, Marie-Elise, and Margaret Walker, along with such expected names as Virginia Woolf, Adrienne Rich, Anaïs Nin, and Anne Sexton.

LITERATURE
Drama
[The scope note for Literature appears on p. 252.]

704   Aidoo, Christina Ama Ata. **Anowa**. Harlow, England: Longmans, 1970.
       [7], 66p. $2.50. ISBN 0582640318. LC 70-504504.
Ama Ata Aidoo's work is an extraordinary fusion of feminism, cultural history,
and dramatic tragedy. Her previous work has been much concerned with marriage,
especially the tragedy of mismatched couples whose cultural values are in
conflict. A grim and classic prologue sets the ritualistic mood for the tragedy.
Based upon a Ghanian legend, the action of the play is built around the marriage
of Anowa and Kofi Ako. Anowa, a beautiful, proud, and independent African
woman, resists marriage to many suitors before she marries the man of her own
choosing, Kofi Ako. Her strength of personality eventually results in his perceiving that his own manliness has been eclipsed. Anowa is not willing to take
responsibility for her husband's unhappiness, but when she decides to leave him,
he kills himself. Anowa drowns herself rather than return to the gossip and
censure of her own village. The dialogue of the old man and the old woman
commenting on the deaths of the couple at the end of the play becomes a stark
statement about the constructions of sex roles: "who knows if Anowa would
have been a better woman, a better person if we had not been what we are?"
reflects the old man.

705   Aidoo, Christina Ama Ata. **The Dilemma of a Ghost**. New York: Collier
       Books, 1971. 93p. $1.25. LC 74-162336.
Eulalie Rush, an American black woman, and Ato Yawson, her African husband,
are living under the illusion that they can disregard local customs and cultural
history when they return to Africa to be with Ato's people. Though women
living within the infrastructure of the small village may complain about their
lots and suggest to each other that childless women are the better off, Eulalie
and Ato's decision to disregard the culture in which they are living and to practice birth control without explaining to anyone in the village what birth control
is, is an ill-considered decision that isolates them from friends and family. Eulalie's
ignorance about the customs of her husband's people is interpreted as an insult.
Ato's mother chastises her son for his short-sightedness in his handling of the
situation. His wife is the stranger and the mother says, "no stranger breaks the
law." Ato presumes that he can bypass tradition and deep-seated religious
and cultural customs; as a consequence, he receives censure for dealing badly
with both relatives and his foreign wife. Aidoo's point appears to be that
estrangement is the result of cultural iconoclasm.

706   Albee, Edward, 1928- . **Who's Afraid of Virginia Woolf?** New York:
       Atheneum, 1962. 242p. $3.45. ISBN 0689100043. LC 62-17691.
This electrifying play may have special interest to women's collections for its
especially negative images of women: woman as bitch and castrator, and woman
as helpless victim.

707   Anouilh, Jean, 1910- . **The Lark.** New York: Oxford University Press, 1956. 103p. $5.95. ISBN 0195003934. LC 56-5472.

The Lark pits Joan of Arc, a pure and unrestrained spirit, against the pretentions and relentless egos of the men about her. Anouilh has made the point that his play "makes no attempt to explain the mystery of Joan." Rather, he sees Joan as a phenomenon "as there is the phenomenon of a daisy or of the sky or of a bird."

708   Bergman, Ingmar, 1918- . **Scenes From a Marriage.** New York: Pantheon Books, 1974. 199p. $6.95. ISBN 0394493052. LC 74-4753.

Of his script portraying marriage and its disintegration, *Scener ür ett äktenskap* (Swedish title), Bergman says he is presenting people who "are nervous, happy, selfish, stupid, kind, wise, self-sacrificing, affectionate, angry, gentle, sentimental, insufferable, and lovable. All jumbled up." This script has been produced as a continuing television series and as a feature length film in Sweden and in the United States. Johan and Marianne seem a conventionally contented and material-istic couple until confronted with painful, inescapable truths about each other, bringing about the dissolution of their marriage. By the sixth scene they have developed much self-knowledge and considerable appreciation for each other, though no immediate resolution is in sight.

709*   Brecht, Bertolt, 1898-1956. **The Mother.** New York: Grove Press, 1965. 158p. LC 65-14211.

Critic Lee Baxandall has suggested that Brecht sees the role of mother as a sphere of primary concern because it is her role that determines the hope of future generations. Vlassova, the Mother, emerges as one of the few positive characters among the complex constellation of dramatic figures created by Brecht in his Marxist period (1929-1956). Her intelligence, independence, and ethical strength define Brecht's notion of the "maternal." Revolutionary maternity becomes, in fact, revolutionary morality, a painful, active, ethical process which takes Vlassova out of the kitchen and her role of passivity toward a position of moral strength.

710   Delaney, Shelagh, 1939- . **A Taste of Honey; a Play.** New York: Grove Press, 1959. 87p. $2.95. ISBN 0394174801. LC 59-8206.

Manchester, England, is the city in which forty-year-old semi-whore (Delaney's term) Helen, whose most distinguishing behavioral response is quiet resignation, is courted by a "slick" car salesman ten years her junior; while seventeen-year-old daughter, Jo, is made pregnant by a 22-year-old black sailor, the first person to show her loving kindness. Jo, whose self-image is one of beauty, accuses Helen of self-centeredness and setting a weak example. The mother does rein-force Jo's undeveloped artistic ability (Jo: "I'm not just talented, I'm geniused.") and says, "You'll be an independent working woman and free to go where you please." Jo, whose lover remains absent, is befriended by the platonic Geof, who hears Jo say, "I used to hold my mother's hands, but she always used to pull them away. . . . She had so much love for everyone else, but none for me," and tells her that she is already like Helen in some ways, attempting to escape, but not knowing from what or to what. Both women are governed by short-term needs and responses to a series of crises, but they have no specific goals beyond simple survival. Jo's major wish is to have no resemblance to her mother's behavior patterns, but she has no plan for self development and has grown increasingly despondent. In the final scene, her mother returns to see her through the birth of her child. Jo, herself the progeny of her married mother's dalliance with the village idiot, seems destined to perpetuate Helen's succession of failures.

711   Euripides. **The Trojan Women.** New York: Vintage Books, 1972. 80p.
       $1.65. ISBN 0394710756.

Adapted by Jean-Paul Sartre (translation of *Les Troyennes* by Ronald Duncan), this particular version of *The Trojan Women* is a fanciful version of the original tragedy. A gallery of women appear, and it is not at all clear who acts out of self-interest and who out of nobility. Hecuba, traditionally considered the most gallant of the Trojan women, sets all blame on Helen, despising her for her destructive narcissistic beauty, warning Menelaus to stay away from Helen, and all the while predicting his vulnerability to her irresistible charms. Helen, meanwhile, blames Menelaus for his carelessness in allowing her abduction. This version could provide much controversy in an "Images of Women" course. Helen is seen quite differently from the poetic perspective of H. D. (*Helen in Egypt*, New Directions, 1974).

712   Ford, John, 1586-ca. 1640. **'Tis Pity She's a Whore.** Lincoln: University
       of Nebraska Press, 1966. 110p. bibliog. $5.95. ISBN 0803252617.
       LC 65-15339.

Incest is the central theme of this play, which also treats narcissism, guilt, murder, and other major tragic themes. First published in 1633, the play depicts the love relationship between Giovanni and Annabella, brother and sister. The friar to whom Giovanni goes for consultation at the beginning of the play warns that death can be the only outcome of such love. The brother is consistently an immovable character, distanced from reality and formulating all manner of illogical arguments to justify his love for his sister. Annabella takes all guilt and repentance on herself and loves less megalomaniacally than the brother. Critics have varied in their response to Annabella's character. T. S. Eliot, for example, refers to her as "virtually a moral defective" (*Collected Essays*, 1932). A disturbing work by any standard, this play offers interesting territory for the discussion of woman's image in seventeenth-century drama.

713   Genet, Jean, 1910- . **The Balcony (Le Balcon): A Play in Nine Scenes.**
       (Rev.). New York: Grove Press, 1960. 115p. $2.95. ISBN 0394172140.
       LC 58-9490.

Genet works out his theories on sexual oppression against the backdrops of brothels and prisons. Carmen, a whore, explains: "entering a brothel means rejecting the world. Here I am and here I stay. Your laws and orders and the passions are my reality." Characters in this surrealistic play of sado-masochism reflect the real and imaginary power elite—the Bishop, the Judge, the Executioner, the Chief of Police, and the forces of the brothel. Genet's is a world where hate is pleasure and in which power is illusion. The whores are mistresses of the ultimate illusions and thus, the actual bestowers of power. Jean Genet wrote his first book, *Our Lady of the Flowers*, in 1943, while serving one of his many lengthy prison terms for theft. For an analysis of the sexual politics in Genet's work, see Kate Millet's treatment in *Sexual Politics*.

714   Giraudoux, Jean, 1882-1944. **Three Plays: Judith, Tiger at the Gates, and Duel of Angels.** New York: Oxford University Press, 1963. 208p. $8.95. ISBN 0195003977.

Translated by Christopher Fry, these plays are full of the impressionistic and fabular touches that characterize Giraudoux's idealistic worldview. Interestingly, he creates woman characters who represent idealism but are generally misunderstood by the world around them. It is a subjective idealism beyond the pale of societally approved heroic and idealistic actions. In *Judith*, Judith kills Holofernes, not to save her people, but because the experience of lovemaking she shared with Holofernes became a transcendent experience that she does not care to eclipse by repeating. Tragically, she accepts the societally approved motive of killing Holofernes and must accept the patriotic role despite the commitment she has made toward the poetic motive. Judith is represented as a virgin, Holofernes as a sensual pagan before the consummation of their love. Drawing on legend and myth, *Tiger at the Gates* recreates the character of Helen of Troy as an indifferent though captivating woman who will survive while the men around her destroy themselves. Many will feel Giraudoux is presenting a negative feminine image, though it may be the chaotic and mad male order of the world that Giraudoux exposes. Lucile, in *Duel of the Angels*, is a character of pure motives suspected of infidelity by her husband. Lucile, who has consistently believed in idealism throughout her life, cannot bring herself to convince her husband of her innocence and commits suicide—it is *his* suspicion that is corrupt and false, and she will keep truth silent and pure.

715   Griffin, Susan. **Voices: A Play.** Old Westbury, NY: Feminist Press, 1975. 159p. $3.50. ISBN 0912670428. LC 75-37540.

Five women speak of their lives to the audience in this moving verse play. Although the characters do not interact, their experiences mingle and overlap, so that the poetic result becomes a *gestalt* of woman's existence in our culture. Adrienne Rich's introduction to *Voices* suggests that Griffin's work "is a search for the words, the rhythms, in which the voiceless can be heard." This is a play of ages, too—of women who are contemporaries yet born into various periods of this century. Griffin feels it is important that women whose real ages correspond to those of the characters should play the parts: Kate, early 70s; Maya, 35; Grace, around 46; Erin, 28; and Rosalinde, 19.

716   Hansberry, Lorraine, 1930-1965. **Les Blancs: The Collected Last Plays of Lorraine Hansberry.** Edited by Robert Nemiroff. New York: Random House, 1972. 370p. $8.95. ISBN 039446480X. LC 69-16462.

With the death of Hansberry at age 34, a bad blow was dealt to black theater. This volume brings together Hansberry's last work in the form of three dramas: *Les Blancs, The Drinking Gourd,* and *What Use Are Flowers? Les Blancs* has been judged Hansberry's best play by many. The action takes place in a white-ruled African country where the black natives are attacking the colonialists. Tshembe Matoseh has returned to his native country to see his father who is dying; the son has been living in England for several years with his white wife. All of the characters of the play are caught up in the revolution whether they wish to be involved or not. Robert Nemiroff provides excellent critical notes to each play.

717   Hansberry, Lorraine, 1930-1965. **A Raisin in the Sun: A Drama in Three Acts.** New York: Random House, 1969. 146p. $6.95. ISBN 0394406885. LC 59-10834.
The action of the play occurs in Chicago's Southside sometime after World War II. It is about a family of "plain people" who show amazing courage, spirit, and pride in deciding to move into the family's dream house in a white neighborhood despite threats of violence "because my father—my father—he earned it." The mother figure is especially strong and nurturant, encouraging her daughter, Beneatha, in her ambition to become a doctor. The title comes from Langston Hughes: "What happens to a dream deferred?/Does it dry up/Like a raisin in the sun?" James Baldwin has written of *Raisin*, "never before, in the entire history of the American theater, had so much of the truth of black people's lives been seen on stage. Black people ignored the theater because the theater had always ignored them."

718   Hellman, Lillian, 1905- . **The Collected Plays.** Boston: Little, Brown, 1972. 815p. $17.50. ISBN 0316355194. LC 79-175482.
Hellman is undoubtedly one of the major playwrights of America in this century. Her most notable successes have been *The Children's Hour, The Little Foxes, The Autumn Garden*, and *Toys In the Attic*. This volume "brings together for the first time all of Miss Hellman's work for the theatre, and supersedes any previous editions and collections. For this edition she has made numerous small revisions and emendations in each of the plays: the texts as given here are henceforth to be regarded as definitive" (publisher's note). Contents: *The Children's Hour, Days to Come, The Little Foxes, Watch on the Rhine, The Searching Wind, Another Part of the Forest, Montserrat, The Autumn Garden, The Lark, Candide, Toys in the Attic*, and *My Mother, My Father and Me*.

719   Ibsen, Henrik, 1828-1906. **The Lady from the Sea; Hedda Gabler; The Master Builder.** New York: Oxford University Press, 1966. 592p. bibliog. $13.75. ISBN 0192113429. LC 71-97819.
This is identified as an excellent edition for *Hedda Gabler* (1890), but there are many cheaper ones without its extensive scholarly apparatus. *The Lady from the Sea* presents an intricate networking of female rivalries, dissatisfactions, and needs. The plot is worked around the family politics of a middle-aged widower with two daughters who remarries a woman close to the age of his elder daughter. Implicit here is the power struggle between wife and daughter, for the daughter has managed the household for some time and has little need of the new wife's affection. The young wife, however, comes to the marriage seeking affection not only from the husband but from his daughters due to her own family background of alienation and her experience of geographical isolation as a lightkeeper's daughter. While *The Lady from the Sea* is energized by the complex working out of family relationships, *Hedda Gabler* is dominated by a single character (though critics have pointed out that rarely has such a major character had so little to say in a play). Hedda's complex character provides inexhaustible material for the image of woman in literature debate.

720   Ibsen, Henrik, 1828-1906. **Pillars of Society; A Doll's House; Ghosts.**
        New York: Oxford University Press, 1961. 499p. bibliog. $17.50.
        ISBN 0192113267. LC 72-93307.

There are, of course, many translations of Ibsen and many editions; R. Farquhar-
son Sharp, Una Ellis-Fermor, and Eva Le Gallienne are among the prominent
translators. All three of these plays manifest Ibsen's condemnation of the
stranglehold on human freedom inherent in institutionalized lifestyles. The
crises of the three major characters in these plays (Bernick, Nora, and Mrs.
Alving) hinge upon their difficult disentanglement from the constrictions on
their liberty imposed by societal morality and custom. There is virtually unlimited
commentary on Nora and *A Doll's House* (1879) and the prototype it portrays
of female unhappiness and suffocation of the self in modern middle-class society.

721   Jellicoe, Ann. **The Knack: A Comedy.** London: Faber and Faber, 1968.
        88p. $3.95. ISBN 0571086179. LC 64-46881.

Jellicoe's play is a feminist statement and a black comedy about the dominant
male and the submissive female who subjects herself to him. Tolen, the most
vital and arrogant of the three young men in the play, takes it upon himself
to instruct his followers in the "knack" of "getting" women. He recommends
that the man be prepared to humiliate himself in the process of the quest. In
the end, this is merely sham humility: "after all, what does it matter? It's just
part of getting her. Once you've got her it's the woman that grovels. Finally,
Collin, the man is the master."

722   Jellicoe, Ann. **The Sport of My Mad Mother: A Play.** London: Faber
        and Faber, 1964. 87p. $3.95. ISBN 057105935X. LC 76-375425.

The idea of the play is introduced by the epigram from a Hindu hymn: "all
creation is the sport/of my mad mother Kali." Jellicoe calls it "an anti-intellect
play," full of irrational forces and spontaneous action which may seem unrelated.
Mainly, she says, it is a play about rites of the tribe and the primal fears shared
by all human beings related to being ostracized from the group. Steve, Dean,
Patty, Fak, Cone, Dodo, and Greta are essentially inarticulate characters whose
words and gestures are seemingly purposeless in advancing any plot in the play.
Gradually, however, a pattern emerges as they begin to repeat certain words
and phrases and to set up a structure of idea repetition. Jellicoe specifies the
use of chanting in the stage directions to underscore the ritualistic, tribal message
of the play.

723   Kuper, Hilda. **Witch in My Heart.** London: Oxford University Press,
        1970. 70p. $7.50. ISBN 0197241808. LC 78-518794.

Set in Swaziland in the 1930s, this is a play about a favored but barren wife
who absorbs the culturally imposed guilt of her childlessness, coming to believe
that being accused of witchcraft may be her just dessert. Written by a respected
anthropologist, the play is ethnographically supported by Kuper's observations
of family organization in Swaziland. In her introduction, Kuper writes, "When
I wrote *A Witch in My Heart* I was not trying, at least at the conscious level,
to interpret a specific situation as an anthropologist. To me the situation was
less about witchcraft and more about the heart—a symbolic heart reflecting
deep human emotions—love, hate, jealousy, hope and despair. It happened that

the people about whom I wrote were Swazi, and among them these emotions were expressed in a particular cultural idiom in which witchcraft was an essential and accepted element, a part of the general order and disorder of life."

724   Kyle, Barry. **Sylvia Plath: A Dramatic Portrait.** New York: Harper and Row, 1977. 92p. $1.95. ISBN 0060804076. LC 76-41603.

Conceived and adapted from Sylvia Plath's writings by Barry Kyle, "the text of this dramatized setting was compiled as a companion piece to *Three Women*, Sylvia Plath's play about childbirth. In *Three Women* there is a constantly shifting perspective as the three separate accounts of childbirth merge and contrast. Similarly, this script is based on the device of three voices; each playing Sylvia Plath at different times." The play has no exits or entrances, and the poetry is spoken directly to the audience as if the audience were participating in the creative process.

725   Lamb, Myrna. **The Mod Donna, and Scyklon Z: Plays of Women's Liberation.** New York: Pathfinder Press, 1971. 200p. $5.95. ISBN 087348164X. LC 71-139788.

In the militant and angry drama of this volume, the common theme is the tyranny of marriage and pregnancy and the victimization of women in society. In the introduction to *The Mod Donna: A Space-age Musical Soap Opera with Breaks for Commercials*, the playwright explains, "The *Mod Donna* main characters are presented in eight 'TV Soap Opera' scenes, with a difference. The mod wife-swapping version of the traditional ménage à trois is turned a bit dissonant, a bit macabre." The play ends with the chorus's refrain against male oppression and the cry, "LIBERATION, LIBERATION, LIBERATION." Of the pieces assembled in the segment titled *Scyklon Z*, the most hard-hitting is the interrogation dialogue "But What Have You Done for Me Lately?," in which a young woman in a surgical smock explains to the young man facing her that he has been implanted with a parasitic impregnated uterus in his abdomen. Against his pleas for mercy, the young woman explains the tortures she suffered as a result of this same man's impregnation of her. In the course of the dialogue, the audience learns that the young man symbolizes the role of any man in the society who seduces and abandons, who denies a woman an abortion, and who perpetuates cruel gynecological and obstetrical practices on women.

726*   Luce, Clare (Boothe), 1903- . **The Women: Play in Two Acts.** (Rev.). New York: Dramatists Play Service, 1966. 92p. LC 67-290.

A brittle little romantic satire, this play was a great success when it was first produced on Broadway in 1936. The action of the play—Mary's losing her husband, Stephen, to a tasteless "shopgirl," Crystal, and then getting him back again—is jungle warfare, Park Avenue style. Indeed, gentle Mary's last line after discovering that she has lost and regained her husband from the clutches of a faithless and undeserving woman is, "well, I've had two years to sharpen my claws." The play provides an interesting study in the image of woman. However, Clare Boothe Luce has used many "types" here and one could argue convincingly that Mary's victory over Crystal is a victory of one social class over another, rather than the deserved victory of one woman, an inherently superior moral being, over another.

726a   McCullers, Carson (Smith), 1917-1967. **The Member of the Wedding**:
          A Play. New York: New Directions, 1963. 118p. $1.75. ISBN
          0811200930. LC 51-10532.

Taken from the 1946 novel, the play was first produced in 1950. As an exploration of the complexity of adolescence in the South the play is compelling.
McCullers excels in creating a world seen through a child-woman's vision. The
black characters are portrayed with sensitivity and warmth. The action centers
around Frankie's desire to accompany her brother and his bride on their honeymoon—even though uninvited. The painful conclusion that Frankie must ultimately draw is that she will be excluded from the special relationship her brother
is forming with his wife as a couple. An excellent play to use with high school
students.

726b   Nemiroff, Robert. **To Be Young, Gifted, and Black: Lorraine Hansberry**
          in Her Own Words. Adapted by Robert Nemiroff. Englewood Cliffs,
          NJ: Prentice-Hall, 1969. 266p. $8.95. ISBN 0139230033. LC 79-80772.

Lorraine Hansberry's biography is important to the understanding of this work.
At 28 when her play *Raisin in the Sun* opened on Broadway and won the New
York Drama Critics Circle Award for the "Best Play of the Year," she was
triply distinguished as the only black writer, the youngest playwright and the
fifth woman to win this honor. She died at 34 of cancer. Nemiroff, Hansberry's
husband and editor, calls this presentation of snippets from manuscripts, essays,
memoirs, journals and correspondence "a small representative sampling, a cross-
section selected and shaped with a particular purpose in mind: to relate the
artist to the person, and place the parts within the context of the whole in such
a fashion as to enable the words she left to tell her story without intrusion or
comment, explanation or footnotes of any kind." A successful off-Broadway
play was conceived and produced from this material (1968-69 off-Broadway
season). The whole of this volume is personal and beautiful. James Baldwin's
"Sweet Lorraine," which introduces the Hansberry material, is a remarkable
comment on Hansberry's artistic process and her spirit.

727   Oates, Joyce Carol, 1938- . **Miracle Play.** Los Angeles: Black Sparrow
          Press, 1974. 87p. $8.95. ISBN 0876852142. LC 74-19270.

The two women in the play—the former lover and the mother of a psychopathic
murderer (Titus Skinner)—form a tableau of almost mute helplessness in this
drama of violence and coercion. Titus Skinner, a black criminal, is a man of
cruelty who proudly admits to the fact. The psychological problem of the play
hinges upon the complexity of Titus's sadistic personality and his destructive
relationship to members of his own family and community, whose testimony
against him could deliver him up to the penalties imposed by white institutional
justice. Titus's mother and lover are clearly terrified of the man but paralyzed
to cope with the situation in the face of such uncomprehending "assistance"
as Titus's slick lawyer, who sees his role as savior of Titus. Only the women,
it seems, understand the true tragedy of Titus: a personality stunted grotesquely
by the circumstances of a racist society to the extent that he develops the personality of a psychopath as a means of gaining recognition.

728   Sartre, Jean Paul, 1905- . **No Exit, and Three Other Plays.** New York:
        Vintage Books, 1955. 281p. $1.95. ISBN 0394700163.
No Exit (*Huis clos*) and *The Flies* (*Les mouches*) were translated by S. Gilbert,
while *Dirty Hands* (*Les mains sales*) and *The Respectful Prostitute* (*La putain
respectueuse*) were translated by L. Abel. Linked together inescapably in a
hotel room in Hell for eternity, Garcin, Estelle, and Inez are caught in an infinite
psycho-sexual battle in *No Exit*. Inez, a lesbian, denies the narcissistic Estelle.
Estelle's total absorption lies in her seduction of Garcin; Garcin's pleasure is
in tormenting Inez. Estelle is an especially fascinating study in woman's passivity,
capable of defining herself only in a man's eyes. Inez possesses the greatest
understanding of who Garcin and Estelle are as individuals entirely bound to
gender roles; she also apprehends the endless hopelessness of their grotesque
ménage à trois. *The Respectful Prostitute* depicts the slavery of woman's lot as
a variant of prostitution and equates this human bondage with the lot of other
oppressed groups, specifically the American black man.

729   Shakespeare, William, 1564-1616. **The Taming of the Shrew.** Edited by
        Sir Arthur Quiller-Couch and John Dover Wilson. Cambridge, England:
        Cambridge University Press, 1962. 194p. bibliog. $12.95. LC 68-91602.
Many courses in women's studies have used *Taming* to illustrate Shakespeare's
image of woman, though others from among his plays could also be fruitfully
explored. Kate's subservient speech in Act V, Scene ii of *Taming* ("I am ashamed
that women are so simple/To offer war where they should kneel for peace,/Or
seek for rule, supremacy, and away,/When they are bound to serve, love, and
obey") is often interpreted as a sexist view rather than as a statement of
seventeenth-century political order with each person occupying a niche so that
society continues in harmony. Some useful critical studies of women in Shakespearean drama are Juliet Dusinberre's *Shakespeare and the Nature of Women*
(Macmillan, 1975), Anna Jameson's *The Heroines of Shakespeare* (Gordon
Press, n.d.), and Agnes Mackenzie's *The Women in Shakespeare's Plays* (Norwood Editions, 1977).

730   Shange, Ntozake. **For Colored Girls Who Have Considered Suicide/When
        the Rainbow is Enuf: A Choreopoem.** New York: Macmillan, 1977.
        64p. $5.95. ISBN 0026098407. LC 77-3034.
In this choreographed tragic-comic poem on the stage, Ntozake Shange has
written a celebration of the strength of black women as sisters and friends,
supporting each other despite the cruel world of poverty, violence, passion,
and male seduction and betrayal. Shange writes in the introduction of the
genesis of these choreopoems: "in the summer of 1974 I had begun a series of
seven poems, modeled on Judy Grahn's *The Common Woman*, which were to
explore the realities of seven different kinds of women. They were numbered
pieces: the women were to be nameless and assume hegemony as dictated by
the fullness of their lives. The first of the series is the poem, 'one' (orange
butterflies & aqua sequins), which prompted the title—*this is for colored girls
who have considered suicide/when the rainbow is enuf*. I was smitten by my own
language, and called all the performances I was to give from then on by that
title." The play opened on Broadway on September 15, 1976. Shange's latest

book, *Nappy Edges* (St. Martin's Press, 1978), explores in poem-essay form the experience of the black woman poet.

731   Shaw, George Bernard, 1856-1950. **Major Barbara.** Northbrook, IL:
       AHM, 1971. 152p. bibliog. $4.95. ISBN 0882950878.
Barbara, the promising daughter of an upper-class English family, has shocked her well-bred relatives by discarding her affluent lifestyle, joining the Salvation Army, and living on a pound a week. To complete the scandal, she has fallen in love with an impecunious classicist who plays the drum for her in public as she begs on behalf of the Salvation Army on street corners. Barbara's father, Andrew Undershaft, armaments tycoon, believes that making money, no matter the trade, is the noblest human endeavor, poverty the basest crime. Barbara decides to turn her father's dubious morality into Salvation Army fodder by using her father's business for future evangelical work. The whole play is an ambitious farce, with Major Barbara's role as proselytizer for morality striking the highest ethical note in the drama. Critics labelled the 1905 play as incomprehensible and unrealistic, especially Barbara's role as a Salvationist refusing money, no matter the source. Readers may want to look at Barbara Watson Bellow's *A Shavian Guide to the Intelligent Woman* (1972) for a defense of Shaw's women from a feminist perspective. "Shaw gifts his strong characters with an awareness that the guilt is society's for having offered them two evils as alternatives, not theirs for having chosen the lesser," Watson writes.

732   Shaw, George Bernard, 1856-1950. **Saint Joan.** Indianapolis, IN:
       Bobbs-Merrill, 1971. 228p. bibliog. $5.65. ISBN 0672610914. LC
       76-134308.
This is edited, with an introduction and notes, by Stanley Weintraub. St. Joan is the most numinous of Shaw's strong-minded women. In her mission of saving a nation, she magnifies all the superior qualities of other Shaw heroines. She manages not a small group of individuals but an entire army. She justifies her task calling not upon a limited code of honor but upon the highest religious principles. Her powers transcend age and sex, yet there is no escaping the fact that she is a young and compelling woman in Shaw's play. As an outsider of established social institutions, Joan's freedom to be domineering, reckless, and creative is limited only by her own personal courage.

733   Williams, Tennessee, 1911- . **The Glass Menagerie: A Play.** New York:
       New Directions, 1945. 124p. $1.75. ISBN 0811202208. LC 49-8373.
Perhaps no other American drama has evoked so poignant a view of woman as a tragic and fragile, crippled creature as Tennessee Williams's *The Glass Menagerie.* In a household in which the mother's anxieties center on marrying off her crippled and obsessively shy daughter, while the daughter is forced to perpetually feed off that anxiety, the son's compelling need to get away from both women clearly is rooted in self-preservation.

734   Woolf, Virginia Stephen, 1882-1941. **Freshwater: A Comedy.** New York:
       Harcourt Brace Jovanovich, 1976. 76p. $6.95. ISBN 0151334870.
       LC 76-1902.

Edited with a preface by Lucio P. Ruotolo and illustrated by Loretta Trezzo, this farce in three acts was performed for eighty invited guests in Vanessa Bell's London studio in 1935. Its importance lies in the fact that it is Woolf's only known play. Woolf herself dismissed it as "tosh." The action of the play is set in the house of the noted Victorian photographer, Julia Margaret Cameron, so it is interesting to read Woolf's witty introduction to Cameron's *Victorian Photographs of Famous Men, Fair Women*, since Cameron's lifestyle and artistic milieu are so much the meat of this play.

LITERATURE
Essays
[The scope note for Literature appears on p. 252.]

734a   Baldwin, James, 1924- , and Nikki Giovanni. **A Dialogue.** Philadelphia,
        PA: Lippincott, 1973. 112p. $5.50. ISBN 039700916X. LC 73-4388.
In this transcribed conversation (1971), Baldwin and Giovanni speak about
the responsibility of the black writer and the ways in which black men and
black women have traditionally viewed each other.

735   Barnes, Djuna. **Ladies Almanack: Showing Their Signs and Their Tides;
        Their Moons and Their Changes; The Seasons As It Is with Them;
        Their Eclipses and Equinoxes; As Well As a Full Record of Diurnal
        and Nocturnal Distempers.** New York: Harper and Row, 1972. (Repr.
        of 1928 ed.). 84p. $7.95. ISBN 0060102217. LC 72-79649.
In her article on lesbian society in Paris of the 1920s (in *Amazon Odyssey*,
edited by Phyllis Birkby, et al.), Bertha Harris describes the *Ladies Almanack*
as an "outrageous lesbian comedy" focusing "on Natalie Barney and her drawing
room and her bedroom to portray the complexities of the social and sexual
games of her little world. Privately printed in 1928 and 'anonymously' presented
by 'A Lady of Fashion,' the little book not only satirized such famous figures
of the inner circle as Radclyffe Hall and Una Troubridge ('Lady Buck-and-Balk
and Tilly-Tweed-in-Blood') it is also in its way and for its time, a document of
lesbian revolution." Barnes calls this fanciful work a "slight satiric wigging."
In the style of fifteenth-century "almanacks," this pokes whimsical fun at the
genres of medieval literature in which woman's place alternated between extremes
of saint and slut.

736   Didion, Joan. **Slouching Toward Bethlehem.** New York: Farrar, Straus
        and Giroux, 1968. 238p. $7.95. ISBN 0374266360. LC 68-14916.
Didion's work is pervaded with California—not just California, the place, but
California, the experience. Los Angeles characterizes her fiction. Most of the
pieces here appeared first in the *Saturday Evening Post*. They are interesting,
splendidly written pieces on contemporary life and culture. Of particular interest
to women are "Slouching Toward Bethlehem," about Haight-Ashbury during
the late 1960s; "Marrying Absurd," on Las Vegas weddings; and "On Keeping
a Notebook."

737   Edgeworth, Maria, 1767-1849. **Letters for Literary Ladies.** London:
        J. Johnson, 1795; repr. New York: Garland, 1974. 11, 74, 79, 47p.
        bibliog. $34.50. ISBN 0824008553. LC 74-8322.
Gina Luria, editor of the Garland Series, The Feminist Controversy in England
1788-1810 (44 works reprinted in photo-facsimile in 89 volumes), suggests
that Edgeworth's inclusion in the series may "provide material for a long-
neglected assessment of her involvement with one of the major questions of
her age: the place of woman in the political, social, and intellectual matrix of
England during the Napoleonic era." As one of the most popular novelists of

the early nineteenth century, Edgeworth was looked to by her contemporaries as "a fount of moral sense and entertaining information." Her most popular works were *Castle Rackrent* (1800) and *The Absentee* (1812). These letters are both fiction and social doctrine, for they comprise the invented correspondence between two educated ladies on the issues of women's rights, social conventions, and marriage. Three separate segments comprise this volume: "Letter from a Gentleman to His Friend upon the Birth of a Daughter, with the Answer"; "Letters of Julia and Caroline"; and "Essay on the Noble Science of Self-Justification."

738   Ephron, Nora. **Crazy Salad: Some Things About Women.** New York: Knopf; distr. New York: Random House, 1975. 201p. $7.95. ISBN 039449735X. LC 74-25227.

Nora Ephron began writing a column in *Esquire* in 1972. The pieces collected here are short, irreverent, and personal insights mainly about changes American women were experiencing in various spheres of American life and culture during the early '70s. She is not attempting to write a history of the women's liberation movement or a statement of weighty political import. (The title comes from William Butler Yeats: "It's certain that fine women eat/A crazy salad with their meat.") Ephron writes honestly; for example, she recounts her own experience in a consciousness-raising group and gives many good reasons why such groups can be harmful and disillusioning. Her point may be summed up neatly from one of her essays "On Never Having Been a Prom Queen": "like all things about liberation, sisterhood is difficult." Some other pieces in this collection are "A Few Words About Breasts"; "Vaginal Politics"; "On Consciousness-Raising"; "The Pig"; and "Women in Israel: The Myth of Liberation."

739   Grier, Barbara [Damon, Gene], 1933- . **Lesbiana: Book Reviews from the Ladder, 1966-1972.** Reno, NV: Naiad Press, 1976. 309p. index. $5.00. LC 76-45683.

Barbara Grier served as editor of *The Ladder*, a well-known lesbian journal of the arts, from 1966-1972. This collection of book reviews provides an excellent bibliographic source of books by and about lesbians. Interested readers should also be aware of another *Ladder* collection edited by Grier (with Coletta Reid), *The Lavender Herring: Lesbian Essays From the Ladder* (Diana Press, 1976).

740   Lessing, Doris May, 1919- . **A Small Personal Voice.** New York: Knopf; distr. New York: Random House, 1974. 171p. $6.95. ISBN 039449329X. LC 74-7724.

In this collection of writings, Lessing speaks in "a small personal voice" about those literary and political insights closest to her mind. Concise and clear about her reasons for writing, she explains what it is to be a "committed" writer; her preferences for Tolstoy, Stendhal, and Balzac; and the terrifying nature of the world we live in. Her preface to *The Golden Notebook* (included here) is the best critical piece available on that complex novel. In that preface, she also speaks of women's liberation, Marxism, the sterility of critical judgment, and the absence of creativity in much literary scholarship. Also included here are three interviews with Lessing conducted by Jonah Raskin, Roy Newquist, and Florence Howe. Essays by Lessing collected here include "My Father";

"Afterword to *The Story of an African Farm* by Olive Schreiner"; and "*Out of Africa* by Karen Blixen [Isak Dinesen] ." These essays span the years 1957-1973 and offer an excellent introduction to Lessing's views of the novel as art and her own function as artist. She defines her role as writer as that of one who "represents, makes articulate, is continuously and invisibly fed by, numbers of people who are inarticulate, to whom one belongs, to whom one is responsible." A favorite Lessing topic is the parochialism of England and the English. For more of Lessing's views on this, see *In Pursuit of the English* (1961).

741   Olsen, Tillie. **Silences.** New York: Delacorte Press/S. Lawrence, 1978.
        306p. index. $10.00. ISBN 0440079004. LC 77-26196.
Tillie Olsen lost twenty years of writing time while raising a family and working. Over the years, Olsen has copiously copied quotations into her notebooks. A notebook subject that has consistently fascinated and depressed her has been creativity—what sustains it, what extinguishes it. The absence of a creative product she terms "silence." Among the varieties of silence (death of creativity, censorship, remaining unpublished), the saddest of all are the silences of those who remain mute because their "waking hours are all struggle for existence; the barely educated; the illiterate; women." In mulling over the silences of women, Olsen speculates that it is the childless and unmarried women who have written most because they have been freed of the obligation to place the needs of others before their own needs to create and to write. Olsen's documentation of silences takes several forms. In the essays she writes of the experiences of women's lives that render them silent in literature, including an essay on Rebecca Harding Davis, whose *Life in the Iron Mills* (1861) chronicles the silences endured by working women of Davis's time. Ironically, Rebecca Harding Davis's work had been forgotten until the Feminist Press issued it in 1972 with an afterword by Olsen. Part 2 of *Silences* records the quotations of great writers on writing, with Olsen's accompanying comments. These "silences of the great in achievement" include Thomas Hardy, Herman Melville, Willa Cather, William Blake, and Jane Austen. Olsen lists and quotes journals, accounts, and letters of writers on the process of writing: Virginia Woolf, Anton Chekhov, Katherine Mansfield, Franz Kafka, Albert Camus, Gide, Rilke, Henry James, Gustave Flaubert, Jessamyn West. The puzzle of creativity that Tillie Olsen has pieced together is as unique and various as it is fragmented. Taken as a whole, this volume speaks tellingly of the perils of writing and of any creative endeavor where commitment must be total and conflict is inevitable.

742   Rukeyser, Muriel, 1913- . **The Life of Poetry.** New York: Kraus
        Reprint, 1968. (Repr. of 1949 ed.). 232p. $14.00. ISBN 0527778001.
Rukeyser introduces her subject: "I have attempted to suggest a dynamics of poetry, showing that a poem is not its words or its images, any more than a symphony is its notes or a river its drops of water. Poetry depends on the moving relations within itself. It is an art that lives in time, expressing and evoking the moving relation between the individual consciousness and the world." In theorizing about the process of poetry, she draws on a dazzling assortment of sources including Whitman, Melville, Dickinson, children's poetry, Sergei Eisenstein, Navajo poetry, black spirituals, Leadbelly, Cole Porter, Arthur Miller, Stevie Smith, and Pu Chu'i. The connections that Rukeyser sees

and the poetic esthetic that she constructs transcend the prose form she is working
with in this volume and become poetry, especially in the final section, "The
Life of Poetry."

743   Sontag, Susan, 1933- . **Against Interpretation, and Other Essays.**
       New York: Farrar, Straus and Giroux, 1966. 304p. $6.95. ISBN
       0374102244. LC 65-20916.
Sontag, recognized as one of the most incisive of contemporary essayists, offers
collected articles, reviews and critical journalism here. She has never been
noted for her championing of feminist issues; she is, however, a consistently
splendid writer. Among the women-related pieces here: "Simone Weil"; "Nathalie
Sarraute and the Novel"; "Psychoanalysis and Norman O. Brown's *Life Against
Death*"; and "Resnais' *Muriel*." Not included in this volume but of interest
to women's studies will be these Sontag articles: "The Third World of Women,"
Partisan Review, (Vol. XL, no. 2, 1973: pp. 180-206); and "Feminism and
Fascism: An Exchange," *New York Review of Books* (Vol. XXII, no. 4, March 20,
1975: pp. 31-32), in which Sontag and Adrienne Rich exchange views on an
earlier Sontag article on the work of Leni Riefenstahl.

744   Sontag, Susan, 1933- . **Styles of Radical Will.** New York: Farrar, Straus
       and Giroux, 1969. 274p. $10.00. ISBN 0374271402. LC 69-15404.
In her second collection of essays, Susan Sontag addresses major intellectual
issues of the day: politics, art and aesthetics, film, theater, pornography, and
radicalism. Of particular interest to women's studies will be the essays "The
Pornographic Imagination" and "Bergman's *Persona*." Sontag's easy shifts from
philosophical to political to literary analysis are dazzling displays of her virtuosity
with the essay form.

745   Stein, Gertrude, 1874-1946. **Lectures in America.** New York: Modern
       Library, 1935; repr. New York: Vintage Books, 1975. 246p. $2.45.
       ISBN 0394714776. LC 74-17454.
First published in 1935, these lectures explicate in Stein's idiosyncratic style
what she is attempting to do in her work and why she has chosen her particular,
peculiar method. Lectures include: "What Is English Literature?"; "Pictures";
"Plays"; "The Gradual Making of the Making of Americans"; "Portraits and
Repetition"; and "Poetry and Grammar."

746   Welty, Eudora, 1909- . **The Eye of the Story: Selected Essays and
       Reviews.** New York: Random House, 1977. 335p. $10.00. ISBN
       0394425065.
Welty is not only a fine fiction writer; her essays and criticism are finely crafted
productions as well. In this book of miscellaneous essays and reviews, Welty
looks at writers and writing. Among the women writers she admires are Jane
Austen, Katherine Anne Porter, and Willa Cather. Her essays on writing include
"Looking at Short Stories" and "Writing and Analyzing a Story."

747   Woolf, Virginia (Stephen), 1882-1941. **Books and Portraits: Some Further
       Selections from the Literary and Biographical Writings of Virginia**

Woolf. New York: Harcourt Brace Jovanovich, 1978. $10.00. ISBN 0151134782. LC 77-85206.

Edited by Mary Lyon, this volume attempts to gather many of the very early Woolf essays, most of which were originally published in the *Times Literary Supplement*, for which Woolf regularly reviewed. Informal essays, sketches, and reviews are the meat of this volume, which should be considered minor Woolf. Of special interest to Women's Studies will be the essays on the lives of women in part 2. It is in these essays that Woolf shows a keen sensitivity to the roles that women have played in public life (mainly oppressive) because of their sex. Portraits include: The Girlhood of Queen Elizabeth; The Diary of a Lady in Waiting; Queen Adelaide; Elizabeth Lady Holland; Lady Hester Stanhope; The Memoirs of Sarah Bernhardt; and Lady Strachey. Essays on women writers include: A Scribbling Dame; Maria Edgeworth and Her Circle; Mrs. Gaskell; Wilcoxiana; and Shelley and Elizabeth Hitchener.

748   Woolf, Virginia (Stephen), 1882-1941. **The Common Reader.** New York: Harcourt, Brace, Jovanovich, 1955. $2.95. ISBN 0156198053. LC 25-10098.

Woolf borrows the phrase "common reader" from Dr. Johnson, and defines such an individual as one who reads for pleasure and judges works outside of the criteria set up by formal critics and scholars. In this collection of elegant essays, Woolf, hardly a common reader, comments upon her favorite writers and dazzles the reader with her intuitive, fresh approach to literature. Her essays—which were taken from her literary writings for newspapers, the *Times Literary Supplement*, and *Dial*—range freely among subjects as diverse as "On Not Knowing Greek" to "Jane Austen" to "The Russian Point of View." One of her finest pieces is her analysis of Jane Austen's work.

749   Woolf, Virginia (Stephen), 1882-1941. **A Room of One's Own.** New York: Harcourt, Brace and World, 1963. 117p. $1.95. ISBN 0156787326. LC 67-31296.

Based on speeches that Woolf prepared for delivery at Girton and Newnham, British women's colleges, this explicitly feminist non-fiction work (originally published in 1929) ranks with Mary Wollstonecraft's work in the profundity of its vision and its ingenious artistic organization of the arguments. Woolf uses the metaphor of having "a room of one's own" to represent the (usually frustrated) need of every woman (in her case, of the creative writer) to separate herself in mind and body from distractions that cripple the creative process. "For my belief is that if we live another century or so—I am talking of the common life which is the real life and not of the little separate lives which we live as individuals—and have five hundred a year each of us and rooms of our own; if we have the habit of freedom and the courage to write exactly what we think; if we escape a little from the common sitting-room and see human beings not always in their relation to each other but in relation to reality . . . then the opportunity will come and the dead poet who was Shakespeare's sister will put on the body which she has so often laid down."

750   Woolf, Virginia (Stephen), 1882-1941. **Three Guineas.** New York:
        Harcourt, Brace and Jovanovich, 1963. 285p. $2.25. ISBN
        0156901773. LC 38-27681.
It would be difficult to find so witty and eloquent an apology for feminism as
Three Guineas (orig. 1932). Woolf's target is male pomposity and the patriarchy
it aggrandizes at every level. For purposes of argument, she singles out the
humorous examples of heralds, a university procession, a judge, and an arch-
bishop—examples of English pageantry that Woolf found ludicrous in all her
writings.

LITERATURE
Fiction
[The scope note for Literature appears on p. 252.]

751   Abeel, Erica. **Only When I Laugh.** New York: Morrow, 1978. 336p.
$9.95. ISBN 068803313X. LC 78-1337.
Abeel writes humorously and well of her experiences covering the traumatic,
exhausting, and exhilarating year following childbirth, the breakup of her
marriage, self-discovery, and independence. The painful experiences of sexual
experimentation, of finding an academic job, of coping alone, of facing a nervous
breakdown, and of daring to write come across honestly. The characters in
Abeel's New York City life are familiar ones: the rejecting but lovable former
husband, the guru therapist, the successful best friend, the sympathetic three-
year-old son, the hippie lover—all familiar but all filtered through Abeel's
incisive perception. Abeel is a survivor and she survives with wit and grace.

752   Aidoo, Christina Ama Ata. **No Sweetness Here.** Garden City, NY:
Doubleday, 1971. 156p. LC 74-144244.
Aidoo, a Ghanian writer, sounds the note of an Africa evolving from colonialism
to independence in these eleven striking, often tragic short stories. In "Everything Counts," a young African professor comes face to face with the cultural
implications of wig-wearing among young black women. Another story, "For
Whom Things Did Not Change," explores the differences in political outlook
between a young African professor and the servant who has been assigned to
wait on him at a government Rest House. While the intellectual chafes at the
servile characteristics of the servant, the servant expresses his private concerns
about independence, concerns that are practically rather than theoretically
based. The title story is a tragic and stark tale about a village woman who divorces,
thus losing her status as mother and wife. When her only son dies suddenly
following the divorce, the mother's grief is augmented by her fear that the
boy's death is a consequence of the family rift. "Life is not sweet" is the conclusion of the villagers. Each story is a carefully wrought sketch of the ambiguous
dynamics of social change.

753   Alcott, Louisa May, 1832-1888. **Behind a Mask: The Unknown Thrillers
of Louisa May Alcott.** New York: Morrow, 1975. 277p. bibliog. $9.95.
ISBN 0688003389. LC 74-31046.
Edited by Madeleine Stern, this collection contains an introduction by her and
four stories by Louisa May Alcott: "Behind a Mask; Or, A Woman's Power,"
"The Abbot's Ghost, or, Maurice Treherne's Temptation," "Pauline's Passion
and Punishment," and "The Mysterious Key and What It Opened." The first
two of these were originally published under the pseudonym of A. M. Barnard.

754   Alcott, Louisa May, 1832-1888. **Little Women; Or, Meg, Jo, Beth,
and Amy.** Boston: Little, Brown, 1968. 444p. $8.95. ISBN
0316030902. LC 68-21171.
Written in 1869, this classic remains a staple in non-sexist children's literature.
The women are strong and independent though not lacking in sensitivity,

kindness, and gentleness. With the absence of the father figure (away in the Civil War), these women depend upon each other for strength while maintaining warm though independent relationships with the men around them. See Nina Auerbach's *Communities of Women* (Harvard University Press, 1978) for an excellent discussion of communities of women.

755   Alcott, Louisa May, 1832-1888. **Work: A Story of Experience.** New York: Schocken Books, 1977. 443p. $10.50. ISBN 0805236562. LC 76-48849.

Sarah Elbert explains in her introduction to this novel (originally 1892) about Alcott's life and times: "work is an expression of Alcott's feminist principles and a major effort toward synthesizing in popular, readable form the broad set of beliefs encompassing family, education, suffrage, labor and the moral reform of social life that defined feminist ideology in the nineteenth century." The novel spans the period 1833 through 1873. The fine introduction by Elbert crystallizes nineteenth-century American woman's experience.

756   Aldridge, Sarah. **Tottie: A Tale of the Sixties.** Bates City, MO: Naiad Press; distr. Reno, NV: The Ladder, 1975. 181p. $4.50.

Distributed by the *Ladder* and rated by *Lesbians in Literature* as an important book for its representation of lesbian relationships, *Tottie* speaks to many contemporary issues (especially those of the '60s—drugs, careerism for women, student activism). Connie Norton, a young attorney in her late 20s, falls in love with a teen-aged runaway from an affluent family. The affair awakens Connie to the sterility of her career and life goals. Though the plot appears to liberate Connie from social conformity, there is much of romanticism here simply transferred from a male object to a female object of love. Some fascinating lesbian themes to explore, though this novel is a mediocre piece of writing.

757   Arnold, June, 1926- . **Applesauce.** New York: Daughters, 1977. 240p. $5.00. ISBN 0913780170. LC 77-80961.

The author explains in the foreword, "I wrote *Applesauce* during the early 1960's. It was partly an attempt to unscramble the tangle my experiences had produced; instead of 'lessons' I ended up with a giant purée of a life . . . ; my only criterion for choosing to include something, imagined or real, was whether or not it touched the floor of me. Among these were children, suicide, mothers, sex, sexual costumes and manners, language, food, nature, and the primary struggle of a woman to be a woman." The book has been compared to *Orlando*; the main character experiences life as woman and man. In trying to fit into the various roles life has assigned her, the woman in *Applesauce* in the form of Liza finally finds her truest self. A very intense experimental novel. See Ellen Morgan's discussion of *Applesauce* in Bazin and Friedman, eds., *Androgyny as Living Myth: Feminist Theory, Criticism and Research.*

758   Arnold, June, 1926- . **The Cook and the Carpenter; A Novel by the Carpenter.** Plainfield, VT: Daughters, 1973. 180p. $3.00. ISBN 0913780006. LC 73-86277.

This is an unusual and difficult book mainly because of the author's use of neuter pronouns. Set in a Texas commune, this novel confronts all manner of societal class and role clashes. It is important for its woman-centered fictional consciousness and experimental use of language.

759   Arnold, June, 1926- . **Sister Gin.** Plainfield, VT: Daughters, 1975. 215p. $4.00. ISBN 0913780340. LC 75-16510.

The women in this novel of life and love shared among women are older women (from 46 to 77). The book is a rich intermingling of contemporary political, health, and sociological issues beautifully and artistically centered in the richly evoked lives of the three major characters—Bettina, Su, and Mamie Carter.

760   Arnow, Harriette Louisa (Simpson), 1908- . **The Dollmaker.** New York: Avon Books, 1972. 608p. $1.95. ISBN 0380009471.

The Dollmaker was originally published in 1954 and tells the story of a Kentucky family's move to Detroit in the later years of World War II so that the father can work in a defense plant. It's an incredibly gripping novel, the kind that immobilizes you in the first five pages. But, more specifically, it is astounding for the way it brings to life the contrast between rural pre-industrial and urban industrial contexts, and for the way it illustrates what the transition from one to the other means to women's lives. This edition includes an afterword by Joyce Carol Oates.

761   Arnow, Harriette Louisa (Simpson), 1908- . **The Weedkiller's Daughter.** New York: Knopf, 1970. 371p. $10.00. ISBN 0394451333. LC 68-23960.

The father of Susan Schnitzer, who is "the weedkiller's daughter," presents the worst face of patriarchy, as a right-wing member of the Establishment whose fears run the gamut from weeds to black people. In Eden Hills, an affluent suburb, Susie finds her life less than a paradise. Her world-view sharply conflicts with that of her parents and her school, an extension of the Establishment. Susie has been compared to Holden Caulfield of *Catcher in the Rye* because of her rejection of adult values and hypocrisy (see Wilton Eckley, *Harriette Arnow*, Twayne, 1974). Though the power of *Hunter's Horn* (1949) and *The Dollmaker* (1954) is absent from this book, Arnow is a formidable writer and presents an admirable portrait of an adolescent girl, amazingly perceptive about the shallowness of the adult-created lifestyle in which she must move in her daughter role. *Mountain Path* (Covici Friede, 1936; repr. The Council of Southern Mountains, 1963) is another of Arnow's novels currently out of print.

762   Atwood, Margaret Eleanor, 1939- . **The Edible Woman.** New York: Popular Library, 1976. 287p. $1.50. ISBN 0445084669.

A humorous dissection of the cult of consumerism is what Atwood is about in this very funny novel about a young woman Marian, who spends her days devising questionnaires for consumer studies and her nights serving herself up to the dull lawyer she is about to marry to escape from her job. Enlightenment takes the form of starvation at first, and finally in a woman-shaped cake that is baked, served, and eaten by Atwood's unusual heroine.

763   Atwood, Margaret Eleanor, 1939- . **Lady Oracle.** New York: Simon and
       Schuster, 1976. 345p. $8.95. ISBN 0671223399. LC 76-15612.
Obvious autobiographical parallels present themselves in this sad/funny novel
of a recently successful young woman novelist who constantly feels her masks
will accidentally slip off and that she, her past and present, will be exposed:
as a writer of trashy gothic novels, as an obese and socially rejected child,
as an adultress. Atwood's use of fragments of the gothic that Joan is writing
even as she is living them is a splendid technique for humorously looking at
feminist concerns, yet never denying or undercutting the quite serious implications of these women's issues—independence, the place of romantic love, the
quest for identity, narcissism.

764   Atwood, Margaret Eleanor, 1939- . **Surfacing.** New York: Simon and
       Schuster, 1973. 224p. $6.95. ISBN 0671214500. LC 72-86983.
The narrator returns to her past in this novel of the quest for self. Home is a
remote Quebec island from which the protagonist's father has disappeared.
Her search for self pits her against the rigors of the rough terrain and the tor-
turous landscape of her own psyche in this rare novel of female adventure.
An interesting article on the religious aspect of the novel is Carol P. Christ's
"Margaret Atwood: The Surfacing of Women's Spiritual Quest and Vision"
in *Signs* (Winter, 1976), an issue that also contains a piece by Atwood herself
on the symbolism of her novels.

765   Austen, Jane, 1775-1817. **Emma.** New York: Oxford University Press,
       1971. 446p. bibliog. $7.25. ISBN 0192253445. LC 78-870114.
There are many fine editions of *Emma* (1816)—perhaps Austen's greatest work—
among them this Oxford edition, edited with an introduction by David Lodge,
and with textual notes and bibliography by James Kinsley. Emma's character
is most complex. Energetic and intelligent, on the one hand, she is excessively
afflicted with narcissism, on the other. She cherishes her self-love and snobbery
but with a style that makes her attractive despite her faults. She manages to
choose wisely and well, as do all Austen's favorite women, when it comes time
to take a husband. But her manipulation of others' lives is insensitive and arrogant until she comes to understand her mistakes. The most impressive aspect
of *Emma* is Austen's artistry in making Emma a sympathetic and attractive
character while exposing her flaws.

766   Austen, Jane, 1775-1817. **Love and Friendship, and Other Early Works.**
       London: Chatto and Windus, 1929; repr. Folcroft, PA: Folcroft Library
       Editions, 1977. 140p. $12.50. ISBN 0841429367. LC 77-22471.
Jane was witty even in her teens—hilariously so, as these youthful parodies
of eighteenth-century fiction demonstrate. G. K. Chesterton says in his introduction that, "it is at least a curiosity of literature that such curiosities of
literature should have been almost accidentally concealed," for this book was
never printed until 1929. Among the things that Jane counted silliest as a
teenager were men, marriage, fainting spells, and admonitions on "the conduct
of young women."

767   Austen, Jane, 1775-1817. **Pride and Prejudice.** New York: Oxford
        University Press, 1970. 352p. bibliog. $5.75. ISBN 0192553321.
        LC 72-541679.

The central irony of this most important nineteenth-century novel of manners
(1813) comes in the first sentence, "it is a truth universally acknowledged,
that a single man in possession of a good fortune, must be in want of a wife."
The plot centers on the single most important social fact of the nineteenth
century: marriage. In the midst of endless machinations occurring around the
marriage theme, the love affair between the cool intelligent Elizabeth Bennet
and the aristocratic and charming Darcy illustrates the best in this tension
between the sexes, in which the clear perceptions of both bring about appropriate
choice of marriage partners. See Nina Auerbach's *Communities of Women*
(Harvard U. Press, 1978) for an excellent discussion of the community of women
in *Pride and Prejudice.*

768   Austen, Jane, 1775-1817. **Sense and Sensibility.** New York: Oxford
        University Press, 1970. 344p. bibliog. $6.00. ISBN 0192553356.
        LC 75-541981.

The dualism expressed in the title of this early (1811) work by Austen mirrors
the conflict within the self between reason and emotion omnipresent in early
nineteenth-century society. Elinor (sense) and Marianne (sensibility) are Austen's
vehicles for expressing this dichotomy, though Austen's favor is clearly disposed
toward Elinor. "she had an excellent heart; her disposition was affectionate,
and her feelings were strong: but she knew how to govern them. . . . "

769   Austin, Mary Hunter, 1868-1934. **A Woman of Genius.** Garden City,
        NY: Doubleday, Page, 1912; repr. New York: Arno Press, 1977. 510p.
        $22.00. ISBN 0405100434. LC 76-51663.

Mary Austin is another midwestern author represented in the Rediscovered
Fiction by American Women writers. Elizabeth Hardwick notes the contemporary
relevance of the themes and situations that the novel presents. "It is the complicated story of [Olive] a woman from Taylorsville—as the town is named—who
meets the dilemma of a serious acting career with its tours, demands and disappointments. The career not only challenges the heroine as a private destiny,
but puts her into conflict with marriage and old friends, and many of the conventions of her youth that mean something real to her." Thematically the novel
might be compared to Willa Cather's *Song of the Lark.*

770*   Baker, Dorothy (Dodds), 1907- . **Cassandra at the Wedding.** Boston:
        Houghton Mifflin, 1962. 226p. LC 62-8115.

When this sensitive novel was published (1962), it received very mixed reviews.
Notable in the "not mentioned" category is the fact that the complex sister,
Cassandra, is a lesbian. Cassandra, Judith's twin sister, is a graduate student
in French literature who comments on the frustration of writing about writers
when it is clear that she wants to be a writer herself. This is not the least of
her frustrations. Her adored sister is getting married, and Cassandra realizes
that Judith will begin an exclusive relationship with her husband that will
distance Cassandra forever. Cassandra makes an abortive attempt at suicide
before the wedding. Cassandra is not a happy character, but she may not be as

"neurotic" as early '60s critics labeled her, either, in this interesting fictional portrayal of a subtle lesbian relationship between sisters.

771   Bannon, Ann. **I Am a Woman.** Greenwich, CT: Fawcett Publications, 1959; repr. New York: Arno Press, 1975. 224p. $9.00. ISBN 0405074069. LC 75-13750.

Bannon writes a torrid, cliché-ridden novel (originally 1959) about a young lesbian, Laura, in love with her straight roommate until she realizes that she has overlooked another woman who has loved her from afar—a woman she previously rejected. As a subplot, Laura's psyche is dominated by her authoritarian father, whom she attempts to kill in a lurid incest scene. This is the second novel in a series of four by Bannon, which comprise a single, connected narrative. The other three are *Odd Girl Out* (originally 1957), *Women in the Shadows* (originally 1959), and *Journey to a Woman* (originally 1960).

772   Barnes, Djuna. **Nightwood.** New York: New Directions, 1946. 211p. $6.50. ISBN 0811202488. LC 49-1384.

This is a novel that vies in fantasy content, intricacy of plot, and richness of language with Virginia Woolf's *Orlando*. Robin Vote—complex, exquisitely beautiful, aloof—inspires passion in all who know her, male and female. Against the rich tapestry of European capitals where the action takes place, these mythic characters move in a sort of trance dance. The transvestite doctor who comments upon life in a series of cryptic aphorisms signals Barnes's most wry commentary on the nature of the chameleon twins order and disorder. Males are portrayed as obsessively concerned with imposing order.

773*   Beauvoir, Simone de, 1908- . **The Mandarins: A Novel.** Cleveland: World, 1956. 610p. LC 56-5315.

Winner of the prestigious French literary prize, the Prix Goncourt, this novel weaves fiction with autobiography drawn from the life of art and politics that de Beauvoir experienced in post-World War II France. In what is probably de Beauvoir's best novel, the women characters are of particular interest—Nadine, the non-conformist rebel and independent spirit, and Paula, who has little identity of her own save for her relationship with Henri. It is interesting to read the third volume of de Beauvoir's autobiography, *The Force of Circumstance*, along with *The Mandarins*, since both are handling the same historical time frame.

774*   Beauvoir, Simone de, 1908- . **The Woman Destroyed.** New York: Putnam, 1969. 254p. LC 69-15486.

The three excellently crafted stories in this volume demonstrate de Beauvoir's virtuosity as a writer. "The Age of Discretion" portrays an aging intellectual facing the spectre of old age and the dimunition of her intellectual and physical powers within the context of a long standing love relationship. "Monologue" consists of the ravings of a woman gone mad because she has taken on societally imposed guilt for her daughter's suicide. Most moving is the title story for the collection, a realistic exploration of the life of Monique, whose seemingly secure and happy life is shattered by her husband's affair with another woman. As she explores her psyche and her life and tries to deal rationally with the situation she comes to recognize the fragility of all the ties and traditions that have defined her life: "I am on the threshold. There is only this door and what is watching behind it. I am afraid. And I cannot call to anyone for help." This is a translation of *La femme rompue.*

775*   Bedford, Sybille, 1911- . **A Compass Error.** New York: Knopf, 1969.
        270p. LC 69-11477.
A sequel to *A Favorite of the Gods* (1963), *A Compass Error* picks up again with the character of Flavia. The story of Flavia's youth emerges during a flashback filtered through the consciousness of Flavia the middle-aged writer. Mainly it is the story of Flavia's two relationships with women, Therese and Andrée, while she is living alone as a young woman in Provence. It is also the story of her guilt about these relationships and loss of confidence in her relationship with her mother.

776   Behn, Aphra Amis, 1640-1689. **The Works of Aphra Behn.** New York:
        Benjamin Blom, 1967. (Repr. of 1915 ed.). 6v. $125.00. ISBN
        0405082533. LC 67-22243.
Aphra Behn (1640-1689), first professional woman writer and one of the earliest English novelists, was labelled "whore" by the public because of the explicit sexual messages in her poems and plays. Her work was largely suppressed and unread, her biography mutilated beyond recognition, her literary output uncollected at worst and at best, poorly edited. This carefully edited text (by Montague Summers) offers a biography of Behn and the most comprehensive collection of her work to date—seventeen plays, several histories and novels, and poems—including *The Rover, The Feigned Curtezans, The Lucky Chance, Oroonoko, The Nun,* and *The Unfortunate Bride.* Volume 6 contains the poetry, an index of first lines, and a general index. (Note: *Books in Print* lists what appears to be an identical collection at a cheaper price. We were unable to obtain a copy for comparison, but offer the following bibliographic information nonetheless: *The Works of Aphra Behn.* Edited by Montague Summers. Staten Island, NY: Phaeton Press, 1967. (Repr. of 1915 ed.). 6v. $75.00. ISBN 0877530041. LC 67-24964.).

777   Blackwood, Caroline. **The Stepdaughter.** New York: Scribner, 1977.
        96p. $6.95. ISBN 0684149346. LC 77-3500.
This prize-winning first novel takes its form in a series of letters to an unnamed correspondent in which K., the writer, pours out her pathological fears and jealousies, focusing mainly on the females in her life: her stepdaughter, her own daughter, the *au pair* girl. The content is conceived as a series of knots, which the writer seems incapable of unloosening as she faces the desertion of her husband and a total dearth of her own inner resources.

778   Blixen, Karen [Dinesen, Isak, pseud.], 1885-1962. **Out of Africa.**
        New York: Random House, 1972. 389p. $2.95. ISBN 0394717406.
Written in 1937, these are short stories that combine fiction, poetry, and autobiography. Isak Dinesen lived on a coffee plantation in East Africa which she ran by herself after her divorce. Danish by birth, her experience of Africa comes from observing those who served under her on her plantation. These stories, aside from their hauntingly beautiful prose style, demonstrate Dinesen's

perceptive observations of the African culture and lifestyle about her. Her description of the Africans is full of common detail of daily existence from the perspective of an independent, sensitive white woman whose work speaks eloquently of her love for human beings and their unique qualities. The stories are divided into five major sections: Kamante and Lulu; Shooting Accident on the Farm; Visitors to the Farm; From an Immigrant's Notebook; Farewell to the Farm.

779   Bowen, Elizabeth, 1899-1973. **The Death of the Heart.** New York: Knopf, 1939. 418p. $8.95. ISBN 0394421728.
Probably Bowen's most respected work, this novel focuses on children. Portia Quayne, another of Bowen's displaced, upper-class children, deals with emotionally paralyzed adults by writing in her diary.

780   Bowen, Elizabeth, 1899-1973. **Joining Charles and Other Stories.** New York: L. MacVeagh, The Dial Press, 1929; repr. St. Clair Shores, MI: Scholarly Press, 1972. 302p. $21.50. ISBN 0403005272.
Young women coming to terms with conventional lives and "wifely" roles is a theme running through several of these stories. On the surface, Bowen sometimes comes across as brittle and unflinchingly British upper class. At a deeper level, the stories speak sensitively of feminine searchings for self and a language in which to communicate the quest for self. Stories: "Joining Charles"; "The Jungle"; "Shoes: An International Episode"; "The Dancing Mistress"; "Aunt Tatty"; "Dead Mabelle"; "The Working Party"; "Foothold"; "The Cassowary"; "Telling"; "Mrs. Moysey."

781   Boyle, Kay, 1903- . **Thirty Stories.** New York: New Directions, 1957. 362p. $4.45. ISBN 0811200132. LC 57-8601.
Kay Boyle, a reviewer, poet, and novelist, is perhaps best known for her short stories, though few could be considered feminist in tone or content. These stories are divided as follows: Early Group, 1927-1934; Austrian Group, 1933-1938; English Group, 1935-1936; French Group, 1939-1942; and the American Group, 1942-1946. A particularly stunning story for its confrontation of social roles is "Your Body Is a Jewel Box," a tale of family politics and female adolescence. Those who appreciate Boyle will find the collection *Three Short Novels* to be of interest (Boston: Beacon Press, 1958). The three novels are *The Crazy Hunter, The Bridegroom's Body,* and *Decision.*

782   Broner, E. M. **A Weave of Women: A Novel.** New York: Holt, Rinehart, and Winston, 1978. 296p. $8.95. ISBN 0030184614. LC 77-13609.
The characters of this novel, which weaves the lives of women together with the cadences and themes of biblical, parabolic, and mythical literature, come from all over the world. Gathered together in the Old City of Jerusalem to participate in the birth ritual of one of the women, Simha, are Terry, director, Home for Jewish Wayward Girls; Hepzibah, religious woman from Haifa; Mickey, woman from Haifa in the process of divorce; Antoinette, Shakespearean from London; Gerda, scientist from Germany; Gloria, the convert from California; two children, and others. This novel celebrates important events in women's lives with the intent of establishing a viable woman-centered tradition: "it is

a story of women who are ceremonious and correct with each other, who celebrate sermons and hermans, birth rites, death rites, sacrificial rites, exodus rites, and exorcism rites." Violence occurs in the novel in the form of protest against masculinist authority and in the disruption of a conference of gynecologists. Broner's first book is *Her Mothers* (Holt, Rinehart, and Winston, 1975).

783   Brontë, Charlotte, 1816-1855. **Jane Eyre.** London: Oxford University Press, 1972. 479p. bibliog. $14.50. ISBN 0192553461.

Among the many acceptable editions of this classic work (1847) is the above, edited with an introduction by Margaret Smith. A feature of the Oxford edition is a descriptive list of the first four English editions of *Jane Eyre*. This novel merits a close reading even if the reader feels that she has had more of Jane than she wishes in high school. The plot is the classic Victorian situation of orphaned governess making good by marrying the master of the house. Brontë has handled this typical Gothic theme with genius, but it is the almost sadistic character of Rochester and the splendidly independent feminist character of Jane that make the novel worth re-reading. Adrienne Rich wrote a particularly fine critique of the novel in *Ms.* (October, 1973) and an article by Sandra Gilbert, "Plain Jane's Progress" (*Signs*, Summer, 1977), is also worth consulting.

784   Brontë, Charlotte, 1816-1855. **Shirley: A Tale.** London: Oxford University Press, 1974. 645p. $8.25. ISBN 0192500147.

At the outset, Brontë announces to her reader: "something real, cool, and solid lies before you; something unromantic as Monday morning. . . ." Her subject is the Luddite disturbances of Yorkshire (1811-1812), a classic confrontation between capital and labor. But this long, drawn-out novel written in 1849 only uses the social issue as a backdrop for the friendship of the two major women characters, Caroline Helston and Shirley Keeldar. If there is a redeeming feature in this ponderous novel with its anemic plot and tidy "all's-well-that-ends-in-marriage" ending, it is the close feminist conversations between these two characters, who have been compared to Emily and Charlotte Brontë, and their relationship to each other.

785   Brontë, Charlotte, 1816-1855. **Villette.** New York: Oxford University Press, 1954. $6.00. ISBN 0192500473. LC 43-21549.

Villette is perhaps Brontë's most stunning effort. Written after the tragic deaths of her brother, Branwell, and her sisters, Emily and Anne, *Villette* (1853) is a very personal tale whose main character, Lucy Snowe, is Charlotte Brontë— plain, witty, distanced, and isolated. At the same time, there is a humorous detachment to the novel that makes it wonderful reading for its comic elements as much as for its passion and power. The plot takes Lucy Snowe to Brussels (Villette) as a governess at a *pensionnat* with her sister, Jane, unfolding the story of her painful, one-sided love for her married tutor, M. Heger. Lucy's (Charlotte's) is a rebellious spirit, attempting to reconcile love with work, striving to deal with the two potential lovers in her life: one who allows her to be passive; the other, active, representing perhaps the two women within Charlotte Brontë, both seeking an outlet for love. Readers who are disappointed with the conclusion of *Jane Eyre* will find Lucy's loss of Paul a more realistic ending and a statement of Brontë's coming to terms with pain. See Charles

Burkhart's *Charlotte Brontë: A Psychosexual Study of Her Novels* (Victor Gollancz, 1973) for an excellent analysis of *Villette*.

786   Brontë, Emily Jane, 1818-1848. **Wuthering Heights.** London: T. C. Newby, 1847; repr. Oxford: Clarendon Press, 1976. 513p. $22.00. ISBN 0198125119. LC 76-378952.

Perhaps no other novel in English has spoken so powerfully to the love-hate bond inherent in male-female relationships as this Gothic love story between Catherine and Heathcliffe. Family pressures keep them apart as lovers, but their spiritual commitment to each other prevents them from finding peace in other relationships. A study of psychic conflict and incest in the Victorian family, *Wuthering Heights* provides a feast for psychological critics. Catherine's personality is as wild and indomitable as the Yorkshire moors, which are the setting for this haunting English novel. Written in 1847, *Wuthering Heights* was Emily's only published novel.

787   Brown, Rita Mae, 1944- . **In Her Day.** Plainfield, VT: Daughters, 1976. 196p. $4.50. ISBN 0913780146. LC 76-7817.

Irreverent, exuberant—Rita Mae Brown writes of lesbian life and culture using snappy dialogue and compelling characters. Carole, Adele, and Ilse are friends who relate with warmth and intensity—very compelling characters. This is a novel of lesbian issues faced with wit: Carole's confrontation with her male department head over her lesbianism; Ilse's dealing with the unwanted attentions of Olive, an aggressive lesbian; Adele and Carole's relating to each other as sisters because of the fidelity each feels to her own lover. Brown is at her best in creating witty dialogue, and there is much of it here.

788   Brown, Rita Mae, 1944- . **Rubyfruit Jungle.** Plainfield, VT: Daughters, 1973. 217p. $4.00. ISBN 0912780022. LC 73-86276.

One of the minor characters in this novel of an unorthodox childhood, a lesbian adolescence, and young adulthood in America says when asked whether he is gay: "Oh, I wouldn't say I was gay. I'd just say I was enchanted." This becomes the meaning and the message of *Rubyfruit*, a chronicle of uninhibited sexual adventures that indicts the culture at large for being ridiculous and hypocritical in its heterosexuality and heterosexism. Despite the serious issues that Brown confronts, *Rubyfruit* is full of humor even when polemical. Brown's latest novel, *Six of One* (Harper and Row, 1978), centers on the lives and relationship of two sisters.

789   Burroway, Janet. **Raw Silk.** Boston: Little, Brown, 1977. 314p. $8.95. ISBN 0316117676. LC 76-48718.

Like many current novels by women, *Raw Silk* is about marriage, career, motherhood, and conflict during a woman's early 30s. Narrator Virginia Marbalestier would seem to have it made as a successful designer, mother of a ten-year-old daughter, and wife of a wealthy English textile businessman. Her account of the floundering of this marriage, her attempts to relate to her daughter, and to fulfill herself in love and in work is witty and brisk. Though the plot may be predictable, the good writing and Virginia's resolution to reclaim her identity by hard work recommend this novel. She concludes: "of the three great options for fulfillment open to a woman, work and motherhood and ecstatic love, I have work left." She resolves to turn her design work toward a new and bold direction. It is good to see women's novels ending with plans for creative growth.

790   Bussy, Dorothy Strachey [Olivia]. **Olivia.** New York: Sloane, 1949; repr. New York: Arno Press, 1975. 135p. $9.00. ISBN 0405073828. LC 75-12342.
Olivia is the story of a young girl's passion for the headmistress of her French school, a first love remembered many years later. Particularly fine is the author's rendering of Olivia's impetuous and uncomprehending love for Mlle. Julie, Julie's reluctant discouragement of her student's overtures, and Olivia's consequent despair and sense of betrayal. Bloomsbury buffs may be interested to know that Dorothy Bussy was Lytton Strachey's sister.

791   Cahan, Abraham, 1860-1951. **Yekl: A Tale of the New York Ghetto.** Gloucester, MA: Peter Smith, n.d. $4.75. ISBN 0844600482.
Readers may remember this tale of family upheaval in the New York Ghetto at the turn of the century from the recent film adaptation, *Hester Street.* Jake (Yekl) at the outset of the story is working in a garment factory in New York City; his life divides itself between work and flirtation with employed, young Jewish women. His conscience bothers him because he realizes he is supposed to be saving his salary in order to bring his wife and son from Russia to New York. When his wife, Gitl, arrives, Jake, who has become a dandy and a snob in his new identity, is revolted by her peasant ways and especially her tenacious regard for old world customs such as the wearing of the formal wig to cover her natural hair in public. Frightened of her husband's rejection, unable to account for his coldness, and unaccustomed to the language and lifestyle of New York's immigrant culture, Gitl tries to accommodate herself to her husband's new tastes before resigning herself to his desire for a divorce from her so that he can be free to marry Maimie, a woman much like Jake himself. The humorous twist to an otherwise grim tale is that Gitl's future looks more promising than Jake's at the conclusion.

792   Cather, Willa Sibert, 1873-1947. **My Ántonia.** Boston: Houghton Mifflin, 1961. 371p. $9.95. ISBN 0395075149. LC 63-2505.
Ántonia is among the finest portraits of women in American literature. Autobiographical in form—the story told by a masculine "I" narrator—rich in details about the Nebraska plains life during the 1880s, *My Ántonia* is dominated by the presence of the patient, simple, philosophical Ántonia. "She was a rich mine of life, like the founders of early races." A "hired girl" and an immigrant, Ántonia has an essential nobility that shines through the center of the story even when she is not center-stage. For an excellent discussion of this novel, see E. K. Brown and Leon Edel's *Willa Cather: A Critical Biography* (Knopf, 1953).

793   Cather, Willa Sibert, 1873-1947. **My Mortal Enemy.** New York: Knopf, 1926. 122p. $7.95. ISBN 0394437527. LC 26-18508.
My Mortal Enemy is important for its portrayal of an aging woman, Myra Driscoll, a masterpiece of a character who is tense, stubborn, and mean, and

somehow magnificent in spite of it. Her ironic story hinges on the fact that she married a good and loving man to spite her rich uncle, thereby losing a fortune. She considers her husband her "mortal enemy," even though he stays faithfully by her to care for her in her final sickness and their mutual state of financial ruin, to a great extent brought about by Myra's systematic obstinacy. The novella form is perfectly suited to its subject.

794   Cather, Willa Sibert, 1873-1947. **The Song of the Lark.** Boston: Houghton Mifflin, 1915; repr. Lincoln: University of Nebraska Press, 1978. 489p. bibliog. $4.95. ISBN 0803263007. LC 77-15596.
Thea is another of Cather's splendid, strong women. A woman who is adamant in her quest to achieve professionally, Thea Kronborg becomes an opera singer at the price of her personal romance. Thea does not inspire pity, though. She is a consummate artist and, like Cather, dedicates her soul to her work and achieves transcendence from her art. As always, Cather conveys the beauty of the country, especially the Southwest.

795   Chopin, Kate O'Flaherty, 1851-1904. **The Awakening.** New York: Norton, 1976. 229p. bibliog. $10.00. ISBN 0393044343.
This authoritative text includes contexts and criticism, edited by Margaret Culley. At first, Edna Pontellier seems to be a conventionally contented heroine of the nineteenth-century domestic cloth—pretty, maternal, reasonable, a pampered woman of means with modest artistic talent. Her life takes a surprising turn when she examines her role as wife, mother, daughter, and dilletante artist and decides to throw over her conventional roles in New Orleans society to explore inner needs and yearnings, artistic and sexual, that she has buried in her identity as wife and mother. A classic novel, *The Awakening* confronts the exhilaration and terror that face a woman who discards societally accepted roles.

796   Chopin, Kate O'Flaherty, 1851-1904. **The Storm, and Other Stories. With The Awakening.** Old Westbury, NY: Feminist Press, 1974. 387p. bibliog. $5.00. ISBN 0912670371. LC 75-9718.
"This concise collection of fiction by Kate Chopin contains all her stories of interest to both general readers and to students and teachers exploring her work in American literature or women's studies courses. More than one-third the size of *The Complete Works of Kate Chopin*, the present volume features not only *The Awakening* and practically all other pieces by her found in anthologies, but many other stories as well" (Per Seyersted's introduction to Feminist Press edition). Chopin is becoming more widely read as she is recognized as more than a regionalist, as an author who wrote searchingly of the female condition. Among the stories here are "A White Eagle"; "Emancipation"; "Ti Démon"; and "A Point at Issue." The introduction is excellent.

797   Colette, Sidonie Gabrielle, 1873-1954. **The Pure and the Impure.** New York: Farrar, Straus and Giroux, 1967. 174p. $7.95. ISBN 0374239207. LC 67-22433.
Colette subtitled this 1933 work "A Case-Book of Love" and maintained that this book was her finest accomplishment. Her subject is love and all its

permutations: lesbian, homosexual, heterosexual. "Charlotte" is "a sensitive disenchanted woman, clever in artifice and in delicacy"; she makes love in opium dens. The "Don Juans" neither give nor take love. The behaviors of all species of lovers interest Colette; for her, love is the most compelling art form. She is receptive to the maleness and femaleness of her own personality and takes a sensual pleasure in observing others work out bisexuality in their lives.

798   Colette, Sidonie Gabrielle, 1873-1954. **Ripening Seed.** Westport, CT:
        Greenwood Press, 1972. 152p. $8.25. ISBN 0837162920. LC 73-178784.
Colette evokes the last sensuous yet innocent summer of Vinca and Philippe, the children of two families of friends who have rented the same villa each summer for many years. Vinca is similar to the characters of Gigi and Claudine— fifteen years old, sensitive, unpredictable, charming. The beautiful narrative hinges on Philippe's sexual awakening by an older, experienced woman (around thirty) at a nearby villa and consequently, Vinca's seduction of Philippe. Through- out, Philippe seems never capable of comprehending the deepest feeling of the women to whom he makes love. Even Vinca, the youngest of the three principal characters, seems capable of greater sensuality than Philippe and appears less obsessed with preserving "fifteen enchanted years of single-minded affection, their fifteen years together as pure and loving twins."

799   Colette, Sidonie Gabrielle, 1873-1954. **The Tender Shoot, and Other**
        Stories. New York: Farrar, Straus and Giroux, 1975. 404p. $10.00.
        ISBN 0374273103. LC 59-9961.
Translated by Antonia White, this collection contains: "Bella Vista," "Gribiche," "The Rendezvous," "The Patriarch," "The Rainy Moon," "The Kepi," "The Tender Shoot," "Green Sealing Wax," "Armande," "The Sick Child," and "The Photographer's Missus." Colette imbues these stories with much autobiographi- cal detail—from "Bella Vista," which has much of the quality of a travelogue, to the title story, in which an older man tells Colette the tale of his seduction of a sixteen-year-old and of his taste for nymphettes. All have the wonderfully sensuous Colette touch.

800   Crane, Stephen, 1871-1900. **Maggie: A Girl of the Streets.** New York:
        Fawcett Publications, 1975. 160p. $1.25.
From her continual rejection by a besotted mother to an early suicidal death by drowning, Maggie endured a frightened existence of poverty and striving for survival. In love with a bartender who seduced and cast her off ("Oh, go teh hell [Maggie]"), she sought acceptance and solace from family; but her mother told her, "Go teh hell an' good riddance." Maggie's despair reflected New York's Bowery district during the 1890s—filthy streets, dingy saloons, miserable tenement houses, hordes of unfortunates swarming through flophouses and pool halls, juvenile violence, and the air redolent of horse manure. Ignored by literary critics when it was first published in 1893, and submerged in the popularity of *The Red Badge of Courage* (1895), this book is now considered by many to be a landmark in American literature. Crane used the theme of destitution in this novel of social protest to illustrate the depravity and vice of urban slums and to comment upon the influence of a broken home and a drunken mother upon an essentially wholesome girl who was driven, by circumstances

seemingly beyond her control, to solicit men on dark streets, merely post-
poning physical death in a jungle populated by the poor and unfortunate.

801   De Jong, Dola, 1911- . **The Tree and the Vine.** London: J. Calder;
       New York: L. Stuart, 1961. 127p. $3.00. ISBN 0818401435.
An explicitly lesbian novel written in the first person about two women in
love with each other during World War II, this novel is unusual for its secondary
plot of Erica's resistance activities in Amsterdam. The novel ends in Erica's
concentration camp death. The narrator, who is Erica's lover, comments on the
inevitability of the tragic end throughout the novel and often entertains the
possibility of leaving Erica. "But it was less than a month later that I came to
the inescapable conclusion that we were tied to each other for life; that the
short year with her had been, at least for me, decisive. I could no longer live
without her; with her I could have only the strange existence that her miserable
childhood had predetermined for her, and in which I could only be the spectator."

802   Didion, Joan. **Play It As It Lays; A Novel.** New York: Farrar, Straus,
       and Giroux, 1970. 214p. $5.95. ISBN 0374234442. LC 79-113779.
Hollywood is Didion's world in *Play It*; shorthand is her method. The imagery
is a montage of sun-baked California plastic: supermarkets, freeways, casinos,
franchise food, motels, and seconals. Life becomes a crap game, and Maria had
learned early in life to "play it as it lays." Silence, passivity, non-movement
are characteristics of the insidious game for which she can find no reason to
play or not to play. Maria, the exploited star of her husband's B movies, breaks
down by novel's end, and we see her lying by the swimming pool concentrating
on life. The lesson she has learned: "I know what 'nothing' means, and keep on
playing."

803   Didion, Joan. **Run River.** New York: I. Obolensky, 1961. 264p. $8.95.
       ISBN 0839210949. LC 62-18792.
Important as Didion's first novel, this work foreshadows themes handled more
deftly by Didion in later work such as *A Book of Common Prayer*. Her *tour de
force* is the character of Lily Knight McClellan, a Californian, and her painful
and self-destructive relationships with husband, lovers, and family.

804   Drabble, Margaret, 1939- . **The Ice Age.** New York: Knopf, 1977.
       295p. $8.95. ISBN 0394417909. LC 77-3319.
Drabble's characters inhabit a "terrible year, a terrible world" set in London
sometime in the future. Recession, bombings, pollution and disease comprise
the lot of Londoners. Alison and Anthony are middle-aged characters in this
depressing world. Both have patiently waited and waded through the problems
of each other's families and former spouses before looking to their own happiness with each other. In this world of technology and foreign relations gone
awry, ordinary human emotional crises and decisions appear unresolvable and
exponentially more complex. Alison and Anthony are victims in a world out
of control in which the next disaster is constantly pending, never knowable or
avoidable. Both are courageous characters who manage to face the despair with
resignation, even nobility. Drabble's skill in evoking the dreadful spiritual landscape is considerable.

805   Drabble, Margaret, 1939- . **The Needle's Eye; A Novel**. New York:
       Knopf, 1972. 368p. $10.00. ISBN 0394479661. LC 79-178957.
A beautifully written novel, this book has for its main character an heiress
of great sensibility and warmth, Rose Vassilou, accustomed to wealth but so
uncomfortable with it that most of her energies are spent in trying to give up
her fortune. Simon, a barrister, provides a wonderful counterpart to Rose's
character, for he has been reared in poverty and has never been able to accustom
himself to the affluence which he finds all about him in his adult life. Drabble
has a wonderful touch with her characters but is especially fine in shaping her
heroines, who are consistently intelligent and human.

806   Drabble, Margaret, 1939- . **The Realms of Gold**. New York: Knopf,
       1975. 354p. ISBN 0394498771. LC 75-8229.
Drabble's main character, Frances Wingate, is as untortured a heroine as one
could ever hope to meet. A renowned British archaeologist, she enjoys her
success and the comfortable globe trotting life that goes along with it. Untroubled about role conflicts, she goes off on long journeys leaving her children
in London with no regrets. She wins back an estranged lover but the victory is
more breezy than labored. She is in control of her world but a sympathetic
character nonetheless. Ironically, it is one of the major male characters who is
devastated in this novel; a young male nephew kills himself and his baby because
he no longer sees any reason to cope with life. Light and airy, the novel raises
some questions about whether untroubled liberated women can be compelling
characters.

807   Drabble, Margaret, 1939- . **Thank You All Very Much**. New York:
       New American Library, 1973. 144p. $0.75. LC 66-16401.
Originally, this was published as *The Millstone*. Drabble has written a fine novel
about a single woman's choice to carry an unplanned baby to term and embark
on parenthood alone. Drabble's evocations of pregnancy, childbirth, motherhood (and the supremacy of bureaucratic, antiseptic medicine over all of these)
are particularly fine and go beyond the specificity of the single parent experience
which is the book's central focus. There are vivid pictures of expectant women,
exhausted and awkward, poor and overworked, with young children clinging
to their skirts. Rosamund (the central character and first-person narrator)
muses as she waits in the ante-natal clinic: "one hears much, though mostly
from the interested male, about the beauty of a woman with child, ships in
full sail, and all that kind of metaphorical euphemism, and I suppose that from
time to time on the faces of well-fed, well-bred young ladies I have seen a certain peaceful glow, but the weight of evidence is overwhelmingly on the other
side. Anemia and exhaustion were written on most countenances: the clothes
were dreadful, the legs swollen, the bodies heavy and unbalanced." Equally
evocative, however, are Rosamund's accounts of the sweetness of new motherhood.

808   Dreiser, Theodore, 1871-1945. **Sister Carrie**. Cambridge, MA: R. Bentley,
       1971. 465p. $8.50. ISBN 083760401X. LC 78-183140.
This didactic classic (1900) about the fortunes of a young woman who loses
her virtue and her ideals in the big city is a commentary on the dependence
of women on men. Carrie learns quickly that life in the city means grim and

tedious work in a shoe factory, until she allies herself with a man who can
provide her with the comforts that give her the confidence and self-esteem to
attract a still more powerful and wealthier man. Although she learns eventually
not to pin her emotional and financial happiness on men, there are subtler
and more amorphous messages about narcissism and the status of women that
make this novel a classic in the fiction that chronicles the anonymous plight
of young women in late nineteenth-century and early twentieth-century industrialized America.

809   Duras, Marguerite. **Destroy, She Said.** New York: Grove Press, 1970.
      133p. $1.25. ISBN 0394171810. LC 70-116170.
This translation of *Détruire, dit-elle*, by Barbara Bray, also includes "Destruction and Language: An Interview with Marguerite Duras," by Jacques Rivette
and Jean Narboni (a translation of "La Destruction et la parole," which was
originally published in *Cahiers du Cinéma*, November 1969; translation is by
Helen Lane Cumberford). Duras is compelled by writing books "that could
be either read or acted or filmed or, as I always add, simply thrown away."
One of her more stunning successes in this genre is *Hiroshima Mon Amour*.
Her cultural manifesto is to destroy knowledge in order to replace it with a
void. This novel is about people watching each other and about nothingness;
the characters (two men and two women) are interchangeable. Duras comments
about this novel and its transformation into film in the interview section.

810   Duras, Marguerite. **Four Novels: The Square, Moderato Cantabile,
      Ten-Thirty on a Summer Night, The Afternoon of Mr. Andesmas.**
      New York: Grove Press, 1965. 303p. $2.95. ISBN 0394174267.
      LC 65-14208.
Duras speaks with a unique voice. The four novels in this edition (with an
introduction by Germaine Brée) are *The Square, Moderato Cantabile, Ten-Thirty
on a Summer Night*, and *The Afternoon of Mr. Andesmas*. Duras is best known
for her script of Alain Resnais's film *Hiroshima Mon Amour*. These works written
between 1955 and 1962 manifest Duras's fundamental preoccupation—that
of the individual facing the dehumanized, distanced world of events. The simple
dialogue is very important in her work. *The Square* has been staged and *Moderato
Contabile* was adapted for film. The novels in this volume have stark, limited
settings and limited time spans—an evening or an afternoon—in which characters
confront an elemental truth about themselves or others.

811   Edgeworth, Maria, 1767-1849. **Castle Rackrent.** New York: Garland,
      1978. (Repr. of 1800 ed.). bibliog. $32.00. ISBN 0824034503. LC
      78-17959.
The critic George Watson identifies *Castle Rackrent* (1800) as the first regional
novel in English. It is a memoir-novel in which the invented male narrator, a
family retainer named Thady Quirk, recounts the details of life at Rackrent
in Irish dialect. In this entertaining tale, much admired by Sir Walter Scott,
Edgeworth has written of successive generations of decadent landlords at a
remote Irish country estate during the eighteenth century. In choosing the
humblest character to display the keenest human insights, Edgeworth asserts

her belief in the intelligence of the human spirit, which transcends class and social station.

812   Eliot, George, pseud., i.e., Marian Evans, afterwards Cross, 1819-
1880. **Adam Bede.** New York: E. P. Dutton, 1960. 515p. bibliog.
$5.00. ISBN 0460000276.

This is Eliot's first novel (1859), and though the plot is compelling, the novelist's powers of characterization do not approach the level of the later novels. Two female characters are important for their illumination of female societal roles: Hetty, who becomes pregnant, the result of a forbidden affair; and Dinah, a Methodist minister who spurns marriage in order to follow the goals of the ministry she has set for herself.

813   Eliot, George, pseud., i.e., Marian Evans, afterwards Cross, 1819-
1880. **Middlemarch: An Anthoritative Text, Backgrounds, Reviews
and Criticism.** New York: Norton, 1977. 770p. bibliog. $15.95. ISBN
0393044300. LC 76-22805.

Among the many fine editions of this staple of Victorian fiction is the Norton critical edition, edited by Bert G. Hornback, which includes background materials and reviews, both contemporary and modern. *Middlemarch* (1828) is a novel of extraordinary scope and depth, leaving no phase of English provincial life unexplored. Its heroine, Dorothea Brooke, is the epitome of nobility and selflessness in contrast to the self-serving, narrow Rosamond. In her missionary zeal to serve others, Dorothea tends to be myopic and, in fact, marries a dull, elderly scholar/fool whom Eliot mercifully kills off, leaving Dorothea to her own devices, which lie predictably in the direction of another marriage. Though Dorothea chooses a much more attractive man on the second go-round, one wishes somehow that she could attain some of her idealistic goals on her own, and one suspects that the romanticism of her second choice may have clinging to it some of the blindness of her first.

814   Eliot, George, pseud., i.e., Marian Evans, afterwards Cross, 1819-
1880. **The Mill on the Floss.** New York: Harcourt, Brace and World,
1962. 508p. $5.95. ISBN 0151598207. LC 62-5698.

The Mill on the Floss (1860) introduces one of the most compelling heroines of English literature, Maggie Tulliver, a tragic victim of the provincial middle-class society that George Eliot knew so well. Maggie even from childhood "rushed to her deeds with passionate impulse," a characteristic that is striking in her adult development as well. Maggie is a deeply divided character, in love with one man, compelled toward another man—a dilemma that flew in the face of nineteenth-century social conventions and mores. In many respects, Maggie Tulliver is important to women's studies scholars for the controversy she has engendered in critical circles both in the nineteenth and twentieth centuries. The manner in which she has been judged and her "tragedy" measured says much about the image of woman in literature and how she has been interpreted and defined by critics and scholars.

815   Emecheta, Buchi. **The Slave Girl.** New York: Braziller, 1977. 179p.
$7.95. ISBN 0807608726. LC 77-77559.

Emecheta writes a novel of a peasant woman's life in twentieth-century Nigeria, managing in the course of the story to depict the struggles that women experience in both a traditional village setting and in a modern city. Ojebeta, the heroine, has been sold into domestic service as the story opens, manages to free herself and return to independence in her village, and is at story's end found in a different kind of domestic bondage as wife and mother in the city of Lagos. The Nigerian author lives in London—an extraordinary woman who manages to pursue a doctoral degree in sociology studying racism, to work among black youth in Paddington, and to write fiction, while raising five children.

816   Fauset, Jessie Redmon. **The Chinaberry Tree: A Novel of American Life.** New York: AMS Press, 1969. 341p. $12.00. ISBN 0404002560. LC 70-95405.
Written in 1931, this is a novel of its time. Jessie Fauset writes of the middle-class black experience, the "dark American who wears his joy and rue very much as does the white American. He may wear it with some differences but it is the same joy and the same rue." This is not a totally successful novel. Perhaps its heavy themes of incest, infidelity, and interracial love are too much for the idyllic landscape of sweetness and flowers sketched in at the outset. Two other Fauset novels that treat the black theme in literature from a middle-class perspective, though sensitive to the issues of bigotry and racism are: *Comedy, American Style* (orig. 1933; Negro Universities Press, 1969), and *There Is Confusion* (orig. 1924; AMS Press, 1974).

817*   Fauset, Jessie Redmon. **Plum Bun: A Novel Without a Moral.** New York: Frederick A. Stokes, 1929. 382p. LC 29-4421.
Fauset addresses the serious issue of "passing" in a white society in this novel about two sisters—one dark-skinned, the other light-skinned. Fauset deals again with middle-class blacks; this time, the problem of the novel centers on Angela Morgan's decision to deny her blackness, even to deny her own sister to preserve her charade. Although Fauset approaches this novel with a light touch and provides a "happy" ending, the racist pressures that have compelled Angela to act as she does are only superficially touched upon. Fauset's handling of this sensitive material is of considerable interest.

818   Ferber, Edna, 1887-1968. **So Big.** Garden City, NY: Doubleday, 1951. 360p. $6.95. ISBN 0385049560. LC 24-26188.
A Pulitzer prize-winning novel, this is the ultimate in "successful son backed by self-sacrificing mother" plots. Selina DeJong is a larger-than-life woman cut out of familiar Ferber cloth—a woman who defies rural High Prairie society to take on her husband's work on the farm after his death. Readers may also be interested in Mary Rose Shaughnessy's recent critical work, *Women and Success in American Society in the Works of Edna Ferber* (Gordon Press, 1977).

819   Fitzgerald, Zelda (Sayre). **Save Me the Waltz.** Carbondale: Southern Illinois University Press, 1967. 255p. $7.95. LC 67-5363.
Save Me the Waltz has two stories—the narrative line of the novel itself, and the story of the painful process of Zelda Fitzgerald's putting the book together against the jealousy of Scott Fitzgerald. Fitzgerald wrote to publisher Maxwell

Perkins at Scribners' in 1932 that Zelda was trying to lift his ideas and to make both him (Scott) and Zelda laughing stocks (due to the autobiographical nature of the material). Critics including Matthew J. Bruccoli have noted that the novel received one of the worst editing jobs ever in American letters, with numerous spelling errors appearing in the 1932 edition. The creative, editorial, and familial interactions occurred against the backdrop of Zelda's hospitalization for a mental breakdown. (See Milford's *Zelda*, 1972). The novel, written in an idiosyncratic style rife with original metaphor and rich, lyrical passages of description, is very much the story of Scott and Zelda in the characters of David and Alabama. David, a lionized young artist is married to Alabama, a young southern woman. Together they become luminaries of the international literary scene. Eclipsed by David's success and disgusted by their way of life, Alabama seeks fulfillment for herself as an artist. The novel has the dubious "happy" ending of David and Alabama's patching up their differences due to an injury to Alabama that necessitates her abandoning a dancing career. This is very definitely a significant novel about female self-realization in its own right.

820   Flaubert, Gustave, 1821-1880. **Madame Bovary: Provincial Manners.**
       New York: Modern Library, 1950. 400p. bibliog. $3.95. ISBN
       0394600282. LC 50-12243.
There are many good editions of this classic about a woman's tragic life, among them the above translation by Eleanor Marx Aveling, with an introduction by Henri Peyre, or the Lowell Bair translation, with introduction by Malcolm Cowley (Bantam, 1959). Originally published in 1857, the novel has been considered a technical triumph of form and plot. In American fiction, the closest counterpart to Emma Bovary is Kate Chopin's Edna Pontellier in *The Awakening*, although Marian Forrester in Willa Cather's *A Lost Lady* also comes close. At any rate, the plight and character of Emma Bovary, a woman who commits adultery to escape the bourgeois monotony and pettiness of her married life in a small village, has evolved into one of the more hotly-debated moral dilemmas in literature, many critics dismissing her as a moral lightweight incapable of seeing the clear light of ethical choice, others arguing that Emma indeed has a defined moral sense and is driven to her death by the oppressive circumstances of her life. Clearly this is an essential literature selection for any discussion of women who have rebelled against the societal fabric of their day.

821   Fowles, John, 1926- . **The French Lieutenant's Woman.** Boston:
       Little, Brown, 1969. 467p. $9.95. ISBN 0316290998. LC 77-86616.
Of most interest to women's studies in this study of the Victorian novel within the form of a Victorian novel are the statements being made about Victorian life and mores, and the roles assigned and played out by the sexes in Victorian society. Taking place in 1867, not by chance the same year when John Stuart Mill argued that the time was ripe for granting women the franchise, this is a love story with some stock Victorian characters. Charles, the hero, is torn between the passionate and imaginative Sarah, who represents unconventionality and a constellation of other qualities seemingly dismissed from the Victorian milieu, and the doll-like Ernestina. Fowles writes a novel at once playful and serious, exploring the paradoxical aspects of a society that sublimates the libido even as it glorifies large families. Fowles has plentifully sprinkled epigrams taken

from major Victorian writers throughout the novel—ironic commentaries on
the plot from the likes of Hardy, Arnold, Clough, Tennyson, and Marx, and from
such odd documents as the *Children's Employment Commission Report* of 1867.

822   Frame, Janet, 1924- . **The Edge of the Alphabet.** New York: Braziller,
       1962. 303p. $4.95. ISBN 0807601942. LC 62-16268.

Tragic and apocalyptic, *The Edge of the Alphabet* is a novel informed by alienation, loneliness, hopelessness, and finally suicide. The characters are Toby Withers,
Zoe Bryce, and Pat Keenan, ordinary people on the outside of things but possessed
of richly symbolic and complex inner worlds. These are characters who in their
ordinary lives have problems in articulating their thoughts and fears and are
emotionally imprisoned and paralyzed in their non-dream existences. As if to
underscore their mute frustration, Frame endows one invisible character, Thora
Pattern, with an eloquent lyrical voice. But Thora is dead and can speak only
through the papers she has left. Literally, she lives on "the edge of the alphabet
where words crumble and all forms of communication between the living are
useless." Frame's concluding message is that we live our lives solitarily caged,
finding our amusements in spite of our frustration and hopelessness. "But like
the yellow birds have we not our pleasures? We look long in mirrors. We have
tiny ladders to climb up and down, little wheels to set our feet and our heart
racing nowhere; toys to play with."

823   Frame, Janet, 1924- . **Faces in the Water.** New York: Braziller, 1961.
       254p. $4.95. ISBN 0807601497. LC 61-12954.

Frame's novel evokes the here and now of a mental hospital and the experiences
of its lyrical narrator, Istina Mavet, in a world of shock treatments, rigid and
mindless behavior codes, perpetual exposure, day rooms and wire cages, domineering nurses and condescending doctors. The novel is informed by a Laingian
view of insanity, which posits that those proclaimed mad may be, in fact, saner
than their accusers and caretakers. The novel is richly hung with the poetic
philosophy of Istina as commentator upon the madhouse experience. Of her own
human condition, despite the barrage of indignities heaped upon her as an inmate
of the asylum, she comments, "living is so much like one of those childhood
games where you keep shutting your eyes and on opening them expect to find
everything changed—a new city with glass towers, a table laden for a feast, a
kindly forest where trees no longer strike blows or twist themselves into fearful
shapes." This novel speaks of Frame's intimate familiarity with the grotesque
routines of mental hospitals.

823a   Frame, Janet, 1924- . **Scented Gardens for the Blind.** New York:
       Braziller, 1964. 192p. $4.50. ISBN 080760268X. LC 64-10786.

Janet Frame's fiction is about inner voyages. In this poetic and allegorical novel,
Frame creates the character Vera Glace, who introduces herself at the outset
of the novel as the grief-stricken mother of Erlene, a mute who sits in the
next room. Vera envisions an important, if not oracular, form of utterance
for her daughter, ". . . the words pleasurably patterned like daisy-chains, with
biting-links, with the smell of the earth and the sun and the juice of man."
The father (a genealogist who is estranged from his own family) is similarly
fixed on the importance of his dumb daughter's speech. Other characters in this

dreamscape include a ridiculous and garrulous psychiatrist and an imaginary character, Uncle Black Beetle, who is the creation of the daughter and the most lyrical voice of the book. All the characters function in a world of imagination, of delusion and illusion. By the end of the novel, it is Vera Glace who remains, a former librarian and a mental patient who has been keeping silence in an asylum for thirty years attended by a faithful nurse. In the final lines of the novel, she breaks silence only to utter an incomprehensible gibberish. Frame's metaphors are complex and her message subtle. The patient reader will find much richness in the work of this New Zealand writer, a major voice in contemporary fiction.

823b   Freeman, Mary Eleanor (Wilkins), 1852-1930. **A New England Nun, and Other Stories.** New York: Harper and Brothers, 1891; repr. New York: Irvington Publications, n.d. $15.00.

The title story is one of Freeman's best—an exquisite portrait of a woman happily living her life as a single woman, rejoicing in her familiar possessions and domestic routine, waiting patiently for the man to whom she has been engaged for fourteen years to complete arrangements for their wedding—a wedding she unconsciously does not want to take place. Freeman wrote nearly a thousand short stories which enjoyed great popularity in their time. At her best, she is an extraordinary writer whose stories have a wonderful New England flavor. "The Revolt of Mother" is another of her particularly fine stories in this volume. *The Revolt of Mother and Other Stories* is also available from Feminist Press, 1974, edited and with an afterword by Michelle Clark.

824   Freeman, Mary Eleanor (Wilkins), 1852-1930. **The Shoulders of Atlas.** New York: Harper, 1908; repr. New York: Arno Press, 1977. 293p. $22.00. ISBN 0405100442. LC 76-51665.

Sylvia is the Atlas of the title and the story is a study of her conscience set against the New England tradition about which Freeman writes so eloquently. The major portraiture is of Sylvia and her jealous and possessive love of a young woman, Rose, who comes to live with her and her husband Henry and to represent for them the daughter they never had. Depiction of the psychological changes that accompany Sylvia and Henry's inheritance of a small windfall becomes more important for Freeman than the mysterious plot, because it is the intricacy and spareness of the New England character that most interest her as a novelist. Other complex moral novels of Freeman currently in print are *Pembroke* (originally 1893) and *Evelina's Garden* (originally 1898).

825   French, Marilyn, 1929- . **The Women's Room.** New York: Summit Books, 1977. 471p. ISBN 067140010X. LC 77-24918.

Similar in theme to Marge Piercy's *Small Changes*, French explores the process of an individual's feminist thinking over 25 years. The narrator, Mira, although actively involved in the women's movement for many years, distances herself from the movement by the novel's end to a position of solitude and contemplation away from active politicizing and radical engagement.

826   Gaskell, Elizabeth Cleghorn (Stevenson), 1810-1865. **Mary Barton.** New York: E. P. Dutton, 1961. 372p. $5.00. ISBN 0460005987. LC 12-999.

This social novel was written in the hope of changing the conditions of workers in Manchester, England. Gaskell writes in the preface to the 1848 edition: "if it be an error, that the woes which come with ever-returning tide-like flood to overwhelm the workmen in our manufacturing towns, pass unregarded by all but the sufferers, it is at any rate an error so bitter in its consequences to all parties, that whatever public effort can do in the way of legislation, or private effort in the way of merciful deeds, or helpless love in the way of 'widow's mites,' should be done, and that speedily, to disabuse the work-people of so miserable a misapprehension." Though the plot may be melodramatic, Gaskell's first novel is perceptive in its dissection of working-class poverty, in industrial Manchester during the 1830s and 1840s. Starvation, disease, and exhaustion characterized the lots of men and women alike. Women were severely limited by the choices of available occupations (prostitutes, seamstresses). *Mary Barton* ends happily in Mary's going to Canada with the man she loves. Death is the lot of less fortunate female characters.

827   Gilman, Charlotte (Perkins) Stetson, 1860-1935. **The Yellow Wallpaper.**
       Boston: Small, Maynard, 1899; repr. Old Westbury, NY: Feminist
       Press, 1973. 63p. bibliog. $1.95. ISBN 0912670096. LC 73-5795.
Literature and feminist politics often do not join together gracefully. Gilman's cameo classic, the tale of a woman going mad due to familial and societal infringements on her individuality, has been revived. Feminist Press has done right by Gilman's little masterpiece, putting it between two covers of its own and including with it an excellent essay by Elaine Hedges, which explains how *The Yellow Wallpaper* intersected with Gilman's own experience of a nervous breakdown and why we have come only recently to the point Gilman was trying to make— namely, that women are imprisoned in gilded, even yellow wallpapered cells. The story was first published in *The New England Magazine* (May 1892), and reaction was that the heroine was insane and a problem to her family, not the other way around.

828   Gippius, Zinaida Nikolaevna [Hippius, Zinaida], 1869-1945. **Selected**
       Works of Zinaida Hippius. Urbana: University of Illinois Press, 1972.
       315p. bibliog. $10.00. ISBN 0252002601. LC 72-188447.
Translated and edited by Temira Pachmuss, this is a collection of fifteen of the best stories of Zinaida Hippius, published in English for the first time. Among the stories are: "Heavenly Words," "Fate," "It's All For the Worse," "The Pilgrim," "He Is White," "There Is No Return," "The Eternal Woman," "The Strange Law," "Memoirs of Martynov," "Julien, Or Not Julien," "Rest, Heart," "With the Star," and "Metamorphosis." Pachmuss states in her lengthy introduction that few Western readers are aware of the works of Zinaida Hippius or her influence upon St. Petersburg's spiritual and cultural life during the Silver Age of Russian poetry, and after the Revolution, upon the Russian émigré circles in Paris. Underestimated by her contemporaries, she wrote both fiction and poetry and gained a place in Russian Modernism through her poetry. Her collected poetry is entitled *Sobranie stikhov: 1889-1903.*

829 Glasgow, Ellen Anderson Gholson, 1873-1945. **Barren Ground.** New
York: Hill and Wang, 1957. 409p. $4.50. ISBN 0809000148. LC
57-9766.

Dorinda Oakley, an exceptionally strong Glasgow heroine, conquers her sense
of futility (after being jilted by her lover) through complete dedication to hard
work. The setting is the Virginia of Glasgow's childhood, complete with "the
endless fields of broomsedge and scrub pine, the low immeasurable horizon,"
which Glasgow loved so well. The story of a typical romance evolves into a
tale of grim realism when Dorinda finds out that her young doctor/fiancé has
brought another woman home to the country as his bride. Dorinda turns the
intensity she felt for Jason to the farm, "the barren ground," and spends all
her energy in making the place fertile and prosperous. In supplanting her
romantic dream with one of strength and purpose, the yield is one of happiness
and a sense of a job well done. She rejects marriage, realizing that such a step
would jeopardize independence and selfhood: "at middle age, she faced the
future without romantic glamour, but she faced it with integrity of vision."

830 Glasgow, Ellen Anderson Gholson, 1873-1945. **The Descendant.** New
York: Harper, 1897; repr. New York: Arno Press, 1977. 276p. $21.00.
ISBN 0405100469. LC 76-51667.

Elizabeth Hardwick tells the reader in the introduction to this work (a volume
in the Arno Rediscovered Fiction by American Women series) that *The Descendant* is Ellen Glasgow's first novel, begun when the author was eighteen, and
finally published in 1897 when Glasgow was 24. The novel's major theme centers around the conflicts between love and career, and career and political
ideals in the relationship of a young couple (artist and journalist) in New York.
The fact that these characters are unmarried yet living together made this an
avant garde novel for 1897 and certainly beyond the social code of Richmond,
Virginia, where Glasgow lived and wrote. The language in this novel tends toward
clichés, especially in the romantic passages, a problem that Glasgow had well
under control in her later work.

831* Glasgow, Ellen Anderson Gholson, 1873-1945. **They Stooped to Folly:
A Comedy of Morals.** Garden City, NY: Doubleday, Doran, 1929.
251p. LC 29-17854.

In this comedy of manners, three generations of women are revealed through
their love affairs as filtered through the narrative consciousness of Victorian
husband and father, Mr. Virginius Littlepage. Glasgow's satire is keen as she
distills the changing mores of Virginian society from the Civil War into the
twentieth century. A brief passage of Littlepage's stream of consciousness about
his wife at the beginning of the novel sets the tone for his expectations of the
perfect woman: "After thirty years of marital happiness, he could still remind
himself that Victoria was endowed with every charm except the thrilling touch
of human frailty. Though her perfection discouraged pleasures, especially the
pleasures of love, he had learned in time to feel the pride of a husband in her
natural frigidity. For he still clung, amid the decay of moral platitudes, to the
discredited ideal of chivalry."

832   Glasgow, Ellen Anderson Gholson, 1873-1945. **Vein of Iron.** New York:
      Harcourt, Brace and Jovanovich, 1967. 462p. $0.95. ISBN
      0156934760. LC 35-27270.
Appalachian Virginia is the setting for this depressing tale of life from 1900
to 1932. Understandably, the tragic economic hardships that plague these years
do not allow Glasgow's characteristic humor and satire to shine through. She
creates a stoic female character, Ada Fincastle, whom we first meet in the
novel at age ten defending an idiot boy from the taunts of jeering children.
Among her childhood longings are "a doll with real hair" and an opportunity
to climb to the top of Thunder Mountain—"that was one of the things Mother
had always longed to do and had never done." The female pattern of this novel
is self-sacrifice and support. Ada marries her childhood sweetheart, a man who
sees her as a rock on whom he can depend, and she is content with this relationship: "because he had been in youth a disappointed romantic, he would inherit
a middle age, and even an old age, if he lived, of cynical realism. But he depended
upon her. . . . And even if his flesh had ceased to desire her, or desired her only
in flashes (she looked down at her withered hands; she remembered her faded
cheeks), some hunger deeper and more enduring than appetite was still constant
and satisfied."

833   Godwin, Gail. **The Odd Woman.** New York: Berkeley Medallion, 1976.
      $1.95. ISBN 0425031675.
In this very intelligent and well-conceived feminist novel, the heroine is torn
between a desire for romantic happiness and dedication to an academic career
and independence. The loneliness and anxiety of Jane Clifford, unmarried
professor of Victorian literature, is always convincing and complex, illustrating
the uncertainty involved in attempting to make choices of growth when there
can be no easy solutions.

834   Gordon, Mary. **Final Payments.** New York: Random House, 1978.
      297p. $8.95. ISBN 0394427939. LC 77-90259.
In this highly praised first novel by Gordon, Isabel Moore puts aside a Catholic
girlhood at age thirty. Out of guilt and love, she has lived the years between
nineteen and thirty as her father's nurse. It is only with his death that she comes
to realize how vacuum-like her existence has been. Gordon renders Isabel's
situation in strokes of great sensitivity and humor. Isabel makes a number of
false starts during her period of adjustment to the world of work and love and
friends after an eleven-year holding pattern. Out of guilt over an affair with a
friend's husband, she almost allows herself to be drawn into another lengthy
nurse-housekeeper situation, this time for a woman she intensely dislikes. She
saves herself from this grim fate and from allowing herself to grow fat and
unattractive by making "a final payment." A novel that speaks articulately
about filial responsibility and female friendship, about aging and self-possession,
Gordon's work will prove of great interest to women.

835   Gould, Lois. **A Sea-Change.** New York: Simon and Schuster, 1976.
      163p. $6.95. ISBN 0671223267. LC 76-13579.
Possible to read as a fantasy, this is a bizarre story about Jessie Waterman,
former model and "golden girl," and her husband, Roy—a much-married,

prolific, macho, even if good-natured man. Rape (real or imagined), solitude, drowning, suicide, helplessness are all elements of this highly symbolic novel, which posits the collaboration of men and women in sustaining patterns of dominance/submission, brutality, and acceptance in their lives as couples.

836   Gray, Francine du Plessix. **Lovers and Tyrants.** New York: Simon and Schuster, 1976. 316p. $8.95. ISBN 0671223380. LC 76-17614.

Gray is noted for her brilliant literary analyses and her elegant exploration of Catholic radicalism in *Divine Disobedience*. In her first novel, she takes on lovers and tyrants in an elegant first-person narrative and concludes that lovers *are* tyrants. Characters in this international intellectual coming of age emerge from the narrator's childhood (a neurotic, hypochondriacal spinster governess), from youth (an adored but absent father), from young womanhood (an adored but cold and mechanical lover), from the years as matron and mother (a companionable, but in the end, boring husband), and finally from middle-age (a bisexual chic, and child-like lover). The equation in du Plessix Gray's fiction world goes like this: sexual love is much like celibacy; it cuts off the possibility of exploration and hence, growth. Lovers are like tyrants; they impose tyranny by their constant presence and the needs that they cannot fulfill within their own beings. This is a powerful novel.

837   Griffin, Susan. **The Sink.** San Lorenzo, CA: Shameless Hussy Press, 1974. 47p. $1.85. ISBN 0915288044.

Small feminist presses are publishing much of the truly experimental fiction of contemporary women writers. Each of these stories is a carefully crafted representation of a girl or woman at a given moment in time. "There Are Already Too Many Candlemakers in Peru" is a dialogue between a girl child and an adult man that begins with the child's plaintive question, "Do you fuck?" "The Sink" is the story of a woman seeking to impose an inner order who becomes obsessed with the pipes and drains in her house. There is a story, "Passage," about the terrifying experience of a woman returning to school who comes to realize that madness is a random reality. Susan Griffin has a gift for recreating the various in women.

838   Guy, Rosa. **Ruby: A Novel.** New York: Viking Press, 1976. 217p. $8.95. ISBN 0670610232. LC 76-2019.

Guy has written successfully for young adult audiences (*The Friends*, 1973). *Ruby* is unusual for its subject matter—a relationship between two black women, Ruby and Daphne. Novels about lesbian relationships between Afro-American women appear rarely. This novel has much to say about friendship between women from two disparate backgrounds—in this case, Ruby from a traditional patriarchal background and Daphne from a leftist political family. Perhaps because Rosa Guy writes for a young adult audience, she felt the need to tack on a conventional love ending for Ruby. At any rate, *Ruby* is an important feminist black novel. *Bird At My Window*, an out-of-print 1966 novel by Guy, deals with a male protagonist so stymied by racism that he turns on those closest to him with tragic consequences.

839   Hall, Radclyffe, 1886-1943. **The Well of Loneliness.** New York: Pocket
       Books, 1975. $1.95. ISBN 0671788086.

The Well of Loneliness is a deservedly classic novel about love between women
that, when first published in England in 1928, triggered enormous controversy
and prosecution for "obscenity." Stephen, the heroine, is the only child of
an aristocratic British couple who had longed for a baby (which they assumed
would be a son) for ten years. Lesbianism as depicted by Hall in her characterization of Stephen is a psychosexual disposition unfolding from birth: the girl
child is named Stephen; something in her appearance inspires repugnance in
her mother, while the child and her father develop an intimate relationship;
a male suitor triggers nothing but repulsion in the adolescent Stephen; and so
on. This is the story of a young woman coming to recognize her "nature" in
a social climate obviously hostile to it, of her love affairs with women, and
particularly of the deep joy and pain of lesbian love. See Una Troubridge's
The Life of Radclyffe Hall (1961, repr. 1975) for its illumination of *Well* and
its public afterbirth.

840   Hardy, Thomas, 1840-1928. **Tess of the d'Urbervilles.** London: James R.
       Osgood, McIlvaine, 1891; repr. New York: St. Martin's Press, n.d.
       $10.95. ISBN 0312793456.

Of this novel, Elizabeth Hardwick writes in *Seduction and Betrayal* (1974):
"Hardy sees Tess as a beautiful, warm soul run down by the dogs of fate, in
her case the bloodhounds of sex and love, Alec d'Urberville and Angel Clare.
Her acceptance, her endurance of the griefs of experience, are of the heroic
kind; she meets suffering without losing her capacity for feeling." Hardwick
goes on to point out that Tess is never stunned by the adversity she faces,
therefore "never degraded by it." *Far from the Madding Crowd* (1874) and
Jude the Obscure (1895) are Hardy novels similarly rich in their characterizations of strong women. In his handling of the complexities of male-female
relationships and the tragedy of passion, Hardy is without peer. Readers with
an interest in Hardy may want to consult Ann Z. Mickelson's *Thomas Hardy's
Women and Men: The Defeat of Nature* (Scarecrow Press, 1976). Lloyd Fernando
in *"New Women" in the Late Victorian Novel* (Pennsylvania State University
Press, 1977) has analyzed Hardy's views on women's liberation and the social
and sexual injustices suffered by women in Victorian society. Fernando gives
particular attention to *Jude the Obscure* and *Tess of the D'Urbervilles* in his
chapter on Hardy.

841   Harper, Frances Ellen Watkins, 1825-1911. **Iola Leroy: Or, Shadows
       Uplifted.** New York: AMS Press, 1971. 282p. $11.00. ISBN
       0404001696. LC 76-153097.

Of pioneering significance, though not a great novel, *Iola Leroy; Or Shadows
Uplifted* (1892) is a didactic novel about the sufferings and travails of a quadroon
sold into slavery. Eventually, Iola is rescued and married to Dr. Latimer and
all is serene. This very popular novel went into three editions. Louis Filler
has written an excellent biographical sketch of Harper's significance as a
nineteenth-century black writer in *Notable American Women* (ed. Edward T.
James, 1971).

842   Harris, Bertha, 1937- . **Lover.** Plainfield, VT: Daughters, 1976. 214p. $4.50. ISBN 0913780138. LC 76-7816.

This lesbian novel is a celebration of loving women in the form of fantasy, history, autobiography, and fiction dazzlingly soldered together.

843   Hawthorne, Nathaniel, 1804-1864. **The Scarlet Letter: Text, Sources, Criticism.** New York: Harcourt, Brace and World, 1961. 217p. bibliog. $4.95. ISBN 0155781677. LC 61-9887.

Published in 1850, perhaps no other American novel has addressed the themes of sexuality and concealed guilt so compellingly as Hawthorne's *Scarlet Letter*. Hester, the heroine, is sentenced to wear a scarlet A attached to her dress at the breast to signify that she is an adultress. The young wife of an aging English scholar, she has been sent alone by her husband to Boston to establish a home, but she becomes involved with Reverend Arthur Dimmesdale, the father of Hester's beautiful child, Pearl. The story centers on the fact that Hester has acknowledged and paid for her sin, but she refuses to implicate Dimmesdale. Dimmesdale is being consumed with hidden guilt but is unable to acknowledge the child as his until the end of the novel, when he makes a public confession at the pillory, where once Hester had been humiliated, and dies in her arms, broken from the experience. Roger Chillingworth, Hester's husband, comes to town in the disguise of a doctor, makes his life quest the discovery of Hester's lover and the father of her child. He becomes crazed in the process, as characters in Hawthorne often do when they either conceal guilt or fix on another's guilt. Hester is the only triumphant character, though feminist critics may wonder at Hester's docility and charity toward the town that has treated her so cruelly. An interesting aspect of her situation by novel's end is that she has been able to adopt an independent manner of life because of the scarlet A—removed from the town and the responsibility of living a married life.

844   Herbst, Josephine, 1897-1969. **Nothing Is Sacred.** New York: Coward-McCann, 1928; repr. New York: Arno Press, 1977. 244p. $20.00. ISBN 0405100507. LC 76-51671.

Josephine Herbst, a midwestern novelist, was a member of the talented, intellectual left-wing society of the '20s. She was a political activist and lived in Cuba for some time. *Nothing Is Sacred* is reprinted as a contribution to the Rediscovered Fiction by American Women series. Elizabeth Hardwick introduces the novel as a "realistic novel of family life in a Middle Western town. Mother and father, their daughters and the daughters' husbands, act and respond and whine with a steady, churning flow, like that of greasy water. Debts, drinking, infidelities, illness and a prolonged, provoking dissatisfaction make up the drama of life."

845   Highsmith, Patricia [Morgan, Claire], 1921- . **The Price of Salt.** New York: Coward McCann, 1952; repr. New York: Arno Press, 1975. 276p. $10.00. ISBN 0405073844. LC 75-12340.

This novel by Claire Morgan (originally 1952) tells the story of two women at different points in their lives (one is nineteen; the other, thirty and in the midst of a divorce) who meet and unexpectedly fall in love. Particularly important in this narrative is Morgan's treatment of the now familiar issue of lesbian motherhood and child custody: the older woman's husband tries to deprive her of custody for her young daughter on the basis of her new lesbian relationship. Marion Zimmer Bradley and Gene Damon described this work in 1960 as "probably the American novel of the Lesbian" (in *Checklist*).

846   Hopkins, Pauline Elizabeth, 1859-1930. **Contending Forces: A Romance Illustrative of Negro Life North and South.** Boston: Colored Co-operative, 1899; repr. Carbondale: Southern Illinois University Press, 1978. 402p. $9.95. ISBN 0809308746. LC 77-18724.

The product of a little-known writer (Hopkins does not appear in *Notable American Women*, for example, despite being a founder of the Colored American League and a playwright, literary editor, novelist, and actor), Hopkins's novel, *Contending Forces*, is very much a period piece, significant for the attention that she hoped to focus on the plight of blacks. The novel was set in late nineteenth-century Boston, Hopkins's home for most of her life. Her information on the historical background of southern slavery was based on her research in archives in South Carolina and Washington, D.C. The author's preface is a particularly moving defense of her purpose "in giving this little romance expression in print." She writes, "fiction is of great value to any people as a preserver of manners and customs—religious, political and social. It is a record of growth and development from generation to generation. No one will do this for us; we must ourselves develop the men and women who will faithfully portray the inmost thoughts and feelings of the Negro with all the fire and romance which lie dormant in our history, and, as yet, unrecognized by writers of the Anglo-Saxon race."

847   Howland, Bette. **Blue in Chicago.** New York: Harper and Row, 1978. 183p. $8.95. ISBN 0060119578. LC 76-26235.

Howland writes from the perspective of a resident of Southside Chicago, specifically from the Hyde Park experience, where she is a graduate student at the University of Chicago. This is a fictional work. Her subject is the tone and temper of life in the city, an ambience that Howland handles in loving detail. Each of the six short stories distills an incredible Chicago essence: Jewish relatives near Sheridan Road; the Borglum Branch of the Chicago Public Library in Uptown; felony court at Twenty-sixth and California; a Jewish funeral. Though Howland is clearly rooted in place, her *tour de force* as a writer is her vivid characterizations drawn from the ethnic richness of urban life.

848   Hurston, Zora Neale, 1902-1960. **Jonah's Gourd Vine.** Philadelphia, PA: Lippincott, 1971. 316p. $5.95. ISBN 039700754X. LC 70-166496.

The hardships of black family life during the Reconstruction period are powerfully depicted here through the characters John and Lucy, who may have been modelled autobiographically on Hurston's own mother and father. Woman's lot appears particularly difficult, as she is still caught in the traditional roles of incessant childbearing and childrearing, a condition hardly alleviated by emancipation. Hurston's dialogue remains strong and true throughout but is especially brilliant in the episodes relating John Pearson's preaching. The novelist's subtle and ironic humor reveals itself in the ending in which John, a philandering husband throughout, receives his just dessert.

849   Hurston, Zora Neale, 1902-1960. **Mules and Men.** New York: Negro
       Universities Press, 1969. (Repr. of 1935 ed.). 342p. $12.00. ISBN
       0837120004. LC 70-90134.
One of the most interesting aspects of this collection of black songs, tales,
and sayings is the personal history Hurston reveals in her introduction about
the gathering of the material. Franz Boas, the noted anthropologist, advised
her on this project. The first place she went to look for material was in her
home town of Eatonville, Florida. "From the earliest rocking of my cradle,
I had known about the capers Brer Rabbit is apt to cut and what the Squinch
Owl says from the house top. But it was fitting me like a tight chemise. I couldn't
see it for wearing it. It was only when I was off in college, away from my native
surroundings, that I could see myself like somebody else and stand off and look
at my garment. Then I had to have the spy-glass of Anthropology to look through
at that." The two parts of this fascinating compendium of black folklore are:
"Folk Tales" and "Hoodoo." Appendix material includes Negro songs with
music, formulae of Hoodoo doctors, paraphernalia of conjure, and prescriptions
of root doctors. A wonderful book of Hurston's in which she plays freely with
folklore, religion, legend, and fiction is her colloquial rendering of the Moses
story, *Moses Man of the Mountain* (orig. 1939; repr. Chatham Bookseller, 1967).

850   Hurston, Zora Neale, 1902-1960. **Their Eyes Were Watching God: A
       Novel.** Urbana: University of Illinois Press, 1978. 296p. $3.95. ISBN
       0252006860. LC 77-18230.
Hurston's most notable novel, set in her native Florida, *Their Eyes Were Watching
God* (1937), is an autobiographical work that states Hurston's position on black
womanhood. Janie Crawford, a proud and beautiful quadroon, is a character
of integrity and truth, who rejects racial and sexual domination at every turn,
though it takes her two disastrous marriages to find a combination that works
in the form of a young laborer with whom she develops a relationship of mutual
respect. Hurston's forte is authentic southern dialect, which she creatively
transcribes and handles in a way quite different from other American writers,
black or white. This is Hurston's most memorable novel and one of the greatest
of black contemporary novels. A less satisfying Hurston novel is *Seraph on the
Suwanee* (orig. 1948; repr. AMS Press, 1974). This edition of *Eyes* has a foreword
by Shirley Anne Williams.

851   James, Henry, 1843-1916. **The Bostonians.** London: Macmillan, 1921;
       repr. New York: Thomas Y. Crowell, 1974. 540p. $4.95. ISBN
       0815203470. LC 73-16075.
In this book about friendship between women, James is ambiguous about how
he views that friendship. To some, James's tone appears to be derisive in his
characterizations of Olive Chancellor, a Boston "spinster" who believes the
woman's movement to be an evangelical cause and who identifies the beautiful,
passive, but verbally assured Verena Tarrant as the medium of her message.
Success in this enterprise seems assured to Olive until Verena falls under the
spell of Olive's cousin, Basil Ransom, who has little sympathy with the ideas
of New England Progressivism and matches Olive's commitment to possess
Verena in the public sphere with a single-minded dedication to restore her to
the domestic world of marriage and motherhood. The characters in this novel

appear uniformly as caricatures whose thoughts surface in utterances of cant or in a parroting of cant. A helpful analysis of female community in *The Bostonians* is to be found in Nina Auerbachs' *Communities of Women* (Harvard University Press, 1978.)

852   James, Henry, 1843-1916. **The Portrait of a Lady: An Authoritative Text, Henry James and the Novel, Reviews and Criticism.** New York: Norton, 1975. 755p. bibliog. $15.00. ISBN 0393043851. LC 74-19457.
Isabel Archer, heroine of *Portrait* (originally 1881) and most famous of James's heroines, has come to represent all that is courageous and true in an American heroine. James allows the intelligent and beautiful Isabel all of the pleasures and pains of choice when she becomes an heiress. Her affection is won by Gilbert Osmond, a man of outward taste and charm but inward shallowness who marries Isabel only for her money. Isabel finally comes to see her husband for what he is, and her best friend and confidante for what she is (the mistress of Osmond and the mother of his lovely daughter, Pansy). Because Isabel is a character who embodies the most severe code of Jamesian honor and duty, even when she sees the mistake she has made and is offered an alternative solution in the form of a proposal by a man for whom she does have affection, she returns to the choice she originally made for better but mostly for worse. Isabel Archer, Pansy, and Madame Merle are classic studies of the images of women in American literature.

853   James, Henry, 1843-1916. **Wings of the Dove.** New York: Scribner, 1909; repr. Fairfield, NJ: A. M. Kelley, 1976. 2v. V.1, $12.50, ISBN 0678028192. V.2, $13.50, ISBN 0678028206. LC 71-158798.
James's 1902 novel, which poses the moral problems and consequences of love and money, is a fiction with two unforgettable female characters. Kate Croy, daughter of an impoverished family who refuses to consider marriage with journalist Merton Densher (though she loves him) because he is without wealth, is contrasted with Milly Theale, an altruistic, dying young heiress and Kate's best friend. It seems to Kate that everyone's problems will be solved if Milly, who is going to die shortly anyway, will simply marry Kate's lover, Merton, giving Milly some sexual happiness for a time and leaving Merton in a financial position that Kate can handle. Neat as such a solution appears, the characters of Milly, Kate, and Merton are in the end too complex to live with such a plan. Milly leaves Merton her money even though she knows Kate and Merton's plan. But the two lovers are finally unable to marry because of guilt, in this classic in the development of the American heroine by the master of morality.

854   Jewett, Sarah Orne, 1849-1909. **A Country Doctor.** New York: MSS. Information; distr. New York: Arno Press, 1972. (Repr. of 1884 ed.). $15.95. ISBN 0842280839.
This is Jewett's first novel, and though not structurally as sound as some of Jewett's other work, the plot of a young woman who rejects traditional goals of marriage and children for a career in medicine is an important one. In addition, the novel is memorable for Jewett's fine, graceful observations of rural life in Maine.

855   Jewett, Sarah Orne, 1849-1909. **Country of the Pointed Firs and Other Stories.** Garden City, NY: Doubleday, 1954. 320p. $2.50. ISBN 0385092148. LC 54-3594.

In this book, which is considered her finest work and a great classic of American prose, Jewett has achieved a triumph of description, concentrating on the austere beauty of New England nature and the spare dignity of New England character. Written in 1896, these are sketches and tales of Dunnet Landing, a small New England coastal village.

856   Johnston, Mary, 1870-1936. **Hagar.** Boston: Houghton Mifflin, 1913; repr. Folcroft, PA: Folcroft Library Editions, n.d. $12.50.

Much of *Hagar* is pretty bland stuff, notwithstanding Tillie Olsen's identification of the book as "a classic of its own kind." Johnston writes about Virginia in most all of her 23 novels. Not surprisingly, her feminist heroine, Hagar Ashendyne, is Virginia-born and bred, heading straight for her destined niche in the domestic sphere. The surprise is that Hagar manages to avoid her assigned lot, though she makes her breaks from family and convention with southern grace and charm. (Some feminist critics find this easy feminism unbelievable and a bit boring.) The final pages of the novel find Hagar an established author deciding to marry the man of her choice on *her* terms. She informs him, "You're aware that you're marrying a working-woman, who intends to continue to work?" He tells her that he plans to help her in her work and her commitment to the woman movement. Johnston's prolific output includes *To Have and To Hold* (1900), a tremendously popular novel about the women of Jamestown; her more mystical works, *Lewis Rand* (1908), *Michael Forth* (1919), and *Sweet Rocket* (1920). A book of love stories unified by a feminist theme about man-woman relations through the ages is her *The Wanderers* (1917).

857   Jones, Gayl, 1950- . **Eva's Man.** New York: Random House, 1976. 177p. $6.95. ISBN 0394499344. LC 75-40565.

Jones has constructed one of the most complex novels to date about the psychology of a black woman criminal. Eva, the narrator, has been in prison for five years at the beginning of the novel. Her crime: the murder and mutilation of a man she met in a restaurant and with whom she had a short, physical affair. Eva's emotions are laid bare as she reconstructs her life in dialogues with prison psychiatrists; her cellmate, Elvira; and with herself. The language of this novel is raw and poetic as Eva gradually comes to realize her hatred of men and to ransack her memory for the reasons behind her violent act. A powerful lesbian theme everges as Eva's conversations with Elvira deepen and she begins to respond to Elvira's lesbian attraction for her. A young novelist of much promise, though her vision is a troubling one, Gayl Jones published *Corregidora* in 1975.

858   Jong, Erica. **Fear of Flying: A Novel.** New York: Holt, Rinehart and Winston, 1973. 340p. $6.95. ISBN 0030107318. LC 73-3697.

Female sexuality is what *Fear of Flying* is about and the heroine, Isadora Wing, in quest of "the zipless fuck," is a twentieth-century female counterpart to Tom Jones. Jong has risked a great deal in this picaresque novel of real and imaginary erotic adventure, in that Isadora cannot be an entirely satisfactory character to readers on either side of the sexual politics question. Erotic,

funny, and intelligent, with a memorable and complex heroine, this is a landmark
woman's novel.

859   Jong, Erica. **How to Save Your Own Life**: A Novel. New York: Holt,
       Rinehart and Winston, 1977. 310p. $8.95. ISBN 003017726X. LC
       76-29905.
An unashamedly autobiographical novel about Jong's life, loves, and quest
after fame and fortune, the narrative begins on Thanksgiving Day with Isadora
(Erica) leaving her husband, psychiatrist Bennett Wing. It ends with her graphic
description of an erotic affair with a young man, followed by a group of fine
love poems by Jong describing many of the conflicts she has narrated in the
novel itself. Isadora remains witty and wry and honest in the second installment.
Though the brittleness of the latest Isadora may be distasteful to some and the
barrage of sexual exploits, heterosexual and lesbian, a bit predictable, none
of these peccadillos are inconsistent with the pleasures available to the famous
Isadora and the pressures that notoriety tends to exert on the successful artist.

860   Kaufman, Sue. **Diary of a Mad Housewife**. New York: Bantam Books,
       1975. 293p. $1.50. ISBN 0553026356.
Originally published in 1967, this novel in the form of a diary fluctuates between
humor and hysteria as Bettina Balser, an affluent Manhattan matron, pours
out her terrors about daily life as a sort of therapy. At the beginning of the
novel, she inventories her many fears—everything from elevators to rapists to
fatal diseases. All of these fears it turns out are symbols for the young woman's
fears of the complexities that urban modern life serves up daily. There is much
wry observation about marriage and children and anxiety here. Its appearance
in the mid-'60s signalled a new approach to women's fiction, which centered
on the daily experience of the ordinary woman searching for identity and
meaning in her superficial life.

861   Kollontai, Aleksandra Mikhailovna, 1872-1952. **Love of Worker Bees**.
       London: Virago, 1977. 232p. $7.95. ISBN 0860680053. LC 78-305830.
Kollontai brings to life her concern with the complex connections between
personal life and political commitments in these three little-known pieces of
fiction dealing with men's and women's lives during and immediately following
the Bolshevik Revolution (originally published in Russia in 1923). Included
in this volume are the novel *Vasilisa Malygina* (originally published in New York
as *Red Love* and in England as *Free Love*), and two short stories, "Three Generations" and "Sisters." Sheila Rowbotham writes in her excellent afterword
to the collection: "though completely opposed to those feminists who thought
there could be women's emancipation within capitalism, [Kollontai] also
fought continually inside the Bolshevik Party against the kind of complacency
which failed to take sexual relations and the positive creation of a new culture
of daily life seriously. She wanted complete equality between the sexes, realizing
that this necessitated big changes in the structure of the family, the organization of domestic work and the economic position of women. . . . In all three
of these stories the relationship between women are close ones. Vasilisa Malygina
overcomes her jealousy for her beautiful rival and is able to see the other woman's
vulnerability—expressed in the remarkable letter to her. In 'Three Generations,'

Olga Sergeevna's daughter affirms her love for her mother despite their very
different views on sexuality. 'Sisters' is a story of the growth of solidarity
between a prostitute and a deserted wife." Cathy Porter translated the three
pieces and writes the introduction to the volume. Readers will find more analysis
of Kollontai's life and her fiction and non-fiction writing in Sheila Rowbotham's
Women, Resistance and Revolution (1972).

862   Larsen, Nella. **Passing.** New York: Negro Universities Press, 1969.
        (Repr. of 1929 ed.). 215p. $9.50. ISBN 0837115418. LC 73-82056.
Highly praised when it was published, *Passing* tells a tale shocking to the audience
of the '20s and '30s—of a light-skinned black woman who "passes" herself in
white society, marries a white man, and never reveals her ancestry until she
accidentally encounters a childhood friend. The encounter triggers feelings of
remorse and guilt in Clare Kendry, the main character. Clare never truly faces
her husband's bigoted rage because of the summary ending: she either kills
herself or is mysteriously killed, in this novel, interesting for the light it sheds
on the reaction to racially mixed couples during the period.

863   Larsen, Nella. **Quicksand.** New York: Negro Universities Press, 1969.
        (Repr. of 1928 ed.). 301p. $11.25. ISBN 037111277. LC 74-75553.
The tragedy of the major character, Helga Crane, a woman born of black and
Danish blood, has little to do with her race and a great deal more to do with
her sex. Though Helga is dissatisfied at first with the hypocrisy of "Negro
society" and chafes under the oppression she feels her lot as private school
teacher to be, her longstanding dissatisfaction resides in her longing for happiness
itself: "always she had wanted, not money, but the things which money could
give, leisure, attention, beautiful surroundings." Her search takes her to New
York, to Denmark, and back to New York after refusing a Danish husband.
She marries an evangelist preacher "in the confusion of seductive repentance."
The author sketches her husband as an unpleasant, even repugnant man. Worn
out by childbearing, Helga's thoughts again turn to luxury and escape. The
novel ends on the depressing note of Helga's giving birth to a fifth child after
a lingering illness.

864   Lavin, Mary, 1912- . **The Shrine, and Other Stories.** Boston: Houghton
        Mifflin, 1977. 156p. $6.95. ISBN 0395257735. LC 77-24044.
An American who has lived and written in Ireland for many years and has emerged
as a major Irish writer, Lavin writes frequently of the experiences of women
alone, either unmarried or isolated in loveless marriages. In this collection,
she writes of a daughter's attempts to cope with her mother's senility, a prudish
nun, a disillusioned bride, and a young woman's religious iconoclasm—all
against the backdrop of Irish life and thought. Lavin has a sharp Irish eye for
the comic and well-trained ear for Irish dialogue. Her novels include *The House
of Clewe Street* (1945) and *Mary O'Grady* (1950). The short story is her métier;
see *Collected Stories* (Houghton Mifflin, 1971).

865   Lawrence, David Herbert, 1885-1930. **The Fox.** New York: Bantam
        Books, 1967. 105p. $1.50. ISBN 0553108484.

Lawrence first published this novella about two single women devoted to each other and living together on a farm in rural England in 1923. Their tranquillity is interrupted by the presence of a young man who decides to marry one of the women, and who wishes the other woman dead. The chosen woman, March, and the young man eventually take the predictable postures one expects in the Lawrentian schema: female passivity yields to male power. At the end of the novella, the man reflects of his wife whom he is taking away from England to Canada to begin a new life: "And then he would have her, and he would have his own life at last. He chafed, feeling he hadn't got his own life. He would never have it till she yielded and slept in him. Then he would have all his own life as a young man and a young male, and she would have all her own life as a woman and a female. There would be no more of this awful straining. She would not be a man any more, an independent woman with a man's responsibility. Nay, even the responsibility for her own soul she would have to commit to him. He knew it was so, and obstinately held out against her, waiting for the surrender." The lesbian theme, though muted, is nonetheless present.

866   Lawrence, David Herbert, 1885-1930. **Lady Chatterley's Lover.** New York: New American Library. 1972. $1.25.
This classic erotic novel banned in 1928 for obscenity, proclaims Lawrence's gospel of sexuality, in which woman is the passive and fertile recipient, man the all-powerful and active depositor of seed. Women's studies courses will find much to debate in this phallocentric novel.

867   Lawrence, David Herbert, 1885-1930. **The Rainbow.** New York: Viking Press, 1973. 495p. $6.00. ISBN 0670589144. LC 67-51882.
Although Kate Millett has criticized Lawrence's sexist worldview, feminist critic Carolyn Heilbrun praises Lawrence in *The Rainbow* (1915) for creating a strong female character emblematic of "the myth of the new female creation born into a world the male spirit has despoiled." Ursula is the hero of this novel and a moral and stable character earnestly searching for truth. In that way, her heroism can be viewed as a quest from which she emerges triumphant at the end of the novel. Her quest includes the tripartite search for knowledge, education and experience, each of which she finds wanting as she defines what she wishes to realize from the self. The novel offers a fine contrast and comparison between mother and daughter and the patterns each chooses to pursue in search of fulfillment. Anna, the mother, seeks to fulfill herself in the repetition of childbearing and childrearing, a pattern that Ursula rejects from the outset. *The Rainbow* is followed by Lawrence's most major novel, *Women In Love*, in which Ursula marries with less heroic implications.

868   Lawrence, David Herbert, 1885-1930. **Sons and Lovers.** New York: Viking Press, 1968. 622p. bibliog. $5.95. ISBN 0670657646. LC 68-28024.
In this autobiographical novel, the son/artist struggles between the engulfing love of the mother and his compelling need to love a younger woman, Miriam Leivers. The theme of *Sons and Lovers*, on one level, becomes the powerful rivalry between women competing for male affection and allegiance. Another significant theme to feminist critics is Lawrence's concentration on the

importance of the nurturing function of the female in the male artist's creative development.

869*   Leduc, Violette, 1907-1972. **Thérèse and Isabelle.** New York: Farrar, Straus and Giroux, 1967. 113p. LC 67-13389.
Thérèse and Isabelle emerge in stark relief against their vaguely sketched boarding school background. The narrative is a montage of erotic scenes between the two young women—rendered in impressionistic scenes of caresses, snatches of conversations, and interruptions. The tension of their forbidden pleasure charges each scene. Leduc's writings have been much praised by de Beauvoir, Sartre, and Camus as successful experiments in new lyrical fiction. The immediacy of sensual experience is the essence of her work. Originally intended as a section of Leduc's very popular *La Bâtard, Thérèse and Isabelle* received separate publication in France before the larger work was published.

870   Le Guin, Ursula K., 1929- . **Earthsea.** Emeryville, CA: Parnassus Press, 1968. $6.95. ISBN 0874660572.
Earthsea contains *A Wizard of Earthsea, The Tombs of Atuan,* and *The Farthest Shore.* Of the three, *The Tombs of Atuan* will be of most interest to women's studies. The main character of *Tombs* is a young girl child, Anna, who is taken from her home at an early age, renamed Tenar, and consecrated as a high priestess. The adventures that befall Tenar chronicle symbolically the maturation of a mind. The escalation of possible choices defines the spiritual growth of Tenar, a female science-fiction character of depth and complexity. *Earthsea* is recommended to young readers, too. Much as Tolkein's work appeals to a wide age range, Le Guin's work transcends age differences.

871   Le Guin, Ursula K., 1929- . **The Left Hand of Darkness.** New York: Ace Books, 1976. 304p. $1.95.
Le Guin's work suggests the possibility of an androgynous fiction in which characters can transcend their gender roles in search of adventure. Le Guin writes a Tolkein-like tale filled with invented language and rosters of characters hailing from exotic galactic locations and involved in complex conspiracies that take the characters on involved and perilous journeys over the mythical terrain. Le Guin was recently the focus of a special issue of *Science-Fiction Studies* (no. 7, Nov. 1975), to which she responded in the subsequent issue (no. 8, March 1976).

872   Lessing, Doris May, 1919- . **African Stories.** New York: Popular Library, 1975. 670p. $1.50. ISBN 0445084375. LC 65-23003.
Growing up in Southern Rhodesia as she did, Lessing's intimacy with African political and social geography has shaped her work from the first. *The Grass Is Singing* and *This Was the Old Chief's Country* (her first two books) were, along with the work of Isak Dinesen, among the few works available that dealt fictionally with Africa. This collection spans Lessing's career and includes every story she wrote about Africa, plus the novella, *Hunger.* A few of these stories appear in *Stories* (1978), but this collection makes especially good sense in light of its African focus. Among the stories: "The Black Madonna" (a

Lessing favorite); "No Witchcraft for Sale"; "The Words He Said"; and "The Story of Two Dogs."

873   Lessing, Doris May, 1919- . **Briefing For a Descent into Hell.** New York: Knopf; distr. New York: Random House, 1971. 308p. $6.95. ISBN 0394421981. LC 71-136325.

Lessing categorizes this book "Inner Space Fiction/for there is never anywhere to go but in." This novel came after the five novels of the "Children of Violence" series, and *The Golden Notebook.* Charles Watkins, a hospitalized professor being treated for loss of his memory, speaks lyrically throughout the novel of his inner voyage. His thought, dreams, and perceptions are counterpointed against the linear, diagnostic reportage of the psychiatrists treating him. Lessing's point of view appears to be close to that of psychiatrist R. D. Laing (*The Divided Self; The Politics of the Family*), who has posited that the apparently insane may have a surer grasp on reality than their "normal" fellow human beings. This is one of the few pieces of Lessing fiction where the main character is male. However, Charles Watkins transcends gender identity. His description of inner space and his revelation of a most intimate self strike familiar chords of Lessing's preoccupation in all her novels: specifically, behind every simple label and easy summation lies a more complex and truer meaning.

874   Lessing, Doris May, 1919- . **The Four-Gated City.** New York: Knopf; distr. New York: Random House, 1969. 613p. $11.95. ISBN 0394425189. LC 69-16611.

The concluding novel of Lessing's series, "Children of Violence" (see annotation to volume 1, *Martha Quest*, for complete list of titles), seems to make radical departures from the first four. The opening finds Martha not only transported to England from her homeland, Rhodesia, but also transported into a very different political and psychological landscape. The predominant concerns have become far more introspective, psychic, and mystical. Eventually, madness takes over as a dominating reality that Martha and other central characters must contend with, while politics is in some ways moved from the center stage it held in the first four volumes. One realizes as the novel progresses, and particularly in its apocalyptic conclusion, that for Lessing (if not for all her characters), there is an increasing convergence of social, political, and psychic realities in a way that denies the primacy of any one of these over the others. There is an important tension in the work between its far-ranging historical and political scope and the apparent isolation and suffocating confinement of the central characters.

875   Lessing, Doris May, 1919- . **The Golden Notebook.** New York: Simon and Schuster, 1962. 567p. $9.95. ISBN 0671287702. LC 62-12412.

"*The Golden Notebook* is Doris Lessing's most important work and has left its mark upon the ideas and feelings of a whole generation of young women," wrote Elizabeth Hardwick in the *New York Times Book Review.* Anna Wulf, one of Lessing's most compelling and complex modern women, uses separate notebooks to record political, personal, and artistic aspects of her life, illustrating the fragmentation and filtering process that individuals use in evading life as a whole. Anna's relentless search for wholeness and truth results in the "golden notebook" and freedom from the arbitrary blocks she had created for herself. Lessing has said that she considers *The Golden Notebook* her most truthful work because of its complexity.

876   Lessing, Doris May, 1919- . **The Grass Is Singing.** New York: Thomas Y. Crowell, 1975. 245p. ISBN 0690007477. LC 50-9419.
In this, Lessing's first novel, she explores her Rhodesian roots in a novel in which sex, race, and class are the important components. The plot revolves around Mary Turner, the dissatisfied and deeply disturbed wife of an unsuccessful farmer, who obsessively turns to a black man for excitement in an attempt to sculpt a relationship that can only result in tragic consequences, given the social milieu of Rhodesia.

877   Lessing, Doris May, 1919- . **The Habit of Loving.** New York: Thomas Y. Crowell, 1957. 311p. $6.95. ISBN 0690005016. LC 58-9187.
The title story of this collection involves a sixtyish romantic writer and play producer who looks for love from a woman much younger than he. Although she is undergoing her own crisis in facing middle age, he thinks of her as a child, as that feeds his own romantic notions of their relationship. He finds it unbearable to relate to her as other than a narcissistic woman-child whose grace and charm exist solely to support his own fantasies of romantic love. Among other stories in the collection: "The Words He Said," "The Woman," "Pleasure," "A Mild Attack of Locusts."

878   Lessing, Doris May, 1919- . **Landlocked.** New York: New American Library, 1970. 280p. $3.95. LC 64-22405.
Volume 4 of Lessing's series, "Children of Violence" (see annotation to volume 1, *Martha Quest*, for complete list of titles), brings many of the involvements of the first three novels to a close, but only painstakingly, slowly. Much of the novel conveys a feeling of disintegration, irresolution, and emotional stultification, as Martha's second marriage drags on indefinitely beyond the point of its obvious failure, as her father's terminal illness drags on, and as the end of World War II ushers in a climate of renewed conservatism and political repression. A momentary high point in this sequence is Martha's love affair with Thomas, her first experience of real passion; but even this is an encounter of despair, ultimately doomed. Martha eventually gathers energy to make her long-dreamed-of trip to England.

879   Lessing, Doris May, 1919- . **A Man and Two Women: Stories.** New York: Simon and Schuster, 1963. 316p. $5.00. LC 63-19277.
In addition to the title story, this collection contains some of Lessing's finest, for example, "One off the Short List" and "To Room Nineteen." Lessing's material here is the bitterness and disappointment of marriage and love. Her people are predominantly drawn from the ranks of peripherally arty and successful middle-class neurotics estranged from their lives, themselves, and from each other. Lessing's character, Susan, in "To Room Nineteen," a desperately unhappy housewife and mother unable to pinpoint the source of her unhappiness, is one of her finest creations. This is a good introduction to Lessing's work in courses where time does not permit exploration of her novels.

880   Lessing, Doris May, 1919- . **Martha Quest**. New York: New American
       Library, 1970. 248p. $3.95.

This is the first in Lessing's amazing five-volume sequence of novels cumulatively
titled "Children of Violence." The series spans a writing and publication period
of nearly two decades, which makes even more awesome its continuity of
character and theme and the entirely convincing evolution from novel to novel.
This continuity is particularly evident in the first four volumes (*Martha Quest,
A Proper Marriage, A Ripple from the Storm*, and *Landlocked*), which form a
whole in themselves in terms of geographical locale (Rhodesia), style, and focus.
The fifth and final volume, *The Four-Gated City*, takes the major character,
Martha, out of Rhodesia to England, into a different psychological and political
context, conveyed by a different literary treatment as well. However, the
reader who sticks with the series until the end will feel that even the departures
of volume 5 are more apparent than real. Though Lessing's themes are always
many and complex, "Children of Violence" does speak powerfully to the
experience of middle-class white women. It also brings to life the motivations,
passions, contradictions, and pain of the Left in Western industrialized societies.
The first volume, *Martha Quest*, takes Lessing's main character from early to
late adolescence in Rhodesia of the late 1930s, through loneliness, sexual
confusion, suffocation within the family, and an unfocused intellectual/
political passion, to her first taste of independence—which she surprises herself by relinquishing almost immediately and whimsically for marriage.

881   Lessing, Doris May, 1919- . **The Memoirs of a Survivor**. New York:
       Knopf; distr. New York: Random House, 1975. 213p. $6.95. ISBN
       0394496337. LC 74-21294.

In her fable of apocalyptic vision, Lessing comments on crumbling society even
as she tells the very simple love story of Emily, a waif aged sixteen, and her
lover, Gerald, a Robin-Hood sort of gang leader who cares for homeless, aban-
doned children. This is a novel about abandonment and responsibility in a nameless and disordered large city like London. A familiar Lessing parable emerges:
no matter how difficult and futile, our only salvation is to take responsibility
for the salvation of others.

882   Lessing, Doris May, 1919- . **A Proper Marriage**. New York: New
       American Library, 1970. 345p. $3.95.

This second volume of Lessing's series, "Children of Violence" (see annotation
to volume 1, *Martha Quest*, for complete list of titles), is in some ways the most
compelling and painful of the five, in its depiction of a woman's alienation in
marriage and the ambivalence of pregnancy (unplanned) and childbirth. Many
of the themes are by now very familiar, but Lessing brings them to life with
a freshness perhaps attributable to the fact that they were anything *but* familiar
in the early 1950s, when this book was written. The novel ends with Martha's
brave and frightening decision to leave not only her husband, but her daughter
as well, in an attempt to reconnect with some of the passions, commitments,
and promise left unfulfilled in adolescence.

883   Lessing, Doris May, 1919- . **A Ripple from the Storm**. New York:
       New American Library, 1970. 262p. $3.95.

Volume 3 of Lessing's series, "Children of Violence" (see annotation to volume 1, *Martha Quest*, for complete list of titles), carries Martha out of her first marriage into renewed independence and the first flush of socialist commitment, within the context of the white Left in racist Rhodesia. Most impressive in this volume is Lessing's depiction of the workings of the Left, a depiction that is critical and alert to the naïveté and contradictions of the political movement without yielding to cynicism. Martha is shown working through the difficult transition from initial inexperienced idealism to a political commitment grounded in a deeper understanding of society and history. At the same time, we see her falling once again into a bad marriage, almost in spite of herself. Lessing manages beautifully to convey the crazy contradictions of the World War II period, with Britain, its colonies, and the United States in the embarrassing predicament of being allied with Communist Russia.

884   Lessing, Doris May, 1919- . **Stories.** New York: Knopf; distr. New York: Random House, 1978. 626p. $15.00. ISBN 0394500091. LC 77-20709.

An obvious purchase for an individual or library who can afford only one volume of Lessing short stories. Thirty-four of the stories here are taken from three major Lessing collections: *The Habit of Loving* (1957), *A Man and Two Women* (1963), and *The Temptation of Jack Orkney* (1972). The novella "The Other Woman" appeared in *Five*, a collection of short novels. Realism is what Lessing has said she admires most in good writing; realism is her métier. Whether writing of marriage, madness, or sexuality (often all three at once), she writes in plain language about the most complex of behaviors; and she consistently states in theme and plot that even the most ordered and simple situations are riddled with complexity. Lessing's own preferences among the stories in this volume are "One off the Short List," "A Man and Two Women," and "To Room Nineteen."

885   Lessing, Doris May, 1919- . **The Summer Before the Dark.** New York: Knopf; distr. New York: Random House, 1973. 273p. $8.95. ISBN 0394484282. LC 72-11044.

Kate Brown, Lessing's protagonist, is faced with a mid-life crisis: freed of family responsibilities for a summer, she takes a job as interpreter at an international conference and takes on a young lover. In the course of the novel, Kate is forced to confront all of the stereotypes of traditional womanhood that have shaped her life: beauty, responsibility, fidelity. Although Kate explores the schizophrenic experience, Lessing brings her back to reality by novel's end, when she returns home. This might be of special interest to older students returning to or beginning college.

886*   Le Sueur, Meridel. **Women on the Breadlines.** Cambridge, MA: West End Press, 1977. 21p. $1.00.

A radical author of the '30s, Le Sueur was blacklisted for over thirty years and her writings restricted to the radical press (*New Masses, The Anvil*). Now in her late 70s, she is being rediscovered by the women's movement and her work reprinted by West End Press. Her short stories and pieces of reportage are distinguished by their vivid evocation of the reality of poverty, unemployment, and oppression and by their particular concern for the struggles of poor women. Each piece in this collection focuses on women and is narrated in the first person by a woman. "Women on the Breadlines" (1932) sketches a bleak portrait of the scene at a city free employment bureau when no jobs are to be had. The woman in "Sequel to Love" (1935) is a single mother whose child has been taken from her and who is now held in an asylum in an attempt to force her to undergo sterilization. "They Follow Us Girls" (1935) is about the particular plight of unemployed women in the cities. The final piece, "Salvation Home" (1939), takes place in a home for "unwed mothers." Eight pieces by Le Sueur written between 1929 and 1946, including reportage, short stories, and humoristic pieces, are gathered together in *Harvest* (West End Press, 1977). Women again figure prominently, and abortion and spinsterhood are among the experiences depicted. Selections from Le Sueur's later writings (1947-1958) are reprinted in *Song For My Time* (West End Press, 1977). Subtitled "Stories of the Period of Repression," this collection evokes the sufferings of the Cold War period, McCarthyism, and the Korean War—the period of Le Sueur's own forced obscurity. All three collections are available from West End Press, Box 697, Cambridge, MA 02139.

887   Lichtenberg, Jacqueline. **Unto Zeor, Forever.** Garden City, NY:
       Doubleday, 1978. 237p. $7.95. ISBN 0385135661. LC 77-12871.
Lichtenberg's fresh plot belongs to the purest strain of science fiction. Two interdependent but absolutely different races (the Gens and the Simes) have evolved from the human race as we know it. Because the Gens manufacture selyn in their bodies—which they cannot use, but which the Simes need in order to survive—the process of this exchange makes the life between the two races incredibly complex and dangerous. The sexual parallels scream out here, though Lichtenberg uses a very technical and detailed vocabulary to explain the intricate selyn transfusion process, leaving the reader to speculate on the social intricacies of the politics between Simes and Gens (men and women). This superb science fiction work is a sequel to Lichtenberg's *House of Zeor*. Among other science fiction novels that metaphorically posit the relationship between the sexes in a visionary world where androgyny imposes order and resolution is Vonda McIntyre's *Dreamsnake* (Houghton Mifflin, 1978). Here the protagonist is a woman and a healer, independent yet loving, who uses snakes for healing and consequently is dependent upon them.

888   McCarthy, Mary Therese, 1912- . **The Company She Keeps.** New York:
       Harcourt Brace Jovanovich, 1960. 304p. $7.50. ISBN 0151203571.
Narcissism, self-analysis and guilt are recurrent themes in this brilliant collection of McCarthy short stories whose central character, Margaret, reappears at different stages of her development as a woman. In the first story, "Cruel and Barbarous Treatment," she is a young woman satirically sketched by McCarthy in the process of shedding her first husband for the object of her adulterous passion. This first story is a showpiece for McCarthy's merciless dissection of female motives; we watch Margaret watch herself as she perceives herself the center of her husband's and lover's attention and the object of the envy and shock of her friends in her roles as Young Wife, Femme Fatale, and Young Divorcée. By the last story, "Ghostly Father I Confess," Margaret is a wiser, much more

experienced woman fusing her background as a Catholic girl and young woman with her present as the unhappy wife of a successful architect. The narrative structure of the last story posits Margaret's experience with her psychoanalyst as parallel to her roles as young confessor with her parish priest, as subservient and adoring daughter with her father, and admiring student with her mentor-husband. McCarthy is particularly incisive in capturing Margaret's awareness of her narcissistic behaviors, and of how her desire to please men, even her analyst, stunts her growth and independence again and again.

889   McCarthy, Mary Therese, 1912- . **The Group.** New York: New American
        Library, 1972. 397p. $1.25.

Mary McCarthy's painstaking and satiric dissection of the lives of eight Vassar friends of the class of '33 is one of the finest women's novels in American literature. This novel (1963), along with Betty Friedan's *The Feminine Mystique*, marked the genesis of women's liberation. McCarthy's characters typified middle-class, well-educated American womanhood coping with the daily realities of marriage, children, divorce, careers, affairs, disillusionment—and mainly, it seems, with boredom. The most vivid characterization is given to Lakey (Elinor Eastlake), who has acknowledged her lesbianism by the end of the novel. Interestingly the lesbian issue threatens to divide "the group" even as it threatens to divide women today: "it occurred to them all that Lakey, who had always been frightening and superior, would now look down on them for not being lesbians." However, it is the men who come off particularly badly in this book—oppressors, bigots, children, psychopaths—even the most successful of them is a failure. The unifying thread to this novel is the marriage of Kay Strong, the first of "the group" to be married after commencement, and her suicide and funeral almost ten years later. The vocabulary of the novel is informed by references to the social thought that ushered in women's liberation: Freud, Spock, and Margaret Mead.

890   McCullers, Carson (Smith), 1917-1967. **The Ballad of the Sad Café
        and Other Stories.** New York: Bantam Books, 1967. 152p. $1.75.
        ISBN 0553115324.

Set in a café owned by Miss Amelia Evans and filled with the commanding presence of a hunchback, Cousin Lymon, the title story could properly be illustrated by the photography of Diane Arbus. It is a story that illustrates McCullers's fondness for the grotesque and the inexplicable in its portrayal of a triangle energized by revenge. Other stories carry out the bizarre *leit motif* that is a hallmark of McCullers's craft of fiction.

891   McCullers, Carson (Smith), 1917-1967. **The Heart Is a Lonely Hunter.**
        Boston: Houghton Mifflin, 1967. 273p. $6.95. ISBN 0395079780.
        LC 40-10298.

McCullers wrote this striking first novel when she was 22 (1940). Set in a southern town, the novel's chief character, John Singer, is a deaf-mute. His is a life of solitude and observation; he has lost his best friend, another mute, who was taken away by relatives and committed to a mental hospital. Singer wanders about the town from café to rooming house, and because he cannot talk, he becomes the silent confidante of several townspeople. The narrative technique is simple and beautiful; the residents of the town appear before the reader each a separate reality yet part of the greater pattern of the town. Mike Kelly, an adolescent girl who would rather be a mechanic than a secretary, is one of the strong characters who tells her story to Singer. Each character is a cameo of working-class life before World War II in the South, whether white or black. McCullers appreciates the experience of the adolescent girl. In *Member of the Wedding* (1946), she creates twelve-year-old Frankie, whose epiphany comes in the form of a new experience presented by an older brother's wedding. Complex and uncontrollable Frankie brushes against violence, confronts sex, makes a friend, and painfully comes of age before the end of the novel.

892   McCullers, Carson (Smith), 1917-1967. **Reflections in a Golden Eye.** Boston: Houghton Mifflin, 1941. 85p. $4.95. ISBN 0395079799. LC 41-2706.

When *Reflections* first appeared, the reviewers praised McCullers for her powerful writing but took her to task for the "morbid and bizarre" characters and plot. The emotional territory that McCullers covers here is set against the background of a southern military post in peacetime. The female characters—one, an adultress and ultra-sensual; the other, an invalid and ultra-sensitive—beautifully contrast against the military forms that stifle and imprison both of them. It is a novel of violence, deviance, insanity, voyeurism—strange and various as human beings are strange and various. The relationships between the officers and their wives are indeed destructive and, in the end, just as peculiar as the undefined relationships between the women and the two subordinate men who asexually and worshipfully stalk them.

893*   MacKenzie, Compton, 1883- . **Extraordinary Women: Theme and Variations.** New York: Macy-Masius, 1928. 391p. LC 28-22880.

MacKenzie depicts the lesbian-oriented, amorous international adventures of wealthy and beautiful young women whose most pressing obligations include frolicking with each other at expensive spas and pursuing each other on the grounds of exotic villas. Each chapter is introduced by an epigraph from Sappho. For an analysis of Compton MacKenzie's *Extraordinary Women* and other lesbian novels of the period based on similar themes of seduction among the wealthy classes with Sappho presiding, see Bertha Harris, "The More Profound Nationality of Their Lesbianism: Lesbian Society in Paris in the 1920's," in *Amazon Expedition* (Times Change Press, 1973).

894   MacKintosh, Elizabeth [Tey, Josephine, pseud.], 1896-1952. **To Love and Be Wise.** New York: Berkeley, 1975. 255p. $1.25. ISBN 0425028984.

A turnabout in sex roles is the device upon which this brief but elegant mystery story hinges. The dénouement is the novel's *tour de force*. Though *To Love and Be Wise* is probably the most appealing of Tey's books to feminist readers, other delightful mysteries by this ingenious writer include *The Franchise Affair* (Berkeley Pub., 1971); *Miss Pym Disposes* (Berkeley Pub., 1971); *A Shilling for Candles* (Berkeley, 1972); and *The Daughter of Time* (Berkeley Medallion Books).

895   Mailer, Norman. **An American Dream.** New York: Dial Press, 1964.
        270p. $6.95. ISBN 0803701306. LC 64-20280.

Perhaps no writer has written so vividly about the MASCULINE experience.
Sample: "I pulled the trigger as if I were squeezing the softest breast of the
softest pigeon which ever flew, still a woman's breast takes me now and then
to the pigeon on that trigger. . . . " As usual, Mailer spends himself in creating
a supermacho character, Stephen Rojack, who compares most physical objects
in the world to some part of a woman's anatomy at the expense of realistic
characterization or coherent plot. The novel illustrates many of Kate Millett's
most salient points in *Sexual Politics.*

896   Mansfield, Katherine, 1888-1923. **Stories.** New York: Vintage Books,
        1956. 348p. $2.95. ISBN 0394700368. LC 56-46420.

The stories here were selected and with an introduction by Elizabeth Bowen,
who comments that Katherine Mansfield was "compelled to experiment" and
thus leaves no typical Mansfield story for the reader and critic to analyze. She
uses prose in a deceptively simple, transparent manner; it is difficult to locate
her style. Yet, this young writer (she died at 34 of tuberculosis) revolutionized
the art of the short story. Her masterpieces have been included here as well as
some of her lesser-known stories, chosen by Bowen because each "exhibits
some characteristic of hers and hers only." Included are: "The Little Governess,"
"Prelude," "At the Bay," "Bliss," "Je ne parle pas francais," "The Man Without
a Temperament," "The Stranger," "The Daughters of the Late Colonel," "The
Voyage," "The Garden Party," "Six Years After"—and many more. Elizabeth
Bowen's discussion of Mansfield's art serves as a valuable introduction to the
collection.

897   Marshall, Paule, 1929- . **Brown Girl, Brownstones.** New York: Random
        House, 1959; repr. Chatham, NJ: Chatham Bookseller, 1972. 310p.
        $7.95. ISBN 0911860118. LC 70-180041.

We first meet Selina, a Barbadian-American girl, at age ten. She is living in a
street of Brooklyn brownstones populated by West Indians in a changing neighborhood during the late 1930s. Marshall's handling of the background and problems of growing up in such a neighborhood is impressive; this is her first novel.
The characters are memorable, especially Selina, but it is the brownstones,
beautiful, ravaged and silently poetic, that shape the novel and its meaning.
Marshall's technical skills in handling characterizations transcend sex, type,
and age. A collection of stories, *Soul Clap Hands and Sing* (orig. 1961; repr.
Chatham Bookseller, 1971), shows her virtuosity. Here the leading character
in each story is an aging man of color.

898   Marshall, Paule, 1929- . **The Chosen Place. The Timeless People.**
        New York: Avon Books, 1976. $1.95.

Published in 1969, Marshall's novel of the poor black inhabitants of a remote
West Indian island, Bournehills, describes lovingly the plight of a forgotten
culture. Merle Kinbona, a black woman of great spirit and integrity, stands
at the center of this complex novel, which pits the old ways against the new,
substantial values against tawdry and temporal ones, a natural environment
against the "improvements" of technology. Tropical underdevelopment takes

second place in the narrative to the superb psychological drama enacted among the open, West Indian woman Merle, the Jewish American research project director, and his ambitious, patrician young wife. The love interest between Merle and Saul is a profound literary achievement in its depiction of a relationship of great dignity and purity, which transcends the color barrier. Paule Marshall is a major black writer; this novel is her most powerful work.

899   Meriwether, Louise. **Daddy Was a Number Runner.** New York: Pyramid Books, 1971. 188p. $1.25. ISBN 0515040312. LC 71-98887.
Meriwether's first novel is the story of twelve-year-old Francie's growing up in Harlem as the daughter of a numbers runner during the late '30s. A novel of the grim reality of poverty and violence in ghetto life, it is also a novel that honestly probes the lives and feelings of those who attempt to survive in this world. Despite flashes of humor, the world filtered through the penetrating eye of a young girl is a hopeless place. "We was all poor and black and apt to stay that way, and that was that," Francie concludes on the novel's last page.

900   Miller, Isabel, 1924- . **Patience and Sarah.** Greenwich, CT: Fawcett Publications, 1976. 192p. $1.50. ISBN 044922953X.
Patience and Sarah's love relationship gets an honest and unmincing portrayal, including their beginning a new life together on a farm during the nineteenth century.

901   Mitchell, Margaret, 1900-1949. **Gone with the Wind.** New York: Macmillan, 1936. 1037p. $8.95. LC 36-27334.
A classic, *Gone with the Wind* offers a panoply of female images and stereotypes from bitch to saint, from Scarlet to Melanie, accompanied by supporting black women cast as loving mammies and stupid servants. The novel seized the American imagination in 1936 like no literary event before it or since, and it understandably shows up on many women's studies syllabi treating literature and the feminine mystique.

902   Morrison, Toni. **Song of Solomon.** New York: New American Library, 1978. $2.50.
Morrison's novel of family life in the South drawing on a rich tradition of black folklore, allegory, and fable, is one of the most important works of contemporary fiction to be written by a black woman in America. Comedy and tragedy blend in a novel of names and places that become a jigsaw puzzle of personal history. By reclaiming the history of buried names, family events, and places, a central character—"Milkman"—comes to realize that under the names and places are real events of meaning and significance to those who did the naming and lived the events. This is a book that celebrates the human dramas, mistakes, comedies and peccadillos that define the "real" history of "real people"— people like Morrison's memorable Macon Dead, Sing Byrd, Crowell Byrd, Pilate, Hagar, Milkman, and other unforgettable characters who come from places like Not Doctor Street, Solomon's Leap, Ryna's Gulch, and Shalimar. The novel won Morrison the 1978 National Book Critics Cricle Award, distinguishing its author as the first black woman to receive that honor.

903   Morrison, Toni. **Sula.** New York: Knopf; distr. New York: Random
         House, 1973. 174p. $7.95. ISBN 0394480449. LC 73-7278.

Morrison explores the risks involved in the friendship between two young black
women who have grown up together in the same small town. Sula Peace and
Nel Wright share an intimate background of adolescent experiences, but their
lives diverge when Sula leaves Medallion, Ohio, for college and later for a free
and roaming existence in the West, while Nel remains in Medallion to marry
young, have children, and absorb fully the social code of Medallion. Morrison's
sensitive portrait of the return of Sula to the town of her youth shows Sula
to be on a destructive path. Her iconclasm isolates her from family, friends,
lovers. In sleeping with any man she can find, Sula manifests her utter loneliness
and in sleeping with her best friend Nel's husband and later rejecting him, Sula
effectively cuts herself off from those for whom she feels the most. The stakes
are too high to undo the damage that she has heaped on the friendship. Morrison's humanity and compassion for both Sula and Nel is plainly visible in the
closing snapshot of Nel attending Sula's funeral, the only black mourner. Friendship between women has always been perilous, especially when their relationships with men may be jeopardized because of it. Morrison has written precisely
of the double-bind in female friendships. Morrison's most recent book, *Song
of Solomon* (Knopf, 1978), is a departure from her realistic treatment of interpersonal relationships among blacks. In this newest novel, Morrison combines
fantasy, allegory and folklore to celebrate four generations of black encurance
in the United States.

904   Mortimer, Penelope, 1918- . **The Pumpkin Eater.** Plainfield, VT:
         Daughters, 1975. 222p. $4.00. ISBN 0913780367. LC 75-16509.

This is a beautiful and ambitious book about a woman and her relationship with
her husband, Jake, and with her many children. Mortimer writes a gauzy narrative
filtered through the consciousness of the main character during a breakdown.
Mrs. Armitage (first name never given) has had four husbands and many children
by the time she is 27. Much of her life seems to have passed in a daze; she has
difficulty remembering her life with her husbands and seems not to remember
the pain of childbirth or even the difficulties of rearing children—though she
has been perpetually pregnant. She has an abortion, followed by a hysterectomy
and breakdown, but this is dimly remembered. Her husband had apparently
been unfaithful to her a number of times. At times his infidelity sparks an
unpleasant memory or a resentment hinging on the fact of her imprisonment
over the years in their house ironically shaped like a tower rather than a pumpkin
shell. The narrator concludes at novel's end: "I have tried to be honest with
you, although I suppose that you would really have been more interested in
my not being honest. Some of these things happened, and some were dreams.
They are all true, as I understood truth. They are all real, as I understood
reality." Two of Mortimer's other fine novels about women dealing with stress
over their dependent relationships with family, lovers, and husbands are *My
Friend Says It's Bullet-Proof* (1968) and *The Home* (1971).

905   Murasaki, Shikibu, b. 978? **The Tale of Genji.** New York: Knopf,
         1976. 2v. $25.00. ISBN 0394483286. LC 76-13680.

Edward Seidensticker's translation of *Genji monogatari* improves on the Arthur Waley translation of the late 1920s. Lady Murasaki, born in tenth-century Japan, was the daughter of a prominent public servant who later took his vows as a Buddhist priest. As a young woman, Lady Murasaki served in the court of the empress and learned much about its amorous intrigues and sexual politics. Her novel of court life in tenth- and eleventh-century Japan is considered by many critics to be the finest literary achievement by a woman in world literature. Set in Heian-kyo (Kyoto), Japan, the story has two major characters—Genji, the son of the emperor and his favorite, and Murasaki, his love. Much of the complexity of the love story derives from the power of lost love. Genji's mother dies when he is a small child, and Genji spends his life in romantic pursuit of women who resemble her. Murasaki has in fact been raised as Genji's daughter, and is the image of his mother. The highly romantic quality of the narrative surfaces in the constant allusions to and examples of poetry and calligraphy. The exchange of notes between lovers and friends raised courtship to the level of art. Though this tale's reputation as erotica has been much discussed, sexual incidents are conveyed frequently by allusion, never by explicit mention. Incidents of forcible sex, incestuous and hintingly incestuous liaisons, polygamy, and female jealousy occur frequently. Genji's mother dies from the strain of the jealous treatment she receives from other ladies of the court, while Murasaki's mother's life is marred by a similar situation. Women in *The Tale of Genji* are estranged from each other because of their competitive relationship to each other. As adored objects of male attention, their role is distinctively passive.

906   Murdoch, Iris. **The Nice and the Good.** New York: Viking Press, 1968. 378p. $5.75. ISBN 0670510254. LC 68-11412.

Murdoch uses many of her familiar techniques and themes with remarkable virtuosity in this quite moral novel of love and Gothic intrigue. Intertwining of lives and loves among disparate people is a frequent narrative technique employed by Murdoch. Here she does it with the object in mind of contrasting the differences between self-serving love and altruistic love. A prevailing sense of order is possibly Murdoch's most notable stylistic and thematic device. No matter how distinct and varied the characters, no matter how labyrinthine the plot, everything is set right in the end with the rigorous application of moral justice. Another of Murdock's ironic and comic novels of incredible complications— this one with incest, homosexuality, adultery, and attempted rape in the hopper—is *A Severed Head* (1961). Again, her achievement is to carry off an intelligent novel with numbers of characters interacting with each other in dazzling constellations of intrigues and dialogues. Murdoch's latest is entitled *The Sea, The Sea* (Viking Press, 1978).

907   Nabokov, Vladimir Vladimirovich, 1899-1978. **The Annotated Lolita.** Edited by Alfred Appel, Jr. New York: McGraw-Hill, 1970. 441p. bibliog. $15.00. ISBN 0070457298. LC 75-95819.

Lolita is the brilliant classic fantasy of the middle-aged white academic male. A comic masterpiece, *Lolita* is dominated by two presences—Lolita, the quintessential nymph, and Humbert-Humbert, her intellectual, tender, and lascivious father-figure lover and the novel's narrator. Narcissists both, Nabokov's lovers undertake an erotic odyssey across the neon wilderness of America. Highways, motel courts, roadside restaurants, and gas stations provide the concrete landscape of this tongue-in-cheek erotic novel. *Lolita* is included in this bibliography as an example of an outrageous caricature of the image of woman in literature and male fantasy. Lolita herself is the embodiment of the myth of the eternally thirteen-year-old, sexually receptive young woman conjured up by the pathetic but sensitive male consciousness obsessed by her elusive sexuality. "She was Lo, plain Lo, in the morning, standing four feet ten in one sock. She was Lola in slacks. She was Dolly at school. She was Delores on the dotted line. But in my arms she was always Lolita." For a topical, feminist discussion of pornography and erotica, see *Ms.* Magazine, November 1978, which contains articles by Kate Millett, Robin Morgan, Alice Walker, and others.

908   Nachman, Elana. **Riverfinger Women.** Plainfield, VT: Daughters, 1974. 183p. $4.00. ISBN 0913780316. LC 74-79916.

Though Inez Riverfingers, the narrator of this sensitively written and humorous novel about women loving each other, calls her effort "the pornographic novel of our lives," it is clear that she uses this term tongue-in-cheek. To Inez Riverfingers, the close friendship she shares with other women will only be considered pornographic in the context of a heterosexist society. Nachman writes playful prose and sprinkles the adventures of the seventeen-year-old lovers, Abby and Inez, with fantasy games and sprightly dialogue. Despite the lightness of touch, however, Nachman lets the reader know even amid the most breezy banter of the characters, that society's censure and society's power over their lives hover threateningly above.

909   Newman, Frances, d. 1928. **The Hard-Boiled Virgin.** New York: Boni and Liveright, 1926; repr. New York: Arno Press, 1977. 285p. $22.00. ISBN 0405100523. LC 76-51674.

The Hard-Boiled Virgin was Newman's first novel, written in 1926, when she was 43 years old (two years before her death). The novel is reprinted as part of the Arno Rediscovered Fiction by American Women series. Elizabeth Hardwick describes the work in her new introduction as, "an intense experiment in fictional form. The work is extremely conscious, mannered, and unrelenting in its commitment to a complex personal style. The material of the book is also complex and even though it was banned in Boston (perhaps for its title) it is a work of intellectual and social skepticism rather than one of sexual astonishment. . . . Frances Newman explains that it was her determination to 'express things only as a woman—as distinct from a man—could express.' " The story is one of a young southern girl's search for sexual initiation.

910   Nin, Anaïs, 1903-1977. **Cities of the Interior.** Chicago: Swallow Press, 1974. 589p. $15.00. ISBN 0804006652. LC 74-21884.

Ladders to Fire, Children of the Albatross, The Four-Chambered Heart, A Spy in the House of Love, Seduction of the Minotaur, and a part of *Solar Barque* are the five organically connected novels that comprise this volume. Nin called this her "endless novel," though each has appeared separately, published by different houses since 1946. Like the *Diary, Cities of the Interior* journeys the inscape of its three unforgettable women characters—Djuna, Lillian, and Sabrina. In her excellent introduction, "The Novel as Mobile in Space,"

Sharon Spencer points out that if one knows Otto Rank's psychoanalytic works, particularly *Art and Artist* and *Will Therapy and Truth and Reality*, which greatly influenced Nin in her artistic translation of the theory of the creative personality, then one begins to understand Nin's fiction, which sees the self as an endless process of change and psychic growth. The center of the person itself is a core in motion. Because fluidity informs each novel, the novels flow into each other; it is unnecessary to read them in sequential order because no boundaries separate the beginning of one character's inner voyage from the ending of another's. Nin states that the continuity of the novels was first established when they were published together under the title *Cities of the Interior* in 1959. Nin writes timeless fiction and characters who represent the numinous.

911   Nin, Anaïs, 1903-1977. **Delta of Venus: Erotica.** New York: Harcourt, Brace, Jovanovich, 1977. 250p. $10.00. ISBN 0151246564. LC 76-54856.

Nin says in her preface that her writing of erotica began as a lark to raise money for expenses. "So I began to write tongue-in-cheek, to become outlandish, inventive, and so exaggerated that I thought he [a book collector] would realize I was caricaturing sexuality." Nin only "decided to release the erotica [originally 1941] for publication [in 1976] because it shows the beginning efforts of a woman in a world that had been the domain of men." Among the stories: "The Hungarian Adventurer," "The Boarding School," "Artists and Models," "The Veiled Woman," "Elena," "The Basque and Bijou."

912   Nin, Anaïs, 1903-1977. **Under a Glass Bell, and Other Stories.** Chicago: Swallow Press, 1961. 101p. $1.50. ISBN 0804003025. LC 61-65444.

This 1948 collection of experimental short stories includes: "Houseboat," "The Mouse," "Under a Glass Bell," "The Mohican," "Je Suis le Plus Malade des Surrealists," "Ragtime," "The Labyrinth," "The All-Seeing," "The Eyes Journey," "The Child Born Out of the Fog," "Hejda," and "Birth." Psycho-analtic themes of individuation, of archetype, of dream symbolism, and of the unconscious are prominent in this collection. "Hejda," for example, sketches the life of an Oriental woman artist whose physical veiling and passive, diminutive art mirrors her inner conflicting need to assert her physical presence and to expand as a woman and artist.

913   Nin, Anaïs, 1903-1977. **Waste of Timelessness, and Other Early Stories.** Weston, CT: Magic Circle Press; distr. New York: Walker, 1977. 105p. $7.95. ISBN 0802705693. LC 74-28648.

A collection of short stories by the famous diarist: "Waste of Timelessness," "The Song in the Garden," "The Fear of Nice," "The Gypsy Feeling," "The Russian Who Did Not Believe in Miracles and Why," "The Dance Which Could Not Be Danced," "A Dangerous Perfume," "Red Roses," "Our Minds Are Engaged," "Alchemy," "Tishnar," "The Idealist," "The Peacock Feathers," "Faithfulness," "A Spoiled Party," and "A Slippery Floor."

914   Oates, Joyce Carol, 1938- . **Do With Me What You Will.** New York: Vanguard Press, 1973. 561p. $8.95. ISBN 0814907504. LC 73-83039.

This controversial novel was much criticized by feminists for Oates's apparent
endorsement of adulterous love as the conduit to greater personal freedom for
women. Elena is a brilliant if depressing Oates character—passive, narcissistic,
the sum of all the parts that the men in her life ask her to play. Afraid, guilty,
possessed during most of the novel, even her assertion in the "Summing Up"
section ("I'm not a thing") should not be taken as Oates's conviction that
Elena has achieved liberation. Oates's writing does not allow for easy character
transformation, and certainly not for facile interpretations.

915   Oates, Joyce Carol, 1938- . **Expensive People.** New York: Vanguard
       Press, 1968. 308p. $8.95. ISBN 0814901700. LC 68-8084.
A macabre, comic novel about phoniness in the suburbs, narrated in the first
person by Richard Everett, eighteen-year-old, 250-pound son and child murderer
of Nada Romanov Everett (really Nancy Romanov) and Elwood Everett, this
novel tells about hate and death in the American family. Richard hates his
mother, his mother hates her husband, and always seemingly has hated herself.
Nada/Nancy is at the center of this novel, a mother that no one deserves. "I
loved her more than ever, of course. Mothers who cringe and beg for love get
nothing, and they deserve nothing, but mothers like Nada who are always backing
out of the driveway draw every drop of love out of us." This could be the most
negative contemporary novel about mothers around.

916   Oates, Joyce Carol, 1938- . **A Garden of Earthly Delights.** New York:
       Vanguard Press, 1967. 440p. $8.95. ISBN 0814901719. LC 67-19288.
Oates has created a strong novel about rural people, especially about Clara
Walpole, a character lacking any compelling or extraordinary quality. Particularly
fine is Oates's detailing of a completely ordinary and inarticulate personality.
Clara Walpole is the prototype of a gallery of Oates's pathetic young women,
who seem at once to have no control over their own passive lives and yet manage
to manipulate those around them with amazing tenacity and effect.

917   Oates, Joyce Carol, 1938- . **The Goddess and Other Women.** New
       York: Vanguard Press, 1974. 468p. $8.95. ISBN 0814907458. LC
       74-81808.
Many critics agree that Oates's major talent reveals itself in her short stories.
These stories take shape in the terrifying crises of ordinary women living out
their daily lives. Housewives, college professors, career women, adolescents,
and young women drift toward destruction and death, caught in their own
erotic fantasies, trapped in neuroses, paralyzed by a pervasive feeling of nothingness. Among the stories here: "The Girl," "The Daughter," "The Maniac,"
"Magna Mater," "The Girl at the Edge of the Ocean," "The Goddess."

918   Oates, Joyce Carol, 1938- . **The Hungry Ghosts.** Los Angeles: Black
       Sparrow Press, 1974. 200p. $8.95. ISBN 0876852045. LC 74-2272.
The absurdity of academe binds these stories together. It is a setting that Oates
knows well, and though there is comedy in the glints of the pompous and
stunted personalities she pens, many of the insights are too acerbic for laughter.
Two stories are particularly fine. In "Up from Slavery," a young black male
professor takes revenge on a young female professor at a small college for

slighting his attentions. The form of revenge is an attack on her competence, which results in her losing her job. Those who have attended a Modern Language Association meeting will experience some discomfort in reading Oates's brilliant evocation of the tone and temper of that gathering in the story "Angst." In it, a young writer (Oates?) attends the MLA Convention to sit in on a panel discussing her work, only to find the papers are wild and pretentious distortions by people who neither understand her work nor recognize her even as she proclaims her identity in their midst.

919   Oates, Joyce Carol, 1938- . **Marriages and Infidelities: Short Stories.** New York: Vanguard Press, 1972. 497p. $8.95. ISBN 0814907180. LC 72-83348.

Many feminist critics feel that Oates's fiction lacks feminist insights. This collection of stories contains a portrait gallery of frightened, crippled, trapped, psychotic, and other psychologically mutilated women. Among the stories here: "The Sacred Marriage," "Puzzle," "Love and Death," "29 Inventions," "Plot," "Did You Ever Slip on Red Blood?," "Where I Lived and What I Lived For," "The Turn of the Screw," and "The Dead." Other important Oates story collections are *The Seduction and Other Stories* (Black Sparrow Press, 1975) and *The Hungry Ghosts* (Black Sparrow Press, 1975).

920   Oates, Joyce Carol, 1938- . **Them.** New York: Vanguard Press, 1969. 508p. $8.95. ISBN 0814906680. LC 74-89660.

Terror is Oates's staple. In an author's note, Oates tells the reader that the history behind this story took shape in Detroit during the 1962-1967 period, when she taught English at the University of Detroit. There she became the confidante of a student, the "Maureen Wendall" of this story. The story is a complex network of social injustice and violence within the Detroit working-class milieu. The problem of the Wendall women is feeling the need for men, which necessitates their coping with male brutality and violence in domestic and sexual arrangements. Oates forges a chain of double-binds that promises more emptiness than relief for the characters she creates. Ambiguous as the choices may be, Oates is compassionate in her characterizations of these desperate and hopeless lives in which men and women are equally victims and oppressors. The scene of the Detroit riots at the end of the novel verifies the chaos inherent in all human interaction and underscores the fearfulness of violence that can neither be controlled nor understood. Readers may be interested in Mary Kathryn Grant's *The Tragic Vision of Joyce Carol Oates* (Duke, 1978), the first full-length study of Oates's work.

921   O'Brien, Edna. **A Scandalous Woman, and Other Stories.** New York: Harcourt, Brace, Jovanovich, 1974. 151p. $6.95. ISBN 0151795584. LC 74-7366.

The stories included in this collection are: "A Scandalous Woman," "Over," "The Favorite," "The Creature," "Honeymoon," "A Journey," "Sisters," "Love Child," and "The House of My Dreams."

922   O'Connor, Flannery, 1925-1964. **Everything That Rises Must Converge.**
       New York: Farrar, Straus, and Giroux, 1965. 269p. $10.00. ISBN
       0374150125. LC 65-13726.
Flannery O'Connor writes searingly humorous fiction about the Bible Belt and
its characters. This group of stories is considered by many her most distinguished
work. The title story (the title is taken from a phrase of the eminent theologian
Teilhard de Chardin) ironically points to the "rising" and "convergence" at
once present and absent in this story and the others in the volume. Always
O'Connor is conscious of the petty, though ultimately death-dealing, clashes
among races, generations, the sexes, and all people. Other stories in the volume
include: "Greenleaf," "A View of the Woods," "The Enduring Chill," "The
Comforts of Home," "The Lame Shall Enter First," "Revelation," "Parker's
Back," and "Judgement Day."

923   O'Connor, Flannery, 1925-1964. **A Good Man Is Hard to Find, and
       Other Stories.** New York: Harcourt, Brace and Jovanovich, 1976.
       251p. $7.95. ISBN 0156364654. LC 77-3306.
O'Connor's ironic eye for the bizarre in southern lower-middle-class society
has produced one of the finest collections of short fiction ever to come out of
the South. In the title story, she pits the religious fundamentalism of a mindless,
meddlesome grandmother against a maniacal, amoral mass murderer. Other
stories in this collection are: "The River," "The Life Your Save May Be Your
Own," "A Stroke of Good Fortune," "A Temple of the Holy Ghost," "The
Artificial Nigger," "A Circle in the Fire," "A Late Encounter With the Enemy,"
"Good Country People," and "The Displaced Person." *Clinical* is a word that
aptly describes O'Connor's style.

924   Olsen, Tillie. **Tell Me a Riddle.** New York: Dell, 1976. 125p. $1.25.
       ISBN 0440385733.
The daily toll of human experience, much of it tragedy-filled, is what Olsen
is about. Olsen considers the difficult and usually insoluble problems of ordinary
people living ordinary lives—a mother looking back at the decisions she made
in rearing her now grown-up daughter in "I Stand Here Ironing"; an elderly
Jewish couple facing the imminent death of the woman in "Tell Me a Riddle."
No answers emerge to the questions—what might have happened if I had done
this rather than that? or might a life have been salvaged? Olsen writes in a
particularly autobiographical and personal style reflecting the difficult life
choices confronting her as woman and artist. (She was forced to put off her
writing career until she had raised four daughters.) The four remarkable stories
here (orig. 1962) represent Olsen's complete oeuvre and mark the beginning
of recognition for a significant woman's voice in fiction.

925   Olsen, Tillie. **Yonnondio: From the Thirties.** New York: Delacorte
       Press, 1974. 196p. $6.95. ISBN 0440091969. LC 73-15555.
The wonder of this book about life in Wyoming during the early '20s is that
it was written by Olsen as a young woman and picked up and reworked forty
years later into a haunting and lyrical fragment of a novel about family life
during the Depression. Remarkable for its sensitive portrayal of both men and
women as victims, the novel contains an especially poignant portrait of Anna

Holbrook, who labors under the yoke of poverty and family strain. No contemporary writer conveys the paradoxical pleasures and pains of motherhood as piercingly and realistically as Tillie Olsen. Much of the beautifully paced narrative of the book is filtered through Anna's narrative consciousness.

926*   Overstreet, Cleo. **The Boar Hog Woman.** Garden City, NY: Doubleday, 1972. 182p. LC 78-182841.
Terse, coarse and depressing, Overstreet's prose is well matched to the hard lives and times she is describing. The setting is California during the Depression; Overstreet describes the small world of an Oakland barbershop for blacks run by a very unattractive woman, Boar Hog Woman. The novel grows out of the adventures and tribulations of the barbershop regulars and their connections. The novelist's acerbic humor and her skill in creating authentic dialogue single out this first novel. Most novels about the Depression speak to the plight of poor whites; Overstreet shows the double stigma that poverty and racism worked on the lives of ordinary black people.

927   Ozick, Cynthia. **The Pagan Rabbi, and Other Stories.** New York: Schocken Books, 1976. 270p. $3.45. ISBN 0805205098. LC 75-36498.
Cynthia Ozick, novelist (*Trust*, 1966) and poet, is a virtuoso story teller in this comic fantasy. Ozick filters her narrative point of view through male characters who are usually on some sort of spiritual quest and often misunderstood by the women who surround them. Stories in this very fine collection are: "The Pagan Rabbi," "Envy; or, Yiddish in America," "The Suitcase," "The Dock-Witch," "The Doctor's Wife," "The Butterfly and the Traffic Light," and "Virility."

928   Packer, Nancy Huddleston. **Small Moments: Stories.** Urbana: University of Illinois Press, 1976. 155p. $6.95. ISBN 0252006151. LC 76-7601.
The first story in this collection, "Early Morning, Lonely Ride," sets the tone of spare vernacular that Packer maintains throughout. A husband and wife bound together in a love-hate relationship kept alive by endless verbal skirmishes encounter a group of thugs on their way home from a party. The frightening experience brings out the mettle of the woman and the cowardice of the man, giving her a chance to gloat in silence over this "small moment." The women are tough in Packer's stories, though the plot turns on the frequent ugliness of men and women's interactions.

929   Paley, Grace. **Enormous Changes at the Last Minute: Stories.** New York: Farrar, Straus and Giroux, 1974. 198p. $6.95. ISBN 0374148511. LC 73-87691.
New York City is the setting for these stories about people on subway trains, in old people's homes, at the city playgounds, and in other city locations. Paley is skillful in her use of dialect in conveying the ethnicity of the city. The title story is a surprising tale about a middle-aged woman's relationship with a cab driver who has propositioned her, running counterpoint to her relationship with her traditional Jewish father, who is growing old and senile. This collection continues the pattern of excellent writing that Paley established in her first book, *The Little Disturbances of Man* (1959).

930*   Petry, Ann (Lane), 1911- . **Miss Muriel and Other Stories.** Boston:
          Houghton Mifflin, 1971. 305p. ISBN 0395126711. LC 75-150139.
In this unusual group of finely crafted stories, Petry considers the position of
blacks in a white society with great subtlety. In the title story, we are given
a careful portrait of the only black family in an upstate New York town through
the perceptions of the young daughter in the family. The family owns a pharmacy,
and the story chronicles a slow-paced summer when Aunt Sophronia, a handsome
unmarried woman trained in pharmacy, attracts many male suitors. Other tales
involve a Barbadian dockworker; the genesis of a riot; and the threatening of
a young black teacher by a gang of rowdies. All of the stories are built on a
narrative principle of quiet tension sustained until a situation demands resolution
in the form of righteous anger. Petry creates women of integrity who have jobs
and professions that make them anomalies in their communities.

931   Petry, Ann (Lane), 1911- . **The Street.** New York: Pyramid Books,
          1975. 270p. $1.25.
Petry's novel tragically depicts the life of a young black woman whose major
goal is to provide a wholesome home for her son in the midst of a rundown
Harlem neighborhood. From the outset, Petry's description of the street in
Harlem where Lutie Johnson will live with her eight-year-old son is graphically
depressing. The setting prefigures the insurmountable human barriers that stand
in the way of Lutie Johnson's finding peace and a good life for herself and her
boy. An attractive woman, she is the prey of any man who sees her—the superin-
tendent at her apartment, the cabaret manager where she works. In her attempt
to work hard to provide and to keep her integrity, she loses everything. Petry's
style is grim realism; her métier is the creation of no-win choices. Her novel
stands as a classic study of the anatomy of family disintegration in a milieu
rife with poverty, racism, and sexism. Lutie Johnson is a noble and memorable
character whose impossible life choices will follow the reader for a long time.
Other Petry novels are *Tituba of Salem Village* (Thomas Y. Crowell, 1964),
Country Place (orig. 1947; repr. Chatham Bookseller, 1971), and *The Narrows*
(orig. 1953; repr. Chatham Bookseller, 1973).

932*   Piercy, Marge. **Dance the Eagle to Sleep.** Garden City, NY: Doubleday,
          1970. 232p. LC 75-124560.
In this apocalyptic tale that pits the counterculture against the establishment,
Piercy sets herself the exacting task of creating realistic political characters.
The militant youths who emerge as strong characters in this novel of rebellion,
sexual awakening, and finally, intensely moral social commitment, are some of
Piercy's most carefully drawn. Unlike the men in her later novels, those in
Dance the Eagle to Sleep have more to their credit than not. Her worldview
here still holds hope for a heterosexual society in which both sexes are equally
valued. The birth at the end assisted by two supportive males prefigures a world
in which human liberation may be possible.

933   Piercy, Marge. **The High Cost of Living.** New York: Harper and Row,
          1978. 268p. $10.00. ISBN 0060133392. LC 77-6149.
Another of Piercy's social explorations, *The High Cost of Living* scrutinizes
the hidden ledgers of human relationships. Piercy writes of the high costs that

must be paid by those who would maintain relationships of freedom and integrity. She also compassionately suggests that those who compromise themselves for relationships that bring security but no personal growth may, finally, fall into moral bankruptcy. Her characters intersect from unlikely social angles: academe, a karate studio, the street, a working-class Detroit neighborhood. They represent a variety of sexual lifestyles: gay man, swinging middle-class couple, lesbian separatist, heterosexual high school woman. Given the volatile quality of the issue—relationships and what men and women expect to gain from them— Piercy remains remarkably unjudgmental, though her women characters are stronger and risk more daringly.

934   Piercy, Marge. **Small Changes.** Greenwich, CT: Fawcett Publications, 1975. 542p. $1.75. ISBN 4492223175.
This novel explores alternative lifestyles of women of the '60s and their relation-ships with themselves and with each other. In a not-so-strange turnabout, the seemingly independent character, Miriam Berg, trades a sensual and unpredictable life for a marriage that leaves her little room for growth, one which appears to stunt her natural and impulsive personality. The more inhibited Beth, fright-ened of her parents and her husband at the beginning of the novel, metamor-phoses into a woman who dares an extraordinary relationship and lifestyle open to many levels of exploration.

935   Piercy, Marge. **Woman on the Edge of Time.** New York: Knopf, 1976. 369p. $10.00. ISBN 0394499867. LC 75-36810.
In her fourth novel, Piercy creates a continuous dialogue between reality and potentiality that succeeds in bringing to life a whole series of political issues and questions. Through the time travel of Piercy's central character, a Chicana named Connie, the reader is flitted back and forth between three different visions: a grimly oppressive present, where the forces of a racist, sexist, and capitalist society are crystallized in the mental hospital that imprisons Connie; a painfully enticing future (Mattapoisett), where the potentiality for renewal of a humane society is struggling to survive in a decentralized, cooperative, loving, feminist community; and an Orwellian vision of future horror, where the worst tendencies in the present society (exploitation, destruction, war, inequality, centralized power) are extrapolated to their logical conclusion. The message seems to be that human nature and history are not fixed or deter-mined. Rather, at any one time, a number of conflicting potentialities are struggling to come into existence. It remains an open question whether people will find the strength and determination to nurture the more humane possibilities. *Woman on the Edge of Time* presents a moving political statement on the nature of struggle and change, an incisive critique of our current reality, and a compelling vision of a socialist feminist future.

936   Plath, Sylvia, 1932-1963. **The Bell Jar.** New York: Harper and Row, 1971. 296p. $10.95. ISBN 0060133562. LC 76-149743.
Because Sylvia Plath had reached an almost mythical stature by the time *The Bell Jar* was published in the United States due to her suicide in 1963, this book tends to be regarded as a brilliant but grim autobiographical prophecy of the inevitable death of a talented, much applauded, but very unhappy woman.

Esther Greenwood is the fictional Sylvia Plath, winner of the *Mademoiselle* college competition, as Plath was. She attempts suicide in the summer of her twentieth year and goes to a mental asylum for shock treatment, as did Plath. Perhaps the most haunting aspect of this probing novel about madness and the schizophrenia of coming of age in American culture is the distance and artistry Plath achieves in looking backward at life during the '50s. She coldly examines the split experience of Esther and the experience of every woman who *appears* to have it all, when what she really has attained is madness.

937   Polite, Carlene Hatcher. **The Flagellants.** New York: Farrar, Straus and
        Giroux, 1967. 214p. $5.95. ISBN 0374156018. LC 67-15013.
Polite represents a very different and angry woman's voice in black fiction. The narrator, in the prologue, characterizes the mood as "hysteria." Ideal and Jimson, a young poet and Ideal's lover, live together in a Greenwich Village apartment. Their confrontations of self and each other, their questionings, and their quarrels, are textured with fear, despair, and rage. Their method is mutual verbal flagellation. As much a sexual as a racial dialectic, Polite's theme appears to be that finding out who one is and cummunicating this identity to the other is the most rigorous and demanding, even brutal, form of interaction. Their arguments puncture standard stereotypes of the Supermasculine and Ultrafeminine black, stereotypes at once racist and sexist. Polite's second novel, set in bohemian Paris instead of Greenwich Village, and again heavily reliant on dialogue to develop deep psychological issues, is *Sister X and the Victims of Foul Play* (Farrar, Straus and Giroux, 1975). The narrative is based on the lives of radical blacks living in Paris. Perhaps this second effort of Polite's is less successful because of her reliance on jive talk to carry her point. Though the book is relatively plotless, Polite ends the novel in a flourish of activity, with the death of a dancer who is killed or commits suicide by falling into an orchestra pit after refusing to do a striptease. Polite is not easy reading, but she is worth the effort.

938   Porter, Katherine Anne, 1894- . **Collected Stories.** New York: Harcourt,
        Brace and World, 1965. 495p. $12.50. ISBN 0151189927. LC 65-14706.
This collection includes *Flowering Judas and Other Stories*, whose Mexican, Cuban, and Spanish characters are graceful foils against the dry awkwardness of Yankee reformers terribly out of place among the Mexican peasants. Also in this collection are the three stories of *Pale Horse, Pale Rider*, whose main character, Miranda, copes with the loss of a southern past with its illusions of dignity and aristocracy ("Old Mortality"), as well as with the horrific present of World War I (in "Pale Horse, Pale Rider"), a present permeated with inexplicable death and doom from flu and from war. *The Leaning Tower and Other Stories* is the other major group of stories included in the collection.

939   Potrebenko, Helen. **Taxi! A Novel.** Vancouver, BC: New Star Books,
        1975. 168p. ISBN 0919888038. LC 76-360540.
Shannon, the heroine of this novel, drives a taxi in Vancouver, and we, the readers, are taken along for the ride. What we see is an at times humorous, at times depressing, always revealing, documentary on class and sex antagonisms and how they're actually played out on the streets. Though all the characters

are fictitious, Helen Potrebenko herself worked as a cab driver in Vancouver for a number of years.

940   Pym, Barbara. **The Sweet Dove Died**. London: Macmillan, 1978. 208p. ISBN 0333233239.
Lenora is the sophisticated central character of this Pym novel about a middle-aged woman, who lives in pursuit of the agreeable life of good food, pleasant company, and tasteful surroundings. Her major activities include the arrangement of flowers, furniture, and other people's lives. Lenora develops an amorous feeling for James, the nephew of an antique collector, and is disappointed to find that his affections lie with his homosexual lover, Ned. Pym presents this tableau of affluent London society and its narcissism with characteristic dry wit. Lenora, like other Pym characters, is a strong-willed and selfish character intent on her own way and completely in synch with the social fabric of which she is an exquisitely designed detail. Pym, an underrated novelist, has been writing during the '50s and '60s for a small but appreciative audience. Single women are staples of her work. See *Excellent Women* (1952) and *Quartet in Autumn* (1977).

941   Radcliffe, Ann Ward, 1764-1823. **The Mysteries of Udolpho: A Romance Interspersed With Some Pieces of Poetry**. New York: Oxford University Press, 1966. 672p. bibliog. $9.75. ISBN 0192553062. LC 66-2628.
An international best-seller well into the nineteenth-century, *The Mysteries of Udolpho* was read, admired, and sometimes, for all intents and purposes, had its plot lifted by the likes of Coleridge, Keats, Sir Walter Scott, and Byron. Today it occupies a hallowed niche as the first English-language Gothic novel. The novel reads as comedy today with its Fair and Lovely Damsel in Distress, Emily St. Aubert, possibly the most saccharine heroine in all literature. Alone in the world, she is prey to the evils of her cruel (also swarthy-complected) Uncle Montoni, who takes her away from southern France and her virtuous lover, Valancourt, to his Italian castle (Udolpho, complete with Gothic trappings—crypts, strange sounds, dark passages, corpses) until her escape to Valancourt.

942   Réage, Pauline. **Story of O**. New York: Grove Press, 1976. 199p. $1.94. ISBN 0802140025. LC 75-43399.
Puzzling but fascinating pornography, the *Story of O* is a narrative of degradation, complete with whips, chains, riding crops, and assorted sadomasochistic paraphernalia. It is difficult to dismiss this as merely a sordid tale of debasement, however; O's complete passivity throughout to her lover's demands that she submit on command to anyone, and her willingness to be abused almost as a martyr of sex, become an allegory of prostitution and oppression in which the victim, O, loses all individuality. Finally, as masked sacrifice indiscriminantly partaken of by all passers by, she discards all gender identity, as well. Jean Paulhan of l'Académie Française writes in his preface to the Grove Press edition, "Happiness in Slavery," that one comes away from *O* hardly knowing what to make of it: "it reminds you more of a speech than a mere effusion; of a letter rather than a secret diary. But to whom is the letter addressed? Whom is the speech trying to convince? Whom can we ask?" The identity of the author, Madame Pauline Réage, has been a mystery, though the book was awarded the

respected Prix des Deux Magots in 1955, a prize reserved for worthy but unconventional works.

943 Rhys, Jean. **After Leaving Mr. Mackenzie.** New York: Harper and Row, 1972. 191p. $8.95. ISBN 0060135344. LC 79-170758.
Rhys has crafted a stark novel about a woman making her way alone in the world who finds that a cycle of affairs with various men has purchased temporary happiness and security though great bitterness and loneliness in the end. The story is filtered mainly through Julia Martin, a single woman whose lover, the cold and stuffy Mr. Mackenzie, has rejected her in Paris. Having no means of support and fewer inner resources, Julia attempts to reconnect with her family after her separation from Mackenzie, only to find that her sister resents Julia for the freedom that she supposes Julia has enjoyed while she was left at home to care for an invalid mother. Julia's attempts to grasp at fragile straws of hope and in the end, her breakdown and her begging money from her former lover, become strategies for survival that many women can identify with. Originally published in 1931, *After Leaving Mr. Mackenzie* is a timeless and grim profile of dependency. A more recent psychological novel by Rhys is *Wide Sargasso Sea* (1967), which some critics consider her best work.

944 Rhys, Jean. **Good Morning, Midnight.** New York: Harper and Row, 1970. 189p. $8.95. ISBN 0060135433. LC 78-96002.
Rhys's subject in this novel (originally 1939), as in *After Leaving Mr. Mackenzie,* is the hopelessness of the situation of a woman alone when she is fearful of growing old, of men, of women, or of herself. Sasha is intelligent; she is also cynical and narcissistic, and she knows these qualities in herself. In her mid-40s, her self-consciousness about her appearance and her financial plight has robbed her of self-respect and peace of mind. Like her counterpart, Julia, in *After Leaving Mr. Mackenzie,* Sasha is in Paris where she has gone for a vacation. Paris becomes the ironically appropriate setting for both of these tormented women who try to fit into the gay and sociable atmosphere of the city, realizing always their rejection by the world. Rhys's power as a novelist is the stark truth of her vision; many women alone are Sashas and Julias, and their lives of dependency and narcissism have brought them to a barren, unlighted place. It is good to see Rhys's work being reprinted.

945 Richardson, Dorothy Miller, 1873-1957. **Pilgrimage.** New York: Popular Library, 1976. 4v. $1.95 ea. ISBN 044508457X(v.1); 0445084693(v.2); 0445084804(v.3); 0445084812(v.4).
The volumes here are 1) Pointed Roofs; Backwater; Honeycomb; 2) The Tunnel; Interim; 3) Deadlock; Revolving Lights; The Trap; and 4) Oberland; Dawn's Left Hand; Clear Horizon; Dimple Hill; March Moonlight. An introduction is provided by Walter Allen. Dorothy Richardson's work occupies a curious place in literature. A pioneer in the use of stream-of-consciousness in her work, and a contemporary of Woolf, Joyce, and Proust, Richardson never received the attention that they did. Until recently her work has not been readily available. *Pilgrimage* is the story of Miriam Henderson's development as a woman from around 1890 to 1915. Miriam's feminism is a very developed part of her personality throughout; the novel has been faulted on that score. Richardson set out

to record the consciousness of Miriam Henderson—not to suggest it, but to explore it in its changes and shadings much as Monet set out to paint haystacks or lily pads in different lights. The task she set herself took a lifetime and filled thirteen volumes. Yet many who do not understand the feminine reality of Richardson's novels—where nothing much happens except the flow of life itself—criticize it for its lack of narrative. The books of *Pilgrimage* follow Miriam's life as governess, dental assistant, Fabianist, and Quaker. But always the emphasis is on the space within. See Gloria Fromm's *Dorothy Richardson: A Biography* (1977).

946   Richardson, Henrietta [Richardson, Henry Handel]. **The End of a Childhood.** Saint Clair Shores, MI: Scholarly Press, 1971. (Repr. of 1934 ed.). 312p. $22.00. ISBN 0403011752.

In addition to the stunning final story of the volume, which conflates the life experiences of an aged woman facing death into a flash ("Mary Christina"), of primary interest to women's studies will be the eight jewel-like stories clustered under the topic "Growing Pains: Sketches of Girlhood." These include "The Bathe," "Three in a Row," "Preliminary Canter," "Conversation in a Pantry," "The Bath," "The Wrong Turning," " 'And Women Must Weep,' " and "Two Hanged Women." Each of these stories is a masterly sketch of scenes in which girls glimpse womanhood. Ranging from the perspective of a six-year-old bathing on the bathing on the beach who watches with awe and later with distaste two middle-aged women stripping for a swim, to the experience of a teen-aged young woman who inadvertently comes upon a group of nude male bathers, each cameo proclaims a conflict and an epiphany for the young woman who learns about something hitherto forbidden. Other titles by Richardson demonstrate similar artistry: *The Fortunes of Richard Mahony, The Getting of Wisdom,* and *Maurice Guest.*

947   Richardson, Samuel, 1689-1761. **Pamela: Or, Virtue Rewarded.** New York: E. P. Dutton, 1955. 2v. $5.00 ea. ISBN 0460006835(v.1); 0460006843(v.2). LC 14-1638.

Published in 1740, *Pamela* was Richardson's first work and has been defined as the first novel of character written in modern language. Pamela's narrative form is a series of letters written by the heroine, Pamela Andrews, a young and unprotected maidservant whose mistress has just died as the story opens. In the first part of the story, Mr. B., the lady's son, falls in love with Pamela; he pursues her dishonorably though Pamela expends considerable energy and skill in fending him off. Finally, the two come to terms (mainly Pamela's) and are married. The second part (published in 1741) sees Pamela in the suffering wife role, married to a profligate husband whom she endures with good grace. This remains an important novel to women's studies for the pattern it establishes in English literature of the superior woman who often endures an impossible man, mainly due to limited social choices, which make him the best in an array of bad possibilities. In *Clarissa*, Richardson presents a heroine who prefers death to societally imposed but morally indefensible choices. Feminist critic Carolyn Heilbron has cited Clarissa's humanity as an androgynous ideal in her discussion of that novel in *Toward a Recognition of Androgyny* (1973).

948*   Riis, Sharon, 1947- . **The True Story of Ida Johnson.** Toronto: Women's
        Press, 1976. 111p. LC 77-370713.
The "true story of Ida Johnson" is a strange one. Ida is a waitress asked by a
passing customer, Luke, to tell her story. She asks him what it's worth to him,
as she would ask what it might be worth for a man to have casual sex with her.
"Jesus. I'll talk your ear off for twenty," she says. Ida tells a rambling story of
working-class Canadian on-the-road life in a hard-hitting vernacular that suggests
that Ida's existence as metaphysical waitress gives her the clearest of windows
on the world.

949   Roberts, Kate, 1891- . **Feet in Chains: A Novel.** Cardiff, Wales: John
        Jones Cardiff, 1977. 133p. $8.95. ISBN 0902375237. LC 78-304060.
As Wales's greatest living author, Kate Roberts at age 86 continues to write
spare prose reflective of the rugged terrain and reserved manner of the people
in Northern Wales. The story that Kate Roberts creates in *Feet in Chains* centers
upon the life of a wife and mother, Jane Gruffydd, a strong and enduring woman
who exists as the still point for her family during three decades. Roberts writes
of the extraordinary courage exemplified in the daily lives of ordinary women.

950   Rolvaag, Ole Edvart, 1876-1931. **Giants in the Earth: A Saga of the
        Prairie.** New York: Harper and Row, 1964. 463p. bibliog. $12.50.
        ISBN 0060135956. LC 64-375.
Translated from the Norwegian (*I de daga*) by Lincoln Colcord and the author,
this was originally published in English in 1927 and widely acclaimed by critics.
Giants in the Earth is an epic tale of Norwegian settlers in the plains of South
Dakota. Rolvaag's novel speaks powerfully to the pioneer experience in America—
both to the formidable struggles with the forces of nature and to the interpersonal and psychological struggles engendered under the difficult pioneer circumstances. Of particular interest to women will be the contrasting portraits
of the key male character, Per Hansa, and of his wife, Beret. Readers with an
interest in fictional renderings of women's pioneer experiences may also want
to turn to Willa Cather's two novels, *O Pioneers!* and *Ántonia*.

951   Rossner, Judith. **Any Minute I Can Split: A Novel.** New York: Warner
        Books, 1973. 253p. $1.95. ISBN 044689169X.
Rossner has created a feminist novel that has at its center a strong and unconventional woman, Margaret. Nine months pregnant, weighing 250 pounds, she
takes off from home on a motorcycle, leaving her breakfast cereal and her
husband behind. Several points make this a refreshing novel: Margaret is an
independent and happy person despite certain insecurities; she does not fear
sexual love nor is she dependent upon it; she does not feel guilty about taking
a lover, nor does she feel resentful about returning to her husband. It is good
to see an eccentric character with a sense of humor, who works out an individual
lifestyle that suits her rather than going insane or committing suicide. Margaret
and her husband both grow during this novel. Their life on a communal farm
with their twin baby daughters signals a positive life for both of them. Rossner's
endowing these two attractive characters with independent wealth is a happy
stroke in a realistic novel, which suggests that excessive psychological pain and

poverty are not necessarily the hallmarks of growth. The dialogue in this novel is consistently witty and intelligent.

952   Roth, Philip. **Portnoy's Complaint.** New York: Random House, 1969. 274p. $8.95. ISBN 0394441982. LC 69-16414.
Mama Portnoy is a caricature of Jewish motherhood drawn by a master. Analysis of what Portnoy is saying about women and family life could trigger spirited discussion in a literature class looking at images of women in contemporary fiction. Mary Allen analyzes Roth's approach in *The Necessary Blankness: Women in Major American Fiction of the Sixties* (1976).

953   Rule, Jane. **The Desert of the Heart.** Cleveland, OH: World, 1964; repr. New York: Arno Press, 1975. 224p. $10.00. ISBN 0405073860. LC 75-12344.
Rule is widely known for her work on lesbian themes and characters. Among her books are *This Is Not For You* (1970) and *Against the Season* (1971). In this novel, she works out the painful conflict faced by a middle-aged college professor, Evelyn Hall, when she falls in love with a very physical, non-cerebral woman, Ann Childs, who works in a Nevada casino. Both women make decisions to throw off more conventional relationships and ties in their commitment to each other.

954   Russ, Joanna, 1937- . **The Female Man.** New York: Bantam Books, 1975; repr. Boston: Gregg Press, 1977. 214p. $11.00. ISBN 0839823517. LC 77-23498.
Five strong women characters emerge clear, true, and unique in this science-fiction, feminist apocalyptic vision of women's freedom. The characters are separate and one at the same time. Joanna represents a contemporary feminist dealing with familiar role conflicts; Janet is a female from a future world where no males exist (a female male); Jael hails from a future separatist society; Jeanine is caught in a somewhat recent time warp set at the time of the Great Depression; and Laura Rose lives sometime in the present, a lesbian mathematician. Using inventive turnabouts, word play, fantasy, and narrative license of every sort, Russ stands every preconceived notion of gender identity on its head. Delightful reading in the unexpected mode of Woolf's *Orlando*.

955   Russ, Joanna, 1937- . **The Two of Them.** New York: Berkeley; distr. New York: Putnam, 1978. 226p. $8.95. ISBN 0399121498. LC 77-26137.
Science fiction is increasingly becoming a popular genre for the woman writer because it gives her the possibility of creating and controlling symbolic rituals that she has either researched or developed in her imagination without having to defend her lack of experience in the realms of derring-do. *The Two of Them* is strongly feminist in tone and narrative structure. The action takes place on the planet Ka'abah, where the culture is racist and sexist. Irene Waskiewics, a feminist undercover agent working for the Trans-Temporal Authority, seeks to change the chauvinist order of affairs on Ka'abah by an elaborate kidnapping scheme involving the daughter of an official of the planet, a strategy that involves the agent's killing of her lover and colleague. Russ deals fantastically with the

conflicts that surface when women become heroes and adventurers and must make difficult personal decisions to advance their quests.

956   Sagan, Françoise, 1935- . **Silken Eyes.** New York: Delacorte Press/
       Eleanor Friede, 1977. 179p. $6.95. ISBN 0440083087. LC 77-21659.
This collection includes: "Silken Eyes," "The Gigolo," "In Extemis," "The Unknown Visitor," "The Five Diversions," "The Gentlemanly Tree," "An Evening Out," "A Stylish Death," "The Fishing Expedition," "Death in Espadrilles," "The Left Eyelid," "A Dog's Night," "Separation Roman-Style," "The Corner Cafe," "The Seven O'Clock Fix," "Italian Skies," "The Sun Also Sets," and "The Lake of Loneliness."

957   Sand, George, pseud. of Mme. Dudevant, 1804-1876. **Indiana.** Chicago:
       Cassandra Editions, 1978. (Repr. of 1900 ed.). 327p. $9.95. ISBN
       0915864584. LC 77-27987.
Finally, George Sand's work is being translated into English. *Indiana* was Sand's first novel. Though Indiana is portrayed as a martyr, unable to help herself and dependent upon her staunch cousin, Ralph, to rescue her from unsuitable and unscrupulous men, still it is a feminist novel that outlines Sand's impatience with the French laws of the day (1831) governing women's position, which she deplored in her preface to the novel as "unjust and barbarous."

958   Sand, George, pseud. of Mme. Dudevant, 1804-1876. **Lélia.** Bloomington:
       Indiana University Press, 1978. 234p. bibliog. $12.50. ISBN
       0253333180. LC 77-23639.
Lélia belongs to the first period of Sand's work (1831-1834), which also includes *Indiana* and *Jacques*. The period is characterized by her rebelliousness against the institution of marriage. This edition, with an excellent translation and informative introduction by Maria Espinosa and a foreword by Ellen Moers (*Literary Women*), marks a resurgence of interest in Sand's work, which has often been overlooked in all the fascination with her flamboyant life and career. Increasingly, Sand is available in English in paperback editions (e.g., *Maurat, Master Mosaic and Devil's Pond, She and He, Country Waif*, and *Fansh and Cricket*).

959   Sand, George, pseud. of Mme. Dudevant, 1804-1876. **She and He.**
       Chicago: Cassandra Editions, 1978. (Repr. of 1902 ed.). 224p. $9.95.
       ISBN 0915864843. LC 78-14444.
Written in 1859, *Elle et Lui (She and He)*, represents an example of George Sand at her most romantic pitch. The plot thinly conceals her own disastrous romance with Alfred de Musset (he, in turn, responded with his own version). Thérèse and Laurent, both artists, are the principles of the contrived plot of passion. Laurent, a maniacal genius, misuses Thérèse and her love to the extent that her only solution is to leave him to rage alone. Thérèse speaks with the voice of reason in this novel and concludes by writing a reasonable letter to Laurent in defense of her leaving him.

960   Sand, George, pseud. of Mme. Dudevant, 1804-1876. **Valentine.**
       Chicago: Cassandra Editions, 1978. (Repr. of 1902 ed.). 336p. $9.95.
       ISBN 0915864606. LC 77-28026.

Originally published in 1852, Sand's second novel, *Valentine*, is a highly senti-
mentalized tale, a pastoral romance. The lovers in the novel (he, a peasant and
she, an aristocrat) transcend barriers of class, property, and familial duty in
their illicit love for each other. The story of Valentine and Benedict is a fictional
working out of Sand's sexual politics: namely, that pure love is possible only
when two people come together out of love unblemished by material interests.
Societal mores are necessarily a distortion of purity, corrupt by their very
righteousness and their infringement on personal liberty.

961   Sarton, May, 1912- . **Crucial Conversations: A Novel.** New York:
       Norton, 1975. 156p. $5.95. ISBN 0393087255. LC 74-32232.
A novel about personal confrontations and about a middle-aged woman who
leaves a long-term marriage in order to salvage a sense of self-worth, this is
quintessential Sarton—full of intelligence, wit, and lyricism. There is much
exploration of the aging process here focusing on both men and women.

962   Sarton, May, 1912- . **Mrs. Stevens Hears the Mermaids Singing.**
       New York: Norton, 1974. 220p. $6.95. ISBN 039308695X. LC
       74-1349.
This new edition of *Mrs. Stevens*, introduced by Carolyn Heilbrun with an
essay on Sarton's place in American fiction, is worth having. Heilbrun feels
that Sarton is "too little celebrated," an exile, an outsider like Hilary Stevens—
the central character in this novel of the woman artist torn between the desire
"to be a woman, simple and fruitful, a woman with many children, a great
husband . . . and no talent," and the driving need to be a creator. Sarton has
explored this theme throughout her work. In this novel, dialogue on the question occurs during an interview that poet Hilary Stevens is granting to a young
couple. Jenny, the young woman interviewer, has a dream of being both artist
and wife/mother. Although Hilary does not look upon marriage and family
with a jaundiced eye, just as Sarton does not, Hilary is bisexual and looks
toward women for inspiration.

963   Sarton, May, 1912- . **The Small Room: A Novel.** New York: Norton,
       1976. 249p. $2.95. ISBN 0393008320. LC 76-25230.
An important later novel (1961) exploring a familiar Sarton theme—a woman's
acknowledgement to herself and to others that she actively seeks excellence.
In this case, the main character, Lucy Winter, went through graduate school
at Harvard in order to remain close to her Harvard Medical School lover. When
the affair died, she found herself with a doctorate and little commitment to
her profession. In her first teaching job at a women's college, Lucy Winter comes
to terms with the meaning of teaching and the definition of total commitment.
" 'People who are rooted in work are rooted in life,' " a beloved colleague tells
her. Mainly, Lucy Winters finds out that she is capable of being an individual
and, in the knowledge of this capacity, frees herself from hinging her own life
choices on the life choices of another. A question that Sarton seems to be throwing out for consideration is whether or not commitment isolates an individual.
Sarton's latest novel, *A Reckoning* (Norton, 1978), has as its major character
a sixty-year-old widow, Laura Spelman, who is dying of lung cancer. This novel

handles important themes of a woman's life—aging, death, lesbianism, and female friendship—with great insight.

964   Schnitzler, Arthur, 1862-1931. **Vienna 1900: Games with Love and Death: The Stories Which Formed the Basis of the BBC TV Serial** . . . Baltimore, MD: Penguin Books, 1973. 356p. $2.50. ISBN 0140037594. LC 74-188252.

The novellas that comprise *Vienna 1900* (four in all) concern "heroines who, racked by frustration and despair, finally rebel, seek a way out of their solitary confinement and pay with their lives for breaking the laws men imputed to God. They make for a bitter commentary on the hypocrisy of men and on the monstrous fate of women in the land of waltzes and whipped cream. . . . " (*New York Times Book Review*, April 9, 1978, pp. 10, 30). Schnitzler, a member of the "Vienna modernist" school, wrote primarily of Viennese upper-class society and was more concerned with psychological portraits than with delineating the goings-on in society.

965   Schreiner, Olive, 1855-1920. **From Man to Man: Or, Perhaps Only** . . . New York: Johnson Reprint, 1972. (Repr. of 1927 ed.). $31.50. ISBN 0384542786. LC 71-38697.

Schreiner's husband states in the introduction to this lyrical novel about two loving sisters that the author loved this book more than anything else she had ever written. It was an unrevised and uncompleted manuscript upon her death in 1920. The novel, like *The Story of an African Farm* (1883), is the story of two sisters who grow up in the isolation of an African farm. Unsophisticated, they expect the best from the world. The elder sister, more prepared for life's disappointments, makes a good marriage that later turns sour, a situation with which she manages to cope despite its difficult consequences. The younger sister, a free spirit and a romantic, chooses to have an affair with the wrong man. When he rejects her, she is left penniless and alone to cope with her plight. Each of the sisters is a victim of a patriarchal society, which posits marriage as the only choice for women. One male character is sympathetic, but the other men are an assortment of irresponsible, selfish, and lecherous beings. Schreiner's description of the South African landscape and lifestyle is vivid and compelling. The setting provides a striking backdrop for the inevitable misfortunes of the two sisters.

966   Schreiner, Olive, 1855-1920. **The Story of an African Farm.** New York: Schocken Books, 1976. 287p. $4.95. ISBN 0805205470. LC 76-9143.

This is an important novel for its confrontation with South African society at the turn of the century, especially in relation to the lot of women. Lyndall, a feminist heroine of bitterness and tragedy, rebels to the grave. Her most passionate speeches reject the narcissistic, ingrown, paralyzed role that society expects of her as the conventional wife and mother: "we fit our sphere as a Chinese woman's foot fits her shoe, exactly, as though God had made both— and yet he knows nothing of either. In some of us the shaping to our end has been quite completed. The parts we are not to use have been quite atrophied, and have even dropped off; but in others, and we are not less to be pitied, they have been weakened and left. We wear the bandages, but our limbs have not

grown to them; we know that we are compressed and chafe against them."
The Story of an African Farm (1893) has been compared to *A Doll's House*
for its influence on the feminist movement. But Schreiner's feminism is not
free of problems. Her women meet hardship and death for perceived sexual
indiscretions and seek martyrdom rather than triumph. See Elaine Showalter's
perceptive analysis of Olive Schreiner's work in *A Literature of Their Own*
(Princeton, 1977). This edition of *Farm* has an introduction by Doris Lessing.

967   Schreiner, Olive, 1855-1920. **A Track to the Water's Edge: The Olive
       Schreiner Reader.** New York: Harper and Row, 1973. bibliog. $6.95.
       ISBN 0060680768. LC 72-78068.

Pacifism, feminism, labor, and freedom for all people were concerns of this
nineteenth-century South African writer, whose first novel, *The Story of An
African Farm*, has served as a manifesto for feminism throughout the world
(though few have read it in its entirety and it has until recently been out of
print along with Schreiner's other books). Her fiction is marked by a keen poetic
sensitivity, which, together with her concern for social issues, makes her writing
a unique experience for the reader first coming to her. Her own life combined
courage, poetry, frustration, and defeat because of her strongly held beliefs.
(See her husband, Cronwright-Schreiner, *The Letters of Olive Schreiner*, 1924
and *The Life of Olive Schreiner*, n.d.). Contents of this reader include selections
from: *The Story of an African Farm*; *Thoughts on South Africa*; *Dreams*;
Woman and Labor; *Trooper Peter Halket of Mashonaland*; *Stories, Dreams
and Allegories*; and *From Man to Man*. Howard Thurman writes a balanced
introduction. Another very similarly arranged selection of Schreiner's work
will be found in *Olive Schreiner: A Selection*, edited by Uys Krige (Oxford
University Press, 1968). Krige has written a long introduction from the perspective of an admiring South African critic. Schreiner's work is uneven; the *Reader*
surveys that inconsistency in quality.

968   Scott, Evelyn, 1893- . **The Narrow House.** New York: Boni and Liveright,
       1921; repr. New York: Arno Press, 1977. 221p. $18.00. ISBN
       0405100558. LC 76-51677.

Elizabeth Hardwick introduces this novel, chosen for the Arno Rediscovered
Fiction by American Women series, as follows: "Evelyn Scott's reputation
as a sophisticated artist, working in the new forms of the 1920's, was very much
alive during her productive period. She wrote poetry, autobiography, juveniles,
criticism, and a number of novels that ranged from a highly individualized
poetic realism to historical subjects. . . . *The Narrow House*, Evelyn Scott's
first novel, was published in 1921. It is a family novel, written in a detached,
unsentimental manner. The Farley family is a worthy one, a group of quite
modest persons who somehow fall under the gloom of depressed spirits and
repressed feelings. . . . The distinction of *The Narrow House* lies in its powerfully
detailed observation, in its radical, slashing understanding of the 'moral cellar'
in which the Farley family is imprisoned. 'The narrow house' is the breathless
space constructed out of confused marriages, empty work, private natures
never acknowledged."

969*   Seid, Ruth [Sinclair, Jo, pseud.]. **Wasteland**. New York: Harper and
        Brothers, 1946. 321p. LC 46-1556.
It is informative to return to the reviews that this controversial novel received
when it came out in 1946. Most reviewers were able to deal with the main
character, Jake, and his problems of inferiority and shame because of his Jewish
background. Jake reveals himself through the course of psychoanalytic dialogues
with his psychiatrist. No reviewer mentions Jake's loving relationship with his
sister, Deborah, a lesbian and a writer, despite the issue's visibility in the book.
At one point the psychiatrist reflects, "he [Jake] feels himself disgustingly
different from most people, and that Deborah's oddness substantiates his own. . . .
He talks of Deborah's oddness, her short hair, her boyishness. He has not used
the word homosexual, or Lesbian. Is he ashamed to use such words, or doesn't
he know the words? Does he know what Deborah is; or is it pure feeling on his
part?" Deborah turns out to be the most liberated character in the novel because
she accepts herself. Sinclair's characters are intensely, painfully realistic. Jake's
stomach-turning fears that he may be rejected by the people he knows and works
with if they know his background become the fears shared by every "out"
group in a culture where the message to conform pervades every aspect of daily
life. The reviews indicate that while critics in the '40s are able to accept ethnic
inferiority as a legitimate problem, they are unwilling to address issues of
sexual preference.

970   Shelley, Mary Wollstonecraft Godwin, 1787-1851. **Frankenstein; Or,
        the Modern Prometheus**. Indianapolis, IN: Bobbs-Merrill, 1974. 287p.
        bibliog. $7.50. ISBN 0672514575. LC 72-80409.
There are several good editions of this classic, including a recently annotated
and generously illustrated edition with introduction and notes by Leonard
Wolf (Crown, 1977). Published in 1818, this gothic story grew out of a wet
summer spent in Switzerland, when the Shelleys and Byron passed the time
telling and writing ghost tales. Mary Shelley wrote a version of "Frankenstein"
which her husband urged her to enlarge. The story that she created was a deeply
philosophical study on isolation and creativity. A Genevan student of natural
philosophy, Frankenstein discovers the key to imparting life to inanimate
matter. The creature that he structures is imbued with human sensibility, but
so ugly in appearance that it inspires dread and revulsion in anyone who sees it.
Because of its abject loneliness and feeling of rejection, it takes revenge on its
creator by murdering Frankenstein's brother and his bride. This results in
Frankenstein's pursuit of the monster to the Arctic, where both monster and
creator die.

971   Shockley, Ann Allen. **Loving Her: A Novel**. Indianapolis, IN: Bobbs-
        Merrill, 1974. 187p. $6.95. ISBN 067251835X. LC 73-13227.
Although a somewhat contrived novel (the lesbian lovers are reunited on Christmas Eve to the melodies of Christmas music), this novel gives fictional representation to the experiences of lesbian mothers and lesbian artists. It also explores
the emptiness of the gay bar scene.

972   Shulman, Alix Kates. **Memoirs of an Ex-Prom Queen: A Novel**. New
        York: Knopf, 1972. 274p. $6.95. ISBN 0394471563. LC 74-171159.

Seen by some feminist critics as a feminist variation of the *bildungsroman* novelistic form, *Memoirs* is a catalog of a young woman's painful coming of age in America. It is standard to comment on the hilarity of this chronicle of sexual initiation, marriage, divorce, abortion, and child-bearing. Yet, the novel so parallels the experiences of many women and speaks so tellingly about the rampant narcissism that contemporary life and culture breeds in women, there seems to be more that is tragic than laughable beneath the witty handling of this predictable plot. A classic, this should be recommended to every college freshman—though she probably won't believe its message.

973   Smedley, Agnes, 1890-1950. **Daughter of Earth.** Old Westbury, NY: Feminist Press, 1973. 429p. $8.00. ISBN 0912670104. LC 72-14442.
Daughter of Earth was originally written, Agnes Smedley tells us, as part of "a desperate attempt to reorient my life." Though she gave the book the form of a novel, it in fact tells the story of Smedley's life until the late 1920s, when *Daughter of Earth* was published. Born on a small farm in northern Missouri, soon to move to southern Colorado and a transient existence in the mining towns of the Rockefeller-owned Colorado Fuel and Iron Company, Smedley's childhood was one of extreme poverty and hopelessness. Her account of this time is painfully moving but also very revealing in its acute sensitivity to the particularly precarious existence of the women she knew while growing up— "the hell of nagging, weeping women, depending for food and clothing upon [their husbands]." The remembered vision of this hell was to haunt her for the rest of her life, causing her, on the one hand, to struggle against formidable odds to escape the feared fate, and, on the other, to commit her life to the struggle of the oppressed for liberation. This commitment led her first to an involvement in the movement for the liberation of India and, later, to her lengthy connection with the Chinese Revolution, about which she wrote extensively. These political commitments undoubtedly help explain the obscurity into which her life and her books had fallen until rediscovered by the contemporary women's movement. This new edition of *Daughter of Earth* includes a fine afterword by Paul Lauter. Readers might also want to look at Smedley's *Battle Hymn of China*, which contains an autobiographical introduction covering her life up to 1929.

974   Sontag, Susan, 1933- . **Death Kit.** New York: Farrar, Straus and Giroux, 1967. 311p. $5.75. ISBN 0374135568. LC 67-22434.
Criticized for its mechanical dullness, this book by essayist and critic Susan Sontag nevertheless is a technically interesting novel about madness and dependence. Diddy, the male character, aged 33, meets a blind girl during a train trip of nightmarish dimensions—he may have murdered someone while the train had stopped, but the reader is not quite sure. He gives up his job to be with the blind young woman and to help her to regain her vision. When this fails, they enter into an existence of complete isolation from the world, total dependence on each other, and eventually the sharing of the same nightmare, leading to madness if not to murder.

975   Spark, Muriel. **The Prime of Miss Jean Brodie.** Philadelphia, PA: Lippincott, 1962. 187p. $3.95. ISBN 0397002327. LC 62-7182.

Miss Jean Brodie may be familiar to former girls' school inmates as the irresistible teacher who commands a coterie of devoted followers. This is a story of emerging adolescent sexuality in a Scottish girls school set in the 1930s and of the "betrayal" of Miss Brodie, a fortyish woman, who protests often that she is in her "prime." Jean Brodie is vividly created, another of Spark's eccentrics, but more memorable and compelling than most.

976   Spark, Muriel. **The Takeover.** New York: Viking Press, 1976. 266p. $8.95. ISBN 0670691070. LC 76-17909.
Spark writes satirical novels about the British upper classes, and she writes with a humorous bite that recognizes life as being serious business but amusing even in its grim moments. Maggie Radcliffe is alternately repelling and endearing as a middle-aged, manipulating, wealthy expatriate in Italy trying to maintain her fortune against the forces of Arab oil power, a sponging former husband, a swindling financial advisor, and other assorted "takeover" types. Maggie may not always be admirable, but underneath the brittleness, she is a survivor.

977   Stead, Christina, 1902- . **The Man Who Loved Children.** (2nd ed.). New York: Holt, Rinehart and Winston, 1976. 527p. $12.50. ISBN 0030472652. LC 65-10128.
Christina Stead, an Australian writer who has lived in the United States, is an enormously gifted writer of books that describe the texture of women's lives, though she has proclaimed her disdain of the women's movement. Very little of her work surfaced until recently. Accused of being a communist during the '50s, she saw her books rapidly go out of print. *House of All Nations* (1938) is perhaps her most noted work. In *The Man Who Loved Children* (1940), she creates a man of great immaturity and egocentricity who is unable to react thoughtfully to adults, including his wife. Henny and Sam Pollit are joined together in a relationship of non-communication, with their children acting as the go-betweens in the battle of sexual and family politics. Sam Pollit's energies are absorbed totally in cultivating the affections of his young children, without the recognition that children must inevitably mature into adults. Henny Pollit is absorbed in herself and the knot of her family relationships; she eventually commits suicide. Of Stead's own tragic lack of recognition, poet Randall Jarrell writes in the introduction: "her books have had varying receptions. *House of All Nations* was a critical success and a best-seller; *The Man Who Loved Children* was a failure both with critics and with the public. It has been out of print for many years, and Christina Stead herself is remembered by only a few readers. When the world rejects, and then forgets, a writer's most profound and imaginative book, he may unconsciously work in a more limited way in the books that follow it; this has happened, I believe, to Christian Stead. The world's incomprehension has robbed it, for twenty-five years of *The Man Who Loved Children*; has robbed it, forever, of what could have come after *The Man Who Loved Children*." For a recent analysis of Christina Stead's own impressions of her work, see the interview material given to Joan Lidoff in *Aphra* (Vol. 6, nos. 3 and 4).

978   Stein, Gertrude, 1874-1946. **Selected Writings of Gertrude Stein.** New York: Vintage Books, 1972. 706p. $3.95. ISBN 0394717104.

This collection was edited, with an introduction and notes, by Carl Van Vechten, and with an essay on Gertrude Stein by F. W. Dupee. It is an excellent choice for individuals and libraries who cannot afford to collect Stein in a comprehensive manner; this collection contains samples of her many periods, techniques, styles, and genres. Van Vechten's essay addresses Stein's habit of dealing with "actualities" and her fondness for describing the people she knew and the places currently on her mind when writing. His essay will serve as a helpful guide to the reader first coming to Stein. Contents include: *The Autobiography of Alice B. Toklas*; two plays: *Ladies' Voices* and *What Happened*; *The Making of Americans* (selected passages); portraits of the painters Cezanne, Matisse, and Picasso; poetry; and miscellaneous writings.

979   Stein, Gertrude, 1874-1946. **Three Lives.** New York: Vintage Books, 1958. 279p. $1.95. ISBN 0394701534.
Subtitled "Stories of the Good Anna, Melanctha, and the Gentle Lena," *Three Lives* (1909) is probably the most immediately comprehensible of Stein's work. Anna, a good-hearted housekeeper, spent her health and her identity on the hard labors of keeping other people's lives in order. Of her, Stein writes simply, "then they did the operation, and then good Anna with her strong, strained, wornout body died." Melanctha Herbert, a black woman, learns her power over men early in her womanhood. She goes through a cycle of relationships with men and women, finally dying as a consumptive. Of her, Stein writes, "Melanctha Herbert was always losing what she had in wanting all the things she saw. Melanctha was always being left when she was not leaving others." Finally, the story of Lena is that of a German servant's being pressured into marrying a man who doesn't want to marry her and dying in childbirth. Hers is a story of numbness: "but mostly Lena just lived along and was careless in her clothes, and dull and lifeless."

980*   Strindberg, August, 1849-1912. **Getting Married.** New York: Viking Press, 1973. 384p. bibliog. ISBN 0670337609. LC 72-11063.
A controversial book, *Getting Married* was attacked by feminists for being sexist and by clergy for being immoral. This particular edition—translated from Swedish, edited, and introduced by Mary Sandback—contains an excellent introduction to Strindberg's philosophy of marriage: namely, that marriage is an admirable institution that most individuals misuse and abuse because of the role that each sex expects the other to play. Strindberg is particularly appalled at the role of "knight" thrust upon the men and the woman's role of "doll," which turn each into a "tyrant" in the marriage relationship. In his preface, Strindberg reacts negatively to the interpretation of Ibsen's *A Doll's House* as a feminist manifesto, claiming that "Ibsen has caricatured the cultured man and woman . . . [in *Doll's House*] which has become the gospel of all the zealots for the Woman Question." In his own fascinating group of short stories (written in 1884) on marriage, he concentrates on several recurrent themes, which he identifies as pathological in modern middle-class marriages and love relationships: the tyranny of wives who expect to be waited upon and catered to after marriage; individuals who marry simply to be married even when the partner chosen is unsuitable; the financial struggles of men to support a married lifestyle; and the struggle for dominance within the marraige. Strindberg believes

that men especially need a sexual relationship for physical and mental well-being and that women are generally happiest when submitting to their husbands and rearing children. However, in his preface, he strongly defends equal education for men and women, marriage contracts, and remuneration for housework in marriage.

981 Suckow, Ruth, 1892-1960. **Iowa Interiors.** New York: Knopf, 1926; repr. New York: Arno Press, 1977. 283p. $22.00. ISBN 0405100574. LC 76-51679.

Iowa Interiors is a collection of sixteen short stories mostly set in rural Iowa by Iowa-born and raised Ruth Suckow. Elizabeth Hardwick introduces the collection, which has been published as part of the Arno series, Rediscovered Fiction by American Women: "*Iowa Interiors* tells of the generations, the difficult hours and working the land, the parents and children caught up in family, small town and village anxieties. Every situation and theme is recorded in a quiet but singularly skillful and serious manner. Ruth Suckow is especially interesting with old couples who have lived together in a compromise that always denies part of their feelings; they live, these enduring couples, usually in a social structure or with the mere bad luck of nature that does not justly accommodate their efforts and needs. . . . The stories are brilliantly alive, truthful, and alert to the rhythms of speech and feeling."

982 Vivien, Renée, 1877-1909. **A Woman Appeared to Me.** Reno, NV: Naiad Press, 1976. 91p. bibliog. $4.00. LC 76-45689.

Although Renée Vivien (born Pauline Mary Tarn) was Anglo-American, she chose to write in French. The translation of *Une femme m'apparut* (1904) rendered here by Jeannette H. Foster makes the now-rare French novel available to non-French readers. Gayle Rubin, a noted lesbian-feminist anthropolotist, has written a fine introduction in which she identifies the work of Renée Vivien as a major contribution to lesbian literature and discusses the remarkable *oeuvre* that Renée Vivien left (over twenty volumes of poetry and prose), each volume a celebration of love between women. Rubin's introduction details the lexbian society of Paris during the late 1890s, a lesbian renaissance that included Colette, Natalie Barney, and Violet Shilleto. *A Woman Appeared to Me* mirrors the events of Renée Vivien's life between 1899 and 1903, the period during which she had a tempestuous affair with Natalie Barney, which failed due to Barney's fondness for eclectic and uncommitted relationships. Rubin writes of the novel: "[it] is biographical, but it has the scrambled quality of inner thought and feeling. It records less the events themselves than Renée's emotional response to them. Moreover, Renée experienced her emotions very symbolically. Perhaps as part of her poetic craft, particular people became associated with any number of levels of imagery and significance. Renée's inner cosmology associated colors, flowers, legendary figures, and personal archetypes." The poetry of Vivien is available in two recent editions, one in English (*The Muse of the Violets: Poems*; Naiad Press, 1977), the other in French (*Poèmes de Renée Vivien*; orig. 1923/24, repr. Arno Press, 1975).

983   Walker, Alice, 1944- . **In Love and Trouble: Stories of Black Women.**
      New York: Harcourt, Brace and Jovanovich, 1973. 138p. $6.50.
      ISBN 0151444056. LC 73-7607.

In this stunning collection of stories, Walker seems to be saying that the permutations of experience even within an oppressed class can be overwhelming and
irreconcilable. In many of the stories, a strong woman is misunderstood, distorted, or ignored by the man with whom she is affiliated. In "Roselily," the
woman "thinks she loves the effort he will make to redo her into what he truly
wants." The deranged woman in "Really, Doesn't Crime Pay" puts herself
through an endless, mindless ritual of perfuming and dressing herself, passively
submitting to her man while plotting her escape from him. The jealous woman
in "Her Sweet Jerome" is married to a man who is in love with revolution
without even knowing his own wife.

984   Walker, Alice, 1944- . **Meridian.** New York: Harcourt, Brace and
      Jovanovich, 1976. 228p. $7.95. ISBN 0151592659. LC 76-941.

Walker paints a moving portrait of a black woman's coming of age during the
Civil Rights Movement. This short novel manages to bring to life a surprising
number of deep political issues, and Walker never balks before their complexity.
Rather it is the ambiguity of political and social life that Walker persistently
brings into focus—whether it be the contradictory reality of race, class, and
sex oppression in people's lives and in political struggle, or the tensions between
liberatory and authoritarian impulses in political movements.

985   Walker, Margaret, 1915- . **Jubilee.** Boston: Houghton Mifflin, 1966.
      497p. $9.95. ISBN 0395082889. LC 66-11218.

Walker has written an epic novel based on careful research of her great grand-
parents from Georgia, the Vyry and Randall Ware of this story. The story
follows the life of the noble slave, Vyry, through the antebellum South, the
Civil War, and the Reconstruction years. Vyry's portrait is that of a real and
human woman, a representative of the underside of the *Gone with the Wind*
fiction. Her decisions are consistently informed with great humanity and the
highest ethical considerations. Despite a lack of formal education herself, she
aspires to this for her children. Her nobility of bearing despite a lifetime of
sorrow and adversity provides a center for her family. Walker sculpts Vyry
and all of the black female characters of *Jubilee* as models of the strength and
peace inherent in the history of Afro-American womanhood. The process of
Walker's writing of *Jubilee* is in itself compelling reading. See *How I Wrote
Jubilee* (Third World, 1972).

986* Weldon, Fay. **Down Among the Women.** New York: St. Martin's
      Press, 1972. 216p. LC 72-78181.

Weldon gives a dry, feminist worldview in this significant contemporary novel:
specifically, life is hard "down among the women," especially if it is measured
in terms of a successful relationship with a man. Nothing is certain or easy
in Weldon's fictional world—relationships crumble; children turn on parents;
men are unfaithful to women; motherhood is bittersweet; childbirth, a torment;
contraception is uncertain; friends turn on each other. Weldon deals uniquely
with the intersecting friendships of women and the chronology of their lives.

Wanda, Scarlet, and Byzantia (grandmother, daughter, and granddaughter, respectively) are spokeswomen for their generations about the problems of women in their dealings with men. Weldon strikes a hopeful note in the character of Byzantia who emerges as a prototype of the New Woman "full and strong" by novel's end.

987   Weldon, Fay. **Female Friends: A Novel.** New York: Avon Books, 1975. $1.95.

Weldon is a humorist with great insights into the lives of women. Here she writes of Chloe, Marjorie, and Grace—three friends who came together during World War II and whose lives remain interwoven to the present day through husbands, lovers, parents, and children. Rich in the details of female life—menstruation, childbearing and rearing—the novel takes form in tracing the chronology of patterns in three women's lives. "We are obliged to agree that there is no such thing as an accident," says the narrator. In this novel of growth and hope, most of the characters see positive change by novel's end, not because they reject men, but because they see themselves in control of the patterns they make.

988   Weldon, Fay. **Remember Me.** New York: Random House, 1976. 248p. ISBN 0394405544. LC 76-14165.

Another of Weldon's positive and humorous novels about female friendships, this novel speaks penetratingly of relationships with men as they affect relationships with women. Lily, the efficient, beautiful, and somewhat shallow second wife must confront the identity and the death of Madeline, the jilted first wife. Margot, a good-natured and complacent wife and mother, faces upheaval of her own worldview through her connections with these two women and their husband, Jarvis. "As we grow older we sense more and more that human beings make connections in much the same manner as the basic materials of matter. . . . The linkages are unexpected; they can be of objects, plants, places, events, anything." Weldon's most recent novel, *Praxis* (Summit Books: Simon and Schuster, 1978), treats many important feminist issues including illegitimacy, incest, and sexual betrayal.

989   Welty, Eudora, 1909- . **Delta Wedding.** New York: Harcourt, Brace, 1946. 247p. $7.95. ISBN 0151247730. LC 46-3217.

Welty's gift is to render the subtle and intricate texture of family traditions and roots in an old southern family. Little happens in this uneventful narrative of the Fairchilds, who live on a large delta plantation. The story of the family's gathering and preparation for the wedding of a favorite daughter, Dabney, is rendered through the eyes of a nine-year-old visiting child, Laura. Thematically this is not a feminist novel, but rather a dazzling display of Welty's talent and her poetic virtuosity in rendering southern life and culture, a culture for which Welty has an obvious fondness. Welty's short fiction is perhaps her truest measure as a writer. See her *Thirteen Stories* (Harcourt, Brace and World, 1965).

990   West, Dorothy, 1909- . **The Living Is Easy.** New York: Arno Press, 1969. (Repr. of 1948 ed.). 347p. $14.00. ISBN 0405019424. LC 71-94139.

This first novel by West, *The Living Is Easy*, is set in Boston during the 1920s and '30s and dominated by Cleo Judson. A beautiful middle-class black woman of great pride and independence, Cleo is chiefly remarkable for her skill at manipulating those around her (especially her husband) for the sake of family obligations. She chose her husband, an older man, specifically for the security that he could provide. As she relates to a younger sister, "I've thought, and planned, and lied, and juggled Mr. Judson's money for this sister and that, so I could always know there was no one of my kin who didn't have food in her belly or clothes on her back." Cleo is compelling despite her machinations, and the dialogue in this spirited novel crackles with individuality and energy.

991   West, Rebecca, pseud. **The Fountain Overflows.** New York: Avon
       Books, 1974. 412p. $1.95.
In this novel originally published in 1956, the plot revolves around the marginal fortunes of the Aubrey family, a gifted if eccentric Victorian family. The strongest characters are women. The mother, a former concert pianist, struggles to provide culturally and financially for her gifted children despite the obstacles set up by a creative, but ne'er-do-well husband. The daughter, Rose, narrates the story of growing up in this late-nineteenth-century London household, emphasizing the strong traits of female family members who manage the tempestuous travails of family life with pride and dignity.

992   West, Rebecca, pseud. **Rebecca West: A Celebration, Selected from Her
       Writings by Her Publishers, with Her Help.** New York: Viking Press,
       1977. 780p. bibliog. index. $20.00. ISBN 0670590614. LC 76-21281.
Though reading an author in unexcerpted form is always preferable, this selection at least provides a glimmer into West's diverse fiction, especially since early works are out of print and unavailable. *St. Augustine* and *The Return of the Soldier*, two difficult-to-find early West works, are given here in their entirety. Cutting mars *Black Lamb and Grey Falcon* and *The Thinking Reed*, two particularly splendid West creations. A useful introduction by Samuel Hynes and a bibliography of her writing contribute to the usefulness of this reader.

993   Wharton, Edith Newbold (Jones), 1862-1937. **The Age of Innocence.**
       New York: Scribner, 1968. (Repr. of 1920 ed.). 361p. $10.00. ISBN
       0684146592. LC 75-41953.
Perhaps one of Wharton's finest novels, this is the love story of Newland Archer and Ellen Olenska, set within the context of the implacability of New York society and cultural mores toward the end of the nineteenth century. May Welland Archer and Ellen Olenska escape representing the stereotypes of the innocent, devoted wife as opposed to the sophisticated "other woman" because of Wharton's brilliant handling of the complexity of their social roles in a world of strict forms.

994   Wharton, Edith Newbold (Jones), 1862-1937. **The House of Mirth.**
       New York: New York University Press, 1977. 335p. $10.00. ISBN
       0814749763. LC 77-77299.
Published in 1905, the theme of this important Wharton novel is the systematic destruction of the vital and sensitive Lily Bart by the cold indifference of

New York society. A striking commentary on the role of women in high society, Lily comes to symbolize her hybrid environment even with her more compelling qualities. The title taken from Ecclesiastes ("The heart of fools is in the house of mirth") describes the shallowness of a world that Lily painfully comes to recognize for what it is.

995   Wittig, Monique. **Les Guerillères.** New York: Viking Press, 1971. 144p. ISBN 0670424633. LC 70-158421.

The vulva and its roundness is the central symbol working in Wittig's experimental novel, a symbol introduced by a large black circle at the beginning of the book. The format of the novel is an ingenious arrangement of literary forms, including litanies, prose poems, chants, hymns, and mythic stories, the whole a ritual chorus of celebration in praise of female heroism. At the same time, Wittig uses forms with such outrageous intent and with such intense abandon that her structure itself becomes a parody of traditional, male literary celebrations of masculine heroism, which employ inflated language as a means of self-aggrandizement. Wittig's work pioneers in finding forms in which to express and establish a feminist mythology.

996   Wittig, Monique. **The Lesbian Body.** New York: Morrow, 1975. 165p. $5.95. ISBN 0688029000. LC 75-7738.

"*Le Corps Lesbien* has lesbianism as its theme, that is, a theme which cannot even be described as taboo, for it has no real existence in the history of literature. Male homosexual literature has a past, it has a present. The lesbians, for their part, are silent—just as all women are as women at all levels. When one has read the poems of Sappho, Radclyffe Hall's *Well of Loneliness*, the poems of Sylvia Plath and Anaïs Nin, *La Bàtarde* by Violette Leduc, one has read everything. Only the women's movement has proved capable of producing lesbian texts in a context of total rupture with masculine culture, texts written by women exclusively for women, careless of male approval. *Le Corps Lesbien* falls into this category" (author's note). So split from male reality is Wittig's vision that she purposefully slashes personal first person pronouns to reflect the separatism. In French she uses "j/e." In the English version, "I" is used but "m/y" is divided. Wittig's novel, a controversial experiment in form, revels in female anatomy. Indeed, the content of the lyrical celebration takes a litany form in praise of each organ and orifice of the woman's body: "Your bare feet touch the blue calyces of the anemones as you walk. The pink violet white yellow snapdragons come to your calves, some as far as your thighs." Margaret Crosland wrote the introduction for this translation; see Crosland's *Women of Iron and Velvet* (Taplinger, 1976) for a full discussion of Wittig as a French woman writer.

997   Wittig, Monique. **The Opoponax.** Plainfield, VT: Daughters, 1976. 256p. $4.50. ISBN 0913780154. LC 76-7818.

Winner of the Prix Médicis in 1964, when Monique Wittig was 28, this experimental novel is a technical triumph in its form of narration. In it, Wittig recaptures a child's perception of the world around her in the person of Catherine Legrand from approximately her fifth to thirteenth year. By using the indefinite pronoun "on" in the French edition ("you" in English) Wittig invents a communication that is poetic and akin to spoken language while at the same time effective in its written form. The child often refers to herself by her full name, which never appears to disturb the hypnotic quality of the sensuous awakening to life and its possibilities that the young girl experiences. The childlike, non-stop flow of perceptions permits the reader to become one with the experience of Catherine Legrand.

998   Wollstonecraft, Mary, 1759-1797. **Maria; Or, The Wrongs of Woman.** New York: Norton, 1975. 154p. $6.95. ISBN 0393087131. LC 74-30341.

In her introduction, Moira Ferguson states that though *A Vindication of the Rights of Woman* is considered one of the most significant documents of early feminism, Wollstonecraft's fiction has been given scant attention. *"Maria or The Wrongs of Woman*, the novel [Wollstonecraft] was writing at the time of her death in 1797, echoes and often transcends the notions expressed in the *Vindication*. That this and her other works of fiction have been virtually inacces-sible till recently reflects not only a judgment on their value as literature in a traditional sense but indicates, in addition, the cultural preferences of the patriarchal society against which she rebelled." The novel depicts realistically the wrongs done to women and translates the more generalized charges that Wollstonecraft makes in *Vindication* into the concrete details of the life of Maria, the heroine, imprisoned in an asylum thanks to the efforts of her husband, who wishes to control her fortune. Jemima, a woman attendant whom Maria meets in the asylum, has formerly been a thief and a prostitute. In the course of the novel as we have it, both narrate their stories; Jemima, who has knowledge of London's street life and pauper institutions, seems to have fared worse than Maria, though both women have been prisoners of their class lots.

999   Wollstonecraft, Mary, 1759-1797. **Mary: A Fiction.** New York: Schocken Books, 1977. 110p. $7.50. ISBN 0805236570. LC 76-39618.

First printed in 1788, *Mary: A Fiction* was written during the period when Wollstonecraft served as a governess in Ireland. As this autobiographical novel reveals, Wollstonecraft was in great sympathy with the plight of her sensitive heroine. An example of the novel of sensibility, the story is about a woman born into a difficult family situation from which she escapes via her friendship with Ann, whose prototype was Wollstonecraft's dear friend, Fanny Blood. Mary is married to an unsympathetic though wealthy and socially prominent young man whom she finds repugnant. Her friend dies. Mary finds herself in a relationship with a sick but sensitive young man whom she cannot marry. Her return to her husband signals the beginning of a life devoted to good works, though not of fulfillment in the romantic sense. A sentimental and didactic work, *Mary* is chiefly interesting for the obstacles to a woman's independence that it chronicles.

1000   Woolf, Virginia (Stephen), 1882-1941. **Mrs. Dalloway.** New York: Harcourt, Brace and World, 1949. 296p. $3.95. ISBN 0151628629. LC 25-9749.

Originally published in 1925, *Mrs. Dalloway* is the stream-consciousness narra-tive of one day in the life of Clarissa Dalloway, socialite party-giving wife of

Richard Dalloway, a wealthy politician. Clarissa possesses an exquisite, even if glacial, sensibility and her entire day works toward climax in the party that she has carefully orchestrated. Counterpointed against this fundamentally ordered vision is the chaos of Septimus Smith's madness. Septimus moves through London during Clarissa's day, though they are not intended to meet. Death enters Clarissa's party when Smith's suicide is mentioned in passing. Clarissa's processing of the suicide remark suggests a much more complex Clarissa than the social woman we have watched during the day. Her meditation on the compelling quality of death reveals her more akin to Septimus than to any of the guests at her party.

1001   Woolf, Virginia (Stephen), 1882-1941. **Night and Day.** New York: Harcourt, Brace and Jovanovich, 1973. 508p. $4.25. ISBN 0156656000. LC 73-5730.
Night and Day (1919) explores straight-forwardly the very real problems of marriage. Like Rachel Vinrace in *The Voyage Out*, Katharine Hilbery cannot reconcile her own expectations of life and love with those of society. She is able to extricate herself from an engagement to an extremely rigid and conventional man in favor of an experimental relationship (a kind of marriage without the constrictions) by the end of the novel. However the experimental relationship of Ralph and Katharine is not tested in the course of the novel, so we can never know whether their plan of separate lives lived together will work. One of the most interesting social commentaries in *Night and Day* comes through in the portrayal of Mary Dachet's professional feminism. A humorless and drab "spinster," Mary works as the unpaid secretary in a suffrage society; her existence seems pale and somewhat comical next to Katharine's more daring and sexual experimentation. Clearly, Woolf's sympathies did not lie with formalized, "serious" feminism.

1002   Woolf, Virginia (Stephen), 1882-1941. **Orlando: A Biography.** New York: Harcourt, Brace and Jovanovich, 1973. 333p. $2.95. ISBN 015670160X. LC 73-5729.
First published in London in 1928, this is the most whimsical of Virginia Woolf's novels. It is an improbable, high-spirited fantasy that zigzags across history and geographical locations with dazzling speed and grace. Orlando begins as a sixteen-year-old male aristocrat serving as page to decrepit Queen Elizabeth I and is metamorphosed by the novel's conclusion into a 36-year-old female Orlando (said to be inspired by Woolf's friend, Vita Sackville-West), elegant in pearls and baring her breasts to the moonlight in October 1928 (near the publication date of *Orlando*). Orlando changed sex toward the end of the seventeenth century; the constant during the three centuries of this engaging chronicle is Orlando's yearning to be a poet, which she achieves at the end of the novel, along with the biologically creative act of giving birth to a son. History is handled with abandon, as Woolf sprinkles the novel with deliberate and irreverent errors. Hallucination is the order of the day, and there is more dashing, leaping, darting—in a word, action—than in any other Woolf fiction. Woolf is wonderful in the liberties she takes with British history. It cannot undercut the fun that she intended to suggest that she was also dealing with the more serious issue of gender-determined historical roles in the "real" world.

1003   Woolf, Virginia (Stephen), 1882-1941. **To the Lighthouse.** New York:
        Harcourt, Brace, 1949. 310p. $3.95. ISBN 0151907374. LC 37-28677.
Probably the most widely read of Woolf's novels, *To the Lighthouse* (1927)
draws heavily on the novelist's background as daughter of the professorial
Leslie Stephen (editor of the *Dictionary of National Biography*) and of Julia,
the ultra-maternal Victorian mother who died young after bearing many children
and sacrificing her strength to her husband's needs and intellectual life. Mrs.
Ramsay of the novel is the perfect wife and mother, the architect of order
and harmony in the house by the sea (St. Ives, summer home of the Stephen
family). In sharp contrast to Mrs. Ramsay—and threatened by Mrs. Ramsay's
presence, a totally commanding one in life and in death—Lily Briscoe (V.W.)
is a "spinster" artist, recoiling from Mrs. Ramsay's domesticity yet fearful of
drawing an essential line down her canvas to complete a creation. The journey
To the Lighthouse after Mrs. Ramsay's death comes to signify a spiritual quest
for the Ramsay children and Professor Ramsay, underscored by the refrain,
"we perish each alone." For Lily, watching the progress of the boat from the
shore while painting, the journey becomes the attainment of artistic inspiration
as she draws the significant line through the center of her picture.

1004   Woolf, Virginia (Stephen), 1882-1941. **The Voyage Out.** New York:
        Harcourt, Brace and World, 1968. 375p. $2.95. ISBN 0156936259.
        LC 68-6631.
Virginia Woolf's first published novel (1915) presages the complexity of later
novels, which become increasingly experimental. Helen Ambrose and her husband
set out on a voyage from London to a mythical South American coastal resort.
Accompanying the couple is their niece, Rachel, a young woman absorbed
by books and music, who has had little experience with the world. The novel
is preoccupied with the question of whether or not married life can be emotionally satisfying to a young, independent woman. If marriage is an unacceptable
choice, then what societally approved alternatives are available to her? The
death by the novel's end of Rachel, who has difficulty dealing with marriage
as the logical corollary to her relationship with a man, may suggest Woolf's
sense of skepticism, or even hopelessness, about the conventional lifestyles
to which young women must conform. Imagery of lighthouses and power
that Woolf uses with great skill in later novels appears in less sophisticated form
in *The Voyage Out*.

1005   Woolf, Virginia (Stephen), 1882-1941. **The Waves.** Toronto: University
        of Toronto Press, 1976. 55, 769, 62-72p. index. $29.50. ISBN
        0802016286. LC 71-185714.
Published in 1931 and the most experimental of Virginia Woolf's novels, *The
Waves* is a lyrical chorus of voices. All six of the voices are friends—three men
and three women. Susan, Rhoda, and Jinny represent familiar female types
in Woolf's fiction: the archetypal mother, the tense and fearful character sym-
bolizing the would-be-artist, and the sensual here-and-now woman emblematic
of the realist aspiring to nothing more than what she senses before her. Against
the swell of life's waves is the omnipresent and immovable spectre of death,
whose constant presence is registered by the absence of Percival, the voice of
a war fatality.

1006   Woolf, Virginia (Stephen), 1882-1941. **The Years.** New York: Harcourt,
        Brace, Jovanovich, 1969. 435p. $3.95. ISBN 0156997010. LC 37-27268.
The Years (orig. 1937) is typically interpreted as Woolf's fictional treatment
of the demise of the Victorian middle class and of its giving way to the emergence
of a liberated younger generation. Critical opinion is divided between those
who see the novel solely as a social document lacking poetry and vision and
those who judge the novel as one of Woolf's most visionary works, cyclical like
The Waves, with all characters transcending individual consciousness to participate in a final, encompassing, cosmic whole. The book's chapters present random
clots of time: 1880, 1891, 1907, 1908, 1910, 1911, 1913, 1914, 1917, 1918,
1936. Each section is preceded by a comment about a season, also random,
since no season follows in natural order. Then there is the presentation of the
diurnal order in which night may come before day, and day may follow close
upon day. Though outwardly events may be disordered and lacking in harmony,
the vision Woolf arrives at is a pattern of order and survival, as the fortunes
of the Pargiter family are traced through the generations, with Eleanor, the
eldest Pargiter daughter being the axis upon which the Pargiters and the years
turn. The scattered family and their many connections, representing diverse
strata of London society, suggest a pattern of human connectedness and meaning
not fully understood until Eleanor apprehends the form of the vision at the end
of the novel.

1007   Woolson, Constance Fenimore, 1840-1894. **Anne.** New York: Harper,
        1882; repr. New York: Arno Press, 1977. 540p. $22.00. ISBN
        0405100590. LC 76-51682.
Set in Fort Mackinac, an old Great Lakes settlement where Constance Woolson
had summered with her family, the novel has a good deal of detail about the
island culture of the Great Lakes, especially about French settlers and descen-
dents of the French and Indian minglings. *Anne* is a novel of the "struggling
young woman-makes good" genre, in which the heroine leaves her native surroundings to go to New York City as the ward of her aunt. Though the ensuing romantic
plot fails artistically, the novel is strong on setting and observations of the social
milieu from which Anne came and to which she came unprepared for snobbery
and hostility. Elizabeth Hardwick writes the introduction to this period-piece
novel in the Rediscovered Fiction by American Women series. This edition
contains the original illustrations by C. S. Reinhart, the popular magazine
illustrator.

1008   Wright, Zara. **Black and White Tangled Threads.** Chicago: Barnard and
        Miller, 1920; repr. New York: AMS Press, 1975. 340p. $24.50. ISBN
        0404113788. LC 73-18566.
"The lives of each character portrayed in this book remind one of tangled skeins
of threads. The heroine of this story portrays a type of womanhood so often
sought for, so rarely found. Circumstances have placed her in a false position,
she sacrifices her principles of right and wrong to save those near and dear to
her from imaginary shame and humiliation. Paul Andrews, a southern planter,
vies with the heroine in sharing honors. One cannot help admiring him. He
plays an important part in this story. There are other characters that play such
distinctive parts that we must leave it to the imagination of the reader to decide

which is the most appealing" (author's note). *Black and White Tangled Threads* appears on a list of important novels published before 1973 in Rita D. Dandridge "On Novels by Black American Women: A Bibliographical Essay," in *Women's Studies Newsletter* (Summer 1978).

1009   Yezierska, Anzia, 1885- . **Bread Givers: A Novel; A Struggle Between a Father of the Old World and a Daughter of the New.** Garden City, NY: Doubleday, Page, 1925; repr. New York: Persea Books, 1975. 297p. $3.95. ISBN 0892550147. LC 74-25319.

Anzia Yezierska takes us inside a world of poverty and patriarchy in her auto-biographical novel, which chronicles Jewish immigrant life on New York's lower east side. Her ear for the idiom is unerring; even passages of description have a colorful Yiddish quality that offers humor even as it conveys the grim reality of the family's impoverished situation. A feminist throughout, Yezierska maintains compassion for the father and mother she describes, though she abhors the tyranny of the Jewish patriarchal tradition that shaped her mother's life of servitude to the father. Yezierska's works, masterpieces about the poverty and culture of ghetto life, have only recently surfaced again after enjoying some popularity in the 1920s. See her short stories, *Hungry Hearts* (orig. 1920, repr. Arno Press, 1975). The introduction to *Bread Givers* is by Alice Kessler Harris.

LITERATURE
History and Criticism
[The scope note for Literature appears on p. 252.]

1010* Adburgham, Alison. **Women in Print: Writing Women and Women's Magazines from the Restoration to the Accession of Victoria.** London: Allen and Unwin, 1972. 302p. bibliog. ISBN 0040700054. LC 72-197099.

Many pre-Victorian women supported themselves by working in the writing trade, though it was considered less than gentlewomanly to make a point of it. This is a first-rate study of the array of pre-Victorian periodical literature for women and of the women who wrote it, spanning 1690-1870.

1011 Aird, Eileen M. **Sylvia Plath.** New York: Harper and Row, 1975. 114p. bibliog. $1.25. ISBN 006080341X.

This small but useful volume contains essays on *The Colossus, Crossing the Water, Winter Trees, Ariel, The Bell Jar* and the imagery found in Plath's work. The introduction makes the point that Plath's originality rests in her insistence that the domestic world, traditionally viewed as a sanctuary, in its preoccupation with childbearing, love, and security can contain the most explosive tragic elements.

1012 Allen, Mary, 1939- . **The Necessary Blankness: Women in Major American Fiction of the Sixties.** Urbana: University of Illinois Press, 1976. 226p. bibliog. index. $8.95. ISBN 0252005198. LC 75-38780.

This examines fiction by Barth, Pynchon, Purdy, Kesey, Roth, Updike, Oates, and Plath. Allen's contention is that women have not escaped from stereotypes in major contemporary American fiction, though she does not examine whether the omnipresence of vapid female characters is due to the fact that art often does imitate life, rather than the contrary. Her parade of losers includes Roth's castrating Jewish mothers; Upkike's dull, bovine beauties; Plath's defiant self-destructive heroines; Oates's terrified victims; and a gaggle of assorted passive types created by Barth, Pynchon, Purdy, and Kesey.

1013 Allphin, Clela. **Women in the Plays of Henrik Ibsen.** New York: Revisionist Press, 1975. bibliog. $34.95. ISBN 0877002118. LC 74-28455.

The author sees two major conflicting roles for women in Ibsen's drama: the traditional woman (usually a wife or fiancee) versus the non-conventional, intellectual, restless woman. Allphin examines and compares several psychological groups that appear prominently in the Ibsen corpus.

1014 Appignanesi, Lisa. **Femininity and the Creative Imagination: A Study of Henry James, Robert Musil and Marcel Proust.** New York: Beekman, 1973. $11.95.

Three major foci occur in this critical study: a) femininity as it is made to work artistically in the work of James, Musil, and Proust; b) analysis of the femininity myth as it occurs in the artistic vision of these three writers; c) an analysis of the femininity myth in all three authors as it might be used to understand the lives of real women. In each of the three writers, the author identifies femininity as a creative, spiritual quality functioning beyond and apart from rational and intellectual spheres.

1015   Arce de Vazquez, Margot. **Gabriela Mistral: The Poet and Her Work.** New York: New York University Press, 1964. 158p. bibliog. index. $2.95. ISBN 081470011X. LC 64-16899.
Gabriela Mistral (Lucila Godoy Alcayaga) was born in Chile in 1889 and achieved early recognition as a poet, enjoying a career rich in literary and diplomatic achievement without interruption until her death in 1957. For the reader first coming to Mistral's poetry, this is an excellent study of her life and work, enhanced by fine translations. The first Hispanic-American writer to receive the Nobel Prize for Literature (1945), Mistral was also a distinguished journalist. Her poetry includes *Antología* (1946); *Poesías Completas* (1958); *Desolacion* (1922); *Ternura* (1924); *Nubes Blancas* (1926); *Tala* (1938); and *Lagar* (1954).

1016   Auchincloss, Louis. **Pioneers and Caretakers: A Study of Nine American Women Novelists.** Minneapolis: University of Minnesota Press, 1965. 202p. index. $8.50. ISBN 0816603448. LC 65-17016.
This book of essays about the work of Sarah Orne Jewett, Edith Wharton, Ellen Glasgow, Willa Cather, Elizabeth Madox Roberts, Katherine Anne Porter, Jean Stafford, Carson McCullers, and Mary McCarthy has as its focus the notion that "our women writers ... have struck a more affirmative note than the men. Their darkness is not as dark as that of Dreiser or Lewis or Faulkner or O'Neill, which is not to say that they see America less clearly, but that they may see it more discriminatingly. ... They never destroy; they never want a clean sweep. They are conservatives who are always trying to conserve" (author's preface).

1017   Auerbach, Nina, 1943- . **Communities of Women: An Idea in Fiction.** Cambridge, MA: Harvard University Press, 1978. 222p. bibliog. index. $11.50. ISBN 0674151682. LC 77-21213.
Auerbach looks closely at the concept of communities of women and compares how it works in seven well-known novels: Austen's *Pride and Prejudice* with Alcott's *Little Women*; Gaskell's *Cranford* with Charlotte Brontë's *Villette*; James's *The Bostonians* with Gissing's *The Odd Women*. Auerbach sees contemporary women characters as mythological types and regrets the loss of individuality that they possessed in nineteenth-century communities of women. She calls this chapter dealing with women's withdrawal into a woman's world, "One Big Miss Brodie" after Muriel Spark's *The Prime of Miss Jean Brodie*, and shows how writers like Barnes and Wittig have implemented Muriel Spark's model. This important book has clear explication and carefully wrought notes.

1018   Auster, Henry, 1938- . **Local Habitations: Regionalism in the Early Novels of George Eliot.** Cambridge, MA: Harvard University Press, 1970. 232p. bibliog. index. $10.00. ISBN 0674536762. LC 74-116734.
In this revision of the author's thesis (Harvard, 1966), the background of Eliot's regionalism is discussed in "The Critics Surveyed: Responses to George Eliot's

Regionalism"; "Country Matters: Regionalism, Realism, and George Eliot's Fiction"; and "Toward Social History: Continuity and Development in George Eliot's Fiction." In the section treating the actual fiction, in-depth analyses are given for *Scenes of Clerical Life, Adam Bede, The Mill on the Floss,* and *Silas Marner.*

1019   Bald, Marjory Amelia. **Women—Writers of the Nineteenth Century.** Cambridge, England: Cambridge University Press, 1923; repr. New York: Russell and Russell, 1963. 288p. $17.00. ISBN 0846203421. LC 63-8356.

This classic work on nineteenth-century women writers has chapters on Jane Austen, the Brontës, Mrs. E. C. Gaskell, George Eliot, Mrs. Browning, and Christina Rossetti. It is useful reading about women's mood or temperament and creative process when read alongside such important recent criticism as Ellen Moer's *Literary Women* (1976).

1020   Basch, Francoise. **Relative Creatures: Victorian Women in Society and the Novel, 1837-67.** New York: Schocken Books, 1974. 360p. bibliog. index. $12.50. ISBN 0805235655. LC 74-8634.

This study of women in the work of major Victorian writers—Dickens, Thackeray, Gaskell, Brontë, and Eliot—is an attempt to study the gap between the reality of the lives of Victorian women and their portrayal in important novels of the day. As such, it is a useful volume for both literature and social history courses. It includes chapters on wives and mothers, single and working women, and fallen women.

1021   Baym, Nina. **Woman's Fiction: A Guide to Novels By and About Women in America, 1820-1870.** Ithaca, NY: Cornell University Press, 1978. 320p. bibliog. index. $15.00. ISBN 0801411289. LC 77-90897.

Novel-writing was an established women's profession between 1820 and 1870. Largely discounted as "feminine fiction" now, this literature has much to say about the experiences of women and the social history of America. Baym makes the point that often literary critics have turned to writers such as Harriet Beecher Stowe for validation of women's place in the mid 1880s, not to the writers who concerned themselves with "woman's place." Novelists whose fiction is discussed: Catharine Sedgwick, Maria McIntosh, E.D.E.W. Southworth, Caroline Lee Hentz, Susan and Anna Warner, Maria Cummins, Ann Stephens, Mary Jane Holmes, Marion Harland, Caroline Chesebro, and Augusta Evans. The critic attempts to prove that characters in the "domestic novel" genre were encouraged by their creators to take responsibility for their lives and to broaden their educational horizons. The chronologically arranged bibliography will interest social historians.

1022   Bazin, Nancy Topping, 1934- . **Virginia Woolf and the Androgynous Vision.** New Brunswick, NJ: Rutgers University Press, 1973. 251p. bibliog. index. $13.50. ISBN 0813507359. LC 72-4198.

Bazin uses a Jungian framework to discuss Woolf's creative process in terms of her effort to fuse masculine and feminine sensibilities in order to arrive at truth: the androgynous vision. Tracing through the major novels and drawing from letters and diary entries, Bazin critically analyzes problems of form and content in Woolf's fiction in terms of her continual examination of the tension between male and female principles—her "quest for equilibrium." This is an important critical study of Woolf.

1023   Beer, Patricia. **Reader, I Married Him: A Study of the Women Characters of Jane Austen, Charlotte Brontë, Elizabeth Gaskell, and George Eliot.** New York: Barnes and Noble, 1974. 213p. bibliog. $15.00. ISBN 0064903451. LC 75-306807.

Beer gives the reader lively essays on the situation of women as handled by four nineteenth-century English women novelists. Because the Woman Question was beginning to burn as a serious matter during this important period in fiction writing, and because there are often considerable gaps between what each novelist thought about feminism and the views of her characters, this analysis is particularly significant. Chapter 1 is an extremely perceptive examination of the private attitudes on women held by Austen, Brontë, Gaskell, and Eliot. For a discussion of this same question at an earlier date, see Joyce Mary Horner, *The English Women Novelists and Their Connections with the Feminist Movement (1688-1797)* (orig. 1930; repr. Norwood Editions, 1977).

1024   Benson, Ruth Crego. **Women in Tolstoy: The Ideal and the Erotic.** Urbana: University of Illinois Press, 1973. 141p. bibliog. $6.95. ISBN 0252002873. LC 72-92631.

Benson concentrates on Tolstoy's treatment of women in *Family Happiness, War and Peace, Anna Karenina*, and three of his late short works and finds that Tolstoy reflected in his fiction his own tormented and divided experience of women: women as saints, devoted to husbands and children; and women as sinners, caught up in adulterous liaisons, threatening to men because of the demanding nature of their uncontrollable sexual appetites. This is an important critical study in that most Tolstoyan critics have concentrated on his heroes. The analysis of *Anna Karenina*, bringing out as it does the range of women's capabilities for building and undermining complex family relationships, is particularly fine.

1025   Blom, Margaret Howard. **Charlotte Brontë.** Boston: Twayne, 1977. 176p. bibliog. index. $8.50. ISBN 0805766731. LC 76-42225.

This is a handy reference tool that undergraduates will surely find useful because of its familiar Twayne format. For any substantive analysis of Brontë from a secondary or biographical perspective, readers will want to go to Margot Peter's *Unquiet Soul* (Doubleday, 1975) and to the classic biographical source, Mrs. Gaskell's *The Life of Charlotte Brontë* (orig. 1924, edited by Alan Shelston, Penguin, 1975).

1026   Bogan, Louise, 1897-1970. **Achievement in American Poetry, 1900-1950.** Chicago: Gateway Editions, 1951. 140p. bibliog. index. $1.25. ISBN 0895269244. LC 56-14022.

This can hardly be considered feminist criticism. Bogan treats the work of important American poets, male and female. She has a particularly excellent chapter, Truth and Feeling, in which she defines the changes in women's verse between the late nineteenth and twentieth centuries. Among the women discussed in this critical volume are Louise Imogen Guiney (1861-1920), Lizette Woodworth Reese (1856-1935), Emily Dickinson (1830-1886), Gertrude Stein (1874-1946), Sara Teasdale (1884-1933), Edna St. Vincent Millay (1892-1952), Elinor Wylie (1885-1928), H.D. (1886-1961), Leonie Adams (1899-), Marianne Moore (1887-1972), and Elizabeth Bishop (1911-). Bogan's 1947 essay "The Heart and the Lyre," from Robert Phelps, ed., *A Poet's Alphabet: Reflections on the Literary Art and Vocation* (1970), is useful to consult on women's experimentation with form and language.

1027   Bradford, Gamaliel, 1863-1932. **Elizabethan Women.** Boston: Houghton Mifflin, 1936; repr. Freeport, NY: Books for Libraries Press, 1969. 242p. bibliog. index. $15.00. ISBN 0836950011. LC 75-75505.
First published in 1936, this is a series of essays by the specialist in Elizabethan literature, Gamaliel Bradford, collected by the editor, Harold Ogden White. The essays are divided into two sections: Part 1, The Daily Life of Elizabethan Women, discusses the education, home life and social life of Elizabethan women; part 2, The Women of Elizabethan Literature, discusses the women of Dekker, Heywood, Middleton, Webster, Beaumont, Fletcher, Massinger, Ford, Shirley, and others, as well as the women of "The Fairy Queen" and the Cleopatra of tragedy.

1028   Brée, Germaine. **Women Writers in France: Variations on a Theme.** New Brunswick, NJ: Rutgers University Press, 1973. 90p. bibliog. $5.00. ISBN 0813507715. LC 73-13700.
Taking up the debate known as the "querelle des femmes," in which a learned fourteenth-century French woman, Christine de Pisan, took issue with her contemporaries on their unenlightened stance toward women, Brée presents cameos of French women writers from the fourteenth to the twentieth centuries: Christine de Pisan, Marguerite d'Angoulême, Simone de Beauvoir, Marguerite Duras, and Nathalie Sarraute. Because this essay was originally presented as a lecture, readers may find it more helpful for its broad analyses than for in-depth development on the topic of women writers in France. For an in-depth examination of women in French literature as related to feminism, see Ian Maclean, *Woman Triumphant: Feminism in French Literature 1610-1652* (Clarendon Press, 1977).

1029   Brewster, Dorothy, 1883- . **Virginia Woolf.** New York: New York University Press, 1962. 184p. bibliog. index. $7.95. ISBN 081470056X. LC 62-19050.
This useful little study was written before the publication of the definitive biography and the collected letters, and thus is somewhat incomplete in its analysis of how Woolf worked and what she thought about her writing. Its three major sections deal with Woolf's biography, her fiction, and her critical writing.

1030   Brown, Cheryl L., 1951- , and Karen Olson, eds. **Feminist Criticism: Essays on Theory, Poetry, and Prose.** Metuchen, NJ: Scarecrow Press, 1978. 369p. bibliog. index. ISBN 081081143X. LC 78-8473.

One hopes that this excellent anthology of feminist criticism will get the wide reading it deserves. Represented are several of the most talented academic feminist critics. Divided into three sections (Theoretical Feminist Literary Criticism; Practical Feminist Literary Criticism: Poetry; Practical Feminist Literary Criticism: Prose), the anthology will find its way into classrooms as a text for women's studies courses. It will be a valuable addition to other courses on literary criticism. Essays are consistently excellent and far-ranging. A sampling: Annette Kolodny, "Some Notes on Defining a 'Feminist Literary Criticism' "; Susan Friedman, "Who Buried H.D.? A Poet, Her Critics, and Her Place in 'The Literary Tradition' "; Suzanne Juhasz, " 'The Blood Jet': The Poetry of Sylvia Plath"; Evelyn Thomas Helmick, "Zora Neale Hurston"; and Agate Krouse, "Toward a Definition of Literary Feminism."

1031   Burkhart, Charles. **Charlotte Brontë: A Psychosexual Study of Her Novels.** New York: Humanities Press, 1973. 159p. bibliog. $8.50. ISBN 0575016612. LC 73-174333.

Burkhart writes an excellent study of Brontë's essential modernity in her search for self, as he demonstrates her Victorian literary consciousness. He examines the reasons that Brontë's novels still capture the popular imagination and theorizes on the reasons for the Victorian audience's acceptance of the sexuality in her novels. So much has been written on Brontë (as Burkhart is quick to recognize) that his thorough bibliography with concise annotations is very useful in placing the various critical approaches to Brontë. As might be expected, he places strong emphasis on the autobiographical parallels in Brontë's work and examines her four novels as chapters in psychosexual development–*The Professor*: Rites of Passage; *Jane Eyre*: The Art of the Adolescent; *Shirley*: The Eternal Feminine; *Villette*: The Art of the Adult.

1032   Butler, Marilyn. **Jane Austen and the War of Ideas.** Oxford: Clarendon Press, 1975. 310p. bibliog. index. $22.50. ISBN 0198120680. LC 75-327777.

The critical approach here is to define Austen's moral goals and to examine the didactic and partisan undercurrents that are so characteristic of Austen's fiction. Butler looks to the novels of the day, attempting both to place Austen in the context of the Jacobin novel and to compare and contrast her work with that of such contemporaries as Maria Edgeworth and Ann Radcliffe. Part 2 of this critical volume discusses each major novel separately, with chapters on *Northanger Abbey, Sense and Sensibility, Pride and Prejudice, Mansfield Park, Emma*, and *Persuasion*.

1033   Butscher, Edward, ed. **Sylvia Plath: The Woman and the Work.** New York: Dodd, Mead, 1977. 242p. bibliog. $8.95. ISBN 0396074979. LC 77-24700.

Butscher is the author of *Sylvia Plath: Method and Madness* (1976). This book is a collection of seventeen essays by friends and critics. The first half of the book ("The Woman") consists of personal memoirs written by Plath's friends recalling her years at Smith, in England and in New York. The second half ("The Work") discusses the poetry both technically and autobiographically. Two of the more interesting essays in this section are Joyce Carol Oates's "The Death Throes of

Romanticism" and Irving Howe's "The Plath Celebration: A Partial Dissent."
Howe asserts, "after the noise abates and the judgment returns, Sylvia Plath
will be regarded as an interesting minor poet whose personal story was poignant."

1034   Calder, Jenni. **Women and Marriage in Victorian Fiction**. New York:
       Oxford University Press, 1976. 223p. bibliog. index. $10.00. ISBN
       0195198565. LC 75-42965.
Calder clearly believes that the themes of literature and the concerns of real
life are worth considering together. Since a given of the Victorian novel is the
exploration of domestic life and relationships, Calder argues that social history
can provide a fuller literary reading of Victorian fiction. Thackeray, Tolstoy,
Charlotte Brontë, Dickens, Eliot, Gaskell, Meredith, and Gissing are among the
novelists that Calder considers. A central thesis is that the institution of marriage
was basic to Victorian society and thus to the plot of the novels; "it was always
there to provide a staple of plot and action, of assumptions about what people
wanted, how they behaved, and what the roots of life were." Among her chapters:
The Moral Marriage; The Perils of Independence; The Uncommercial Marriage;
The Doll in the Doll's House; Passionate Women and Predatory Men. A selective
chronology at the end of the book gives dates of nineteenth-century books
pertinent to the subject and of important legislation affecting the status of
women.

1035   Coffin, Tristram Potter, 1922- . **The Female Hero in Folklore and
       Legend**. New York: Seabury Press, 1975. 223p. $10.95. ISBN
       0816492638. LC 75-14412.
Coffin explores types—"The Golden Girl" and "Grotesque Roses"—and includes
a portrait gallery of magical ladies, feminists, and reformers (Cleopatra, Guinevere,
Eleanor of Aquitaine, Zelda Fitzgerald, Mata Hari, Annie Oakley, Sarah Bernhardt, and Lydia Pinkham). This is a book of snippets from sources such as
Andreas Capellanus and *De Amore Libri Tres* to Erich Fromm's interpretation
of "Little Red Riding Hood." The treatment is topical, and Coffin makes a
case that despite women's liberation, these larger-than-life female heroes will
always be around. Good photographs and illustrations enhance the work.

1036   Colby, Vineta. **The Singular Anomaly: Women Novelists of the Nineteenth
       Century**. New York: New York University Press, 1970. 313p. bibliog.
       index. $11.00. ISBN 0814700969. LC 70-92522.
This critical study considers that group of late nineteenth-century English novels
written by women novelists, which enjoyed huge popular success mainly because
they didactically interpreted Victorian bourgeois domestic society. Among
the prominent practitioners of this literary genre were Mrs. Eliza Linton, Olive
Schreiner, Mrs. Humphrey Ward, John Oliver Hobbes, and Vernon Lee. Although
these novels are seldom read today, a study of these works provides a clear
insight into Victorian values and mores.

1037   Colby, Vineta. **Yesterday's Woman: Domestic Realism in the English
       Novel**. Princeton, NJ: Princeton University Press, 1974. 269p. bibliog.
       index. $14.00. ISBN 069102633. LC 73-2469.

Novels that centered on home life and bourgeois domestic values were the literary mainstay of English households during the first half of the nineteenth century. Female-dominated, these novels were written by female authors, read by a largely female audience, and peopled by domestic heroines. Colby traces the history of the novel of domestic realism as a genre and discusses at length its variations in the work of Mrs. Gore, Maria Edgeworth, Charlotte Elizabeth, Charlotte Yonge, and Harriet Martineau.

1038   Cornillon, Susan Koppelman, comp. **Images of Women in Fiction:**
        Feminist Perspectives. (Rev. ed.). Bowling Green, OH: Bowling Green
        University Popular Press, 1972. 399p. bibliog. index. $10.00. ISBN
        0879720484. LC 72-89999.
Cornillon's volume of collected feminist criticism is exemplary for the quality of the essays included and for the organizing principles used to order the material. "This book is divided into four sections depicting the roles women have been forced to assume in society and are now beginning to occupy, beginning with the most desiccated and lifeless traditional stereotypes of woman as heroine, and as invisible person, progressing through an awakening to reality, wherein the woman is treated as person, and ending with the newest insistence by women that we are equal in all respects to men." The section "Women as Heroine" contains Joanna Russ's classic essays "What Can a Heroine Do? Or Why Women Can't Write" and "The Image of Women in Science Fiction." "The Invisible Woman" segment contains personal essays such as Tillie Olsen's "Silences: When Writers Don't Write" and Carole Zonis Yee's "Why Aren't We Writing about Ourselves?" In "The Woman as Hero" section, Ellen Morgan writes of the neo-feminist novel and Nan Bauer Maglin of fictional feminists. Dawn Holt Anderson writes an important essay on women in May Sarton's fiction, and Judith Little, on heroism in *To the Lighthouse* Perhaps the section on "Feminist Aesthetics" is the true marrow of this book, with significant essays on feminism and the study of literature by Florence Howe, Marcia R. Lieberman, and Josephine Donovan, among others. Included is one of the most useful bibliographies available on women writers.

1039   Daiches, David, 1912- . **Virginia Woolf.** (Rev. ed.). New York: New
        Directions, 1963. 169p. $2.75. ISBN 0811200310. LC 62-16926.
This excellent little volume of criticism is one of the jewels of critical thought on Woolf. Written in 1942, it remains one of the essential critical companions to Woolf. In addition to Daiches's discussion of the fiction, he writes a very tight, sound biographical chapter, which serves to introduce his critical discussion, and concludes with a splendid chapter on Woolf's *The Common Reader* and the novelist's unique critical facility.

1040   Deegan, Dorothy (Yost). **The Stereotype of the Single Woman in**
        American Novels: A Social Study with Implications for the Education
        of Women. New York: King's Crown Press, 1951; repr. New York:
        Octagon Books, 1969. 252p. bibliog. index. $10.50. ISBN 0374920907.
        LC 69-16754.
Fiction from before 1951 is used here as a social document to study the "problem" of the single woman. Though the author argues that the rights of single women

must be respected, it is clear that she subscribes to some of the assumptions imposed by the stereotype even as she seeks to expose "the derogatory social attitude toward women who do not marry" that novelists have "unwittingly" reinforced. Her chapter defining the research problem and reviewing the literature on single women will be very helpful for those researching American attitudes toward single women pre-1950. She uses 125 novels of the Dickinson lists of American fiction as the base for her data. The numerically demonstrated conclusion that Deegan draws from looking at the novels is predictably that the single woman "is at best, an unfortunate member of society. She may be useful in her small sphere, but in a humble way. She may be loved and respected, but she is likewise pitied or ridiculed." The list of single women characters, the novels from which they are taken, and the dates of the novels could be of considerable use to the researcher.

1041   Diamond, Arlyn, 1941- , and Lee R. Edwards, eds. **The Authority of Experience: Essays in Feminist Criticism.** Amherst: University of Massachusetts Press, 1977. 304p. bibliog. $15.00. ISBN 0870232207. LC 76-8755.

Broadly organized around the principle that the contributing "authors should address themselves generally to the problem of defining feminist criticism and/or deal in some declaredly feminist way with significant English or American texts," this volume of sixteen essays illustrates that literary materials can be legitimately examined in a feminist context. Included here are three theoretical essays on feminist criticism, by Annette Barnes, Marcia Landy, and Lynn Sukenick; essays on Chaucer, by Maureen Fries and Arlyn Diamond; an essay on *The Taming of the Shrew*, by Coppelia Kahn; on *Moll Flanders*, by Miriam Lerenbaum; on Samuel Richardson, by Katherine Rogers; on *Jane Eyre*, by Maurianne Adams; on *Mrs. Dalloway*, by Lee R. Edwards; and on *The Golden Notebook*, by Mary Cohen. Other essays deal with works by Kate Chopin, Katherine Anne Porter, Herman Melville, and Ernest Hemingway.

1042   Donovan, Josephine, 1941- , ed. **Feminist Literary Criticism: Explorations in Theory.** Lexington: University Press of Kentucky, 1975. 81p. bibliog. $4.00. ISBN 0813113342. LC 75-12081.

Among the essays gathered here from a symposium on feminism and literature at the University of Kentucky in 1973 are: Cheri Register's "American Feminist Criticism: A Bibliographical Introduction"; Dorin Schumacher's "Subjectivities: A Theory of Critical Process"; Marcia Holly's "Consciousness and Authenticity: Toward a Feminist Aesthetic"; Bell and Ohmann's "Virginia Woolf's Criticism: A Polemical Preface"; Heilbrun and Stimpson's "Theories of Feminist Criticism: A Dialogue"; and Josephine Donovan's "Afterword: Critical Re-Vision." This collection of essays offers a good cross section of the concerns of feminist literary critics and of the problems which they face in formulating a method and in pioneering new critical approaches. The bibliographical introduction will be very helpful to students coming to a women's literature course with little or no background in feminist criticism. A theme that runs throughout is the need for personal, human literary criticism.

1043   Douglas, Ann, 1942- . **The Feminization of American Culture.** New
         York: Knopf, 1977. 403p. bibliog. index. $15.00. ISBN 0394405323.
         LC 76-47923.
Douglas brilliantly probes "the drive of nineteenth-century American women
to gain power through the exploitation of their feminine identity as their
society defined it." She equates "feminizing" forces with sentimental influences
which circumvented possibilities of growth and change in American culture.
She critically examines culture heroines such as Little Eva, clerical and feminine
patterns of disestablishment, the alliance between the institutions of clergy and
motherhood, and the role of the periodical press. Part Three, Protest: Case
Studies in Romanticism, contains chapters on Margaret Fuller and Herman
Melville. The notes are first-rate and Douglas supplies the reader with fascinating
appendices of the women she discusses and the men with whom they were
affiliated.

1044   Earnest, Ernest Penney, 1901- . **The American Eve in Fact and Fiction,
         1775-1914.** Urbana: University of Illinois Press, 1974. 280p. bibliog.
         index. $9.50. ISBN 0252004485. LC 74-19339.
Earnest's book is a study of American "girls" rather than women between the
Revolution and World War I. Central to his study are the works of Henry James
and William Dean Howells. He deals with common stereotypes of American
girlhood and womanhood and with familiar figures in history and in literature.
Chapters include: The Revolutionary Women; Girls and Goddesses; Daisy and
Jenny—The American Girl in Europe; The College Girl, the Gibson Girl and
the Titaness. Particularly fascinating are the diary excerpts that Earnest chose
for inclusion—revelations often at odds with the popularized Victorian stereotypes.

1045   Eckley, Wilton. **Harriette Arnow.** New York: Twayne, 1974. 138p.
         bibliog. index. $7.50. ISBN 0805700234. LC 73-18406.
According to Eckley, his study is the first substantial secondary source to appear
on Harriette Arnow, a fine writer of fiction and social history whose work
first appeared in the thirties. Arnow's novels *Hunter's Horn* (1949) and *The
Dollmaker* (1954) were among the best sellers of their time, yet she is only
now being rediscovered and accorded critical acclaim. In his first chapter,
Eckley presents a biographical sketch of Arnow—of her childhood in Kentucky,
her early compulsion to write, her marriage and efforts to combine writing
and parenthood. The next six chapters discuss her work: chapter 2, her novel
Mountain Path (1936); chapter 3, her short stories; chapter 4, *Hunter's Horn*;
chapter 5, *The Dollmaker*; chapter 6, her social histories, *Seedtime on the
Cumberland* (1963) and *Flowering of the Cumberland* (1960); and chapter 7,
her most recent novel, *The Weedkiller's Daughter* (1970). In his final chapter,
Eckley offers a critical assessment of Arnow's work as a whole. Eckley's biography of Arnow is based on taped interviews with her and her husband and also
on her unpublished notes, letters, and manuscripts. A bibliography of Arnow's
work is appended.

1046   Ellmann, Mary. **Thinking about Women.** New York: Harcourt, Brace
         and World, 1968. 240p. bibliog. index. $3.45. ISBN 0156899000.
         LC 67-20309.

Ellmann writes a witty, often acerbic analysis of the sexes perceiving each other in literature and literary criticism. She is difficult reading because she moves so dazzlingly and irreverantly among an enormous number of literary concepts and personalities. "Sexist" critics merit her special scorn. She writes of the sexual analogy between the writer's art and the writer's sex, of phallic criticism, of feminine stereotypes from formlessness to compliancy, of shrews and witches, of differences in tone of female and male writers, and of nineteenth-century women writers' response to life and the living of it.

1047*   Evans, Patrick David, 1944- . **Janet Frame.** Boston: Twayne, 1977.
        228p. bibliog. index. $9.50. ISBN 080576254X. LC 77-4752.
Janet Frame, a New Zealand novelist noted for her lyrical style and innocent perception of the world, deserves more attention than she has received. A parabolic novelist, her work transcends the regionalism of New Zealand. *Scented Gardens for the Blind* (1963) is the novel that brought her an international audience. Evans links Frame's personal tragedies to her metaphoric worldview. The first bibliography of Frame's work appears here, as well as a good bibliography of the relatively scarce secondary sources.

1048   Ferlazzo, Paul J. **Emily Dickinson.** Boston: Twayne, 1976. 168p.
        bibliog. index. $7.95. ISBN 0805771808. LC 76-48304.
Ferlazzo writes an introductory study to Dickinson, her life, and work that will be useful to the undergraduate trying to sort through the maze of Emily Dickinson scholarship. Format follows the Twayne series style with a chronology and a selected, briefly annotated bibliography. A very clear and direct presentation, this incorporates a good selection from Dickinson's poetry.

1049   Ferrante, Joan M., 1936- . **Woman as Image in Medieval Literature, from the Twelfth Century to Dante.** New York: Columbia University Press, 1975. 166p. bibliog. index. $10.00. ISBN 0231039298. LC 74-26652.
Drawing upon the images of Eve (temptress) and Mary (inspiration and virgin), the author traces the treatment of woman in medieval literature, specifically in the symbolic genres of allegory, lyric romance, and biblical exegesis. The image of woman in medieval literature reflects a symbology in shift: from a negative image in biblical exegetical literature, woman moves toward a positive twelfth-century interpretation, then back to a negative thirteenth-century representation, until in the work of Dante she becomes a celebration of the immortal and the instrument of man's salvation.

1050   Fiedler, Leslie A. **Love and Death in the American Novel.** (Rev. ed.). New York: Stein and Day, 1966. 512p. index. $10.00. ISBN 0812811054. LC 66-14948.
Fiedler set out to prove that the American novel "has a character and fate different from the novel in France, Germany, even Russia." He has concentrated on the themes of love and death treated by major American novels, giving full-scale analyses to novels such as *Moby-Dick, The Scarlet Letter*, and *Huckleberry Finn*. He is firmly rooted in Freudian and Jungian theory. Of most interest to women's studies scholars will be part 2 of Fiedler's study and the chapters:

Clarissa in America: Toward Marjorie Morningstar; Good Good Girls and Good
Bad Boys: *Clarissa* as a Juvenile; The Failure of Sentiment and the Evasion
of Love; The Revenge on Woman: from Lucy to Lolita. Fiedler's exploration
of sentimental archetypes, of mythic romance, of marriage, and of mythical
heroines is important as it offers some theory of why it has been "almost
impossible for our novelists to portray adult sexual passion or a fully passionate
woman."

1051 Finkelstein, Bonnie Blumenthal. **Forster's Women: Eternal Differences.**
New York: Columbia University Press, 1975. 183p. bibliog. index.
$9.00. ISBN 0231038933. LC 74-18418.
This critic identifies Forster's greatest characters as women and suggests that
there is an androgynous ideal in the novelist's works, a radical notion of sexuality
in Victorian society shared by his contemporary, Virginia Woolf. In this competent critical study, the author analyzes the novels: *Where Angels Fear to
Tread, The Longest Journey, A Room with a View, Howards End, A Passage
to India*, and *Maurice.*

1052 Fleishman, Avrom. **Virginia Woolf: A Critical Reading.** Baltimore, MD:
Johns Hopkins University Press, 1975. 232p. bibliog. index. $12.00.
ISBN 0801816165. LC 74-24375.
Fleishman sums up his critical study as "simply a reading of Woolf's nine major
fictional works." His approach is eclectic, resulting in a guide to mythic, historical,
biographical, and symbolic truths in Woolf's novels, which he names "fictions."
He posits a theory of Woolf's "repetitive style," one that seeks to define the
truth of past experiences by recreating them in their infinite variety. Chapters
are arranged by novels, considered in order of publication, beginning with
The Voyage Out.

1053 Fryer, Judith. **The Faces of Eve: Women in the Nineteenth Century
American Novel.** New York: Oxford University Press, 1976. 294p.
bibliog. index. $11.95. ISBN 0195020251. LC 75-32345.
Although Fryer has been faulted for discussing male notions of the "faces of
Eve" rather than concentrating on women writers, Fryer writes well and her
analyses of Henry James, Nathaniel Hawthorne, and Herman Melville are
important explorations of "the myth of America as the New World Garden of
Eden, which I believe to be the dominant myth of American culture." Peopling
this Garden are the various forms of the American Eve in the guises of Temptress,
American Princess, Great Mother, and New Woman.

1054 Gasiorowska, Xenia. **Women in Soviet Fiction, 1917-1964.** Madison:
University of Wisconsin Press, 1968. 288p. bibliog. index. $14.00.
ISBN 0299047806. LC 68-16060.
Gasiorowska's study traces four major types of women found in Soviet literature.
The pre-1917 peasant housewife and her transformation into the heroine of
the Revolution is the first characterization examined here. The second part
of the study treats ethical problems of young working women and their relationship with the Communist Youth League (*Komsomol*). Another prominent
heroine during the decade following World War II is the typical proletarian woman

of the "industrial" novels. The third part of the study examines the Amazon-type as she appears in all strata of Soviet society and thus in Soviet fiction. The last part of the study concentrates on upper-middle class women, especially the post-Stalinist women without prerevolutionary ties who have experienced psychological stresses in the conflicts that evolve in their careers and emotional lives. The bibliography offers a good list of English translations of Russian literature. The study itself could be hard going for those without a background in Russian literature.

1055   Gerber, Philip L. **Willa Cather.** Boston: Twayne, 1975. 187p. bibliog. index. $7.50. ISBN 0805771557. LC 75-2287.
Gerber's explication of Cather's life and works approaches the novelist's development as one that was consistent throughout her career. Following the familiar Twayne format, Gerber gives a chronology, an integrated sketch of Cather's life along with an analysis of her fiction, concluding with a chapter that describes the critical reception accorded Cather both during her life and after her death (he notes an increase in her popularity). The selected bibliography will serve all but the most scholarly interests.

1056   Gutwirth, Madelyn. **Madame de Staël, Novelist: The Emergence of the Artist as Woman.** Urbana: University of Illinois Press, 1978. 344p. bibliog. index. $12.95. ISBN 0252006763.
Gutwirth, a feminist critic, sets Madame de Staël and her novels in the context of eighteenth-century French life and literature. The book contains a very detailed analysis of *Delphine* and *Corinne*, centering the analysis on the problems woman faces as artist in society. Gutwirth's reading of the novels and examination of Madame de Staël's life undercut notions that eighteenth century literature in France was controlled by women.

1057   Hardwick, Elizabeth. **Seduction and Betrayal: Women and Literature.** New York: Random House, 1974. 208p. $6.95. ISBN 039449069X. LC 74-19117.
Hardwick is the mistress of the graceful contemporary essay on literature. Easily, and without the scholarly apparatus of footnotes, indexing, or bibliography, she covers the pivotal literary figures considered in major discussions of women and literature, both the heroines and the women writers. On the one hand, we get Hardwick's always reasonable and direct analysis of the significance of the Brontës, Dorothy Wordsworth, Virginia Woolf, Jane Carlyle, Sylvia Plath, and Zelda Fitzgerald. On the other hand, we find essays summarizing the characters themselves: Hardy's Tess; Hawthorne's Hestor Prynne; Ibsen's Nora, Rebecca West, and Hedda; Dreiser's Roberta; Zola's Nana; Richardson's Clarissa; and Eliot's Hetty. Hardwick has a way of grounding literary issues, themes, and figures that threaten to blow away like helium balloons. It is refreshing to read Hardwick's analysis of Virginia Woolf's fiction, wherein she states, "and what is the point of paraphrasing *The Waves*, of trying for your own circles of ebb and flow to compete with hers? I was immensely moved by this novel when I read it recently and yet I cannot think of anything to say about it except that it is wonderful." In her chapter "Seduction and Betrayal,"

Hardwick marks the death of sex as an exalted, epic theme; rather, she maintains, sex in contemporary fiction is a passing event often presented in ironic terms.

1058   Heilbrun, Carolyn G., 1926- . **Toward a Recognition of Androgyny.**
        New York: Knopf, 1973. 189p. bibliog. index. $6.95. ISBN
        0394461754. LC 77-171149.

Heilbrun's belief is that "our future salvation lies in a movement away from sexual polarization and the prison of gender toward a world in which individual roles and modes of personal behavior can be freely chosen." She feels that androgyny (andro=male; gyn=female) is an appropriate term to describe this process. Heilbrun mines the literature of mythology and archaeology for references to androgyny manifested in "masculine" and "feminine" impulses and principles. She finds examples of androgyny in Genesis, the New Testament's portrayal of Jesus, medieval romance, *The Fairie Queen*, Shakespearian comedies, and in the persistent use of opposite-sex twins in world literature. In part 2, the Woman as Hero, Heilbrun comments on the prominence of female heroic figures in nineteenth-century novels—novels in which the woman consistently emblemizes a spiritual identity. *Wuthering Heights, The Scarlet Letter, Clarissa*, and *Vanity Fair* are to Heilbrun's mind the "great androgynous novels before the twentieth century." Heilbrun takes a different stance on Lawrence from the other feminist critics (notably, Kate Millett), seeing him as subscribing to androgynous principles in his creation of the new Eve. Part 3 discusses the practical working out of the androgynous spirit in Bloomsbury culture where amazing creative outpourings emanated from a group in which "masculinity and femininity were marvelously mixed in its members." Heilbrun concludes by prophesying the creation of major androgynous literary works by women where the themes of marriage and sexual conquest will be replaced by new possibilities. Readers with a further interest in exploring the idea of adrogyny may want to look at June K. Singer's *Androgyny: Toward a New Theory of Sexuality* (Anchor Press, 1976). Singer's work looks for examples of androgyny in "Alchemy and Gnosticism, the Kabbalah, the Tao, Tibetan Tantrism, Kundalini Yoga." Also included are discussions of Plato, Freud, and Jung.

1059   Hoffman, Michael J., 1939- . **Gertrude Stein.** London: George Prior;
        Boston: Twayne, 1976. 159p. bibliog. index. $7.50. ISBN 0805771689.
        LC 76-2661.

Though readers with a serious interest in Stein will want to consult James Mellow's *Charmed Circle: Gertrude Stein & Company* (1974) and Donald Sutherland's *Gertrude Stein: A Biography of Her Work* (1931), Hoffman provides a neat introduction to Stein which will be helpful to most undergraduates. Hoffman's introduction examines "The Paradoxes of Gertrude Stein"; chief among them is that as controversial a writer as Stein is, few people have bothered to actually read her work. Stein's work is somewhat clarified by the tight Twayne format. Hoffman spends most time in his discussion of *The Making of Americans* (1925), which he describes as Stein's most ambitious book.

1060   Jessup, Josephine Lurie. **The Faith of Our Feminists: A Study in the
        Novels of Edith Wharton, Ellen Glasgow, Willa Cather.** New York:

R. R. Smith, 1950; repr. New York: Biblo and Tannen, 1965. 128p. bibliog. $5.50. ISBN 0819601586. LC 65-23482.

Jessup groups Wharton, Glasgow, and Cather together as serious writers, each living and writing into old age, each born of American stock and of an Anglican religious tradition. More, their fiction attests to their philosophical and moral commitment to feminism. Interestingly, Glasgow and Cather never married, while Wharton remained separated from her husband for many years until their eventual divorce. Jessup's examination of the fiction reveals that the treatment of the masculine character in the work of all three is "dwarfed and straitened." In Glasgow's novels, women are oppressed by men; in Wharton's, women are misunderstood; but in Cather's, women's preeminence and dominance are tacitly accepted. If feminism can be defined as a woman's quest for independence, Jessup's study shows that each author has succeeded in creating memorable women characters who strive in this direction, though each has had problems in translating a feminist viewpoint into characters who are, after all, products of their times. Useful biographical sketches and bibliographies are given for each author.

1061   Juhasz, Suzanne, 1942- . **Naked and Fiery Forms: Modern American Poetry by Women: A New Tradition.** New York: Octagon Books, 1976. 212p. bibliog. $11.00. ISBN 0374944504. LC 76-16672.

Juhasz considers the work of Emily Dickinson, Marianne Moore, Denise Levertov, Sylvia Plath, Anne Sexton, Gwendolyn Brooks, Nikki Giovanni, Alta, and Adrienne Rich to make up a significant corpus that can be identified as speaking in a new woman-oriented tradition. She is particularly insightful in her introductory essay when she alludes to the "double-bind" situation in which the female poet necessarily finds herself. Because the role of the poet is to proclaim her art, ego (generally associated with assertiveness and masculinity) is an important attribute. Yet, sensitivity and intuition, qualities that usually mark the creativity of a male poet, can be the undoing of a female poet if she channels these qualities into the traditional and accepted female nurturing patterns that society expects of her. Juhasz is attuned to the coping devices these poets have used in working toward the resolution of the "double bind." Serious questions are addressed here, questions that define feminist criticism (e.g., what characterizes the content of "good" poetry written by women? can its excellence be judged by male standards?). Clearly, Suzanne Juhaxz considers herself to be a feminist literary critic: "I base my assumptions about the work of women poets in my belief that their interactions between self and society are related to the poetry that they write. I see their relationship to one another occurring in an historical and social context."

1062   Kannenstine, Louis F., 1938- . **The Art of Djuna Barnes: Duality and Damnation.** New York: New York University Press, 1977. 194p. bibliog. index. $12.50. ISBN 0814745644. LC 76-55152.

Because Djuna Barnes was a writer of incredible diversity—experimental fiction, poetry and drama—and of considerable talent, it is odd that she is just now beginning to receive some critical attention. *Nightwood* (1936) is her best-known work, but generally, she is considered a minor writer. Kannenstine's critical study examines separately six aspects of her work—Early Journalism and Essays;

The Early Poems; *Ryder* and *Ladies Almanack*; The Short Stories, *Nightwood*; Early Plays; and *The Antiphon*. Strange, unpredictable, and melancholy is the judgment that Kannenstine places on her work. The only previous book-length study was James B. Scott's *Djuna Barnes* (1976), which focused on her experimentation with language and its form and on her association with other literary expatriated men and women of the '20s—Natalie Clifford Barney, Margaret Anderson, James Joyce, and T. S. Eliot. Because her literary output has been slim, her dabbling in different genres frequent, and her life one of isolation, she has not emerged as an important literary figure. This study assesses Barnes's achievement as an organic one with the entire corpus of flawed and better work related to the masterpiece, *Nightwood*.

1063   Kelley, Alice Van Buren. **The Novels of Virginia Woolf: Fact and Vision.** Chicago: University of Chicago Press, 1971. 279p. bibliog. index. ISBN 0226429857. LC 73-77134.

"Thematically . . . Virginia Woolf presents a dual world of fact and vision that can function within the life of the individual or create a larger pattern in the realm of history—the life of mankind as a whole. Stylistically, this same pattern of fact and vision grows within her novels in at least two ways. First of all, the pattern emerges through her use of image. Solid objects in Virginia Woolf's novels demonstrate her notion that fact may become vision either directly, by taking on universal meaning for one of her characters in a moment of vision or, indirectly, by recurring throughout one or more works to give a pattern of order and meaning similar to that created by accumulating, recurrent visions in the lives of her men and women" (from the introduction). Kelley gives chapter-length analysis to *The Voyage Out* (1915), *Night and Day* (1919), *Jacob's Room* (1922), *Mrs. Dalloway* (1925), *To the Lighthouse* (1927), *The Waves* (1931), *The Years* (1937), and *Between the Acts* (1941), with appendix treatment of the critical approaches to Virginia Woolf's fiction. Woolf's concentration on the repetition of patterns and her conscious imposition of form upon chaos in the representation of life and art in her novels are points that Kelley critically examines in her detailed study.

1064   Lansbury, Coral. **Elizabeth Gaskell: The Novel of Social Crisis.** New York: Barnes and Noble, 1975. 230p. bibliog. index. $15.00. ISBN 064940462. LC 75-325048.

Lansbury's study of Elizabeth Gaskell—Victorian novelist, social critic, and biographer of Charlotte Brontë—reveals a critic who clearly admires her subject. "Elizabeth Gaskell was less concerned with describing events than with intimating the way in which people regarded those events and themselves. Rather than engage in the current fashion for depreciation of her talents, I would argue that it is high time that Elizabeth Gaskell was accorded her place in the company of Thackery and Dickens, George Eliot and Jane Austen" (preface). This study examines Gaskell's perspective as a writer from her position as a writing woman and Unitarian in Victorian society. Lansbury devotes a chapter-length treatment to each of Gaskell's major works: *Mary Barton, Ruth, Cranford, North and South, The Life of Charlotte Brontë, Sylvia's Lovers,* and *Wives and Daughters.* Her notes for each chapter serve to outline the prominent critical treatments of these works. Two useful features are the chronology of Gaskell's life and works and the bibliographic essay. It is helpful to consult the letters along with Lansbury's critical treatment. See J. A. V. Chapple and Arthur Pollard, eds. *The Letters of Mrs. Gaskell* (Manchester, 1966).

1065   Legman, Gershon, 1917- , comp. **Rationale of the Dirty Joke: An Analysis of Sexual Humor.** New York: Grove Press, 1968-1975. 2v. v.1, $2.95, ISBN 0394172612; v.2 (distr. New York: Breaking Point), $18.00, ISBN 0917020014. LC 68-29924.

The material for these two volumes was laboriously collected and analyzed over the course of three decades. The result is an attempt "to give reasonably full and authentic texts of almost the entire basic float of bawdy jokes of sexual or scatological nature found in oral folk-transmission in the English language, in either America or Britain, over the last fifty to one hundred years— basically, the late-nineteenth and twentieth centuries." Legman does far more, however, than merely present the collection of jokes; he analyzes them by topic as folklore for what they reveal about social relations and human psychology. What is more, he examines them for their revelations about male/female relations—and, most often, male fear and dislike of women. While this often makes for painful and infuriating reading, it is at the same time fascinating and invaluable as a basis for analysis of the relationships of men and women in contemporary patriarchal society. Among the topics discussed are: Children; The Male Approach; The Sadistic Concept; Women; Premarital Sexual Acts; Marriage; Adultery; Homosexuality; Prostitution; and Castration. Readers may also be interested in a hard-to-obtain study entitled *An Intelligent Woman's Guide to Dirty Words: English Words and Phrases Reflecting Sexist Attitudes toward Women in Patriarchal Society, Arranged According to Usage and Idea* (vol. 1 of the *Feminist English Dictionary*; Chicago: Feminist English Dictionary, 1973).

1066   Leighton, Jean. **Simone de Beauvoir on Woman.** Rutherford, NJ: Fairleigh Dickinson University Press, 1975. 230p. bibliog. index. $10.00. ISBN 083861504X. LC 74-3615.

Leighton considers de Beauvoir's *The Second Sex* to be a negative projection of the image of woman, even of the supposedly emancipated woman. By subjecting de Beauvoir's major novels—*L'Invitée* and *Les Mandarins*—to a biographical analysis, Leighton attempts to show how the autobiography, the theoretical work on woman's destiny, and the feminine characters of the novels support a negative view of women held by the celebrated French author. Although Leighton concedes that de Beauvoir may have conflicting feelings about women, she ultimately accuses the author of misogyny. Leighton's study has its controversial aspects, attempting to judge fiction from autobiographical and theoretical perspectives as it does. However, it makes a number of perceptive observations concerning the parallels between Simone de Beauvoir's imaginative presentation of women and de Beauvoir's own experiences as a talented and emancipated woman attempting to maintain intense relationships with men and caught in a web of immanence and narcissism.

1067*   Lindberg, Gary H., 1941- . **Edith Wharton and the Novel of Manners.** Charlottesville: University Press of Virginia, 1975. 186p. bibliog. index. ISBN 081390563X. LC 75-17504.

Edith Wharton dealt exclusively with the world of manners, where each character's
social and historical connections are not merely a part of the self, but rather
these connections are the self. In this world (mainly of New York society),
all actions are observed by witnesses, and characters are unable to free themselves even when alone of the pressure of an all-seeing audience. In the truest
sense, all Wharton characters are bound to their society. Lindberg's is a brilliant
anatomy of the novel of manners and Wharton's achievement as one of its
finest practitioners. His major attention falls on *The House of Mirth, The Custom
of the Country*, and *The Age of Innocence* as her most distinguished contributions to American literature. His final assessment of her fiction suggests
that she may have overemphasized the psychic bind in which the societal milieu
can hold the individual. Lindberg includes a fine bibliographic essay, which
might serve as a starting point for anyone beginning an analysis of Wharton's
work.

1068*   Link, Frederick M. **Aphra Behn.** New York: Twayne, 1968. 183p.
         bibliog. index. LC 68-17246.
Link introduces his subject by stating simply the facts of the case: "much of
what has been written about Aphra Behn's life is based on conjecture and
misinformation. For example, after three hundred years we do not yet know
her maiden name, the date of her birth, or the circumstances surrounding her
trip to Surinam and her marriage." Similarly, Link notes a dearth of criticism
on her work. What he has done here is to critically survey Aphra Behn's work—
plays, poems, translations, and novels—though her plays are acknowledged to
be of chief importance. Behn is a writer who received much adverse criticism
in her day (1690s), as much for the quality of her life as for the quality of her
work. Her plays were labeled "obscene" and she herself, "a harlot." Link does
a commendable job of introducing the writer and her work, of dealing with
the chronology of her life and the critical heritage of her work. It is only recently
that Behn's work has become more available; Link's excellent bibliography is
welcome as well as his liberal use of quotations from Behn's work to illustrate
her virtuosity as a writer.

1069   McClatchy, J. D., 1945- , ed. **Anne Sexton: The Artist and Her Critics.**
        Bloomington: Indiana University Press, 1978. 320p. bibliog. $12.95.
        ISBN 0253307481. LC 77-23646.
First-rate criticism, interviews, reviews of Sexton's books, and personal recollections by friends have been included in this memoir of Sexton. Though the
criticism is both positive and negative, critics Maxine Kumin, Richard Howard,
Robert Lowell, Denise Levertov, and J. D. McClatchy agree that her poetry
addresses questions of the most serious nature about the relationship between
art and life.

1070   McDowell, Margaret Louise Blaine, 1923- . **Edith Wharton.** Boston:
        Twayne, 1976. 158p. bibliog. index. $6.95. ISBN 0805771646. LC
        75-44094.
McDowell's tight study of Wharton's life and work will serve well the reader
who is first coming to Wharton as well as someone who wishes a review. Because
Margaret McDowell has been an active participant in women's studies, she

brings a significant, though not substantially different, perspective to Wharton's life and work. Hers is an inclusive approach to Wharton, encouraging a wider reading of the lesser-known novels, novellas, and short stories in the post-1920 period. As always, the Twayne format for handling the select bibliography of primary and secondary sources is helpful.

1071   McKendrick, Melveena. **Woman and Society in the Spanish Drama of the Golden Age: A Study of the Mujer Varonil.** New York: Cambridge University Press, 1974. 346p. bibliog. index. $24.50. ISBN 0521202949. LC 73-82457.

McKendrick has used the approach of the social historian—scrutinizing memoirs, letters, diaries, sermons, legal codes, poetry, novels, and other secondary and primary sources—to formulate a construct of the norm of Spanish womanhood during the seventeenth century. In establishing a norm, she is able to prove how seventeenth-century Spanish dramatists consistently used the *mujer varonil*— a type of feminist heroine—in the major plays of the period. Male clothing, assertive expression, bold action, and uninhibited patterns of thought are the characteristics of this Spanish heroine. McKendrick traces her development in the theater of the pre-Lopistas, and in the work of Cervantes and the Valencians. Typical of the various forms in which this special heroine appeared were the *bondolera*, the *mujer esquiva*, the amazon, leader, warrior, scholar, career woman, the bella cazadora, the avenger. McKendrick accounts for the popularity of these stock heroines as natural attractions in a world where women were *never* allowed to rival men. The heroine's unreality was her most compelling quality.

1072   Marder, Herbert. **Feminism and Art: A Study of Virginia Woolf.** Chicago: University of Chicago Press, 1968. 190p. bibliog. index. $8.50. ISBN 0226504603. LC 68-16704.

Marder's purpose is to study the relationship between Woolf's feminism and her novels. Barbarism, insensitivity, patriarchy, and lack of receptivity to new ideas were among the world's evils that Woolf counted most odious. Marder's succinct introduction outlines Woolf's approach to these feminist concerns in her art: "The way to remedy these evils, according to Virginia Woolf, is to let feminine influences act freely, both within society and within the individual. Our only hope, as far as she is concerned, lies in cooperation between the sexes, and the extent to which such cooperation actually exists is an index of the extent to which a society has become civilized. When the wife is permitted to administer the law of sympathy in the home, domestic harmony becomes possible. When women take part in national affairs the evils of politics are mitigated. When the individual learns to cultivate both masculine and feminine sides of his mind he approaches unity of being. Wholeness—integration of the personality—is the ultimate goal, and the symbol Virginia Woolf uses to represent this ideal condition is the androgynous mind, the mind in which masculine and feminine elements attain a perfect balance." Marder arrives at his analysis through a critical examination of her biography and of the social and economic realities of late nineteenth and early twentieth-century Britain which shaped her vision. He weaves these perceptions into his discussion of the individual works.

1073   Marks, Elaine. **Simone de Beauvoir: Encounters with Death.** New
        Brunswick, NJ: Rutgers University Press, 1973. 183p. bibliog. index.
        $12.50. ISBN 0813507073. LC 72-4199.
Marks states her thesis in the first chapter, "Death and Sensibility": "Simone
de Beauvoir always writes about or around the major preoccupation of the
modern sensibility, the preoccupation with death, and she does this in a manner
that reaches a wide and varied audience." Stating that de Beauvoir's *corpus* is
obsessively concerned with death and staving off confrontation with the void,
Marks demonstrates how the author attempts to exorcise death in her fiction,
in her autobiography, in her relationships with God, her friends, lovers, mother,
and finally, in the fear and anguish of contemplating her own death.

1074   Mason, Bobbie Ann. **The Girl Sleuth: A Feminist Guide.** Old Westbury,
        NY: Feminist Press, 1975. 176p. bibliog. $3.95. ISBN 0912670177.
        LC 74-22313.
Mason believes that series mystery books (e.g., Nancy Drew, the Dana Girls,
and Cherry Ames) have enthralled girls between nine and fourteen, though
educators and critics have dismissed the importance of this genre of adolescent
literature and ignored the attraction of their heroines. In this study, the critical
approach is to examine form and content of several series books which appeal
to girls, "to comment on their quality and their possible impact on young girls'
imaginations, and to examine the stereotypes which have been popularized
by the books." The influence of fictional characters such as Nancy Drew has
been considerable according to Mason, who believes that the conventional and
revolutionary were often paradoxically packaged in the heroine. Among the
series noted here are the Beverly Gray College Mystery Series, the Blythe Girls
Books, the Bobbsey Twins Books, Connie Blair Mysteries, the Vicki Barr Flight
Stewardess Series, along with the most famous, Dana Girls Mystery Stories and
Nancy Drew Mystery Stories.

1075   Mews, Hazel. **Frail Vessels: Woman's Role in Women's Novels from
        Fanny Burney to George Eliot.** London: Athlone Press; distr. New York:
        Humanities Press, 1969. 209p. bibliog. $10.75. ISBN 0485111055.
        LC 78-447404.
This book analyzes the effect that changes in women's role had upon the work
of women novelists writing before 1870. Mews feels that novelists from Burney
to Eliot presented a realistic view of women's work and presented women as
fuller characters operating in dimensions outside of home and family. Women
ceased to be static and stock characters in these novels, according to Mews.

1076   Moers, Ellen, 1928- . **Literary Women.** Garden City, NY: Doubleday,
        1976. 336p. bibliog. index. $10.00. ISBN 0385074271. LC 74-33686.
History, biography, criticism: the subject of Moers's book is major women
writers. She divides her material into two sections, the first dealing with women's
literary history and traditions, the second, with heroinism. Among the important
writers included are Jane Austen, Elizabeth Barrett Browning, Kate Chopin,
Christina Rossetti, Emily Dickinson, the Brontës, George Sand, and Madame
de Staël. Moers moves about her subject with scholarly flair and stylistic grace.

An unfortunate aspect of the book is the notes section, difficult to use and to follow even with Moers's guide.

1077   Myer, Valerie Grosvenor. **Margaret Drabble: Puritanism and Permissiveness.** New York: Barnes and Noble, 1974. 200p. index. $12.00. ISBN 0064950549.

Myer approaches Drabble's novels by looking at the women characters and examining their "conflicting claims of selfhood, wifehood and motherhood. . . . " She identifies the profile of the Drabble woman as that of an intelligent woman and mother, leading a bourgeois life of domestic confinement from which she tries to escape, but remaining sucked into the vortex of home and family because of deep feelings of duty. Characters whom Myer discusses come from the following Drabble novels: *A Summer Birdcage* (1963); *The Garrick Year* (1964); *The Millstone* (1965); *Jerusalem the Golden* (1967); *The Waterfall* (1969); and *The Needle's Eye* (1972). A major point in this study is Drabble's firm placement of characters in a clearly defined socio-economic niche, in which they must deal with the constraints imposed by class, societal mores, power, and money. There is little critical work on Drabble, so this can be considered a major study. The lack of a bibliography is noticeable here.

1078   Oates, Joyce Carol, 1938- . **The Hostile Sun: The Poetry of D. H. Lawrence.** Los Angeles: Black Sparrow Press, 1973. 60p. $3.00. ISBN 0876851685. LC 73-8763.

Oates sees Lawrence as a mystic poet and accounts his best single volume of poetry to be *Birds, Beasts, and Flowers* (1923) in this beautifully produced critical volume. Joyce Carol Oates's critical appraisal is sympathetic to the Lawrentian schema, and this volume is as interesting for what it reveals about Oates as critic as for its interpretation of D. H. Lawrence's poetry.

1079   Oliphant, Margaret Oliphant Wilson, 1828-1897, et al. **Women Novelists of Queen Victoria's Reign: A Book of Appreciations.** London: Hurst and Blackett, 1897; repr. Folcroft, PA: Folcroft Library Editions, 1974. 311p. $20.00. ISBN 0841465215. LC 74-34124.

The Brontë sisters, George Eliot, Mrs. Gaskell, and lesser literary luminaries such as Mrs. Crowe, Mrs. Archer Clive, Mrs. Henry Wood, Lady Georgiana Fullerton, Mrs. Stretton, Anne Manning, Dinah Mulock, Julia Kavanagh, Amelia Blanford Edwards, Mrs. Norton, and Mrs. Ewing (all leading novelists during Victoria's reign) are celebrated in criticism by leading English novelists of the 1890s. It is interesting to see the Brontës, George Eliot and Mrs. Gaskell filtered through the literary sensibilities of Mrs. Oliphant, Mrs. Lynn Linton and Edna Lyall. Oliphant, for example, suggests naively at the end of her essay on Charlotte Brontë that "no more should be said" about the poor woman.

1080   Page, Sally R. **Faulkner's Women: Characterization and Meaning.** De Land, FL: Everett/Edwards, 1972. 233p. bibliog. index. $12.00. ISBN 0912112166. LC 78-172792.

Page takes the corpus of secondary criticism about Faulkner's fiction to task for over-simplifying and sometimes distorting Faulkner's actual view of women. Though she concedes that several of Faulkner's women manifest extremes of creativity or destructiveness, Page suggests that his mythic, symbolic novels must be read outside of the context of realism. Perverted sexuality characterizes negative female characters, while devotion to duty and a maternal sexuality are positive attributes of womanhood in Faulkner's fictional world. Chapters include: The Ideal of Motherhood: *Sanctuary*; The Feminine Ideal of *Light in August*; and Sexual Perversity and Sterility. The large bibliography of secondary sources gives general studies of Faulkner from a variety of perspectives. This edition contains an introduction by Cleanth Brooks that defends Faulkner's polarization of sexual types—decent women vs. depraved women.

1081   Pratt, Annis, and L. S. Dembo, eds. **Doris Lessing: Critical Studies.** Madison: University of Wisconsin Press, 1974. 172p. bibliog. $4.50. ISBN 029906506X. LC 74-5909.
The essays here cluster mainly around Lessing's most discussed work, *The Golden Notebook*. Particularly interesting is Florence Howe's much cited interview with Lessing in 1966, during which Lessing informally explains what she is attempting in *The Golden Notebook* and her rather pragmatic and unstuffy notions about writing. Other pieces are: John L. Carey, "Art and Reality in *The Golden Notebook*"; Evelyn J. Hinz and John J. Teunissen, "The Pieta as Icon in *The Golden Notebook*"; Michele Wender Zak, "*The Grass Is Singing*; A Little Novel about the Emotions"; Dagmar Barnouw, "Disorderly Company: From *The Golden Notebook* to *The Four-Gated City*"; Lynn Sukenick, "Feeling and Reason in Doris Lessing's Fiction"; Sydney Janet Kaplan, "The Limits of Consciousness in the Novels of Doris Lessing"; Douglas Bolling, "Structure and Theme in *Briefing for a Descent into Hell*"; Nancy Shields Hardin, "Doris Lessing and the Sufi Way"; Agate Nesaule Krouse, "A Doris Lessing Checklist"; and Ellen Morgan, "Alienation of the Woman Writer in *The Golden Notebook*."

1082   Richmond, Merle A. **Bid the Vassal Soar: Interpretive Essays on the Life and Poetry of Phillis Wheatley (ca. 1753-1784) and George Moses Horton (ca. 1797-1883).** Washington: Howard University Press, 1974. 216p. bibliog. index. $8.95. ISBN 0882580019. LC 73-85493.
In making a decision to ignore the question of the literary merit of Wheatley's and Horton's work, Richmond has done a creditable job of examining the poetry and other relevant documents with the idea of seeing what these writings reveal of the poets' lives and time, and particularly of the institution of slavery. Richmond's writing is crisp and clear. "Their poetry as poetry is not the main thing," she writes. Consequently, she has shaped a study that makes sense and is probably the best current critique of Wheatley. Excellent notes are included.

1083   Richter, Harvena, 1919- . **Virginia Woolf: The Inward Voyage.** Princeton, NJ: Princeton University Press, 1970. 273p. bibliog. index. $12.50. ISBN 0691061793. LC 74-90958.
In this excellent study of Virginia Woolf, Richter examines her subjective methods. "Using principles of perception and mind function, she seeks to approximate the actual ways in which man sees, feels, thinks, and experiences time and change. The reader, placed within the mind of the character, becomes to some extent that mind, receiving certain of the emotional stimuli and sharing in the response" (introduction). Among the host of subjective issues to which Richter

gives attention are Woolf's relationship to the age in which she lived; the woman novelist; the influences of her father and Bloomsbury on her work; how Woolf translated emotion as reality; point of view in her fiction; the influence of psychoanalytic theory on her work; the use of mirrors, reflections, and surfaces in her work; multiplicity of self; the handling of time in the fiction; metaphors and symbols; rhythm, pattern, and space. Perhaps Richter's most important chapter is her analysis of the demands made upon the reader by Woolf's work.

1084   Rigney, Barbara Hill, 1938- . **Madness and Sexual Politics in the Feminist Novel.** Madison: University of Wisconsin Press, 1978. 148p. bibliog. index. $15.00. ISBN 0299077101. LC 78-53291.
Taking four well-known novels—Charlotte Brontë's *Jane Eyre*, Virginia Woolf's *Mrs. Dalloway*, Doris Lessing's *The Four-Gated City*, and Margaret Atwood's *Surfacing*—Rigney uses the psychoanalytic approach to literary criticism to demonstrate how major feminist writers have linked madness and women in their work. "Each novel presents a criticism of a patriarchal political and social system, a universe dominated by masculine energy, which, in itself, manifests a kind of collusive madness in the form of war or sexual oppression and is thereby seen as threatening to feminine psychological survival. Most of these novels depict a female protagonist who, in spite of such oppression achieves a superior sanity and at least a relative liberty in the assertion of a self" (introduction). Rigney invokes R. D. Laing's theories as "a base from which to begin a feminist psychoanalytic approach to literature." Since Laing posits that madness may be the logical coping process for an individual oppressed by the larger society and that schizophrenia or the divided self may symbolize the lot of oppressed individuals in the society, his paradigm of insanity becomes descriptive of the feminist character at odds with society until she finds within the means to heal herself.

1085   Rogers, Katharine M. **The Troublesome Helpmate: A History of Misogyny in Literature.** Seattle: University of Washington Press, 1966. 288p. bibliog. index. $8.95. ISBN 0295739738. LC 66-19565.
Rogers maintains that the biological love that men have for women has consistently been accompanied by negative feelings of fear and antagonism. In this ambitious undertaking, she has examined mysogynistic trends in American and English literature and tried to differentiate between misogyny as a convention of the era in which an author was writing and misogyny as a personal philosophy of the author. Chaucer, Ben Jonson, Swift, Thackeray, Dickens, Wycherley, Congreve, Lawrence, and Henry James are among the authors whose work she examines. Hers is an essentially Freudian perception of misogyny as a behavior of displacement, of projection, or of defensiveness.

1086   Rule, Jane. **Lesbian Images.** Garden City, NY: Doubleday, 1975. 246p. bibliog. index. $8.95. ISBN 0385042558.
"From the ugly masochism of Violette Leduc to the lyric wonder of Margaret Anderson, from the moral earnestness of Gertrude Stein to the ambivalent cynicism of Colette, from the neutered sexuality of Ivy Compton-Burnett to the blatant sexual hunger of Vita Sackville-West, from the silence of Willa Cather to the confessions of May Sarton, the reality of lesbian experience

transcends all theories about it. If this book astonishes simply by the number of women, and very gifted women, who have been concerned about love between women, it will have fulfilled its purpose, for no one can comfortably dismiss all those who find a place in these pages" (preface). Rule's major concern is to unearth images of lesbians that women writers have created in autobiography and fiction. Herself a lesbian fiction writer and university teacher, Rule writes courageously in her introduction of the risks of writing about the lesbian experience; she has accepted that she can never be totally palatable to the militant lesbian community or to the straight academic community. *Lesbian Images* is an excellent starting point, along with Barbara Grier's *Lesbian Lives* (1976), for those who wish to read a sound and well-written account of the lesbian experience in literature. Radclyffe Hall, Gertrude Stein, Willa Cather, Vita Sackville-West, Ivy Compton-Burnett, Elizabeth Bowen, Colette, Violette Leduc, Margaret Anderson, Dorothy Baker, May Sarton, and Maureen Duffy each get chapter-length treatments. Rule comments on the trends of lesbian fiction from the 1930s to the 1970s and on recent nonfiction about lesbians, noting that despite breakthroughs, a hostile climate still prevails. Among Rule's own novels are *This Is Not for You* (1970) and *Desert of the Heart* (1964). Unavailable for examination and out of print, *This Is Not for You* is the story of Kate, a lesbian since high school, and her feelings of guilt and awkwardness about expressing her love for women. She falls in love with Esther at college, though she abandons the idea of consummating this affair. The novel explores her hesitation and difficult decision.

1087   Shapiro, Marianne. **Woman, Earthly and Divine, in the Comedy of Dante.** Lexington: University Press of Kentucky, 1975. 187p. bibliog. index. $9.95. ISBN 0813113113. LC 73-96407.

Inheriting a pervasive misogynous tradition, Dante accepted the prescribed view of Eve's being the causal factor in man's downfall. Shapiro's analysis explicates the various roles of women found in Dante, demonstrating that the portrayal of a complete woman was impossible for Dante given the religious, chilvalric, moral and aesthetic temper of his time. She notes in Dante a preponderance of good and evil mother-figures—separated extremes that cannot come together in the same figure. Women who are depicted as virgins and mothers have no sexual role, and hence are not dangerous. Women who are lovers are mainly destructive and emblematic of female destruction. Though Shapiro agrees that Dante used all the poetic conventions of his time to exalt Beatrice and "to reconcile the love of woman with that of God," she sees this as only a supernatural solution and not one that works in the temporal society of the Middle Ages. This study, although complex, is worth looking at for its analysis of the perplexing position of women in the Middle Ages, in which Beatrice becomes an affirmation of the masculine value system of the period.

1088   Sherman, Joan R. **Invisible Poets: Afro-Americans of the Nineteenth Century.** Urbana: University of Illinois Press, 1974. 270p. bibliog. index. $10.00. ISBN 025200325X. LC 73-81569.

"Anthologies of Afro-American literature typically imply that black poetry began with Phyllis Wheatley (1753-84), disappeared for over one hundred years, and only reemerged with Paul Lawrence Dunbar (1872-1906). Actually, however, at least 130 black men and women published poetry in America during the nineteenth century. I have chosen twenty-six of these individuals for intensive study, hoping to construct for the first time certain significant profiles of their life experiences and to appraise the qualities and import of their poetry" (from the preface). Women poets included in this study are Ann Plato (1820?-?), Frances Ellen Watkins Harper (1824-1911), Charlotte L. Forten Grimké (1837-1914), Henrietta Cardelia Ray (1852?-1916), and Eloise Bibb Thompson (1878-1927). In addition to a fine bibliographical essay—which discusses bibliographies, other reference aids, books of biography and criticism, periodicals, anthologies, and manuscript collections relating to black literature—Sherman has provided useful appendix material on Afro-American poets for further research: occasional poets, anonymous poets, turn-of-the-century poets, and poets erroneously identified in various bibliographies as Afro-American. Although this work does not specifically and only relate to women, its consistent scholarly quality, excellent notes, and good bibliography of works by each poet suggest that it can be of great value to those wishing to identify Afro-American women poets who have previously gone unnoticed.

1089   Showalter, Elaine. **A Literature of Their Own: British Women Novelists from Brontë to Lessing.** Princeton, NJ: Princeton University Press, 1977. 378p. bibliog. index. $17.50. ISBN 0691063184. LC 76-3018.
Showalter underscores major phases during which a shift of literary emphases took place: the feminine phase, from 1840 (which marked the use of the male pseudonym) to George Eliot's death in 1880; the feminist phase, 1880-1920, marking the struggle to gain the franchise; the female phase, from 1920 to the present, which was accelerated by increased self-awareness in 1960. Casting her critical eye on the works and lives of less famous writers, many of whom have been virtually excluded from literary history, Showalter comes up with a list of her own to consider: Mary Braddon, Rhoda Broughton, Dina Mulock Craik, Margaret Drabble, Doris Lessing, Margaret Oliphant, Dorothy Richardson, Olive Schreiner, Charlotte Yonge. There is plenty, too, about Woolf, Brontë, and Eliot. Showalter is explicitly opposed to the consideration of such concepts as "female aesthetic" and "female imagination," because she sees them as calling up a constellation of stereotypes—subjectivity, illumination, lyric prose, intuitive perception, for example. "Androgyny" is another term that gives Showalter trouble; she calls it "a myth that helped [Virginia Woolf] . . . to choke and repress her anger and ambition." She includes a biographical appendix as well as a bibliography listing "the most useful sources for studying nineteenth- and twentieth-century English women novelists."

1090   Sibley, Agnes Marie, 1914- . **May Sarton.** New York: Twayne, 1972. 160p. bibliog. index. $6.95. ISBN 0805706569. LC 70-187610.
May Sarton (1912-) counts her true creativity to be in her poetry; she is acknowledged, however, chiefly for her fiction. In her finest novel, *Mrs. Stevens Hears the Mermaids Singing* (1965), the main character is an aging poet who describes the process of writing poetry and the nature of her Muse. Sibley's little study summarizes the connections between Sarton's forms—poetry and fiction. Two prominent themes she notes in the fiction are detachment in the early novels, communion in the later novels. Sarton has written about these conflicting

themes in her life in her beautiful autobiographical *Journal of a Solitude* (1973).
Sibley's is a useful sketch of Sarton's life and literary work accompanied by a
chronology and a bibliography of primary and secondary sources.

1091   Spacks, Patricia Ann Meyer. **The Female Imagination.** New York:
        Knopf; distr. New York: Random House, 1975. 326p. bibliog. index.
        $10.00. ISBN 039449184X. LC 74-21320.
Because Spacks invokes Pascal's "the truth of the heart," and suggests that
looking closely at the work of women can be therapeutic in "helping" undergraduates (Spacks calls them "adolescents") to achieve "self-realization," a
slightly condescending tone seeps through her analysis of major women writers.
Still, her question—what are the themes that have occupied women writers—
is an interesting one and her tracing of the "special" literary heritage left by
women a formidable excursion into fictions, essays, diaries and autobiographies
written by women from the seventeenth century to the present. Narcissism,
the yearnings for power and love, the idea of virtue, the balancing of independence
with a relationship: unsurprisingly these become the foci for women's fiction.
Spacks's analysis takes the reader to the work of Austen, the Brontës, Burrey,
Chopin, Colette, Eliot, Gaskell, Gilman, Hellman, James, Lessing, Nin, Welty,
Wharton, Woolf, and many more. Her list of works cited in the text constitutes
an excellent basic collection to support women's studies literature courses.

1092   Spark, Muriel. **Child of Light: A Reassessment of Mary Wollstonecraft
        Shelley.** Hadleigh, Essex, England: Tower Bridge Publications, 1951;
        repr. Folcroft, PA: Folcroft Library Editions, 1976. 235p. bibliog.
        index. $25.00. ISBN 0841478074. LC 76-47464.
Expensive in the reprint and certainly well worth watching for as a used book,
this is a biographical and critical study of Mary Shelley (1787-1851). Spark's
critical judgment is that Mary's association with poet Percy Shelley obscured
her considerable literary talents and the fact that she was a writer for all the
28 years of her life following Shelley's death. She suggests that the novel *The
Last Man* is Mary's most brilliant work—even more extraordinary than *Frankenstein*, her youthful Gothic. The appendix is an abridged version of *The Last
Man*, a relatively unknown work. As for Mary Shelley's editing of her husband's
work, Spark sees her as an illustrator of the text rather than an interpreter;
but Mary never claimed to have a keen critical ability: "I have, however, the
liveliest recollection of all that was done and said during the period of my
knowing him."

1093   Spencer, Sharon. **Collage of Dreams: The Writings of Anaïs Nin.**
        Chicago: Swallow Press, 1977. 188p. bibliog. index. $10.00. ISBN
        0804007608. LC 77-78781.
Spencer sees Nin's life as one with her art. " . . . Nin is a ragpicker of experience.
And from the rags, debris, and especially from the broken fragments she has
gathered up, Nin has made a large body of highly inventive books." Her form
is "collage composition," her goal, "to redeem experience." Spencer gives Nin
a sympathetic feminist reading and appropriately deals with Nin in broad thematic
sweeps (e.g., Rediscovering Woman; Symphonic Writing; Transforming the
Muse), as Nin deals with life in an expansive, free-flowing, free-floating manner.

Spencer traces the influence of music, dance, and painting in Nin's work; the importance of Otto Rank and psychoanalysis in her writing process; and her ties to surrealism, symbolism, and the Proustian style. Spencer has written extensively on Nin. See her *Space, Time and Structure in the Modern Novel* (New York University Press, 1971) and her introduction to Nin's *Cities of the Interior*.

1094 Stanford, Ann. **Ann Bradstreet, the Worldly Puritan: An Introduction to Her Poetry.** New York: B. Franklin, 1975. 170p. bibliog. index. $14.95. ISBN 0891020306. LC 74-22319.

In this concise and well-documented study, Stanford shows clearly how the Puritan influence was worked into Bradstreet's poetry. Puritan theology wages a dialogue between the joys of temporal life and the incomprehensible joys of eternal life; Bradstreet reflects this preoccupation. Stanford spends much time discussing the range of forms in Bradstreet's poetry: metrical prayers, rhymed histories, love poems, meditative poems, elegies. The study is divided into The Ipswich Poems and The Andover Poems. The appendixes are quite interesting, including a frequency list of images in her poetry and a list of books with which she was acquainted. Two other books on Bradstreet that deserve attention are Josephine K. Piercy, *Anne Bradstreet* (New Haven, 1965) and Elizabeth Wade White, *Anne Bradstreet: "The Tenth Muse"* (New York, 1971).

1095 Stein, Gertrude, 1874-1946. **A Primer for the Gradual Understanding of Gertrude Stein.** Ed. by Robert Bartlett Haas. Los Angeles: Black Sparrow Press, 1971. 158p. $10.00. ISBN 0876851375. LC 75-32292.

The aim of the primer is to focus attention on the work of Stein rather than on her publicly or privately held beliefs. Since conversation was one of the great Stein strengths, the "Transatlantic Interview" included here (given by Stein at age seventy) offers significant insight into the writer's interpretation of her own work. She explicates a number of her poetic experiments through specific examples from her books. Also included in this volume is an anthology of Stein from 1895 to 1946, which offers a sampling of her writings illustrative of various innovations (literary music, disembodied movement, etc.). Two essays by Gertrude Stein Raffel and Donald Sutherland further illuminate this difficult author for those first coming to her work.

1096 Thomson, Patricia. **George Sand and the Victorians: Her Influence and Reputation in Nineteenth-Century England.** New York: Columbia University Press, 1977. 283p. bibliog. index. $17.50. ISBN 0231042620. LC 76-30654.

Since most studies of George Sand center upon her personal reputation, rather than on her influence as a writer, it is good to see this measured and careful study of Sand's impact on Victorian writers. Thomson has traced the effect of George Sand on writers such as Elizabeth Barrett, the Brontës, George Eliot, and Henry James—citing from Victorian letters, periodicals, and essays, and from works that Sand influenced. Thomson's introduction states her conviction of Sand's enormous influence "as the missing link between the earlier nineteenth-century writers and those of the Victorian period, in her introduction of passion as a major theme in the novel."

1097   Wasserstrom, William. **Heiress of All the Ages: Sex and Sentiment in the Genteel Tradition.** Minneapolis: University of Minnesota Press, 1959. 157p. index. $5.00. ISBN 0816601852. LC 59-7949.

Wasserstrom attempts to define the genteel tradition, a cultural force that he sees beginning in the 1830s and concluding with the First World War. "The American girl" is the heiress of all that was coherent and ordered in the American tradition of literature. Popular fiction that contained the image of the good and true American woman served a therapeutic social function in a land where wilderness and political disorder might otherwise have bred disorientation. Major writers discussed are Henry James, William Dean Howells, Robert Penn Warren, and Edith Wharton. Each chapter deals with a dominant image in the genteel tradition: Steel-Engraving Ladies and Gibson Girls; The Lily and the Prairie Flower; Fortune's Darlings; The Spirit of Myrrha; Nymph and Nun; Sugar and Spice.

1098   Watson, Barbara Bellow. **A Shavian Guide to the Intelligent Woman.** New York: Norton, 1972. 250p. bibliog. index. $2.45. ISBN 0393006409. LC 72-194120.

Watson's new introduction reflects the emergence of a more feminist perspective since the 1964 edition. Watson's major point remains that Shaw's work is filled with strong and witty women, significant protagonists who assert themselves as individuals above and apart from their sex roles. In most of Shaw's plays, the women emerge as the triumphant characters. *Candida, Mrs. Warren's Profession, Major Barbara, Saint Joan*, and *The Millionairess* are titles that suggest the important parts that women play in Shaw's drama. Watson's thesis contends that the only men who are able to match Shavian women for wit, charm, and intelligence are characters like Dick Dudgeon, King Magnus, and King Charles, whose notions about the conventional relations between men and women have given way to thought and conduct that reject the hypocrisy of "ladylike" behavior dictated by Victorian mores. An excellent bibliography illuminates many issues surrounding Victorian thought on "the woman question."

1099   Watts, Emily Stipes. **The Poetry of American Women from 1632 to 1945.** Austin: University of Texas Press, 1977. 218p. bibliog. index. $13.95. ISBN 0292764359. LC 76-43282.

Watts's purpose is to examine the rich tradition of American poetry pre-1945, which she suggests provided the underpinnings for the more sophisticated post-1945 diversity found in American poetry by women. She divides her study into six major sections. The 1632-1758 section deals with Anne Bradstreet and other Puritan poets. The 1735-1804 section introduces the contributions of women poets writing during the period in which poetic conventions dictated imitative verse; Jane Colman Turrell, Phyllis Wheatley, Mercy Warren, and Susanna Haswell Rowson are notable examples. The 1800-1850 analysis covers the rise of "female" poetry, largely characterized by attention to feminine American domestic experience; notable practitioners of this poetic school were Lydia Huntley Sigourney, Elizabeth Oakes Smith and Frances Sargent Osgood. Watts marks 1850-1900 as a benchmark of women's poetic achievement, with the innovative work of Emily Dickinson. 1900-1945 is bound up with the diverse poetic achievements of H.D., Gertrude Stein, Edna St. Vincent Millay, and

Elinor Wylie. Much of Watts's analysis concentrates on thematic development in American women's poetry and concludes that women's contributions have shaped much of what we consider to be the American tradition in poetry. The bibliography features a comprehensive listing of work by American women poets.

1100*   White, Cynthia Leslie. **Women's Magazines, 1693-1968.** London: Joseph, 1970. 348p. bibliog. index. ISBN 0718106873. LC 70-483235. White applies a historical perspective to the field of women's publishing and draws upon the techniques of sociology, literary analysis, and marketing in her survey of representative women's magazines appearing between 1800 and 1968. White concentrates on British magazines but includes a significant chapter on American women's magazines. "The aims of this survey, therefore, are to analyse the modern women's periodicals against their historical background, relating the development of the industry to social, economic and technological change, and showing how these three sets of factors have affected its structure and evolution, and influenced the scope and character of magazine content" (introduction). White's conclusions suggest that editors must be responsive to social change, including the needs of older women, expanding roles for women, and changing sexual mores and family roles. "Society's interests can never be served by influential periodicals which are so closely circumscribed by financial considerations that they cannot readily respond to changing social requirements," White concludes. The appendix material will be invaluable for anyone doing research in this area. It includes a list of periodicals for women from 1693-1968; circulation figures for principal women's magazines from 1938-1968; classified lists (fashion, service, etc.) of British and American women's periodicals in 1968; and graph material comparing circulation histories of American and British women's periodicals, 1948-1968. The bibliography provides an excellent historical grounding in the subject of women readers and many aspects of women's periodicals in Britain and the United States, including advertising and reader research patterns and studies.

1101   Williams, David L. **Faulkner's Women: The Myth and the Muse.** Montreal: McGill-Queen's University Press, 1977. 268p. bibliog. index. $16.00. ISBN 0773502572. LC 77-379597.
Williams relies heavily on Jung's theory of archetypes in arguing that the Christ symbol is one of impotence in Faulkner and that Deity takes on a feminine essence. His chapter "Cultural Failure and the Modulation of Idiom: A Critical Orientation to Faulkner's Women" is the most useful chapter, though the book is unnecessarily freighted throughout with obfuscating terminology and literary-speak.

1102   Wright, Frederick Adam, 1869-1946. **Feminism in Greek Literature from Homer to Aristotle.** Port Washington, NY: Kennikat Press, 1969. 222p. bibliog. $8.00. ISBN 0804607206. LC 71-95337.
Wright's argument suggests that the Greek world fell because of the degradation of women: "the position of women and the position of slaves—for the two classes went together—were the canker-spots which, left unhealed, brought about the decay first of Athens and then of Greece." Since Greece is the source on which

most Roman writers based their work, Wright finds an "undercurrent of mysogyny which permeates Latin literature, and finds its fullest expression in Juvenal." Wright gives chapter-length analyses to Aeschylus, Sophocles, Euripides (four feminist plays), Aristophanes, Plato, and Aristotle.

LITERATURE
Poetry
[The scope note for Literature appears on p. 252.]

1103 Atwood, Margaret Eleanor, 1939- . **Selected Poems.** New York: Simon and Schuster, 1978. 240p. $9.95. ISBN 0671228854. LC 77-18042.
Atwood has chosen the best from her individual volumes of poetry—*The Circle Game* (1966), *The Animals in That Country* (1968), *The Journals of Susanna Moodie* (1976), *Procedures for Underground* (1970), *Power Politics* (1971), and *You Are Happy* (1974)—a prolific corpus for the 1966-1974 years, which have also produced three major novels. Carolyn Forche has said that these poems are a "chronicle of her preoccupation with surfaces. . . . Her language carves—and the instrument used is tonally blunt, laconic, as incisive as suits the purpose. What emerges is a bare outline: runner tracks on the ice, white scars on the body, an engraving on the shells of things, attempting to suggest the pattern of some internal order" (*New York Times Book Review*, May 21, 1978, pp. 15, 42). The Canadian poet has always been interested in the rugged terrain of Canada as metaphor for the vast inner geography we all must learn to track and to trace. Hers is a major poetic voice.

1104 Bishop, Elizabeth, 1911- . **The Complete Poems.** New York: Farrar, Straus and Giroux, 1969. 216p. $7.50. ISBN 0374127441. LC 69-15407.
Collected here are three decades of Bishop's poetry, including *North and South* and *A Cold Spring*, for which she received the Pulitzer Prize in 1955. One of the most individual poets of our time, her work has been called revolutionary, not experimental. See David Kalstone's perceptive essay on Bishop in *Five Voices* (Oxford University Press, 1977).

1105 Bishop, Elizabeth, 1911- . **Geography III.** New York: Farrar, Straus and Giroux, 1976. 50p. $7.95. ISBN 0374161356. LC 76-49930.
Bishop continues to explore the world as it is, incomprehensible and difficult and other, without despair or even judgment about what ought to be. Like geography (defined as the description of the earth's surface), Bishop describes the surface of experience without questioning. The precision is exquisite whether the topic is "The End of March," "Objects and Apparitions," or "12 O'Clock News." Other Bishop volumes are *North and South, A Cold Spring, Questions of Travel*, and *The Complete Poems*.

1106* Bradstreet, Anne (Dudley), 1612?-1672. **The Works of Anne Bradstreet.** Edited by Jeannine Hensley. Cambridge, MA: Belknap Press of Harvard University Press, 1967. 320p. index. LC 67-17312.
This edition of Anne Bradstreet is a good one to use. It is authoritative and contains an eloquent essay on Bradstreet's poetry by Adrienne Rich as well as an excellent introduction by Jeannine Hensley. The second edition of Bradstreet's work, *Several Poems* (printed in 1678), is considered closest to the

form that Anne Bradstreet intended for her poems, and it is the 1678 text that has been carefully followed in this edition. The first edition, *The Tenth Muse*, was published in London in 1650 and stands as the first known volume of poetry printed in New England except for the *Bay Psalm Book*. Bradstreet is at the height of her powers when she lays aside mimetic poetry with its conventions and concentrates on her fears and experiences as a wife, lover, mother, and woman. "Before the Birth of One of Her Children" is one of these poems. "Upon the Burning of Our House" is yet another brilliant example. Rich assesses Bradstreet's importance by saying, "Anne Bradstreet was the first non-didactic American poet, the first to give an embodiment to American nature, the first in whom personal intention appears to precede Puritan dogma as an impulse to verse."

1107   Brooks, Gwendolyn, 1917- . **In the Mecca: Poems.** New York: Harper and Row, 1968. 54p. $7.95. ISBN 0060105372. LC 68-26544.
Many of these poems articulate the Chicago ghetto experience. "Gang Girls" is a particularly powerful statement of the black woman's *persona* in a climate of violence and is the only poem in this collection relating specifically to woman's experience. This verse appears in *The World of Gwendolyn Brooks* (Harper and Row, 1971).

1108   Brooks, Gwendolyn, 1917- . **Selected Poems.** New York: Harper and Row, 1963. 127p. $10.00. ISBN 0060105356. LC 63-16503.
Most of the poems here appear in *The World of Gwendolyn Brooks* (Harper and Row, 1971). Exceptions occur in the section, New Poems: "Riders to the Blood-Red Wrath"; "The Empty Woman"; "To Be in Love"; "Of Robert Frost"; "Langston Hughes"; and a cycle of poems, "A Catch of Shy Fish."

1109   Brooks, Gwendolyn, 1917- . **The World of Gwendolyn Brooks.** New York: Harper and Row, 1971. 426p. $10.95. ISBN 0060105380. LC 74-16046.
Essential to every poetry collection is this comprehensive volume, which contains the poet's work published previously under the titles: *A Street in Bronzeville* (1945), *Annie Allen* (1949), *Maud Martha* (1953), *The Bean Eaters* (1960), and *In the Mecca* (1968). Brooks has always been a sensitive black woman poet in her writing, articulating the black urban experience. However, she reveals in her autobiographical *Report from Part One* that she is in the process of liberating herself from "conditioned" poetry imposed by a white world to write more consciously black poetry. *Riot* (1969) is not included in this collection. *Annie Allen* won the Pulitzer Prize for Poetry in 1950. It deals with a favorite Brooks theme, the development process of a young black woman. *Maud Martha*, Brooks's only novel, is another sensitive work about growth to black womanhood.

1110   Broumas, Olga, 1949- . **Beginning with O.** New Haven, CT: Yale University Press, 1977. 74p. $6.95. ISBN 0300021062. LC 76-49697.
Stanley Kunitz writes in his forword to *Beginning with O*, "among the most impressive features of Broumas's supple art is her command of syntax, rhythm, and tone. Her hedonism extends to the use of language itself; she rollicks

in 'the cave of sound.' " This volume won for Broumas the distinction of being the first winner of the Yale Series of Younger Poets who is not a native speaker of English. Broumas is Greek, her orientation, Sapphic; the sensuality of her poetry is consistently female and Greek: beaches, the clitoris, the sea, stone, the moon, menstruation—all occur and recur. Her poetry is political, often using the metaphor of language to posit the necessity for decisive action: "We must/find words/or burn." Broumas is a significant poetic voice, and her volume of poetry is quite possibly the best verse of 1977.

1111   Brown, Rita Mae. **Songs to a Handsome Woman.** Baltimore: Diana
        Press, 1973. 839p. $2.00. ISBN 0884470016. LC 74-13541.
This is an indispensable collection of lesbian poetry by the author of *Rubyfruit Jungle, Plain Brown Rapper, In Her Day*, and *The Hand That Cradles the Rock*.

1112   Browning, Elizabeth Barrett, 1806-1861. **Aurora Leigh.** Chicago:
        Academy Press, 1978. 400p. $10.95. ISBN 091586486X.
A novel/poem of 10,000 lines in blank verse, this is an extraordinary achievement, written in 1855 or '56. Renewed interest in Browning's long narrative romance has stemmed partly from Ellen Moers's evaluation of the work in *Literary Women*. Aurora Leigh, like her creator, is a writer determined to perfect her artistry at all costs. Aurora agonizes over the conflict between love and writing and in doing so, fictionally represents a realistic conflict in Victorian society that permitted women to write but not to talk about it as their vocation. Of it, Elizabeth Barrett Browning said, "this book is the most mature of my works, and the one into which my highest convictions upon Life and Art have entered."

1113   Browning, Elizabeth Barrett, 1806-1861. **The Poetical Works of Elizabeth
        Barrett Browning.** Boston: Houghton Mifflin, 1974. 548p. index.
        $10.95. ISBN 0395180120. LC 73-20373.
Ruth M. Adams, who writes a new introduction to the Cambridge Edition (orig. 1900), states, "this Cambridge Edition is without question the best single volume of the poetical work of Elizabeth Barrett Browning." The remarks of the original editor, Harriet Waters Preston, have been retained and they represent "a sympathetic but not uncritical" reading of Elizabeth Barrett Browning. Adams's introduction considers Elizabeth Barrett Browning's critical heritage and devotes attention to the two most significant of her poetic achievements: *Sonnets from the Portuguese* and *Aurora Leigh*. Adams's assessment of *Aurora Leigh*'s "too discursive, too tedious, too platitudinous" qualities are sharply at odds with more recent feminist interpretations. The Cambridge Edition is not as complete as the six-volume Coxhoe Edition or the Arno Edition (1901), but it should serve all but the specialist reader.

1114   Browning, Elizabeth Barrett, 1806-1861. **Sonnets from the Portuguese:
        A Facsimile Edition of the British Library Manuscript.** Barre, MA:
        Barre; distr. New York: Crown, 1977. [112] p. $7.95. ISBN
        051753178X. LC 77-24631.
Virtues of this particularly attractive edition of the sonnets (1849) include the facsimile presentation of each sonnet with a printed version on the facing page, a useful introduction, and a lovely pastel portrait of Elizabeth Barrett

Browning. Peterson's introduction "demythologizes" the relationship between Elizabeth Barrett Browning and her father immortalized in the stage play, *The Barretts of Wimpole Street*, by Rudolf Besier. The father may not have been such an ogre, after all. Peterson also addresses the issues of illness, death, and aging that Elizabeth Barrett Browning thematically explores in the *Sonnets*.

1115   Cooper, Jane, 1924- . **Maps and Windows: Poems.** New York: Macmillan, 1974. 80p. bibliog. $6.95. ISBN 0025280600. LC 74-10975.
This is a lovely slim volume of thoughtful lyrics—new and selected verse from 1961-1973 and 1947-1951 poems. Most interesting perhaps is Cooper's prose digression, "Nothing Has Been Used in the Manufacture of This Poetry That Could Have Been Used in the Manufacture of Bread," an essay that explores the poet's autobiography ("I've never married, have no children, so you could say my case was always different") and a poet's block that kept her from publishing for several years. In examining the process of creating and writing, she comes to realize that she was not free to give her whole being to poetry as a younger woman because she was hinging survival on the chance of establishing a permanent family relationship with husband and children. At fifty, Cooper seems to have concluded that writing is necessary for her survival and that there is no final solution "to the questions that confront women writers."

1116   Danner, Margaret. **The Down of a Thistle: Selected Poems, Prose Poems, and Songs.** Waukesha, WI: Country Beautiful, 1976. 144p. index. $9.95. ISBN 0872940845. LC 75-38873.
Danner's work is elegant and simple, though not necessarily easy to understand. She uses the imagery of nature to make dramatic statements about African culture (e.g., "The Down of a Thistle"). There is much of Chicago in this collection—the Art Institute, Lake Michigan, the Baha'i Temple. A joyful poetry, Danner's work deserves increased visibility and is suitable for a variety of libraries.

1117   Dickinson, Emily, 1830-1886. **The Poems of Emily Dickinson.** Cambridge, MA: Belknap Press of Harvard University Press, 1955. 3v. $40.00. ISBN 0674676009. LC 54-8631.
Edited by Thomas M. Johnson, this is the authoritative text for Emily Dickinson's poetry, including variant readings critically compared with all known manuscripts—especially important since Emily used letter stationary, envelope flaps, wrapping paper, and bits of newspaper in various states and stages of composition. In most cases, Johnson has indicated the poet's preferred copy of the poem. Volume 1 contains a lengthy essay on Emily's creative process, another on the editing process from 1890-1945, notes on manuscript and publication symbols, and the first group of poems, arranged chronologically 1-494 (1850-1862); volume 2 contains poems 495-1176 (1862-1870); and volume 3, poems 1177-1775 (1870-1886), along with a great deal of appendix material on the recipients of Emily's poetry and the dating and arrangements of packets. Subject index and index of first lines are included in volume 3.

1118   Doolittle, Hilda [H.D.], 1886-1961. **Helen in Egypt.** New York: New Directions, 1974. 304p. $9.00. ISBN 0811205436. LC 74-8563.

As the founder of the *imagiste* movement and as an innovator in American poetry, H.D. is known for economy in the use of words. This book-length poem is a re-creation of the Helen-Achilles myth, in which H.D. adopts the *persona* of Steisichorus. Susan Friedman's analysis of H.D. in *Women's Studies* (Winter 1978) provides a thoughtful interpretation of her imagery. The introduction is by Horace Gregory.

1119   Doolittle, Hilda [H.D.], 1886-1961. **Trilogy: The Walls Do Not Fall, Tribute to the Angels, The Flowering of the Rod.** New York: New Directions, 1973. 172p. $6.95. ISBN 0811204901. LC 73-78848.

Three distinct H.D. voices are heard in *Trilogy*. *The Walls Do Not Fall* (1944) was inspired by the air raids of World War II in London. For H.D., the bombings were to be witnessed, endured, and finally energized in the poet's consciousness. *Tribute to the Angels* (1945) was written in the pause before D-Day. Again, the apocalyptic tone was inspired by the stopping and starting of bombings. Much of the material has reference to the Old Testament (e.g., much is done with the symbolism of sevens in reference to the Old Testament and the Apocalypse of St. John, most obviously the 43 sections, with four and three adding up to seven). *The Flowering of the Rod* (1946) has little to do with war and much to do with resurrection. H.D. is drawn to the figure Mary-of-Magdala, who is reborn by washing the feet of Christ with perfumed ointment. Norman Holmes Pearson writes the introduction to this edition.

1120   Evans, Mari, 1923- . **I Am a Black Woman.** New York: Morrow, 1970. 95p. $2.45. ISBN 068830494X. LC 72-121690.

"I Am a Black Woman" is the title poem of this collection, which asserts the beauty and pride of black womanhood. The poet's major themes are love, black solidarity and community, death, and the black experience in America. Stunning photographs illustrate selected lyrics throughout the text.

1121   Gilman, Charlotte (Perkins) Stetson, 1860-1935. **In This Our World.** Boston: Small, Maynard, 1899; repr. New York: Arno Press, 1974. 217p. $15.00. ISBN 040506098X. LC 74-3951.

"While waiting for her divorce to become final, Charlotte Anna Perkins Gilman (1860-1935) sought to support herself and her family by lecturing and writing and keeping boarders. But people in her hometown and elsewhere in California knew her as one who had suffered nervous collapse, had voiced strange ideas about sex and marriage, then later had remained on most friendly terms with her closest friend who had married her ex-husband. Debt and failure pursued her, including the demise of the weekly paper she edited with Helen Campbell. San Franciscans killed it, one of them explaining that 'nothing that Mrs. Stetson (Gilman) does can succeed here.' In her autobiography, *The Living of Charlotte Perkins Gilman* (Arno Press, 1972), she noted that "there was really something exquisitely funny in . . . the moral superiority of attitude in the 'society' of that city." At that time she published her only book of poetry, elixers of her experiences, for which she earned a modest reputation as poet (A Note about This Volume," L. Stein and A. K. Baxter, editors). Many of the poems cluster around the subjects of woman's role at home and in Gilman's contemporary society. There are also a number about California scenery and climate, and, more seriously, about social conditions.

1122   Giovanni, Nikki. **Black Feeling, Black Talk, Black Judgment.** New York: Morrow, 1970. 98p. $2.25. ISBN 068825294X. LC 70-119846.
The Afro-American experience is the content of Nikki Giovanni's first published collection. "Nikki-Rosa" is perhaps the best known title of the group. Other poems interesting for their militancy and direct language are "Black Separatism," "Black Power," "Poem for Black Boys," "Revolutionary Music," "Woman Poem," and "Beautiful Black Men."

1123   Giovanni, Nikki. **My House: Poems.** New York: Morrow, 1972. 69p. $7.95. ISBN 0688000215. LC 72-116.
Nikki Giovanni's poetry is uneven. She has been compared in style and technique with Rod McKuen for some of the poems in this volume. Yet, there are outstanding moments, too. When Nikki Giovanni is into her most angry, most radical stride, she is at her best. See "Atrocities," "I Laughed When I wrote It," and "On Seeing Black Journal etc."

1124   Giovanni, Nikki. **The Woman and the Men.** New York: Morrow, 1975. [64]p. $5.95. ISBN 0688029477. LC 75-16237.
One of the three major sections of this volume is titled "The Women." Among other poems about women are: "The Women Gather," "Poem for Aretha," "For a Lady of Pleasure Now Retired," and "Mother's Habits." Giovanni's latest volume of poetry is entitled *Cotton Candy on a Rainy Day* (Morrow, 1978).

1125   Godoy Alcayaga, Lucila [Mistral, Gabriela, pseud.], 1889-1957. **Selected Poems of Gabriela Mistral.** Bloomington: Indiana University Press, 1957. 119p. $1.75. ISBN 0253299152. LC 57-13189.
Gabriela Mistrel, Chilean poet and stateswoman, won the Nobel Prize for Literature for her volume of poetry *Desolación* (Despair), said to be a memorial to death. (In 1907, Mistral's young lover had killed himself by putting a bullet through his head.) Hers is a maternal poetry and a woman's poetry with segments titled "Cradle Songs," "Poems for Mothers," "For the Saddest of Mothers," "Earth and Women," though she was not a mother herself but a beloved teacher and a lover of her native country.

1126   Grahn, Judy, 1940- . **Work of a Common Woman: The Collected Poems of Judy Grahn, 1964-1977.** Oakland, CA: Diana Press, 1978. $8.75. ISBN 0884470237. LC 78-16250.
This new edition makes more accessible the work of an important lesbian poet, Judy Grahn. Included here are her "Edward the Dyke and Other Poems," "The Common Woman," "She Who," "A Woman Is Talking to Death," and "Confrontations with the Devil in the Form of Love."

1127   Harper, Frances Ellen Watkins, 1825-1911. **Atlanta Offering: Poems.** Miami, FL: Mnemosyne, 1969. (Repr. of 1895 ed.). 70p. $7.00. ISBN 0836985885. LC 70-79027.

As is the case with many black authors, material by and about Harper is difficult to obtain. However, her poetry has begun to be reprinted in the last ten years. A lecturer, reformer, and author born in Baltimore, she was educated in her uncle's school for free Negroes and published her first work in 1845, *Forest Leaves*. Of her work, Louis Filler says in *Notable American Women* that she was influenced by Longfellow and other popular English authors following the prescribed sentimental formula poetry of the day. "Though conventional in form, her work was earnest in content and evidently gained from personal presentation." Her book *Poems on Miscellaneous Subjects* (1854) sold 12,000 copies by 1858. She has been compared to Phyllis Wheatley. Among the themes treated by Harper are nature, slavery, and religion. Editions of her work currently in print include *Poems* (Freeport, NY: Books for Libraries Press, 1970, Repr. of 1895 ed.) and *Poems* (New York: AMS Press, 1975, Repr. of 1871 ed.).

1128   Jong, Erica. **Fruits and Vegetables: Poems.** New York: Holt, Rinehart, and Winston, 1971. 86p. $5.95. ISBN 0030859980. LC 74-138876.
Onions, avocados, tomatoes, pears, apples, and grapes are the makings of this sensual and serious-comic collection about love, sexuality, and poetry. The message might best be summed up in the poet's "Arse Poetica": "Item: the poet has to feed himself and fuck himself." Rooting, giving birth, and organic growth mark the moments of motion in Jong's first book of poetry—along with eating, sucking, and nurturing. Jong's poetry is rendered in clear, exhuberant feminist language. Certain incidents and preoccupations appear in the later well-known picaresque novel, *The Fear of Flying*.

1129   Jong, Erica. **Half-Lives.** New York: Holt, Rinehart and Winston, 1973. 127p. $6.95. ISBN 0030074266. LC 72-11067.
Half-Lives follows close on the heels of *Fruits and Vegetables* and picks up thematically and metaphorically on the poetry she introduced in that first volume. "The Eggplant Epithalamion" is one of the best examples of Jong's skill with this type of verse. Her repetition of lines and phrases works particularly well (e.g., in "Seventeen Warnings in Search of a Feminist Poem"). Her subject matter is always contemporary, much of it exploring the double-bind of the woman in love, much of it informed by the experience of psychoanalysis. Segments in this collection: The Wives of the Mafiosi; A Crazy Salad; The Age of Exploration; and Sleeping with Death.

1130   Levertov, Denise, 1923- . **Footprints.** New York: New Directions, 1972. 58p. $5.00. ISBN 0811204545. LC 72-80972.
The most powerful poem in this collection, "The Day the Audience Walked Out on Me, and Why," tells of the poet's experience giving a poetry reading at Goucher College, where the audience reacted well to the commemoration of the student murders at Kent State but negatively when Levertov reminded them of "the black students shot at Orangeburg two years ago/and Fred Hampton murdered in his bed/by the police only months ago." A beautiful verse memory of the poet's experiences teaching at MIT is "A New Year's Garland for My Students/MIT 1969-70." Levertov captures the unique qualities of an entire class by writing a verse portrait of each member, which speaks persuasively of the poet's fondness for teaching. Woven through the collection are some of

Levertov's most compelling and simple nature poems, influenced by the Oriental style of Rexroth and Gary Snyder.

1131   Levertov, Denise, 1923- . **The Freeing of the Dust.** New York: New
        Directions, 1975. 114p. $7.00. ISBN 0811205819. LC 75-8568.
Levertov's poetry is so consistently excellent that it is difficult to say that one collection or another is her best. Yet the verse in this eleventh collection is so spare and unadorned, so tender and chastened, it does deserve to be ranked among Levertov's best. "The Woman" and the "Living Alone" poems are particularly memorable for their eloquent simplicity.

1132   Levertov, Denise, 1923- . **The Jacob's Ladder.** New York: New Direc-
        tions, 1961. 87p. $2.25. ISBN 0811200833. LC 61-17868.
Lyrically beautiful, and not yet into the political vein of Levertov's poetry of the late '60s and early '70s, *The Jacob's Ladder* is strongly influenced by the work of William Carlos Williams. Poems such as "A Common Ground," "The Tulips," and the "Air of November" are imagistic.

1133   Levertov, Denise, 1923- . **O Taste and See: New Poems.** New York:
        New Directions, 1964. 83p. $2.75. ISBN 0811200841. LC 64-16820.
The seasons are here in this wonderful collection—fall and spring and a bit of winter. Marriage, love, and the experience of being a woman, however, mark this collection like no other book by Levertov. She sculpts such stark and magnificent lines as these on the marital welding of a couple: "two by two in the ark of/the ache of it."

1134   Levertov, Denise, 1923- . **Relearning the Alphabet.** New York: New
        Directions, 1970. 121p. $6.00. ISBN 0811203034. LC 72-103373.
The poems here comprise a varied collection, with beautiful lyric verse descriptions of embroideries appearing in the same volume with Levertov's eloquent revolutionary poetry taken from her 1968-1969 notebook. The title poem catalogs the range of the poet's insights darting backward and forward in time and concludes in a passionate statement of poetics: "Relearn the alphabet,/ relearn the world . . . " Levertov reworks some of the themes introduced in *Relearning the Alphabet* and in *The Sorrow Dance* (1967) in *To Stay Alive* (1971), notably the "Notebook" poems and the "Olga Poems." She says of this reintroduction of material, "the artist as explorer in language of the experiences of his or her life is, willy-nilly, weaving a fabric, building a whole in which each discrete work is a part that functions in some way in relation to all others." During the late '60s and early '70s, Levertov's poetic voice chronicles demonstrations, the struggle for human rights, and pacifism against "this obscene system."

1135   Lifshin, Lyn. **Upstate Madonna: Poems, 1970-1974.** Trumansburg, NY:
        Crossing Press, 1975. 127p. bibliog. $8.95. ISBN 0912278587. LC
        75-11946.
Lifshin has a strong following in the Midwest as well as upstate New York and has emerged as one of the better young, vocally feminist poets in the states. She won considerable acclaim with her book of poetry, *Black Apples* (The

Crossing Press, 1973). In *Upstate Madonna*, her concerns are heavily autobiographical; much of it deals with sexual politics. For those interested in following her prolific progress, Lifshin includes a bibliography of her work to 1975, both books and in anthologies. Not mentioned in the bibliography is *Some Madonna Poems* (Buffalo, NY: White Pine Press, 1976).

1136   Madgett, Naomi Cornelia (Long). **Pink Ladies in the Afternoon: New Poems, 1965-1971**. Detroit, MI: Lotus Press, 1972. 63p. $2.00. ISBN 0916418014. LC 72-93588.
Madgett has been published in *Black World, Poet, Journal of Black Poetry, A Broadside Treasury* (edited by Gwendolyn Brooks, 1971), and *New Black Voices* (1972). Her literary situation is like that of many lesser recognized black poets: her work is often not readily available. Relatively few of the titles here speak directly of the black experience; most are occasional poems. Particularly successful are "Glimpses of Africa" and "Black Woman." Another in-print volume of Madgett's poetry is *Star By Star* (2nd ed., Lotus Press, 1970).

1137   Millay, Edna St. Vincent, 1892-1950. **Collected Lyrics of Edna St. Vincent Millay**. New York: Harper and Row, 1943. 279p. $10.95. ISBN 0060129301. LC 43-51349.
Millay's best volumes of poetry are *Renascence and Other Poems* (1917), *A Few Figs from the Thistles* (1920), *The Harp-Weaver and Other Poems* (1923), and *The Buck in the Snow and Other Poems* (1928). This volume contains the verse from these volumes and other work less highly regarded: *Wine from These Grapes, Huntsman, What Quarry?, Second April*, and *Selected Poems for Young People*.

1138   Millay, Edna St. Vincent, 1892-1950. **Collected Sonnets of Edna St. Vincent Millay**. New York: Harper and Row, 1941. 161p. $11.95. ISBN 0060129409. LC 41-52020.
Arranged chronologically, the 160 sonnets here selected from the works *Renascence* (1917) to *Make Bright the Arrows* (1940) represent Millay's finest work. One sonnet written by Millay when she was fifteen and three other previously unpublished sonnets appear in this volume. Her technical ability with the sonnet form is apparent throughout the collection, but a maturer tone and tighter metrical forms distinguish the poetry beginning with *Second April* from the gayer, more flippant earlier poetry. Love and the human condition emerge as prominent themes in *Collected Sonnets*.

1139*   Moore, Marianne, 1887-1972. **A Marianne Moore Reader**. New York: Viking Press, 1961. 301p. index. LC 61-17409.
For its foreword by the poet alone, this volume is worth having. Marianne Moore writes a convoluted, idiosyncratic style of prose that is the correlative to her brilliant, telegraphic style of poetry. This volume contains: the best from *Collected Poems* (1951), including "Marriage" and "The Mind Is an Enchanted Thing"; *Like a Bulwark*; *O to Be a Dragon*; *Other Poems*; selections from *The Fables of La Fontaine*; and selections from *Predilections*. *Predilections* has some interesting prose pieces—an admiring essay on Ezra Pound, another on Henry James. Other prose includes review literature, obituaries, and a

fascinating correspondence between Moore and the Ford Motor Company, which asked her to come up with "a colossal name" for a new car. "May I submit UTOPIAN TURTLE TOP? Do not trouble to answer unless you like it," wrote the poet. Ford finally chose "Edsel," not submitted by Miss Moore. The interview with Donald Hall is a rare statement of Moore's poetic beliefs in which she explains her fondness for borrowing quotations to use in her poetry, her aversion to planning stanza forms, her editorship of *The Dial*, and her association with other well-known poets. Readers may wish to consult a recent critical appraisal of Moore's work, Laurence Stapleton's *Marianne Moore: The Poet's Advance* (Princeton University Press, 1978).

1140   Morgan, Robin. **Lady of the Beasts: Poems**. New York: Random
        House, 1976. 131p. $8.95. ISBN 039440758X. LC 76-10750.
Following her first collection, *Monster* (1973), which denounces the distortions imposed on women by modern society, Morgan's feminism is less angry, more muted in this second collection. Here, she speaks of woman's powerful mythic role as Great Goddess and Lady of the Beasts, mostly lost now amid the ordinary, subservient rhythms of her life. An impressive cycle is "The Network of the Imaginary Mother," a poetic meditation on woman's roles as mother, consort, sister, child, and on the self. Another of Morgan's developmental handlings of woman's mythology is "Voices from Six Tapestries," inspired by the *La Dame à la Licorne* (The Lady with the Unicorn) tapestries hanging in the Musée de Cluny in Paris.

1141   Morgan, Robin. **Monster: Poems**. New York: Random House, 1972.
        86p. $5.95. ISBN 0394482263. LC 72-5810.
Robin Morgan edited *Sisterhood Is Powerful* (Random House, 1970), an anthology of feminist writings that became a standard Movement text. Identified as a feminist militant, her verse in this, her first published volume of poetry, is a strong collection, explicitly feminist in form and content. Marriage (her own and the institution), love between women, revolution, child-bearing, Vietnam, and mothers are Morgan's subject matter in poems such as "Matrilineal Descent" and "Letter to a Sister Underground." Perhaps most striking is Robin Morgan's translation of old, negative images into images of strength and power. "Monster" becomes an image embraced by the poet as a notation of positive identity. In "Monster," she writes that her infant son has looked at her naked body and cooed the word "monster." Morgan concludes the poem and her collection: "I am a monster/And I am proud."

1142   Newlin, Margaret, 1925- . **The Snow Falls Upward: Collected Poems**.
        Ann Arbor: Ardis, 1976. 176p. $8.95. ISBN 0882331698. LC
        76-380761.
This volume of Newlin's poetry won a National Book Award nomination in 1976. Verse here spans the years 1963-1975 and includes all poems from her first two books, *The Fragile Immigrants* (1971) and *Day of the Sirens* (1973), along with more recent verse. Ordinary life and domesticity characterize Newlin's quiet, spare verse. Some titles of poems: "Occupation: Housewife"; "The Wedding Dress"; "Washing Machine"; "Firstborn"; "A Plant for Mother"; "Nursery Song"; and "Marriage Song." Sanity and optimism are what Newlin

is about. She concludes with a cycle about an aging mother, her illness, and eventual death, seen through the poet's observant and compassionate but not despairing eye.

1143   Parker, Dorothy (Rothschild), 1893-1967. **The Portable Dorothy Parker.** (Rev. and enl. ed.). New York: Viking Press, 1973. 610p. index. $8.95. ISBN 0670540161. LC 74-180479.

Published in 1944 under the title, *Dorothy Parker*, the 1973 edition contains an introduction by Brendan Gill admirable for its precise placement of Dorothy Parker as an important minor American literary personage. Noted for her wit— "the wittiest member of the Algonquin Round Table"—she lived a long life, Gill notes ironically, and quotes a memorable Parker witticism: "People ought to be one of two things, young or old. No; what's the use of fooling? People ought to be one of two things, young or dead." Parker's work has survived, a fact that Brendan Gill comments would have surprised her. Part 1 of the 1973 edition contains the original *Portable* as arranged by Parker in 1944 (poems and short stories); part 2 contains her later stories and reviews and articles from magazines such as *New Yorker* and *Esquire*, for which she frequently wrote. Those with a serious interest in Parker's work will want to look at *The Collected Poetry* of Dorothy Parker (New York, Modern Library, 1944).

1144*   Parker, Pat. **Pit Stop.** Oakland, CA: Women's Press Collective, 1975. 44p.

Pat Parker writes explicitly of the black lesbian experience. Thematically, her poetry is deeply caught up in the struggle of all oppressed people, especially blacks and women. Her collected work is contained in *Movement in Black*, unavailable for examination at this writing (Diana Press, 1978); foreword by Audré Lord and Judy Grahn.

1145   Piercy, Marge. **Hard Loving.** Middletown, CT: Wesleyan University Press, 1969. 77p. $7.50. ISBN 0819520462. LC 70-82544.

The dedication to this volume reads, "from the Movement/for the Movement." The verse speaks of Movement experiences—of anger, confrontation, alternative lifestyles, wrenchings from familiar traditions. Many are love poems. Among the best: "Community," "Wedding Pictures," "Trajectory of the Traveling Susan," "I Am a Light You Could Read By," "I Still Feel You," "The Death of a Small Commune," "How We Marry Each Other," "The Morning Half-Life Blues," "The Organizer's Bogeyman," and "In Praise of Salt and Water."

1146   Piercy, Marge. **Living in the Open: Poems.** New York: Knopf, 1976. $6.95. ISBN 0394499875. LC 75-37525.

Piercy has said of the women's movement, "since 1969 I have been active mainly in the women's movement, which has been a great energy source (as well as an energy sink!) and healer of the psyche for me." In this collection of poetry, Piercy captures the pain in individual experience against the larger concerns of the feminist movement. Essential Piercy, among the most explicitly feminist poems in this volume are "Make Me Feel It," "The Token Woman," and "Rape Poem." There is much landscape poetry here, especially verse inspired by Cape Cod. The title poem, "Living in the Open," is a poetic manifesto for independent love. Though Piercy has often expressed a preference for lesbian love, this poem simply states the poet's belief in emotional independence for all lovers: "You wear your own flags and colors and your own names./I will never have you./ I am a friend who loves you."

1147   Piercy, Marge. **The Twelve-Spoked Wheel Flashing.** New York: Knopf; distr. New York: Random House, 1978. 130p. $7.95. ISBN 0394424387. LC 77-15020.

Divided into seasons—Winter, Spring, Summer, Fall—this collection is about cycles. The poet writes about this volume: "as I cannot separate the personal and political in my life, as I will not separate emotional and intellectual judgment and experience but try to weld them, as I go back and forth from the vital dying city with its wars of plunder and the vital dying country with its wars of plunder I have tried to shape this book as a growth ring, the record of a year." Domestic poems, love poems, situational poems about cocktail parties and airports—a stunning collection this is not, but it has the clear prose voice of Piercy.

1148   Plath, Sylvia, 1932-1963. **Ariel.** New York: Harper and Row, 1968. 85p. $7.50. ISBN 0060133589. LC 66-15738.

"In these poems, written in the last months of her life, and often rushed out at the rate of two or three a day, Sylvia Plath becomes herself, becomes something imaginary, newly, wildly and subtly created . . . " (Robert Lowell's introduction). This volume of poetry has risen to the stature of myth among Plath's vast following. Contents include: "Morning Song," "The Couriers," "Cut," "Lesbos," "A Birthday Present," "Daddy," "The Bee Meeting," "Contusion," "Edge," and "Words."

1149   Plath, Sylvia, 1932-1963. **Crossing the Water: Transitional Poems.** New York: Harper and Row, 1971. 56p. $7.95. ISBN 006013366X. LC 71-138756.

Crossing contains poems written between the British publication of *The Colossus* (1960) and the composition of the *Ariel* poems in 1961. Many of the poems have appeared in the British (not the U.S. edition) of *Colossus*. Others have appeared in the limited edition of *Uncollected Poems* (1965) and in various periodicals. Although there are glimmers of Plath's humor and compassion here, mostly there is the terror of Plath's dangerous, death-dealing vision. Among the poems: "Wuthering Heights," "Insomniac," "I Am Vertical," "Stillborn," "Widow," "Love Letter," "Sleep in the Mojave Desert," "Mirror," "Two Sisters of Persephone," "Maenad," "Witch Burning," "Crossing the Water."

1150   Rich, Adrienne Cecile, 1929- . **Adrienne Rich's Poetry: Texts of the Poems; The Poet on Her Work; Reviews and Criticism.** Ed. by Barbara and Albert Gelpi. New York: Norton, 1975. 215p. bibliog. index. $7.95. ISBN 0393043991. LC 75-315494.

For students, teachers, and poets wishing to examine the Rich texts, this Norton critical edition will be useful. The Gelpis write about the intended use of the book in the preface: "this book was planned for use in a variety of courses: poetry courses, women's studies, freshman writing." The study is organized

into three major sections: a generous sampling of Rich's major collections, from
A Change of World (1951) to *Poems: Selected and New* (1975); selections from
Rich's poetic statements and conversations (1964-1974); and finally a selection
of critical readings of Rich including W. H. Auden, Randall Jarrell, Albert Gelpi,
Robert Bowers, Helen Vendler, Erica Jong, Wendy Martin, and Nancy Milford.

1151　Rich, Adrienne Cecile, 1929- . **Diving into the Wreck: Poems, 1971-
　　　　1972.** New York: Norton, 1973. 62p. $5.95. ISBN 0393043703.
　　　　LC 73-2626.
This, the seventh book of Rich's poetry, contains some of the poet's most
important work about woman's awakening consciousness and her expectations
of what Rich defines as a new reality for women: "I am the androgyne/I am the
living mind you fail to describe/in your dead language/the lost noun, the verb
surviving/only in the infinite/the letters of my name are written under the lids/
of the newborn child." Poems include: "Trying to Talk with a Man," "Rape,"
"For a Sister," "For the Dead," "From a Survivor."

1152　Rich, Adrienne Cecile, 1929- . **The Dream of a Common Language:
　　　　Poems, 1974-1977.** New York: Norton, 1978. 96p. $9.95. ISBN
　　　　0393045021. LC 77-28156.
In this powerful collection, Rich writes of lesbianism, of feminism, of being
a woman, and of being a poet. It is the dream of finding a "common language"
to express the hitherto unarticulated lyricism of woman's collective experience
toward which she strives. For Rich "The drive/to connect. The dream of a common
language," is what poetry is about. Rich is much too complex to be summed
up as a poet whose work is about this or that ideology. The political truths
after which she quests cannot be slotted. The poetry in this collection is divided
into three parts: I. Power ("Origins and History of Consciousness" is probably
the most stunning poem of the collection and appears in this section); II.
Twenty-One Love Poems (a cycle of poems celebrating the love between two
women, first published in a limited edition by Effie's Press, Emeryville, California,
1977); III. Not Somewhere Else, but Here (these poems trace the various relationships between women as sisters, friends, mothers and daughters).

1153　Rich, Adrienne Cecile, 1929- . **Poems: Selected and New, 1950-1974.**
　　　　New York: Norton, 1975. 256p. index. $8.50. ISBN 0393043924.
　　　　LC 74-10781.
A long-standing concern of Rich's has been to explore the unexpressed feelings
of women. For those libraries who cannot afford to collect each of the individual
volumes of Rich's poetry, this collection draws from all seven of the poet's
earlier books, spanning 25 years. It includes eight poems not published in earlier
volumes as well as thirteen poems written since *Diving into the Wreck* (1973).
Rich writes in her introduction to *Poems: Selected and New*: "I think of this
book, not as a summing-up or even a retrospective, but as a graph of a process
still going on." Liberal selections appear from these groups: *A Change of World*
(1951), *The Diamond Cutters* (1955), *Snapshots of a Daughter-in-Law* (1963),
Necessities of Life (1966), *Leaflets* (1969), uncollected poems (1957-1969),
The Will to Change (1971), *Diving into the Wreck* (1973), and poems (1973-1974).
A stunning collection, Rich's work is personal and intense even when dealing

with public and political themes. For a particularly fine essay on the evolving voice of Rich, see David Kalstone's *Five Voices* (Oxford University Press, 1977), pp. 129-169.

1154*   Rukeyser, Muriel, 1913- . **Breaking Open.** New York: Random House, 1973. 135p. ISBN 039448696X. LC 73-5045.

In her eleventh volume of poetry, Rukeyser shows her mastery of many forms and her flexibility and openness in writing poems about various subjects. The repetitive theme of *Breaking Open* is the poets' quest for truth. "What kind of woman goes searching and searching?" she asks in one poem. "What do we see? What do we not see?" she asks repeatedly in another poem. Her poetic statement, "I want to break open," becomes a commitment to strip sway sham and untruth and to confront self, other, ugliness, and beauty. Among these poems about love, the Vietnam War, protesting, pacifism, and self-examination is a cycle of fifteen stark Eskimo songs, which she translated with Paul Radin. The simplicity of these Northern verses in subject and their chant-like quality seem to represent the kernel of direct experience only possible after "breaking open."

1155   Sanchez, Sonia, 1935- . **A Blues Book for Blue Black Magical Women.** Detroit, MI: Broadside Press, 1974. 62p. $5.00. ISBN 0910296782. LC 72-77309.

Dedicated to the Honorable Elijah Muhammad, this book of poetry is inspired by Sanchez's deep Muslim beliefs. Many poems in the collection lyrically project a positive and noble image of black womanhood. In the sequence titled "Past," Sanchez amplifies this positive view in segments she names "woman," "earth mother," "young/black/girl," "young womanhood," and "womanhood." As the title suggests, there is much music and song in her verse.

1156   Sanchez, Sonia, 1935- . **Homecoming.** Detroit, MI: Broadside Press, 1969. 32p. $1.00. ISBN 0910296057. LC 77-78640.

Don L. Lee writes the introduction to this political, angry, and stark collection mapping the black experience in racist America. "Her ABC's were learned in alleys & corner bars; she knows what motivates her blk/sisters & she understands the hurt of the blackman . . . The love of blackpeople, the love of blackness. That's what it is all about, the love of self & people. That's why/what Sonia writes. She doesn't have time to indulge in meaningless poetics. She need not talk about the aesthetics of a tree; there are no trees in Harlem or on the west-side of Chicago."

1157   Sanchez, Sonia, 1935- . **Love Poems.** New York: Third Press, 1973. 101p. $4.95. ISBN 089388104X. LC 73-83168.

In these stark and simple poems, Sanchez favors the haiku form. Though mainly addressing a male lover, Sanchez also explores other relationships, for example, in her father-daughter sequence.

1158   Sanchez, Sonia, 1935- . **We a BaddDDD People.** Detroit, MI: Broadside Press, 1970. 72p. $4.50. ISBN 0910296278. LC 73-121886.

Anger characterizes this early Sanchez verse through Survival Poems, Love Songs/Chants, and TCB/EN Poems (taking care of business). She begins with a celebration of black womanhood, "for i will be called QUEEN." Her anger strikes out at white America, at black complacency, at the senseless use of drugs. Sanchez chastizes those who are unable to see that true revolution is made impossible by senseless hedonism, which deflects black men and women from the serious revolution of educating black children to value themselves and their unique culture. Highly moralistic poetry, Sanchez's purpose here is to raise consciousness.

1159　Sexton, Anne, 1928-1974. **All My Pretty Ones.** Boston: Houghton Mifflin, 1962. 68p. $3.95. ISBN 0395081777. LC 62-14201.
The title poem of this volume places the poet in the autobiographical context of reflection over the death of her father, memories triggered while looking through family memorabilia—an album, a scrapbook, snapshots, a diary. Sexton was strongly attached to memorabilia during her lifetime and uses this imagery to reconcile herself to the relationship she had with her father during life and the deaths of both of her parents within a few months of each other in the early 1960s. Preoccupations of the poet in this volume are fear, death, physical and mental illness, marriage, and the emotional price of being a poet ("A woman who writes feels too much"). Among the poems: "The Truth the Dead Know," "The Operation," "The Abortion," "Ghosts," "Housewife," "Love Song for K. Owyne," "The Black Art."

1160　Sexton, Anne, 1928-1974. **The Awful Rowing toward God.** Boston: Houghton Mifflin, 1975. 86p. $5.95. ISBN 0395203651. LC 74-23618.
Ironically, Sexton spent the afternoon of her death reading galley sheets for *The Awful Rowing.* The title poem, a capsulized autobiography, finishes with the line: "This story ends with me still rowing." While previous poetry has been obsessed with death, this volume of verse deals consistently with the quest for God: "I cannot walk an inch without trying to walk to God." Poems include: "The Room of My Life," "The Sermon of Twelve Acknowledgements," "The Sickness Unto Death," "Jesus, the Actor, Plays the Holy Ghost," "Mothers," "Doctors," "Frenzy," "When the Saints Come Marching In," "The Rowing Endeth." Another posthumous collection of Sexton's work is entitled *Words for Dr. Y* (Houghton Mifflin, 1978); it includes poems and three brief Gothic stories, of which "The Ghost" is the most effective.

1161　Sexton, Anne, 1928-1974. **The Book of Folly.** Boston: Houghton Mifflin, 1972. 105p. $5.95. ISBN 0395140145. LC 72-3839.
Sexton experiments with form in this collection, which includes thirty poems, three stories in the style of fables, and a section she titles, "The Jesus Papers." Of the poetry, Sexton is at her most moving in a poem called "Mother and Daughter," addressed to her daughter, Linda Gray. "The Wifebeater" is a powerful statement about familial violence. The stories plot the course of love and marriage in strokes of bitterness and despair. Women are zombie-like victims being led to mindless slaughter. Men, though oppressors, are also victims in the brutal cycle.

1162   Sexton, Anne, 1928-1974. **The Death Notebooks.** Boston: Houghton
        Mifflin, 1974. 97p. $5.95. ISBN 0395182816. LC 73-17311.
It is no secret that Anne Sexton was preoccupied with death. She takes the
epigram for this volume from Hemingway: "Look, you con man, make a living
out of your death." This group of poems, published in the year of her suicide,
contains a number of autobiographical poems drawing on biblical imagery and
structure. Among the poems: "Gods," "Making a Living," "For Mr. Death Who
Stands with His Door Open," "The Furies" (a cycle of poems), and "O Ye
Tongues" (a cycle of psalms). The poet casts a clear cold eye on death. The
final poem proclaims: "For God was as large as a sunlamp and laughed his heat
at us/and therefore we did not cringe at the death hole."

1163   Sexton, Anne, 1928-1974. **45 Mercy Street.** Ed. by Linda Gray Sexton.
        Boston: Houghton Mifflin, 1976. 113p. $6.95. ISBN 0395242959.
        LC 75-38707.
Linda Gray Sexton, Sexton's daughter, edited the unpublished manuscript
after the poet's suicide in 1974 and has made editorial decisions concerning
arrangement, handwriting problems, and the like, while preserving the original
text. Certain poems have been omitted "because of their intensely personal
content," though the complete manuscript, along with worksheets, private
papers and letters, is in the Anne Sexton Archive at Boston University. This
volume of verse records the poet's growth and events of her life from 1971
to 1974. Many of the poems deal with divorce, especially the lengthy section
"The Divorce Papers." This is a haunting, tortured collection by a gifted poet.

1164   Sexton, Anne, 1928-1974. **Live or Die.** Boston: Houghton Mifflin,
        1966. 90p. $5.95. ISBN 0395081815. LC 66-22961.
Sexton introduces this Pulitzer-Prize winning collection: "to begin with, I have
placed these poems (1962-1966) in the order in which they were written with
all due apologies for the fact that they read like a fever chart for a bad case
of melancholy." Autobiographical in content, Sexton's verses speak of an
unhappy childhood and disillusioned marriage, of mental asylum routines and
drug addiction, of traveling abroad and traveling inside the poet's tortured
head. Among the poems: "Flee on Your Donkey," "Love Song," "Man and
Wife," "Two Sons," "Sylvia's Dead," "For the Year of the Insane," "Menstruation at Forty," "Wanting to Die," "The Wedding Night," "Suicide Note," "Pain
for a Daughter," "The Addict," "Cripples and Other Stories," "Live."

1165   Sexton, Anne, 1928-1974. **Love Poems.** Boston: Houghton Mifflin,
        1969. 67p. $6.95. ISBN 0395081831. LC 69-12444.
These 25 love poems can be read as the continuing chronicle of a single lover,
or as individual poems. The epigram by Yeats states the thematic preoccupation
of this volume: "Everything that has been shall be again." Among the poems:
"The Touch," "The Kiss," "The Breast," "In Celebration of My Uterus,"
"For My Lover Returning to His Wife," "Moon Song, Woman Song," "The
Ballad of the Lonely Masturbator," "Eighteen Days without You."

1166   Sexton, Anne, 1928-1974. **To Bedlam and Part Way Back.** Boston:
        Houghton Mifflin, 1960. 67p. $3.95. ISBN 0395081793. LC 60-5221.

The poet's voice in this first collection is the anguished cry of a solitary soul—solitary in madness; solitary in asylum life; solitary and reviled as a witch, as the mother of an illegitimate child; alone and bereft as the survivor of airline disasters and the death of parents. Somehow the poet hangs on even after two suicide attempts—"I pretended I was dead/until the white men pumped the poison out,/putting me armless and washed through the rigamarole/of talking boxes and the electric bed." In this first collection, Sexton establishes her poetic control of the ironic line that turns back upon itself. Of life in the asylum: "Once I was beautiful. Now I am myself/counting this row and that row of moccasins/waiting on the silent shelf."

1167   Sexton, Anne, 1928-1974. **Transformations.** Boston: Houghton Mifflin, 1971. 111p. $5.00. ISBN 0395127211. LC 71-156489.

It is common to read that Anne Sexton "transformed" Grimm's fairy tales into frightening story-poems in this volume. It may be that Sexton is saying in her verse that Grimm's little tales were rather frightening of themselves; we simply didn't listen closely enough as children to the messages. There are seventeen familiar tales here, including "Snow White and the Seven Dwarfs," "Rapunzel," "Cinderella," and "Briar Rose (Sleeping Beauty)." The foreword is by Kurt Vonnegut, with drawings by Barbara Swan.

1168   Smith, Florence Margaret [Smith, Stevie], 1902-1971. **The Collected Poems of Stevie Smith.** New York: Oxford University Press, 1976. 591p. index. $20.00. ISBN 0195198166. LC 75-4322.

Because of her playfulness and fondness for doggerel, Stevie Smith's poetry has never received the critical acclaim it deserves, though her reputation fares better in Britain than in the United States. As easy as she is to read, her simplest lines generally contain word play of great sophistication and complex wit, as in "I was much too far out all my life/And not waving but drowning." Stevie Smith's unique personality radiates throughout this handsome edition of her poetry, much of the verse accompanied by her fanciful doodles. Her friend and the editor of this volume, James MacGibbon, writes a brief, fond memoir of the poet in the preface. *The Collected Poems* contains *A Good Time Was Had By All* (1937), *Tender Only to One* (1938), *Mother, What Is Man?* (1942), *Harold's Leap* (1950), *Not Waving But Drowning* (1957), *Poems* (1962), and *Scorpion and Other Poems* (1971). Readers with an interest in Stevie Smith may want to look at Hugh Whitemore's *Stevie: A Play*, a drama based on Smith's life and work (S. French, 1977).

1169   Sturgeon, Mary C. **Michael Field.** London: G. G. Harrap, 1922; repr. New York: Arno Press, 1975. 245p. bibliog. $10.00. ISBN 0405074018. LC 75-12361.

Perhaps the most interesting aspect of this volume of verse by Michael Field (the combined pen-name of two late-Victorian Englishwomen—Katharine Bradley, 1846-1914, and Edith Cooper, 1862-1913) is the biographical note about the two women collaborators (pp. 13-64), who spent much of their lives together writing poetry and drama and advocating women's rights. The two women were much influenced in their art by the Sapphic fragments.

1170*   Swenson, May. **Half Sun, Half Sleep: New Poems**. New York: Scribner, 1967. 128p. LC 67-11638.

In her poetry, May Swenson uses a mixture of new and old forms and experiments with spatial, imagist, surrealist, and calligraphic verse. She consistently surprises. Here she favors observations of natural phenomena—in "October Textures," "A City Garden in April," "Hearing the Wind at Night," and translations of Ingemar Gustafson, Werner Aspenström, Eric Lindegren, Gunner Ekelof, Harry Martinson, and Karin Boyle (six Swedish poets). She explores female experience in a poem such as "Motherhood," though her verse is not generally feminist.

1171*   Swenson, May. **To Mix with Time: New and Selected Poems**. New York: Scribner, 1963. 183p. LC 63-10635.

Swenson has been compared with Marianne Moore for her idiosyncratic use of language and experimental use of imagery in the description of concrete objects. In this volume, she writes of people-watching in parks, museums, subways, gardens, and churchyards in Europe and in the States (most frequently in New York City). One reads Swenson in much the same way as one looks at an impressionistic canvas, especially in such deftly painted scenes as "Spring in the Square," "Horses in Central Park," "Looking Uptown," "Water Picture," and "Ornamental Sketch with Verbs."

1172   Teasdale, Sara, 1884-1933. **The Collected Poems of Sara Teasdale**. New York: Macmillan, 1967. 224p. $5.95. LC 37-28625.

The collections included here are *Sonnets to Duse and Other Poems* (1907), *Helen of Troy and Other Poems* (1911), *Rivers to the Sea* (1915), *Love Songs* (1917), *Flame and Shadow* (1920), *Dark of the Moon* (1926), *Stars To-Night* (1930), and *Strange Victory* (1933). Teasdale's poetry is distinguished by an exquisite sensibility, which reaches its highest emotional pitch in *Flame and Shadow, Dark of the Moon*, and *Strange Victory*. Her life was marked by physical frailty and deep depressions. She died of an overdose of barbituates in 1933 after serious illness followed by severe depression. See Harriet Monroe, *A Poet's Life* (1938), and Margaret Haley Carpenter, *Sara Teasdale: A Biography* (1960).

1173   Urdang, Constance. **The Picnic in the Cemetery: Poems**. New York: Braziller, 1975. 67p. $6.95. ISBN 0807607959. LC 75-7653.

Richard Howard writes in the introduction to this collection, "though of course [Urdang] writes most deliberately as a woman, a wife, a daughter, a mother, a maiden, a whore, a crone (the nurse, the sibyl, and the hag are favorite inflections), she is astonishing among the women poets I know for her egalitarianism, for her coupled measurements of what it must be to be fully human. What bothers her into poetry is not resentment but response, not competition but replenishment. For she is supremely aware of the metamorphoses—even in the cemetery, even in the nursery, in the nursery most of all." Titles of poems in this collection speak to her preoccupation with the woman theme: "Abortion," "Woman in the Attic," "Becoming a Woman," "Adultery," "Because the Oracle Is a Woman," and "Childless Woman." Among her other works are *Charades and Celebrations* (poems, 1965) and *Natural History*, a novel.

1174   Wakoski, Diane. **Dancing on the Grave of a Son of a Bitch.** Los Angeles:
        Black Sparrow Press, 1975. 137p. $10.00. ISBN 0876851804. LC
        73-16395.
Wakoski has emerged as an important voice in contemporary American feminist
poetry. She has said that the important details of her life can be found in her
poetry, and indeed her poetry is personal, unashamedly autobiographical,
often accompanied by a note describing the circumstances of the poem's
creation. The poems in this volume are divided into five sections: The Astronomer
Poems; Dancing on the Grave of a Son of a Bitch (in which the title poem,
one of her most beautiful poems—"The Purple Finch Song"—and a number
of chant poems appear); Some Poems for the Buddha's Birthday; The Diamond
Merchant; and Esoteric Fables.

1175   Wakoski, Diane. **The Man Who Shook Hands.** Garden City, NY:
        Doubleday, 1978. 118p. $6.95. ISBN 0385134088. LC 77-80917.
Wakoski looks at her body and its imperfections with a sense of humor, despite
her admission that she fantasizes about possessing personal beauty so compelling
that she could attract the lovers for whom she longs. She equates communication
through poetry to communication through music. Her poetry is music, and other
poets she admires have left their music in her head: Wallace Stevens, Charles
Olson, Robert Duncan, and others. Her introductory essay, "The Blue Swan,
an Essay on Music in Poetry," contains the most remarkable writing in this
volume. "Running men" is Wakowski's song of humor and healing expressing
the plight of the plain woman who must learn to live with the images of physical
perfection imposed from within and without.

1176   Wakoski, Diane. **Trilogy: Coins and Coffins; Discrepancies and Appari-
        tions; The George Washington Poems.** Garden City, NY: Doubleday,
        1974. 166p. $6.95. ISBN 0385089104. LC 73-10548.
Three early and out-of-print collections of Wakoski's poetry—*Coins & Coffins*
(1962), *Discrepancies and Apparitions* (1966), and *The George Washington
Poems* (1967)—appear here in their entirety. Wakoski writes in the introduction
to *Trilogy* that she does not see her poetry as progressing from one form to
another. Rather, she conceives of each collection as a separate and self-contained
developmental process. She describes the poems in *Coins & Coffins* as surrealistic
creations built around dream images. "*The George Washington Poems* are all
poems in which I address some man in my life as well as his alter ego, George
Washington, a mysterious mythical figure, both representing the world I live
in, 'the man's world,' with its militaristic origins and the glorification of fact
over feeling." Wakoski deflates the image of reality, seeing humor in the human
situation for both men and women. In *Discrepancies and Apparitions*, a collection built from three smaller manuscripts, Wakoski transcends the mundane
qualities of describing ordinary experience by using imagery that is purposefully extravagant and surreal. Among the most striking individual poems here are
"Elizabeth and the Golden Oranges," "Poem to the Man on My Fire Escape,"
"Coins and Coffins Under My Bed," "Follow That Stagecoach," "Apparitions
Are Not Singular Occurrences," and "George Washington: The Whole Man."
Diane Wakoski is a poet clearly involved with men; she writes her perplexities
about her relationships into her poetry, reinventing her experiences with

men and with women. The result is magical, surprising, personal, compassionate, contradictory, and humorous poetry.

1177   Walker, Alice, 1944- . **Once: Poems.** New York: Harcourt, Brace,
         Jovanovich, 1976. 81p. $2.45. ISBN 0156687453. LC 75-29307.
Written when the poet was 24, this volume (originally 1969) of simple poems about Africa and about the civil rights conflicts in the South was recognized immediately as the work of a formidable poetic sensibility.

1178   Walker, Alice, 1944- . **Revolutionary Petunias and Other Poems.**
         New York: Harcourt, Brace, Jovanovich, 1973. 70p. $2.95. ISBN
         0156766205. LC 72-88796.
Alice Walker writes at the beginning of the volume: "these poems are about Revolutionaries and Lovers; and about the loss of compassion, trust, and the ability to expand in love that marks the end of a hopeful strategy. Whether in love or revolution. They are also about (and for) those few embattled souls who remain painfully committed to beauty and to love even while facing the firing squad." Accordingly, the poems here depict three faces of a black woman: poems that look to ancestors and childhood in rural Georgia; poems that comment upon revolution and what commitment demands of the Self; poems of gentle love.

1179   Walker, Margaret, 1915- . **For My People.** New Haven, CT: Yale Univer-
         sity Press, 1942; repr. New York: Arno Press, 1968. 58p. $8.00. ISBN
         0405019025. LC 73-4377.
Originally published in 1942 as the winner of the Yale Series of Younger Poets award, this collection was noted for its "straightforwardness," "directness" and "reality" by Stephen Vincent Benét, who wrote the foreword. Benét went on further to remark that these qualities were "combined with a controlled intensity of emotion and a language that, at times, even when it is most modern, has something of the surge of biblical poetry." Many of the poems here have been anthologized, but most famous is her eloquent title poem, which is a dedication to blacks scattered geographically throughout the country and a celebration of their diversity and resiliancy.

1180   Walker, Margaret, 1915- . **October Journey.** Detroit, MI: Broadside
         Press, 1973. 38p. $1.50. ISBN 0910296960. LC 73-82444.
The title poem takes the reader on a visually magnificent journey from North to South in October and sets the tone for the impressive verse to follow, a celebration of notable names in black history and culture, and a personal celebration of the major influences on Walker's poetry. Among the most memorable selections: "Harriet Tubman," "Epitaph for My Father," and "A Litany from the Dark People." Margaret Walker's poetry displays admirable control over a number of quite different verse forms.

1181   Walker, Margaret, 1915- . **Prophets for a New Day.** Detroit, MI: Broad-
         side Press, 1970. 32p. $1.00. ISBN 0910296219. LC 78-130304.
Walker's civil rights poetry focuses on desegregation struggles and the days of street marches and sit-ins, murdered civil rights workers, and assassinated

heroes. The verse is noble, strong, and remarkably free from rancor. Particularly intense is her elegiac "For Andy Goodman—Michael Schwerner—and James Chaney."

1182   Wheatley, Phillis, afterwards Phillis Peters, 1753?-1784. **Life and Works of Phillis Wheatley. Containing Her Complete Poetical Works, Numerous Letters, and a Complete Biography of This Famous Poet of a Century and Half Ago.** Plainview, NY: Books for Libraries Press, 1970. (Repr. of 1916 ed.). 112p. $12.25. ISBN 0836986857. LC 70-83899.
This volume contains a lengthy essay on Wheatley's life, a sampling of her letters, and the 1773 text of her poems. Another good edition of *The Poems* is the volume edited by Julian D. Mason (Chapel Hill, 1966).

1183   Wheatley, Phillis, afterwards Phillis Peters, 1753?-1784. **Memoir and Poems of Phillis Wheatley: A Native African and Slave.** Miami: Mnemosyne, 1969. (Repr. of 1838 ed.). 155p. $9.25. ISBN 0836986865. LC 76-83898.
Not until 1834, when abolitionist acitivity was at high pitch, did Margaretta Odell, a distant relative of the Wheatleys, publish a "Memoir" of the poet in a new edition of the *Poems*. It was with this edition of the *Poems* that Wheatley achieved some recognition as the first Negro woman poet in America. By conventional standards, her poetry is not first-rate. Her quest for education and her personal qualities of charm and poise were extraordinary. Odell addresses her remarks to Wheatley's personal attributes. The poems in this edition, which cluster around epic and religious themes, were first published in London in 1773.

1184   Wier, Dara, 1949- . **Blood, Hook and Eye.** Austin: University of Texas Press, 1977. 70p. $7.95. ISBN 0292707207. LC 76-30772.
Wier spares the reader no directly observed inscapes or landscapes either beautiful or ugly. The 51 poems arranged here to comment on the outward and inward lives of women are: "Blood"—family life in Missouri poverty; "Hook"—the buttons, hooks, and artifacts that hold a woman's life in, as well as her biological openings, mysterious yet mechanical at times; and "Eye"—everything that we see, including "Mexico, West Virginia, Where"; and "The Direction to the Left of Sunrise." Dara Wier is an unusual new voice in feminist poetry. *Blood, Hook and Eye* is an exceptional collection.

1185   Wylie, Elinor (Hoyt), 1887-1928. **Collected Poems of Elinor Wylie.** New York: Knopf, 1932. 311p. $8.95. ISBN 0394403347. LC 32-26577.
Elinor Wylie's four volumes of verse are included here: *Nets to Catch the Wind* (1921), *Black Armour* (1923), *Trivial Breath* (1928), and *Angels and Earthly Creatures* (1929). The order and sequence of their original publication have been maintained. In addition, there is a section of previously uncollected poems that Wylie published in periodicals. Edited and selected by her husband, William Rose Benét, this volume reflects the best work of the poet, which often has a light tone and songlike quality. Among the most interesting work here: "The

Heart's Desire," "The Madwoman's Miracle," "The Pebble," "Little Eclogue,"
"A Tear for Cressid," and the nineteen sonnets from *Angels and Earthly Creatures.*
A recent biography of Wylie is Stanley Olson's *Elinor Wylie: A Life Apart* (Dial
Press, 1978).

MEDICINE, HEALTH,
SEXUALITY, BIOLOGY

The resources in this chapter extend over the range of scholarly and general
interest materials available on women's health care, female sexuality and biology,
and the male-dominated medical system under which the majority of American
women receive care. Though the emphasis is on feminist and woman-related
materials suitable for supporting women's studies courses on topics related to
women's biology and health, much of the material supports library collection
development in the area of general health materials. Clusters include books on
the history of the medical profession and midwifery (see Donnison); the contemporary medical education situation (see Campbell); resource guides on women's
health care (see Cowan); histories of childbirth and female disorders, both
political and social (see Corea). Standard survey and report literature on sexuality
(see Hite) and particular women-related health clinical issues (Cope) are examples
of the core literature in this area. See the Reference chapters for additional
sources and bibliographies. The journal *Women & Health* (published by the
Biological Science Program at SUNY—Old Westbury) stands out as the most
significant periodical resource in this area, providing ongoing identification or
important print and non-print resources addressing women's health issues.

1186*   Alsop, Gulielma Fell, 1881- . **History of the Woman's Medical College,
        Philadelphia, Pennsylvania, 1850-1950.** Philadelphia, PA: Lippincott,
        1950. 256p. bibliog. index. LC 50-10367.
This is a history of the Woman's Medical College of Pennsylvania, "the first
medical college for women in the history of education . . . ," by a 1908 graduate.

1187   Arms, Suzanne. **Immaculate Deception: A New Look at Women and
        Childbirth in America.** Boston: Houghton Mifflin, 1975. 318p. bibliog.
        index. $11.95. ISBN 0395198933. LC 74-28129.
"For the midwives," reads Suzanne Arms's dedication in this remarkable and
upsetting analysis of childbirth in America. Ehrenreich and English have written
a brief history of the usurpation of the midwife's function at normal births
by the medical profession (see their *Witches, Midwives, and Nurses*, 1973).
What Arms does in *Immaculate Deception* is to describe the consequences of
this for the childbirth process, for laboring women, and for their babies. It is
a chilling story, one that any woman socialized in the U.S.—with its mystifica-
tion of the medical profession—will find hard to accept. The basic question
Arms raises is whether unnecessary medical intervention into the normal birth
process has not succeeded in rendering hospital birth *more* rather than less
risky to mother and child than home birth. Arms offers detailed evidence indicting routine obstetrical use of drugs, fetal monitors, IVs, episiotomies, forceps
in deliveries, and hormones to induce or speed up labor. She also presents
moving testimony and suggestive evidence on the harmful effects of hospitals'
dehumanizing and inflexible routine on the labor process and the mother, father,
and child. This powerful indictment of current obstetrical practice is further

strengthened by Arms's discussion, in the second half of the book, of traditional practices of midwifery in a home birth situation—where obstetrical faith in complex technology and a crisis mentality is replaced by the midwife's faith in nature, patience, and caring. Interviews with and statements by mothers, midwives, nurses, and doctors alternate with Arms's own analysis throughout. Readers might also want to look at Doris Haire's *The Cultural Warping of Childbirth* (orig. 1972; included in *The Cultural Crisis of Modern Medicine*, edited by John Ehrenreich, 1978), Jane B. Donegan's *Women and Men Midwives: Medicine, Morality, and Misogyny in Early America* (Greenwood Press, 1978), Judy Barrett Litoff's *American Midwives, 1860 to the Present* (Greenwood Press, 1978), and Nancy Stoller Shaw's *Forced Labor: Maternity Care in the United States* (Pergamon Press, 1974).

1188   Ashdown-Sharp, Patricia, 1941- . **A Guide to Pregnancy and Parenthood for Women on Their Own.** New York: Vintage Books, 1977. 200p. bibliog. index. $3.95. ISBN 0394722728. LC 76-62491.
Ashdown-Sharp writes with sensitivity and respect for her reader. In addition, she is very conscious of and well informed about the problems that women face in pregnancy and childrearing, and her concern is to provide women with as many positive alternatives as possible. This *Guide* has much that would interest any woman, but the author is addressing herself to single women in particular. Her chapters on the specific situations of single pregnant women and single mothers are most valuable ("Marriage"; "Adoption and Fostering"; "Bringing Up a Child on Your Own"). These speak to both the emotional experience and to the practical needs of single women, and they include concrete suggestions and lists of relevant organizations and publications. Her chapters on diagnosing pregnancy, abortion, pregnancy, and contraception are also responsibly and sensitively written, but they duplicate other widely available sources—for example, the Boston Women's Health Book Collective's *Our Bodies, Ourselves*, a classic that the reader will also want to consult.

1189   Ashley, Jo Ann, 1939- . **Hospitals, Paternalism, and the Role of the Nurse.** New York: Teachers College Press, 1976. 158p. bibliog. index. $9.95. ISBN 0807724718. LC 76-7908.
Based on the author's doctoral dissertation ("Hospital Sponsorship of Nursing Schools: The Influence of Apprenticeship and Paternalism on Nursing Education in America, 1893-1948," Teachers College), this is a much needed study of the development of nursing in the United States as a "female profession" subject to the authority and control of the male-dominated medical profession. Ashley is concerned about the increasingly recognized crisis in health care and analyzes the contributions of the hierarchical and sex-stratified organization of Health care systems to this crisis.

1190   Bell, Alan P., 1932- , and Martin S. Weinberg. **Homosexualities: A Study of Diversity Among Men and Women.** New York: Simon and Schuster, 1978. 505p. bibliog. index. $12.95. ISBN 0671242121. LC 78-7398.
Concluding that homosexuals reflect both diversity in their lives and the stable, ordinary mental health of the general population, Bell and Weinberg proclaim their Kinsey Institute Study, a ten-year project, to be "the most ambitious

study of homosexuality ever attempted." Interviews of 1,500 persons found among other things that "homosexual people" rarely adhere to traditional sex roles, do have long-lasting love relationships, and tend to be more liberal in their political views and less religious than the general population. Few respondents expressed regret about being gay. Lesbian critics will note that Bell and Weinberg have focused on homosexuality in males. They justify their emphasis rationalizing that the "problems and adaptations" of the male homosexual population were "of greater interest" to the National Institute of Mental Health, than the experiences of lesbian women. The typology that Bell and Weinberg have devised pertains to homosexual men. Similarly, the authors have taken a narrow approach in the racial composition of their study—white and black only. Many charts, graphs, and tables support the study, though the statistical apparatus will not save the study from controversy regarding the values and assumptions that underlie it. Weinberg and Bell's controversial study is an important middle-ground approach, despite its shortcomings, in the area of socio-sexuality.

1191   Boston Women's Health Book Collective. **Our Bodies, Ourselves: A Book By and For Women.** (2nd ed.). New York: Simon and Schuster, 1976. 383p. bibliog. index. $12.95. ISBN 0671221450. LC 75-25802.
This is the best fundamental resource available on woman's mental and physical health needs, her physiology, and her sexuality. The second edition is over 100 pages longer than the first and more than two-thirds revised, in some cases in response to readers' requests, in other cases to report changes in and new information about the health field. Each chapter has excellent illustrations and bibliographies. By 1976, *Our Bodies, Ourselves* had sold over a million copies and was being published in many countries outside the United States. It should be in all library reference collections. Readers who have found the approach of *Our Bodies, Ourselves* helpful will undoubtedly be interested in the collective's new book, *Ourselves and Our Children* (Random House, 1978). This resource book on parenting is informed by the same self-help perspective that shaped the Collective's first book, building on the testimony of some 200 parents. "Our feeling is that no one knows more about being parents than parents do," said one collective member. The book seeks to demystify romantic conceptions of parenthood at the same time that it affirms much of the parenting experience. Practical information is offered about day care, pregnancy and childbirth, gay parents, and more.

1192   Campbell, Margaret A. (pseud.). **Why Would a Girl Go into Medicine? Medical Education in the United States: A Guide for Women.** (3rd ed.). Old Westbury, NY: Feminist Press, 1974. 114p. $3.50. ISBN 0912670339. LC 74-16326.
"This report is an attempt to inform all who are concerned about health care, about the relationships between the prejudice that describes women as 'girls,' the effects of that prejudice on women being trained to become physicians, and the inappropriate attitudes and assumptions that color the behavior of many physicians toward their women patients." The author uses her own experiences and date collected from 146 women medical students to address the major issues of institutional discrimination, overt discrimination, subtle discrimination, and organizing and surviving as women in medical schools. Especially interesting

is the table provided listing individual medical schools, the sexual breakdown of their admissions, and identification of their support groups. Readers should be aware of an earlier (and inevitably dated) study by Carol Lopate entitled *Women in Medicine* (Johns Hopkins Press, 1968).

1193   Clay, Vidal S. **Women: Menopause and Middle Age.** Pittsburgh, PA: Know, 1977. 157p. index. $5.00. ISBN 091278637X. LC 76-26455.
Jessie Bernard, a prominent sociologist, has written about this book that "it helps women feel good about themselves. Though it romanticizes nothing, promises no miracles, offers no placebos, it offers constructive, non-patronizing information. It treats women as strong and capable of managing their own lives." Clay discusses physical, social and psychological sides of menopause, estrogen replacement therapy, women's different experiences of menopause, and menopause and middle age. Readers may also want to look at Paula Weideger's *Menstruation and Menopause: The Physiology and Psychology, the Myth and the Reality* (Knopf, 1976).

1194   Cope, Oliver, 1902- . **The Breast: Its Problems, Benign and Malignant: and How to Deal with Them.** Boston: Houghton Mifflin, 1977. 240p. bibliog. index. $8.95. ISBN 0395257093. LC 77-9045.
For many years a surgeon at Massachusetts General Hospital in Boston and professor of surgery at the Harvard Medical School, Dr. Oliver Cope has based his treatise on breast cancer on twenty years' experience in pursuing alternatives to mastectomy. Cope has a definite point of view he wants to get across: namely, that the disfigurement of radical mastectomy is not only no longer necessary, but that it, in fact, is a less effective treatment than other methods available today. Medicine being reluctant to change, it is Cope's belief that an informed public must demand the changes in its interests. In this volume, he discusses the physiology of the breast, benign tumors and their relation to the menstrual cycle, and effective alternative treatments for malignancies (irradiation, the palliative hormones, chemotherapy, and immunotherapy).

1195   Corea, Gena. **The Hidden Malpractice: How American Medicine Treats Women as Patients and Professionals.** New York: Morrow, 1977. 309p. bibliog. index. $10.00. ISBN 068803148X. LC 76-53556.
This is a highly readable feminist analysis of women's health care and how it is shaped by male domination of the medical profession in general and of gynecology and obstetrics, specifically. Corea first gives a historical account of the exclusion of women from medicine, then proceeds with a critical analysis of health care practices relating to veneral disease, birth control, abortion and sterilization, childbirth, and common female health problems. There are also chapters on the patient-doctor relationship, medicine and social control, the history of the birth control movement, and midwives. In an epilogue, she discusses the women's health movement, to which is appended a list of names and addresses of organizations, clinics, films, and publications pertaining to the health movement and to self-help in general.

1196*   Cowan, Belita. **Women's Health Care: Resources, Writings, Bibliographies.**
         Ann Arbor, MI: Anshen, 1977. 52p. $4.00. LC 77-71904.
Conscientiously researched, to the point, and current, this resource guide—
which features a mixed format of questions, answers, essays, readings, recommended
periodicals, films, and organizations—will supplement existing materials on
important women's physical and mental health issues. Topics include: patients'
rights, malpractice, medical research, women in health, childbirth, abortion,
birth control, menopause, estrogens, breast cancer, alcoholism, psychotherapy,
drug abuse, and rape prevention. The author is active in the women's health
movement as a college health care instructor. The publication is available from
Anshen Publishing, 556 2nd Street, Ann Arbor, MI 48103.

1197   Crile, George, 1907- . **What Women Should Know about the Breast
         Cancer Controversy.** New York: Macmillan, 1973. 179p. bibliog.
         index. $4.95. LC 73-7142.
This is an important book written by a physician who has spent his professional
life studying the causes and cures for breast cancer. It is written to be accessible
to lay readers and with a commitment to the right of the patient to be informed
and involved in decision-making about her treatment. A further recommendation
for the book is Crile's critical examination of alternative methods of treatment
("If your surgeon refuses to consider anything but a radical mastectomy, find
one who will."). Among the topics he considers are: The History of the Treatment
of Breast Cancer; Why Different Types of Treatment Give Similar Rates of Cure;
Why American Surgeons Have Been Slow to Abandon Radical Mastectomy;
The Right to Choose; and A Summary of the Advantages and Disadvantages
of Various Treatments.

1198   Donnison, Jean. **Midwives and Medical Men: A History of Inter-
         Professional Rivalries and Women's Rights.** New York: Schocken
         Books, 1977. 250p. bibliog. index. $14.95. ISBN 080523652X.
         LC 76-48763.
Based on Donnison's thesis entitled *The Development of the Profession of
Midwife in England, 1750-1902, Midwives and Medical Men* is a historical account
of the profession of midwifery in England: the historical tradition of women
tending women in pregnancy and childbirth; the usurpation of obstetrical
functions by a rising male medical establishment during the eighteenth and
early nineteenth centuries; the reorganization and reappropriation of midwifery
by women in the nineteenth-century women's movement, seeking to open up
medical education and opportunities for employment to women; the struggle
for the Midwives Act of 1902, which granted professional status to midwives;
and contemporary threats to midwifery, such as that posed by routine hospitalization and obstetrical intervention in childbirth. The history of midwifery in
England differs markedly from the American experience. Readers will want
to compare Donnison's account with, for example, Barbara Ehrenreich and
Deirdre English's two pamphlets, *Witches, Midwives and Nurses* (1974) and
Complaints and Disorders (1973). Readers should also be aware of Suzanne
Arms's important book, *Immaculate Deception* (1975).

1199   Dreifus, Claudia, ed. **Seizing Our Bodies: The Politics of Women's Health.** New York: Vintage Books, 1977. 321p. bibliog. $4.95. ISBN 0394723600. LC 77-76554.

Seizing Our Bodies pulls together an excellent collection of articles from the women's health movement. Articles were culled from such publications as *Health/PAC Bulletin, Majority Report, Mother Jones, New York Times Magazine, off our backs,* and *Science for the People.* The writings are organized into five major topics: 1) History/Herstory; 2) The Means of Reproduction (i.e., contraception, abortion, and sterilization); 3) Institutionalized Male-Practice (sex hormones, breast cancer, unnecessary surgery, class dimensions of medical malpractice); 4) Women Workers in the Medi-Business; and 5) Taking Our Bodies Back: The Women's Health Movement. Among the contributors are G. J. Barker-Benfield ("Sexual Surgery in Late-Nineteenth-Century America"), Barbara Ehrenreich and Deirdre English ("Complaints and Disorders: The Sexual Politics of Sickness"), Barbara Seaman ("The Dangers of Oral Contraception," "The Dangers of Sex Hormones"), Adrienne Rich ("The Theft of Childbirth"), Claudia Dreifus ("Sterilizing the Poor"), and Ellen Frankfort ("Vaginal Politics"). Readers might also want to be aware of Sheryl K. Ruzek's *The Women's Health Movement: Feminist Alternatives to Medical Control* (Praeger, 1978).

1200   Ehrenreich, Barbara, and Deirdre English. **Complaints and Disorders: The Sexual Politics of Sickness.** Old Westbury, NY: Feminist Press, 1973. 94p. bibliog. $2.50. ISBN 0912670207. LC 73-18356.

In this classic analysis of the sexual politics of sickness, Ehrenreich and English argue that the medical system is strategic to women's oppression and for women's liberation. On the one hand, it has been a bulwark of "scientific" justification of sexual inequality, while, on the other, it is the guardian of potentially liberating reproductive technology. In this pamphlet, the authors discuss 1) medicine's contribution to sexist ideology and sexual oppression in the late nineteenth and early twentieth centuries (the period that witnessed the shift from religious to bio-medical rationales for sexism, as well as the rise of the male medical establishment), and 2) women's relation to the medical establishment today.

1201   Ehrenreich, Barbara, and Deirdre English. **For Her Own Good: 150 Years of the Experts' Advice to Women.** Garden City, NY: Anchor Press, 1978. bibliog. index. $8.95. ISBN 0385126506. LC 77-76234.

Ehrenreich and English write from a distinctly socialist feminist perspective in this telling historical study of women and medicine. The central questions they address here are simple and direct: why have women been systematically excluded from the policy and practice of medicine? and what have been the consequences of their exclusion? They chronicle medicine's transformation in America from a family art, where the skills of women healers were valued and the sensibilities of people as human beings respected, to a commodity relation dominated by "experts," where healing becomes regulated by the market and human interaction takes a distinctly secondary role to the dictates of commercialism—competition for patients, for financial reward, for prestige—all in Science's holy name. Whether charting the growth of the popular health movement, sketching the nineteenth-century malady of hysteria, delineating the uterus-vs.-brain controversy, or tracing the scientific mystique, this book delivers American medical history with the sharp sting of truth.

1202   Ehrenreich, Barbara, and Deirdre English. **Witches, Midwives and Nurses: A History of Women Healers.** (2nd ed.). Old Westbury, NY: Feminist Press, 1973. 48p. bibliog. $1.95. ISBN 0912670134.

"Women have always been healers . . . They were called 'wise women' by the people, witches or charlatans by the authorities." This important pamphlet analyzes the repression of women healers and the usurpation of healing by a male medical establishment that is both part of and subservient to the ruling class. Ehrenreich and English see the struggle over medicine as intimately linked to the history of both sex struggle and class struggle. Two specific phases in the male takeover of health care are analyzed here: the suppression of witches in medieval Europe and the rise of the male medical profession in nineteenth-century America. Readers might also want to look at Jean Donnison's *Midwives and Medical Men*, a history of midwifery in England, and Jane B. Donegan's *Women and Men Midwives: Medicine, Morality, and Misogyny in Early America* (Greenwood Press, 1978).

1203   Ehrenreich, John, 1943- , ed. **The Cultural Crisis of Modern Medicine.** New York: Monthly Review Press, 1978. 300p. bibliog. $16.50. ISBN 0853453488. LC 78-465.

John Ehrenreich has brought together in this collection twelve important articles, previously published in journals or other anthologies, which (as Ehrenreich describes them, "unlike most radical critiques of health care, are not concerned primarily with the problem of the distribution of health care (who gets what kind of care and how do they pay for it) but rather with the nature of modern medical care itself. They examine medical care as science and as social interaction" (from the introduction). Section 2 of the anthology, "Medicine and Women: A Case Study in Social Control," will be most directly relevant to women's studies. It includes the following pieces: "The 'Sick' Women of the Upper Classes," by Barbara Ehrenreich and Deirdre English; "The Politics of Birth Control, 1920-1940: The Impact of the Professionals," by Linda Gordon; "The Cultural Warping of Childbirth," by Doris Haire; "Pediatricians and Mothers," by Mary C. Howell; and "A Funny Thing Happened on the Way to the Orifice: Women in Gynecology Textbooks," by Diana Scully and Pauline Bart. Other important articles in the collection include: "Medicine and Social Control," by Barbara and John Ehrenreich; "Medicine as an Institution of Social Control," by Irving Kenneth Zola; "Medicine and Colonialism," by Frantz Fanon; and "Public Health in Imperialism: Early Rockefeller Programs at Home and Abroad," by E. Richard Brown.

1203a   Fisher, Seymour. **The Female Orgasm: Psychology, Physiology, Fantasy.** New York: Basic Books, 1973. 533p. bibliog. index. $16.00. ISBN 0465023738. LC 72-89173.

A condensed version was published in 1973 under the title: *Understanding the Female Orgasm.* Fisher states in his introduction "this book seeks to understand the psychological aspects of the various kinds of sexual behavior studied by Kinsey et al. (1953) and Masters and Johnson (1966). It is concerned with how a woman's personality influences her sexual responsiveness as well as her experiences with body functions such as menstruation and pregnancy." Particularly interesting are the conclusions Fisher makes on the psychological correlates of orgasm consistency and the preference women express concerning clitoral versus vaginal orgasm. A scholarly treatment supported by extensive appendices, tables, and references.

1203b*   Forbes, Thomas Rogers, 1911- . **The Midwife and the Witch.** New Haven, CT: Yale University Press, 1966. 196p. bibliog. index. LC 66-21519.
Though it is out of print and the perspective is not feminist, *The Midwife and the Witch* will be of interest to readers intrigued by the close historical connections between women's healing, midwifery and persecution of witches (the most well known feminist treatment of the topic is Ehrenreich and English's *Witches, Midwives, and Nurses,* 1973). Forbes's book is perhaps most interesting *because* its conceptualization and writing preceded feminist formulations of the issue. The connections Forbes emphasizes emerge from the fear and superstitiousness humans display in the face of the mysterious and unknown—in this case, reproduction—rather than from sexual antagonism and power struggle. His lengthy bibliography including works in several languages other than English, should be of interest to researchers.

1204*   Francke, Linda Bird. **The Ambivalence of Abortion.** New York: Random House, 1977. ISBN 0394410807. LC 77-90257.
Francke's book addresses some very difficult and painful issues about abortion. A committed advocate of women's right to abortion ("I would march myself into blisters for a woman's right to exercise the option of motherhood . . . ") and a woman who herself experienced an emotionally painful abortion, she wants to understand the ambivalence of the act. This is dangerous territory, as she discovered when her original piece on the Op-Ed page of the New York *Times* (signed "Jane Doe") was avidly pounced upon by Right-to-Lifers and widely reproduced in their literature. Woman's right to abortion has such precarious standing that its advocates are understandably reluctant to qualify their views or admit the complexity of the issue. Francke takes the position that one can be pro-abortion but still admit to ambivalence. Here she presents material collected in interviews held across the U.S. with single women, married women, teenagers, couples, doctors, clinic staffs, men in abortion waiting rooms, and parents. This is not a scientific survey, but an impressionistic portrait which succeeds in raising important questions. A more systematic study of the subjective reality of abortion is Mary K. Zimmerman's *Passage Through Abortion: The Personal and Social Reality of Women's Experiences* (Praeger, 1977).

1205   Francoeur, Robert T. **Eve's New Rib: Twenty Faces of Sex, Marriage and Family.** New York: Harcourt Brace Jovanovich, 1972. 253p. bibliog. index. $6.50. ISBN 0151293848. LC 78-182328.
Francoeur is the author of *Utopian Motherhood* and a married former Catholic priest. His preoccupation here is with monogamous marriage as an ideal of Western civilization, in the context of the new technology of human reproduction (including artificial insemination, test-tube fertilization, embryo transplantation, and contraceptive pills). Because of this technology, Francoeur insists that the

present vocabulary and traditional conceptualization of male-female relationships, marriage, and the family are quite inadequate. Among chapters in this volume are: Population Control and the Sexual Revolution; Serial Polygamy, Infidelities, and Modern Affairs; Comarital Concubines, Bigamy, and the Obsolete Mistress; Polygamy for Senior Citizens; Contract, Unisex, and Celibate Marriages. Francoeur's approach is popular. His bibliography is a selected list of annotated sources on alternatives in marital and other sexual arrangements.

1206   Francoeur, Robert T. **Utopian Motherhood: New Trends in Human Reproduction.** (3rd ed.). South Brunswick, NJ: A. S. Barnes, 1977. 307p. bibliog. index. $3.95. ISBN 0498040941. LC 77-362417.

The prospect of "artificial insemination, frozen germ cells, the artificial womb, embryo transplants, prenatal monitoring and manipulations, genetic engineering, and asexual clonings" clearly has Francoeur worried. Are we wise enough, holy enough, god-like enough to meet the "brave new world's" challenge? Francoeur's contention is that embryology will force men and women to rethink the myths of masculinity and femininity with the potential for males and females to realize their humanity—but also to "cast us into an asexual, impersonal world of assembly-line produced, thought controlled, genetically engineered ghosts of men." This is a popularized treatment of a complex biological issue, but his point that sexual intercourse and procreation will become increasingly unlinked human activities is a valid one that raises many questions in male-female dialogue.

1207   Frankfort, Ellen. **Vaginal Politics.** New York: Quadrangle Books, 1972. 250p. $6.95. ISBN 081290284X. LC 72-83623.

This important exposé of the American medical establishment charges women to acquire knowledge about their own bodies and to demand excellent non-sexist medical care. Among the issues that Frankfort raises are the elitist hierarchy of a male-dominated medical profession and the consequences of a medical mystique; the legal and economic issues that surround abortion; drugs, prescriptions, and consumer education; breast cancer and gonorrhea; psychotherapy and sexual therapy; women's health courses and centers.

1208   Gordon, Linda. **Woman's Body, Woman's Right: A Social History of Birth Control in America.** New York: Grossman, 1976. 479p. bibliog. index. $12.50. ISBN 0670778176. LC 76-22691.

While different bits and pieces of the history of birth control in the United States have been available before, Linda Gordon pulls together a tremendous amount of material and in a novel way. As her subtitle informs us, this is a *social history* of birth control, as opposed to a medical or technological account. What this means is that the story of the development of birth control methods and of the struggle over their availability is set into the context of the on-going social currents and struggles of the time—feminism, socialism, Malthusianism and eugenics, the evolution of the medical establishment, and so on. Noting that many birth control methods have been known since antiquity, her major argument is "that birth control has always been primarily an issue of politics, not of technology." This book is crucial background for those interested in issues of women's reproductive freedom.

1209   Grissum, Marlene, and Carol Spengler. **Womanpower and Health Care.**
       Boston: Little, Brown, 1976. 314p. bibliog. index. $6.95. ISBN
       0316328952. LC 75-41571.
Nursing is a profession possessing the classic characteristics of a "female"
occupation: while the vast majority of the work force is composed of women,
the occupation is locked into a hierarchy over which men retain authority and
control. In *Womanpower and Health Care*, two nurses analyze the oppression,
frustration, and sense of powerlessness felt by women in the nursing profession.
Part of their analysis focuses on socialization processes, which favor hierarchical
sexual relations as they get played out between the medical and nursing professions. The second and potentially more radical thrust in the analysis considers
possibilities for change and for a movement by the workers who actually deliver
health care to demand control over the terms and the quality of that care—a
possibility with clear and far-reaching implications not just for working conditions of nurses but for the crisis-ridden health care system in this country as
well.

1210   Haller, John S., and Robin M. Haller. **The Physician and Sexuality in
       Victorian America.** Urbana: University of Illinois Press, 1974. 331p.
       bibliog. index. $10.00. ISBN 0252002075. LC 73-2456.
The authors define sexuality very broadly to encompass the totality of social
relations between the sexes. Their concern in this important study is with the
tensions which arose in these relations as Victorian America made the transition from a rural, preindustrial to an urbanized, industrial society—a transition
creating dramatically new social patterns and necessitating the invention of new
values and behaviors. In particular, the transformation of the family from a
sphere of production to a sphere of privatized consumption threatened disruption of the traditional sexual division of labor. Haller and Haller see the manifestation of these tensions in Victorian society's preoccupation with sexuality;
in the endless diagnoses of, treatises on, and claimed cures for the ills of masturbation, prostitution, pregnancy, menopause, women's "nervous disorders,"
and so on. The authors advance three particularly important theses concerning
this period. First, they argue, it was at this time that physicians increasingly
usurped the role formerly played by ministers as society's confessors and moral
guardians. Second, they note that in this role physicians exercised a very conservative influence, particularly with regard to women's efforts to escape constricting sex roles. And third, they make a radical reinterpretation of the supposed
"prudery" of Victorian women, viewing it as a form of sexual rebellion and as
the only line of defense available under prevailing conditions. Readers may
want to read in conjunction with this study Linda Gordon's *Woman's Body,
Woman's Right* (1976) and Ehrenreich and English's *For Her Own Good* (1978).

1211   Hardin, Garrett James, 1915- . **Mandatory Motherhood: The True
       Meaning of "Right to Life."** Boston: Beacon Press, 1974. 136p. bibliog.
       $4.95. ISBN 0807021768. LC 74-4880.
Hardin, an outspoken critic of the "Right to Life" Movement, challenges all
of the arguments of the large anti-abortion mobilization. Hardin's main point
is that Right to Life "is dedicated to forcing motherhood onto women who
don't want to be mothers." Appendixes include: Organizations Supporting

Abortion; Gallup Poll on Abortion; The Swedish Study; a reading list of significant
works on abortion; Educational and Activist Organizations.

1212   Himes, Norman Edwin, 1899-1949. **Medical History of Contraception.**
        New York: Schocken Books, 1970. 521p. bibliog. index. $4.50. ISBN
        0805202463. LC 70-102799.
First published in 1936, this massive study (the product of ten years' research)
presents a comprehensive and panoramic history of human contraceptive theory
and practice over the course of 3,000 years. Today the work remains indispensable background for readers interested in reproduction and its control. Himes,
who was professor of sociology at Colgate University, investigates contraceptive
technique in preliterate societies, in the world of antiquity (Eqypt, Greece,
and Rome), in early Eastern cultures (China, India, and Japan), and in the West
during the Middle Ages and early modern times. He then moves on to give a
historical account of what he calls the "democratization of technique" in England
and the U.S. since 1800. He concludes with a discussion of the probable future
impact of this democratization. Himes emerges from this exhaustive investigation with a conclusion of radical import: namely, that—whatever the level of
understanding of reproductive processes and whatever the level of success in
contraceptive practice—the *desire* and *striving* of human beings to control
reproduction are ancient and universal. Himes has provided massive historical
documentation for this argument, whose implications for a theory of the origins
and evolution of patriarchy have only begun to be explored (see, for example,
Linda Gordon, *Woman's Body, Woman's Right*, especially her first chapter).
Himes's study concludes with a bibliography of some 1,500 items, covering the
literature up to the mid-1930s.

1213   Hite, Shere. **The Hite Report: A Nationwide Study on Female Sexuality.**
        New York: Macmillan, 1976. 438p. bibliog. $12.50. ISBN 0025518518.
        LC 76-6944.
Hite claims in the preface that "the first half of the book is devoted basically
to a discussion of orgasm, and the second half to a critique of our culture's
definition of sex." Hite's questionnaire asked women how they felt about sex
and the book that resulted is one of women sharing their experiences about
all facets of their sexual lives rather than a statistical tabulation of female
response. Major chapters on: masturbation, orgasm, clitoral stimulation, lesbianism, sexual slavery, sexual revolution, older women, and the new female sexuality.

1214   Hite, Shere. **Sexual Honesty by Women for Women.** New York: Warner
        Paperback Library, 1974. 294p. $1.95. ISBN 0446894648.
Shere Hite brought this book out several years before the now better known *Hite
Report*. Though it comes out of the same questionnaire study on women's
sexuality and covers much of the same ground, there's much to recommend
it in addition to or even over the more recent book. Aside from its relative
brevity, its primary distinction is the presentation of each woman's questionnaire response *as a whole*, rather than scattered through the book by topic as
is done in the *Hite Report*. This permits the reader to get a sense of the *person*
whose views on sexuality are being expressed.

1215 Hughes, Muriel Joy, 1903- . **Women Healers in Medieval Life and Literature.** Freeport, NY: Books for Libraries Press, 1968. 180p. bibliog. index. $12.75. ISBN 0836905520. LC 68-57322.

First written and published in 1943 as a doctoral dissertation (Columbia University), this study is an early foray into a field of inquiry that has greatly intrigued feminist historians of the contemporary women's movement (see the now-classic pamphlet by Ehrenreich and English, *Witches, Midwives, and Nurses*, 1973). Hughes looked at the woman healer and her practices from the eleventh through the fifteenth century, with particular emphasis on the English woman. She investigated examples of famous women healers in medieval literature and researched the history of the actual practices and status of women physicians, surgeons, nurses, and midwives—showing that "as one might expect, the records bear out, in the main, what imaginative literature describes."

1216 Indiana. University. Institute for Sex Research. **Sexual Behavior in the Human Female.** By the staff of the Institute for Sex Research, Indiana University: Alfred C. Kinsey and others. Philadelphia, PA: Saunders, 1953. 842p. bibliog. index. $19.00. ISBN 0721654509. LC 53-11127.

The Institute for Sex Research, under the direction of Alfred C. Kinsey, opened the door to the scientific study of sexual behavior. Its studies, initiated in 1938, revolutionized scientific and popular understanding of human sexuality. The pathbreaking work of Havelock Ellis and of Freud is acknowledged by Kinsey et al., but they note that prior to the Institute studies there had been no general survey of *normal* human sexual behavior. What studies existed were of the case history variety, thus failing to provide a sample adequate for scientific conclusions. This volume followed the Institute's initial publication, *Sexual Behavior in the Human Male* (Saunders, 1948). It is based on the case histories (secured in personal interviews) of 5,940 white women living in the U.S. Data are presented on preadolescent sexual development, masturbation, nocturnal sex dreams, "pre-marital" petting, "pre-marital" coitus, marital coitus, extra-marital coitus, lesbianism, and the comparative anatomy, physiology, and psychology of male and female sexual response and orgasm. This report was instrumental in counteracting many of the myths surrounding women's sexuality and the female orgasm. Interested readers will want to turn to the more recent work of Masters and Johnson, who took the scientific study of sexuality a step further than Kinsey with their laboratory observations of actual behavior.

1217 Jex-Blake, Sophia, 1840-1912. **Medical Women: A Thesis and a History.** New York: Source Book Press, 1970. (Repr. of 1886 ed.). 256, 99p. bibliog. $16.50. ISBN 0442810776. LC 72-133996.

Sophia Jex-Blake, M.D., was a member of the Irish College of Physicians, a lecturer on hygiene at the London School of Medicine for Women, and attending officer at the Edinburgh Hospital and Dispensary for Women and Children. In part 1 of *Medical Women*, she sketches a history of women in medicine— men's monopoly on healing by the time of the nineteenth century; women healers in earlier times; medieval midwifery and the recent emergence of "man-midwifery"; medical women in England, Italy, France, the United States; and the author's suggestions for change. In part 2, the Medical Education of Women, Jex-Blake gives an account of the struggle of five women to graduate from the University of Edinburgh in the 1870s and their ultimate victory. A brief summary of their legal case is included as an appendix. Readers may want to look at a recent anthology entitled *Women Physicians of the World: Autobiographies of Medical Pioneers*, edited by Leone McGregor Hellstedt (Hemisphere, 1978).

1218   Lader, Lawrence. **Abortion II: Making the Revolution.** Boston: Beacon Press, 1973. 242p. bibliog. $3.95. ISBN 0807021814. LC 72-6228.
Lader writes a history of the abortion movement in the United States from 1966 to 1973. Though he brings together much material that the student or researcher will find of interest, he has a tendency to place himself and his own political work at the center of the history he is reconstructing. This is first evident in his choice of 1966 as the beginning point for this study—the year in which his earlier book, *Abortion*, was published. His introductory chapter describes his reluctant venture into that research, and the considerable controversy it provoked upon publication, as the "preface to revolt." In Lader's perspective on abortion history, the struggles of women are viewed sympathetically but as somewhat peripheral and after the fact. For example, Lader writes, "It took only a few of us in 1966—the early fanatics—to break the silence and unleash the moral fury of women. Once the National Organization for Women and Women's Liberation groups joined the abortion movement, we were ready to shake the country." Readers will undoubtedly want to consult other perspectives on this history, as well as more recent accounts.

1219   Lee, Nancy Howell. **The Search for an Abortionist.** Chicago: University of Chicago Press, 1969. 207p. bibliog. $9.50. ISBN 0226470016. LC 74-75135.
Published in 1969, this study is based on doctoral research conducted from 1965 to 1967. The fact that the study predated the Supreme Court decision legalizing abortion makes it particularly valuable as testimony on women's struggles for reproductive control—in the late 1970s more than ever, as the legal status of abortion is increasingly under attack. The research was based on lengthy questionnaires filled out by 89 women and extensive interviews with an additional 25 women who had had abortions. While Lee incorporates statistical tables into the text, the main body of the account is written in non-technical language; frequent reference to personal details about or verbatim quotations from particular subjects humanize the analysis. Lee questioned her subjects about their social backgrounds, the circumstances of the unwanted conception, the decision to seek an abortion, the personal networks through which an abortionist was found, and the type of abortion and its aftermath. In a concluding chapter, Lee considers the question of differential access to abortion and abortionists by social class.

1220*   McDermott, Sandra. **Female Sexuality: Its Nature and Conflicts.** New York: Simon and Schuster, 1971. 223p. index. ISBN 0671209523. LC 77-154551.
First published in England under the title *Studies in Female Sexuality*, this volume is the result of a series of three- to four-hour interviews with women over the course of two years on the subject of their sexuality. The bulk of

the subjects were enlisted in the study through the British monthly periodical, *Forum*. Topics discussed include fantasy, morality, love, marriage, orgasm, lesbianism, and masturbation. McDermott's perspective is that sexuality must not be viewed as an isolated activity, but rather as an integral part of personality and human relationships. The study seems less effective than those of Shere Hite (*Sexual Honesty, The Hite Report*) due to the author's decision to use interview material only as illustration for her own argument rather than letting the women speak for themselves. While the approach is generally feminist, this predominance of the author still makes for the kind of dangerous substitution of opinion and judgment for fact that characterizes most treatises on sexuality. While the book is out of print in the U.S.—representing a further disadvantage—it may be recommended especially for the comparisons it makes possible between women in the U.S. and in Britain.

1221   Masters, William H., et al., eds. **Ethical Issues in Sex Therapy and Research.** Boston: Little, Brown, 1977. 227p. bibliog. index. $12.50. ISBN 0316549835. LC 77-70467.
A dry but very significant reference source in the field of human sexuality. Topics evolved out of a conference organized and sponsored by the Reproductive Biology Research Foundation (January 22-23, 1976). In addition to the notable editors (Masters, Johnson, and Robert C. Kolodny), women's studies individuals will recognize the names of many participants: Mary Calderone, Helen Kaplan, Judith Long Laws, Pepper Schwartz, Sallie Schumacher, Mary Jane Sherfey, and Emily Hartshorne Mudd. Discussions were convened around the topics: The Historical Background of Ethical Considerations in Sex Research and Sex Therapy; Theological Perspectives on the Ethics of Scientific Investigation and Treatment of Human Sexuality; Ethical Issues and Requirements for Sex Research with Humans: Confidentiality; Issues and Attitudes in Research and Treatment of Variant Forms of Human Sexual Behavior; The Ethics of Sex Therapy; and The Training of Sex Therapists. William H. Masters summed up the conference in an expression of the need for the incorporation of acceptable ethical standards in both treatment and research. He called for the establishment of training centers and treatment programs with appropriate institutional connections, stating that human sexology has yet to come into its academically recognized and legitimized scientific place in the medical community.

1222   Masters, William H., and Virginia E. Johnson. **Human Sexual Inadequacy.** Boston: Little, Brown, 1970. 467p. bibliog. $15.00. ISBN 0316549851. LC 71-117043.
This volume follows up the authors' earlier *Human Sexual Response* with a discussion of common problems in sexual expression, including premature ejaculation, ejaculatory incompetence, impotence, orgasmic dysfunction, vaginismus, dyspareunia, and sexual inadequacy in the aging. Suggested treatments for impotence and orgasmic dysfunction are also outlined. The approach and style is highly clinical (for example, "The marital unit also must be encouraged continually to create an environment that fulfills the stimulative [biophysical and psychosocial] requirements of each partner and in which sex-tension can occur without any concept of performance demand."). Some readers may prefer

Fred Belliveau and Lin Richter's popularized and simplified *Understanding Human Sexual Inadequacy* (Little, Brown, 1970).

1223   Masters, William H., and Virginia E. Johnson. **Human Sexual Response.**
        Boston: Little, Brown, 1966. 366p. bibliog. $15.00. ISBN 0316549878.
        LC 66-18370.

Acknowledging the enormous contributions of Alfred C. Kinsey and the Indiana University Institute for Sex Research to the scientific understanding of human sexuality, Masters and Johnson make a case for the necessity of direct observation and physical measurement of male and female sexual response—an empirical approach they have pioneered. In this report based on the study of 382 female and 312 male subjects, the authors present an analysis of comparative male and female sexual response and of geriatric sexual response. The chapter on female sexual response discusses: female extragenital response, the anatomy and physiology of female external genitalia, the clitoris, the vagina, the artificial vagina, the uterus, the female orgasm, and pregnancy and sexual response. Readers who find this clinical report heavy-going may prefer to look at the popularized and simplified *An Analysis of Human Sexual Response,* by Ruth and Edward Breecher (Little, Brown, 1966), or Mary Jane Sherfey's *The Nature and Evolution of Female Sexuality* (J. Aronson, 1974), which was based in large part on the work of Masters and Johnson.

1224   Masters, William H., and Virginia E. Johnson. **The Pleasure Bond:**
        A New Look at Sexuality and Commitment. Boston: Little, Brown,
        1975. 268p. $8.95. ISBN 0316549819. LC 74-18390.

Each chapter of this exploration of sexuality between couples focuses on the question of how to maintain sexual interest in an ongoing relationship. The approach is definitely geared to heterosexual couples. In each of the various group situations described in the book—young marrieds, individuals who engage in extramarital sex, "swinging" couples, second marriage couples—individuals describe their situations, and Johnson and Masters offer thoughtful comments in a non-judgmental way. It is impossible not to note that in the profiles of the couples, the man almost invariably has a more interesting and challenging job, though this is never discussed in the therapy sessions. Some especially interesting chapters to those looking at Masters and Johnson from a women's studies perspective: How the Double Standard Influences Sexual Pleasure; What Men Stand to Gain from Women's Liberation; and What Sexual Fidelity Means in a Marriage.

1225   Miniconsultation on the Mental and Physical Health Problems of
        Black Women, Washington, D.C., 1974. **Miniconsultation on the**
        Mental and Physical Health Problems of Black Women, Washington,
        D.C., March 29-30, 1974. Washington: Black Women's Community
        Development Foundation, 1975. 136p. bibliog. LC 75-325602.

This book is a follow-up to a conference on the mental and physical health problems of black women sponsored by the Black Women's Community Development Foundation of Washington, D.C., in March 1974. The central focus of the conference was the impact on black women of the class-, race- and sex-biased United States health care system. Among the problems of particular concern to black women that are inadequately addressed by U.S. health care are hypertension, cancer, fibroids, sterilization abuse, suicide, and depression. Contributors to this readable volume include both health care professionals and laypersons.

1226   Nightingale, Florence, 1820-1910. **Notes on Nursing: What It Is and What It Is Not.** London: Harrison, 1859; repr. Philadelphia, PA: Lippincott, 1946. 79p. $4.75. ISBN 0397540000.

In outlining some general principles of nursing practice—both to professional nurses and to women performing nursing duties for their own families—Nightingale reveals much about the status of nurses and the state of the medical art of her day. Stating that one out of seven babies born in England died before the first birthday, she argued that women had best not leave medical and physiological knowledge only to medical men. Much of her advice was common sense, which often contradicted ignorant and unhygienic medical practice of the day. Among topics on which she dispensed advice: Ventillation and Warming; Food; Bed and Bedding; Chattering Hopes and Advices; and Observation of the Sick. Though Nightingale never specifically indicts doctors for careless medical practices, she gives enough examples from her observations of faulty medical practice to make a strong case for good nursing as the salvation of many a patient. Nightingale concludes that "surgery removes the bullet out of the limb, which is an obstruction to cure, but nature heals the wound. So it is with medicine; the function of an organ becomes obstructed. Medicine, so far as we know, assists nature to remove the obstruction, but does nothing more. And what nursing has to do in either case, is to put the patient in the best condition for nature to act upon him. Generally, just the contrary is done. You think fresh air, and quiet and cleanliness extravagant, perhaps dangerous, luxuries, which should be given to the patient only when quite convenient, and medicine the *sine qua non*, the panacea. If I have succeeded in any measure in dispelling this illusion, and in showing what true nursing is, and what it is not, my object will have been answered."

1227   Robinson, Paul A., 1940- . **The Modernization of Sex: Havelock Ellis, Alfred Kinsey, William Masters and Virginia Johnson.** New York: Harper and Row, 1976. 200p. bibliog. index. $8.95. ISBN 0060135832. LC 75-24500.

For readers interested in the history of "the modernization of sex," Paul Robinson provides a helpful summary and comparative analysis of four key sexual theorists of this past century who together can be credited with opening the door to the systematic study of human sexuality. Robinson's approach is that of the intellectual historian. He tells us, "I have examined their writings very much as one might those of a major philosopher or political theorist . . . to identify the assumptions, the biases, the tensions, and the modes of reasoning that characterize their work. . . . " Robinson is also attentive to the perspective of each theorist on female sexuality, male/female sexual relations, and feminism.

1228   Seaman, Barbara. **Free and Female.** Greenwich, CT: Fawcett Publications, 1973. 320p. bibliog. index. $1.50.

The sexual life of women, including the medical profession's approach to female-related diseases, is the subject of Seaman's sometimes angry but uniformly interesting study. "This book deals with body issues. I hope that it will help women to appreciate how exquisitely formed and beautiful their natural bodies are and what great instruments of pleasure these bodies can be," she writes in her introduction. Chapters are: Is Woman Insatiable; The Liberated Orgasm; 100 Sensuous Women—part 1; 100 Sensuous Women—part 2; How To Liberate Yourself from Your Gynecologist; Men, Love and Marriage; A Skeptical Guide to VD and Contraception; The Children of Liberated Women; The Middle-Class Male as Mighty Joe Young, or Can Men Be Rehumanized? Complementary reading to Seaman's analysis of gynecology is Gena Corea's well-researched feminist indictment of the medical profession's shocking approach to female health problems, *Women's Health Care: The Hidden Malpractice* (1977).

1229   Seaman, Barbara and Gideon Seaman. **Women and the Crisis in Sex Hormones.** New York: Rawson Associates, 1977. 502p. bibliog. index. $12.95. ISBN 0892560037. LC 76-53297.
In this controversial study, the Seamans indict doctors' massive prescription of sex hormones for women in the face of substantial evidence suggesting their dangers. They tell the story of DES (diethylstilbestrol), a synthetic estrogen shown to be associated with vaginal cancer in daughters of women who took the drug in pregnancy, and still prescribed as replacement therapy for menopausal women, for the prevention of post-partum breast engorgement, and in the form of the "morning-after" pill. The physiology of menopause and the hazards of estrogen replacement therapy (ERT), natural remedies for the discomforts of menopause, complications known and suspected to be associated with oral contraceptives, and alternatives to the pill for men and women are among the study's other major foci. Central to the analysis is the Seamans' radical opposition to the medical profession's crisis- and disease-oriented approach to normal female biological functions. Barbara Seaman is also author of two earlier studies on women's health care entitled *The Doctors' Case Against the Pill* (Wyden, 1969) and *Free and Female* (Fawcett, 1973).

1230   Sherfey, Mary Jane, 1933- . **The Nature of Evolution of Female Sexuality.** New York: J. Aronson, 1974. $10.00. ISBN 0876681321. LC 73-18627.
Originally published in 1966, this study is dedicated to Masters and Johnson, whose observations of the workings of female sexuality Sherfey did much to popularize. Sherfey discusses the nature of female sexual response and its implications for the psychoanalytic theory of female sexuality. In particular, she denies the distinction between "vaginal" and "clitoral" orgasms and emphasizes that women's capacity for sexual arousal and orgasm far exceeds that of men, being limited only by the onset of fatigue. Women's sexual capacity has been historically repressed, she argues, to guard the maternal function and to protect men's property rights. This classic study has been the basis of many of the more recent feminist writings on female sexuality.

1231   Sisley, Emily L., and Bertha Harris. **The Joy of Lesbian Sex: A Tender and Liberated Guide to the Pleasure and Problems of a Lesbian Lifestyle.**

New York: Crown, 1977. 223p. bibliog. index. $12.95. ISBN 0517531593. LC 77-22418.

A follow-up to *The Joy of Sex* and *More Joy of Sex*, this guide is written by lesbians for lesbians, addressing social and emotional concerns as well as lesbian sexuality. Readers will find a more complete resource guide in Ginny Vida's *Our Right to Love* (1978).

1232   Skowronski, Marjory, 1948- . **Abortion and Alternatives.** Millbrae, CA: Les Femmes, 1977. 145p. bibliog. $4.95. ISBN 0890879230. LC 76-53342.

Written "in simple language from a woman's viewpoint," *Abortion and Alternatives* is intended for: women who have decided on abortion but still have questions about it; women who have had abortions and still experience ambivalence; men who are participating in a decision about abortion; parents and friends of a woman considering an abortion; and professionals. Skowronski discusses abortion law, the abortion debate, medical questions related to abortion, alternatives to abortion, contraception, fears and psychological consequences, and abortion and men. Information on abortion referrals and starting a women's health collective is included in appendices.

1233   Stellman, Jeanne M., 1947- . **Women's Work; Women's Health: Myths and Realities.** New York: Pantheon Books, 1977. 262p. bibliog. index. $12.95. ISBN 0394410386. LC 77-5200.

While Stellman's field is occupational health, she succeeds in placing the issue of women and occupational health within a broad sociological and historical and political context. Her concerns in *Women's Work, Women's Health* are: first, the real hazards confronted by women in the work they do, both inside and outside the home; second, how the problem of women's exposure to these hazards is handled legally and by corporations; and, third, the assumptions about women, the sexual division of labor, and workers' rights in general that are the ideological underpinnings of occupational health policy. Just as with the abortion issue, concern is often expressed for the rights of the fetus, while the sufferings of the mother and even the child, once born, are ignored. So too, with the issue of occupational health, a woman's mere *capacity* for child-bearing (even in the absence of any intention to have children) often becomes the focus of concern to the neglect of the general health of adult workers, male and female. Fertility in and of itself is made a basis for the exclusion of women workers from hazardous occupational environments, which themselves go uncorrected. This is a valuable book, combining social and political analysis with much concrete information. Arguments in the text are frequently supported by statistical tables and illustrations. Two appendices provide detailed (and chilling) lists of health hazards encountered in particular occupations and their observed effects.

1234   Tavris, Carol, and Susan Sadd. **The Redbook Report on Female Sexuality: 100,000 Married Women Disclose the Good News about Sex.** New York: Delacorte Press, 1977. 186p. bibliog. index. $8.95. ISBN 0440075602. LC 77-24616.

In 1974, *Redbook* published a questionnaire entitled "How Do You Really Feel about Sex?" and received more than 100,000 replies to questions that ranged over the intimate topography of women's sexual life. Issues raised include premarital sex, promiscuity, religious background, initial sexual experimentation, oral sexuality and other sexual mores, extramarital sex, and aging and sexuality. Tavris and Sadd selected 2,300 married respondents from the 100,000; the result of their analysis showed that most were happy with their marriages, their husbands, and their sex lives. They explore the problems and advantages of using a questionnaire as a sex research tool and make comparisons with other major reserach strategies and projects in the area of human sexuality: Kinsey, Shere Hite, Masters and Johnson, and Morton Hunt. The questionnaire and responses appear as an appendix. The style is readable and the data, readily accessible to the layperson.

1235   Walsh, Mary Roth. **"Doctors Wanted; No Women Need Apply"; Sexual Barriers in the Medical Profession, 1835-1975.** New Haven, CT: Yale University Press, 1977. 303p. bibliog. index. $15.00. ISBN 0300020244. LC 76-44416.

With great attention to medical manuscript and historical sources, Walsh, a professor of psychology and American studies, offers a careful analysis of the changing tides of women's experiences in the short history of American medical training. During the late nineteenth century, which saw the "professionalization" of medical schools and medical practice, feminists made inroads into the "regular" medical schools, and by 1910, 6 percent of the country's physicians were women. Walsh's study demonstrates how short-lived this female impact on the medical profession proved to be, what with the rapid establishment of quota systems and other barriers, such as denial of financial aid, of admission into state medical societies, and of internships. Perhaps more insidious were the psychological ploys used to discourage women's medical school ambitions. These were based, it seems, on the profession's fears that the "feminization" of the profession would reduce medical fees due to the decreased status that has inevitably followed in the wake of female dominance of a profession.

The medical profession had good reason to fear an influx of women practitioners, since women constitute the patient majority. Barbara Ehrenreich and Deirdre English cover similar territory with regard to the nineteenth-century medical profession in *For Her Own Good* (1978).

Because the chapter on Women's Movement and Feminist Theory handles materials on the politics of the women's movement and significant feminist theoretical works, this chapter is restricted mainly to works on political science: political participation (see Gruberg); contemporary political issues (see Bryant); voting studies, women's experiences in negotiating the political process; and the new feminist political science including anthologies (see Jaquette). General radical political writings—for example, works by Emma Goldman, Rosa Luxemburg, and Hannah Arendt—also appear in this section. Consult the Reference chapter for bibliographies and biographical reference books on politics.

1236   Amundsen, Kirsten. **A New Look at the Silenced Majority: Women and American Democracy.** Englewood Cliffs, NJ: Prentice-Hall, 1977. 172p. bibliog. index. $8.95. ISBN 0136153364. LC 76-58411.
This is an updated version of the author's 1970 book entitled *The Silenced Majority*. In her preface, Amundsen writes, "As some colleagues and many friends in the movement suspect, there is no reason to change the key conclusions arrived at in the [sic] *The Silenced Majority*. What the new findings reveal is the superficiality and token nature of the changes that have come about in recent years." The book surveys discrimination against women in the labor market and in politics. It analyzes the ideology of sexism and the limits of United States democracy, and it speculates about what the "liberated society" might look like.

1237   Bernard, Jessie Shirley, 1903- . **Women and the Public Interest: An Essay on Policy and Protest.** Chicago: Aldine-Atherton, 1971. 293p. bibliog. index. $12.95. ISBN 0202250245. LC 79-140005.
"This essay is an attempt to bring into focus, from a wide variety of researched sources in quite different research traditions, some of the issues that policy makers are going to have to wrestle with in relation to the functions of women in modern society" (from the introduction). Bernard considers research findings on the sexual division of labor in United States society and then discusses, on the one hand, attempts to adjust the lives of women to what she calls the "Establishment," and, on the other, demands by women that the "Establishment" be adjusted to their lives. A major focus is the conflict between demands on women as workers in the labor force and as workers in the home.

1238   Besant, Annie (Wood), 1847-1933. **A Selection of the Social and Political Pamphlets of Annie Besant.** New York: A. M. Kelley, 1970. 1v. (various pagings). $17.50. ISBN 0678006385. LC 78-114024.
This is a collection of very rare writings by an important nineteenth-century British social theorist and journalist. Besant's intellectual and political career included an atheist, a reformist, a socialist, and, finally, a theosophical period. The writings gathered here are from her radical and socialist years (1874-1889). They cover a wide range of topics—trade unionism; land tenure; civil and religious liberty; the status of women; neo-malthusianism; questions of British

foreign policy, with particular attention to Ireland; and Fabian socialism. Her writings on women include the essays, "The Political Status of Women," "The Legalisation of Female Slavery in England," and "Marriage, As It Was, As It Is, and As It Should Be: A Plea For Reform.

1239   Binkin, Martin, 1928- , and Shirley J. Bach. **Women and the Military.** Washington: Brookings Institution, 1977. 134p. bibliog. $8.95. ISBN 0815709668. LC 77-24040.
"The U.S. armed forces employ some two million people, yet by 1982, according to the Pentagon, only 7 percent of them will be women." Increased participation by women in the military is one of the most inflammatory prospects associated with feminism, the women's movement and the ERA (the only specter more feared is integrated restrooms). It is useful to find in one slim volume a discussion of the key issues involved in sexual integration of the military. The authors provide a brief history of men, women, and the U.S. military in the twentieth century, then go on to discuss current policies in the military and their implications, women's rights and military benefits, institutional attitudes (public opinion and congressional, judicial, and military attitudes), the economics of sex integration, and military effectiveness and sex composition. An appendix gives a brief summary of how sex integration has been treated in the countries of Western and Eastern Europe, Asia, Australia, and the Middle East.

1240   Bryant, Anita. **The Anita Bryant Story: The Survival of Our Nation's Families and the Threat of Militant Homosexuality.** Old Tappan, NJ: Revell, 1977. 156p. $6.95. ISBN 0800708970. LC 77-88806.
On June 7, 1977, Dade County, Florida, voted by a margin of more than two to one to repeal the homosexual rights ordinance of the Dade County Code—an event that marked the beginning of a national movement by the organized Right in the United States against homosexual rights. This book tells the story of the Dade County crusade in the words of the woman who led it, Anita Bryant, orange juice queen and president of Save Our Children, Inc.

1241*   Calkin, Homer L. **Women in American Foreign Affairs.** Washington: Dept. of State, 1977. 311p. bibliog. LC 77-604551.
Because this report contains information that has long presented difficult access problems, it is a very useful and unique publication. Calkin examines the status and role of women in the Department of State and the Foreign Service, as well as the history of the employment of women by the Federal Government. Not surprisingly, the history of the Department of State with regard to the employment of women is one of discrimination; women were not appointed to diplomatic posts (except as clericals) based on the Department's reasoning that women could not withstand social, political, or even adverse world climate conditions. The author adds that the prevailing attitude toward women in the Department of State differed little from prevailing attitudes toward women in the country as a whole. Calkin shows the programs in which women have held top policy positions; only 25 women in 44 years have reached the positions of minister and ambassador. The appendices contain much interesting documentation on policy within the Department of State regulating the hiring and promotion of women. One appendix lists names of women in key

positions. While the tone of this report is laudatory of the efforts of individuals to improve the attitude toward women officers in the Department, the bulk of the information appears factual and non-propagandistic. Sections are: Status of American Women during Two Centuries; Women and the Department of State, 1800 to 1940; Women in the Foreign Service, 1851 to 1940; The Foreign Service Examination; Entrance into the Foreign Service by Other Means; Impact of War; Various Roads to Joining the Foreign Service; Women in the Postwar Period; The 1970's and Women of the Department. Considerable biographical material is assembled on important women in foreign affairs. Many charts and tables are also included.

1242   Canovan, Margaret. **The Political Thought of Hannah Arendt.** New
        York: Harcourt Brace Jovanovich, 1974. 136p. bibliog. index. $6.50.
        ISBN 0151728151. LC 74-3037.
In this small and readable volume, Canovan discusses the key areas of Hannah Arendt's political thought: totalitarianism, the human condition, the modern world, and politics and thought.

1243*   Catt, Carrie (Lane) Chapman, 1859-1947, and Nettie Rogers Shuler,
        1865-1939. **Woman Suffrage and Politics: The Inner Story of the
        Suffrage Movement.** Seattle: University of Washington Press, 1969.
        504p. bibliog. index. LC 70-8954.
First published in the 1920s in the aftermath of the victory of woman suffrage, this is a historical analysis by two women important in the movement of the relation of woman suffrage to United States politics as a whole. The authors do not aim to provide anything but brief summaries of suffrage history, biographies of suffragists, and American political history. Rather, "this book's essential contribution must be sought in its revelation of the bearing of American politics upon the question of woman suffrage." A particular focus here is on the long delay of suffrage victory, until fully 26 other countries had already granted women the right to vote. Catt and Shuler's argument is that the delay was due not to an antagonistic, uninformed, or indifferent public, but to "the deflecting and the thwarting of public sentiment, through the trading and the trickery, the buying and the selling of American politics. . . . [Suffragists] consider that they have a case against certain combines of interests that systematically fought suffrage with politics and effectively delayed suffrage for years. We think that we can make that case."

1244   Deutsch, Richard. **Mairead Corrigan, Betty Williams.** Woodbury, NY:
        Barron's, 1977. 204p. $8.95. ISBN 0812052684. LC 77-17696.
Mairead Corrigan, Betty Williams, and Ciaran McKeown won the 1976 Nobel Prize for peace because of their organization of a movement in Northern Ireland, popularly called Peace People. The women's movement for peace, including both Catholics and Protestants sickened by the bloodshed and violence of the complex Irish conflict, has made a modest non-violent impact on Catholic and Protestant communities in Northern Ireland. In addition to biographical material on these women, this book diagrams a successful program for peace, worthy of celebration in a world that more often remarks on the politics and strategies of war.

1245   Diamond, Irene, 1947- . **Sex Roles in the State House.** New Haven, CT: Yale University Press, 1977. 214p. bibliog. index. $12.50. ISBN 0300021151. LC 76-49708.

Diamond explains in her preface that the major hypothesis that she seeks to "develop and test—that sex differentiation decreases as competition for political office increases—relates to the sexes and politics in contemporary America. State legislatures are the particular focus because this is the one political arena where the question of sex differences can be examined in a systematic and quantitative fashion." Diamond uses aggregate data, survey data, and personal interviews in her analysis of where women are elected to the legislature, sex differences between male and female legislators, and possibilities for change.

1246   Giffin, Frederick C., ed. **Woman As Revolutionary.** New York: New American Library, 1973. 256p. $1.75. LC 73-83408.

This collection of excerpts from the writings of women revolutionaries has the advantages and disadvantages of the genre: it is useful as an introduction to these women and their thought, but the brief excerpts are bound to misrepresent or superficially characterize any particular woman. Though each of the women represented here can be seen as a feminist, they were chosen rather as strong women who fought for the cause of *human* liberation, a criterion reflected in Giffin's choice of writings (so, for example, Alexandra Kollontai is represented by her writing on the Workers' Opposition rather than on sexual relations and the family). Included here are: Christine de Pisan, Joan of Arc, Saint Teresa of Avila, Olympe de Gouges, Mary Wollstonecraft, Mercy Otis Warren, Maria Weston Chapman, Susan B. Anthony, Sofia Perovskaya, Annie Besant, Jane Addams, Helen Keller, Emma Goldman, Rosa Luxemburg, Alexandra Kollontai, Isadora Duncan, Margaret Sanger, Dolores Ibarruri, Elizabeth Kenny, Maria Montessori, Joan Baez, and Francoise Parturier. Giffin has provided brief biographical introductions to each of the women, and Anne Fremantle has written an overall introduction to the anthology.

1247   Goldman, Emma, 1869-1940. **Anarchism and Other Essays.** Port Washington, NY: Kennikat Press, 1969. (Repr. of 1910 ed.). 277p. bibliog. $10.00. ISBN 0804606110. LC 71-86017.

There is considerable overlap between this collection and that edited by A. K. Shulman, *Red Emma Speaks.* Both are included here because each lacks important essays reprinted in the other and because the more inclusive of the two, *Red Emma Speaks,* is currently out of print. Included here (and not in the Shulman edition) are the following pieces: "Minorities Versus Majorities"; "Patriotism: A Menace to Liberty"; "The Hypocrisy of Puritanism"; "The Drama: A Powerful Disseminator of Radical Thought"; and "Woman Suffrage."

1248   Goot, Murray, and Elizabeth Anne Reid. **Women and Voting Studies: Mindless Matrons or Sexist Scientism?** Beverly Hills, CA: Sage Publications, 1975. 44p. bibliog. $3.00. ISBN 0803999119. LC 74-18746.

In this very brief paper, Goot and Reid critically analyze the political science literature on sex differences in voting behavior. They find this literature rife with unexamined assumptions, sexist prejudice, biased research design, and contradictory conclusions. Among the truisms of the field are the assertions

that women personalize politics, that wives' political behavior conforms to
that of their husbands, and that women are more conservative than men.
Readers interested in feminist critiques of the political science discipline should
also look at Jane Jaquette's anthology, *Women in Politics* (1974).

1249   Gruberg, Martin. **Women in American Politics: An Assessment and
        Sourcebook.** Oshkosh, WI: Academia Press, 1968. 336p. bibliog.
        index. $7.50. ISBN 091188002X. LC 68-27151.
Useful in the information it gathers up to 1967, the work is journalistic in its
style. Gruberg has divided his research into two major segments—an assessment
and a sourcebook. In the assessment section, he looks at "The Achievement
of American Women in Politics since 1920," including issues such as their
indirect influence on politics and their political powerlessness. Other chapters
in the first section are "Women as Political Party Members" and "Women's
Political Achievements in Other Countries." The sourcebook segment provides
lists and biographies including "A Survey of Women's Organizations in America"
and "Women in Government since 1920." For more recent material look to Susan
and Martin Tolchin, *Clout* (1974), and to the Rutgers University Center for the
American Woman and Politics, *Women in Public Office* (1976).

1250   Iglitzin, Lynne B., 1931- , and Ruth A. Ross, 1933- , eds. **Women
        in the World: A Comparative Study.** Santa Barbara, CA: Clio Books,
        1976. 427p. bibliog. index. $19.75. ISBN 0874362008. LC 74-14197.
"This volume is the result of a series of seminar meetings sponsored jointly
by the Department of Political Science of the University of California, Santa
Barbara, and the Center for the Study of Democratic Institutions." Part 1,
"Conceptualizing the Cross-Cultural Study of Women," handles issues of
patriarchy and the political participation of African and Latin American women.
Part 2, "Women in Europe and the United States," treats the status of women
in Italy, Ireland, France, West Germany, Great Britain, and the United States.
Part 3, "Women in Developing Countries," contains essays on women in Ghana,
Iran, Algeria, Columbia, Mexico, and Hong Kong. Part 4, "Women in Nations
Mobilized for Social Change," includes papers on Yugoslav women, changing
roles for women in the USSR, kibbutz women, and Chinese and Scandinavian
women.

1251   Jaquette, Jane S., 1942- , comp. **Women in Politics.** New York: Wiley,
        1974. 367p. bibliog. index. $16.75. ISBN 0471440221. LC 74-1037.
A collection of articles on women's political experiences in the U.S. and else-
where, this includes: "The Making of the Apolitical Woman: Femininity and
Sex-Stereotyping in Girls" (Lynne B. Iglitzin); "Women and Political Socializa-
tion: Considerations of the Impact of Motherhood" (Cornelia B. Flora and
Naomi B. Lynn); "Ideology and the Law: Sexism and Supreme Court Decisions"
(Susan Kaufman Purcell); "Contemporary Feminism, Consciousness-Raising,
and Changing Views of the Political" (Nancy McWilliams); "The Tyranny of
Structurelessness" (Jo Freeman); "Women Under Communism" (Barbara
Jancar); "A Marxist Analysis of Women and Capitalism" (Temma Kaplan);
"The Mobilization of Women in Allende's Chile" (Elsa M. Chaney); "Memsahib,
Militante, Femme Libre: Political and Apolitical Styles of Modern African

Women" (Judith Van Allen); "The Politics of Cultural Liberation" (Kay Boals).
Also included is an extensive bibliography on the subject of women in politics
by Mary Cornelia Porter. Another useful (but hard to obtain) bibliography
is Virginia Sapira's *A Guide to Published Works on Women and Politics, II*
published by the Center for Political Studies, Institute for Social Research,
University of Michigan (1975).

1252   Keller, Helen Adams, 1880-1968. **Helen Keller: Her Socialist Years;**
        Writings and Speeches. Ed. by Philip S. Foner. New York: International
        Publishers, 1967. 128p. LC 67-13214.
The story of Helen Keller's struggle against the blindness and deafness which
struck her at the age of ten months and of her teacher Anne Sullivan's tutelage
is well known. Keller's first autobiographical account, *The Story of My Life*
(1902), was an immediate best-seller, and her life history was further immortalized through the play and movie, "The Miracle Worker." Less familiar is the
story of Keller's years of political activism. Her general empathy for others'
sufferings came together with her specific interest in social and industrial causes
of blindness to create receptiveness to the socialist ideas to which she was
exposed after 1905. She read voraciously in socialist and Marxist literature
and, in 1909, joined the Socialist Party. Until 1922, when her commitment
to the American Federation for the Blind limited her political work, Keller
was an active spokeswoman and writer in the socialist movement, decrying
the "mental blindness" (as she saw it) all around her. Among the pieces collected
here are: "How I Became a Socialist"; "Social Causes of Blindness"; "To an
English Woman-Suffragist"; "The Unemployed"; "Why Men Need Woman
Suffrage"; "Birth Control"; "Strike Against War"; "Why I Became an IWW";
"The New Woman's Party"; and "End the Blockade of Soviet Russia." Foner
provides a lengthy biographical introduction to the volume. Keller's second
autobiographical account is entitled *Midstream: My Later Life* and is available
in a reprint edition (orig. Doubleday, Doran, 1929; repr. Greenwood Press,
1968).

1253   Kelly, Rita Mae, and Mary Boutilier. **The Making of Political Women:**
        A Study of Socialization and Role Conflict. Chicago: Nelson-Hall,
        1977. 376p. index. $16.95. ISBN 0882292900. LC 77-17081.
Though many may disagree with Kelly and Boutilier's approach—their reliance
on recognized women to posit a theory of what makes the political woman
go—still, the portraits of 36 political women (including Eleanor Roosevelt,
Shirley Chisholm, Golda Meir, Angela Davis, Charlotte Corday, and Maud
Gonne) yield fascinating conclusions about lifestyles, family backgrounds,
and family expectations of the women studied. Though their findings about
the small sample of extraordinary women may be questioned, their conclusion
that it is important for *every* member of a society to be encouraged to act as
a public individual is both indisputable and a prerequisite to seeing a change
in the sexual arrangements that now exist in politics. A familiar, out-of-date
title that profiles the paucity of American women in politics is Peggy Lamson,
Few Are Chosen: American Woman in Political Life Today (Houghton Mifflin,
1968).

1254   Kirkpatrick, Jeane J. **Political Woman.** New York: Basic Books, 1974.
        274p. bibliog. index. $10.00. ISBN 0465059708. LC 73-90130.
Commissioned by the Center for the American Woman and Politics at Rutgers
University, this book seeks to assess the validity of the hypothesis that women
seeking higher office face obstacles that differ in degree or kind from their
male counterparts. Data are based on interviews and questionnaires gathered
from the fifty women state senators and representatives selected for their
diversity to attend a conference on women in politics in 1972. Kirkpatrick
analyzes the four hypothetical constraints that have been seen as explaining
women's low profile on the political scene: physiological constraints, cultural
constraints, role constraints, and male conspiracy. She introduces four political
styles that characterize the women in this study, including The Leader, The
Moralizer, The Personalizer and The Problem Solver, noting that the problem-
solving style characterizes over half the sample. Very interesting material is
here on what motivates and sustains political women.

1255   Luxemburg, Rosa, 1870-1919. **Selected Political Writings of Rosa
        Luxemburg.** New York: Monthly Review Press, 1971. 441p. bibliog.
        $11.50. ISBN 0853451427. LC 75-142991.
Rosa Luxemburg was a key political theorist of turn-of-the-century German
Social Democracy and a revolutionary active in the German, Polish, and Russian
movements. She is noted in particular for her devastating critique of revisionism
within the German party in *Reform or Revolution* and for her conception of
socialism as the creation of a democratic mass movement rather than the
execution of a blueprint ordered by an elite. Luxemburg was murdered in Berlin
in 1919 in the aftermath of the German Revolution of 1918-1919. Collected
here are selections from her writings on revisionism (including *Reform or
Revolution*), on tactics (including excerpts from *Mass Strike, Party, and Trade
Unions*), on the role of the party (including "Organizational Questions of Russian
Social Democracy"), on the International (including "The Crisis in German
Social Democracy," from *The Junius Pamphlet*), and on the beginnings of the
German revolution. In the section on tactics is reprinted a little-known but
remarkable essay entitled "Women's Suffrage and Class Struggle." Readers
may want to look at another collection of Luxemburg's writings that overlaps
only slightly with this one: *Rosa Luxemburg Speaks*, edited by Mary-Alice
Waters (Pathfinder Press, 1970). Two biographies may be recommended: J. P.
Nettl's two-volume *Rosa Luxemburg* (Oxford University Press, 1966) and
Paul Frölich's *Rosa Luxemburg: Her Life and Work* (1940; repr. H. Fertig,
1970). The present edition of her writings was edited and introduced by Dick
Howard.

1256   McCourt, Kathleen. **Working-Class Women and Grass-Roots Politics.**
        Bloomington: Indiana University Press, 1977. 256p. bibliog. $10.00.
        ISBN 025336650X. LC 76-26340.
McCourt's study is based on in-depth interviews conducted in 1972 with a
small sample of white working-class women from Chicago's Southwest side.
Twenty-three women were selected for their activism in local community
organizations that had used direct action tactics in their political organizing.
An additional seventeen women who were not politically active were selected

for comparison. Interviews were several hours in length, covering such topics as the woman's feelings about her community; her assessment of problems faced by the community; her sense of public officials' responses to these problems; her organizational memberships; her attitudes toward the local and national political system; her political behavior; her attitudes towards women's roles, integration, and social class; and her ethnic background. McCourt presents statistical analyses of her data, bringing these to life with her own perceptive text and extensive quotations from interviews. The material is organized topically, however, and thus the reader is unable to develop a sense of these women as individuals. Nancy Seifer's *Nobody Speaks for Me!* (1976) would be interesting to read in conjunction with McCourt for its oral histories of ten working-class, politically active women.

1257   Mass, Bonnie. **Population Target: The Political Economy of Population Control in Latin America.** Toronto: Latin American Working Group, 1976. 299p. bibliog. index. ISBN 0889610356. LC 77-372439.
This well-researched study explores United States governmental and social policy with regard to contraception and sterilization programs in Latin America, which the author considers sexist, neo-malthusian, and imperialistic in that such population control programs are oppressing women who have been designated inferior because of race and class. This book stands as a stunning exposé of policies that limit reproductive freedom for women and is must reading for those who would understand the political economy of reproduction.

1258   Milwaukee County Welfare Rights Organization. **Welfare Mothers Speak Out: We Ain't Gonna Shuffle Anymore.** New York: Norton, 1972. 190p. bibliog. $1.95. ISBN 0393010732. LC 72-3963.
Edited by Thomas Howard Tarantino and Dismas Becker, this important anthology has an introduction by Dr. George A. Wiley. It alternates chapters on the sociology of welfare with testimony of Welfare Rights Organization workers and welfare mothers. In plain language, the volume demystifies the reality of welfare in America, demonstrating that 1) nearly everyone in the U.S. is on welfare, and corporations and the wealthy receive far more than do the poor; 2) that most money channeled into "poverty programs" never reaches the poor, but is siphoned off by professionals and "experts" who run the programs; 3) that behind the apparent charity of welfare are innumerable insults to people's dignity, denials of justice and basic rights, and cases of welfare fraud (committed, for example, by doctors connected with the Medical Assistance Program); 4) that welfare myths are contradicted by reality. The book also critically evaluates various guaranteed income proposals, including Nixon's Family Assistance Plan, and counterproposes a Guaranteed Adequate Income Plan devised by the National Welfare Rights Organization. Testimony by women on welfare speaks directly to real issues. For example, Mrs. Anne Henderson of Milwaukee, Wisconsin, says of the myth that welfare mothers "breed" to get more money: "If you think that I'm gonna have a baby—and watch that child grow up with no food or clothing; and then watch him go to school where teachers don't teach him anything; and worry that he's gonna become a pimp or start shooting up dope; and finally, when he's raised, see him go into the army and get really shot up in there—if you think I'm gonna go through all

that pain and suffering for an extra $50, or $100 a month, why you must be crazy."

1259   Morgan, Marabel. **The Total Woman.** Old Tappan, NJ: Revell, 1973.
            192p. bibliog. $5.95. ISBN 0800706080. LC 73-11474.
Dedicated to Anita Bryant, this simplistic recipe for marital bliss has made the phrase "Total Woman" a recognized expression for a mindset that supports traditional values, deplores women's liberation, applauds fundamentalist religious doctrines, and is anti-ERA. Because of its impact on a significant segment of American women, it is an important sourcebook on the thought patterns of women who subscribe to feeble-minded solutions to save crumbling institutions. Sample chapters: Interior Decorating; Admire Him; Adapt to Him; Rocks in the Mattress; Super Sex.

1260   Tolchin, Susan, and Martin Tolchin. **Clout: Womanpower and Politics.**
            New York: Coward, McCann and Geoghegan, 1974. 320p. bibliog.
            index. $10.00. ISBN 0698106008. LC 74-79677.
The barring of women from mainstream politics is part of the story told by the Tolchins. The better part of the tale is the "coming of age of women in politics," an emergence that the authors attribute to an amalgam of political and social upheavals: Watergate, women's liberation, the McGovern campaign, the peace movement, and increased education for women. The authors believe that the political sphere is open to women and the only true guarantor of improved status for women. The people they acknowledge for assistance in research reads like a who's who of the women's political vanguard. Among the many recognizable names who appear often in the book are Bella Abzug, Sissy Farenthold, Shirley MacLaine, Gloria Steinem, and Patricia Schroeder. Among the interesting appendices are Schroeder's speech on political clout, "You Can Do It," and "Tips on Running for Public Office," from the Office of Women's Activities, Democratic National Committee, Washington, D.C.

1261   Weisbord, Robert G. **Genocide? Birth Control and the Black American.**
            Westport, CT: Greenwood Press; distr. New York: Two Continents,
            1975. 219p. bibliog. index. $7.95. ISBN 0837180848. LC 75-13531.
Weisbord tries to unravel the tangled web of issues surrounding birth control for black Americans, at the heart of which is the difficult question of what constitutes reproductive freedom and choice in a context shaped by the forces of race, class, and sex oppression. Distinctions are rarely made between political intent, ideology, and social reality in this inflammatory debate. Weisbord attempts to draw these distinctions through a historically-grounded analysis of, on the one hand, centuries of white genocidal practices against black Americans, the eugenic intent of many birth-control programs, and forced sterilization of poor black women; and, on the other hand, the forced breeding of the slave era and the problem of poor black women's lack of access to birth control. He counterposes black nationalist pronatalism to black women's concrete desires and demands for reproductive freedom and choice. Parallel conflicts surrounding

the question of birth control policy in Puerto Rico, Latin America, Africa, and Native American communities are usefully explored. Readers wishing to pursue these topics should also look at Linda Gordon's *Women's Body, Women's Right: A Social History of Birth Control in America* (1976) and Bonnie Mass's *Population Target: The Political Economy of Population Control in Latin America* (1976).

The works presented here have been drawn from the popular, general, and theoretical constellation of psychological literature. The profile of the selection that emerges is chiefly contemporary. Popular works treat subjects such as assertiveness, mothers and daughters, and life crises. Psychology texts range from the classic works to the new feminist psychology. Psychoanalytic studies represent the classic theoretical positions (Deutsch, Horney, Freud) as well as the new psychoanalytic foci on such topics as *anorexia nervosa* and women's mental health, which is often anti-psychiatry in approach. Feminist therapy books represent still another approach. Theoretical works that link patriarchy and psychology (see Dinnerstein) are significantly represented here as are counseling, clinical, and sex differences studies. Psychological studies of lesbianism, battered women, and other topical issues can be found here, though studies on these issues from a sociological perspective appear in the Sociology chapter. The journal *Psychology of Women* offers consistently good reviews of current material in this field.

1262   Barber, Virginia, 1935- , and Merrill Maguire Skaggs. **The Mother Person.**
        Indianapolis, IN: Bobbs-Merrill, 1975; repr. New York: Schocken
        Books, 1977. 220p. bibliog. $3.95. ISBN 0805205659. LC 76-48850.
Barber notes the visibility of books on children and childrearing, as well as books addressing the problems of parents coping with children. "For the new mother, however, there are two chief problems with these books: they don't agree, and few of them are addressed to her as a person. Only recently has any attention been paid to the *mother's* stages, fears, anxieties and problems. And so far, we believe, no book adequately analyzes the changes that becoming a mother may bring–changes in the woman's own self-concept or personality, in the realities of her daily life, in her relations with her husband and her community." This book develops the idea of "mothering," particularly in relation to babies and very small children. A survival guide for expectant mothers and for those who have recently given birth, *The Mother Person* dispenses advice in a moderate voice on the subjects of tolerance, stress, fears, expectations, the pain and pleasure all associated with the role of "mother." Barber advises mothers to see themselves as people and supports paternity leave for fathers, childcare facilities for all who wish to use them, and a more humane system of family responsibility for the sake of everyone. The tone is feminist. The bibliography lists a number of useful non-sexist books on childbearing.

1263   Bardwick, Judith M., 1933- . **Psychology of Women: A Study of Bio-
        Cultural Conflicts.** New York: Harper and Row, 1971. 242p. bibliog.
        index. $15.95. ISBN 0060404965. LC 70-137799.
This contemporary discussion of the psychology of women begins with a dismissal of both biological and cultural determinism as explanations of sex differences, arguing that these differences originate in the interaction of biology and culture. Much of the discussion is based on psychology research, which, as Bardwick admits, means it is largely limited to data on middle-class American whites, primarily college undergraduates. Among the topics considered are

psychoanalytic theory, sex differences in personality and learning ability, dependence, passivity and aggression, and the motive to achieve.

1264   Bardwick, Judith M., 1933- , comp. **Readings on the Psychology of Women.** New York: Harper and Row, 1972. 335p. index. $9.95. ISBN 0060404930. LC 71-188199.

This collection is a companion to Bardwick's own book, *The Psychology of Women.* As Bardwick is anxious to point out in her preface and elsewhere, this book is not a part of the "rhetoric, passion, and extremism" that she sees as characterizing most recent publications on women's liberation. Rather, this "is an academic's collection of theory and research papers from the professional literature of psychology, sociology, anthropology, endocrinology, obstetrics, and psychosomatics." Major subject areas are: the Development of Sex Differences; Socialization, Cultural Values, and the Development of Motives; the Traditional Role; the Women's Liberation Movement; Intercultural Comparisons; Women in Their Relationship to Their Bodies; and Women and Criteria of Mental Health. An introduction by Bardwick precedes each section.

1265   Bloom, Lynn Z., 1934- , et al. **The New Assertive Woman.** New York: Delacorte Press, 1975. 230p. bibliog. $7.95. ISBN 0440064392. LC 75-25569.

This is a book about assertiveness training for women, written by three women who have worked with assertiveness training groups. It serves both as a description of the ideas and process of assertiveness training and as a kind of self-help manual. The authors illustrate most of their points with examples from the groups they've worked with and, in some cases, with verbatim interactions.

1266   Bruch, Hilde, 1904- . **The Golden Cage: The Enigma of Anorexia Nervosa.** Cambridge, MA: Harvard University Press, 1978. 150p. $8.95. ISBN 0674356500. LC 77-10674.

Bruch, a psychiatrist, writes a readable analysis of the puzzling illness *anorexia nervosa*, which is occurring with increased frequency among affluent young women. *Anorexia* is characterized by self-starvation even to the extent of causing death. Bruch is particularly interesting in her discussion of how the disease starts and the family's role in the progress and control of *anorexia*. The disease is of great interest to women's studies because it occurs only in females and because of the implications of problems in the mother-daughter relationship, which appear to be part of the pattern of the disease. A feminist analysis of the disease can be found in Marlene Boskind-Lodahl's "Cinderella's Stepsisters: A Feminist Perspective on Anorexia Nervosa and Bulimia" (*Signs*, Winter 1976).

1267   Castillejo, Irene Claremont de, 1896- . **Knowing Woman: A Feminine Psychology.** New York: Putnam for the C. G. Jung Foundation for Analytical Psychology, 1973. 188p. bibliog. index. $8.00. ISBN 0913430013. LC 72-80470.

A series of meditations on the psychology of women and male-female relations, these were written from a Jungian perspective by an analyst of twenty years experience. Some of the chapters were previously published elsewhere, and most can stand on their own. Castillejo writes in her preface, "I describe here what I have learned of woman's present psychology. Perhaps I am only describing myself." Some readers may find disturbing the author's tendency to express her thoughts, observations, and speculations about such a controversial subject in absolute terms; for example, "Many women have forgotten, in the modern emphasis on career and economic independence, that woman has a role to play towards man which is inherent in her nature . . . her role is still as it always has been, to be a mediator to man of his own creative inspirations. . . . "

1268   Chasseguet-Smirgel, Janine, 1928- . **Female Sexuality: New Psychoanalytic Views.** Ann Arbor: University of Michigan Press, 1970. 220p. bibliog. $8.95. ISBN 0472219006. LC 79-107974.

First published in 1964, this collection of essays predates the contemporary women's movement and retains an approach more psychological than political or social to the subject of female sexuality. Nonetheless, the authors are all committed to the project of re-examining the theories of female sexuality, using the psychoanalytic method, and to avoiding "the misleading theoretical path which attempts to approach the problems of femininity through the study of male sexuality." The collection includes: "A Masculine Mythology of Femininity," by Christian David; "Outline for a Study of Narcissism in Female Sexuality," by Béla Grunberger; "The Change of Object," by Catherine Luquet-Parat; "Feminine Guilt and the Oedipus Complex," by Janine Chasseguet-Smirgel; "The Significance of Penis Envy in Women," by Maria Torok; and "Homosexuality in Women," by Joyce McDougall. There is, in addition, a lengthy introduction by the editor, who reviews the main theories of Freud, his disciples, and his opponents.

1269   Chesler, Phyllis. **About Men: A Psycho-sexual Meditation.** New York: Simon and Schuster, 1978. bibliog. $9.95. ISBN 0671229397. LC 77-20486.

This ambitious study by Chesler is highly controversial, containing as it does psychiatric interpretations of history, autobiographical accounts of the men in Chesler's own life, interviews with unfamiliar men on "maleness," and a sustained analysis of the male condition. The book lets itself in for the same criticism leveled at *The Second Sex*, by de Beauvoir: many generalizations and interpretations cannot be justified and are often shaky on scholarship.

1270   Chesler, Phyllis. **Women and Madness.** Garden City, NY: Doubleday, 1972. 359p. bibliog. index. $8.95. ISBN 0385026714. LC 72-76136.

This important book belongs to the emerging anti-psychiatry analysis (e.g., Thomas Szasz, R. D. Laing) and social movement. Chesler's particular contribution was to explore the *patriarchal* dimensions of the psychiatric social control indicted by earlier critics. She notes that, given the differing social expectations governing men's and women's lives, it is none too surprising that men and women are sanctioned for different behaviors and in different ways. Expectations and sanctions are further defined by class, race, and nationality. At the simplest level, she points out that mental institutions serve a social control function for women comparable to that served by prisons for men: unhappy women turn inward in self-destructiveness and depression where men become violent. The script between female client and male psychiatrist repeats the typical sexual power relation of our society, facilitating the labeling of deviance from prescribed feminine norms as neurosis or psychosis. *Women and Madness* is an exploration of these questions and themes at several levels: statistical profiles of female patients, interviews with sixty women of diverse backgrounds with psychiatric histories (these are particularly moving and revealing), and theoretical conclusions. Readers may also be interested in the recent personal account by a longtime woman psychiatric patient, Janet Gotkin's *Too Much Anger, Too Many Tears: A Personal Triumph Over Psychiatry* (Quadrangle/New York Times, 1975).

1271   Chodorow, Nancy. **The Reproduction of Mothering: Psychoanalysis and the Sociology of Gender.** Berkeley, CA: University of California Press, 1978. 263p. bibliog. index. $12.95. ISBN 0520031334. LC 75-27922.
Chodorow's central concern is to explore the significance and implications of the near-universal fact that *women mother*, as well as to consider how women's exclusive responsibility for child care has been historically reproduced. While she is convinced of the value of the psychoanalytic method of analysis, her perspective is well grounded in history and sociology. She sees "the reproduction of mothering as a central and constituting element in the social organization and reproduction of gender" and argues "that the contemporary reproduction of mothering occurs through social structurally induced psychological processes. It is neither a product of biology nor of intentional role-training. I draw on the psychoanalytic account of female and male personality development to demonstrate that women's mothering reproduces itself cyclically. Women, as mothers, produce daughters with mothering capacities and the desire to mother." Intimately linked to Chodorow's historical and theoretical concerns is her commitment to discovering potentials for change. Her view is that the social organization of gender requires an analysis and a strategy for change related to but distinct from analyses and strategies concerned with the organization and relations of production. Her book is divided into three major sections—1) Setting the Problem: Mothering and the Social Organization of Gender; 2) The Psychoanalytic Story; and 3) Gender Personality and the Reproduction of Mothering—followed by a brief afterword, "Women's Mothering and Women's Liberation." Readers interested in this topic will also want to consult Dorothy Dinnerstein's *The Mermaid and the Minotaur.*

1272   Deaux, Kay. **The Behavior of Women and Men.** Monterey, CA: Brooks/Cole, 1976. 168p. bibliog. index. $4.95. ISBN 0818501774. LC 75-23856.
Social psychologist Deaux examines sex roles and stereotypes, psychological androgyny and achievement motivation, as well as conformity and compliance behaviors, male/female difference in communication styles and leadership styles, differences in self-esteem and self-evaluation, and other topics that have received only limited attention in the field of social psychology. The book has been applauded for its skillful handling of sex role topics and for its criticism of sex bias in experimental design, but it was criticized for Deaux's failure to point out that sexism may be accountable for the different behaviors of men and women.

1273   Deutsch, Helene, 1884- . **The Psychology of Women: A Psychoana-
        lytic Interpretation.** New York: Grune and Stratton, 1944-1945.
        2v. bibliog. v.1: $12.75, ISBN 080890115X; v.2: $14.50, ISBN
        0808901168. LC 44-5287.
Deutsch was one of the early and unreservedly devoted disciples of Freud. In
this two-volume work, the "psychology of women" becomes equated with
the psychology "of female instinctual development and its relation to the
reproductive function." Though in her 1944 preface to the work, Deutsch makes
some claim to objectivity based on empirical data gathered in her sessions
with patients and from other records, in her 1973 autobiography (*Confrontations with Myself*), she confesses that the *Psychology* contains hidden within
it her own personal experience generalized as normal experience. There is much
in these volumes to irritate or at least puzzle the reader, particularly in her
orthodox Freudian outlook and her failure to consider questions of social
structure and context. Nonetheless, the work is important in the history of
theoretical perspectives on the psychology of women. Volume 1 discusses
prepuberty, adolescence, menstruation, eroticism (the "feminine woman"),
feminine passivity, feminine masochism, the "active" woman ("the masculinity
complex"), homosexuality, and—belatedly—"the influence of the environment."
All of volume 2 is devoted to the psychology of motherhood, including "motherhood, motherliness, and sexuality," problems of conception, pregnancy, delivery,
lactation, the mother-child relation, unmarried mothers, adoptive mothers,
stepmothers, and menopause.

1274*   Diamond, Esther E., ed. **Issues of Sex Bias and Sex Fairness in Career
        Interest Measurement.** Washington: Department of Health, Education,
        and Welfare, National Institute of Education, Career Education Program,
        1975. 219p. bibliog. index. LC 75-603045.
The purpose of this NIE-sponsored study is to examine the social and technical
issues in career interest inventories to determine whether they reflect sex bias
in career counseling. Chapters include Cole and Hanson, "Impact of Interest
Inventories on Career Choice"; John Holland, "The Use and Evaluation
of Interest Inventories and Simulations"; Lenore Harmon, "Technical Aspects";
and Mary Faith Tanney, "Face Validity of Interest Measures," among other
essays exploring racial, legal, and financial implications in development and
change of interest inventories. Abstracts are provided for each paper. Of particular interest may be the paper by Mary Ellen Verheyden-Hillard, "Expanding
Opportunities for the Reentry Woman: The Use of Interest Inventories with
the Mature Woman."

1275   Dinnerstein, Dorothy. **The Mermaid and the Minotaur: Sexual Arrange-
        ments and Human Malaise.** New York: Harper and Row, 1976. 288p.
        bibliog. $10.95. ISBN 0060110473. LC 72-23879.
Dinnerstein has written a penetrating analysis of the consequences for human
personality and society of women's monopoly in childraising. She defines
"sexual arrangements" as a universal condition in which women take primary
responsibility for babies and small children. "Human malaise" is what she
names this maladaptive position, which resists change because change is tem-
porarily painful and disorienting. She has chosen the symbols minotaur and

mermaid to represent "the pernicious prevailing forms of collaboration between the sexes" in which "both man and woman will remain semi-human, monstrous." Dinnerstein suggests that her treatment of sex roles and childrearing is neither scholarly nor scientific—"Its method is to appeal to the reader's own experience." She admits that the conclusions she draws are threatening ones. The maiming patterns of behavior she identifies are grounded in traditional views of women as monogamous in their sexuality and as infantile in their relations with the world at large. Further, as mothers and representatives of nature rather than human beings in their own right, as symbols of the flesh and thus as "dirty goddesses," and as acceptors of the status quo in the form of adult male dominion, women accept the patterns of continuity and thus both men and women collaborate in the distortion of their human potential. Dinnerstein clearly sees this collaboration as destructive and life-rejecting. Women are effectively sealed off from history, a contemporary history of madness and megamachines. This is an extremely important book on the labyrinth of sex roles.

1276   Donelson, Elaine, and Jeanne E. Gullahorn, eds. **Women: A Psychological Perspective.** New York: Wiley, 1977. 342p. bibliog. index. $13.95. ISBN 0471217794. LC 76-54924.

This anthology is intended primarily as a basic text for undergraduates in psychology and women's studies courses. Topics covered include: 1) General Orientation (an overview of the psychology of women and personality theory); 2) Psychobiological Foundations of Sex-Typed Behavior (gender in the animal world and human society, menstruation, and sex differences in language use); 3) Social Influences on the Development of Sex-Typed Behavior (socialization processes, friendship, achievement); and 4) Adult Involvements and the Quest for Androgyny (sex roles, sexuality, the family, single women, women professionals, equality, and social structure). Because the scope of this collection is far-reaching (from biology to social structure) yet sketchy, it would prove inadequate as a text on its own. Contributors are Elaine Donelson, Jeanne E. Gullahorn, Stanley C. Ratner, Glenn I. Hatton, Audrey D. Landers, Lauren Jay Harris, Hiram E. Fitzgerald, Ellen A. Strommen, and Lucy Rau Ferguson.

1277   Franz, Marie Luise von, 1915- . **Problems of the Feminine in Fairytales.** New York: Spring Publications, 1972. 194p. $7.00. ISBN 0882141058.

Because Franz uses a classically Jungian approach to her material, it is advisable that the reader have some familiarity with Jungian terminology before tackling these lectures (originally presented at the C. G. Jung Institute, 1958-1959). The lectures deal with the feminine in fairytales in terms of animus/anima, father-complex, collective unconscious, the archetype, and individuation by subjecting various fairytale characters to Jungian analysis. This is indeed an interesting process, though one that some feminists will reject.

1278   Friday, Nancy. **My Mother/My Self: The Daughter's Search for Identity.** New York: Delacorte Press, 1977. 425p. bibliog. $10.00. ISBN 0440060060. LC 77-23571.

The thesis of this book, which explores mother-daughter relationships, is that daughters reflect in their own lives many aspects of their mothers, even if they dislike them. A significant aspect of the relationship between mother and daughter, according to Nancy Friday, is the dishonesty that goes on between the two. Daughters want to believe the fantasy that the mother is a madonna figure because mothers want their daughters to believe the fantasy that they are madonna figures, beings without sexual lives. "Whether we want our mother's life or not, we never escape the image of how she was. Nowhere is this more true than in our sexual lives," writes Friday. Nancy Friday's analysis of the dangerous fantasies that symbiotically link mothers and daughters suggests that we can become free women, mothers and daughters if we can give up our fantasies of magical mothers and perfect daughters and look at each other as the sexual women that we know we are. Among the women with whom Friday consulted in the process of writing the book are Pauline Bart, Jessie Bernard, Helene Deutsch, Mary Calderone, Cynthia Fuchs Epstein, and Virginia Pomeranz. Friday's earlier work, *My Secret Garden: Women's Sexual Fantasies* (Trident Press, 1973), was a compilation of women's fantasies gathered by Friday through an ad placed in several national magazines and newspapers and through follow-up interviews.

1279   Frieze, Irene H., et al. **Women and Sex Roles: A Social Psychological Perspective.** New York: Norton, 1978. 444p. bibliog. index. $13.95. ISBN 0393011631. LC 78-15651.

In this book intended as a basic text for courses in the psychology and sociology of women, and for multidisciplinary women's studies courses, the authors have attempted to review the research and literature in psychology relevant to women from a feminist perspective, challenging basic psychological assumptions as sexist and biased. Major chapters are: The Psychology of Women and Sex Roles; Doing Psychological Research; Theories of Feminine Personality (Freud, Deutsch, Horney, Thompson, Jung, and Erikson are briefly discussed); Sex Differences in Personality and Abilities; Is Anatomy Destiny? Classic Theories of Sex-Role Socialization; Cognitive-Developmental Theories of Sex-Role Socialization; Changes in Women's Role Participation; Women's Adult Development; Biosocial Aspects of Reproduction; Sexual Roles of Women (includes material on lesbianism); Achievement and Nonachievement in Women; Psychological Disorders in Women; Indices of Role Strain; Prejudice and Discrimination; Women and Interpersonal Power; Being Feminine or Masculine Nonverbally; Politics and Power; Making Life Decisions.

1280   Green, Richard, 1936- . **Sexual Identity Conflict in Children and Adults.** New York: Basic Books, 1974. 327p. bibliog. index. $15.00. ISBN 0465077269. LC 73-76589.

A thorough review of the work done in recent times on sex and gender, the material here is presented in language suitable for a general audience. The chapter bibliographies are quite helpful. Contributions range the territory of the natural, social, and applied sciences. Green has made extensive use of direct quotations from his interviews with transsexuals and those who have close relationships with them. Chapters are Historical and Cross-Cultural Survey; Psychologic Theories; Biologic Studies; Men Who Want to Become Women; Boyfriends and Husbands of Male-to-Female Transsexuals; Treatment of Men Who Want to Become Women; Women Who Want to Become Men; Girlfriends

and Wives of Female-to-Male Transsexuals; Treatment of Women Who Want to
Become Men; Feminine Boys: Behavioral Overview; Feminine Boys: Parental
Descriptions; Feminine Boys: Their Stories; Feminine Boys: Psychologic Testing.

1281   Hammer, Signe. **Daughters and Mothers: Mothers and Daughters.** New
        York: Quadrangle Books/New York Times, 1975. 175p. bibliog.
        $7.95. ISBN 0812905911. LC 75-9211.
This study of the psychology of the mother-daughter relationship focuses
particularly on the transitions now taking place in this relationship. Hammer
interviewed over 75 mothers, daughters, and grandmothers, from the ages of
four-and-one-half to eighty, in preparation for the book. Her own discussion is
frequently interrupted by illustrative quotations from these interviews. Readers
might want to look at Dorothy Dinnerstein's book, *The Mermaid and the
Minotaur*, which analyzes some of the consequences of women's monopoly
on childcare, in conjunction with *Daughters and Mothers*.

1282   Harding, Mary Esther, 1888-1971. **The Way of All Women: A Psycho-
        logical Interpretation.** New York: Putnam for the C. G. Jung Founda-
        tion for Analytical Psychology, 1970. 314p. bibliog. index. $9.00.
        ISBN 0913430137. LC 78-97582.
Like Harding's *Woman's Mysteries* (1936), *The Way of All Women* (1933)
is rooted firmly in Jungian theory. Two types of women are differentiated here:
the man's woman (or the anima-woman) and the woman's woman (or the individual woman). Harding stresses the importance of a woman's freeing herself
from the anima projection of man with all the illusions of womanhood and
femininity that he may be unconsciously attaching to that projection. She
must assert her real self yet let her instinct surface at the same time. Despite
the date of the original edition, there is much material here to explain "the
myth of womanhood," derived from far-flung and often esoteric sources. Although
some feminists dismiss Jungian theory because of its reliance on masculine and
feminine principles, the material is worth reading carefully. The introduction
is by C. G. Jung.

1283   Harding, Mary Esther, 1888-1971. **Woman's Mysteries, Ancient and
        Modern: A Psychological Interpretation of the Feminine Principle
        As Portrayed in Myth, Story, and Dreams.** New York: Putnam, 1972.
        256p. bibliog. index. $9.00. ISBN 039910917X. LC 72-184527.
Originally published in 1936 and revised in 1955, this edition with an introduction by Jung explores moon symbolism in Jungian terms. The moon, in the
Jungian schema, represents the feminine principle, "the Lesser Light which
rules the night of instinct and the shadowy perceptions of the inner intuitive
world." Among the chapters: Myth and the Modern Mind; The Moon as Giver
of Fertility; The Moon in Modern Life; The Moon Cycle of Women; The Moon
Mother; Priests and Priestesses of the Moon; Ishtar; Isis and Osiris. Many illustrations of the sacred representation of the moon in art accompany the text.
It is Harding's and Jung's view that modern women must learn to reclaim the
Eternal Feminine within by recognizing the Moon Mother in the unconscious.

1284   Harmon, Lenore W., et al., eds. **Counseling Women.** Monterey, CA:
       Brooks/Cole, 1978. 315p. bibliog. index. $6.95. ISBN 0818502401.
       LC 77-22343.

The essays in this volume have been developed from two special issues of *The
Counseling Psychologist*, a publication of the Division of Counseling Psychology
of the American Psychological Association. "The first issue of 'Counseling
Women'—which represents Section 1 of this book—was designed to highlight
the deficiencies in our counseling theories and practices as applied to women.
The second issue dared to 'go further' in another sense by talking about counseling women with very specific problems in their lives—the single-again woman,
the rape victim, the mastectomy patient, and the 'perfect mother,' just to cite
a few. Discussions of these and other crisis situations, together with articles
dealing with other dimensions and aspects of counseling interventions for women,
make up Section 2 of the book and provide an especially useful tool for members
of the counseling profession. The book is intended for them and for graduate
students. It will also be useful for some undergraduates" (from Harmon's
preface).

1285   Horney, Karen, 1885-1952. **Feminine Psychology.** New York: Norton,
       1967. 269p. bibliog. $6.95. ISBN 0393010457. LC 67-12439.

Edited and with an introduction by Harold Kelman, this volume brings together
Karen Horney's articles on the psychology of women, spanning the period from
1922 to 1936. Horney was important as one of the early Freudian revisionists
and was pathbreaking as a feminist critic of Freud. Her psychoanalytic approach
emphasized human plasticity and potentiality for growth. She sought explanation for repression and blockage in the social context as well as in family history.
This theoretical perspective is particularly apparent in her writings on women,
where she repeatedly indicts our phallocentric culture. Attacking orthodox
psychoanalysis for its assumption of a male model of development and a male
viewpoint, Horney makes a major departure in attributing much of female
neurosis and of male fear and dislike of women to patriarchal culture. Included
in this collection are: "The Flight from Womanhood"; "Inhibited Femininity"
(on the problem of frigidity); "The Problem of the Monogamous Ideal"; "The
Distrust between the Sexes"; "Problems of Marriage"; "The Dread of Woman";
"The Denial of the Vagina"; "Maternal Conflicts"; "The Overvaluation of Love";
"The Problem of Feminine Masochism"; and "The Neurotic Need for Love."
Readers may want to look at a recent work on Horney by Jack L. Rubins
entitled *Karen Horney: Gentle Rebel of Psychoanalysis* (Dial Press, 1978).

1286   Laing, Ronald David, and Aaron Esterson, 1923- . **Sanity, Madness,
       and the Family: Families of Schizophrenics.** (2nd ed.). New York:
       Basic Books, 1971. 272p. bibliog. index. $8.95. ISBN 0465071759.
       LC 78-150224.

Laing and Esterson's eleven case histories of schizophrenic families are profoundly
absorbing and thought-provoking. Their approach was to study the family
relationships and dynamics of eleven women between the ages of fifteen and
forty who had been clinically diagnosed as schizophrenic. In each case, the
woman was interviewed and observed both alone and with each family member,
in all possible combinations. Questioning the view of schizophrenia as a

biochemical, neurophysiological, or psychological fact, Laing and Esterson
strive to understand the woman's behavior within her family context. The cases
are presented descriptively, with liberal quotations from interviews. The authors'
presence is definitely low-profile, yet their analytic approach shapes the description and makes clear the conclusion that "the experience and behavior that
psychiatrists take as symptoms and signs of schizophrenia [are] more socially
intelligible than has come to be supposed" (from the preface). The case histories
are also very ripe for a feminist analysis, though Laing and Esterson neglect
to pursue it. The pattern of an overbearing mother's fostering a symbiotic tie
to her daughter and an ineffectual father is remarkably consistent across these
cases, suggesting the atypical sex-role socialization may have something to do
with these young women's "abnormality." Interested readers will also want to
look at Laing's *Politics of the Family and Other Essays* (Pantheon Books, 1971)
and at Juliet Mitchell's feminist analysis of Laing in her *Psychoanalysis and
Feminism* (1974).

1287   Maccoby, Eleanor E., 1917- , ed. **The Development of Sex Differences.**
        Stanford, CA: Stanford University Press, 1966. 351p. bibliog. $11.50.
        ISBN 0804703086. LC 66-22984.
This well-respected anthology consists of papers based on the discussions of
a work group that met at Stanford University, 1962-1964, sponsored by the
Committee on Socialization and Social Structure of the Social Science Research
Council. Included here are: "Sex Hormones in the Development of Sex Differ-
ences in Human Behavior" (David A. Hamburg and Donald T. Lunde); "Sex
Differences in Intellectual Functioning" (Eleanor E. Maccoby); "A Social-
Learning View of Sex Differences in Behavior" (Walter Mischel); "A Cognitive-
Developmental Analysis of Children's Sex-Role Concepts and Attitudes"
(Lawrence Kohlberg); "Sex Differences and Cultural Institutions" (Roy G.
D'Andrade); "Afterword" (Sanford M. Dornbusch); and "Annotated Bibliog-
raphy" (Roberta M. Oetzel). A classified summary of research in sex differences
is appended.

1288   Maccoby, Eleanor E., 1917- , and Carol Nagy Jacklin. **The Psychology
        of Sex Differences.** Stanford, CA: Stanford University Press, 1974.
        634p. bibliog. index. $18.95. ISBN 0804708592. LC 73-94488.
This work reviews the literature (primarily empirical) on the psychology of sex
differences: perception, learning, intellectual abilities, achievement motivation,
temperament, power relationships, and more. Possible explanations of the origin
of perceived sex differences are also discussed—in particular, sex typing and
the role of modeling and differential socialization of boys and girls. This
invaluable reference source attempts the difficult task of ordering the voluminous
and scattered literature on these topics. However, the approach and language
are demanding and technical. Maccoby and Jacklin's "Summary and Commentary" is recommended for the non-specialist. The massive annotated bibliography (232p.) at the end of the volume will greatly aid the researcher in this
field.

1289   Marcuse, Herbert, 1898- . **Eros and Civilization: A Philosophical Inquiry into Freud.** Boston: Beacon Press, 1955. 277p. bibliog. index. $8.95. ISBN 0807015547. LC 66-3219.

Eros and Civilization belongs to a political and theoretical tradition that has sought a basis for the integration of Marx and Freud (other important figures in this tradition are Wilhelm Reich, Reimut Reiche, Juliet Mitchell, and Richard Lichtman). Marcuse takes issue with Freud's view that sexual repression is the hallmark of civilized society. In Freud's view, Marcuse tells us, "the methodical sacrifice of libido, its rigidly enforced deflection to socially useful activities and expressions, *is* culture." While Marcuse acknowledges the operation of this equation historically, he proposes that "the very achievements of repressive civilization seem to create the preconditions for the gradual abolition of repression." In a society where plenty rather than scarcity is the universal condition, the "reality principle" could be left behind and Eros, play, and gratification could take its place. *Eros and Civilization* was originally published in 1955. In a new introduction written in 1966, Marcuse critically analyzes his work, finding it over-optimistic. Like Reiche (in *Sexuality and Class Struggle*), he notes the transition to a society where the forces of domination exploit sexual "liberation" itself to their own ends.

1290   Miller, Jean Baker, comp. **Psychoanalysis and Women: Contributions to New Theory and Therapy.** New York: Brunner/Mazel, 1973. 418p. bibliog. $12.50. ISBN 0876300697. LC 72-97730.

An anthology of writings on women by psychoanalysts. Part 1, Pertinent Pioneers, includes "The Flight From Womanhood" and "The Problem of Feminine Masochism," by Karen Horney; "Sex," by Alfred Adler; and " 'Penis Envy' in Women," "Some Effects of the Derogatory Attitude Toward Female Sexuality," and "Cultural Pressures in the Psychology of Women," by Clara Thompson. Part 2, The Emergence of New Evidence, includes "On the Nature of Female Sexuality," by Mary Jane Sherfey; "Personal Identity and Sexual Identity," by Mabel Blake Cohen; and "The Sense of Femaleness" and "The 'Bedrock' of Masculinity and Femininity: Bisexuality," by Robert J. Stoller. The final section, Present Problems and Some Future Possibilities, includes "Phobias After Marriage: Women's Declaration of Dependence," by Alexandra Symonds; "Is Anatomy Destiny?," by Robert Seidenberg; and "Masculinity-Feminity: A Study in Imposed Inequality," by Lester A. Gelb. The introduction and conclusion are by the compiler, Jean Baker Miller.

1291   Miller, Jean Baker. **Toward a New Psychology of Women.** Boston: Beacon Press, 1976. 143p. bibliog. index. $9.95. ISBN 0807029580. LC 75-36043.

This is a book about the psychology of women as Miller sees it, as well as about the changes that women are making in their lives and outlooks. As the author admits in her foreword, she has not dealt with issues of class and race differences, but rather has chosen to focus "on the forces which I believe affect all women, by virtue of the fact of being women." Points of emphasis are on the dynamics of domination and subordination, recognizing women's strengths in characteristics that have normally been seen as weaknesses, and women's movement toward authenticity, self-determination, and power. The discussion of these issues is somewhat limited by Miller's exclusive focus on psychology and interpersonal relations and by her failure to consider the way these are shaped and constrained by political, social, and economic realities.

1292   Mitchell, Juliet, 1940- . **Psychoanalysis and Feminism.** New York: Pantheon Books, 1974. 456p. bibliog. index. $10.00. ISBN 0394474724. LC 73-18717.

This book argues that "a rejection of psychoanalysis and of Freud's works is fatal for feminism. However it may have been used, psychoanalysis is not a recommendation *for* a patriarchal society, but an analysis *of* one" (p. xv). In this book, Mitchell provides a painstaking exposition of Freud's theory, a comparative and critical analysis of radical psychotherapy (Wilhelm Reich and R. D. Laing), of feminist theorists (de Beauvoir, Friedan, Figes, Greer, Firestone, and Millett), and a concluding theoretical discussion. The book's major weaknesses are its difficult style and its ambitiousness; the latter can be held responsible for the tenuous nature of her conclusions. A clearer argument for the usefulness of psychoanalytic theory to feminism can be found (in much briefer form) in Gayle Rubin's article, "The Traffic in Women," in *Toward an Anthropology of Women* (edited by Rayna Reiter). Readers interested in delving into Freud's own writings on women and sexuality might begin with his *Three Contributions to the Theory of Sex* (Johnson Reprint, 1970) and *Dora: An Analysis of a Case of Hysteria* (Macmillan, 1963).

1293   Neugarten, Bernice Levin, 1916- , comp. **Middle Age and Aging: A Reader in Social Psychology.** Chicago: University of Chicago Press, 1968. 596p. bibliog. $17.50. ISBN 0226573818. LC 68-55150.

Many well-known names appear in this book of readings on the aging process, among them Masters and Johnson, Robert Havinghurst, and Erik Erikson. The volume provides a useful background review of theories and research on aging. Sections included are: Age Status and Age-Sex Roles; The Psychology of the Life Cycle; Social-Psychological Theories of Aging; The Social Psychology of Health; Family Relationships; Work, Leisure and Retirement; The Immediate Social Environment; Aging in Other Societies; Time, Dying and Death; and Research Strategies.

1294   O'Leary, Virginia E., 1943 - . **Toward Understanding Women.** Monterey, CA: Brooks/Cole, 1977. 253p. bibliog. index. $8.95. ISBN 0818502282. LC 77-5103.

O'Leary designed this book as an introductory text in the psychology of women. As a social psychologist, she limits the scope of the analysis to the realms of biology, psychology, and sex roles. That is, behavioral and power differences between men and women are primarily attributed to innate differences and cultural expectations. An analysis of the social structure that shapes culture and interpersonal relations is lacking. Specific foci include genetic determinants of sex, theories of sex-role development, psychological differences between men and women, female achievement, sex-role stereotypes, black women, female sexuality, and the female life cycle. O'Leary combines extensive discussion of the empirical literature with occasional references to her personal experiences.

1295   Rawlings, Edna I., and Dianne K. Carter, eds. **Psychotherapy for Women:
       Treatment Toward Equality.** Springfield, IL: C. C. Thomas, 1977.
       477p. bibliog. index. $17.50. ISBN 0398035849. LC 76-23165.
This textbook was written with the professional community as the intended
audience and was designed as "a guide to psychotherapeutic treatment which
encourages women to develop as complete human beings." The papers support
psychotherapy as a valid tool but seek to incorporate the theoretical frameworks
of feminism and radical therapy. Broad headings under which the papers are
grouped include: Feminist and Nonsexist Psychotherapy; Nonsexist Approaches
to Psychotherapy for Women; Assertion Training for Women; Career Counseling
as Therapy for Women; Psychotherapy for Lesbians; Feminism as Therapy;
Radical Feminism: A Challenge to Professional Psychotherapy; and Social
Activism as Therapy. Contributors represent a range of theoretical perspectives
that support feminism and challenge traditional techniques. The section on
lesbians is written by lesbian therapists. An article by Sanders and Stewart,
"Feminist Bibliotherapy—Prescription for Change," offers materials giving
therapists and clients a basic grounding in feminist thought through non-fiction
articles and books.

1296   Reich, Wilhelm, 1897-1957. **Sex-Pol: Essays, 1929-1934.** Ed. by Lee
       Baxandall. New York: Random House, 1972. 378p. bibliog. index.
       $2.45. ISBN 0394717910. LC 72-2735.
The essays collected in this volume are probably the most important of Reich's
work for feminist theory. Edited by Lee Baxandall and with a superb introduction by Bertell Ottman, this edition is particularly valuable. The texts "are the
first straightforward, unrevised English translations of any of the writings of
Wilhelm Reich from his Marxist years." Ostracized in the early '30s by both
Marxists and psychoanalysts in Germany, Reich drastically revised his works
from this period as he drifted further from Marxism in later years. In the *Sex-
Pol* essays, Reich is developing his theory of sexual repression and alienation,
exploring the nature of the relation of these to class domination in history and
to the specifically capitalist domination of the contemporary era. Writing
in Germany on the eve of the rise of fascism, Reich is clearly concerned with
the contribution of sexual repression to the authoritarian personality structure
and to problems of class consciousness and political mobilization of the working
class. His political organizing during this period followed from these theoretical
concerns, until he was expelled from the German Communist Party in 1933.
Included in this collection are: "Dialectical Materialism and Psychoanalysis"
(1934); "Psychoanalysis in the Soviet Union" (1929); "The Imposition of
Sexual Morality" (1935); "Politicizing the Sexual Problem of Youth" (1932);
"What Is Class Consciousness?" (1934); and "Reforming the Labor Movement"
(n.d.). Among Reich's other works are *Mass Psychology of Fascism* and *The
Sexual Revolution.* Readers may want to look at Juliet Mitchell's critical analysis
of Reich in her *Psychoanalysis and Feminism* (1974). A pathbreaking work that
shares some of Reich's ideas and takes issue with others is Michel Foucault's
The History of Sexuality (volume 1 of the projected six volumes, *An Introduction,*
published by Pantheon Books, 1978).

1297   Rogers, Carl Ransom, 1902- . **Becoming Partners: Marriage and Its Alternatives.** New York: Delacorte Press, 1972. 243p. bibliog. $7.95. ISBN 044000604X. LC 72-3868.

The psychotherapist writes of experiences in marriages, his own included, and other relationships involving a wide spectrum of people and situations. These cross-sectional pictures and perceptions are from male-female relationships spanning three to fifteen years; most subjects are twenty to 36 years of age. The focus is upon developing relationships, breakdowns, and restructurings; the excitement of growth as individuals, sometimes in spite of and often because of agonizing events, dull plateaus, blissful interludes, and occasional ecstasies. It is not an advice book on how to behave; there are few statistics and only a handful of observations on sociological trends. Rogers does make a few generalizations, including the notion that the most successful partnership arrangements are based upon mutual support of each other's personal growth. Marriage and the nuclear family are cited as failing institutions, but the author feels optimistic about these ways of life in the future because young people, represented by his interviewees, are exploring new ways of relating and are inventing improved futures for themselves. The 22-page carefully annotated bibliography, prepared by Dr. Alice Elliott, covers a broad range of topics.

1298   Rosen, David H., 1945- . **Lesbianism: A Study of Female Homosexuality.** Springfield, IL: C. C. Thomas, 1973. 123p. bibliog. index. $7.95. ISBN 0398029245. LC 73-11067.

"The fundamental question to which Dr. Rosen addresses himself in this book is a very timely one: Is female homosexuality a psychiatric disorder or a way of life? The book appears at a time when the American Psychiatric Association is engaged in an intense controversy on the issue of whether to delete homosexuality (male and female) from the Diagnostic Manual of Psychiatric Disorders. The author is firmly on the side of those who recommend deletion and uses his review of the literature as well as his own study of twenty-six lesbians to support his position; thus, he joins a distinguished group of psychiatrists and behavioral scientists who believe that the mental health professions should no longer continue to use their power in stigmatizing a large sexual minority and, by doing so, contributing to the social and psychological problems of the individuals involved" (Evelyn Hooker, "Foreword"). Rosen became interested in this question after hearing a talk by Phyllis Lyon in 1965, and he worked closely with the Daughters of Bilitis (which she had helped to found) in gathering material for the study. Readers may also want to consult *Male and Female Homosexuality: A Comprehensive Investigation* by Marcel T. Saghir and Eli Robins (Williams and Wilkins, 1973).

1299   Roy, Maria, ed. **Battered Women: A Psychosociological Study of Domestic Violence.** New York: Van Nostrand Reinhold, 1977. 334p. bibliog. index. $10.95. ISBN 0442272014. LC 77-8697.

An anthology of articles (some original, some previously published) by psychiatrists, psychologists, neurologists, sociologists, criminologists, and others, these were collected by the founder and director of Abused Women's Aid in Crisis, Inc., a New York City organization offering help to battered women since 1975. Included are articles on the history of wifebeating, demographic characteristics

of battered women, a comparison of wifebeating and husbandbeating, the neurology
of explosive rage, the psychology of wifebattering, the legal system and legal
solutions, and future trends and prevention.

1300   Schaffer, Rudolph, 1926- . **Mothering.** Cambridge, MA: Harvard
        University Press, 1977. 120p. bibliog. index. $6.95. ISBN 0674587456.
        LC 76-56852.
Schaffer's research documents the lack of any evidence to suggest that women
are more particularly suited to caring for children than men. By "mothering,"
Schaffer means the child's involvement with another in a love relationship—
but this does not have to be one-to-one, exclusively between biological mother
and child. This slim volume summarizes past research on mothers and "mothering"
and suggests that research on child development, especially on the influence of
the mother, may have been asking the wrong questions. Given a changing society,
Schaffer posits the need for further study into the precise nature of the "mothering" function.

1301   Sheehy, Gail. **Passages: Predictable Crises of Adult Life.** New York:
        E. P. Dutton, 1976. 393p. bibliog. index. $10.95. ISBN 03553103067.
        LC 76-4907.
Based upon her own and others' research, Sheehy documents the "predictable
crises of adult life" from the late teens through the 50s, arguing that humans
continue growing up through a series of steps that are the same for everyone,
although the developmental rhythms are different for women and men. The
theories and exposition of the developmental ladder presented in chapter two
are a synthesis of the sources and interviews upon which the writer drew, and
they present an essential framework within which the reader can understand
the rest of the book. The seven parts of the book (there are 25 chapters) are:
Mysteries of the Life Cycle, Pulling up Roots, The Trying Twenties, Passage
to the Thirties, But I'm Unique, Deadline Decade, and Renewal. The last six
represent the passage intervals, or developmental steps. The writer maintains
that understanding how the predictable crises will occur can help one maximize
personal potential. One limitation of the analysis, however, is Sheehy's tendency
to gloss over the ways in which concrete social circumstance (for example, race
or class) shapes these crises and constrains attempts to actualize potential.
The implicit model for Sheehy's generalizations is that of the middle- or upper-
middle-class white person, whose primary barriers to success are likely to be
motivational. Detailed notes and sources are appended, followed by publishing
data in the bibliography and by an index.

1302   Sherman, Julia Ann, 1934- . **On the Psychology of Women: A Survey
        of Empirical Studies.** Springfield, IL: C. C. Thomas, 1971. 304p.
        bibliog. index. $10.75. ISBN 0398017441. LC 77-149194.
Julia Sherman's *On the Psychology of Women* is a widely-cited text, noted for
its careful and extensive review of empirical literature. Sherman puts particular
emphasis on Freud's theory of female development because of its continuing
influence, but she finds little empirical support for its validity. Literature
pertaining to the following topics is discussed: biological and psychological
sex differences, Freudian and other theories of moral and sex-role development,

adolescence, cyclic changes, female sexuality, pregnancy, motherhood, and the later years. Sherman's approach is geared to the specialist; the casual reader will probably find the peppering of citations overwhelming. However, the book should be helpful to students and researchers at diverse levels as a reference tool and road map to the terrain of psychological research on women. The bibliography is extensive, though it only covers work up through 1970. Readers will also want to consult Maccoby and Jacklin's more recent literature review, *The Psychology of Sex Differences* (1974). Virginia O'Leary's *Toward Understanding Women* (1977) covers a considerable amount of psychological research at an introductory level.

1303   Strouse, Jean, comp. **Women and Analysis: Dialogues on Psychoanalytic Views of Femininity.** New York: Grossman, 1974. 375p. bibliog. $12.50. ISBN 0670778419. LC 73-7313.

Strouse is one among a significant number of contemporary feminists who believe that feminism has much to lose by falling into simplistic dismissal of Freud and psychoanalysis. She has compiled a very useful collection of writings on the question of psychoanalysis and women, a collection that can provide an excellent introduction to the questions at issue and to some key participants in the debate. Strouse chose ten articles written about women by psychoanalysts and invited ten writers to respond to these articles, so that the original and the commentary are, in effect, in dialogue. The pairs of writers are as follows: Juliet Mitchell on Freud; Elizabeth Janeway on Freud; Margaret Mead on Freud; Joel Kovel on Karl Abraham; Marcia Cavell on Helene Deutsch; Robert Coles on Karen Horney; Barbara C. Gelpi on Emma Jung; Ethel Person on Marie Bonaparte; Ruth Moulton on Clara M. Thompson; Erik Erikson on himself; and Robert J. Stoller on Freud.

1304   Veith, Ilza. **Hysteria: The History of a Disease.** Chicago: University of Chicago Press, 1970. 301p. bibliog. index. $3.25. ISBN 0226852539. LC 65-24429.

"In ancient Egypt the conduct of certain unstable females was attributed to peregrinations of a discontented womb, and the Greeks, who retained this association, gave the disorder its name by calling it hysteria derived from *hystera*, the Greek word for womb" (from the preface). While not specifically feminist in approach, Veith's study is an invaluable source on the "mental disease" known as hysteria and associated primarily with women. Veith traces the history of popular conceptions and treatments of the "disease" from antiquity, through the Middle Ages (when hysteria was thought to arise from witchcraft), to the Victorian Era and the emergence of psychoanalysis. Much of this story is chilling. For example, the nineteenth-century French neurologist, Jean-Martin Charcot, is described as having employed an "ovary compressor" in his efforts to treat women's "hysterogenic zones." The connection between women's sexuality— its expression and its repression—and the attribution of "hysteria" is a theme that runs throughout the study.

1305   Williams, Elizabeth Friar. **Notes of a Feminist Therapist.** New York: Praeger, 1976. 194p. index. $7.95. ISBN 0275521303. LC 73-19466.

Williams has written a particularly readable and personal view of her notion of feminist psychotherapy and her definition of the feminist therapist. She strongly states that a feminist therapist needs to be supportive and avoid taking the traditional "expert" approach, should avoid presenting herself/himself as a sexual manipulator, must encourage independence rather than dependence in the client, and understand and implement a therapy that will overcome a woman's feelings of inadequacy and dependence, which may be contributing to her unhappiness. Much of her philosophy of therapy takes a common-sense approach that women should be open about their sexual relationships and free in the relationship to take as much as they receive. She sees two major outcomes of feminist therapy: that women should see themselves and other women as being as worthy of friendship and respect as men, and that women should experience satisfaction and self-esteem in the roles that they have chosen. Though Williams feels that sexual separatism is destructive and a limiting, unliberated behavior, her book is supportive of sexual choice and lesbianism. Chapters on love, work, loneliness, transference behaviors, and defensive roles are shaped around questions and problems that clients have articulated in therapy. Williams believes that men can be feminist therapists, but that an anti-feminist therapist (one who believes that the woman who challenges sex-role stereotypes is a neurotic) is anti-humanist and can be destructive in his/her sexism. It is Williams's contention that even an excellent male therapist may have to work very hard to understand the effects of sexism on women's self-esteem.

1306   Williams, Juanita H. **Psychology of Women: Behavior in a Biosocial Context.** New York: Norton, 1977. 444p. bibliog. index. $13.50. ISBN 0393011348. LC 76-56740.

This is intended as an introductory text for courses in the psychology of women, covering the following topics: myths, stereotypes, and the psychology of women; psychoanalysis (orthodox and revisionist); biological sex differences; sex-role socialization; sexuality; birth control; pregnancy, childbirth and breast-feeding; lifestyles; deviance; and aging. As should be apparent from the list of contents (and the title), Williams's approach is not narrowly psychological, but rather tries to understand psychology within its social context.

1307   Wolff, Charlotte, 1897- . **Love Between Women.** New York: Harper and Row, 1972. 303p. bibliog. $2.45. ISBN 0060910097.

Wolff, a German-born psychiatrist, reports here on her research on lesbians, which was based on questionnaires and twenty years of psychiatric practice. She was interested in exploring determinants of lesbian sexual preference and concludes on the basis of her study that mother-daughter relationships are central. Wolff includes three brief autobiographies and transcripts of two interviews from her sample.

1308   Wortis, Helen, and Clara Rabinowitz, comps. **The Women's Movement: Social and Psychological Perspectives.** New York: Wiley, 1972; repr. New York: AMS Press, 1973. 151p. bibliog. $10.00. ISBN 0404105203. LC 72-6125.

Originally a special section for the *American Journal of Orthopsychiatry*, a publication which speaks to anthropologists, educators, lawyers, psychologists, psychiatrists, nurses and social workers on topics of mental health, the essays in this volume represent the various perspectives of the behavioral sciences. Among the essays: Klapper, "The Impact of the Women's Liberation Movement on Child Development Books"; Miller and Mothner, "Psychological Consequences of Sexual Inequality"; Adams, "The Single Woman in Today's Society: A Reappraisal"; Walker, "Recent Writings of the Women's Movement"; Keiffer and Warren, "Resource Bibliography."

REFERENCE
Audiovisual

Reference materials appear under four major divisions to facilitate use: Audiovisual Materials, Bibliographies, Biographical Materials, and General. Bibliographies and other works identified in the Reference sections will lead users to a vast array of materials not cited under specific subject chapters, especially to periodical and report literature not included in the scope of this bibliography. Recent bibliographies, such as Krichmar's *The Women's Movement in the Seventies* (1977) and Hughes's *The Sexual Barrier*, give direction in the area of periodical literature that supports the core book sources annotated here. A first-priority purchase for reference should be Elizabeth Oakes and Kathleen Sheldon's *Guide to Social Science Resources in Women's Studies*, (ABC-Clio, 1978). *American Reference Books Annual* (ARBA) offers continuing assistance in selecting reference books for women's studies.

From its beginnings in the late 1960s and early 1970s, women's studies has been a bibliography-conscious phenomenon. Much informal sharing of mimeographed and xeroxed book lists and syllabi has occurred. Journals of the quality of *Signs* and *Chrysalis* have consistently published fine bibliographic work. A high-calibre bibliographic essay, Patricia K. Ballou's "Bibliographies for Research on Women" in *Signs* (Winter, 1977), is typical of the careful identification work encountered in almost each number of that journal. *Chrysalis* has been strong in the area of non-traditional bibliographies detailing often overlooked sources on such topics as menstruation, entrepeneurship for women, and women artists. Book reviews in *Signs, Chrysalis, Women Studies Abstracts*, and *off our backs* (a feminist newspaper) offer full and thoughtful critical essays and evaluation of women-related reference books.

Further bibliographic assistance for reference has come in the form of bibliographies and annotated lists available from centers for research on women and from which are producing their own lists of materials and recent acquisitions. The Center for Research on Women at Wellesley College, for instance, periodically distributes a list of its working papers and publications, while Ohio State University's Women's Studies Library publishes a monthly listing of new materials, *Women Are Human*.

1309   Artel, Linda J., and Susan Wengraf. **Positive Images: A Guide to Non-Sexist Films for Young People.** San Francisco: Booklegger Press, 1976. 167p. bibliog. index. $6.00. ISBN 0912932031. LC 75-46089.
Films, videotapes, slide shows, filmstrips, and photographs that overturn sexual stereotypes are the resources identified here. Much of the material identified is generated by alternative companies and independent feminist groups, which often are overlooked in more general sources. Fine critical annotations increase its value.

1310   Betancourt, Jeanne. **Women in Focus.** Dayton, OH: Pflaum, 1974.
        186p. bibliog. $14.60. ISBN 0827802617. LC 74-78728.
This is an excellent sourcebook for feminist films and films that do not stereotype women. Written by a film teacher in an all-women's high school in New York
City, the book reviews ninety films—features and shorts, fiction and documentary, contemporary and rediscovered older films—providing descriptions of the
films, suggestions for appropriate audiences, rental information, suggested
feminist reading in conjunction with the films, and, in many cases, brief sketches
of the filmmaker. There are in addition three indexes (by film title, filmmaker,
and theme), a list of suggested programs, an annotated bibliography of feminist
books (by Madeline Warren), and a section on distribution information. Betancourt has seen all the films reviewed several times and has shown many of them
to her classes.

1311   Dawson, Bonnie. **Women's Films in Print: An Annotated Guide to 800
        16mm Films by Women.** San Francisco, CA: Booklegger Press, 1975.
        165p. bibliog. index. $5.00. ISBN 0912932025. LC 74-80642.
Women's film courses will find this source of 800 films by 370 women directors
particularly useful. Alphabetical listings by filmmaker include distributor,
price, and a short note on film content. The subject-index is an especially
useful feature—everything from AT&T to Emile Zola. Particularly rich clusters
occur around the subjects sexuality, portraits of women, occupations, music,
adolescence, and dance. Readers might also want to consult a new sourcebook
on women directors: *Early Women Directors* by Anthony Slide (A. S. Barnes,
1977).

1312*   **Women's Films: A Critical Guide.** Bloomington: Indiana University
        Audio-Visual Center, 1975. 121p. bibliog. index. LC 75-328487.
This bibliography provides annotations, distribution and technical information
for over 170 films, on topics such as rape, jobs, historical studies, personal
statements, working mothers, and biographical portraits.

REFERENCE
Bibliographies
[The scope note for Reference appears on p. 460.]

1313   Adell, Judith and Hilary Dole Klein, 1945- . **A Guide to Non-Sexist Children's Books.** Chicago: Academy Press, 1976. 149p. index. $7.95. ISBN 0915864010. LC 75-34396.

This annotated bibliography of non-sexist children's books is divided into three sections: pre-cshool through third grade, third grade through seventh grade, and seventh grade through twelfth grade. Within each of these sections, fiction and non-fiction books are distinguished. The authors include publication information, price (when the book is in print), and an approximate grade level for each book. Annotations are brief and to the point. This would be a useful tool for libraries interested in developing their collections of children's literature and parents looking for non-sexist reading material for their children.

1314*   Al-Qazzaz, Ayad, 1941- . **Women in the Middle East and North Africa: An Annotated Bibliography.** Austin: Center for Middle Eastern Studies, University of Texas at Austin, 1977. 178p. index. ISBN 0292790090. LC 77-73039.

Al-Qazzaz notes in the introduction that materials on Middle Eastern women lag behind the mushrooming literature on women in Western countries. This bibliography is an invaluable resource for research on this topic, including the specific question of women in Islam. Only English-language materials are included, but the scholars represented are diverse in background. The author has listed books, articles, and unpublished papers; in the case of unpublished material, annotations are more detailed. In general, the annotations are quite lengthy and very precise. Al-Qazzaz also directs the researcher to a number of other bibliographies on the general topic for further information. The bibliography is indexed by country and topic. The author intends to update the volume periodically.

1315*   Arthur and Elizabeth Schlesinger Library on the History of Women in America. **The Arthur and Elizabeth Schlesinger Library on the History of Women in America, the Manuscript Inventories and the Catalogs of Manuscripts, Books and Pictures.** Boston: G. K. Hall, 1973. 3v. ISBN 0816110530.

This superb collection developed originally out of the Woman's Rights Collection, a gift of the papers of approximately 100 suffrage leaders and other woman suffrage memorabilia donated by Maud Wood Park, herself an active suffragist, in 1943. Since then, the library has maintained a strong commitment to developing the collection, and it has branched out into the areas of the anti-slavery movement, temperance, prison reform, organized charities, the settlement house movement, the labor movement, and more, while continuing to update the women's movement materials even to the present. Manuscripts represent the core of the collection, but books, periodicals and pamphlets are collected as well. These three volumes reproduce the catalog of library holdings.

1316   Ashton, Jean. **Harriet Beecher Stowe: A Reference Guide.** Boston:
        G. K. Hall, 1977. 168p. index. $18.00. ISBN 081617833X. LC
        76-51433.
Ashton details the 125-year critical heritage of Harriet Beecher Stowe, noting
that "although much of this material has been perfunctory or piously biographical, at least four major concerns can be traced through the serious [critical]
work: the related issues of slavery and race; the definition and discussion of
protest literature and its function; religion; i.e., the manifestation and fragmentation of nineteenth-century Calvinist thought; and, to a lesser degree, feminism"
(introduction). Because Stowe's precise position in the history of American
letters has been the subject of continual debate, it is interesting to follow the
chronological annotations of the criticism that Ashton provides in this bibliography. The arrangement: Writings of Harriet Beecher Stowe; Writings about
Harriet Beecher Stowe, 1843-1974; Appendix I: Fictional Responses to *Uncle
Tom's Cabin*, 1852-1861; Appendix II: Plays Based on the Life of Harriet Beecher
Stowe; Appendix III: *Uncle Tom's Cabin* on Stage (Selected Articles). A thorough
author/title index is included.

1317*   Astin, Helen S., 1932- , et al. **Sex Roles: A Research Bibliography.**
        Rockville, MD: National Institute of Mental Health; Washington:
        for sale by the Supt. of Docs., U.S. Govt. Print. Off., 1975. 362p.
        index. LC 75-602869.
Included in this annotated research bibliography are 346 journal articles, 54
books, 49 chapters of books, proceedings of two conferences, and five unpublished papers and speeches. While the materials were drawn from all the social
sciences plus medicine, approximately two-thirds come from the fields of
sociology and psychology, and the predominant approach throughout is social
psychological. History is excluded. Items are organized into the following
subject areas: Sex Differences; The Development of Sex Differences and Sex
Roles; Specialized Sex Roles in Institutional Settings; Cross-Cultural Overviews
of the Status of the Sexes; and Reviews and Theoretical Expositions. Author
and subject indexes are provided.

1318   Astin, Helen S., 1932- , et al. **Women: A Bibliography on Their Education
        and Careers.** Washington: Human Service Press, 1971; repr. New York:
        Behavioral Publications, 1974. 243p. index. $12.95. ISBN 087705701X.
        LC 74-5124.
An annotated bibliography of articles, monographs, and books on the topic of
women's education and careers, with primary emphasis on empirical research
since the 1960s. The entries are divided by subject categories, among them:
Determinants of Career Choice, Marital and Familial Status of Working Women,
Women in the World of Work, and so on. The bibliography is preceded by two
short essays, "Overview of the Findings," by Helen S. Astin, and "Beyond the
Findings: Some Interpretations and Implications for the Future," by Nancy
Suniewick.

1319*   Bass, Dorothy. **American Women in Church and Society, 1607-1920:
        A Bibliography.** New York: Auburn Program at Union Theological
        Seminary, 1973. 36p. $1.00. LC 73-161124.

This partially annotated bibliography has sections on: general works on women's history, American women before 1830, women on the frontier, women and slavery, black women after Emancipation, family life and the cult of domesticity, sects and utopias, women and their bodies, the education of women, women in the church, working women, women and social change, the struggle for political equality, foreign observers of American women, and popular literature for women.

1320   Bickner, Mei Liang. **Women at Work: An Annotated Bibliography.**
        Los Angeles: University of California, Institute of Industrial Relations.
        Vol. I: 1974. $6.50. ISBN 0892150432. Vol. II (Marlene Shaughnessey,
        co-author): 1977. $7.50. ISBN 0892150645. LC 77-622630.
A good selective bibliography of many types of publications on working women, this has been "prepared primarily for persons who teach, conduct research, or are serious students in the general area of working women." Thus, "how-to" information and practical handbooks and information are absent from the 600 entries here. What do appear are topical reports, government publications, serious studies, and articles from refereed journals. Most of the material is post-1960. Topics of special interest are: publications dealing with non-professional women and minority women; legal developments that affect working women, including legislation, court decisions, decisions of the Equal Employment Opportunity Commission, and the National Labor Relations Board. Annotations are organized by: 1) general studies; 2) historical developments, education, and training; 3) working women; 4) specific occupations and professions; 5) special groups, including aging, minority, teenaged women, and mothers; and 6) public policy materials. Bibliographies are selectively identified. Author, title, category, and keyword indexes are provided.

1321   Blouin, Lenora P. **May Sarton: A Bibliography.** Metuchen, NJ: Scare-
        crow Press, 1978. 236p. bibliog. index. ISBN 0810810549. LC 77-14311.
Sarton's work, published over a period spanning a half century, ranges literary genres: novels, poetry, essays, memoirs, and short stories. Recognized as an outstanding writer, she is now receiving increased attention due to the theme of women's self-exploration that has been her focus for many years, especially women's role as artist, whether painter, sculptor, writer, or poet. This excellent annotated bibliography seeks to order the sizeable Sarton corpus as well as the critical attention she has received in book reviews, scholarly and biographical articles, and unpublished papers. Additional features are a partial checklist of individual poems and an author index.

1322   Bullough, Vern L., et al., eds. **A Bibliography on Prostitution.** New
        York: Garland, 1977. 419p. index. $19.00. ISBN 0824099478. LC
        75-42891.
5494 entries on twenty subject categories are included in this, the most comprehensive work on prostitution currently available.

1323   Burkom, Selma R. **Doris Lessing: A Checklist of Primary and Secondary
        Sources.** Troy, NY: Whitston, 1973. 88p. index. $7.50. ISBN
        0878750398. LC 72-87109.

A slim but useful unannotated bibliography, "this checklist enumerates the basic editions of Doris Lessing's works and the critical responses they have elicited. The catalog of secondary materials makes no claim to being exhaustive; no chronicler can keep up with the mass of Lessing criticism which has begun appearing recently. Hopefully, the most important pieces written to date [1973] have been included" (introduction).

1324* Business and Professional Women's Foundation. Library. **Women and Work in U.S. History: An Annotated, Selected Bibliography.** Washington: Business and Professional Women's Foundation, 1976. 28p. index. LC 76-377333.

An excellent and concise annotated bibliography of women's history materials, this contains both monographs and articles. Materials are included for the following categories: Methods and Theory in Women's History; Earlier Scholarship; Contemporary Scholarship (including document collections, books and journals); and Guides to Further Resources. With 105 items in all, this pamphlet is a good beginning road map to a field that is quickly gaining overwhelming proportions.

1325 Cabello-Argandoña, Roberto, et al. **The Chicana: A Comprehensive Bibliographic Study.** Los Angeles: Bibliographic Research and Collection Development Unit, Chicano Studies Center, University of California, 1976. 308p. $7.95.

An indispensible reference given the mounting demand for information dealing with the Chicana and the increasing visibility of a Chicana movement, this offers a systematic inroad to various significant source materials. Excellent descriptive and evaluative annotations. Periodicals dealing with the Chicana are listed but not evaluated. Under the major subject headings, periodical, book, document, and report citations appear. Major topics: Films; Serials; General Readings; The Chicana and the Women's Liberation Movement; Civil Rights; Culture and Cultural Processes and Folk Culture; Demography; Economics; Education; Family, Marriage and Sex Roles; Health and Nutrition; History; Labor and Discrimination in Employment; Literature; Politics; Religion; Social Conditions. Indexing is both by title and author. This bibliography is the first major bibliographic project on the Chicana and is informed throughout by a scholarly and orderly point of view.

1326 California. Equal Rights Amendment Project. **The Equal Rights Amendment: A Bibliographic Study.** Westport, CT: Greenwood Press, 1976. 367p. index. $19.95. ISBN 0837190584. LC 76-24999.

Anita Miller was project director, and Hazel Greenberg was the editor and compiler of this project. The ERA is a complicated subject. Information about it lies buried in many difficult-to-access sources—newsletters, House and Senate hearings, debates and reports, and other government publications. Numerous brochures, leaflets, and flyers also contain kernels of valuable ERA information. Miller and Greenberg have done a painstaking job in locating the sources. Especially excellent features are their separate treatments of legal periodical literature, of *Equal Rights* (National Woman's Party Magazine chronologically indexed from 1923 to 1954), and of newsletters (most are from the Herstory

collection, which previously has never had *any* subject access). Newsletters
are especially difficult to locate and to index; for this coverage of the ERA
alone, the bibliography is worth the price. Newspaper coverage of the ERA
includes a listing of articles and editorials appearing in the *Chicago Tribune,
Christian Science Monitor, Honolulu Advertiser, Los Angeles Times, National
Observer, New Orleans Times-Picayune, New York Times, Wall Street Journal,
Washington Post,* and *Editorials on File.* Indexing is by author and organization.
The compilers have also provided sixty citations to books, articles and dissertations. Throughout, the explanatory notes are first-rate in this excellent tool,
which should be a starting point for any ERA research.

1327*   Cardinale, Susan. **Special Issues of Serials About Women, 1965-1975.**
         Monticello, IL: Council of Planning Librarians, 1976. 41p.
As more research is done on women by women, a variety of serials have focused
on women for special issue coverage. This annotated bibliography looks at
scholarly journals, popular magazines, and alternative press outlets. In most
cases, the issue is addressed to women or a woman-related subject. Several are
about a specific woman (e.g., Virginia Woolf). General women's periodicals
(e.g., *McCall's*) are for the most part excluded. A scholarly bibliography useful
to update Cardinale is "Special Issues of Periodicals" in *Canadian Newsletter
of Research on Women* (v. 7, no. 1, March 1978). The present work is no. 995
in the CPL Exchange Bibliography series.

1328   Cassirer, Sidonie, ed. **Teaching about Women in the Foreign Languages:
        French, Spanish, German, Russian.** Old Westbury, NY: Feminist Press,
        1975. 237p. bibliog. $5.00. ISBN 091267038X. LC 76-365623.
Volume IX of the Female Studies series, this is a useful collection of materials
for women's studies courses in the fields of French, Spanish, German, and
Russian, including both essays in feminist criticism and course outlines. The
quantity of material in each of the four disciplines varies considerably, with
French the most thoroughly covered and Russian, the least—reflective of the
response received by the Commission on the Status of Women of the Modern
Language Association (which initiated this project) in reply to its requests to
150 faculty for women's studies course outlines.

1329   Chaff, Sandra L., et al. **Women in Medicine: A Bibliography of the
        Literature on Women Physicians.** Metuchen, NJ: Scarecrow Press, 1977.
        1136p. index. $35.00. ISBN 0810810565. LC 77-24914.
Citing more than 4,000 items about women physicians in all parts of the world,
mainly from English-language sources, this vast listing must be considered the
most comprehensive bibliography about women physicians to date. The earliest
cited item is a German work by F. Boerner translated as *Should Women Practice Medicine?* (Leipzig, 1750). Chaff draws on sources published in books,
medical and non-medical periodical literature, alumni and alumnae magazine
articles, and doctoral theses. The annotations are full and "convey the flavor
as well as the content of the items." The substantial subject and personal name
index should provide good access to the material. Topics under which the material is organized: History of Women in Medicine; Biographies; Recruitment;
Medical Education; Graduate Medical Education; Medical Activity; Specialties;

Missionary Activity; Wartime Activity; Psychosocial Factors; Medical Institutions, Societies, and Their Journals; General Literature; and Fiction.

1330   Common Women Collective. **Women in U.S. History: An Annotated Bibliography.** Cambridge, MA: The Collective, 1976. 114p. $2.25. ISBN 0960112219. LC 77-350179.

An annotated bibliography of books and articles on U.S. women's history compiled by the Common Women Collective, this grew out of the 1973-1974 Women's History Project in the Goddard-Cambridge Graduate Program. While the listings on any particular topic are brief, the range of topics is very broad and the selection of books, discriminating. Annotations are concise yet manage to convey the book's contents; its sensitivity (or lack of it) on questions of class, race, and sex; and its ideological slant. The absence of subject, author, or title index is a limitation, but there is some cross-listing between subject areas. In addition to sections covering particular periods in United States history, there are chapters isolating works on Native American women, black women, abolitionism and feminism, temperance, pioneer women, institutionalized women, anarchists, communists and socialists, Chicanas, and lesbians. It is a very thoughtful overview of sources in U.S. women's history. Another overview that would be useful in conjunction with this bibliography is *Women in American Society* (by Gordon, Buhle, and Schrom), an essay on sources and problems in U.S. feminist historiography.

1331   Cromwell, Phyllis E., ed. **Woman and Mental Health: Selected Annotated References, 1970-1973.** Rockville, MD: Division of Scientific and Technical Information, National Institute of Mental Health; Washington: U.S. Govt. Print. Off., 1974. 247p. index. $2.45. LC 75-601067.

"This bibliography is designed to provide information on the social, economic, and psychological pressures on women and to show the diversity of, or lack of, expert opinion on female psychological and sociocultural processes. The material was selected from the behavioral science literature and audiovisual resources" (from the editor's preface). Topics covered include abortion, aging, divorce, lesbianism, motherhood, rape, roles, stereotypes and the Women's Liberation Movement, sexuality and sexual development, and widowhood. An author index is included at the end.

1332   Crump, Rebecca W., 1944- . **Christina Rossetti: A Reference Guide.** Boston: G. K. Hall, 1976. 172p. index. $19.00. ISBN 081617847X. LC 75-28008.

An annotated secondary bibliography, this book includes introductions from selective editions of Rossetti's poetry, introductions from major anthologies of Victorian poetry in which she appears, reviews of works about her, reminiscences, sketches, memorials, essays, articles, theses, chapters of works, books, and dissertations. The materials are arranged by year, 1862-1973, the better to observe, compare, and contrast the tides of critical response to Rossetti. The annotations are detailed, and there is an author/title index.

1333   Davis, Audrey B. **Bibliography on Women: With Special Emphasis on Their Roles in Science and Society.** New York: Science History Publications, 1974. 50p. $3.00. ISBN 0882020145. LC 74-7229.

This is an unannotated list of books and articles selected from subject headings relevant to research on women in *The Library of Congress Catalogue: A Cumulative List of Works* for the years 1950 to March 1973, and unprinted cards for the preceding years. No subject categories or indexing are provided. "The purpose of the selection is to show the numerous possibilities for locating research materials on the roles and accomplishments of women and the attitudes toward them" (from the introduction).

1334   Davis, Lenwood G. **The Black Family in the United States: A Selected Bibliography of Annotated Books, Articles, and Dissertations on Black Families in America.** Westport, CT: Greenwood Press, 1978. 132p. index. $11.95. ISBN 0837198518. LC 77-89109.

Any work on the family necessarily pertains to women as essential members of that unit. Davis has compiled the most comprehensive available bibliography on the black family. The fully annotated bibliography handles books, articles, and dissertations on every aspect of the black family—rural and urban; poor and middle-class—covering issues of health, sex, religion, education, occupation, and economics. In browsing the index, subjects like abortion, contraceptives, birth control, and divorce surface. Surprisingly, references to motherhood and marriage do not. This may be more a function of poor subject indexing than any other factor, as in a random sample of two pages all of the articles dealt specifically with women.

1335   Davis, Lenwood G. **The Black Woman in American Society: A Selected Annotated Bibliography.** Boston: G. K. Hall, 1975. 159p. index. $17.00. ISBN 0816178585. LC 75-33275.

Davis, a professor of black American studies, has produced many fine bibliographies on black America. [See *The Black Family in the United States: A Selected Bibliography of Annotated Books, Articles, and Dissertations on Black Families in America* (Greenwood, 1978), among other works.] His concisely annotated *Black Woman in American Society* contains 1,186 citations covering works about black women from all periods of American history. Davis's introduction surveys the corpus of bibliographic literature on black women to 1976. Contents: Books, Articles, General Reference Works, Selected Current Black Periodicals Directory; Reports, Pamphlets, Speeches and Government Documents; United States Libraries with Major Black History Collections; National Organizations; Newspaper Publishers and Editors; Elected Officials. Statistical tables on black women in urban and rural areas add a useful ready reference feature.

1336   Davis, Lenwood G. **Black Women in the Cities, 1872-1975: A Bibliography of Published Works on the Life and Achievements of Black Women in Cities in the United States.** (2nd ed.). Monticello, IL: Council of Planning Librarians, 1975. (CPL Exchange Bibliography No. 751-752). 75p. $7.50. LC 75-313749.

Many of the books and articles included in this selective bibliography are out of print though likely to appear in reprint in the future. Current material on

black women in the cities can be found on an ongoing basis from the Women's
Bureau of the U.S. Dept. of Labor, which often issues bulletins on black women.
Davis covers general reference works, selected black periodicals, major black
history collections held by U.S. libraries, urban affairs journal literature, bibliographies, government documents, reports and pamphlets, articles and books.
Although the stated focus is black women in urban areas, there is a great deal
of material which relates to the American black woman, in general. There are
no annotations. It includes a list of black women's national organizations and
a list of black women elected officials.

1337   Drake, Kirsten, et al. **Women's Work and Women's Studies, 1971.**
        Pittsburgh, PA: Know, 1972. $4.50. ISBN 0912786183.
The purpose of this bibliography was to keep track of published studies and
research in progress about women and feminism that had been identified during
the preceding year, with concentration on scholarly books, articles, papers,
and pamphlets. This bibliography will be especially useful for women's studies
programs and libraries supporting such programs.

1338   Een, Jo Ann Delores, and Marie Barovic Rosenberg-Dishman. **Women
        and Society, Citations 3601 to 6000: An Annotated Bibliography.**
        Beverly Hills, CA: Sage Publications, 1978. index. $17.50. ISBN
        0803908563. LC 77-18985.
This is volume 2 of the annotated bibliography, *Women and Society*. Volume 1
was co-authored by Marie B. Rosenberg and Len V. Bergstrom (see entry 1378).

1339   Eichler, Margrit, et al. **Women: A Bibliography of Special Periodical
        Issues (1960-1975).** Toronto: Canadian Newsletter of Research on
        Women, 1976. 76p. $2.75. LC 77-371663.
In this special publication of the *Canadian Newsletter of Research on Women*,
the special issues identified here span the years 1960-1975. "Selection was made
on the basis of academic quality, although a few issues are included not because
of their quality but because they deal with some question of import about which
there is scarce information." Bibliographic information is given, along with
contents. Covered are: Anthropology, Arts and Literature, Business Administration, Criminology, Education, Folklore, Futurology, Health, Industrial and
Labor Relations, Interdisciplinary Social Science, Philosophy, Political Economy,
Political Science, Psychology, Primatology, Religion, Sexology, Social Psychology,
Sociology, and Work. The compilers do not quarantee that they are identifying
feminist sources. A second volume of this bibliography is also available, compiled
by Jennifer L. Newton and Carol Zavitz (1978). Both volumes are available
from the *Canadian Newsletter of Research on Women*, c/o Sociology Department
OISE, 252 Bloor Street West, Toronto, Ontario M5S 1V6, Canada.

1340   Farmer, David R. **A Descriptive Bibliography of the Works of Flannery
        O'Connor.** New York: B. Franklin, 1977. 160p. index. $17.95. ISBN
        0891021132. LC 77-12010.
O'Connor's primary writings in print, including those published during her
lifetime and posthumously, appear in this basic reference guide. Separate treatment is given to her other work—contributions to books and periodicals, for

example, and miscellaneous writing. Translations and film adaptations of her work are listed here.

1341   Foster, Jeannette Howard, 1895- . **Sex Variant Women in Literature.**
        (2nd ed.). New York: Vantage Press, 1956; repr. Baltimore: Diana
        Press, 1975. 420p. bibliog. index. $8.00. ISBN 0884470075. LC
        75-33857.
Foster discusses 324 works of French, German, English and classical literature
which treat lesbianism. Works range from Sappho's poetry to novels of the 1950s.
Attention is given to the lesbian stereotype and to male critical responses to
women's writing in general and lesbian writing in particular. This edition has
a new afterword by Barbara Grier.

1342   Friedman, Leslie, 1948- . **Sex Role Stereotyping in the Mass Media:**
        An Annotated Bibliography. New York: Garland, 1977. 324p. index.
        $25.00. ISBN 082409865X. LC 76-52685.
Drawing from scholarly and popular sources, from print and non-print materials,
documents, report literature, and speeches, among other items, Friedman manages
to survey an incredible diversity of literature about sex stereotypes in the
media. Clearly feminist in tone (though the author maintains that she included
all articles she found defending sexism—0.01 percent), this bibliography begins
with the assumption that the media have not met their responsibility, even
minimally, to provide positive images of women to the public. Mass Media,
Advertising, Broadcast Media, Film, Print Media, Pop Culture, Media Images
of Minority Group Women, Media Images of Men, Children's Media, and Impact
of Media Stereotypes on Occupational Choices broadly define Friedman's chapters,
though specific content ranges from airline ads to comic strips, from daytime
programming to skin magazines.

1343   Froschl, Merle, and Jane Williamson. **Feminist Resources for Schools**
        and Colleges: A Guide to Curricular Materials. (2nd ed., rev. and enl.).
        Old Westbury, NY: Feminist Press, 1977. 67p. $1.95. ISBN
        0912670142.
This is an annotated bibliography of nonsexist articles, books, pamphlets, and other
materials for teachers and students from preschool through college and university. In this selective list, Froschl and Williamson carry on the purpose of
Ahlum and Fralley's original bibliography to locate materials to support a
nonsexist and feminist curriculum. Topics covered in the overview: Basic Readings,
Book Studies, For the Counselor, Sports, Law, and Strategies for Change. For
preschool, elementary, and secondary education, topics include: Readings
and Curriculum. Under higher education are listed Resources for the Teacher
and Anthologies for Anthropology, History, Law, Literature, and Psychology.
Perhaps most useful is the segment, Sources of Further Information, listing
Bibliographies, Guides to Nonprint Resources, Organizations, Periodicals, and
Publishers/Book Distributors.

1344   Fulmer, Constance Marie. **George Eliot: A Reference Guide.** Boston:
        G. K. Hall, 1977. 247p. index. $20.00. ISBN 0816178593. LC
        76-58431.

The indexing and the introduction are helpful in this partially annotated guide to George Eliot studies. The standard items are present, so that this bibliography covers the material adequately. The annotations are rather brief when they appear, though they do point the way. Indexing provides excellent access to the items by: 1) specific Eliot works, 2) authors of items, 3) titles of items, 4) subject. This last is not so helpful as it might be, because items are indexed more by genre of critical materials than by specific topics.

1345   **A Gay Bibliography: Eight Bibliographies on Lesbian and Male Homo-sexuality.** New York: Arno Press, 1975. 410p. $25.00. ISBN 0405073496. LC 75-12317.
Bringing together eight annotated or coded bibliographies on lesbians and homo-sexuality, this volume provides access to a great deal of literature, chiefly from the late '50s and the '60s. Because several of the bibliographies were originally mimeographed and privately distributed (which speaks of the underground nature of lesbian and homosexual writings until quite recently), the quality of indexing and annotations varies from one bibliography to another. Speaking to English-language novels, short stories, poetry, and other literature by and/or about lesbians and homosexuals are: Marion Bradley's *Astra's Tower* (1958 and 1959, plus three checklists for 1960, 1961, and 1962); Gene Damon's *The Lesbian in Literature* (1967); Noel Garde's (pseud.) *The Homosexual in Literature: A Chronological Bibliography, Circa 700 B.C.-1958* (1959). The final bibliography, William Parker's *Homosexuality: Selected Abstracts and Bibliography* (1966), deals with the sociological literature on homosexuality and includes abstracts of documents, books, articles, and court cases relevant to homosexuality, along with a wide-ranging supplemental bibliography. Parker's bibliography is primarily confined to materials on men, but the abstracts are so thorough as to provide an excellent guide to the legal, religious, political, medical, and social climate of opinion concerning homosexuality during the 1950s and 1960s. Researchers may also wish to consult Martin S. Weinberg and Alan P. Bell's *Homosexuality: An Annotated Bibliography* (Harper and Row, 1972).

1346   **The Gerritsen Collection of Women's History: A Short Title List for Nos. 1-1959.** Glen Rock, NJ: Microfilming Corporation of America, 1975. 76p. [*List of Addenda to the Basic Collection,* 1977; 34p.].
The original Gerritsen Collection, a nineteenth-century collection obtained by Carl Gerritsen and his wife, Aletta Jacobs Gerritsen (the first female doctor in the Netherlands), was acquired by the University of Kansas in 1954. The strength of the collection is in continental and ethnic American materials on women's history in a variety of languages, including English. The addenda identified in this temporary list complement the first checklist (1976). Although the collection is quite expensive ($21,000) and therefore cannot be considered a core item, the index can be used with or without fiche to identify important international materials on the history and status of women. It should be consulted by those wishing to make use of primary materials. Prostitution, women's rights, birth control, marriage, the education of girls and young women, and the female offender are a few of the strong subject areas in the collection. The permanent *Guide* will not be available until June 1979 (*The Gerritsen Collection of Women's History: A Bibliographic Guide to the Microform Collection*;

Glen Rock, NJ: MCA, 1977; ISBN 0884559998). The *Guide* will contain information on 260 periodical titles and 4,700 monographic titles. It will be priced at $150.00.

1347   Golden, Robert E., and Mary Carmel Sullivan. **Flannery O'Connor and Caroline Gordon: A Reference Guide.** Boston: G. K. Hall, 1977. 342p. index. $22.00. ISBN 0816178453. LC 76-44334.

Robert E. Golden has authored the Flannery O'Connor (1925-1964) section of the reference guide. Covered are: Published Writings about Flannery O'Connor, 1952-1976; Ph.D. Dissertations on Flannery O'Connor (also arranged chronologically); and a list of Flannery O'Connor's First Editions. Annotations are concise, frequently quoting from the reviewer or critic's work. The introduction traces the thread of criticism on O'Connor, noting that discussions of O'Connor's religious intent are the nucleus of criticism about her work. Caroline Gordon (b. 1895-) is a lesser-known writer than O'Connor. Mary Sullivan authors the section on Caroline Gordon and notes that "of her nine novels and two volumes of short stories, eight titles have been recently reprinted." Her introductory essay explores the modest critical history of Gordon's work. Sullivan has annotated all published writings about Caroline Gordon and her work for 1931-1973. Listed are: Works by Caroline Gordon; Published Writings about Caroline Gordon, 1931-1975 (only two entries for 1974-1975, due to print lag in bibliographies, probably); Ph.D. Dissertations on Caroline Gordon. Indexing for both bibliographies is separate, using a single alphabetical listing for authors of critical works and titles of works by Gordon and O'Connor. Subject approaches for both are by bibliography and biography. Format for the G. K. Hall series on literature is attractive and allows easy access to the material. It should be noted that neither Golden nor Sullivan appears to have done critical work on O'Connor or Gordon.

1348   Goodwater, Leanna, 1950- . **Women in Antiquity: An Annotated Bibliography.** Metuchen, NJ: Scarecrow Press, 1975. 171p. index. $7.00. ISBN 0810808374. LC 75-23229.

At Goodwater's writing, only a single survey of the literature existed, Sarah B. Pomeroy's "Selected Bibliography on Women in Antiquity" in *Arethusa* (VI, Spring 1973, pp. 125-127). Goodwater notes that women's studies has tended to do work on the history of women since the sixteenth century, neglecting the study of women in classical antiquity. The scope here includes materials about times to 476 A.D. Covered are women from the Minoan, Etruscan, and Hellenistic kingdoms and some provinces of the Roman Empire; African and Near Eastern women of antiquity do not appear. A heavy emphasis is on biographical materials on specific women, though Cleopatra has been excluded because of the sheer volume of work on her. Goodwater lists some of the major bibliographic treatments of Cleopatra and Sappho in her introduction (p. 22). English, Greek, Latin, French, German, and Italian sources published since 1972 are listed, though comprehensiveness has been directed toward English-language materials only. Goodwater is a careful bibliographer, and the 534 annotations reflect only material she has examined.

1349　Grier, Barbara [Damon, Gene], 1933- , et al. **The Lesbian in Literature: A Bibliography.** (2nd ed.). Reno, NV: Ladder Publications, 1975. 96p. $10.00. LC 75-319976.

The compilers explain in their introduction that, for the most part, their bibliography includes novels, short fiction, poetry, drama, and fictionalized biography concerned with lesbianism, plus many non-fiction works on the subject. They exclude works dealing with male homosexuals except when such works also treat lesbians. An interesting feature of this bibliography is the coding of entries indicating whether the work has major lesbian characters or action as contrasted to a minor lesbian interest; whether the characters manifest latent or repressed lesbianism. The symbol (T) is used to indicate a book which the compilers feel to be of poor quality—the symbol signifies "trash." The compilers state that they have examined all of the English-language titles in the field inclusive of 1974 copyright dates. This bibliography is undoubtedly the best single source available on lesbian literature even though unannotated. An important book to use along with this one is Jeanette Foster's *Sex Variant Women in Literature* (Diana Press, 1975). The 1967 edition of *The Lesbian in Literature* is also available in the Arno Press reprint anthology, *A Gay Bibliography* (1975).

1350　Haber, Barbara. **Women in America: A Guide to Books, 1963-1975.** Boston: G. K. Hall, 1978. 230p. index. $18.00. ISBN 0816178771. LC 78-17724.

It is rare to find an annotated bibliography that is worthy of praise most particularly for its lucid commentaries. Haber has pulled off the rare feat of organizing a bibliography around a difficult and various subject, and defining a precise scope to which she adheres. Throughout, she writes with grace and style informed with a superb knowledge of the literature in the area of American women and social thought. She is clearly comfortable with feminist theory and demystifies it for the reader. As curator of printed books at Radcliffe's Arthur and Elizabeth Schlesinger Library on the History of Women in America, Haber has utilized the selection principles governing the collection policy for the splendid Schlesinger collection in determining entries for this highly selective, comparative 450-item bibliography. It documents the contemporary female experience in such areas as physical and mental health, ethnicity, prostitution, rape, sex roles, abortion, religion, and history in books published from 1963-1975. Her section on feminism is especially fine. Fiction, poetry, drama, and reference books do not figure in Haber's bibliography. Though librarians will want to be sure to check their collections against this important core listing, all readers interested in the women's movement will find Haber a reliable and intelligent tutor in the best of its growing literature.

1351　Hirschfelder, Arlene B. **American Indian and Eskimo Authors: A Comprehensive Bibliography.** New York: Association on American Indian Affairs; distr. New York: Interbook, 1973. 99p. $4.00. ISBN 0913456608. LC 73-82109.

This very comprehensive, annotated bibliography of American Indian and Eskimo authors updates an earlier edition published in 1970. It contains more than twice the titles of the first edition, amounting to almost 400 titles written or narrated by nearly 300 Indian and Eskimo authors representing more than 100 tribes. All works are listed under the names of the Indians or Eskimos who narrated or wrote them, rather than under the names of the investigators or editors who recorded or revised the material. Bibliographic information is provided for citations, including whether or not the item is print; however, readers would do well to check whether sources listed as out-of-print have been reissued since the 1973 publication of this bibliography. Annotations are brief, but informative and to the point. The bibliography is indexed only by tribe. Readers with a primary interest in women authors will have to search the alphabetical list for likely names.

1351a* Hollenshead, Carol. **Past Sixty: The Older Woman in Print and Film.**
Ann Arbor: Institute of Gerontology, University of Michigan—Wayne State University, 1977. 52p. $3.00. LC 78-103540.
This annotated bibliography covers books, journal articles, pamphlets, and films relevant to older women. Among the topics covered are social-psychological perspectives, legal and economic issues, widowhood, sexuality, marriage and the family, health and ethnicity. Available from IOG Publications, 520 E. Liberty, Ann Arbor, MI 48109.

1351b Hughes, Marija Matich. **The Sexual Barrier: Legal, Medical, Economic, and Social Aspects of Sex Discrimination.** (Enl. and rev. ed.). Washington: Hughes Press, 1977. 843p. index. $40.00. ISBN 0912560045. LC 77-83214.
An annotated list of 8,000 items concerned with women's rights, this bibliography is invaluable for its coverage of longstanding legal issues of interest to women (e.g., employment and the ERA) as well as new issues: aging, child care tax deductions, credit in a woman's own name, social security, life insurance, law and medical school admissions, sports, maternity leave, part-time employment, family violence, child-custody, marriage contracts, side effects of the pill and intrauterine devices, abortion, unnecessary surgery (e.g., hysterectomies and radical mastectomies), private clubs, lesbianism, minority women, and issues related to unpaid homemakers. Sex discrimination receives attention from medical, legal and economic vantage points. The author's experience as a law librarian is reflected in her extensive listing of cases: over 325 separate cases are cited in the table of cases. "Entries are divided into 17 chapters arranged alphabetically. They include sources from 1960 to 1975 dealing with women's rights and feminist issues, including books, articles, pamphlets and government documents. They cover material from the United States, Great Britain, Australia, Canada, and other foreign countries. Documents of the United Nations and other international organizations are included. Each of these sources is classified by subject and is identified by author, title, publisher and date of publication." Hughes has compiled an indispensible bibliography which should be a "must" purchase for libraries of all types serving women.

1352 **International Bibliography of Research in Marriage and the Family.**
Minneapolis: Minnesota Family Study Center and the Institute of Life Insurance; distr. Minneapolis: University of Minnesota Press, 1967-1974.
2v. v.1: $17.50. ISBN 0816604150. v.2: $35.00. ISBN 0816607265.
LC 67-63014.

Volume 1: 1900-1964, is by Joan Aldous and Reuben Hill; volume 2: 1965-1972, by Joan Aldous and Nancy Dahl. It is continued by *Inventory of Marriage and Family Literature*; volume 3, 1973/74, by David H. L. Olson and Nancy S. Dahl. There are currently four volumes in this series covering the literature in this field to 1977. It provides a comprehensive inventory of literature on marriage and the family from scholarly journals, but it will be of greatest interest to academic libraries. Subject, author, and key word indexes facilitate use, as does the periodical listing.

1353   Jacobs, Sue-Ellen. **Women in Perspective: A Guide for Cross-Cultural Studies.** Urbana: University of Illinois Press, 1974. 299p. $3.45. ISBN 0252003484. LC 72-93987.

This invaluable bibliography provides access to more than 3,500 citations on women in Africa, the Middle East, Asia, Europe, Oceania, North and South America. Part 1 is devoted to general geographical treatments by area, and part 2, to topical treatments of wide-ranging subject interest (e.g., misogyny, futurism, and primate studies). This guide is an excellent beginning point for cross-cultural studies.

1354*   Jacobson, Angeline, 1910- . **Contemporary Native American Literature: A Selected and Partially Annotated Bibliography.** Metuchen, NJ: Scarecrow Press, 1977. 262p. index. ISBN 081081031X. LC 77-5614.

While this bibliography on contemporary works (1960- to mid-1976) by Native American authors does not focus exclusively on women, the index indicates that much work by women has been identified here. Literary efforts may be reflected in a single poem, a group of poems, or a group of stories. Some entries are for periodical publications, some, for book-length works. Significantly, legends, myths, and autobiographies transmitted through interpreters are included. Eskimos, Canadian, and Mexican tribal writers are included as well as United States Native Americans. In this very important tool for a difficult-to-access and important segment of literature, many bibliographies, indexes, and important periodicals are identified, which will facilitate continued work in this area.

1355   Kemmer, Elizabeth Jane. **Rape and Rape-Related Issues: An Annotated Bibliography.** New York: Garland, 1977. index. $18.00. ISBN 0824098730. LC 76-52701.

Kemmer dedicated this book "to all victims of rape, with the hope that this bibliography may, in some way, lead to an increased understanding of the crime and its victims." The book lists over 340 books and articles published between 1965 and 1976. It includes a short subject index and an excellent introduction outlining the major trends in rape literature.

1356   Kiernan, Robert F. **Katherine Anne Porter and Carson McCullers: A Reference Guide.** Boston: G. K. Hall, 1976. 194p. index. $19.00. ISBN 0816178062. LC 76-2357.

Kiernan provides two separate bibliographies surveying the book and periodical (mainly) literature about Porter from 1924-1974 and about McCullers, 1940-1975. He handles the bibliographic essays well, noting the trends in reviews and critical literature over the years. While Kiernan notes the general high quality and intricate analysis in the Porter commentary, he finds that the substantial material published about McCullers has clustered around the same subjects—the use of lonely characters and freaks by McCullers and her consistently tragic portrayal of love. He notes little disagreement among McCuller's critics, contributing to a relatively redundant critical heritage.

1357   Knaster, Meri. **Women in Spanish America: An Annotated Bibliography from Pre-Conquest to Contemporary Times.** Boston: G. K. Hall, 1977. 696p. bibliog. index. $38.00. ISBN 0816178658. LC 76-46413.
This bibliography contains over 2,500 entries to Spanish and English-language works, published from the 1600s to 1974. Items range from the scholarly to the popular. Major subject divisions are subdivided into four geographical areas: Spanish America—General, Middle America, South America, and the Caribbean. The author has lived and taught in Colombia.

1358   Kowalski, Rosemary Ribich. **Women and Film: A Bibliography.** Metuchen, NJ: Scarecrow Press, 1976. 278p. index. $11.00. ISBN 0810809745. LC 76-25051.
This bibliography surveys reference, historical, and specific works (both books and periodicals) about women performers, film-makers, and images of women in film. An interesting section entitled "Women Columnists and Critics" gives references to critical work of Penelope Gilliatt, Pauline Kael, Judith Christ, Renata Adler, Maya Deren, and Susan Sontag, among others. Much material about women directors surfaces here among the 2,300 entires. Although the annotations are extremely brief, copious mention is made of names and specific films. Kowalski has organized an excellent subject index. Included are some non-English citations.

1359   Krichmar, Albert, 1940- . **The Women's Rights Movement in the United States, 1848-1970: A Bibliography and Sourcebook.** Metuchen, NJ: Scarecrow Press, 1972. 436p. $13.50. ISBN 0810805286. LC 72-4702.
Bringing together significant literature related to the women's rights movement from 1848 to 1970, this partially annotated bibliography speaks to women's status, to legislative issues, and to the attitudinal questions surrounding the women's rights movement. Types of literature included are: periodicals, books, pamphlets, dissertations, organizational listings, and state and federal publications (mainly from the United States Women's Bureau). Manuscript collections have been identified that offer possibilities for future research. The subject index is a good one, particularly helpful for finding information on a state-by-state basis. Author indexing and a periodicals checklist are provided. Krichmar's *The Women's Movement in the Seventies* (1977) picks up the literature published or reprinted from 1970 to 1976, and with 8,600 citations, is a more ambitious project in scope.

1360   Krichmar, Albert, 1940- . **The Women's Movement in the Seventies: An International English-Language Bibliography.** Metuchen, NJ: Scarecrow Press, 1977. 891p. index. $30.00. ISBN 0810810638. LC 77-21416.

International in scope, this bibliography of 8,600 items covers women's issues in about 100 countries. Publications included are books, pamphlets, report literature, periodical articles, government documents, and Ph.D. dissertations. The brief annotations are descriptive rather than evaluative. Two hundred reference works, including 63 bibliographies, are listed. The very large subject index must be mined patiently and carefully to access relevant items. A nice feature is the inclusion of review essays. The concerns of this bibliography fall broadly within these categories: cultural and literary studies; economic studies; educational studies; legal and political studies; psychological studies; religious and philosophical studies; scientific and technological studies; sociological and anthropological studies. The huge scope of this project is overwhelming; in many cases, this bibliography touches on the most important literature, but not always. For example, there is only one citation for "witches." The author index will be the most helpful access point for those familiar with the literature on women. All libraries and programs will want to own this.

1361   Leonard, Eugenie Andruss, 1888- , et al. **The American Woman in Colonial and Revolutionary Times, 1565-1800: A Syllabus with Bibliography.** Philadelphia: University of Pennsylvania Press, 1962; repr. Westport, CT: Greenwood Press, 1975. 169p. bibliog. $12.25. ISBN 0837178835. LC 74-27221.

By Eugenie Andruss Leonard, Sophie Hutchinson Drinker, and Miriam Young Holden, this is an excellent source on colonial and revolutionary women and their various roles. It treats areas as diverse as the marital, inheritance, and political rights of colonial women. Journals, diaries, memoirs, and correspondence of colonial women appear. Citations to 104 specific, notable colonial women are given, as well as extensive citations to the occupational roles of women— as entrepreneurs, attorneys and administrators, scientists and craftspersons. The section "Women in the Religious Life of the Colonies" cites literature pertaining to many different religious movements, with sizeable sections on witchcraft and women as preachers. Though this reprint does not include contemporary contributions to the literature about colonial women, its almost 1,100 entries provide an excellent base for the study of American women during this period.

1362*   Levenson, Rosaline. **Women in Government and Politics: A Bibliography of American and Foreign Sources.** Monticello, IL: Council of Planning Librarians, 1973. 80p.

This is the Council of Planning Librarians' Exchange Bibliography no. 491. Levenson has organized her unannotated bibliography into four major sections: Bibliographies and Indexes; Women in Government; Women in Politics; and Women in Government and Politics in Other Countries. Each major section is divided by subject matter and cites both book and periodical literature. Coverage is rather consistently limited to publications since 1940, and major emphasis is on U.S. information. However, Asia, Canada, Europe, Great Britain, India, Latin America, and the Middle East receive English-language coverage. Definitely worth consulting, this is not a comprehensive bibliography. Another CPL bibliography on this topic is Meredith Kirkpatrick's *Women in Public Service: A Selective Bibliography* (CPL Exchange Bibliography 1465, 1978).

1363*   Loyd, Bonnie. **Women and Geography: An Annotated Bibliography and Guide to Sources of Information.** Monticello, IL: Council of Planning Librarians, 1976. 18p.

This is CPL Exchange Bibliography no. 1159. "Part I of the bibliography contains references on women in the field of geography. Some citations are published articles. Others are films, unpublished papers, theses, special sessions, and work in progress. The listings provide evidence of women's participation in the profession, and they suggest people and organizations to contact for more information. Part II lists geographic research on women in society. . . . Research on women is expanding quickly, and it is being done by both male and female geographers" (author's introduction). Topics covered include the spectrum of geographical themes: cross-cultural comparisons, spatial behavior and spatial distribution, ecological studies, models, social justice, and landscape modification.

1364   Lyle, Katherine Ch'iu, 1939- , and Sheldon Jerome Segal, 1926- , eds. **International Family Planning Programs, 1966-1975: A Bibliography.** New York: Population Council, 1977. 207p. index. $11.00. ISBN 0817345019. LC 77-21322.

This international bibliography covers medical, sociological, and behavioral literature, including books, chapters of books, conference papers, and journal articles published in English on family planning programs from 1966 to 1975. General aspects of family planning are cited first; treatment of the subject thereafter is arranged by location, from Afghanistan to Zaire. Predictably, the majority of the literature falls under the United States heading. Dense areas of the subject index are: Adolescent Pregnancy Prevention; Birth Rate; Knowledge, Attitude, and Practices; Midwives and Nurses; and Population Policy.

1365   McKee, Kathleen Burke. **Women's Studies: A Guide to Reference Sources.** Storrs: University of Connecticut Library, Storrs, 1977. 112p. index. $5.00. ISBN 0917590015. LC 77-1747.

McKee's guide might be used profitably by anyone interested in researching from a women's studies perspective. Specifically intended to direct students to resources at the University of Connecticut, Storrs, the sources cited are general enough to be helpful in almost any university or college reference collection. The arrangement of materials: Guides; Library Catalogs and Collections; Handbooks; Directories; Statistics; Indexes, Abstracts and Bibliographies (this includes women's studies and many related fields, with coverage of all sorts of literatures—periodical and monographic); and a supplement listing women's serials in the University of Connecticut Library's Alternative Press Collection. With good annotations throughout, this also has title, author, and admirable subject indexing.

1366   McKenney, Mary, 1946- . **Divorce: A Selected Annotated Bibliography.** Metuchen, NJ: Scarecrow Press, 1975. 157p. index. $6.00. ISBN 0810807777. LC 74-22423.

"The annotations in this book reflect my political point of view, but I have in no way prejudiced my case in terms of what I have chosen to include in the bibliography: every 'significant' writing on divorce in English through 1972

I could find, as well as some items of debatable significance but some interest; all popular legal works and all statistical works I could locate; a sample of the literature and films dealing with divorce; and a few items published after 1972 that seemed to warrant inclusion" (from the preface). Materials are divided into the following broad subject areas: General and Historical Works; Legal Aspects; Financial Aspects; Statistics; Divorce Outside the United States; Divorcées: Women; Divorcés: Men; Children of Divorce; Psychological and Sociological Aspects; Religious and Moral Aspects; and Miscellaneous Works: Literature, Films, etc. Two appendices (Resource People; American Divorce Laws by State) and author and subject indexes are included. Annotations are brief but informative. A more recent bibliography on divorce is Kenneth D. and Betty H. Sell's *Divorce in the United States, Canada, and Great Britain: A Guide to Information Sources* (Gale Research, 1978).

1367*   Moser, Collette, 1940- , and Deborah Johnson. **Rural Women Workers in the 20th Century: An Annotated Bibliography.** East Lansing: Michigan State University, Center for Rural Manpower and Public Affairs, 1973. 63p. LC 74-622968.

We were unfortunately unable to retrieve a copy of this bibliography for review, but we include it because its focus on rural women is an important one. Two other sources on this topic we were unable to obtain are Audrey Wipper's *Rural Women: Development or Underdevelopment?* (East Lansing: African Studies Center, Michigan State University, 1976; 230p.; LC 77-622806) and Linda Joyce's *Annotated Bibliography of Women in Rural America: With a Review of the Literature about Women in Rural America, Bibliography of Women in Rural Areas Worldwide, and Resource Material* (University Park: Dept. of Agricultural Economics and Rural Sociology, Agricultural Experiment Station, Pennsylvania State University, 1976; 62p.).

1368   Myers, Carol Fairbanks. **Women in Literature: Criticism of the Seventies.** Metuchen, NJ: Scarecrow Press, 1976. 256p. index. $10.00. ISBN 0810808854. LC 75-35757.

With coverage of books and periodicals from 1970 to 1975, this unannotated bibliography examines literary criticism about women characters, feminist literary criticism, critical and biographical studies of women writers, and interviews with women writers, and selected reviews of women writers. This is a very helpful general bibliography. A new bibliography, revised and expanded, is expected from Myers under the title *More Women in Literature: 1970-Present* (Scarecrow, 1979).

1369   Myerson, Joel. **Margaret Fuller: An Annotated Secondary Bibliography.** New York: B. Franklin, 1977. 272p. index. $19.50. ISBN 0891020268. LC 77-3187.

Myerson's bibliography, the first formal secondary bibliography of Sarah Margaret Fuller, Marchesa d'Ossoli, will give substantial assistance to scholars. The annotations presume some familiarity with Fuller's life, writing, and the intellectual milieu in which she moved. Thirteen hundred works between 1834 and 1975 are arranged chronologically, with helpful critical evaluations. This volume complements the forthcoming *Margaret Fuller: A Descriptive Bibliography*, which will list all of Fuller's writings published separately, in collections, and during her lifetime in newspapers, magazines, and journals. The arrangement here hinges upon the completion of that volume, although this bibliography can be used productively without the descriptive bibliography. Myerson is Fuller's definitive bibliographer. As he is a scholar of American Transcendentalism, his bibliography will be of use to those interested in this period as well as to individuals specifically focusing on Fuller.

1370   Nagel, Gwen L., and James Nagel. **Sarah Orne Jewett: A Reference Guide.** Boston: G. K. Hall, 1978. 178p. index. $15.75. ISBN 0816178488. LC 77-7392.

Though scholars will definitely want to consult Clara C. and Carl J. Weber, *A Bibliography of the Published Writings of Sarah Orne Jewett* (1949), those wishing secondary sources of her work and a treatment of the critical heritage will find this reference guide a helpful source.

1371   National Association for Girls and Women in Sport. Research Committee. **Bibliography of Research Involving Female Subjects: A Compilation of Theses and Dissertations in Physical Education, Health and Recreation: NAGWS Research Committee Project, Part of the Research Model for Investigating the Woman Athlete.** Washington: American Alliance for Health, Physical Education, and Recreation, 1974. 212p. $5.25. LC 75-313612.

Two hundred colleges and universities were surveyed for lists of their theses and dissertations on "studies related to women as subjects of exercise and sport." Motor Learning; Sport Psychology; Physiological Aspects of Motor Performance; Sport Studies; Physical Education for the Handicapped; Health; Teaching Methods, Curriculum, Administration; and Recreation—Leisure are the topics under which this literature has been arranged. Considering the dearth of printed information available on women and sport, this should prove a useful tool.

1372   Newton, Jennifer L., and Carol Zavitz, comps. **Women: A Bibliography of Special Periodical Issues.** Toronto: Canadian Newsletter of Research on Women, 1978. 300p. $5.00.

Special Publication no. 4 of the *Canadian Newsletter of Research on Women*, this bibliography updates (but does not supersede) the earlier volume compiled by Margrit Eichler, et al., covering the years 1960 to 1975. Volume 2 lists approximately 375 special issues devoted to women, outlining the table of contents and often information on availability, publisher's address, etc. Together, volumes 1 and 2 index approximately 500 special periodical issues, including a fair amount of European material. Items in volume 2 are organized into the following categories: Anthropology; Art and Architecture; Black and Minority Studies; Criminology and Law; Health and the Sciences; History; Industrial and Labor Relations; Interdisciplinary Social Sciences; Literature and Literary Criticism; Philosophy and Political Theory; Psychiatry and Counseling; Psychology; Religion; Sexology; Sociology; and Third World Studies. Special indices (Men; The Family; Judaism and Israeli Studies; Immigration/Migration; Unions and Unionization; Agriculture and Rural Women) are included to cover areas scattered across categories. Both volumes of this bibliography are available from the *Canadian Newsletter of Research on Women*, c/o Sociology Dept. OISE, 252 Bloor Street West, Toronto, Ontario M5S 1V6, Canada.

1373   Nierman, Judith. **Edna St. Vincent Millay: A Reference Guide**. Boston: G. K. Hall, 1977. 191p. index. $16.00. ISBN 0816179506. LC 77-5400.

Readers should be aware that Nierman's annotations and introduction express some bias against Millay and her work, though the review of critical literature in the introduction is useful. The 1,070 annotated entries covering dissertations, reviews, articles, and books from 1918-1973 are more complete than any Millay bibliography to date. Arrangement is by year of publication, which gives some indication of the shifting sands of Millay's cirtical acclaim. The author/title/ subject index will consistently get the user to the material.

1374   Northouse, Cameron, and Thomas P. Walsh. **Sylvia Plath and Anne Sexton: A Reference Guide**. Boston: G. K. Hall, 1974. 143p. index. $9.50. ISBN 0816111464. LC 74-14965.

This is a very helpfully annotated and arranged guide to the works of Plath and Sexton. It is organized into two sections for each poet: works by and works about. The index section is divided by poet and takes the researcher to articles and books about the poets which have been chronologically arranged. One can tell at a glance everything that Ted Hughes, for example, has written about Plath—what years the Hughes criticism appeared and whether the form was book or article.

1375*   Pask, Judith M., comp. **The Emerging Role of Women in Management: A Bibliography**. West Lafayette, IN: Institute for Research in the Behavioral, Economic, and Management Sciences, Purdue University, 1976. 49p. index.

This is an important research tool catering to business students and women in the business world.

1376   Phelps, Ann T., et al. **New Career Options for Women: A Selected Annotated Bibliography**. New York: Human Sciences Press, 1977. 144p. index. $9.95. ISBN 0877052735. LC 77-23125.

New Career Options can be used profitably with or without the companion volumes by Helen S. Farmer, *New Career Options: A Woman's Guide* (1977) and *New Career Options for Women: A Counselor's Sourcebook* (1977). The annotated bibliography contains 240 abstracts of selected research studies and documents related in the '70s to many significant aspects of contemporary career possibilities, challenges, and problems facing women. It could be helpful in many different situations with girls and women of all ages.

1377*   Rom, Christine Carol, 1951- . **Women's Writings: Feminist Little Magazines in the Rare Book Department**. Madison: University of Wisconsin-Madison, 1978. [12p.]

This is a guide to the collection of women's little magazines held in the University of Wisconsin—Madison Memorial Library Rare Book Department. Entries are grouped into the following three categories: Currently Publishing Magazines; Non-Current Magazines; and Issues of Special Interest. Full bibliographic information is listed for each entry, including dates and place of publication, subscription price (if current), illustrations, contents, where the magazine is indexed, and Rare Book holdings. The 1977 edition of this pamphlet was issued under the title *Feminist Little Magazines in the Rare Book Department, University of Wisconsin, Memorial Library*.

1378   Rosenberg, Marie Barovic, and Len V. Bergstrom. **Women and Society: A Critical Review of the Literature with a Selected, Annotated Bibliography.** Beverly Hills, CA: Sage Publications, 1975. 354p. index. $17.50. ISBN 0803902484. LC 73-77874.

This annotated bibliography provides the reader with an excellent survey of the literature on women vis à vis history, work, and politics in its thoughtful and well-written introduction. The notes on scope at the beginning of each section are helpful, as is the breakdown of subjects covered in the major divisions (Sociology, Political Science, History, Philosophy, Medicine, Biography, Literature and the Arts, Psychology, Anthropology, Economics, and General Reference). Brief annotations. The second volume of this bibliography was co-authored by Jo Ann Een and Marie B. Rosenberg (1978) and follows the pattern of the first bibliography.

1379   Rosenfelt, Deborah Silverton. **Strong Women: An Annotated Bibliography of Literature for the High School Classroom.** Old Westbury, NY: Feminist Press, 1976. 56p. index. $1.95. ISBN 0912670401. LC 76-375218.

Although this bibliography is directed to high school teachers and students, the materials annotated here can be used to good advantage by undergraduates and those teaching undergraduates since many students are not exposed to works by and about strong women before their college work. Organized by genres— anthologies, autobiography/biography, drama, novels, short stories, and poetry— the annotations are pithy and the number of reading suggestions, manageable. Use is facilitated by a cross-topical index giving access to materials in the areas of adolescence, female sexuality, women in the arts and professions, women in politics, Third-World women, and working-class women.

1380*   Roysdon, Christy. **Women in Engineering: A Bibliography on Their Progress and Prospects.** Monticello, IL: Council of Planning Librarians, 1975. 22p. $2.00. LC 76-350346.

This is CPL Exchange Bibliography no. 878. Relatively little has been done on women in engineering; this bibliography cites materials and analyzes briefly the dearth of material in this field. "Some interesting finds emerge from the bibliographic data alone. For example, the fact that most aritcles encouraging women to become engineers bear wartime or 'Cold War' dates adds credence to the conventional wisdom that most technical women have been but emergency 'spares' to be sent home after the passing of each manpower crisis. Further study of the patterns of the dates and titles of the literature could prove rewarding" (from the preface). Entries are organized around the following subjects: The Professional Woman; Major Conferences; Major Books; The Status of Women

Engineers; Recruitment; Education and Training; On the Job: Performance, Opportunity, Satisfaction; "Role Models"—Success Stories; Government Publication of Women in Engineering; and Relevant Organization: Addresses, Services, Publications. Libraries catering to young readers may also want to acquire Nancy Kreinberg's *I'm Madly in Love with Electricity and Other Comments about Their Work by Women in Science and Engineering* (Berkeley: Lawrence Hall of Science, University of California, 1977; $1.00), in which women scientists, engineers, and mathematicians speak about their work and job opportunities.

1381   Schlacter, Gail, and Donna Belli. **The Changing Role of Women in America: A Selected Annotated Bibliography of Reference Sources.** Monticello, IL: Council of Planning Librarians, 1975. 36p. index. This is CPL Exchange Bibliography no. 931. Gail Schlacter, who writes this as head of social sciences in the library at California State University, Long Beach, has written much on the changing role of women. "This bibliography has been prepared to assist the researcher interested in the changing social, educational, psychological, political, economic, or historic aspects of women's role in American society" (introduction). Principal sources are dictionaries, encyclopedias, handbooks, statistical compilations, documents, biographical sources, directories, and major bibliographies.

1382   Schlachter, Gail Ann. **Minorities and Women: A Guide to Reference Literature in the Social Sciences.** Los Angeles: Reference Service Press, 1977. 349p. index. $19.50. ISBN 0918276012. LC 76-53061. Especially for libraries that are inadequately fixed for bibliographies surveying recent reference literature on minorities and women in America, this will be a priority purchase. Schlachter has previously done a good deal of reliable work on both topics. The annotations are critical and thorough. However, the title confuses the user, since minorities necessarily encompass women. Titles up to mid-1976 in this valuable source include all standard types of reference works—biographical sources, documentary sources, etc. Native Americans, Spanish Americans, black Americans, and Asian Americans are the foci of the 738 citations. Author, title, and subject indexing are provided.

1383   Schwartz, Narda Lacey, 1948- . **Articles on Women Writers: A Bibliography.** Santa Barbara, CA: Clio Books, 1977. 236p. index. $24.95. ISBN 0874362520. LC 77-9071. Citing works which appeared in scholarly and popular periodicals between 1960 and 1975, Schwartz has filled a pressing need in providing references to over 600 writers. Her bibliography lists the writers alphabetically by last name along with birth and death dates and nationality. Types of critical works about the author (bibliographies, general works, including biographical and critical treatments, and individual works) are followed by citations culled from *Humanities Index*, the *MLA Bibliography*, and *Biography Index*, to name only a few of the 21 major literature sources Schwartz consistently consulted. The 600 names of women writers represent work from the Middle Ages to the present, from major geographical English-speaking areas. A superb and much-needed reference source, it should provide a starting point for research, especially on obscure writers.

1384   Selig, Robert L. **Elizabeth Gaskell: A Reference Guide.** Boston:
        G. K. Hall, 1977. 431p. index. $30.00. ISBN 0816178135. LC
        76-30505.
Noting that the pattern of criticism on Gaskell over 128 years shows that she
received favorable acceptance during her lifetime, when she was considered a
major novelist, a sharp decline after her death, and only recently an enthusiastic
resurgence, Selig states that he sees Gaskell in a class with Eliot, Hardy, and
Trollope. While this may be overstating the case, Selig has written a good
introductory bibliographic essay and has listed and annotated book and periodical literature on Gaskell from 1848 to 1974. There is extensive indexing. Spot
checking indicates that this reference guide to Gaskell supersedes Jeffrey Welch's
Elizabeth Gaskell: An Annotated Bibliography 1929-1975 (1977) for all except
1975 items.

1385*   Sharma, Prakash C. **Female Working Role and Economic Development:
        A Selected Research Bibliography.** Monticello, IL: Council of Planning
        Librarians, 1974. 16p. $1.50. LC 75-311534.
This is CPL Exchange Bibliography no. 663. "The present bibliography contains
nearly 250 selected references on 'Female Working Role and Economic Development,' published chiefly during 1940-1972. The references listed in the bibliography are by no means definitive nor are they meant to be, but they represent
many of the old and current publications which may be used as guides for further
research. The bibliography is divided into two parts: Part One contains the listing
of books and monographs and Part Two is a listing of articles and periodicals"
(author's preface).

1386   Shreemati Nathibai Damodar Thackersey Women's University, Bombay.
        Research Unit on Women's Studies. **A Select Bibliography on Women
        in India.** Bombay: Allied Publishers; distr. Columbia, MO: South Asia
        Books, 1976. 131p. index. $5.50. ISBN 0883868776.
The material listed here represents the first comprehensive bibliography on
women in India, according to the Women's Studies Research Unit at SNDT
Women's University, Bombay. Topics covered include historical studies, biographies, women's status and role, health, education, employment, legal status,
women in art and folklore, and psychological studies. All materials are English-
language; many are theses and dissertations written at U.S., English, and Indian
institutions.

1387   Skowronski, Joann. **Women in American Music: A Bibliography.**
        Metuchen, NJ: Scarecrow Press, 1978. 225p. index. $8.00. ISBN
        0810811057. LC 77-26611.
Two hundred years of women in American music is the scope of this listing.
Covering popular, religious, and classical music from 1776 to 1976, the bibliographer has gathered citations from *Readers' Guide* and *Music Index*, but
relies mainly on books. This is a worthy effort to document the scarcely visible
but substantial contributions of women to American music. A project underway
but incomplete and unavailable for examination is *Women in American Music:
A Bibliography*, being prepared by the Graduate School CUNY with support
from the National Endowment for the Humanities.

1388   Soltow, Martha Jane, and Mary K. Wery. **American Women and the Labor Movement, 1825-1974: An Annotated Bibliography.** (2nd ed.). Metuchen, NJ: Scarecrow Press, 1976. 247p. index. $8.00. ISBN 0810809869. LC 76-40169.

This updates an earlier edition, published in 1972 under title: *Women in American Labor History, 1825-1935.* Treated here are articles, books, papers, pamphlets, and U.S. government documents. Major topics are: Employment, Trade Unions, Working Conditions, Strikes, Legislation, Worker Education, and Labor Leaders. The well-executed subject index allows fine access to the materials described here.

1389   Sophia Smith Collection. **Catalog of the Sophia Smith Collection Women's History Archive.** (2nd ed.). Northampton, MA: Smith College, 1976. 78p. index. $3.00.

"The Sophia Smith Collection, named in honor of the founder of Smith College, and established there in 1942, is today an internationally known women's history archive that contains thousands of manuscripts, pamphlets, broadsides, books, miscellanea and periodicals that document the intellectual and social history of women—present and past. This revised, expanded catalog analyzes selected major primary and secondary holdings to aid scholars contemplating major research projects in the field of women's history. The scope of The Sophia Smith Collection is international; its principal holdings date from 1790" (from the introduction). This pamphlet is an annotated list of selected archival holdings, including manuscript collections of individuals (e.g., Jane Addams, Susan B. Anthony, Mary Ritter Beard, Carrie Chapman Catt, the Garrison family, Margaret Sanger) and international and national organizations (e.g., International Congress of Working Women; Women's International League for Peace and Freedom; American Association for Health, Physical Education and Recreation; American Association of University Women; National American Woman Suffrage Association; National Women's Trade Union League of America, YWCA); subject collections (e.g., birth control, civil rights, literature, industry, medicine, settlement work/social reform, suffrage/anti-suffrage, women's liberation); and selected periodicals. The printed list of the entire holdings of the Sophia Smith Collection is available in an expensive seven-volume edition published by G. K. Hall: *Catalogs of the Sophia Smith Collection, Women's History Archive, Smith College, Northampton, Massachusetts*; Boston: G. K. Hall, 1975; $535.00; ISBN 0816100012; LC 76-358485.

1390   Springer, Marlene. **Edith Wharton and Kate Chopin: A Reference Guide.** Boston: G. K. Hall, 1976. 305p. index. $24.00. ISBN 0816110999. LC 76-1831.

Criticism, reviews, and miscellaneous writings of Edith Wharton from 1897 to 1973 appear in this bibliography, which seeks to identify the most significant critical works on Wharton. Since Wharton published prolifically, crossing a number of genres, and usually to critical acclaim, Springer has had no shortage of sources from which to select. During Wharton's sixty-year career, she authored seventeen novels, seven novelettes, many volumes of verse and short stories, in addition to works on interior decoration, estates, and gardens. Though Kate Chopin's canon is considerably smaller than Wharton's, the critical works about

her are organized along the same lines as for Wharton. Springer has been less
selective in her inclusions for Chopin. Chopin only recently has been accorded
a strong critical response with the reissuing of *The Awakening* in 1964 and
The Complete Works of Kate Chopin in 1969. Critical works about Chopin
date from 1890 to 1973 in this volume.

1391   Stanwick, Kathy, and Christine Li. **The Political Participation of Women
       in the United States: A Selected Bibliography, 1950-1976.** Metuchen,
       NJ: Scarecrow Press, 1977. 160p. index. $6.50. ISBN 0810810751.
       LC 77-23036.
This updating and expansion of Stanwick and Li's *Women and American Politics:
A Selected Bibliography, 1965-1974* includes over 1,500 references to published and unpublished works from 1950 to 1976 on American women's political
participation at all levels of society. The authors are staff members of the Center
for the American Woman and Politics, Eagleton Institute of Politics, Rutgers
University. All types of printed literature are included in this bibliography,
which contains information on such topics as women holding elective and
appointive offices; voting patterns; biographies and autobiographies of political
women; and political volunteer work.

1392* Swanick, M. Lynne Struthers. **A Checklist of Canadian Federal, Provin-
       cial and Municipal Government Publications of Special Significance
       for Women.** Monticello, IL: Council of Planning Librarians, 1976.
       20p. $2.00. LC 77-360102.
This is CPL Exchange Bibliography no. 1118. An extensive checklist, it could
be of help to someone doing work on Canadian women. Publications are grouped
by location—Quebec, Toronto, etc.

1393   Thompson, Victor H. **Eudora Welty: A Reference Guide.** Boston:
       G. K. Hall, 1976. 175p. index. $18.00. ISBN 0816178011. LC 76-
       1983.
Thompson has organized and annotated critical writing about Eudora Welty
from 1936 to 1975, revealing a considerable critical heritage. Criticism of
Welty's photographs also appears here. The introduction traces Welty's rise as
a major American writer, showing her to be an author of great accessibility
(many published interviews and newspaper stories about her). Regionalism,
mystery, myth, colloquialism in her creation of dialogue, and her comic sense
are frequent concerns of Welty's critics. A critics index is provided.

1394   Tominaga, Thomas T., and Wilma Schneidermeyer. **Iris Murdoch and
       Muriel Spark: A Bibliography.** Metuchen, NJ: Scarecrow Press, 1976.
       237p. index. $10.00. ISBN 0810809079. LC 76-909.
Two bibliographies in one, this Murdoch/Spark bibliography draws together
"all their writings, and the accompanying criticism and translations, from the
beginning of their careers to 1975." Critical works about the authors cover
books, dissertations, critical essays, motion pictures, interviews, biographies,
and bibliographies.

1395   Turner, Darwin T., 1931- . **Afro-American Writers.** Northbrook, IL:
        AHM, 1970. 117p. $6.95. ISBN 0882955276. LC 72-79171.
This useful bibliography points the way to research methodology and excellent
general literary research tools in the area of Afro-American literature; among
the Afro-American women writers who surface here are: Mary Breechwood,
Gwendolyn Brooks, Alice Childress, Maud Cuney-Mare, Jessie Redmond Fauset,
Angelina Grimké, Rosa B. Guy, Lorraine Hansberry, Frances Ellen Watkins
Harper, Kristin Hunter, Elizabeth Maddox Huntley, Zora Neale Hurston, Georgia
Douglas Johnson, Nella Larsen, Audré Lorde, Naomi Long Madgett, Paule
Marshall, May Miller, Ann Petry, Carlene H. Polite, Sadie Roberson, Letty Shaw,
Mary Elizabeth Vroman, Margaret Walker, Dorothy West, Phillis Wheatley.
Evidence that more work needs to be done on the work of black writers becomes
obvious in a glance at the appendix, "Selected Criticism of Africans and Afro-
Americans as Characters." Most of the criticism studies the presence of blacks
in fiction written by preeminent male white writers.

1396   Walstedt, Joyce Jennings. **The Psychology of Women: A Partially
        Annotated Bibliography.** Pittsburgh, PA: Know, 1972. 76p. $2.25.
This is a partially annotated bibliography on the psychology of women, with
items organized into the following categories: Infancy and Childhood; Adolescence; Young Adulthood; Middle and Old Age; Cross-Cultural; General Source
Material; Primate Studies; Minority Group Status, Discrimination; Psychoanalytic Theories, Mental Health; and Sexuality and Physiology. Annotations are
brief but informative. No indexing is provided. Readers will want to be aware
of two more extensive reviews of the psychological literature on women: Julia
Sherman's *On the Psychology of Women* (1971) and Eleanor Maccoby and
Carol Jacklin's *The Psychology of Sex Differences* (1974).

1397*   Westervelt, Esther Manning, and Deborah A. Fixter. **Women's Higher
        and Continuing Education: An Annotated Bibliography with Selected
        References on Related Aspects of Women's Lives.** New York: College
        Entrance Examination Board, 1971. 67p. $1.50. LC 74-174883.
The sources identified here represent a modest selection of what is available,
with most citations clustering around the mid-'60s. However, the annotations
are informative and identify the work of leaders in the area of programs and
theory about women's work and women's development. The literature covers
general citations to women's status and the education of women, basic research
on women's education vis à vis social and cultural roles, female psychology,
and sex role research. Educational behavior and aspirations of high school,
college, graduate school, and mature women are covered. The broad area of
women and employment receives attention; topical, report, journal, and reference literature is cited. The bibliographies cited represent a broad approach
to diverse materials: Education and Continuing Education; Women in the
Labor Force; and General, Multi-faceted or Specialized Bibliographies. This
volume works well when used concurrently with Astin, et al., *Women: A
Bibliography on Their Education and Careers* (Human Service Press, 1971).

1398   Wheeler, Helen Rippier. **Womanhood Media: Current Resources about Women.** Metuchen, NJ: Scarecrow Press, 1972. 335p. $8.50. ISBN 0810805499. LC 72-7396.

For book, non-book, and non-print material relevant to women up to 1972, Wheeler is an invaluable source. Among her useful sections of annotated entries are general reference sources and their use in Women's Studies research, a basic book list, and a significant section of audio visual materials. The *Supplement* (1975) is the item to purchase if a library is unable to afford both volumes.

1399   Wheeler, Helen Rippier. **Womanhood Media: Supplement: Additional Current Resources about Women.** Metuchen, NJ: Scarecrow Press, 1975. 482p. $15.00. ISBN 0810808587. LC 72-7396.

Although this supplement to *Womanhood Media: Current Resources about Women* (1972) suggests consulting the original volume first, the *Supplement* for the most part supersedes the 1972 edition. The Basic Book Collection is a briefly annotated guide to 826 books coded for reading level and availability in Spanish. Non-book resources cited include pamphlets, movement periodicals, and audiovisual resources. The Directory of Sources (including media and information outlets, women's liberation groups and centers, rosters for employment) is very valuable, though this is constantly shifting information. The index to the Basic Book Collection provides access to fully annotated titles as well as to references within the annotations. *Womanhood Media: Supplement* is informed throughout by Wheeler's feminist perspective. Lesbiana, Canadiana, material on Chicanas, affirmative action, and black women have been strengthened since the 1972 bibliography.

1400*   White, Anthony G. **Rape: An Urban Crime?: A Selected Bibliography.** Monticello, IL: Council of Planning Librarians, 1977. 15p.

This is CPL Exchange Bibliography no. 1367. The position of the compiler is that rape is no more an urban crime than a sexual act: "it is an assault." The preface to the bibliography contains an analysis of patterns in the literature: "Material written prior to the 1920's demonstrates a curiosity (perhaps a titillating one) and an expression of male fears. From the 1920's through the 1950's, the literature centers on the scientific establishment of medical evidence and standards for determining whether a rape has been committed. The 1960's show a growing openness to discussion of the effects of rape upon the victim, an anger, and the beginnings of activism as the feminist movement gathers steam. Finally, the literature of the 1970's demonstrates a call to action, for the development of practical programs to aid the victims, and a desire to improve the management of repairing the victims' lives." Approximately 150 citations mainly from the '60s and '70s, though several earlier citations that bear out the analysis above are also included.

1401   White, Barbara Anne. **American Women Writers: An Annotated Bibliography of Criticism.** New York: Garland, 1977. 126p. index. $12.50. ISBN 0824098870. LC 76-52677.

White, a literature scholar and librarian, has successfully brought off a major reference *tour de force* in producing an annotated bibliography as fascinating to read as it is effective to use in locating significant books, articles, chapters, and introductions to critical materials that deal generally with the work of American women writers. Her purpose is to provide access to the vast range of secondary sources on women's writing from almost every conceivable frequency of the critical spectrum. Researchers who are trying to find critical works on specific authors will do better to start with Carol Fairbanks Myers's annotated *Women in Literature: Criticism of the Seventies* (Scarecrow Press, 1976), which has an author arrangement. Using Fairbanks and White together works well. Because White's book lacks a subject index, one is forced to sort through the broad chapter headings, e.g., Special Topics, Feminine Sensibility, to find the specific criticism on a dazzling array of topics—female eroticists, Appalachian writers, domestic novels of the 1850s, and angry poetry to name a few. The search is never dull, however, and White does provide a helpful index to critics and editors.

1402   Williams, Ora, 1926- . **American Black Women in the Arts and Social Sciences: A Bibliographic Survey.** (Rev. ed.). Metuchen, NJ: Scarecrow Press, 1978. 197p. bibliog. index. $8.00. ISBN 0810810964. LC 77-17055.

Ora Williams, professor of English, scholar of comparative culture, and member of the Women's Studies Department at CSU—Long Beach, has updated her 1974 first edition of this important prime checklist to present a more comprehensive bibliographic inventory of the American black woman's substantive contributions to the arts and social sciences. New features of the revised and expanded edition include a chronology of significant dates in American black women's history from 1619 to 1977; a short biographical section listing important ideas and achievements of forty selected women—unfortunately and inexplicably, Williams leaves out dates of births and deaths; a brief listing of recordings for artists like Julia Perry, Gertrude Reiney, Florence Price, and Leontyne Price; many black and white photos of authors and artists, with a special photographic section of paintings and ceramics. Williams does a nice job in her comprehensive listing of reference materials, anthologies, various genres of literature, and subjects in the social sciences. She includes a section of criticism by black women and a very important list of works by illustrators, painters, sculptors, arrangers, composers, and lyricists. Seventeen individual unannotated bibliographies appear: among others are Maya Angelou, Zora Neale Hurston, and Naomi Long Madgett. Williams has concentrated on work by black women and has clearly identified non-black-generated work.

1403   Women and Literature Collective. **Women and Literature: An Annotated Bibliography of Women Writers.** (3rd ed.). Cambridge, MA: Women and Literature Collective, 1976. 212p. index. $3.50. ISBN 0915052024. LC 76-47335.

Carefully annotated, this book, international in scope, has "focused particularly on women's fictional writings plus other forms of expressive prose." The annotations are the work of several women, all of whom seem very familiar with the works they have annotated. The perspective is uniformly feminist. Entries include useful information about the author and her place in literary history. The authors handled selection by making an effort to include some grossly overlooked areas in women's fiction: Canadian writers, lesbian literature, black literature, labor movement and working class novels, works coming out of feminist presses. Effort has been made to include relatively unknown authors of quality. The book is arranged by country, then by period. Subject and author indexes are provided.

REFERENCE
Biographical Materials
[The scope note for Reference appears on p. 460.]

1404   **The Biographical Cyclopaedia of American Women.** New York:
        Halvord, 1924; repr. Detroit: Gale Research, 1974. $45.00. ISBN
        0810339900.
        This is a good supplementary resource to *Notable American Women.*

1405   Brignano, Russell Carl. **Black Americans in Autobiography: An Anno-
        tated Bibliography of Autobiographies and Autobiographical Books
        Written Since the Civil War.** Durham, NC: Duke University Press,
        1974. 118p. index. $7.75. ISBN 0823303175. LC 73-92535.
A bibliography that lists and annotates autobiographies and autobiographical
works, including diaries, written by black Americans from the end of the Civil
War to early 1973, this is a valuable source for locating material on black women.
The annotations make little judgment on the literary quality of the work but
concentrate on essential information, both biographical and geographical, about
the authors' public lives. Three indexes give access to black Americans: 1)
experiences, occupations, and professions; 2) geographical locations and educational institutions mentioned in annotations; and 3) titles of works.

1406   Cederholm, Theresa Dickason, comp. **Afro-American Artists: A Bio-
        Bibliographical Directory.** Boston: Trustees of the Boston Public
        Library, 1973. 348p. bibliog. $10.00. ISBN 0890730075. LC
        73-84951.
This is a "bio-bibliographical" dictionary of Afro-American artists from the
eighteenth century to the present: painters, sculptors, photographers, illustrators, printmakers, graphic artists, weavers, curators, etc. The amount of information provided for a given artist varies tremendously, but, in general, the
following is included: artistic medium, year and place of birth, education,
works, where exhibited, and bibliographical sources. For better-known and
more prolific artists, we are also given lists of collections, awards, and artists'
memberships. A lengthy bibliography of general works is appended, including
books, exhibition catalogues, magazines, and newspapers. While this directory
would obviously be useful only as a beginning point in research on a particular
artist, it is nonetheless an invaluable reference tool, offering information not
elsewhere available. It is included here because of the dearth of information
sources on Afro-American women.

1407   Chamberlin, Hope. **A Minority of Members: Women in the U.S.
        Congress.** New York: New American Library, 1974. 391p. index.
        $2.25.
This is a biographical index to the careers of the 75 women who served in the
U.S. Congress from Jeannette Rankin's election in 1917 to the 1972 election.
Chamberlin's synopses are very brief (1-15 pages) and offer no guide to further

sources. The book, therefore, will be most helpful as an introduction to the topic. An alphabetical chart at the back provides a quick summary of these women's congressional careers. Despite the limitations of brevity, this remains the best available directory on women who have served in Congress.

1408* Dannett, Sylvia G. L., 1909- . **Profiles of Negro Womanhood.** Yonkers, NY: Educational Heritage, 1964-1966. 2v. bibliog. index. LC 64-25013.
Two volumes of information about black women and their notable achievements in American history make this set an important source in this neglected area of women's biography. The first volume spanning the years 1619-1900 treats black women notable in a variety of social, political, and intellectual concerns. The biographies are brief, accompanied by a few notes; this brevity is understandable given the dearth of printed information available on black women. Among the many women included: Candy and Mary Black (Salem witchcraft trials); Lucy Terry and Phyllis Wheatley (literary heritage); Sarah Mapps Douglass, the Forten Sisters, Charlotte Forten Grimké (noted Philadelphia black women); Elizabeth Taylor-Greenfield and Edmonia Lewis (artistic contributions); Mary McCleod Bethune and Mary Church Terrell (contributions to the advancement of blacks) and many others. Volume 2 treats twentieth-century black women and follows the same format as volume 1. A sampling of those included in this volume are Meta Vaux Warrick Fuller and Geraldine Hamilton McCullough (Fine Arts); Dr. Helen Dickens and Dr. Juliette Simmons (Physicians); Susan Elizabeth Freeman and Mary Elizabeth Carnegie (Nurses); Helen Eugenia Hagan and Nora Douglas Holt (Performing Arts); Jessie Redmon Rauset, Zora Neale Hurston and Ellen Tarry (Literary Figures). Other categories are Lawyers, Civil Rights Activists, and Government Officials. A bibliography follows that would be especially useful to high school or lower division undergraduates. This is a difficult-to-obtain work, which may indicate the lack of accessibility of works on black women. It has an attractive format and illustrations. Other sources should be consulted, but *Profiles* is a good beginning.

1409 Ellet, Elizabeth Fries (Lummis), 1818-1877. **The Women of the American Revolution.** (4th ed.). New York: Haskell House, 1969. (Repr. of 1850 ed.). 3v. bibliog. $49.95. ISBN 0838301975. LC 68-31269.
Elizabeth Fries Lummis Ellet was quite a prolific writer throughout her lifetime of poetry, essays, translations, and—what eventually became her predominant concern—history. She embarked upon this three-volume opus, *The Women of the American Revolution*, in an attempt to counterbalance the complete neglect of the contributions of women in all sources she could find on the American Revolution. In this work, she tells the stories of more than 170 women—well-known and obscure—who played important roles in the Revolution. In preparation for the volume, Ellet unearthed and studied numerous unpublished letters and interviewed descendants, in addition to researching what little was available in print. The style is popular and much of the material anecdotal, but the work has been praised by later writers, including the historians Charles and Mary Beard, for its contribution to the task of adding women to the historical record.

1410*   Engelbarts, Rudolf. **Women in the United States Congress, 1917-1972: Their Accomplishments; With Biographies.** Littleton, CO: Libraries Unlimited, 1974. 184p. bibliog. index. ISBN 0872870839. LC 73-93278.

The format of this reference book on women in the Congress allows the reader a brief biographical glimpse of the woman along with a bibliography of works by and about her. The introduction is poor, and the biographical information suffers from Engelbart's unfortunate style. Yet, it is a good source for fast, easy-to-absorb portraits of these notable women, and it leads the user to other sources. A better source is Hope Chamberlin's *Minority of Members* (New American Library, 1974).

1411   **Foremost Women in Communications: A Biographical Reference Work on Accomplished Women in Broadcasting, Publishing, Advertising, Public Relations, and Allied Professions.** New York: Foremost Americans, 1970. 788p. index. $35.00. ISBN 0835204146. LC 79-125936.

The title accurately describes this massive reference source edited by Barbara Love providing brief biographical information on nearly 8,000 women in communications, defined to include publishing, broadcasting, advertising, public relations and "allied professions." Information was compiled from questionnaires completed by the biographees and includes education and employment history, memberships, awards, birth place and date, parents, address, and publications. It should be noted that this is a directory to living women active in the communications field in the late 1960s, not a history of women in the field. Geographical and subject indexes are appended.

1412   Fremantle, Anne Jackson, 1909- . **Woman's Way to God.** New York: St. Martin's Press, 1977. 255p. bibliog. $7.95. ISBN 031288690X. LC 76-10553.

This is a collection of very brief biographies of women who have led intensely religious lives, from the familiar cases of Anne Hutchinson and Fatima to those of lesser known women from pre-Christian and medieval times. Fremantle also provides an introductory summary of the role and image of women in Western religion. The approach throughout is cursory and, therefore, the book will be found most useful as a beginning biographical reference tool.

1413   Hinding, Andrea, ed. **Women's History Sources: A Guide to Archives and Manuscript Collections in the United States.** New York: Bowker, 1979. 2v. bibliog. index. ISBN 0835211037.

Women's studies students and scholars agree that primary-source information by and about women is essential to creative, ground-breaking research on the lives and experiences of women. This guide to archival and manuscript material relevant to women describes more than 18,000 collections in more than 1,600 repositories throughout the United States. Funded by a grant from the National Endowment for the Humanities and the University of Minnesota; supported by the American Historical Association; endorsed by the Executive Council of the Society of American Archivists and numerous other professional organizations; and completed with the nationwide help of archivists, librarians, researchers, historians, and editors—*Women's History Sources* must be considered a major resource for any collection with an interest in the lives of American women and is a landmark publishing event. Each individual entry is described by title, type of documents, inclusive dates and collection size, access information to the collections, and bibliographic control by guides, card catalog, etc. A concise content description accompanies each entry. Volume 1 lists the 18,000 entries, volume 2 is the index. Examples of entries are the papers of Tallulah Bankhead and the papers of the Mobile Suffrage Association. An extremely valuable feature of this guide is its commitment to provide access to women who may not have achieved "notable" status nationally, but whose achievements were outstanding in their own sphere. Also important is its mining of archives to locate the papers of wives, daughters, and sisters of famous men. Under Mencken, for example, we find a description of the papers of Sarah Haardt Mencken— the wife of Henry L. Mencken. Price has not yet been set.

1414   Hixon, Donald L., and Don Hennessee. **Women in Music: A Biobib-
        liography.** Metuchen, NJ: Scarecrow Press, 1975. 347p. bibliog. $12.50.
        ISBN 0810808692. LC 75-23075.
Hixon and Hennessee provide basic biographical and bibliographical information on more than 4,000 women "classical" musicians, U.S. and foreign. Included for each entry are the musician's name (and variant names, stage names, etc.), place and dates of birth and death, field of musical activity, and a bibliography of further biographical sources. Musicians are additionally listed alphabetically within specific areas of musical expertise in an appendix.

1415   Ireland, Norma (Olin), 1907- . **Index to Women of the World from
        Ancient to Modern Times: Biographies and Portraits.** Westwood, MA:
        F. W. Faxon, 1970. 573p. bibliog. $16.00. ISBN 0873050975. LC
        75-120841.
Thirteen thousand women are listed in this work, which provides a beginning for further research.

1416*   Jackson, George F. **Black Women, Makers of History: A Portrait.**
        (Rev. ed.). Sacramento, CA: Fong and Fong, 1977. 289p. bibliog.
        index. LC 76-57082.
George Jackson (black history teacher in Sacramento, California) has compiled this important biographical directory as a contribution to the rediscovery of the suppressed history of black women in the United States. The biographies of over 100 black women, from the slave era to the present, are briefly sketched; graphics and photographs illustrate the accounts. While these sketches can only offer a starting point for the researcher, Jackson provides numerous references to further sources throughout, as well as a general selected bibliography and a list of relevant periodicals, reference works, and almanacs at the end. Included in this directory are slave women, abolitionists, businesswomen, civil rights activists, doctors, teachers, writers, singers, academics, artists, actresses, athletes, and military women.

1417   James, Edward T., et al., eds. **Notable American Women, 1607-1950:
        A Biographical Dictionary.** Cambridge, MA: Belknap Press of Harvard
        University Press, 1971. 3v. $75.00. ISBN 0674627318. LC 76-152274.

Prepared under the auspices of Radcliffe College, *Notable American Women* is an unexcelled compilation of well-written, thoroughly researched biographical sketches for over 1,300 American women who died no later than 1950. Excellent bibliographies accompany each article, though care should be taken to identify new material that has surfaced since 1971. Janet Wilson James writes a superb introduction giving an historical survey of women in America from colonial times to the present. Volume 3 features a Classified List of Selected Biographies, which offers invaluable assistance in identifying abolitionists, actresses and theater managers, anthropologists and folklorists, architects and interior decorators, art collectors and patrons, art critics and historians, art educators, astronomers, authors (by literary period), botanists, chemists and physicists, children's authors, Civil War figures, circus performers, classicists, college administrators, composers, dancers, editors, educational reformers, explorers, entrepreneurs, feminists, heroines, historians, Indian women, and many, many more.

1418   Logan, Mary Simmerson (Cunningham), 1838-1923. **The Part Taken by Women in American History.** New York: Arno Press, 1972. (Repr. of 1912 ed.). 927p. index. $41.00. ISBN 0405044674. LC 72-2613.
"Mary Simmerson Cunningham Logan (1838-1923) grew up in a southern Illinois pioneer community. Married at 17, she travelled with her husband, a state attorney, on his court circuit, then into the field while he served as colonel in the Union army, and finally on the campaigns that brought him to Congress and the Senate. Her home was a center of social life in Washington. She and her daughter, Mary Logan Tucker, prepared this compendium of lives of famous and not-so-famous women ... between 1902 and 1909" ("A Note about This Volume"; A. K. Baxter and L. Stein, eds.). This is a monumental biographical dictionary of U.S. women, first published in 1912. Included are sections on: Native American women; women pioneers; women of the Revolution; women in the Civil War; women of the "New South"; women's clubs; women of the Confederacy; woman suffrage; women reformers and sociologists; Catholic and Jewish women; women temperance workers; women educators, artists, actresses, lecturers, playwrights, and authors; women inventors; women in business, and more. A name index is provided.

1419   Macksey, Joan, and Kenneth Macksey. **The Book of Women's Achievements.** New York: Stein and Day, 1976. bibliog. index. $6.95. ISBN 0812822382. LC 75-38771.
First published as *The Guinness Guide to Feminine Achievements*, this is a compendium of unusual and entertaining information about women arranged in an attractive format. The biographies are short and the writing style, snappy rather than scholarly.

1420   O'Neill, Lois Decker. **The Women's Book of World Records and Achievements.** Garden City, NY: Doubleday, 1979. 720p. index. $19.50. ISBN 0385127324.
Who is a leading woman viticulist? the first woman commander of the Salvation Army? the first black woman to receive an M.D.? the first woman Rhodes scholar? the first woman to walk across the United States? More complete than Joan and Kenneth Macksey's *Book of Women's Achievements* (1976), O'Neill's

marathon treatment of approximately 5,000 firsts, greats, and achievers documents heroic efforts in every field of human endeavor from agriculture to women activists. More, it offers state-of-the-art reports about women's achievements written by experts in each field along with an information mine of statistical tables, lists, and biographical facts, which are the daily grist of every reference operation. Though emphasis is on American women, international, minority, and Third-World women figure prominently.

1421   Ross, Ishbel, 1897- . **Ladies of the Press.** New York: Harper and Brothers, 1936; repr. New York: Arno Press, 1974. 622p. index. $36.00. ISBN 040506120X. LC 74-3972.

The subtitle of the original 1936 edition reads, "The Story of Women in Journalism by an Insider." Ishbel Ross *was* an insider to the newspaper world, reporting for more than a decade for the New York *Herald Tribune. Ladies of the Press* is a monumental biographical directory to newspaper women in the United States through the mid-thirties, but Ross managed to convert this tremendous amount of detail into a very readable book in which one vignette flows gracefully into the next. She covers news-feature and news writers, columnists, fashion experts, and other specialists. Though the biographies are arranged topically (e.g., "Front-Page Girl," "War and Suffrage," "The New York *Times*"), an index provides access by name, newspaper, geographical locale, and so on. Sketches of particular women are brief, and Ross provides no list of further references. Hence, the book will serve only as a starting place for researchers in this field.

1422   Rush, Theressa Gunnels, et al. **Black American Writers Past and Present: A Biographical and Bibliographical Dictionary.** Metuchen, NJ: Scarecrow Press, 1975. 2v. bibliog. $30.00. ISBN 0810807858. LC 74-28400.

This book, which includes over 2,000 black men and women American writers, living and deceased, was designed as a single source to provide information about both these writers' lives and their works, from the early eighteenth century to the present. It includes those writers whose works are studied in black literature courses and whose works appear in black literature anthologies, and those writers from Africa and the West Indies who live and/or publish in the U.S. Each writer's entry includes a biography, a list of all known published works by the person, and secondary sources for criticism of the writer's work.

1423   Rutgers University, New Brunswick, NJ: Center for the American Woman and Politics. **Women in Public Office: A Biographical Directory and Statistical Analysis.** New York: Bowker, 1976. 455p. bibliog. index. $21.50. ISBN 0835208613. LC 75-37487.

Local, state, and federal women public officeholders surface in this important biographical source. A massive identification project profiling 13,000 women in a geographically-arranged directory, this tool arranges the subjects by level of office and often provides the following information: biographical data including address information, committee and commission appointments, past political involvement, education and publications. The Statistical Essay manipulates the biographical data in a number of ways: for example, state summaries; elected officeholders by office; minority women in office;

populations of states analyzed by percentage of women in the legislature; family characteristics; education patterns; occupational array; economic status; membership in feminist organizations; and party affiliation. The conclusions drawn by the Eagleton Institute indicate that "women are not well integrated with the political life of the nation. The number of women active in the polity is small. The few women who do hold office are found most frequently in positions with little potential for affecting broad segments of the population." The 1978 second edition of this work (Scarecrow Press; LC 78-7463; ISBN 0810811421; $29.50) is important to collect, as it updates and expands the earlier profile, identifies 17,000 women serving as public officials since 1976, reports on women who have left office since 1975, and provides a biographical sketch for more than 3,000 women officials. This edition contains the first analysis of national data comparing male and female office holders, which reveals a distinct women's point of view on political issues. Both volumes represent significant and unique resource materials on women and politics.

1424   Taylor, Kathryn. **Generations of Denial: 75 Short Biographies of Women in History.** Washington, NJ: Times Change Press, 1971. 64p. bibliog. index. $2.00. ISBN 0878100148.
A slim volume of very brief biographies of: suffragists, feminists and political leaders; military leaders, queens, martyrs, heroines, and lesbians; witches; reformers and revolutionaries; educators; scientists, and inventors; writers, journalists, and printers; entertainers; explorers; and artists. Though compiled from secondary sources, "most written by men—many of whom were defiantly sexist and all of whom were biased," these sketches are frequently enlivened by Taylor's feminist sarcasm. Biographies average around 400 words and therefore will obviously serve only as the barest introduction to these women's lives.

1425   **Who's Who of American Women.** (10th ed.). Chicago: Marquis, 1977. $52.50. ISBN 0837904102. LC 58-13264.
Produced biennially, this reference work gives brief biographies of living women prominent in many fields using a standard format. Public and academic libraries will want to purchase it as a current biographical reference source.

REFERENCE
General
[The scope note for Reference appears on p. 460.]

1426   Abarbanel, Karin, and Gonnie McClung Siegel. **Woman's Work Book.**
        New York: Praeger, 1975. 327p. bibliog. $9.95. ISBN 027552203.
        LC 74-6723.
Subtitled "How to get your first job. . . . How to re-enter the job market. . . .
How to fight for your rights in the work world . . . and more," this book has
lots of useful information for women from all backgrounds, including practical
advice on writing resumes and using employment agencies. The directory section
listing organizations and centers is a bit dated; addresses should be checked
before using.

1427*   Adams, Edith L., comp. **Where to Find Foundation Money for Women's
        Projects: A Directory to Who's Giving Money to Women's Projects.**
        Yonkers, NY: Independent Women's Press, 1977. 119p.
An address book of foundations funding projects in areas such as abortion,
abused women, health care, research, minorities, and sports, it is indexed by
name of foundation. It would be a good supplementary tool to the standard
grant and foundations directories.

1428   Allen, Martha Leslie, ed. **Media Report to Women: Index/Directory.**
        Washington: Women's Institute for Freedom of the Press, 1978. $8.00.
This annually-updated reference work indexes recent documents available only
in *Media Report to Women*, a monthly founded in 1972 by the Women's Institute for Freedom of the Press. Information about developments in the media
and in women's media is also included. The *Index/Directory* is available from
the Women's Institute for Freedom of the Press, 3306 Ross Place, N.W., Washington, DC 20008.

1429   Bagnall, Carlene, et al. **New Woman, New World: The American Exper-
        ience.** Ann Arbor: Women's Studies Program, University of Michigan,
        1977. 117p. bibliog. $2.50.
This is one of the four interdisciplinary courses created by women's studies
teachers and scholars from southern Michigan as part of the Women's Studies
Curriculum Series. These course outlines are intended as guides for the creation
of interdisciplinary women's studies courses at an intermediate level; together,
they could form the basis for a developing women's studies program. Introductions, lecture outlines, required reading and suggested fiction, questions for
discussion, and bibliographies for further reading and research are provided
for different topics in the courses. *New Woman, New World* covers the following
topics, among others: Growing Up Female in the New World; Learning to be
Female; The Patriarchal Family; Matriarchies, Communes and Extended Families; Women and Work in America; Health Care System and Its Effects on Women's
Bodies; The Status of Women; and Women as Agents of Social Change. The other

three courses in this series are *Women and Identity* (by Ann Coleman, et al.), *Women's Art and Culture* (by Conklin and Patraka), and *A Cross Cultural Study of Women* (by Margot Morrow, et al.). These courses can be ordered from: Women's Studies Curriculum Series (Order), Women's Studies Program, 1058 L.S.A. Building, The University of Michigan, Ann Arbor, Michigan 48109 (add $0.50 per course for third class mailing within the U.S.).

1430   Barrer, Myra E., 1927- , ed. **Women's Organizations and Leaders Directory, 1975-1976.** Washington: Today Publications and News Service, 1976. $46.00. ISBN 0879990074. LC 72-86473.

This is the second edition and the first international edition of this directory, with twice the entries of the original 1973 edition. It is an invaluable resource for women and organizations in the women's movement, as well as for employers or affirmative action officers seeking to identify pools of women applicants. The main text gives name, address, telephone number, and a short descriptive paragraph for each entry. In addition, there are five indexes to the text: an alphabetical, geographical and subject index, and two periodical indexes.

1431   Berkowitz, Tamar, et al., eds. **Who's Who and Where in Women's Studies.** Old Westbury, NY: Feminist Press, 1974. 308p. $12.50. ISBN 0912670363. LC 75-313864.

"Whatever the future of women's studies, *Who's Who and Where in Women's Studies* provides an exhaustive record of the movement's history as well as a view of its [1973] size and scope. The volume was organized so that it might serve not only as a guide to the thousands of feminist scholar/teachers, but also as a reliable data base for historians and other scholars. Its three sections light up three different faces of women's studies: institutional development of courses; the pioneering faculty; the sponsoring departments. Dates chart the annual increment in the number of courses; combined with the individual histories of feminist teachers, dates also chart the geographical dispersal of women's studies. In addition the volume contains a list of women's studies programs, the degrees they offer, and their coordinators or directors" (Florence Howe, introduction). Despite the obvious problems of dating because of academic mobility, the 2,964 feminist teacher/scholars listed here represent an important source list for those teaching or studying in this field.

1432   Bolles, Richard Nelson. **What Color Is Your Parachute? A Practical Manual for Job Hunters and Career Changers.** (Rev. ed.). Berkeley, CA: Ten Speed Press, 1977. 233p. bibliog. index. $8.95. ISBN 091366863X. LC 72-92348.

Noting that workers metamorphose into job-hunters and job-hunters, into career-changers, Bolles writes a lively job manual. The first eight chapters erase many of the common myths about finding a job, covering such recognizable landmarks of job-hunting as screening, recruiters, ads, agencies, free and professional help, résumés, "how to get in to see the boss," interviews, career and life-planning. There is much here of interest to those thinking of retraining for another career, switching fields, and going back to school. The meatiest sections are the appendices: a bibliography broken into topics—work, job-hunting, vocational counseling, skills, women (with emphasis on the mature woman), executives, mid-life and second careers, and a directory section listing workshops, seminars, agencies, organizations, and individuals helpful in the job-finding process. A state-by-state section lists local resources for women. Bolles has written a practical book that will be useful to women from high school to retirement—entertaining, too.

1433   Boulding, Elise, et al. **Handbook of International Data on Women.**
        Beverly Hills, CA: Sage Publications; distr. New York: Halsted Press,
        1976. 468p. bibliog. $25.00. ISBN 0470151838. LC 76-20609.
Because the data here are based on existing UN statistics describing the status of women in member countries, the researcher needs to be aware that completeness and reliability of the data may fluctuate depending on the sophistication of data-gathering of the reporting country. Among the indicators covered are: General Economic Activity; Economic Activity by Status; Economic Activity by Industry; Economic Activity by Occupation; Literacy and Education; Marital Status; Migration; Life, Death and Reproduction; Political and Civic Participation; and World Overview. The authors have devised an "index of femaleness" and a "distribution index" to compare cross-cultural data, which needs explanation unless the user has considerable sociological research expertise.

1434   Coleman, Ann, et al. **Women and Identity.** Ann Arbor: Women's Studies
        Program, University of Michigan, n.d. 120p. bibliog. $2.50.
This is one of the four interdisciplinary courses created by women's studies teachers and scholars from southern Michigan as part of the Women's Studies Curriculum Series. These course outlines are intended as guides for the creation of interdisciplinary women's studies courses at an intermediate level; together they could form the basis for a developing women's studies program. Introductions, lecture outlines, required reading and suggested fiction, questions for discussion and bibliographies for further reading and research are provided for different topics in the courses. *Women and Identity* covers the following topics: Sexuality; Fertility; Work and Family; Fear and Envy; Women's Networks; Individuality; Women and Social Change. The other three courses in this series are *Women's Art and Culture* (by Conklin and Patraka), *A Cross Cultural Study of Women* (by Margot Morrow, et al.), and *New Woman, New World: the American Experience* (by Carlene Bagnall, et al.). These courses can be ordered from: Women's Studies Curriculum Series (Order), Women's Studies Program, 1058 L.S.A. Building, The University of Michigan, Ann Arbor, Michigan 48109 (add $0.50 per course for third class mailing within the U.S.).

1435   Conklin, Nancy Faires, and Vivian M. Patraka. **Women's Art and
        Culture.** Ann Arbor: Women's Studies Program, University of Michigan,
        1977. 80p. bibliog. $2.50.
Another of the four interdisciplinary courses created by women's studies teachers and scholars from southern Michigan as part of the Women's Studies Curriculum Series. These course outlines are intended as guides for the creation of interdisciplinary women's studies courses at an intermediate level; together, they could form the basis for a developing women's studies program. Introductions, lecture outlines, required reading and suggested fiction, questions for discussion, and bibliographies for further reading and research are provided

for different topics in the courses. *Women's Art and Culture* covers the following topics: Women in the Arts: A Conceptual Framework; Women's Oppression and Creativity; Women on Women; Art and Politics; and Great Women and Great Art. The other three courses in this series are *Women and Identity* (by Ann Coleman, et al.), *New Woman, New World: The American Experience* (by Carlene Bagnall, et al.), and *A Cross Cultural Study of Women* (by Margot Morrow, et al.). These courses can be ordered from: Women's Studies Curriculum Series (Order), Women's Studies Program, 1058 L.S.A. Building, The University of Michigan, Ann Arbor, Michigan 48109 (add $0.50 per course for third class mailing within the U.S.).

1436*   Danky, James Philip, 1947- . **Undergrounds: A Union List of Alternative Periodicals in Libraries of the United States and Canada.** Madison: State Historical Society of Wisconsin, 1974. 206p. $12.95. ISBN 0870201425. LC 74-8272.
Danky has compiled a useful list of underground and alternative periodicals giving location information. Since there is no subject index, those periodicals that are women-oriented must be sought by looking for titles beginning with words "Female," "Feminist," "Women." If you know the title and simply need locations, Danky is very helpful. A more recent checklist, one with subject access, is Joanne V. Akeroyd's *Alternatives* (2nd ed.), Bibliographic Series, No. 5 (University of Connecticut Library, April 1976; include $3.00 with order); or use the special supplement listing feminist serials from Akeroyd's list, which appears as a source in Kathleen Burke McKee's *Women's Studies: A Guide to Reference Sources*, Bibliography Series, No. 6 (University of Connecticut Library, 1977; $5.00 with order).

1437   Farmer, Helen S., and Thomas E. Backer. **New Career Options: A Woman's Guide.** New York: Human Sciences Press, 1977. 60p. $2.95. ISBN 0877052727. LC 77-853.
A slender, useful volume in the three-part series designed for use in female career counseling (see also Farmer and Backer's *New Career Options for Women: A Counselor's Sourcebook* and Ann Phelps's *New Career Options for Women: A Selected, Annotated Bibliography*), this booklet briefly examines new opportunities for working women as well as the problems that remain; sketches the opportunities for women in crafts, management, and the professions; and discusses laws, misconceptions, sociological issues, planning strategies, training possibilities, and information sources dealing with getting a job. There is good information on relevant agencies to contact and government publications with current information. Care should be used with names and addresses provided in organizational listings, as this type of information dates quickly.

1438   Farmer, Helen S., and Thomas E. Backer. **New Career Options for Women: A Counselor's Sourcebook.** New York: Human Sciences Press, 1977. 349p. bibliog. index. $16.95. ISBN 0877052972. LC 77-5721.
Essential reference reading for those dealing with career guidance for women and girls, this is a valuable guide for general reference on a variety of topics clustering around the changing role of women. The emphasis is on how to get

and use information in this rapidly expanding area of women in the labor market. Among the chapters included: Women's Opportunities in Training and Education; Career Counseling for Women: Theories and Concepts; The Law: Recent Legislation and Its Impact. The authors direct the reader to very specific sources and techniques. Of particular interest is the resources section, giving several listings of published products, organizations, films, workshops, and miscellaneous materials directed toward expanding options for women. Charts and tables address the gamut of issues centering on women and work. The appendices alone are indispensible ready reference items: for example, listings of earned degrees by field, race, sex; preparing a work résumé; a question-and-answer section on ERA; a list of court actions on sex discrimination.

1439   **A Gay News Chronology, January 1969-May 1975: Index and Abstracts of Articles from the New York Times.** New York: Arno Press, 1975. 1v. (various pagings). $12.00. ISBN 0405074093. LC 75-14265.
"This volume comprises abstracts of all material on homosexuality published in *The New York Times* from January 1, 1969, to May 15, 1975. . . . The abstracts were obtained by tapping the New York Times Information Bank, a pioneering computerized system in which abstracts of all material published in *The Times* and of selected material published in some sixty other newspapers and magazines are stored 'on-line' and may be retrieved by entering inquiries on a computer terminal" (from the introduction). A single weakness of this volume is its lack of any indexing, which effectively cuts off access to its material by subject. Its primary value, therefore, is likely to be simply as an historical chronology; one can, in one volume, follow the progression of events and their treatment in a major U.S. newspaper from 1969 to 1975, key years for the emergence of Gay Liberation and lesbian feminism. Researchers with a need to pinpoint specific topics will undoubtedly do better to use the New York Times *Index*.

1440   **The Good Housekeeping Woman's Almanac.** By the editors of the *World Almanac.* New York: Newspaper Enterprise Association, 1977. 576p. index. $7.95. ISBN 0385133774. LC 77-75353.
This book touts itself as "the book with all the answers for women"; and it does contain a mix of general and specific information, strange and useful facts, biographical sketches on notorious and important women, charts, graphs, and lists. Major topics include: education, health, money, work, the arts, women's liberation, etc. Though the information is somewhat unsystematically arranged, this is an adequately indexed and handy reference tool, with an emphasis on the practical, which will be of use in almost any library situation.

1441   Grimstad, Kirsten, and Susan Rennie, eds. **The New Woman's Survival Sourcebook.** New York: Knopf, 1975. 245p. bibliog. index. $5.00. ISBN 0394730356. LC 75-8260.
A useful source for information on every current women's issue and topic (health and child care, employment, discrimination, women's literature and publishing, etc.), this is a book to browse in and to look to for ready reference. Care should be used with addresses, as they may be dated. Visually, this is an attractive book in *Whole Earth Catalog* format, with interviews, notices of

books and periodicals, articles, announcements, and lists sprinkled throughout its fifteen sections.

1442   Harrison, Cynthia. **Women's Movement Media: A Source Guide**. New York: Bowker, 1975. 269p. index. $14.95. ISBN 0835207110. LC 75-2484.

A guide to the services, products and information available to women in most states and in Canada, this directory lists 560 various organizations, including feminist publishers, news services, distributors, women's research centers, library research collections, governmental and affiliated organizations and agencies. Four indexing systems provide easy access: by name, by subject, by media, and by geographical area. As with all such reference books, care must be taken when using address information.

1443   Joan, Polly, and Andrea Chesman. **Guide to Women's Publishing**. Paradise, CA: Dustbooks, 1978. 296p. bibliog. index. $8.95. ISBN 0913218804. LC 77-29143.

A comprehensive guide to the women's publishing movement. It lists presses, newspapers, periodicals of all types, archives, libraries, and organizations that are feminist, lesbian, and non-sexist. It also describes the kind of work that these publishers are likely to publish for those looking to place their writing.

1444   Lembeck, Ruth. **1,001 Job Ideas for Today's Woman: A Checklist Guide to the Job Market**. Garden City, NY: Doubleday, 1975. 268p. index. $2.50. ISBN 0385045921.

Originally published under the title: *Job Ideas for Today's Woman*, and written primarily for those who want to get out of the house or to develop a gainful in-home occupation, this is a cookbook approach with step-by-step recipes for getting jobs: what the job seeker needs (personal traits, materials, education, training), costs, potential earnings, a brief description of such jobs, and how one gets started. Few professions are included, a lack attributed by the author to space limitations, infeasibility for most women, and an already high motivational level that characterizes women seeking a professional position. Examples of real women, drawn almost altogether from the East Coast, are included as models. Major fields covered include animal care, health, fashion, education, child care, communications, office, writing, home economics, librarianship, travel, and house maintenance. Definitely not a laundry list, this covers most major fields in sufficient depth to provide ideas for the reader who wants to follow through. The appendix of organizations lists over a hundred professional and trade associations, ranging from Advocates for Women to Women's Bureau, U.S. Department of Labor. When using address information and salary data, the 1975 publication date should be kept in mind.

1445   Loring, Rosalind, and Herbert Arthur Otto, eds. **New Life Options: The Working Woman's Resource Book**. New York: McGraw-Hill, 1976. 487p. bibliog. index. $10.95. ISBN 0070387427. LC 76-25092.

The editors bring to this work much experience in the fields of continuing education and human potentialities. Divided into five parts—New Perspectives, Getting the Best from Your Career, Taking Good Care of Yourself, The Potential of

Your Relationships, Managing Your Options—the book is geared toward working women committed to helping themselves deal with issues of home and career conflict, job-hunting, sexism at work, managing a business, mental and physical health issues, single parenthood, childcare, assertion, and personal finance— in short, the constellation of complex, and to an extent, unresolvable problems facing working women. Clearly written by people who have published, consulted, and lectured extensively in these areas, the text is supported by notes on additional reading. It could be of significant assistance to young women first facing the job market, older women re-entering the labor force, and women who have not done basic reading in these topical work-related areas.

1446   Lynn, Naomi B., et al. **Research Guide in Women's Studies.** Morristown, NJ: General Learning Press, 1974. 194p. bibliog. $3.95. ISBN 0382180917. LC 74-75728.
This work speaks to the need for identification of existing scholarly offerings in the field of women's studies, concentrating on United States resources. Chapters deal with researching, selecting, and citing sources for topics on women; annotating basic resources and surveying diverse tools in women's studies; reviewing general social science tools concerned with women, as well as specific subject-relevant tools; and reviewing sources of statistical information. A helpful listing of research centers and women's organizations appears at the end. This volume provides a blueprint for any reference librarian to assist a client (whether student or independent researcher) in using existing tools.

1447*   Marshall, Joan K. **On Equal Terms: A Thesaurus for NonSexist Indexing and Cataloging.** New York: Neal-Schuman, 1977. 152p. $14.95. ISBN 0918212022. LC 77-8987.
This is an excellent reference tool for public use as well as for catalogers, as it lists in one useable volume those terms that the Library of Congress presently uses for subjects of interest to the individual researching issues on women, sex roles, etc. It also provides a model for what catalogers should be using to avoid sexist terms.

1448   Mitchell, Joyce Slayton. **I Can Be Anything: Careers and Colleges for Young Women.** (Rev. and exp. ed.). New York: College Entrance Examination Board, 1978. 315p. $12.95. LC 77-95209.
A straight-forward approach to 108 careers from A to Z (actually from Accountant to Writing Career), this answers very simple questions for each career listed, using a standard format for questions like: What's It Like to Be an ____? What Education and Skills Will I Need? How Many Women in the Field and Where Do They Work? What Are the Salaries? What Is the Future? What Colleges Award the Most Degrees to Women in ____? Where Can I Get More Information? In short, this reference book holds someone's hand through the initial process of investigating careers. A school, college, and university directory is appended at the end of the volume. Though the approach may have been designed for *young* women, any woman who is contemplating career training and confused about the options could use this easily.

1449   Morrow, Margot, et al. **A Cross-Cultural Study of Women.** Ann Arbor:
        Women's Studies Program, University of Michigan, 1977. 132p. bibliog.
        $2.50.

This is one of the four interdisciplinary courses created by women's studies
teachers and scholars from southern Michigan as part of the Women's Studies
Curriculum Series. These course outlines are intended as guides for the creation
of interdisciplinary women's studies courses at an intermediate level; together,
they could form the basis for a developing women's studies program. Introductions, lecture outlines, required reading and suggested fiction, questions for
discussion, and bibliographies for further reading and research are provided
for different topics in the courses. *A Cross-Cultural Study of Women* covers
the following topics: Theoretical Overviews; Male Dominance; Women and
Economics; Women and Religion; Area Studies; Women in China; Women in
Melanesia; Women in Sub-Saharan Africa; Women in Latin America; and Islamic
Middle East and North Africa. The other three courses in this series are *Women
and Identity* (by Ann Coleman, et al.), *Women's Art and Culture* (by Conklin
and Patraka), and *New Woman, New World: The American Experience* (by
Carlene Bagnall, et al.). These courses can be ordered from: Women's Studies
Curriculum Series (Order), Women's Studies Program, 1058 L.S.A. Building,
The University of Michigan, Ann Arbor, Michigan 48109 (add $0.50 per course
for third class mailing within the U.S.).

1450   Partnow, Elaine. **The Quotable Woman, 1800-1975.** Los Angeles:
        Corwin Books, 1977. 539p. index. $20.00. ISBN 0894740067. LC
        77-76016.

Most astounding of all when one considers this book of insights, perceptions,
epigrams, musings, commentaries, exclamations, tributes, and lyrics all authored
by women, is that no one thought of undertaking the project before this. The
enormity of the task may have discouraged even those who saw the need; from
the outset this was clearly a labor of retrieving women's buried and lost thoughts.
The author's preface notes that .5 percent of the total number of quotations in
Bartlett's Familiar Quotations and only 1 percent in the *Oxford Book* can be
attributed to women. Assuredly, it cannot be that women have had nothing
worthwhile to say. Partnow's sifting, selecting and ordering of over 8,000
quotations, authored by some 1,300 women from Bernice Abbott to Clara
Zetkin, proves that much has been said well both aloud and in print by women,
later to be mislaid, minimized, and forgotten. Chronologically arranged by
author's birthdate from 1800 on (didn't any woman before the nineteenth
century utter a pithy phrase?), these quotations span a dazzling subject array
from abandonment to Zionism, with predictable clusters at such terms as aging,
children, freedom, love, marriage, motherhood, men, sexuality, war, work, and,
of course, women. The carefully wrought author index alone qualifies this book
as an essential reference tool: each entry gives the author's full name including
married name, dates, nationality, relationships to other notables, profession,
outstanding contributions, and honors. Partnow has handled the selection of
most quotable lines with great skill when one considers the editorial problems
of choosing lines from writers as eloquent and prolific as Simone de Beauvoir,
Virginia Woolf, and George Eliot, or as obscure as Olive Custance and Katherine
Hankey.

1451   Paulsen, Kathryn, and Ryan A. Kuhn, comps. **Woman's Almanac: 12 How-To Handbooks in One.** New York: Lippincott, 1976. 624p. bibliog. index. $12.50. ISBN 039701113X. LC 76-2055.

This belongs in all reference collections that serve women. It is an attractive encyclopedic collection of articles on women's issues by persons with expertise in particular areas (such as psychology, sexuality, law, handywork, etc.). The Women's Directory gives classified listings of 1,500 local and national women's services, resources, and special interest organizations.

1452   Schlachter, Gail Ann. **Directory of Financial Aids for Women.** Los Angeles: Reference Service Press, 1978. 200p. bibliog. index. $15.95. ISBN 0918276022. LC 77-78149.

This up-to-date directory is divided into four sections: 1) scholarships, fellowships, loans, grants, etc., designed primarily or exclusively for women (includes address, availability, purpose, eligibility, financial data, duration, deadline, number awarded); 2) women's credit unions (lists addresses and phone numbers); 3) state sources of educational benefits (gives addresses, organized by state); and 4) annotated bibliography of general financial aids directories. The over 600 different financial aids described here are indexed by sponsoring organization, by geographic region, and by subject.

1453   Schwartz, Felice N., et al. **How to Go to Work When Your Husband Is Against It, Your Children Aren't Old Enough, and There's Nothing You Can Do Anyhow.** New York: Simon and Schuster, 1972. 348p. $2.95. ISBN 0671215345. LC 74-165539.

A primer for women who want to find meaningful work while juggling domestic responsibilities, this book has much useful information on locating a job: letter-writing, interview techniques, résumé preparation and an excellent career Baedeker describing occupations alphabetically (from accountant to vocational guidance counselor) with useful information on the field, training, earnings, opportunities, and part-time possibilities. Addresses for additional information and suggestions for further reading are listed. The approach is geared toward women who may have to overcome resistance at home to their seeking employment and who may be lacking self-confidence to initiate a job search. No index is provided.

1454   **Sourcebook of Equal Educational Opportunity.** (2nd ed.). Chicago: Marquis Academic Media, 1977. $34.50. ISBN 0837929024. LC 77-75482.

Formerly titled *Yearbook of Educational Opportunity*, the *Sourcebook* puts together a comprehensive portrait of the current state-of-the-art with regard to equal educational opportunity. Statistical and narrative data have been collected from both government and private sources, identified with each excerpt. In addition to a general section which analyzes mainstream thinking about equal educational opportunity and treats the topics of population characteristics, cultural pluralism, sexism, and racism, six large areas receive in-depth treatment: American Indian/Native Alaskan; Asian American/Pacific Islander; Black; Disadvantaged/White Ethnic; Hispanic; and Women. All sections contain a wealth of statistical information. The section on women has much relevant appendix material, including "A Guide to Federal Laws and Regulations Prohibiting Sex Discrimination," summaries of the educational status of minority women, and lists of women's organizations and women's studies programs.

1455   Task Force on Alternative Books in Print. **Alternatives in Print, 77-78: The Annual Catalog of Social Change Publications.** (5th ed.). San Francisco: Glide Publications, 1977. 198p. $12.95. ISBN 0912078499. LC 76-54384.

This catalog is very helpful in the identification of new women's periodicals and the addresses of their publishers. The 1977-78 edition lists 175 entries under the subjects Women in Industry and Women's Liberation Movement, and 110 entries under Feminism.

1456*   United States. Bureau of the Census. **A Statistical Portrait of Women in the United States.** Washington: U.S. Dept. of Commerce, Bureau of the Census: for sale by the Supt. of Docs., U.S. Govt. Print. Off., 1976. 90p. bibliog. LC 76-10850.

Check here first for statistical information related to women. "This report presents a statistical portrait of the changing role of women in the United States during the twentieth century. Data are from United States Government sources— from surveys, decennial censuses, vital statistics, and administrative records. The majority of the statistics have been published previously, either in government documents or professional journals, but are brought together here to highlight the demographic, social and economic conditions of women" (from the introduction). Chapters are: Population Growth and Composition; Longevity, Mortality, and Health; Residence and Migration; Marital and Family Status; Fertility; Education; Labor Force Participation; Occupation and Industry; Work Experience; Income and Poverty Status; Voting and Public Office Holding; Crime and Victimization; Black Women; Spanish Women. Tables support each chapter. A privately produced statistical source that augments the *Statistical Portrait* is Abbott L. Ferris, *Indicators of Trends in the Status of American Women* (Russell Sage Foundation, 1971).

1457*   United States. Equal Employment Opportunity Commission. **Employment Profiles of Women and Minorities in 23 Metropolitan Areas, 1974.** Washington: EEOC, 1976. 314p. LC 76-603564.

This is a standard and essential statistical source for information profiling the employment of women and minorities in Standard Metropolitan Statistical Areas (SMSA). For each area, the profile provides a summary of findings.

1458   United States. Women's Bureau. **Mature Women Workers: A Profile.** Washington: U.S. Dept. of Labor, Employment Standards Administration, Women's Bureau: for sale by the Supt. of Docs., U.S. Govt. Print. Off., 1976. 118p. LC 76-602592.

For the purposes of this study, the mature woman is defined as 45 years or older. The profile documents the presence in the labor force of older women (in 1975, one-third of *all* women workers were 45 or older). The mature married woman is less visible in the working force than her widowed, divorced, or separated counterpart. This reflects the reentry difficulties that married women

face in convincing employers of their skills and future potential. "These entry
or reentry difficulties are reflected in mature women's occupational status and
earnings, in the incidence of poverty, and in the duration of their unemployment.
On the other hand, once mature women obtain jobs, they have a lower incidence
of unemployment than younger women" (from the introduction). Statistics
are grouped under: Labor Force Status, Education, Marital Status, Occupations,
Income, and Unrelated Women Living Alone.

1459*   United States. Women's Bureau. **Minority Women Workers: A Statisti-
        cal Overview.** (Rev.). Washington: The Bureau, 1977. 14p. bibliog.
        LC 77-603426.
This documents 1974-76 statistics on minority women workers "including Negro,
American Indian, Japanese, Chinese, Filipino, Korean, Hawaiian, Eskimo,
Aleut, and all other nonwhite races." Negroes constitute 89 percent of persons
of minority races. Persons of Spanish origin are included in the white population.
Statistics cover: Labor Force Participation, Unemployment Status, Reasons
for Unemployment, Unemployment During the Recession, Occupations, Marital
Status, Women Heads of Families, Working Mothers, Children of Working
Mothers, Education, Employment Status of High School Dropouts, and Earnings.
The report concludes that during 1976, minority women held 4,140,000 jobs,
thus experiencing proportionally greater employment increases when compared
with their white counterparts.

1460*   United States. Women's Bureau. **1975 Handbook on Women Workers.**
        Washington: U.S. Dept. of Labor, Employment Standards Administra-
        tion, Women's Bureau, 1975. 435p. bibliog. index. LC 76-601044.
The periodically updated Women's Bureau *Handbook* is an indispensable source
of statistical information and analysis on women workers in the U.S. Part 1,
Women in the Labor Force, covers demographic characteristics of women
workers (age, marital status, children, race, employment patterns, distribution
in the various occupations, income and earnings, education and training). Part
2, Laws Governing Women's Employment and Status, discusses federal and
state laws of particular relevance to women, maternity standards, and the
civil and political status of women (including the ERA). Part 3, Institutions
and Mechanisms to Advance the Status of Women, enumerates avenues of legal
remedy at the federal level and also considers commissions on the status of
women and international activities (e.g., IWY). The highly current statistical
data (1974 in most tables) are in many cases presented in the context of comparative data for this century, revealing historical trends. Considerable effort
has been expended to render both the tables and the text with utmost clarity.

1461   University of Wisconsin-Extension. Family Living Education and Women's
        Education Resources. **Women's Issues Packets.** Madison, 1978. $1.50ea;
        $12.00 for 12.
The first twelve of these award-winning packets were compiled by Carolyn
Wilson. They include interesting topical materials: articles, speeches, reports,
government documents. They are particularly useful for discussion groups
planning meetings, students preparing papers, and reference librarians. The
following titles are now available: Battered Women, Displaced Homemaker,

Equal Rights Amendment, Legal Status of Wisconsin Homemakers, Marital
Property Reform, Teenage Pregnancy, Women in Elective and Appointive
Office, Female Offenders, Women and Employment, Women and Credit, Older
Women, and Physical and Mental Health of Women. Women's Education Resources
of the UW-Extension has plans to update the packets, which provide an orderly
approach to establishing vertical file materials on these important topics. The
packets may be ordered from: University Extension Bookstore, 432 North
Lake Street, Madison, WI 53706.

1462   Vida, Ginny, 1939- , ed. **Our Right to Love: A Lesbian Resource Book.**
        Englewood Cliffs, NJ: Prentice-Hall, 1978. 325p. bibliog. $12.95.
        ISBN 0136444016. LC 77-20184.
With its impressive bibliographies, lists, and informative articles, this book is
a definitive source on lesbianism and is essential for reference collections.
Divided into thirteen sections, including identity, health, law, and media, the
format is designed to intersperse personal testimonies with articles. It was
produced in cooperation with women of the National Gay Task Force.

1463*   Warrior, Betsy. **Working on Wife Abuse.** (5th ed.). Cambridge, MA:
        Warrior, 1977. 114p. ISBN 0960154418.
In this highly respected practical guide to resources for battered women, Warrior
lists places of refuge, contact persons throughout the world (but primarily in
the U.S.), and publications and films relevant to battered women. Arrangement is geographical. While much of this sort of information is quickly dated,
Warrior has issued five editions since her pamphlet was first published in April
1976. *Working on Wife Abuse* is available from Betsy Warrior, 46 Pleasant
Street, Cambridge, MA 02139.

1464   Wisconsin. Governor's Commission on the Status of Women. **Working
        Together: A Directory for Wisconsin Women's Groups.** (2nd ed.).
        Madison, 1977. 30p. $2.00.
This directory locates statewide women's organizations or those with a national
affiliation, provides the name of a contact person, and notes if a newsletter
is published. Local women's centers and strictly occupational or professional
groups are not included. A list of acronyms and an organization index with
name variations are in the directory. It is available from the Governor's Commission on the Status of Women, 30 West Mifflin Street, Rm. 210, Madison,
WI 53703.

This slender chapter indicates the limited number of books currently available on these significant subjects. Recent bibliographic essays on women and religion have begun to identify the important book and periodical literature related to the roles of women in philosophy and religion. See especially "Women's Survival Catalog: Spirituality" in *Chrysalis* (No. 6, 1978) and review essays by Mouton and Driver on philosophy and religion in *Signs* (Vol. 2, No. 2, Winter 1976). Articles on contemporary religious concerns emerge in bibliographies such as Krichmar (1977) and Haber (1978), identified in the Reference chapter.

1465   Agonito, Rosemary, ed. **History of Ideas on Woman: A Source Book.** New York: Putnam, 1977. 414p. index. $7.95. ISBN 0399119647. LC 77-5061.

Agonito states in her preface: "Despite a burgeoning body of materials in virtually all areas of women's studies, there continues to exist no single collection of primary sources in the history of ideas on Woman. This book is designed to fill that gap by presenting the most significant and representative thinking in the history of Western civilization on all aspects of the Woman Question." Selections include writings from Plato, Aristotle, Plutarch, Paul, Augustine, Thomas Aquinas, Francis Bacon, Hobbes, Locke, Rousseau, Hume, Kant, Wollstonecraft, Hegel, Kierkegaard, Schopenhauer, Emerson, Mill, Darwin, Nietzsche, Engels, Russell, Freud, Horney, de Beauvoir, Montagu, Friedan, and Marcuse. Agonito gives us a capsule view of each writer's stance on women preceding the selection and includes a section of short "Biographical Notes" at the end of the book. A useful reference book, this could be of special interest to introductory women's studies courses. Studies of women and philosophy have been invisible until only recently. Recent literature includes Mary Mahowald, ed., *Philosophy of Woman* (Indianapolis: Hackett, 1978); Sharon Hill and Marjorie Weinzweig, eds., *Philosophical Aspects of Women's Liberation* (Belmont, CA: Wadsworth, 1978); and Carol Gould and Marx Wartofsky, eds., *Of Women and Philosophy* (New York: G. P. Putnam, 1976). Also see the Review Essay on Philosophy by Jane English, *Signs*, v.3, no. 4, (Summer 1978), pp. 823-831.

1466   Coriden, James A., ed. **Sexism and Church Law: Equal Rights and Affirmative Action.** New York: Paulist Press, 1977. 192p. bibliog. index. $7.95. ISBN 0809120100. LC 77-70638.

The articles in this collection were originally written for a symposium on "Women and Church Law" held at Rosemont College in October 1976. Among the topics considered are: "The Juridical Status of Women in Contemporary Ecclesial Law," by Francis Morrisey; "Women in Relation to Orders and Jurisdiction," by Katherine Meagher; "Changing Forms of Ministry in the Early Church," by Hamilton Hesse; and "Women in Vatican Documents 1960 to the Present," by Nadine Foley. Also included is the "Consensus Statement," which emerged from discussions at the symposium. The overall tone of the book is optimistic, noting progress made and evincing hope in future changes.

1467   Daly, Mary, 1928- . **Beyond God the Father: Toward a Philosophy of Women's Liberation.** Boston: Beacon Press, 1973. 225p. bibliog. index. $8.95. ISBN 0807041645. LC 73-6245.

This is a landmark critical analysis of Judeo-Christian theology in its sexist, repressive, and destructive dimensions. Daly writes from a radical feminist perspective, viewing male supremacy and "phallic morality" as being at the source of the "most unholy trinity"—rape, genocide, and war. Her analysis is not purely critical, but moves toward the creation of a new feminist spirituality at the same time that it dismembers prevailing theological outlooks. Her use of language as a tool of liberation is breathtaking at times. Rosemary Ruether's book, *New Woman, New Earth*, would make for an interesting contrast with *Beyond God the Father*, covering similar territory but from a socialist feminist perspective.

1468   Daly, Mary, 1928- . **The Church and the Second Sex.** New York: Harper and Row, 1975. 229p. bibliog. index. $3.45. ISBN 0060613759. LC 75-301799.

Originally published in 1968, reflecting the views of a "Catholic Feminist," the 1975 edition contains a much more radical "new feminist postchristian" introduction by the author, describing her views of the church as a sexist and oppressive institution. Daly writes with great acerbity of the Catholic church, drawing on Simone de Beauvoir's criticism of the church in *The Second Sex*. Her point in the original edition, which she disowns in the 1975 introduction, is that the church is guilty of contributing to the subjection of women but capable of radical transformation. Readers interested in Daly's more recent views should look at her *Beyond God the Father*.

1469*   Doely, Sarah Bentley, ed. **Women's Liberation and the Church: The New Demand for Freedom in the Life of the Christian Church.** New York: Association Press, 1970. 158p. bibliog. ISBN 0809618141. LC 70-129441.

Contributors to this volume on women's liberation and the church represent many positions and speak to the disappointment, disillusionment, and anger of women who find the church inconsistent in its teachings on "humanity" and women. Contents are: Davida Foy Crabtree, "Women's Liberation and the Church"; Rosemary Radford Ruether, "Women's Liberation in Historical and Theological Perspective"; Sidney Cornelia Callahan, "A Christian Perspective on Feminism"; Susan Copenhaver Barrabee, "Education for Liberation: Women in the Seminary"; Norma Ramsey Jones, "Women in the Ministry"; Sisters of the Immaculate Heart of Mary, Los Angeles, "The Sisters Join the Movement"; and Peggy Ann Way, "An Authority of Possibility for Women in the Church." Of these, the essay by Rosemary Ruether is particularly lucid, tracing the historical and theological background of women's subordination in a Christian society, which is most prominently expressed in her dualistic position as both the salvation and greatest temptation of man. Another recent collection is entitled *Sexist Religion and Women in the Church: No More Silence!* (Association Press, 1974). Edited by Alice L. Hageman, the volume consists primarily of lectures delivered at the Harvard Divinity School in 1972-1973.

1470   Emswiler, Sharon Neufer, and Thomas Neufer Emswiler. **Women and Worship: A Guide to Non-Sexist Hymns, Prayers, and Liturgies.** New York: Harper and Row, 1974. 115p. bibliog. $5.95. ISBN 0060622458. LC 73-18681.

"This book was written to try to provide guidelines for those who wish to learn how to develop creative, meaningful non-sexist worship. It is intended not just for the concerned minister or professional worship leader but also for lay women and men. . . . " (from the introduction). The authors briefly discuss "how the new woman feels in the old worship service," then attempt to establish a biblical rationale for the sort of changes they propose. In the second half of the book, they provide examples of "liberated" prayers, affirmations, responses, and services. A list of non-sexist hymns and a brief bibliography of further resources are appended. The style is popular and the perspective is decidedly "integrationist," in contrast with the more radical approaches of Mary Daly or Rosemary Ruether.

1471   English, Jane, 1947- , ed. **Sex Equality.** Englewood Cliffs, NJ: Prentice-Hall, 1977. 250p. bibliog. $11.95. ISBN 0138075948. LC 76-53000.

This is an anthology of writings by Plato, Aristotle, Locke, Rousseau, J. G. Fichte, J. S. Mill, and F. Engels; and by contemporaries, among them de Beauvoir, Joyce Trebilcot, Irving Thalberg, Sam Ervin, Ruth Bader Ginsburg, Steven Goldberg, Naomi Weisstein, and Robin Lakoff. The collection "is designed for use as a basic text in a philosophy of feminism course, as a second text in an introductory ethics course, or as 'issues' reading in a general introduction to philosophy. Nearly all of the articles included are accessible to undergraduates with no previous philosophical training" (from the preface). Central issues under discussion include: equality, equal opportunity, preferential treatment, the family, education, political equality, natural sex differences, self-respect, language, and sex roles. These issues are set out in English's introduction to the volume.

1472   Gage, Matilda (Joslyn), 1826-1898. **Woman, Church, and State.** New York: Arno Press, 1972. (Repr. of 1900 ed.). $24.00. ISBN 0405044585. LC 72-2602.

Born in New York State, the only child of a physician of progressive political bent, Matilda Joslyn Gage first entered politics in 1852 when she addressed the National Woman's Rights Convention held in Syracuse, New York. She was henceforth deeply committed to and involved in the suffrage movement, as member of the advisory council of the National Woman Suffrage Association; contributor to its newspaper, *Revolution*; as head of the National and New York State suffrage associations in 1875; as co-editor (with Elizabeth Cady Stanton and Susan B. Anthony) of the first three volumes of the *History of Woman Suffrage* (1881-1886). *Woman, Church, and State* (first published in 1893) represented the culmination of her views, developed from the late 1870s on, that the cause of the tremendous opposition to woman suffrage must be sought, and that the explanation would be found in the ascendancy of Christian church doctrine, which preaches the inferiority of women. The book is dedicated "to all Christian women and men, of whatever creed or name who, bound by Church or State, have not dared to think for themselves," and explores various dimensions of Christianity—its views on and control of marriage, celibacy of the clergy and the denigration of women, marriage and property in women, etc.—which help cement the structure of sexual inequality. Particularly interesting is her analysis of witchcraft: Gage prefigures contemporary theorists in her assertion that it was women's possession of knowledge, particularly of healing, that brought them under the suspicion and persecution of the Church. This work represents important historical background to contemporary feminist critiques of religious doctrine.

1473   Gould, Carol C., and Marx W. Wartofsky, eds. **Women and Philosophy: Toward a Theory of Liberation.** New York: Putnam, 1976. 364p. bibliog. $8.95. ISBN 0399116524. LC 75-33604.

Women and Philosophy is based on a special issue of the quarterly journal, *The Philosophical Forum* (v. V, nos. 1-2). The articles collected here seek to clarify the philosophical conceptions underlying the different theories and strategies of feminism (liberal feminism, radical feminism, and socialist feminism). Involved are key questions such as: is there such a thing as women's nature? what are the origins of women's oppression? what is the meaning of women's liberation, and how can it be achieved? and, what is the relation of women's struggle to the struggles of other oppressed peoples? The anthology is divided into four sections. Part 1 analyzes why women's oppression is not considered a relevant question by conventional philosophy and argues for a reconceptualization of philosophy. Part 2, Historical Critique, analyzes the history of theories of sex differences and sexual identity from Plato and Aristotle to Freud and Sartre. Part 3, Analysis and Critique of the Present, includes articles on forms of women's oppression and their relation to other forms of exploitation in society. The final section, What's to be Done, considers different strategies for liberation. The contributors are Elizabeth Lane Beardsley, Larry Blum, Margery Collins, Anne Dickason, Marlene Gerber Fried, Carol C. Gould, Diana Long Hall, Sandra G. Harding, Hilde Hein, Virginia Held, Marcia Homiak, Judy Housman, Alison Jagger, Carolyn W. Korsmeyer, Mihailo Markovic, Michael Martin, Onora O'Neill, Christine Pierce, Elizabeth Rapaport, Naomi Scheman, Irving Thalberg, Judith Farr Tormey, Mary Vetterling, Robert Paul Wolff, and Caroline Whitbeck.

1474   Gross, Rita M., ed. **Beyond Androcentrism: New Essays on Women and Religion.** Missoula, MT: Scholars Press, 1977. 347p. bibliog. $7.50. ISBN 0891301968. LC 77-13312.

This collection of essays came out of the 1975 meeting of the Women and Religion section of the American Academy of Religion. The papers are organized into five broad themes: The Feminist Transformation of Religious Studies: statements from several disciplinary perspectives; Rediscovering the Data: cross-cultural and historical studies on women and religion; Our Foremothers (and Forefathers) Revisited: rereading the biblical narrative; The Women's Movement and Feminist Theology: nineteenth-century arguments and twentieth-century continuities; and Feminine Language and Imagery in Constructs of Ultimacy: cross-cultural examples and theological proposals. These are statements by specialists, and thus the collection would not be appropriate for readers seeking an introduction to feminist theological approaches.

1475   Institoris, Henricus [Kramer, Heinrich], d. 1508, and Jakob Sprenger,
        1436or8-1495. **Malleus Maleficarum.** New York: B. Blom, 1970.
        (Repr. of 1928 ed.). 277p. $17.50. LC 68-57193.
"It is hardly disputed that in the whole vast literature of witchcraft, the most
prominent, the most important, the most authoritative volume is the *Malleus
Maleficarum* (*The Witch Hammer*) of Heinrich Kramer (Henricus Institoris)
and James Sprenger," writes Montague Summers in his introduction to this
classic, late fifteenth-century treatise. The *Malleus* gained particular prominence
from the Bull of Pope Innocent VIII (1484) designating Kramer and Sprenger
as inquisitors into alleged witchcraft networks throughout northern Germany.
Appearing in numerous editions during the course of the fifteenth to seventeenth
centuries, the *Malleus* "lay on the bench of every judge, on the desk of every
magistrate." The *Malleus* is important for feminist studies as *the* authoritative
statement on the identification and punishment of witches, which many feminist
historians have seen as an especially virulent form of patriarchal repression.
The vast majority of the accused and murdered were women; women's sexual
expressiveness, healing activities, and, perhaps most important, control over
reproduction were important among the alleged heretical activities. Among the
topics discussed by Kramer and Sprenger are: "Concerning Witches who copulate
with Devils: Why is it that Women are chiefly addicted to Evil Superstitions?";
"That Witches who are Midwives in Various Ways Kill the Child Conceived
in the Womb, and Procure an Abortion . . . "; "How Witches Impede and Prevent
the Power of Procreation"; "How, as it were, they Deprive Man of his Virile
Member." Other questions considered by the pious authors are "Who Are Fit
and Proper Judges in the Trial of Witches?" and various methods of sentencing
the guilty. Readers will want to look at Ehrenreich and English's *Witches,
Midwives, and Nurses* (1973) in conjunction with this demanding text.

1476   Kerenyi, Karoly, 1897-1973. **Eleusis: Archetypal Image of Mother
        and Daughter.** New York: Bollingen Foundation (distr. Pantheon
        Books), 1967; repr. New York: Schocken Books, 1977. 257p. bibliog.
        index. $9.90. ISBN 0805205489. LC 76-9148.
The text of this volume on the Eleusinian Mysteries (commemorating the grief
of Demeter at the rape of her daughter Persephone, "the ineffable maiden")
tends to be obscure and somewhat difficult to follow for the non-classicist.
The visual representation of the Mystery or Secret of Eleusis, however, makes
this particularly worthwhile for all collections. An important section of the
study, entitled "Reconstruction," explores geographical, chronological, and
mythological settings; contrasts and compares the Lesser Mysteries and the
Great Mysteries; and details the Secret of Eleusis. Part 2 contains a "Hermeneuti-
cal Essay on the Mysteries."

1477   Koltun, Elizabeth, ed. **The Jewish Woman: New Perspectives.** New York:
        Schocken Books, 1976. 294p. bibliog. $12.95. ISBN 0805236147.
        LC 75-35445.
Jewish attitudes toward women rooted in doctrine, tradition, and law form
the basis of this collection of essays, which looks to the past and to the sources
of the traditional Judaic views of women even as it looks to the future and a
reexamination of the law. Among the essays here are: Judith Plaskow's "The

Jewish Feminist: Conflict in Identities"; Cherie Koller-Fox's "Women and Jewish Education: A New Look at the Bat Mitzvah"; Paula Hyman's "The Other Half: Women in the Jewish Tradition"; Carol Clapsaddle's "Flight from Feminism: The Case of the Israeli Woman"; Sonya Michel's "Mothers and Daughters in American Jewish Literature: The Rotted Cord."

1478   Ochs, Carol. **Behind the Sex of God: Toward a New Consciousness— Transcending Matriarchy and Patriarchy.** Boston: Beacon Press, 1977. 177p. bibliog. index. $9.95. ISBN 0807011126. LC 76-48519.

Carol Ochs writes in her prologue: "The major concern of this book is to show how the dichotomy of matriarchy and patriarchy has affected religious thought. . . . I will suggest that the opposition of matriarchy and patriarchy can be overcome not by opting for one rather than the other, nor even by combining the two. I will suggest that the apparent duality can be transcended and a genuine unity achieved." Ochs examines and analyzes the concept of creation; the Eleusinian mystery religion, a predominantly matriarchal system; the sacrifice of Isaac, the stories of Cain and the Tower of Babel, and the emphasis on exile within the Judaeo-Christian (essentially patriarchal) tradition; the persistence of matriarchal elements within the Judaeo-Christian tradition as revealed by the cult of Mary; and the constellation of opposing categories in matriarchy and patriarchy (e.g., between spirit and matter).

1479   Richardson, Herbert Warren. **Nun, Witch, Playmate: The Americaniza- tion of Sex.** New York: Harper and Row, 1971. 147p. bibliog. index. $2.50. LC 76-85064.

Richardson, a theologian, claims that he has used an "historical evolutionary approach" in positing a general theory of sexuality, one that discounts religious, metaphysical and moral considerations. The first sentences of the book ("How a man views the world always expresses his own view of himself—even though he may not be aware of this. The evolution of human consciousness includes, therefore, the evolution of man in all the dimensions of his being") serve as typical examples of the extent to which Richardson himself is caught up in the problem of patriarchy in Western society that he describes. He then goes on to enumerate five major evolutions in consciousness that mark transformations of sexual consciousness: 1) mimetic consciousness; 2) ego-consciousness (7000- 1000 B.C.); 3) rational consciousness (800-400 B.C.); 4) self-consciousness (1300-1700 A.D.); 5) and polyconsciousness, still in its developing stages. Key concepts in this very theological schema of love and sexuality are that virginity is a higher form of love, that genital sexuality is somehow less than ascetical freedom (chastity); courtly love is superior to orgasmic sexual experience. Mariology, the tenets of courtly love, the history of witchcraft, romantic marriage as an institution, the emergence of the playmate as a function of the petting process, and American utopian communities all receive attention. Richardson sees the Hebrews, the Catholic monastics and the American Puritans, along with sects of the American utopian tradition, as pioneers in forging new sexual and spiritual possibilities for both men and women. Many feminists will disagree with Richardson's notion. Mary Daly's books will be useful to consult for a contrasting viewpoint.

1480   Ruether, Rosemary Radford. **Liberation Theology: Human Hope**
         Confronts Christian History and American Power. New York: Paulist
         Press, 1972. 194p. bibliog. $3.95. ISBN 0809117444. LC 72-92263.
Ruether brings together in this volume a collection of her essays (some previously
published) on the theology of liberation. The essays "focus on the question of
human liberation primarily from the situation of the 'oppressor-oppressed'
relationship, as this applies to Christian anti-Semitism, racism, sexism and
colonialism." They also raise questions about what resources the Christian
tradition possesses "to provide symbols for the liberation of peoples whom
the very culture created in the name of Christianity has helped to oppress . . .
and what transformations need to take place to transform Christianity . . . from
an ideology of the oppressor to a gospel of liberation for the oppressed, and
through the oppressed, for the oppressor as well." Two essays that may be
of particular interest to women are "Is Christianity Misogynist? The Failure
of Women's Liberation in the Church" and "Mother Earth and the Megamachine:
A Theology of Liberation in a Feminine, Somatic and Ecological Perspective."
Other topics she specifically addresses are the counter-culture, the suppression
of Christian radicalism, Christian anti-Semitism, black theology, the dilemma
of the white Left in the U.S., and Latin American theology of liberation.

1481   Ruether, Rosemary Radford, ed. **Religion and Sexism: Images of**
         Woman in the Jewish and Christian Traditions. New York: Simon
         and Schuster, 1974. 356p. bibliog. index. $10.95. ISBN 0671216929.
         LC 74-2791.
Included in this important book of essays are: Bernard Prusak's "Woman:
Seductive Siren and Source of Sin?"; Constance Parvey's "The Theology and
Leadership of Women in the New Testament"; and Ruether's "Mysogynism and
Virginal Feminism in the Fathers of the Church." Each area of historical theology
treated is written by a scholar in that specific area. Each essay attempts to trace
the traditional cultural images that have subjugated women.

1482   Stanton, Elizabeth (Cady), 1815-1902. **The Woman's Bible.** New York:
         Arno Press, 1972. (Repr. of 1895-1898 ed.). 2v. in 1. $16.00. ISBN
         040504481X. LC 72-2626.
"The Bible teaches that woman brought sin and death into the world, that she
precipitated the fall of the race, that she was arraigned before the judgment
seat of Heaven, tried, condemned and sentenced. . . . From the inauguration
of the movement for woman's emancipation the Bible has been used to hold
her in the 'divinely ordained sphere' prescribed in the Old and New Testaments"
(from the introduction). This radical critique of how religious ideology buttresses
the structure of sexual inequality is a clear example of the broad feminist concerns of Elizabeth Cady Stanton. Suffrage was the key focus of her political
activism, but not the sum total of her feminist vision. *The Woman's Bible*
alienated many of her more conservative suffragist contemporaries, and the
National American Woman Suffrage Association voted to officially dissociate
itself from Stanton's views in 1896. Part 1 contains "Comments on Genesis,
Exodus, Leviticus, Numbers and Deuteronomy." Part 2 comments on the Old
and New Testaments from Joshua to Revelation. This is essential historical

background to the contemporary feminist analysis of the Judeo-Christian religious tradition (e.g., Mary Daly, Rosemary Radford Ruether).

1483   Stone, Merlin. **When God Was a Woman.** New York: Dial Press, 1976. 265p. bibliog. index. $7.95. ISBN 0803794746. LC 76-22544.

Originally published in Great Britain under the title, *The Paradise Papers*, in this popularized treatment of goddess-worship and its transformation into more modern patriarchal religions, Stone explains the role of ancient worship in the formation of Judeo-Christian attitudes toward women. A major point is that female religion "flourished for thousands of years before the advent of Judaism, Christianity and the Classical Age of Greece." She also points out frequently that most scholarly archaeological accounts of female religion are written by men who dismiss worship of female deities as "fertility cults." She attempts to unravel the legend of Adam and the fallen Eve, suggesting that the myth's basis was a Levite strategy to suppress female religion. Stone herself is an art historian who became interested in the topic of female religion from her study of goddess sculpture. The bibliography is rich in sources on ancient religions and the place of the goddess in these religious traditions.

1484*   Stuart, Martha, and William Thomas Liu, 1930- , eds. **The Emerging Woman: The Impact of Family Planning; An Informal Sharing of Interests, Ideas, and Concerns, Held at the University of Notre Dame.** Boston: Little, Brown, 1970. 329p. index. ISBN 0700001905. LC 75-112013.

The purpose of the conference that gave rise to this publication was to bring together panelists, delegates, and observers representing public and private life to discuss changes in women's roles around the world resulting from the use of contraceptives. Participants represented a variety of religions, countries, disciplines, and institutions. Each subject was introduced and explored by a man and a woman who were working together; panelists included such persons as Martha Stuart (who edited the text) and William V. D'Antonio; William H. Masters and Virginia E. Johnson; and Joseph W. Bird and Lois F. Bird. The final chapter asks the question, "what are we free for?," and concludes that traditional structures cannot be dropped without replacing them, that morality and responsibility are evolving as symbolic values but have in some instances been irresponsibly removed from a religious foundation and secularized in certain cultures. There was a consensus that women's freedom provides unprecedented opportunities for us all to live and work together, as female assertiveness supplants a diminishing passivity. Given its sponsorship, the conference discussions ranged over many pejorative issues that one might not expect in such a setting.

1485*   Swidler, Arlene, ed. **Sistercelebrations: Nine Worship Experiences.** Philadelphia, PA: Fortress Press, 1974. 88p. bibliog. $2.50. ISBN 0800610849. LC 74-80414.

Women have been looking at their churches and synagogues with the idea of creating new roles for women in the liturgy which will incorporate feminist ideas and concerns. Nine sample liturgies have been collected here that will provide ideas for women eager to create their own liturgical celebrations. Titles of liturgies: "God of the Matriarchs"; "Motherhood Reborn"; "Brit

Kedusha: A Home Ceremony Celebrating the Birth of a Daughter"; "A Mass
for Freedom for Women"; "A Celebration on the Opening of the Ecumenical
Women's Centers"; "Sister-celebration: To Cultivate the Garden"; "The Trial
of the Halloween Six" (in memory of the persecution of witches); "Sisterhood
Service on Mother's Day"; and "Jewish Women's Hagada."

1486   Vetterling-Braggin, Mary, et al., eds. **Feminism and Philosophy**. Totowa,
        NJ: Littlefield, Adams, 1977. 452p. bibliog. $7.95. ISBN 0822603357.
        LC 77-25464.
Feminism, sex roles and gender, sexism in ordinary language, equal opportunity
and preferential hiring, marriage, rape, and abortion are major areas of philo-
sophical inquiry in this important collection of articles on feminism and philosophy. Each section is supplemented by an excellent bibliography. Contents
include: Alison Jaggar, "Political Philosophies of Women's Liberation"; Sandra
Lee Bartky, "Toward a Phenomenology of Feminist Consciousness"; Joyce
Trebilcot, "Two Forms of Androgynism"; Janice Moulton, "The Myth of
Neutral 'Man' "; Carolyn Korsmeyer, "The Hidden Joke: Generic Uses of
Masculine Terminology"; Onora O'Neill, "How Do We Know When Opportuni-
ties Are Equal?"; Alan H. Goldman, "Limits to the Justification of Reverse
Discrimination"; Sara Ann Ketchum, "Liberalism and Marriage Law"; Susan
Griffin, "Rape: The All-American Crime"; Susan Nicholson, "The Roman
Catholic Doctrine of Therapeutic Abortion"; and Jane English, "Abortion and
the Concept of a Person."

1487   Warner, Marina, 1946- . **Alone of All Her Sex: The Myth and the Cult
        of the Virgin Mary.** New York: Knopf; distr. New York: Random House,
        1976. 400p. bibliog. index. $15.00. ISBN 0394499131. LC 76-13682.
Warner's Catholic background gave rise to a desire and need to research the
paradox inherent in the cult of Mary: the most holy and chaste of women is
celebrated for her removal from humanity and from other women. This is an
important and readable study of the Mary myth done from the perspective
of a scholar of comparative religion. Warner refrains from using polemic, presenting a painstakingly researched examination of Mariological scholarship drawn
from a diversity of sources: church history, secular history, biblical exegesis,
legend, iconography, dogma, and literature. A particularly useful chronology
maps historical events and developments in arts and letters as the cult of the
Virgin evolved. Warner approaches Mary via her five personae: Virgin, Queen,
Bride, Mother, and Intercessor.

1488   Weil, Simone, 1909-1943. **The Simone Weil Reader.** Ed. by George A.
        Panichas. New York: McKay, 1977. 529p. bibliog. index. $17.50.
        ISBN 067950656X. LC 77-692.
Since Simone Weil's recent "rediscovery" by the public, the definitive biography
by Pétrement has appeared (*Simone Weil: A Life*, 1977) as have the *Notebooks*
(translated by Arthur Wills, reissued 1976). Though not a substitute for the
First and Last Notebooks (Oxford University Press, 1970), the *Reader* (edited
by George A. Panichas) draws together essays and excerpts from her most important writings, all of which manifest her deep involvement with militant politics
in France and on an international scale, as well as her saintly mysticism. Because

she was at once a political activist and a mystic/philosopher, it may be a fault of the *Reader* to segment the readings under headings such as A New Saintliness, Prelude to Politics, Language and Thought, Criteria of Wisdom, Paths of Meditation, when these categories may suggest arbitrary and artificial separations in her thought and action. "As a book *The Simone Weil Reader* has its own special and autonomous identity, containing the essence of Simone Weil's thought in its representative scope, range, focus. The concentrated form of the book should help the reader to grasp the syncretizing intellectual variety (and vitality), and internalizing spiritual unity, in outlook and overview, of her writings on religion, politics, sociology, anthropology, philosophy, economics, science, aesthetics and education."

SOCIOLOGY

The intent of this chapter is to survey the current sociologically based book offerings on women-related topics. Popular treatments of current issues, texts and anthologies, theoretical and empirical studies, as well as anecdotal, impressionistic accounts constitute this chapter. Topics such as women offenders, abortion, careers, media, aging, single women, marriage, motherhood, sex roles, rape, black women, lesbians, battered women, racism, housework, and childcare suggest the diversity of the published contemporary sociology material. Also in this section are contemporary sociological surveys of women in other countries. The women's studies journal literature keeps the user current in this area (see Periodicals). Many fine bibliographies that support the topics mentioned above appear in the Reference chapter.

1489 AAAS Seminar on Women in Development, Mexico, 1975. **Women and World Development: With an Annotated Bibliography.** Ed. by Irene Tinker, Michèle Bo Bramsen, and Mayra Buvinić. New York: Praeger, 1976. 382p. bibliog. index. $21.50. ISBN 0275565203. LC 76-20602.

This volume presents background papers and proceedings of the Seminar on Women in Development convened by the American Association for the Advancement of Science (AAAS) in Mexico City, June 15-18, 1975—just prior to the World Conference of International Women's Year. The Seminar was envisaged as preparation for and a parallel to the IWY Conference and brought together 95 men and women—academics, staff members of development agencies, activists—from 55 countries. Emphasis from the outset was on the failures of development strategies with regard to women, and a key goal of the Seminar was the generation of concrete proposals for change. Participants divided into five workshops with the following foci: food production and the introduction of small-scale technology into rural life; urban living, migration, and employment; education and communication; health, nutrition, and family planning; and women's formal and informal organizations. There was general agreement among participants that development strategies are having a negative impact on women through their failure to recognize women's traditional productive roles, through reinforcement of prevailing patriarchal values, and through introduction of Western patriarchal values. Participants were divided, however, in their strategies for change between those whose vision was one of reform and those convinced of the necessity of revolution. Included in this volume are twelve background papers prepared for the Seminar by Margaret Mead, Irene Tinker, Teresa Orrego de Figueroa, Kenneth Little, Mary Elmendorf, and others; descriptive summaries of the proceedings of the Seminar; and an extensive annotated bibliography on women and development prepared by Mayra Buvinić and others (also separately published by the Overseas Development Council, 1976). Good background reading for this volume is Ester Boserup's *Woman's Role in Economic Development* (1974).

1490   Addams, Jane, 1860-1935. **The Social Thought of Jane Addams.** Ed. by
        Christopher Lasch. Indianapolis, IN: Bobbs-Merrill, 1965. 266p. bibliog.
        $5.20. ISBN 0672601109. LC 65-22345.

Christopher Lasch brings together here a collection of writings by Jane Addams
with the hope of dispelling "the impression that Miss Addams was important
solely for her services to the poor." He acknowledges the greatness of Addams
as founder of Hull House, activist and social reformer who struggled for child
labor legislation; for tenement reform and public health; for pacifism, internationalism, and feminism; who chose to live and work in Chicago's West Side.
But he also wants to acquaint his readers with the power of her intellect and
the quality of her social analysis and criticism. The essays include "Twenty
years at Hull-House" (1910), "Why women should vote" (1910), "The Progressive Party and the Negro" (1912), "The Second twenty years at Hull-House"
(1930), and "Peace and bread in time of war" (1922).

1491   Adler, Freda. **Sisters in Crime: The Rise of the New Female Criminal.**
        New York: McGraw-Hill, 1976. 287p. bibliog. index. $3.95. ISBN
        0070004161. LC 76-23387.

"Women are indeed committing more crimes than ever before. Those crimes
involve a greater degree of violence, and even in prison this new breed exhibits
a hitherto unmatched pugnacity." Adler sees the increase in crimes committed
by women as "but one wave in [the] rising tide of female assertiveness" dating
from the Civil Rights Movement. Her book is concerned with providing documentation of changing patterns of female crime in the United States, projections
for the future, and a psychosocial interpretation. Readers might want to compare
Adler's interpretation with the view that emerges from Kathryn Burkhart's
Women in Prison, a descriptive and analytic account of women prisoners' interpretations of their experiences.

1492   Andreas, Carol. **Sex and Caste in America.** Englewood Cliffs, NJ:
        Prentice-Hall, 1971. 146p. bibliog. index. $2.95. ISBN 0138074380.
        LC 74-160532.

This introduction to the study of sexual inequality was written—as were several
other such general texts—because the author (a professor of sociology) felt
the lack of such a book when she first taught a college course on sex roles.
The topics covered include sex-role socialization, education, work, religion
and academe, law and morals, and politics and history. Her perspective is sensitive to questions of class, race, and imperialism as well as to sexual inequality.
The treatment of each topic is necessarily brief, and hence the book will be
most useful in introductory courses and for readers relatively new to the subject.

1493   Andrews, Stephen Pearl, 1812-1886, ed. **Love, Marriage, and Divorce,
        and the Sovereignty of the Individual: A Discussion between Henry
        James, Horace Greeley and Stephen Pearl Andrews; And a Hitherto
        Unpublished Manuscript, Love, Marriage and the Condition of Woman.**
        Boston: B. R. Tucker, 1889; repr. Weston, MA: M and S Press, 1975.
        13, 121, 55p. $12.50. ISBN 0877300100. LC 75-310761.

"As part of the debate over divorce in the 1850's, Horace Greeley, Henry
James, Sr., and Stephen Pearl Andrews offered representative arguments in an

extended exchange in the New York *Tribune*. Greeley, reformer and editor/ publisher of the *Tribune*, defended 'indissoluable marriage.' James wanted a liberalized divorce law that could rectify improper marriages. Andrews provided an anarchist/socialist critique of existing marriage and sought to delineate another system of male/female relations based upon love and equality" (from the introduction, by Charles Shively). This is a good edition of the debate, with an interesting introduction by Shively. It also includes Andrew's unpublished essay, "Love, Marriage and the Condition of Woman"—a "masterpiece in the literature of sexual liberation."

1494   Angrist, Shirley S., and Elizabeth M. Almquist. **Careers and Contingencies: How College Women Juggle with Gender.** New York: Dunellen, 1975. 269p. bibliog. index. $15.00. ISBN 0804671001. LC 75-326795.
In this book, the authors present the results of a longitudinal study of college women—their attitudes and their plans and aspirations for adult life, especially career aspirations. The 87 subjects of the study entered college in 1964 and were given questionnaires and interviews throughout their four years of study. The authors utilize both statistical analyses of the questionnaire data and direct quotations from interviews to illustrate their conclusions. The primary focus is on the women's career orientation, or lack of it, anticipated role conflict between work and children, and the relation between these and the influences of parents, teachers, "boyfriends," and "girlfriends." The book includes a foreword by Jessie Bernard.

1495   Ashton, Winifred [Dane, Clemence, pseud.]. **The Women's Side.** Freeport, NY: Books for Libraries Press, 1970. 144p. $13.00. ISBN 0836915666. LC 70-99629.
First published in 1926, this is a series of essays "on subjects that concern women," written by a feminist, hoping, she says, at a minimum to spark healthy disagreement from women. "For even in this year of grace there are still women who evade the responsibilities of citizenship by declaring that 'woman's sphere is the home' and sitting down in it with the windows shut: forgetting that if they will not take their share of national housekeeping they run the risk of having their private housekeeping threatened by forces—laws, wars, strikes and revolutions—outside their control." Among the topics discussed by Dane are the vote, capital punishment, education, marriage laws, and "sex and the business woman."

1496   Baum, Charlotte, 1934- , et al. **The Jewish Woman in America.** New York: Dial Press, 1976. 290p. bibliog. index. $8.95. ISBN 0803797079. LC 75-33895.
This book was written collectively by three women—Charlotte Baum, Paula Hyman, and Sonya Michel—who, despite very different economic and cultural backgrounds, all became interested in trying to understand how the positive images of Jewish women in the old country and during the immigrant period evolved in this century into the degrading stereotypes of "Jewish Mother" and "Jewish American Princess." They soon came to suspect that the change in image reflected a transformation in the Jewish woman's real social role, and it is this transformation they explore in their book. Among the topics

they discuss are: Women in the Jewish Tradition; The German Jewish Woman in America; Jewish Women in Eastern Europe; Eastern European Jewish Women in America; Jewish Women in the Union Movement; and Jewish Women Today. It includes a lengthy bibliography.

1497*   Beasley, Maurine Hoffman, and Sheila Silver. **Women in Media: A Documentary Source Book.** Washington: Women's Institute for Freedom of the Press, 1977. 198p. bibliog. $5.95. ISBN 0930470001. LC 77-82376.

Beasley and Silver bring together much unpublished material about the women's media phenomenon as it is taking shape in this country and the world. Documentation is selected and arranged to describe historical development from 1790 to 1977, illustrating the worst trends and the most hopeful developments regarding portrayal and employment of women in the media. Biographical portraits and brief selections appear for women such as Anne Royall, Margaret Fuller, Ida Tarbell, Rheta Childe Dorr, and Margaret Bourke-White. Several chapters deal with media issues such as broadcast licenses, monitoring television, newspapers, and advertising. Publishing and IWY guidelines are included. "Journalism of the Women's Liberation Movement" covers the genesis of publications such as *Ms.* and *off our backs.* Excellent selection of bibliographical notes, including materials on black women journalists, license challenges, federal complaints, agreements, and prime time/daytime portrayal.

1498   Beauvoir, Simone de, 1908- . **The Coming of Age.** New York: Putnam, 1972. 585p. bibliog. index. $10.00. ISBN 0399109110. LC 75-189781.

De Beauvoir calls the reluctance of Western society to deal with old age "a conspiracy of silence." As with other oppressed groups, she sees the aged as a group without economic strength, without rights, and without solidarity as an exploited class. By exploring societal definitions and stereotypes of the aged, the aging process and its meaning, and the existential quality inherent in change and process, de Beauvoir attempts to look at the aging process as a cultural fact. Although de Beauvoir is interested in exploring the fact of growing old for both men and women, there is much here about aging in women, treating issues of sexuality, narcissism, cultural difference, and employment as they apply to women. It is worthwhile to look at Elaine Marks's *Simone de Beauvoir: Encounters with Death* (1973) along with *Coming of Age* to trace de Beauvoir's preoccupation with the subject. This is a translation of *La vieillesse.*

1499*   Benet, Mary Kathleen. **The Secretarial Ghetto.** New York: McGraw-Hill, 1973. 181p. bibliog. ISBN 0070045364. LC 72-10053.

Six out of ten office workers in the United States are women, and most of these are secretaries. This book is a classic study of what Benet calls the "secretarial ghetto." "Interviews with several hundred secretaries supplemented the reading that went into this book. Offices in the United States and Europe yielded a story of discontent that was hotly challenged by the bosses, personnel managers, and employment agents whose views were also sought. Sometimes it was hard to believe that the two sides were talking about the same offices. The views expressed by secretaries in all situations and all countries were remarkably similar, as were the men's opinions. It seemed, finally, that there really was a sex

war going on in the office, and that it bore some similarity to a class war—
but with a female proletariat and a male capitalist class" (from the author's
note). The experience recounted here of life in the secretarial ghetto is surely
thought provoking on at least two counts—first, with its depiction of the sexual
division of labor and dynamics characterizing the ghetto, as noted by the author;
and secondly, as a testimonial of discontent, suggesting that more might be
needed for its relief than a modification of this sexual division of labor in the
form of women bosses. Benet's chapters are: The Rise of the Secretary; Substitute Wives: The Making of a Secretary; The Ambitious Secretary; and The Pool
Proletariat.

1500   Bequaert, Lucia H. **Single Women: Alone and Together.** Boston:
        Beacon Press, 1976. 256p. bibliog. index. $8.95. ISBN 0807027561.
        LC 75-36038.
"Autobiographical statements, contemporary research findings, and practical
coping information are interwoven to delineate the social and emotional realities of women who live alone by choice or by marital dissolution. After looking
at the special challenges confronting different categories of single women—
never-married, divorced, and widowed—Lucia N. Bequaert explores general
issues, such as loneliness, sexuality, and economic insecurity, that are important
in the life patterns of all single women" (Marion Kilson, *Harvard Magazine*).
Bequaert includes at the end a selected bibliography and a list of useful addresses,
including both organizations and periodicals.

1501   Bernard, Jessie Shirley, 1903- . **The Future of Marriage.** New York:
        Bantam Books, 1973. 409p. bibliog. index. $2.25. ISBN 055310165X.
Bernard notes in her introduction that "the future of marriage" has long been
and continues to be an issue of great concern to society largely because it is
presumed that the sexual controls instituted in marriage are fundamental to
the stability of the whole social fabric. Her focus in this book is not on marriage
as a system for the control of sexuality, but on "the commitment which men
and women make to each other—including the sexual commitment but not
restricted to it—that constitutes their marriage." A second focus is the lifestyles that accompany this commitment and their future evolution. In her
analysis, Bernard is careful to make distinctions between men's and women's
experience of marriage. She is also attentive to the important relationship between
men and women's feelings about their work, about themselves, and the quality
of their interpersonal relationships. The book is written in a popular style but
with careful footnoting of sources.

1502   Bernard, Jessie Shirley, 1903- . **The Sex Game.** New York: Atheneum,
        1972. 372p. bibliog. index. $4.95. ISBN 0689702930. LC 68-13219.
Bernard writes in a new introduction to this book on communication between
the sexes (first published in 1968) that it, "in fact, constitutes in a way wholly
unintended a portrait of the relations between the sexes which are the prime
targets of [feminists]. It is, par excellence, a statement of precisely what it
is they wish to be liberated from." Bernard sees many of her conclusions, reached
before the most explosive period of the women's movement, as being too mildly
stated, but argues that the portrait presented by the book remains essentially valid.

1503   Bernard, Jessie Shirley, 1903- . **Women, Wives, Mothers: Values and Options.** Chicago: Aldine, 1975. 286p. bibliog. index. $15.00. ISBN 0202302806. LC 74-18210.

A portion of this collection of essays is taken from Bernard's earlier book, *The Future of Motherhood.* The other articles are, however, not available elsewhere, as they were for the most part prepared as talks for scholarly meetings. Among these are: "Research on Sex Differences: An Overview of the State of the Art"; "Sex-Role Transcendence and Sex-Role Transcenders"; "Adolescence and Socialization for Motherhood"; "The Impact of Sexism and Racism on Employment Status and Earnings"; and "The Bitter Fruits of Extreme Sex Specialization." Each group of essays is given a short introduction by Bernard.

1504   Bettelheim, Bruno. **The Children of the Dream.** New York: Macmillan, 1969. 363p. bibliog. index. $7.95. LC 69-10505.

"How intimate is the link between the nature of a society and how its children are raised? Or as we have so often asked: Is man the father of society, or society the father of man?" Thus opens Bettelheim's study of childraising in the Israeli kibbutz. There is much material here on the ideas and practice of collective childrearing, on the commitment to egalitarianism and community, and on the differences that Bettelheim observed between the new generation and the founders. While contemporary feminists have pointed out the limitations of "women's liberation" on the kibbutzim, the kibbutz experiments are important as examples of attempts by men and women to live together, work together, and raise children in new ways.

1505   Blood, Robert O., and Donald M. Wolfe. **Husbands and Wives: The Dynamics of Married Living.** New York: Free Press, 1965. 293p. bibliog. index. $2.95. ISBN 0029040701. LC 59-6824.

This is a classic empirical study of marriage. Conducted in the late 1950s, this study obviously suffers from preconceptions and blindspots characteristic of the period. However, it has historical importance as one of the pieces of research first studied and critiqued by the feminist sociologists who emerged in the late '60s and early '70s. The authors report their findings from interviews with wives in 731 families from metropolitan Detroit and 178 farm families (husbands were excluded as subjects because they are "less available"). The subjects were questioned on the following topics (it's important to note that the format was multiple-choice rather than open-ended, thus putting prior constraints on the results): power and decision-making; division of labor; employment; children; companionship; understanding and emotional well-being; love; and stresses and strengths in American marriages (this last is actually based on questions about "marital satisfaction"). This book will be of more interest to persons with extensive interest in the field of marriage and the family than it will be to the casual reader.

1506   Bracey, John H., et al., comps. **Black Matriarchy: Myth or Reality?** Belmont, CA: Wadsworth, 1971. 217p. bibliog. $4.95. ISBN 0534000495. LC 77-154815.

This anthology represents an important sourcebook on the history of the debate over the black family in the United States—whether or not it can be described as "matriarchal" and, if it can, whether the implications of "matriarchy" for the black community are good or bad. Represented here are E. Franklin Frazier, black sociologist who first made the argument that the black family was "matriarchal," in his view as a result of the stresses of slavery; anthropologist Melville J. Herskovits, who disagreed with Frazier's attribution of causality, contending that black "matriarchy" was a remnant of West African culture and had been important in the survival of the black community in the U.S.; three empirical studies (by Charles S. Johnson, Lee Rainwater, and Elliot Liebow) that essentially are interested in applying Frazier's thesis; Daniel P. Moynihan's apocalyptic report (*The Negro Family: The Case for National Action*, 1965), which argued that the problems of the black community were caused by the "breakdown in black family life," i.e., black "matriarchy"; Hylan Lewis, who simply repeats (in answer to Moynihan) the argument that the weakness of the black family is result, not cause, of black status; and two final articles by Herbert H. Hyman and Virginia Heyer on new approaches to the problem. It should be noted that a feminist viewpoint is nowhere represented in this collection. Readers interested in the feminist critique might want to consult Carol Stack's *All Our Kin* or Rosaldo and Lamphere, *Woman Culture and Society*. For a recent comprehensive history of the black family in the U.S., see Herbert Gutman, *The Black Family in Slavery and Freedom, 1750-1925* (1976).

1507   Brown, Donald R., 1925- , ed. **The Role and Status of Women in the Soviet Union.** New York: Teachers College Press, 1968. 139p. bibliog. $8.95. ISBN 0807711284. LC 68-27326.

This is a collection of articles on the subject of the status of women in the Soviet Union: "Workers (and Mothers): Soviet Women Today," by Mark G. Field; "The Woman Student in Russia," by Patricia Carden; "The Changing Image of Women in Soviet Literature," by Vera S. Dunham; "The Changing Soviet Family," by Urie Bronfenbrenner; "The Childbearing Functions of the Soviet Family," by David M. Heer; and "Marriage and the Family," by Rachel Dunaway Cox.

1508   Burgess, Ann Wolbert, and Lynda Lytle Holmstrom. **Rape: Victims of Crisis.** Bowie, MD: R. J. Brady, 1974. 308p. bibliog. $9.95. ISBN 0876180292. LC 74-7577.

Ann Burgess, a psychiatric nurse, and Lynda Holmstrom, a sociologist, initiated a counseling program for rape victims at Boston City Hospital in 1972. This book is an analysis of the first year in the program, during which the authors interviewed and followed up all rape victims admitted to the hospital. In this volume, they discuss the victim's and the rapist's view of rape, victims' reactions to rape, community reaction to rape (police, hospital, and community programs for rape victims), and the crisis intervention techniques that they developed. They make frequent use of examples taken from their counseling work, including verbatim accounts of conversations, statements by victims, and court interrogation. This book is written in a highly readable style for a varied audience, including professionals, crisis workers, and victims and their families.

1509   Burkhart, Kathryn Watterson. **Women in Prison.** Garden City, NY:
        Doubleday, 1973. 465p. bibliog. $10.00. ISBN 038504674X.
        LC 72-92195.

In preparation for this book, Kathryn Burkhart made visits to 21 jails and
prisons for women, eight jails and prisons for men, and five juvenile jails. She
interviewed 400 women in depth and had conversations with approximately
500 more. In addition, she interviewed administrators of prisons, heads of
bureaus of correction and more than 250 guards and prison employees, correc-
tional counselors, deputy sheriffs, police, lawyers, judges, parole and probation
officers and criminologists. She writes that "it's adding all these pieces together
that gives us a fuller picture of what's going on. No single person has a full
measure of truth." As Burkhart points out, prisoners—male or female—are
rarely asked for their interpretation of their experiences. What makes this book
extraordinarily powerful and valuable is Burkhart's commitment to letting
the women she met speak for themselves, in their own words.

1510   Butler, Josephine Elizabeth (Grey), 1828-1906, ed. **Woman's Work
        and Woman's Culture.** New York: Gordon Press, n.d. $35.00. ISBN
        0849013194.

This is a group of essays on sexual inequality and women's rights, first collected
in one volume by Josephine Butler in 1869. Among the articles: a lengthy
introduction, by Butler; "The Final Cause of Woman," by Frances Power
Cobbe; "Medicine as a Profession for Women," by Sophia Jex-Blake; "On
Some Historical Aspects of Family Life," by Charles H. Pearson; "The Property
Disabilities of a Married Woman, and Other Legal Effects of Marriage," by
Herbert N. Mozley; "Female Suffrage, Considered Chiefly with Regard to Its
Indirect Results," by Julia Wedgwood; "The Education of Girls, Its Present and
Its Future," by Elizabeth C. Wolstenholme; and "The Social Position of Women
in the Present Age," by John Boyd-Kinnear.

1511   Carson, Josephine, 1919- . **Silent Voices: The Southern Negro Woman
        Today.** New York: Delacorte Press, 1969. 273p. $6.95. ISBN
        0440078997. LC 69-17530.

"Black woman, silent, almost invisible in America, has been speaking for three
hundred years in pantomime or at best in a borrowed voice. She has moved
silently through the mythological roles forced upon her—from chattel to Mammy
to Matriarch. She has solaced and fortified the entire South of the United States,
black and white, male and female, a South which reveres and heeds her in secret,
which confides in her and trusts her to rear its children, black and white, yet
which—like the rest of America—has never asked her to speak, to reveal her
private history, her knowledge, her imaginings, never asked her participation
in anything but maintenance of humanity by way of the back door." In preparation for this book, Carson asked many southern black women to speak and reveal
their histories, knowledge, and imaginings. What resulted is a moving account,
a series of images and stories written in a vivid style.

1512   Cater, Libby A., 1925- , et al., eds. **Women and Men: Changing Roles,
        Relationships and Perceptions: Report of a Workshop.** New York:

Praeger, 1977. 270p. bibliog. index. $17.50. ISBN 0030214769.
LC 76-14472.

Consists of transcriptions of discussions and essays written for a workshop
held in Aspen, Colorado, August 3-10, 1975, under the auspices of the Aspen
Institute for Humanistic Studies. Represented among the participants were
men and women from a variety of professions—academia, business, labor unions,
law, etc.; no non-professionals were included. Among the essayists are Tamara K.
Hareven, Marcia Guttentag, Joseph Pleck, and Catharine R. Stimpson.

1513   Chafetz, Janet Saltzman. **Masculine/Feminine or Human? An Overview
       of the Sociology of Sex Roles.** Itasca, IL: F. E. Peacock, 1974. 242p.
       bibliog. index. $4.95. ISBN 0875811663. LC 73-85770.

This introductory text in the sociology of sex roles is intended for the undergraduate level. Chafetz examines theories on the origins of patriarchy, sex-
role stereotyping, socialization processes, sex discrimination, the impact of
sex roles on relationships between men and women, and possibilities for change.
Her emphasis is on the relation between male and female sex roles and the
different constraints of each. Another basic text in the sociology of sex roles
is Betty Yorburg's *Sexual Identity: Sex Roles and Social Change* (Wiley, 1974).
Yorburg gives an overview of variations in sex roles historically and cross-
culturally, in addition to her analysis of sex roles in the contemporary United
States.

1514* Conference on Black Women in America, University of Louisville, KY,
       1974. **Perspectives on Afro-American Women.** Ed. by Willa D. Johnson
       and Thomas L. Green. Washington: ECCA Publications, 1975. 197p.
       bibliog. LC 75-4204.

Most of the papers collected in this anthology were written for the Conference
on Black Women in America held in Louisville, Kentucky, in March 1974.
All of the writers represented are university faculty members, but various
disciplines are reflected: literature, education, and the various social sciences.
Among the articles: "The Black Struggle, Affirmative Action, and Women's
Liberation: Establishing Priorities," by Willa D. Johnson; "Diamond in Dirt
Theory of Slavery, Seasoning the Female Slave," by Margo Crawford; "The
Status of Black Women: Sex, Marriage and the Family," by Robert Staples;
"Comparative Life Styles of the Black Female in the United States and the
Black Female in Lesotho," by Nellie B. Kanno; "Black Eve or Madonna? A
Study of the Antithetical Views of the Mother in Black American Literature,"
by Daryl Dance; and "The Role of Black Women in Black Families: Teaching
About Black Families on a Predominantly White Campus," by Priscilla White
and Patricia Scott.

1515   Coolidge, Mary Elizabeth Burroughs (Roberts) Smith, 1860-1945.
       Why Women Are So. New York: Arno Press, 1972. (Repr. of 1912
       ed.). 371p. $17.00. ISBN 0405044526. LC 72-2595.

"To D. C. and other new men who set human quality above femininity in women,"
reads the dedication of this work by sociologist Mary Roberts Coolidge. Her
major concern in this book is the origin of "femininity." "As a working hypothesis it is assumed that the women of the nineteenth century in America were

for the most part what men expected them to be; modified only by the disinte-
grating, and at the same time reconstructive, forces of modern society. In
other words, sex traditions rather than innate sex character have produced what
is called 'feminine' as distinguished from womanly behavior." The study is
divided into four sections: The Domestic Traditions (includes "The Conventions
of Girlhood," "The Career of Motherhood," and "Domesticity as a Vocation");
The Effect upon Women (includes "The Feminine Temperament" and "The
Virtues of Subservience"); Some Exceptions (includes "Women Insurgents");
and From Femininity to Womanhood.

1516   Cormack, Margaret Lawson, 1912- . **The Hindu Woman.** New York:
        Teachers College, Columbia University, 1953; repr. Westport, CT:
        Greenwood Press, 1974. 207p. bibliog. $12.25. ISBN 0837175577.
        LC 74-6750.
Margaret Cormack was born in India and lived there 21 years, her experiences
"being chiefly connected with the South, in villages, and with the lower
classes. . . . " This background may temper somewhat the major limitation of
her study (originally 1953) of women in India—namely, that it is based almost
entirely on material obtained from ten Indian informants who were all graduate
students at Columbia University, and all from educated, urban, middle-, and
upper-class backgrounds. Cormack discusses birth and infancy, childhood,
socialization, puberty, betrothal, marriage, motherhood, single women, older
women, widowhood, divorce, and self-concept.

1517   Cory, Donald Webster, pseud. **The Homosexual in America: A Subjective
        Approach.** New York: Greenberg, 1951; repr. New York: Arno Press,
        1975. 326p. bibliog. index. $15.00. ISBN 0405073658. LC 75-12310.
Originally published in 1951, three years after the publication of the first volume
of the Kinsey Report had startled United States society into a new awareness
of homosexuality, Cory's book was well-timed and made an important contribution to the changes that ensued in the next two decades. The work developed
an analysis (the author claims it was the first such analysis) of homosexuals
as a minority group, though in the moderate tone prevalent in that period.
In his introduction to the reprint edition, Cory says he sees the book as having
mainly historical importance today, due to the significant changes that have
taken place in society, in gay liberation, and in his own views, which appear
to have moved in more conservative directions (he concludes the introduction
by declaring his belief that homosexuality is, after all, a form of mental illness).
A further limitation of the book is its tendency to assume male homosexuality
as a model, giving lesbianism scant treatment.

1518   Curtis, Jean, 1939- . **Working Mothers.** Garden City, NY: Doubleday,
        1976. 214p. $7.95. ISBN 0385037864. LC 75-18370.
Curtis interviewed over 200 women, their husbands, and children from various
geographical and social backgrounds across the United States for this book,
which addresses these questions: should a mother work outside the home or
not? if she does, what does it do to the children? the marriage? the husband?
the woman herself? This is not a how-to book, and the emphasis appears to be
on re-examination of roles and family life. The old traditions are scrutinized

and the literature on wage-earning mothers re-evaluated; contrasts and comparisons are drawn between mothers who do and don't work outside the home. Child care, housework, sex, stereotypes of husbands, and methods of coping are dealt with at length.

1519   David, Deborah Sarah, and Robert Brannon, eds. **The Forty-Nine Percent Majority: The Male Sex Role.** Reading, MA: Addison-Wesley, 1976. 338p. bibliog. $6.95. ISBN 0201014483. LC 75-18152.
Noting the lack of materials available for an analysis of male sex roles and the inaccessibility of what has appeared for undergraduate students, the editors have put together a useful reader on the topic. Materials are drawn from both books and journals and organized into the following sections: Part 1, Dimensions of the Male Sex Role (deals with male fears of expressiveness, vulnerability, "sissy stuff," homosexuality; success imperatives; competiveness; expectations of toughness, confidence and self-reliance; male aggression and violence; My Lai); part 2, Learning the Role (sex role socialization); and part 3, Changing the Roles (Men's Liberation). Among the contributors are Warren Farrell, Marc Feigen Fasteau, Robert Gould, Michael Korda, Lucy Komisar, Kate Millett, Joseph Pleck, and Jack Sawyer.

1520   Davidson, Terry. **Conjugal Crime: Understanding and Changing the Wifebeating Pattern.** New York: Hawthorn Books, 1978. 274p. bibliog. index. $9.95. ISBN 0801517311. LC 76-56524.
Terry Davidson was raised in a household where mother, son, and daughter were held captive and terrorized by the husband/father, a thoroughly respectable minister who just happened to brutalize his wife and children at home. Davidson was a survivor and has put her unhappy experience to use in trying to understand the social phenomenon of woman-battering and to work towards changing that pattern. In this book, she discusses both the problem and the growing movement that is confronting woman-battering through consciousness-raising, education, building shelters, working on legislation. One of the key messages of this book is that the crime is not restricted to the working class, the poverty-stricken, and the slums. Rather, it is all too common in middle-class families. A list of shelters, hotlines, addresses, and relevant publications is appended, along with a checklist of legal procedures for battered women. Two other works relevant to Davidson's topic (which we were unable to retrieve for review) are Roger Langley and Richard C. Levy, *Wife Beating: The Silent Crisis* (E. P. Dutton, 1977) and Erin Pizzey, *Scream Quietly or the Neighbors Will Hear* (R. Enslow, 1977).

1521   Donovan, Frances R. **The Saleslady.** Chicago: University of Chicago Press, 1929; repr. New York: Arno Press, 1974. 267p. bibliog. index. $17.00. ISBN 0405060882. LC 74-3942.
A study of a "female" occupation—sales—in the twenties, in the participant observation tradition. Donovan worked as a "saleslady" in a New York City department store during one summer vacation (her permanent occupation was as a schoolteacher; see her book, *The Schoolma'am*). She records her experiences on the job and with co-workers, attentive to the social backgrounds and pastimes of other saleswomen, their attitudes towards work and romance or marriage,

their relationships with each other, and their working conditions. Donovan also experimented with waitressing, writing about her impressions in *The Woman Who Waits*. Her works would be interesting to compare with recent descriptions of "female" occupations, for example, Louise Howe's *Pink Collar Workers* (1977).

1522 Donovan, Frances R. **The Schoolma'am.** New York: F. A. Stokes, 1938; repr. New York: Arno Press, 1974. 355p. bibliog. $22.00. ISBN 0405060874. LC 74-3943.

Donovan was interested in exploring the characteristics of "female occupations" in the twenties and thirties. She wrote two earlier books, one on waitressing and another on saleswork, based on her brief experiences in these jobs. This book is an account of her own occupation: at the time of writing, Donovan had spent nineteen years as a teacher in several different types of schools and communities in the United States. Perhaps as a result of her more extensive experience in teaching, *The Schoolma'am* is much less anecdotal than her other two books; it is written more as sociological analysis, though based primarily on Donovan's personal observations. Among the topics: Why She Is Unmarried; The Married Teacher; Who She Is and Why She Teaches; Teacher Mobility; Her Private Life; Her Economic Position; and Teaching as a Career.

1523 Donovan, Frances R. **The Woman Who Waits.** Boston: R. G. Badger, 1920; repr. New York: Arno Press, 1974. 228p. $15.00. ISBN 0405060890. LC 74-3941.

Donovan's study of a "female" occupation—waitressing—early in the century, is in the participant observation tradition. Donovan waitressed in Chicago off and on for nine months, writing her impresssions in between jobs. This book is a record of her experiences on the job and with her co-workers, written in a chatty style frequently interspersed with dialogue. Donovan writes about working conditions, the social origins of other waitresses, their interests, their relative commitment to work and to romantic or family involvements, and about the Illinois Waitresses' Alliance. The author has also written about women teachers and saleswomen; her descriptions would make for interesting comparisons with recent books on the "female" occupations, such as Louise Howe's *Pink Collar Workers* (1977).

1524 Duberman, Lucile, 1926- . **Gender and Sex in Society.** New York: Praeger, 1975. 274p. bibliog. index. $10.00. ISBN 0275521109. LC 73-10658.

Duberman sees this book as "an effort to bring together current theory and research in the sociology of sex status and gender roles." Chapters are as follows: 1) Women Then and Now; 2) Socialization, Sexuality, and Sex; 3) Love Thine Enemy: Male-Female Relationships; 4) Men and Women at Work; 5) Class and Race Differences in Gender Roles, by Helen Mayer Hacker; 6) Gender Roles from a Cross-Cultural Perspective, by Helen Mayer Hacker; and 7) Beyond Masculinity: Liberating Men and Their Relationships with Women, by Warren T. Farrell.

1525   Ellis, Havelock, 1859-1939, and John Addington Symonds, 1840-
        1893. **Sexual Inversion.** London: Wilson and Macmillan, 1897; repr.
        New York: Arno Press, 1975. 299p. bibliog. index. $20.00. ISBN
        0405073631. LC 75-12312.
An important early study of homosexuality, *Sexual Inversion* treats the subject
from historical and cross-cultural perspectives, also examining earlier theories
of the "cause" and "treatment" of "sexual inversion" in men and women.
In the Victorian context from which he wrote, Ellis felt compelled to justify
exploration of heterosexual practices at length; to study and write about homosexuality was obviously even more taboo. Ellis writes in his preface that he
"realised that in England, more than in any other country, the law and public
opinion combine to place a heavy penal burden and a severe social stigma on
the manifestations of an instinct which to those persons who possess it frequently
appears natural and normal. It was clear that the matter was in special need of
elucidation and discussion." The subject of "Sexual Inversion in Women" is
accorded a separate chapter.

1526   Epstein, Cynthia Fuchs. **Woman's Place: Options and Limits in Profes-
        sional Careers.** Berkeley: University of California Press, 1970. 221p.
        bibliog. index. $7.95. ISBN 0520015819. LC 75-98139.
Drawing data mainly from the professions of law, medicine, science, teaching
and engineering, Epstein examines social forces and trends that have limited
women's access to the professions and barred their way to higher level positions.
Chapters include Ideals, Images, and Ideology of Women and Women's Roles
in Society; The Socialization Process and Its Consequences: Roads to Careers
and Dead Ends; Reconciliation of Women's Roles: Paths and Obstacles; The
Structure of the Professions: How They Affect Women's Participation; Inside
Professional Life: Interaction, Performance, and Impediments; Professions
in a Changing World: New Contexts. A highly relevant list of tables supports
the author's thesis in this classic work. Readers may want to look at the more
recent historical work on women professionals, Barbara J. Harris's *Beyond Her
Sphere: Women and the Professions in American History* (Greenwood Press,
1978).

1527   Etzioni, Amitai. **The Semi-Professions and Their Organization: Teachers,
        Nurses, Social Workers.** New York: Free Press, 1969. 328p. bibliog.
        index. $10.95. ISBN 0029096006. LC 69-10481.
Because this study of the "semi-professions" is focused on occupations in which
the majority of the work force is women, and because it is considered a basic
source in the field, it merits attention from those interested in the sociology of
women's work. However, there is much in its ideological premises and the attitudes
evinced toward women that will go further to offend than to inform. A key
weakness in the approach is its neglect of the reality of power struggle as instrumental to the historical emergence of and attainment of legitimacy by "the
professions" (medicine, law, academia). As a result, the self-congratulatory
self-image of these occupations is accepted as fact: for example, Etzioni writes,
"The basis of professional authority is knowledge. . . . " In contrast, then, to
the autonomy of "the" professions, the "semi-professions" (teaching, nursing,
social work) are characterized by hierarchy and bureaucratic control. And if

the basis of autonomy in "the" professions is superior knowledge, the explanation for bureaucratic control in the "semi-professions" is . . . that the workers
are *women*: "A woman's primary attachment is to the family role; women are therefore less intrinsically committed to work than men and less likely to maintain a
high level of specialized knowledge. Because their work motives are more utilitarian
and less intrinsically task-oriented than those of men, they may require more control" (from "Women and Bureaucracy in the Semi-Professions," by Richard L.
Simpson and Ida Harper Simpson). Other contributors to this volume are Dan C.
Lortie (on elementary school teaching), Fred E. Katz (on nursing), W. Richard
Scott (on social work), Nina Toren (also on social work), and William J. Goode
(on the theoretical limits of professionalization).

1528   Fleming, Jennifer Baker, and Carolyn Kott Washburne. **For Better,**
        For Worse: A Feminist Handbook on Marriage and Other Options.
        New York: Scribner, 1977. 406p. bibliog. index. $14.95. ISBN
        0684149192. LC 77-8017.
This book grows out of the experiences of a group called Women in Transition,
Inc., who provided legal support and emotional support to women "who were
in some kind of marital transition—separated, divorced, raising children alone—
or who were being beaten by their husbands." In the course of their work,
the women involved formulated some strategies and solutions to dealing with
potential problems in marriage and adjustment difficulties in alternative lifestyle arrangements. Chapters here are directed to: romantic illusions about
marriage; dependence and independence in marriage; marriage as a legal institution; economic factors in marriage; motherhood; alternatives to marriage; lesbian
relationships; violence in marriage; a male perspective of marriage. The bibliography and resource materials include many local and regional sources and
agencies.

1529   Gager, Nancy, and Cathleen Schurr. **Sexual Assault: Confronting**
        Rape in America. New York: Grosset and Dunlap, 1976. 336p. bibliog.
        index. $10.00. ISBN 0448115271. LC 73-18531.
Sexual Assault presents a feminist analysis of the problem of rape, focusing
in particular on the ways in which the socialization of passivity in women
and aggression (including sexual aggression) in men contributes to the creation
of our "rape-prone environment." Authors Gager and Schurr have been active
and written on the subject of rape since the early '70s. They approach the
problem from a variety of angles: the victim—who is she?; the police; the
medical complex; the courts, the law, and legal reform; the rapist—who is he?;
and women's struggle against rape (crisis centers, counseling, and institutional
change).

1530   Gelles, Richard J. **The Violent Home: A Study of Physical Aggression**
        Between Husbands and Wives. Beverly Hills, CA: Sage Publications,
        1974. 230p. bibliog. index. $11.00. ISBN 0803903812(C). LC
        73-94288.
Little emerges that can be considered surprising in this study of familial violence
(e.g., abusive parents and spouses seem to have received this violent treatment
from their own parents). Gelles notes that husband-wife violence has been a

muted topic (1974) since it only surfaces when people have contact with social agencies or the police. Though Gelles provides the standard sociological statistical apparatus in the form of tables and figures, the significance of this study lies in the interview material with eighty individuals, most of whom were wives. One of the more important findings: most of the domestic violence "occurs in families with low income, low educational achievement, and where the husband has low occupational status." Gelles's early study on conjugal violence was undertaken before the acknowledgement of this national scandal became a "hot" media issue. Because of this, his findings and bibliography are valuable in documenting how little had been undertaken on this immense social problem before 1974.

1531　Giele, Janet Zollinger, and Audrey Chapman Smock, eds. **Women: Roles and Status in Eight Countries.** New York: Wiley, 1977. 443p. bibliog. index. $17.50. ISBN 0471015040. LC 76-39950.
This surveys women's roles and status in eight countries: Egypt, Bangladesh, Mexico, Ghana, Japan, France, the United States, and Poland. The chief flaw of this collection is the superficial treatment imposed by brevity. The chief attraction is the uniformity of framework and approach employed by authors commissioned to write chapters for this volume, which facilitates an international comparison. "Each chapter begins with the historical and cultural background necessary to put contemporary conditions in [the given] country into perspective. Then women's roles and status are examined in the context of the family, educational system, economic system, family planning facilities, and political system prevailing in that society" (from the preface). Contributors are: Janet Zollinger Giele, Audrey Chapman Smock, Nadia Haggag Youssef, Mary Elmendorf, Susan J. Pharr, Catherine Bodard Silver, and Magdalena Sokolowska.

1532　Glazer, Nathan. **Affirmative Discrimination: Ethnic Inequality and Public Policy.** New York: Basic Books, 1975. 248p. bibliog. index. $11.95. ISBN 0465020763. LC 74-25924.
While Glazer is addressing himself to the question of affirmative action specifically for minorities, the discussion is clearly relevant to issues of sex discrimination. Like all opponents of affirmative action, Glazer exaggerates the impact that it has had and the gains that minorities have made. He raises serious and important questions about the contradictions of legal remedies based on racial and ethnic (and, by extension, sexual) categories, which evade altogether the question of the *class* inequality that cuts across racial, ethnic, and sex groupings. However, he ultimately retreats from any serious grappling with these contradictions into a defense of the ideology of equal opportunity. Affirmative action threatens, he says, "the abandonment of our concern for individual claims to consideration on the basis of justice and equity. . . . " This polemic by a prominent social scientist will undoubtedly continue to serve as the effective weapon against affirmative action that it has already shown itself to be. Another work that attracted considerable attention for its attack on affirmative action (specifically in universities, in this instance) is Richard Lester's *Antibias Regulation of Universities: Faculty Problems and Their Solutions* (McGraw-Hill, 1974). Also

relevant is Oceana Publications' issuing of the judicial record of the Bakke case, *Allan Bakke versus Regents of the University of California* (1978).

1533   Glazer-Malbin, Nona, 1932- , and Helen Youngelson Waehrer, comps. **Woman in a Man-Made World: A Socioeconomic Handbook.** (2nd ed.). Chicago: Rand McNally, 1977. 443p. bibliog. index. $6.95. ISBN 0528680854. LC 76-17193.

The first edition of *Woman in a Man-Made World* appeared in 1971 and quickly became a standard text for sociology of women courses. The second edition is extensively revised and enlarged; considerable effort has been made to broaden the approaches and perspectives represented in the volume and the result is a much stronger collection. Part 1, General Perspectives, considers the meaning of feminist scholarship (e.g., "Some Implications of a Sociology for Women," by Dorothy E. Smith) and historical perspectives on women's oppression (including excerpts from Eli Zaretsky's now classic essay, "Capitalism, The Family, and Personal Life" and from Heidi Hartmann's "Capitalism, Patriarchy, and Job Segregation by Sex"). Part 2, The Subjection of Women, provides sociological perspectives on sex differences, gender roles ("A Note on the Division of Labor by Sex," by Judith K. Brown), women as a minority group (Helen Mayer Hacker's classic article by that name), and on Engels's theory of sex oppression and a contemporary Marxist approach ("Women: The Longest Revolution," by Juliet Mitchell). Also included in part 2 are economic perspectives on labor force activity, labor market differences (especially sex segregation) and "nonmarket activity" (i.e., women's work in the home: Margaret Benston, "The Political Economy of Women's Liberation"). In part 3, Sex and Social Roles, a variety of sociologists (e.g., Talcott Parsons, Peter Berger, Lenore J. Weitzman) and economists (e.g., Victor Fuchs) discuss gender role differentiation, the marriage relationship and the job market (including an article on the particular oppression of black women). Part 4 considers a number of myths about women related to divorced women and their families, housework, women's status in academia, women's contribution to family income, and women and wealth. Part 5, Toward Sex Equality, considers the question of liberation: "Have Swedish Women Achieved Equality?," by Nancy S. Barrett; "The Chinese Family Revolution and Feminist Theory," by Judith Stacey; and "Family Structure and Communism," by Agnes Heller. Brief introductions to each section are provided by the editors. The bibliographies following each article will direct readers to basic sources in specific areas.

1534   Goode, William Josiah. **World Revolution and Family Patterns.** New York: Free Press of Glencoe, 1970. 432p. bibliog. index. $4.95. ISBN 0029124603. LC 63-13538.

This is a useful summary (orig. 1963) of women and the family cross-culturally, by a sociologist well-known for his work on the family and for his insistence that family sociology (and sociology as a whole) must be historical and comparative. Goode introduces his study: "Whether or not this book meets contemporary standards of excellence, it must be adjudged presumptuous. For it seeks to describe and interpret the main changes in family patterns that have occurred over the past half-century in Japan, China, India, the West, Sub-Saharan Africa, and the Arab countries, and to relate them to various alterations in other institutional areas." Goode does focus specifically on questions relating to the position of women, husband-wife relations, polygyny, infanticide, matriliny, women's rights, contraception, prostitution, women's work, divorce, and other such foci of particular interest to women's studies.

1535   Gorney, Sondra, and Claire Cox. **After Forty.** New York: Dial Press, 1973. 256p. bibliog. index. $7.95. ISBN 0803709471. LC 72-13463.
Campuses that are noting significant numbers of reentry women will want to have this moderate, inoffensive book about aging in their collection. Simone de Beauvoir's *Coming of Age*, this book is not. Chapter titles give a good idea of the tone and content: You're Not Getting Older, You're Getting Better; No Need to Sing the Menopause Blues; What Every Young Woman over Forty Should Know about Sex; Mirror, Mirror on the Wall; Tuning in on Marriage and Family Life; Women Alone: The Widowed, Divorced, and Unmarried; Out to Work: Be Back after Sixty-five; Retirement: Time to Take a New Lease on Life; The Best Is Yet to Come.

1536   Hagood, Margaret Jarman, 1907- . **Mothers of the South: Portraiture of the White Tenant Farm Woman.** Chapel Hill: University of North Carolina Press, 1939; repr. New York: Arno Press, 1972. 252p. $11.00. ISBN 0405038623. LC 70-169384.
Hagood's important study, conducted during the Depression and recently reprinted, was based on lengthy discussions with 129 mothers in southern white tenant farmer families. Her eye for detail and her abundant anecdotes enliven the account as she describes the tenant farm system and the women's lives—field work, housekeeping, childbearing, childraising, wifehood, community participation, middle age. She writes early on in the book that southern "tenant farm mothers compose a group who epitomize, as much as any, the results of the wastes and lags of the Region. They suffer the direct consequences of a long-continued cash crop economy; they undergo extreme social impoverishment from the lack and unequal distribution of institutional services; and they bear the brunt of a regional tradition—compounded of elements from religion, patriarchy, and aristocracy—which subjects them to class and sex discrimination." Hagood creates a vivid picture of the struggles of women in underdeveloped regions—in this instance, not far off in the Third World, but right here in the United States.

1537   Harris, Janet. **The Prime of Ms. America: The American Woman at Forty.** New York: Putnam, 1975. 250p. bibliog. $7.95. ISBN 0399114424. LC 74-16600.
The fortieth birthday is taken as the milestone in this commentary about the unfairness of society's treatment of middle-aged women. Harris seems to have built her study on informal interviewing of women between the ages of forty and sixty. The portrayal of women in the media, the physical effects of aging, marriage and the double standard, the single woman, work, mental and physical health, leisure and self-realization—these are the issues that Harris finds important for middle-aged women, who have nearly half a lifetime remaining to them beyond the end of their childbearing years. Harris stitches together with skill much of the existing popular literature about women in a sexist, ageist society.

1538   Hartman, Mary S. **Victorian Murderesses: A True History of Thirteen Respectable French and English Women Accused of Unspeakable Crimes.** New York: Schocken Books, 1977. 318p. bibliog. index. $15.00. ISBN 0805236082. LC 75-34877.

In this scholarly and readable volume, Hartman describes the cases of thirteen rather ordinary Victorian women from Great Britain and France who employed bizarre measures to resolve some rather pedestrian problems. Time covered spans 1840-1890. Hartman writes that often these women were poor practitioners of the murderous art. Their real interest lies in the portrait they make depicting "the domestic confines of middle class families and . . . the problems even the terrors that women faced there." Extensive documentation is provided.

1539   Hate, Chandrakala Anandrao. **Changing Status of Woman in Post-Independence India.** New York: Paragon, 1969. bibliog. index. $9.00. ISBN 0818810491.

Hate bases her study of women in post-independence India primarily on statistical data, covering the following topics: marriage, the family, family planning, education, career, politics, leisure. Extensive use of tables is made.

1540   Hazleton, Lesley. **Israeli Women: The Reality behind the Myth.** New York: Simon and Schuster, 1977. bibliog. index. $8.95. ISBN 0671225316. LC 77-21587.

This is a controversial and thoroughly documented study of the inequities in the legal, social, religious, and political structures of Israel that define the status of Israeli women as one considerably less than that of Israeli men. Hazleton carefully examines the complexities of Jewish divorce law: an Israeli woman cannot divorce her husband, though a husband may divorce his wife. Similar inequalities occur in marriage law, which treats adultery more severely for women, and in the military, where women perform mainly clerical tasks. This is enlightening reading that exposes a widely-held myth and is written by an Israeli woman.

1541   Hernton, Calvin C. **Sex and Racism in America.** New York: Grove Press, 1966. 180p. bibliog. $1.95. ISBN 0394174097. LC 64-20576.

Hernton, a black author, takes on a thorny problem that has rarely been addressed—the "sexualization of racism" in the United States. He argues that an integral component of racism is the fear of white men that black men desire sexual access to white women. Hernton explores the racist sexual dynamics that have created the myths of the "pure" white woman, of the hypersexed black male, and of the black female slut. He points to the white male fears and white female desires that underlie lynchings of innocent black men, and he indicts the arrogance of white men's assumption of a right of sexual access to black women. Missing from the analysis is an exploration of the male supremacist roots of the sex/race dynamic. Women's status as sexual property to be fought over by men is clearly of some importance here. Nonetheless, Hernton's study represents an important contribution toward an understanding of the interconnections between sex, race, and class oppression in U.S. society.

1542   Holmstrom, Lynda Lytle. **The Two-Career Family.** Cambridge, MA:
        Schenkman; distr. Morristown, NJ: General Learning Press, 1972.
        203p. bibliog. $8.95. ISBN 0382211294. LC 70-189095.
The "two-career family" refers not to families in which both the man and the
woman are in the paid labor force (an increasingly common pattern), but
to families in which both are employed in the *professions*. This pattern continues
to be rare and to pose significant problems for the families involved. Holmstrom
reports here on her study of twenty two-career families and seven comparison
couples (in which the women "had significantly limited their careers"). Data
were obtained through interviews. Holmstrom discusses the life-cycle of the
family; the inflexibility of occupations; sexual division of labor; allocation
of time, effort and money; competitiveness; colleagueship; the male view;
and breakdown of the dual-career pattern through divorce or the wife's abandonment of career. Her suggestions for change go no further than advocating an
enlarged role for the husband in childrearing, increased availability of child
care centers (with male and female staff), and "greater flexibility" in the
professions. The interested reader will also want to consult *Dual-Career Families*
(1971) and *Dual-Career Families Re-examined* (1977), by Rhona and Norman
Rapoport.

1543   Huber, Joan, 1925- , ed. **Changing Women in a Changing Society.**
        Chicago: University of Chicago Press, 1973. 295p. bibliog. $9.50.
        ISBN 0226356442. LC 72-96342.
This collection of articles first appeared as v. 78, no. 4 of *American Journal
of Sociology* (January 1973). Included are: "The Origins of the Women's Libera-
tion Movement" (Jo Freeman); "Cultural Contradictions and Sex Roles: The
Masculine Case" (Mirra Komarovsky); "Positive Effects of the Multiple Negative:
Explaining the Success of Black Professional Women" (Cynthia Fuchs Epstein);
"Women and Social Stratification: A Case of Intellectual Sexism" (Joan Acker);
"Demographic Influence on Female Employment and the Status of Women"
(Valerie Kincade Oppenheimer); "Income Differences between Men and Career
Women" (Larry E. Suter and Herman P. Miller); "Women, Work, and Wedlock:
A Note on Female Marital Patterns in the United States" (Elizabeth M. Havens);
"Impediment or Stimulant? Marital Status and Graduate Education" (Saul D.
Feldman); "A Review of Sex Role Research" (Arlie Russell Hochschild); "A
Funny Thing Happened on the Way to the Orifice: Women in Gynecology Text-
books" (Diana Scully and Pauline Bart).

1544   Klaich, Dolores. **Woman + Woman: Attitudes toward Lesbianism.** New
        York: Simon and Schuster, 1974. 287p. bibliog. index. $8.95. ISBN
        0671216953. LC 73-21052.
Klaich neither editorially champions nor condemns lesbianism. "I do not believe
that lesbianism is a sin, a crime, or a sickness. I do feel that lesbianism is a
way of loving, a natural possibility, and as such, like the other possibilities,
it can be a matter of joy, of mutual growth, of constructive human interaction.
But also, like other possibilities, it can be a matter of mutual stagnation, even
destruction" (prelude). The book examines past and contemporary attitudes
toward lesbianism and is directed toward the individual who knows little about
the subject and may even be hostile toward it. Among the materials included

are interviews, question and answers, and some biographical material on Gertrude
Stein, Radclyffe Hall, Virginia Woolf, Renée Vivien, Natalie Clifford Barney,
and Colette. A good bibliography is appended.

1545   Klein, Carole. **The Single Parent Experience.** New York: Avon Books,
        1973. 304p. bibliog. $1.95.
"The single parent within these pages is the person who has *chosen* this role,"
writes Carole Klein in her introduction. Stereotypes of single mothers as either
promiscuous "unwed mothers" or pathetic widows and divorcees are demeaning
and inaccurate. Amidst today's widespread experimentation with alternative
lifestyles, ventures into parenthood outside marriage and the nuclear family
are increasingly common. Klein discusses the idea of the separation of parenthood from marriage, the male single parent, the "unmarried mother" of today,
homosexual parents, adoption, the single parent's family, child care, the social
realities of single parenthood, alternative lifestyles, and psychological effects
of having a single parent. This is a popular account, with illustrations from Klein's
interviews with single parents frequently interspersed. The bibliography is
extremely brief. An appendix of state sources for adoption, pregnancy, and
related counseling is included. Another book of related interest is *Momma:
The Sourcebook for Single Mothers*, edited by Karol Hope and Nancy Young
(New American Library, 1976).

1546   Ladner, Joyce A. **Tomorrow's Tomorrow: The Black Woman.** Garden
        City, NY: Doubleday, 1971. 304p. bibliog. index. $2.95. ISBN
        0385009410. LC 78-139038.
A revision of the author's thesis, Washington University, *Tomorrow's Tomorrow*
is the culmination of Ladner's four-year study of the lives of black preadolescent
and adolescent girls in a slum neighborhood of St. Louis, Missouri (beginning
in 1964). In her honest and introspective introduction, Ladner writes of the
conflicts she had to work through between her experience as a black woman
and her socialization as a doctoral candidate in a racist, classed society. Her
graduate training predisposed her to assume a posture of objective detachment;
her theoretical background prepared her to see black cultural patterns as
"deviant" and "pathological" and to hold the victims responsible for their
own oppression. Her life experiences, on the other hand, contradicted these
theoretical presuppositions, affirmed the validity of her "subjects' " perspectives
on their own lives and recognized their strength in coping with institutional
racism. Ladner ultimately decided to break with the traditions of her academic
training and to write what seemed true from her perspective. Her chapters are:
Yesterday: Black Womanhood in Historical Perspective; Growing Up Black;
Racial Oppression and the Black Girl; The Definition of Womanhood; Becoming
a Woman; and Conclusions.

1547   Lasch, Christopher. **Haven in a Heartless World: The Family Besieged.**
        New York: Basic Books, 1977. 230p. bibliog. index. $15.00. ISBN
        0465028837. LC 77-75246.
Lasch sets himself an ambitious goal in this study: to order and make sense
of all the endless debate over the status of the family and to better understand
the reality of the family in the present. While this is a task at which he was

bound to fail, the fact that he has strived for an overall view strongly recommends this work. "The crisis of the family," he tells us, is not at all new but a product of the nineteenth century. The social sciences and "helping professions" arose largely in response to this crisis and must be seen as bearing "the same relation to the later stages of the industrial revolution that the science of political economy bore to the earlier stages." Just as Marx found a critique of classical political economy to be necessary preparation for an analysis of the capitalist transformation of production, Lasch argues that a critique of social science and its theories of the family must underlie an analysis of the capitalist transformation of *reproduction*. This is really the task that Lasch undertakes (though he claims his subject is broader than this—"the intersection of theory, ideology, and social practice"). In the course of the work, Lasch critically analyzes the rise of social science, the sociology of "rating and dating" (courtship), culture and personality theories (psychoanalysis, anthropology, the Frankfurt School), Parsonsian theory, sociological revisionism, and more. His chief argument—that the family can be no "haven" due to increasing state intervention and socialization of reproduction—can be faulted as overstatement and as failing to sufficiently distinguish the roles of men and women within the family. Nonetheless, his effort to come to grips with an enormous body of social theory remains an important contribution.

1548   Laslett, Peter. **Family Life and Illicit Love in Earlier Generations: Essays in Historical Sociology.** New York: Cambridge University Press, 1977. 270p. bibliog. index. $24.50. ISBN 0521214084. LC 76-21010.
As founder and director of the Cambridge Group for the study of family history, Laslett has shaped this area as a scholarly field. Among the family-related topics given essay treatment here are bastardy, old age, and age at menarche. The introductory essay discusses historical sociology as an important interdisciplinary approach in the social sciences. Another important work edited by Laslett is *Household and Family in Past Time* (Cambridge University Press, 1972), which includes information and analyses on England, France, Serbia, Japan, North America, and Western Europe.

1549   Lifton, Robert Jay, 1926- , ed. **The Woman in America.** Boston: Beacon Press, 1965. 293p. bibliog. $3.95. ISBN 0807041971.
Most of these essays first appeared in the Spring 1964 issue of *Daedalus* and are the result of the *Daedalus* conference on women held at the House of the American Academy of Arts and Sciences, Boston. They include Erik Erikson, "Inner and Outer Space: Reflections on Womanhood"; Robert Jay Lifton, "Woman as Knower: Some Psychohistorical Perspectives"; Diana Trilling, "The Image of Women in Contemporary Literature"; David Riesman, "Two Generations"; Alice S. Rossi, "Equality Between the Sexes: An Immodest Proposal"; Ester Peterson, "Working Women"; David McClelland, "Wanted: A New Self-Image for Women"; Carl Degler, "Revolution Without Ideology: The Changing Place of Women in America"; and Edna G. Rostow, "Conflict and Accommodation."

1550   Lopata, Helena Znaniecki, 1925- . **Occupation: Housewife.** New York: Oxford University Press, 1971. 387p. bibliog. index. $12.95. ISBN 0195014685. LC 77-83046.

Lopata tells us that her interest in doing a study of housewives "began to take shape when we moved out to a suburb near Chicago while I was simultaneously finishing my doctoral dissertation and juggling Teddy, our daughter, on my lap." *Occupation: Housewife* is a summation of Lopata's eleven years of research on housewives in the Chicago area. The sample used in this study was composed of 571 informants (279 suburban housewives, 192 non-working housewives, and 100 working wives) who were extensively interviewed in 1964-1965. Lopata's sociological perspective is that of "role theory," in which individuals are seen as filling a variety of culturally-dictated, interrelated (though possibly conflicting), evolving roles in the course of their lives. Lopata conceptualizes the housewife role as moving through a specifiable series of stages constituting a life cycle: Becoming a Housewife; The Expanding Circle (first children); The Full-House Plateau (last child born, but children remain at home); and The Shrinking Circle (the "empty nest" stage). Lopata's study of role shifts in widowhood for women fifty years and older is separately published as *Widowhood in an American City* (Schenkman, 1973).

1551   Mandel, William. **Soviet Women.** Garden City, NY: Anchor Books,
        1975. 350p. bibliog. index. $3.50. ISBN 0385032552. LC 74-12732.
Mandel is very enthusiastic about his subject and very impressed with the achievements of the Soviet Union in working towards sexual equality. The comprehensiveness of this study—combining historical records, contemporary statistical surveys, case histories, biographical sketches, illustrations from literature, and Mandel's own personal experience based on six trips to the Soviet Union—should go far in mitigating possible uneasiness of American readers accustomed to more critical views of the Soviet system. Mandel shows how women's advancement in the public sphere has been possible because of the commitment of the Soviet Union to meeting certain preconditions—not just legal equality of men and women, but also full employment, equal pay, free education, reproductive freedom, paid maternity leave, and extensive and cheap child care facilities. Readers may want to take a comparative look at Hilda Scott's *Does Socialism Liberate Women?* (1974). Scott casts a more critical eye on the achievements of the Soviet Union and the Eastern European countries with regard to sexual equality, though sharing with Mandel a fundamental admiration of these societies' guarantees of basic social and economic rights.

1552   Martin, Del. **Battered Wives.** San Francisco: Glide Publications, 1976.
        269p. bibliog. $7.95. ISBN 0912078456. LC 75-24031.
This analysis of the problem of male violence against women within the home was written by the woman who co-authored *Lesbian/Woman*. What distinguishes Martin's approach to the subject is a) her desire to understand the seeming paradox whereby society stigmatizes and blames the battered woman and vindicates the battering man; and b) her belief that the problem of battered women cannot be understood apart from the larger web of male/female power relations in society. Chapters are included on the following topics: Violence in the Home; Wife-Beating and the Marriage Contract; The Batterer—What Makes Him a Brute?; The Victim—Why Does She Stay?; The Failure of the Legal System; Social Services—The Big Runaround; Survival Tactics; Remedial Legislation; and Refuges for Battered Women. The last chapter ("Refuges")

contains descriptions of seven refuges in the U.S. and several in other countries; and information on how to set up a refuge and prepare a funding proposal, on funding sources, and on the network developing around this issue.

1553   Medea, Andra, and Kathleen Thompson. **Against Rape.** New York: Farrar, Straus and Giroux, 1974. 152p. bibliog. $7.95. ISBN 0374102333. LC 74-4099.

Medea and Thompson argue that although most women would rather not think about rape, our society and its attitude toward male sexual violence force contemporary women to fear the crime even more than did our grandmothers and mothers. "Although women are expected to be attractive, if they are attractive to the wrong person at the wrong place and time, they must take responsibility for some stranger's actions. For women the luxury of going out for a walk alone, of getting away for a few minutes, is almost impossible. Every day of their lives, women learn to accept the fact that their freedom is limited in a way that a man's is not. There is a curfew on women in this country and it is enforced by rapists" (introduction). The authors call for the crime of rape and any attack made upon a woman to be treated seriously by the law. Chapters include: What Is Rape?; Why Do Men Rape Women?; Who Is the Rapist?; Rape and Social Patterns; The Little Rapes; Precautions and Preventions; Self-Defense; Psychological Reactions; and The Movement Against Rape. This is excellent for its thoughtful if discouraging discussion of the psychological double-bind in which the crime of rape places women.

1554   Mednick, Martha T., et al., eds. **Women and Achievement: Social and Motivational Analyses.** Washington: Hemisphere; distr. New York: Halsted Press, 1975. 447p. bibliog. index. $19.95. ISBN 0470590254. LC 75-22047.

This anthology was developed from a 1972 special issue of the *Journal of Social Issues* entitled "New Perspectives on Women." It brings together articles by major researchers in the field of women, sex roles, and achievement. (It should be noted that achievement is here limited to activities outside the home.) Among the articles are the following: "Sex Roles and Social Change" (Harriet Holter); "Sex-Role Stereotypes: A Current Appraisal" (Inge K. Broverman, et al.); "The Employment of Women, Education, and Fertility," "Early Childhood Experiences and Women's Achievement Motives," and "Fear of Success in Males and Females, 1965 and 1971" (Lois Wladis Hoffman); "The Socialization of Achievement Motivation in Females" (Aletha H. Stein and Margaret M. Bailey); "Toward an Understanding of Achievement-Related Conflicts in Women" (Matina S. Horner); "Determinants of Occupational Role Innovation Among College Women" (Sandra Schwartz Tangri); "A Summary of Psychological Sex Differences" (Julia A. Sherman); "The Sex-Labeling of Jobs" (Valerie Kincade Oppenheimer); "Sex Discrimination Against the American Working Woman" (Teresa Levitin, et al.); "Women As New Students" (K. Patricia Cross); and "Sex Discrimination in Academe" (Helen S. Astin and Alan E. Bayer).

1555   Mernissi, Fatima. **Beyond the Veil: Male-Female Dynamics in a Modern Muslim Society.** Cambridge, MA: Schenkman; distr. New York: Halsted Press, 1975. 132p. bibliog. $12.50. ISBN 0470596120. LC 75-29283.

A basic assumption of this exploration of the traditional view of Muslim women
in the social order and of the present modernizing trend for Muslim women to
gain educational and employment equity, is that comparisons between East
and West with regard to discrimination against women and issues of women's
status do not assist in understanding the sexual dynamics of Muslim society.
Since laws and customs in Morocco posit that the family is based on male
supremacy and female subordination, the question of women's liberation becomes
one of strife between modernity and tradition, which threatens to tear apart
the Muslim society. While in Western society, sexual inequality is in part based
on a belief in women's biological inferiority, Muslim views of women posit
the female sex as a dangerous enemy whose power must be controlled by segregation. This is an extremely helpful overview of a very complex religious and social
pattern, with a tightly argued position that women's liberation must be seen
in the cultural context of the society in which it is occurring. Topics covered
by the author include the Muslim notion of female sexuality, the relationship
between husband and wife in Muslim society, the position of the mother-in-law,
and the economic basis for loss of traditional sex roles in modern Morocco.

1556   Millman, Marcia, and Rosabeth Moss Kanter, eds. **Another Voice:**
        Feminist Perspectives on Social Life and Social Science. New York:
        Anchor Press/Doubleday, 1975; repr. New York: Octagon Books,
        1976. 382p. bibliog. $16.00. ISBN 0374957282. LC 76-27716.
This group of articles ranges from studies of institutions to studies of special
groups of women and finally to general themes in social interaction. The contents
include: Thelma McCormack, "Toward a Nonsexist Perspective on Social and
Political Change"; Rosabeth Moss Kanter, "Women and the Structure of Organiza-
tions"; Judith Lorber, "Women and Medical Sociology: Invisible Professionals
and Ubiquitous Patients"; Sara Lawrence Lightfoot, "Sociology of Education:
Perspectives on Women"; Lyn H. Lofland, "The 'Thereness' of Women: A
Selective Review of Urban Sociology"; Gaye Tuchman, "Women and the Creation
of Culture"; Pamela Roby, "Sociology and Women in Working-Class Jobs";
Lena Wright Myers, "Black Women and Self-Esteem"; Marcia Millman, "She
Did It All for Love: A Feminist View of the Sociology of Deviance"; Arlie
Russell Hochschild, "The Sociology of Feeling and Emotion: Selected Possibili-
ties"; David Tresemer, "Assumptions Made About Gender Roles"; Arlene
Kaplan Daniels, "Feminist Perspectives in Sociological Research."

1557   Money, John William, 1921- , and Patricia Tucker. **Sexual Signatures:**
        On Being a Man or a Woman. Boston: Little, Brown, 1975. 250p.
        bibliog. index. $6.95. ISBN 0316578266. LC 74-26632.
A primer on the issues of gender identity and gender role as two separate
aspects of the gender schema, this readable treatment of complex issues explores
the topics of cultural gender stereotypes, individual gender schemas, transsexualism, homosexuality, transvestism, and hermaphroditism with the purpose
of convincing people to relax rigid gender expectations. "The more of his
individual self a man can develop without having to question his masculinity,
the more of her individual self a woman can develop without having to question
her femininity, the more of a person each can be, and the more fully they can
complement and enhance each other," the authors conclude. Chapters include:

Prenatal Stages, Sex Hormones on the Brain, Gender Identity, Childhood, Adolescence, and the Sex Revolution. One of their most interesting analyses concerns the issue of sex polarization and elitism through genderized language (e.g., "How can a child fail to put laundering into his or her female schema when the only common words for one who launders are washer-woman and laundress?").

1558   Myers, Margaret, and Mayra Scarborough, eds. **Women in Librarianship:
        Melvil's Rib Symposium.** New Brunswick, NJ: Bureau of Library and
        Information Science Research, Rutgers University School of Library
        Service, 1975. 112p. bibliog. $4.95. ISBN 081350807X. LC 75-325598.
The most readable contributions to this volume on the female-dominated profession of librarianship are Anita Schiller's "Sex and Library Careers" and Carolyn Sherif's "Dreams and Dilemmas of Being a Woman Today." Schiller traces the fortunes (or perils) of women in librarianship from the time of Melvil Dewey's opening the first professional library school in America at Columbia in 1887. Dewey was forced to close the school and to resign from Columbia because the school admitted women. From the beginning, Schiller points out, women were employed in libraries because they were willing to work for little money, though this arrangement has rarely been seen as one of gross exploitation. The notion of equal opportunity in librarianship for women is characterized by Schiller as bogus, since women account for 82 percent of the profession but are paid less than men and rarely appear in top positions. The larger and more prestigious the library, the less the likelihood that there will be women appearing prominently on the ascending career ladder. Carolyn Sherif calls the stereotype of the woman librarian "perhaps the most vicious of all stereotypes." She suggests that the low status of librarianship as well as of all traditionally "female" jobs is based on a cultural definition of women's work as inferior held by both males and females. Such "social arrangements" must be corrected, according to Sherif, if anything like equal pay for equal work is to be achieved.

1559   Myrdal, Alva (Reimer), 1902- , and Viola Klein. **Women's Two Roles:
        Home and Work.** New York: Humanities Press, 1970. bibliog. index.
        $8.75.
This is a revision of work initially published in 1956; the reprint changes some emphases of the former volume, and more recent research findings are added. Part of the discussion is about psychological conflicts as symptoms of women's uncertainties about their economic and social roles. The authors believe that both men and women would have more time and energy to devote to home and family if the employment of women beyond childbearing age becomes a widespread practice, which could theoretically result in reduced work hours for all. They express hope for increased leisure for all workers as a period of rest and recreation within a full life. It is hypothesized that fewer hours of work would make possible a "complete renaissance of home life" (p. 192), especially increasing participation by the husband in family life. They point to the change of public opinion, a reduction of prejudices against employing married women, concluding that women in their thirties and forties who fail to work, at least part time and irrespective of social class, "now almost have to give an explanation of staying at home." Chapters include Women in an Ageing Society; The Phases of a Life-Span (which Myrdal and Klein aver has become a commonly

accepted concept and remains essentially unchanged in the reprint); Women in the Labour Force Today; Why Married Women Seek Employment; Employers' Problems; The Effects on Children; and Contemporary Female Dilemmas. A brief but diversified bibliography is included.

1560   Oakley, Ann. **Sex, Gender and Society.** New York: Harper and Row, 1972. 220p. bibliog. $2.95. ISBN 0060903201.
"In 1969, when I first decided to do a study of housework, I was interested not only in women's attitudes to housework in industrial society now, but in the historical background to the housewife role, in the cross-cultural patterning of the division of labour, and in ideologies of women's domesticity" (from *Woman's Work*). Three books resulted from Oakley's research: *Woman's Work: The Housewife, Past and Present*; *Sex, Gender and Society*; and *The Sociology of Housework*. *Sex, Gender and Society* is a discussion of sex differences, with emphasis on cross-cultural variation in sex roles. Topics include The Biology of Sex, Sex and Intellect, Sexuality, Sex and Social Role, and The Learning of Gender Role.

1561   Oakley, Ann. **The Sociology of Housework.** New York: Pantheon Books, 1975. 242p. bibliog. index. $10.00. ISBN 0394497740. LC 75-4668.
The Sociology of Housework contains a detailed analysis of Oakley's study of women's attitudes to housework, based on interviews conducted with London housewives. She discusses, among other topics, Images of Housework, Social Class and Domesticity, Work Conditions, Socialization and Self-Concept, and Marriage and the Division of Labour. Case-studies of four housewives, taken from this same study, are presented in *Woman's Work*, which also gives historical and anthropological background on the role of housewife.

1562   Oakley, Ann. **Woman's Work: The Housewife, Past and Present.** New York: Pantheon Books, 1974. 275p. bibliog. index. $8.95. ISBN 0394460979. LC 74-4765.
The British edition was published in 1974 under the title, *Housewife*. It deals with the historical and ideological questions, together with case-studies of four housewives and their situation today. The two chapters on pre-industrial society and industrialization are particularly valuable in their demonstration of the historicity of the idea and the actuality of the "housewife." A related source that is somewhat difficult to obtain, but has nonetheless circulated fairly widely and won high praise, is Heidi Hartmann's dissertation, *Capitalism and Women's Work in the Home, 1900-1930* (Yale University, 1974; distr. University Microfilms, 1976).

1563   O'Brien, Patricia. **The Woman Alone.** New York: Quadrangle Books, 1973. 285p. bibliog. $7.95. ISBN 0812903382. LC 72-94650.
"I have tried to write about the experience of being female from the perspective of women alone—drawing first on my own experience and then moving the focus to the lives of the women I searched out, the single, widowed, and divorced women of this country, women without men, who want and need as much as anyone else to be part of a whole, not just fragments isolated from society and

from one another." This is a subjective, popular treatment of living alone in
a culture that sanctions "twoness" and often ostracizes those people who are
not involved in a coupled relationship. The epilogue is particularly revealing;
it contains edited conversations from interviews with individual women relating
their experiences of being alone. The model of togetherness that is being talked
about here when women express the need for a relationship—whether married
or a living together arrangement—is exclusively heterosexual.

1564   O'Hare, Kate Richards, 1877-1948. **In Prison.** New York: Knopf,
        1923; repr. Seattle: University of Washington Press, 1976. 211p.
        bibliog. index. $15.00. ISBN 0295954515. LC 76-7793.
This edition has a new introduction by Jack M. Holl who writes: "Kate Richards
O'Hare's *In Prison* is a remarkable memoir written by a socialist agitator who
served fourteen months as a political prisoner of the United States. Because
she opposed American participation in World War I, Mrs. O'Hare was arrested,
tried and convicted under the provisions of the Espionage Act of 1917. Sentenced
to five years in prison, she was incarcerated on April 14, 1919, five months
after Armistice Day. Because the federal government owned no women's prisons
(there were only three federal prisons for men in 1920) the forty-year-old
convict was 'boarded' in the state prison at Jefferson City, Missouri, where,
along with other federal prisoners such as Emma Goldman, her labor was ille-
gally sold by the state to a private manufacturer of overall jackets. Understandably,
when her sentence was commuted by President Woodrow Wilson in May 1920,
Kate Richards O'Hare walked out of the Missouri State Penitentiary determined
to expose the brutality of American prisons and to destroy the prison contract
labor system." *In Prison* is the result, and it was received by a sympathetic prison
reform-conscious audience.

1565   Pescatello, Ann M. **Female and Male in Latin America: Essays.**
        Pittsburgh, PA: University of Pittsburgh Press, 1973. 342p. bibliog.
        $9.95. ISBN 0822932555. LC 72-81794.
Included in this collection are essays on the image of Latin American women,
their history, and the particular example of Cuba. Among the pieces are: "The
Passive Female and Social Change: A Cross-Cultural Comparison of Women's
Magazine Fiction" (Cornelia Butler Flora); "*Marianismo*: The Other Face of
Machismo in Latin America" (Evelyn P. Stevens); "Women in Latin American
Politics: The Case of Peru and Chile" (Elsa M. Chaney); "Women: The Forgotten
Half of Argentine History" (Nancy Caro Hollander); "The Pursuit of an Ideal:
Migration, Social Class, and Women's Roles in Bogota, Colombia" (Shirley J.
Harkess); and "Modernizing Women for A Modern Society: The Cuban Case"
(Susan Kaufman Purcell). Another recent collection of related interest is *Sex
and Class in Latin America*, edited by June C. Nash and Helen Icken Safa
(Praeger, 1976). The authors of this volume consider implications of the sexual
division of labor in industrial, agricultural, and domestic labor for the process
of capital accumulation in Latin America.

1566   Rainwater, Lee. **And the Poor Get Children: Sex, Contraception, and
        Family Planning in the Working Class.** New York: New Viewpoints,
        1974. 202p. bibliog. index. $5.00. LC 74-10181.

Rainwater's study was sponsored by the Planned Parenthood Federation of America. The data are drawn from interviews conducted with a sample of 46 married men and fifty married women from the working class in Chicago and Cincinnati. Reviewing the book at the time of its first publication (1960), Margaret Mead wrote: "Extensive verbatim quotations provide a dreary documentation of what happens to communication when the working class deal with interviewers from another class and cast their remarks in the stilted, evasive, embarrassed language of partial respectability. . . . Seen through the eyes of those who would prefer members of the lower classes to have fewer children, it is clear that it is necessary to introduce into the picture middle-class attitudes, planning, more 'communication between husband and wife,' and more technical knowledge. It seems doubtful that the population explosion can be dealt with by such methods" (*American Anthropologist* 63 [April 1961] : p. 458). Among the topics discussed by Rainwater and his subjects are: Assumptions and Orientations in Family Planning; Social Role and Self-Concept in the Marital Relationship; Mutuality and Rejection in Sexual Relations; and Sexual Relations, Family Planning, and Contraception.

1567*   Rainwater, Lee, et al. **Workingman's Wife: Her Personality, World and Life Style.** New York: Oceana Publications, 1959. 238p. bibliog. index. LC 59-9845.

Though this book is out of date and out of print, and much better and more recent books on the subject are available, there are at least three important factors that make *Workingman's Wife* worth examining. First of all, it's a "classic" study of the working-class married woman, one invariably mentioned— if critically—in later works. Second, though the approach is clearly not feminist, some valuable material emerges from the study, particularly from the lengthy direct quotations from interviews which are liberally scattered throughout. And finally, this study—which was published in conjunction with a consumer research firm and whose stated purpose is to help advertisers better understand how to reach a mass market through working-class women—provides ample material confirming feminist analyses of women's exploitation as consumers and of the formidable economic interests that have a stake in the sexual division of labor. Readers might find Stuart Ewen's *Captains of Consciousness* helpful in putting *Workingman's Wife* into perspective. Other relevant works are the also-dated *Blue-Collar Marriage*, by Mirra Komarovsky (Random House, 1964), and the recent *Worlds of Pain: Life in the Working-Class Family*, by Lillian B. Rubin (1976).

1568   Rainwater, Lee, and William L. Yancey. **The Moynihan Report and the Politics of Controversy.** Cambridge, MA: MIT Press, 1967. 493p. bibliog. $8.95. ISBN 0262680092. LC 67-15238.

"The evidence—not final, but powerfully persuasive—is that the Negro family in the urban ghettos is crumbling. A middle-class group has managed to save itself, but for vast numbers of the unskilled, poorly educated city working class the fabric of conventional social relationships has all but disintegrated. . . . So long as this situation persists, the cycle of poverty and disadvantage will continue to repeat itself." This was the central argument of Daniel Patrick Moynihan's 1965 *The Negro Family: The Case for National Action*. Moynihan found the "roots of the problem" in the conditions of slavery, and saw the "matriarchal" family structure of blacks as central to the contemporary "tangle of pathology." This report elicited immediate and heated controversy, which Rainwater and Yancey attempt to document in this reader. They reprint the original report, provide background on the controversy, and present examples of response to the report from the government, President Johnson, civil rights leaders, and academics. Selected newspaper and magazine articles are included as well. No feminist viewpoint is represented. Other related sources are Herbert Gutman's *The Black Family in Slavery and Freedom, 1750-1925* (1976), John Bracey's *Black Matriarchy: Myth or Reality?* (1971), and Carol Stack's *All Our Kin* (1974).

1569   Roby, Pamela A. **Child Care—Who Cares? Foreign and Domestic Infant and Early Childhood Development Policies.** New York: Basic Books, 1975. 456p. bibliog. index. $3.95. ISBN 0465095267. LC 72-89179.
This is an excellent primer in the history and theory of child care in the United States and abroad. Major sections are: Who Needs Child Care?; Child Care: A Basic Right; Does the United States Care?; and A Look Abroad. "Child Care and Women's Liberation," an essay by Elizabeth Hagen, offers an excellent analysis of the conflicts that the issue of child care presents. Does child care merely "liberate" woman for the endless routine of carting children to distant centers, so that she is free to work at a job she doesn't enjoy? What constitutes a good daycare program? How can parents control the center if their schedules are too busy to contribute to the shaping of the program? The international section highlights daycare in Sweden, Finland, Norway, England and Wales, the Soviet Union, Japan, and Israel. Authors of the essays have first-rate credentials as specialists in this area. Readers should also be aware of Margaret O'Brien Steinfels's study, *Who's Minding the Children? The History and Politics of Day Care in America* (Simon and Schuster, 1973).

1570   Ross, Heather L., and Isabel V. Sawhill. **Time of Transition: The Growth of Families Headed by Women.** Washington: The Urban Institute, 1975. 223p. bibliog. index. $10.00. ISBN 0877661480. LC 75-38209.
Transition is used in two contexts here. First, it includes single, divorced women who are heads of households and marry within five years of their divorce; thus, the status of single-parent households shifts constantly as the marital situations in these households undergo transition. Second, the economic factors governing the traditional roles of women and marriage are changing; women may find that the economic stability that marriage may once have provided is no longer as necessary to them when they are economically self-sufficient. Ross and Sawhill, who may be considered representative of "the new home economics," which applies economic models to quantifiable data on the family—its fertility, dissolution, productivity, etc.—suggest that social policy should meet the needs of the transitional family. They argue that two-parent families need economic incentives to stay together, since financial pressures are a key cause of family breakup, and that income support for female-headed households will encourage women to make more considered choices concerning remarriage. Extensive use is made of tables.

1571   Rubin, Lillian B. **Worlds of Pain: Life in the Working-Class Family.**
New York: Basic Books, 1976. 268p. bibliog. index. $11.95. ISBN
0465092454. LC 76-21648.

Worlds of Pain has been praised for its successful evocation of the texture of
working-class family life in the U.S. and of the concerns of working-class
people. Rubin conducted intensive interviews with fifty white working-class
families and, for purposes of comparison, 25 professional, middle-class families.
She made the sensitive decision to speak with husbands and wives separately
so that their experiences of marriage and family life—when different—could
more easily surface. Two important preoccupations of Rubin were the effect
of class on family life and the contradictory nature of the family as both a
constricting institution and source of human warmth and security. Rubin
describes the central concerns of her book as "the nature of the strains, the sources
of the conflicts, and the quality of the struggles which engage [the women and
men who live in white working-class families]. It is about their origins; about
how they came to marry; about the quality of their family life; about their
definitions of a good life, a good marriage, a good family; about the set of
values, norms, and lifeways to which they give allegiance; about how they are
responding to the forces insisting upon change; about their hopes and dreams
for the future ... [and] about how intimately connected all these experiences,
attitudes, and behaviors are with the work people do, their place in the class
structure of our society." Rubin writes in a simple, non-academic style, alter-
nating her own analysis with frequent excerpts from her interviews. Her perspective is clearly feminist, which is reflected in the questions she chose to ask,
especially of the women. Readers interested in a standard but now dated
treatment of working-class family life should look at Mirra Komarovsky's
Blue-Collar Marriage (Random House, 1964).

1572   Russell, D. E. H. **The Politics of Rape: The Victim's Perspective.**
New York: Stein and Day, 1975. 311p. bibliog. $10.00. ISBN
0812816579. LC 73-90697.

This book is built around interviews with rape victims. A fundamental view is
that, contradictory to a widely-held male view of rape, rape victims do not
enjoy being raped. Four main sections indicate primary foci: The Victim;
The Rapist; Rape and Race; Rape and Society. A sampling of chapters describes
the range of materials: The Stigma of Being Raped; Fathers, Husbands and
Other Rapists; Rape and Black Rage; White Man Wants Black Piece; Keep It
to Yourself; Psychiatrists, Husbands and Others Find the Victim Guilty. The
appendix offers Rape Prevention Tactics.

1573   Safilios-Rothschild, Constantina, 1934- , comp. **Toward a Sociology
of Women.** New York: Wiley, 1972. $7.25. ISBN 0471006858. LC
70-168398.

This collection has been widely used as a basic text for introductory-level
sociology of women courses. Eleven of the 31 articles were commissioned for
this book; the other twenty were drawn from journals such as *Social Policy,
Acta Sociologica,* and *Michigan Law Review.* Articles are grouped into the
following topics: The Making of Men and Women; The Images of Women;
Money, Sex and Women; The Options of Women; On Combining of 'Deviant'

and a Conventional Option; Women in 'Deviant' Occupations; and Projections about the Women's Liberation Movement and the Future of Men and Women. Each section is followed by a discussion by Safilios-Rothschild.

1574   Scanzoni, John H., 1935- . **The Black Family in Modern Society**:
        Patterns of Stability and Security. Chicago: University of Chicago
        Press, 1977. 365p. bibliog. index. $5.95. ISBN 0226733416.
In this text on black family structure written by white sociologist John Scanzoni, the focus is on black households "headed by a *man* with his wife present." While Scanzoni hopes to counterbalance certain prejudices and ideological assumptions about black family patterns, he brings substantial white, middle-class male biases of his own to bear on this work. Among the topics are: denigration of the black male self-concept, the urban experience, lower-class socialization patterns, the linkage of family structure and parental functionality, parental role models, achievement and mobility, husband-wife relationships, and parent-child relationships. Readers will find a radically different approach in Carol Stack's study, *All Our Kin: Strategies for Survival in a Black Community* (1974).

1575   Sheehan, Susan. **A Welfare Mother**. Boston: Houghton Mifflin, 1976.
        109p. $6.95. ISBN 0395245052. LC 76-13439.
Michael Harrington writes the introduction to this superb piece of advocacy journalism in which Carmen Santana, a welfare mother with four children, tells her story through Susan Sheehan's spare, factual reportage. Harrington, himself an advocate of reforming governmental dealings with the poor (*The Other America*, 1962), points out the complicated truth that underlies our entire welfare system. He states that it *is* true that people such as Mrs. Santana "cheat" in terms of their reporting of earnings to the Welfare Department but for a complex of reasons: the money allocated is not sufficient for the culture in which we live, the rules are often baffling to the welfare client, and the clients cannot really see any reward in adhering to the letter of the law of a system that makes them victims and certainly not victimizers. This book grew out of a *New Yorker* "Profile" article. Sheehan virtually lived with Mrs. Santana and her Puerto Rican welfare family in the Williamsburg section of Brooklyn while researching the article. Their violent and complex family and social life, as well as the incredibly tangled bureaucratic structure that Mrs. Santana accepted as her daily lot as a welfare mother, were directly observed by Sheehan. Sheehan's conclusions about the future for Mrs. Santana and her children are grim. One son has died of an overdose of heroine, and it is likely that the disadvantages of their alienated situation due to poverty and lack of education will see a third generation of Santanas on welfare.

1576   Sheehy, Gail. **Hustling: Prostitution in Our Wide Open Society**. New
        York: Dell, 1974. 254p. $1.50. ISBN 0440138000.
Writing in *New York* magazine style, and using the sketch-like approach she used in *Passages*, Sheehy manages to portray the daily lives of prostitutes working on many different levels—from the street walker to the courtesan. Her conclusion is that our supposedly liberated culture has created "a prostitution boom," mainly because men fear the intimacy of demanding interpersonal relationships and because "the gospel according to *Playboy*" has preached that a woman must

be a playmate, a role difficult to maintain when a woman is living in a permanent relationship. Although Sheehy's approach is readable and engaging, it is often more a vehicle of experimental journalism than an analysis of the prostitution situation. Her technique to gain information about the world of prostitution has been to do street research, to interview arrested prostitutes, and to cultivate connections associated with the "*haute monde* of hustling."

1577   Simpson, Ruth, 1926- . **From the Closet to the Courts: The Lesbian Transition.** New York: Viking Press, 1976. 180p. $8.95. ISBN 0670331651. LC 75-25658.
The writer, a lesbian, deals with the "specific problems of the lesbian as particularly illustrative of problems which confront every member of any oppressed group who takes a step away from the hiding place toward the hostile ground known as our society." Contents: What Is Lesbianism?; The Family; Social Attitudes; Lesbianism and Feminism; The Oppressor Church; Lesbianism and Psychiatry; Homosexuals—In and Out of the News; Lesbians and Law Enforcement; The Homosexual Movement; Lesbians and the Courts of Justice.

1578   Skolnick, Arlene S., 1933- , and Jerome H. Skolnick, comps. **Family in Transition: Rethinking Marriage, Sexuality, Child-rearing, and Family Organization.** (2nd ed.). Boston: Little, Brown, 1977. 592p. bibliog. $6.95. ISBN 0316797146. LC 77-358226.
A reader on the changing nature of the family, this is "addressed mainly to those who hold conventional assumptions about the necessity of the nuclear family, the inherent nature of male and female sex-role differences, and the unchangeability of human nature." The compilers see as their purpose "to do for the family what some poets have described as the main aim of poetic art: to make the familiar seem strange." Chief topics are: Conceptions of the Family; The Politics of Sex and Marriage; The Politics of Child Rearing; and The Politics of Household and Life Style. Among the contributors are: Margaret Mead, Claude Lévi-Strauss, Philippe Ariès, William J. Goode, Karl Marx, Eleanor Maccoby, Juliet Mitchell, R. D. Laing, Alice S. Rossi, Talcott Parsons, Elliott Liebow, and Melford Spiro.

1579   Smart, Carol. **Women, Crime, and Criminology: A Feminist Critique.** Boston: Routledge and Kegan Paul, 1977. 208p. bibliog. index. $11.25. ISBN 0710084498. LC 77-350404.
This study of female crime looks at emancipation and its link with crime rates, rape, prostitution, female criminality and mental illness, and the profile of the female offender. Though it is focused chiefly on Britain, and supported by U.K. statistics, the feminist conclusions that Smart draws and the research that she targets as imperative in the field of female criminality will be of interest to anyone trying to understand the sexist trends in the present state of criminology literature. A good bibliography draws from medical, sociological, psychological and feminist sources. Readers may also be interested in the anthology compiled by Carol Smart and Barry Smart entitled *Women, Sexuality and Social Control* (Routledge and Kegan Paul, 1978). This collection of articles, primarily by British scholars, addresses the issue of social control as expressed in medical practice, prostitution, sexual codes, criminology, and rape.

1580   Stack, Carol B. **All Our Kin: Strategies for Survival in a Black Community.**
New York: Harper and Row, 1974. 175p. bibliog. index. $7.95. ISBN
0060139749. LC 73-4126.

Carol Stack is a white anthropologist. Her particular achievement in *All Our Kin*
is that by using participant observation methods to study survival strategies in
a black community, she has succeeded in bypassing the white middle-class
models that ordinarily structure such studies (see, for example, John Scanzoni's
The Black Family in Modern Society). Black family patterns as Stack describes
them emerge as culturally distinct forms rather than as deviations from white
patterns. Specifically, Stack reveals "patterns of co-residence, kinship-based
exchange networks linking multiple domestic units, elastic household boundaries,
lifelong bonds to three-generation households, social controls against the formation of marriages that could endanger the network of kin, the domestic authority
of women, and limitations on the role of the husband or male friend within
a woman's kin network." These patterns represent creative survival responses
in lives shaped by poverty, structural unemployment, and the welfare system.
Interested readers will also want to look at Herbert Gutman's *The Black Family
in Slavery and Freedom, 1750-1925* (1976).

1581   Staples, Robert. **The Black Woman in America: Sex, Marriage, and the
Family.** Chicago: Nelson-Hall, 1973. 269p. bibliog. index. $12.95.
ISBN 0911012559. LC 72-95280.

Robert Staples is a black sociologist whose major focus is black women. Staples
begins his study noting that black women in America have, out of necessity,
had to cope with blurred identities, responsibilities, standards of behavior and
family roles. "Economic inequities forced many to carry the burden of responsibility for their entire families without the security offered to women of other
racial and ethnic groups. At the same time, they were coerced into taking on
some of the purely feminine characteristics that prevail in mainstream American
society" (foreword). Staples emphasizes the patience and courage of black women
in dealing with abdication of responsibilities by many black men, as well as
with the oppressive conditions of a racist society. Chapters are: Black Womanhood: Myth and Reality; The Sexual Life of Black Women; Bodies for Sale:
Black Prostitutes in White America; Being Married—and Black; The Joy and
Pain of Motherhood; Black Women and Women's Liberation; Voices of Black
Womanhood. Other very relevant literature appeared around the same time as
Staples's study, and complements Staples: Andrew Billingsley, *Black Families
in White America* (1968); Toni Cade, *The Black Woman* (anthology; 1970); Jay
David and Melvin Watkins, *To Be a Black Woman* (anthology; 1971); Mari
Evans, *I Am a Black Woman* (poetry; 1970); Joyce A. Ladner, *Tomorrow's
Tomorrow: The Black Woman* (1971).

1582*   Stephenson, Marylee. **Women in Canada.** (Rev. ed.). Don Mills, ON:
General, 1977. 368p. bibliog. index. $8.95. ISBN 077361026X.
LC 77-373935.

A collection of articles on the changing status of Canadian women, this volume
contains the following: Dorothy E. Smith, "Women, the Family and Corporate
Capitalism"; Margrit Eichler, "Women as Personal Dependents"; Sherrill Cheda,
"Indian Women"; Vera Rosenbluth, "Women in Prison"; Jennifer Stoddart,

"The Woman Suffrage Bill in Quebec"; Esther Greenglass, "The Psychology of
Women; Or, The High Cost of Achievement"; and other papers touching on:
Marriage and the Family; Work outside the Home; Changing Things. Particularly
fine is the bibliography of materials relevant to Canadian women from 1950
to the present.

1583   Stoll, Clarice Stasz, comp. **Sexism: Scientific Debates.** Reading, MA:
        Addison-Wesley, 1973. 137p. bibliog. $3.95. ISBN 0201073080.
        LC 72-11077.
Approaching the social sciences from a feminist perspective, Stoll finds serious
methodological errors in empirical studies and other scholarship that researches
sex differences, marriage and the family, sexual behavior, and women. *"There
is growing evidence that the social sciences are sexist*; this should not be surprising given that white males predominate in virtually every scientific profession.
In addition, these males run the professional societies, are overrepresented on
editorial boards and granting agencies, and therefore become public figures. . . .
These men have shared a socialization process and set of experiences quite different in many respects from those experienced by females. Consequently,
they are likely to perpetuate certain attitudes toward the world that are based
on sexist assumptions. Female scientists learn this tradition and may unwittingly
perpetuate it" (from Stoll's introduction). The readings that Stoll has brought
together explore questions about sex roles raised by social scientists and suggest
policy changes for the elimination of sexism. The papers do not necessarily
represent feminist positions. Contents: John Money, "Developmental Differentiation of Femininity and Masculinity Compared"; Judith Bardwick, "Infant Sex
Differences"; Lionel Tiger, "Sex and Politics"; Patricia Sexton, "The Feminized
Male"; Stoll and McFarlane, "Sex Differences in Game Strategy"; Marijean
Suelzle, "Women in Labor"; Charles Winick, "Toward a Society of Neuters";
and Jesse Bernard, "Adjusting the Lives of Women to the Establishment."

1584*   Theodore, Athena, comp. **The Professional Woman.** Cambridge, MA:
        Schenkman, 1971. 769p. bibliog. index. ISBN 0870739662. LC
        72-169697.
The tone of this book of readings is set early on by a quotation of Julia Ward
Howe's: "The professions indeed supply the keystone to the arch of woman's
liberty." Fifty-two readings are included under these rubrics: The Sexual Freedom
of Professions; Cultural Definitions of the Female Professional; Career Choice
Processes; Adult Socialization and Career Commitment; Career Patterns and
Marriage; The Marginal Professional; and Female Professionalism and Social
Change. In the introductory section, Theodore provides an overview ("The
Professional Woman: Trends and Prospects") of the book's major subject headings. In her concluding remarks for that preview (pp. 32-35), she cites declining
female participation at professional levels and concludes that it is too early to
judge from recent changes whether the trend might be reversed. She suggests
that additional research concerning the husbands of "achieving women" might
improve understanding of whether the dynamics of female motivation might
change the existing situation. She states that women who consider work to be
equal or superior to family endeavors are too few to effect changes that would
lead to economic equality. Yet, she is optimistic that the recent resurgence of

a social movement to establish economic equality between the sexes offers
hope for improving the lot of professional women.

1585   Tobach, Ethel, 1921- , et al. **The Four Horsemen: Racism, Sexism,**
        Militarism, and Social Darwinism. New York: Behavioral Publications,
        1974. 123p. bibliog. $9.95. ISBN 0877051216. LC 73-18052.
The four brief essays collected here are based on a panel discussion at the
American Orthopsychiatric Association's 1972 national convention. What
unifies the four authors (Howard Topoff on racism, C. G. Gross on sexism,
John Gianutsos on militarism, and Ethel Tobach on Social Darwinism) is their
concern with the rise within the scientific and social scientific disciplines of
social engineering and sociobiological perspectives. They are disturbed by theories
that see social problems as biological in origin and as susceptible to biological
intervention as cure. Gross's essay, "Biology and Pop-Biology: Sex and Sexism,"
critically reviews the main tenets (or myths) of sociobiological theories of male
supremacy: for example, that dominance and leadership are "male" characteristics, while child care is "female"; or that male monopoly on political leadership
is biologically based in "male bonding"; or that sex differences in personality
are genetic in origin and thus resistant to environmental influences.

1586*   United States. Commission on Civil Rights. **Window Dressing on the**
        Set: Women and Minorities in Television. Washington: The Commission,
        1977. 181p. bibliog. LC 77-603555.
Due to this study's separate treatment of blacks, Native Americans, Asian
Americans, and "Women," it is not able to deal adequately with the question
of the double discrimination faced by minority women. Introducing the study
with statistics concerning the average time that audiences spend viewing television each day (over six hours), the Commission outlines criticisms leveled
against television for its continued portrayal of women and minorities in stereotyped roles, and for the low visibility of these groups in news reporting positions
and in the industry. The study cites liberally from the existing programming,
tracing portrayal from the 1950s to the 1970s. Many statistics and tables support
the Commission's recommendation that the FCC take a more active role in
remedying stereotyped portrayals of women and minorities. The study also
asserts that "representation of women and minorities in key editorial, reporting
and writing positions is critical to the development of a broader and more
varied concept of what constitutes the news."

1587*   Ward, David A., and Gene G. Kassebaum. **Women's Prison: Sex and**
        Social Structure. Chicago: Aldine, 1965. 269p. index. LC 65-12460.
The focus of this study is "female homosexuality" in prisons for women,
differentiating those who engaged in lesbian behavior while in prison, and further
refining the differences between those who play "masculine" versus "feminine"
roles in such prison relationships. Research was conducted at the California
Institution for Women, Frontera. Chapters are: The Pains of Imprisonment;
Female Prisoners and the "Inmate Code"; The Reaction of Female Inmates
to the Pains of Imprisonment; The Extent of Homosexual Behavior in the
Prison Setting; Social-Psychological Bases of Homosexual Role Differentiation;
The Dynamics of Prison Homosexuality; The Course and Character of the Love

Affair; Some Implications of the Homosexual Adaptation for the Prison Staff. The researcher sees homosexuality as a pathology, using the terms "butch" and "femme" to designate roles played in the lesbian relationship. The term "lesbian" is not used. The author emphasizes that homosexual adaptation is the inmate's method of coping with the stress and deprivations of prison life and that homosexual behavior will continue unless non-traditional approaches are sought to control and counsel prisoners.

1588   Watkins, Mel, and Jay David, comps. **To Be a Black Woman: Portraits in Fact and Fiction.** New York: Morrow, 1970. 285p. $6.95. ISBN 0688000118. LC 74-125348.

The authors state that the American black woman has suffered doubly on account of sex and race. "In part, this may explain the conspicuous absence of a substantial body of literature written by or about black women; the black female writer has been more rare than her white counterpart, and black men, overwhelmed with their own emasculation, have usually avoided the subject. Consequently, the black woman has been treated only tangentially in American literature and in most previous sociological studies, and no in-depth portrait has been available in a single volume" (introduction). Sources for the readings in this book (out of 39, all but six are written by black writers) are various: literature, biography and autobiography, and sociology. Taken together, a collage of images of and roles assumed by black women from the antebellum period to contemporary times takes shape. Among the writers represented are: B. A. Botkin, Frances E. W. Harper, Langston Hughes, Nina Simone, Richard Wright, Calvin C. Hernton, Martin Duberman, Frank Yerby, Alex Haley, Mari Evans, Claude Brown, Robert Coles, William Grier, Lena Horne, Billie Holiday, James Baldwin, Lorraine Hansberry, Maya Angelou, Gwendolyn Brooks, Lethonia Gee, Josephine Carson, Paule Marshall, Don L. Lee, and Eldridge Cleaver. Clearly the perspective is weighted toward a male view, but the book is nonetheless useful because of its topic.

1589   Weibel, Kathleen, and Kathleen Heim, eds. **Women in Librarianship**: **1876-1976.** New York: Neal-Schuman; distr. Phoenix, AZ: Oryx Press, 1979. bibliog. index. $12.95. ISBN 0912700017.

Weibel and Heim have gathered a group of significant readings that comprehensively reviews the historical and sociological status of women in libraries during the last hundred years. The bibliography they have put together is the most complete available survey of the literature on women in the library profession with over 1,500 items. Since librarianship, like teaching and social work, is a female-dominated, relatively low status profession with males occupying the great majority of power positions, this anthology will surely be of interest to librarians, but also fascinating to readers who wish to understand the sociology of sex roles and sex-role stereotyping in the professions. Readers may also wish to look at a collection entitled *Women in a Woman's Profession: Strategies*, edited by Betty-Carol Sellen and Joan K. Marshall, and based on the Preconference on the Status of Women in Librarianship held at Douglass College in 1974.

1590   Weibel, Kathryn. **Mirror, Mirror: Images of Women Reflected in Popular Culture**. Garden City, NY: Anchor Books, 1977. 256p. bibliog. index. $3.95. ISBN 0385111312. LC 76-47835.

Popular fiction, movie images, advertising, and popular magazines are major topics covered in this illustrated treatment of mass media and the enormous role that mass media play in the shaping of women's perceptions of themselves—all in the interest of big business, it seems. A huge subject that deserves greater in-depth treatment, sex-role portrayal in the mass media is also the subject of a very recent collection of pioneer studies by social science researchers, *Hearth and Home: Images of Women in the Mass Media*, edited by Gaye Tuchman, Arelene Kaplan Daniels, and James Benet (Oxford University Press, 1978). Such studies as Weibel's and Tuchman's can always be faulted for subjectivity, over-generalizations, and blurring of categories. In-depth analysis becomes very difficult because of the sheer volume of the popular cultural output. Nevertheless, these studies are valuable for their documentation of the distorted images that the communications media continually stress and for their suggestions for a change in cultural norms.

1591   Woolley, Persia, 1935- . **Creative Survival for Single Mothers**. Millbrae, CA: Celestial Arts, 1975. 144p. $4.95. ISBN 0890870179. LC 74-25829.

How to balance the maternal role with managing a fulfilling personal life that includes men is the focus of this self-help book for divorced women, which incorporates the author's "12 years of accidental research." The common sense suggestions that Woolley offers could be helpful for an individual who has no support group or friends with whom to discuss these matters.

1592   Young, Michael Dunlop, 1915- , and Peter Willmott. **The Symmetrical Family**. New York: Pantheon Books, 1974. 398p. bibliog. index. $10.00. ISBN 0394487273. LC 73-7009.

Young and Willmott (authors of the highly respected *Family and Kinship in East London*, Penguin, 1962) take a historical and sociological approach in their survey of changes in family structure in London. They see the evolution of "technology" since industrialization as the prime trigger for the historical transformation of the family: from the preindustrial family, which functioned as the societal productive unit; to the family of the Industrial Revolution, disrupted by the advance of wage labor and the decline of family production; to the contemporary "symmetrical family," in which, they assert, a return to the family-centeredness of the preindustrial era is made possible by technological advance ("technological advance . . . has made the home a machine for believing in"). While their view of this "alliance of family and technology" seems unusually optimistic, they see a social cost in the developing pattern of increased employment of wives outside the home and increased participation of men in work within the home. "The losses in tranquillity, and in stability for the children, are almost too obvious to need stressing." On the one hand, this study may be recommended for a commitment to historical perspective unusual in sociological research. On the other hand, the work seems limited in its analysis of sources of change due to its failure to investigate the actual social forces underlying what the authors have termed "technological advance." Readers may want to compare Lawrence Stone's more recent monumental study, *The Family, Sex and Marriage in England, 1500-1800* (1977). The foreword to the present work is by Lee Rainwater.

SPORTS

The literature of women and sport is sparse, considering the amount of speculation voiced about women's lack of visibility in sports. Additional assistance in this area comes from bibliographies cited in the Reference chapter. The Feminist Press publication, *Feminist Resources for Schools and Colleges* (1977), suggests a number of organizations to which users might write for current report literature. This list presents a sampling from the current state of the literature: the history of sport dealing specifically with women; the psychology of women in sport; texts on physical education programs and teaching techniques applied to women. In the last few years, books have begun to appear that profile noted women athletes, especially tennis players and gymnasts. Another trend in sports books about women are those that emphasize strategies for women to succeed in individual sports—running and tennis, particularly.

1593   American Association for Health, Physical Education, and Recreation. **Women's Athletics: Coping with Controversy.** Ed. by Barbara J. Hoepner. Washington, 1974. 120p. bibliog. $3.75. LC 74-170341.
These selected papers from the 1973 AAHPER national convention in Minneapolis speak to the issues of equal opportunity for women in sports. Papers are divided in four major areas—Women's Rights; Women's Intercollegiate Athletics—Past, Present, Future; The Olympic Games: Women in Athletics; Welfare of Women in Sports. Some of the more interesting papers: Margaret C. Dunkle's "Equal Opportunity for Women in Sports," which reviews Title IX compliance; Lucille Magnusson's "The Development of Programs," which describes national organizations determining the directions being charted for women's intercollegiate athletics; Jack Scott's "The Masculine Obsession in Sports," which describes "the stag party atmosphere of American athletics" and the concern with the words "masculine" and "feminine" in sports; and Betty Menzie's "Sociological Aspects of Women in Sports," which talks, among other things, of the emergence of a sport subculture for women.

1594   Bowers, Carolyn Osborn, et al. **Judging and Coaching Women's Gymnastics.** Palo Alto, CA: National Press Books, 1972. 217p. bibliog. $9.95. ISBN 0874841496. LC 70-142368.
This is a technical discussion of the rules of competition in women's gymnastics and of technique, composition, style, and current trends in specific areas of women's competitive gymnastics. The book is intended as an aid to coaches, gymnasts, and judges in their preparation for competition. Illustrations are provided throughout the discussions of technique.

1595*   Bowers, Carolyn Osborn, comp. **Selected Gymnastics Articles.** Washington: American Association for Health, Physical Education, and Recreation, 1971. 128p. LC 78-175621.
Topics included in this collection of articles covering the period (1963-72) are: Gymnastics in the Physical Education Program; Specialized Skills; Theory; and Competition. Included also are the Federation of International Gymnastics

rule interpretations from the 1972-1974 *Gymnastics Guide*. A brief description
of the history and scope of gymnastics is written by Andrea Bode Schmid.
Readers may also be interested in the recent *Women's Gymnastics*, by Jill Coulton
(Charles River Books, 1977).

1596   Brailsford, Dennis. **Sport and Society: Elizabeth to Anne.** Toronto:
        University of Toronto Press, 1969. 279p. bibliog. index. $15.00.
        ISBN 0802016227. LC 70-437885.
A general study of sport between 1560 and 1714, this book documents the non-
participation of women in sport, especially in the chapter "Sporting Theory
and Practice," which treats of gentlewomen and sports. Brailsford writes:
"The courtly experience of the Renaissance provided boys' physical education
with a perpetual image of what was possible, while girls' schooling, even in its
Elizabethan heyday, had developed no comparable pattern of exercise or play
as part of its system. Court ladies shared a few of the physical benefits of the
Renaissance cult; some of them, like Elizabeth herself, would join in hunting
expeditions (which had, as we have seen become so organized as to make ladies'
participation possible) and show their skill with the bow; they also went hawking,
to judge from their portraits with hooded falcons at the wrist. These, however,
were fringe benefits from the courtly mode of training enjoyed by the men.
The nobly-born girls' education might often, in the earlier part of the Queen's
reign particularly, bring her to a high level of classical scholarship, but it would
involve little if any physical training." This is a good source for this period,
with citations pointing to contemporary education manuals for women.

1597   Butt, Dorcas Susan. **Psychology of Sport: The Behavior, Motivation,
        Personality and Performances of Athletes.** New York: Van Nostrand
        Reinhold, 1976. 196p. bibliog. index. $12.95. ISBN 0442212267.
        LC 76-24853.
Butt, who played on the international tennis circuit between the age of nineteen
and 23, has much personal experience with both the destructive and constructive
psychological aspects of sport. Although her general discussion of the subject
applies to both male and female athletes, she includes an excellent chapter
entitled "Sex Roles in Sport," in which she examines role conflict for the
female athlete, sexuality of the female athlete, and lesbianism among female
athletes. Particular female athletes (e.g., Billie Jean King, Nancy Green) are
introduced in the context of the general discussion. A good bibliography supports
the chapter on sex roles in sport.

1598   Gibson, Althea, 1927- . **I Always Wanted to Be Somebody.** New York:
        Harper and Row, 1958. 176p. $8.79. ISBN 0060115165. LC 58-12447.
Althea Gibson begins her autobiography, "I always wanted to be somebody. I
guess that's why I kept running away from home when I was a kid even though
I took some terrible whippings for it. It's why I took to tennis right away and
kept working at it, even though I was the wildest tomboy you ever saw and my
strong likings were a mile away from what the tennis people wanted me to
do. . . . " Gibson is a black woman tennis champion, the first to invade the snob-
bish white game. Here she tells her story: how she was born to a share-cropping
family in a small town in South Carolina, moved as a child to Harlem, spent

her childhood loving nothing better than playing ball, couldn't stay in school
or hold a job, and was finally removed from her home by the Welfare Department and placed in a private home, where, happy coincidence, she was introduced
to tennis. From here, it is a story of Gibson's struggle to learn and succeed in
the monolithically white sport, getting a scholarship to college, raising money
in black communities to pay her way to tournaments, traveling around the world
trying to build her game and reputation, and finally, in 1957, winning the
Wimbledon singles championship.

1599   Klafs, Carl E., and Muriel Joan Lyon. **The Female Athlete: Conditioning,**
       Competition, and Culture. St. Louis, MO: Mosby, 1973. 216p. bibliog.
       index. $8.25. ISBN 0801626803. LC 72-86405.
"The main focus of this book has been the female athlete herself–her structural,
physiological, and psychological characteristics and capacities. We earnestly
hope that it will provide those persons in positions of leadership in girls' and
women's athletics–coaches, administrators, etc.–greater insight and understanding regarding the nature of their young and enthusiastic competitors"
(preface). Chapters include: Historical Background; Anatomical and Physiological
Factors in Sports Performance; Psychological and Cultural Influences; Conditioning and Training; a glossary of terms useful in athletic training; and useful
appendices on training room supplies and record keeping.

1600   Lance, Kathryn. **Getting Strong: A Woman's Guide to Realizing Her**
       Physical Potential. Indianapolis, IN: Bobbs-Merrill, 1978. $6.95. ISBN
       0672523884. LC 77-15433.
Included here as an example of a well-written guide for building up physical
strength with clear instructions on how to do so, *Getting Strong* is intended
specifically for women. It contains good tips on a number of various sports
and activities. A worthwhile specific treatment of a single sport is Joan Ullyot's
Women's Running (World Publications, 1977). The author is chief of the aerobics
division of San Francisco's Institute of Health Research.

1601   Lichtenstein, Grace. **A Long Way, Baby: Behind the Scenes in Women's**
       Pro Tennis. New York: Morrow, 1974. 239p. $7.25. ISBN 0688002633.
       LC 74-1166.
A Long Way Baby is an example of popular sportswriting that has long been
accorded to male athletes and only recently to women, complete with a fourteen-
year-old girl expressing her admiration for women tennis players outside the locker
room door in a conversation with the author. The author views women "superstar"
tennis players as "true pioneers of the women's movement . . . carving out a
place for themselves in what, throughout history, had been strictly a man's
world–that of the sports superstar." Lichtenstein writes in the dedicated prose
of the serious sportswriter about Astrotennis, Philadelphia tournaments, St.
Petersburg, Wimbledon, Forest Hills, and other official territories of great
tennis. Billie Jean King dominates the text in the company of Rosie Casals,
Margaret Court, Francoise Duir, Nancy Richey, and Evonne Goolagong. Some
feminists may be disturbed by the emphasis on money and media. However,
it is good to see women being seriously written about as major competitors.

1602   Sage, George Harvey, comp. **Sport and American Society: Selected Readings.** Reading, MA: Addison-Wesley, 1974. 489p. bibliog. $10.95. ISBN 020106703X. LC 73-14353.

Though the intent of the volume is to bring together a number of readings on the general subject of sport in society, one chapter has been assigned to "Women and Sport." The tone of the essays is feminist, and the introduction provides a brief but cogent description of the transformations of woman's role in sport and its relation to woman's position in the culture. Essays in this chapter include Eleanor Metheny, "Symbolic Forms of Movement: The Feminine Image in Sports"; Smith, Rosenberg, and Morgan, "Development of Sex Differences in Play Choice During Preadolescence"; Dorothy V. Harris, "The Sportswoman in Our Society"; and Carolyn Sherif, "Females in the Competitive Process."

1603   Spears, Betty Mary, and Richard A. Swanson. **History of Sport and Physical Activity in the United States.** Dubuque, IA: Wm. C. Brown, 1978. 402p. bibliog. index. $11.95. ISBN 0697071618. LC 77-88350.

A general survey of sport in the United States, which includes excursions into international sport with a chapter on the ancient and modern Olympic Games, this book bears consulting for information on: Native American women's games, dance, sports in girl's schools and women's colleges, organized sport for women, and women in athletic festivals of the ancient world. Many female athletes receive mention. Among the references to specific women's groups in sport: Woman's Football League, Women's Division of the National Amateur Athletic Association, Women's Intercollegiate Skiing Conference, and the Women's Professional Golf Association.

1604   Ullyot, Joan, 1940- . **Women's Running.** Mountain View, CA: World Publications, 1976. 153p. bibliog. $5.95. ISBN 0890371008. LC 75-20962.

Ullyot confesses to a lifelong hatred of exercise but a passionate love of running: "This is the key. You aren't going to do any exercise unless you love it and discover you're not a whole person without it." *Women's Running* is a primer on: training for beginners, intermediates, and racers; proper clothing, shoes, and diet; safety; and injuries and their treatment. Ullyot is a graduate of the Harvard Medical School; her specialty is exercise physiology.

1605   **Women and Sport. A National Research Conference Held at the Pennsylvania State University, August 13-18, 1972. Proceedings.** Ed. by Dorothy V. Harris. University Park: Pennsylvania State University, 1972. 416p. bibliog.

Dorothy Harris, conference chair, writes in the preface that the conference papers spoke to specific research issues of women and sport related to psychological, sociological, physiological, and biomechanical considerations, rather than to the issues of distinction between "women and sport" and "men and sport." Twenty-five papers cluster around these four major topics, hitting upon an array of controversial issues concerning women's participation in athletics. A sampling: Joan Strati, "Body Image and Performance"; Michael Smith, "Aggression and the Female Athlete"; Judith Zoble, "Femininity and

Achievement in Sports"; Eileen Portz, "Influence of Birth Order and Sibling Sex on Sports Participation"; Buskirk and Haymes, "Nutritional Requirements for Women in Sport"; and Barbara Drinkwater, "Sex Differences in Biomechanics."

WOMEN'S MOVEMENT AND
FEMINIST THEORY

This chapter represents an eclectic gathering of the signal works on feminist theory and theories of inequality, regardless of historical treatment or nationality, though the majority emanate from British and American feminists. Wollstonecraft, Mill, Gilman, Millett, Firestone, and Rowbotham, predictably, are represented; but representative works of anti-feminists (see Steven Goldberg) should be considered core comparative examples and are included here also. Only post-1960s women's movement works appear in this section. Historical treatments of the women's movement and the "First Wave" of feminism books (e.g., Seneca Falls, woman suffrage) are listed under History. Look to the Reference chapters for additional direction to bibliographies and biographical materials. Barbara Haber's *The Woman in America: A Guide to Books* (1978) and Oakes and Sheldon's *Guide to Social Science Resources in Women's Studies* also cover the literature of the contemporary women's movement in some depth, while Krichmar's *Women's Movement in the Seventies* (1977) offers a comprehensive list of citations, though the annotations are sketchy. *Quest: A Feminist Quarterly* is perhaps the most outstanding of the scholarly feminist theory journals.

1606   Abbott, Sidney, and Barbara Love. **Sappho Was a Right-On Woman:**
        A Liberated View of Lesbianism. New York: Stein and Day, 1972.
        251p. bibliog. $1.95. ISBN 0812815904. LC 77-160348.
This book is an early statement of lesbian feminism. Part 1, What It Was Like, analyzes the experience of lesbian oppression—more specifically, the internalized guilt, fear of societal sanctions and consequent closeted lifestyles, the bars, and role-playing. In part 2, Living the Future, the authors trace the history of the lesbian/straight split within the National Organization for Women and the emergence of lesbian-feminism as an open political stance.

1607   Adams, Elsie Bonita, 1932- , and Mary Louise Briscoe, comps. **Up**
        Against the Wall, Mother . . . On Women's Liberation. Beverly Hills,
        CA: Glencoe Press, 1971. 521p. bibliog. $7.95. ISBN 0024702005.
        LC 74-131473.
This is an early and very general anthology of women's liberation materials. Its attempt to reflect the past as well as the present, and anti-feminism as well as feminism, makes for something of a hodge-podge: for example, John Stuart Mill is followed by the U.S. Dept. of Labor, which is followed by Eve Merriam. It would be most appropriate as a source of introductory readings.

1608*   Altbach, Edith Hoshino, comp. **From Feminism to Liberation.**
        Cambridge, MA: Schenkman, 1971. 275p. bibliog. LC 70-137492.
This collection of essays grew out of the February 1970, "Special Issue on Women's Liberation" of the journal *Radical America*, at that time published in Madison, Wisconsin. Most of the contributors wrote from a socialist feminist perspective. It is unfortunate that the volume should be so soon out of print, as many of the articles are classics of the women's liberation movement. Among

these: "Bread and Roses," by Kathy McAfee and Myrna Wood; "Where Are We Going?," by Marlene Dixon; "Women and the Socialist Party, 1901-1914," by Mari Jo Buhle; "The Political Economy of Women's Liberation," by Margaret Benston; "A Woman's Work Is Never Done," by Peggy Morton; and "On Abortion and Abortion Law," by Lucinda Cisler.

1609*   Altman, Dennis. **Homosexual: Oppression and Liberation.** New York: Outerbridge and Dienstfrey, 1971. 242p. bibliog. index. ISBN 0876900392. LC 79-178894.

Altman sees gay liberation as a product of the counter-culture and a force within the movement of the '60s and early '70s. Radicalizing the homosexual to demand a revision of society's norms and mores is a central concern of this extended essay on gay liberation, which frequently invokes the likes of Norman O. Brown and Herbert Marcuse. A particularly interesting chapter on the impact of gay liberation explores the relationship between gay liberation and women's libera- tion, and the ideological hostilities between gay men and heterosexual women and between lesbians and male homosexuals. Though the author clearly imparts his viewpoint as a practicing homosexual, this book is very strong on arguments supporting the philosophy of human liberation and its contingency on sexual liberation. Chapters include: Coming Out: The Search for Identity; The Oppres- sion of Identity; Liberation: Toward the Polymorphous Whole; The Movement and Liberation; America, the Counter-Culture and Gay Liberation; The Impact of Gay Liberation; and The End of the Homosexual?

1610*   Andersen, Margret, comp. **Mother Was Not a Person.** (2nd ed.). Montreal: Black Rose Books, 1974. 253p. bibliog. $10.95. ISBN 901961812X. LC 76-350834.

This collection of feminist writings by Canadian women resulted from a course taught by Margret Andersen at Loyola of Montreal in 1971-1972, entitled "Women in Modern Society," and it gathers together work by students in that course as well as by professional women in Montreal. Written in English, the collection does not reflect the experiences of Quebecois women. Included are writings by early Canadian feminists (e.g., Nellie McClung and Therese Casgrain); analyses of education, law, marriage, the media, and the employment situation; selections of feminist criticism and poetry; a section on women and their bodies; writings about women's liberation; critical analyses of the Report of the Royal Commission on the Status of Women; and, lastly, a critique of the feminist movement from a socialist perspective by Marlene Dixon.

1611   Anthony, Katharine Susan, 1877-1965. **Feminism in Germany and Scandinavia.** New York: Holt, 1915; repr. New York: Russell and Russell, 1977. 260p. bibliog. index. $18.00. ISBN 084621752X. LC 73-86716.

This work was originally published in 1915 by Katharine Anthony, an American writer and educator, with the hope of breaking through the ethnocentric outlook of the American women's rights movement and of introducing American feminists to German and Scandinavian feminism. The material that she brings together is of historical interest, and her central message is relevant once again within the contemporary U.S. women's movement, which remains largely ignorant of women's struggles and feminist theory outside the U.S. Anthony authored two other feminist studies, which, unhappily, have not been reissued but are in some ways even more pertinent today than *Feminism in Germany and Scandinavia*—for both address the difficult problem of women's unrecognized and uncompensated labor in the home and what to do about it. *Mothers Who Must Earn* (Russell Sage Foundation, 1914) is a detailed study of a group of women wage-workers living in the middle west side of New York—their families and financial situation, their occupations, hours of work, wages and income, home life, and the physical and human cost. Anthony tells us she chose her rather awkward title in an attempt to avoid the more common term, "working mothers," "which married housekeepers who do not receive wages justly resent." *The Endowment of Motherhood* (B. W. Huebsch, 1920) is an argument and plan for a national allowance to be paid directly to mothers to cover the needs of the woman and each of her children. Readers will find much here that prefigures current writings in the wages for housework debate (see, for example, Dalla Costa and James, *The Power of Women and the Subversion of the Community*).

1612   Astell, Mary, 1666-1731. **Some Reflections upon Marriage**. New York: Source Book Press, 1971. 128p. $9.50. ISBN 0442810563. LC 70-134178.
"That the Custom of the World has put Women, generally speaking, into a State of Subjection, is not denied; but the Right can no more be prov'd from the Fact, than the Predominancy of Vice can justify it." In this work, Astell discusses the problems of marriage, given the unequal power of men and women and the denial of education to women. Especially interesting is her sarcastic reply to readers included as an appendix in this edition. For a short biographical note on Astell, see entry under her *A Serious Proposal to the Ladies* (1701; repr. 1971).

1613   Atkinson, Ti-Grace. **Amazon Odyssey**. New York: Links Books; distr. New York: Quick Fox, 1974. 258p. $15.00. ISBN 0825630231. LC 73-80394.
This is an important document in the evolution of feminist theory. Atkinson has pulled together a collection of her essays and speeches ranging over the period from 1967 to 1972. As a result, the book gives a sense of how she changed during those years, as well as how the women's movement changed, rather than presenting a static theory of women's oppression. Her main concerns are to understand the roots of women's oppression and the nature of power relations in society, and to develop tactics for the struggle for change. The method of analysis is philosophical.

1614   Babcox, Deborah, and Madeline Belkin, comps. **Liberation Now! Writings from the Women's Liberation Movement**. New York: Dell, 1971. 382p. bibliog. $1.50. ISBN 0440147875. LC 74-27571.
This is an excellent early movement anthology. It includes writing by Marlene Dixon, Vivian Gornick, Alice Rossi, Margaret Benston, Marge Piercy, Eve Merriam, Juliet Mitchell, Naomi Weisstein, Radicalesbians, Anne Koedt, Charlotte Bunch, and many more contemporary writers. In addition, there are a few classical excerpts: for example, from Charlotte Perkins Gilman's *Women*

and Economics, Emma Goldman's "Marriage and Love," and from Virginia
Woolf's *A Room of One's Own.*

1615   Beard, Mary (Ritter), 1876-1958. **On Understanding Women.** New
        York: Longmans, Green, 1931; repr. New York: Greenwood Press,
        1968. 541p. bibliog. index. $24.75. ISBN 0837103029. LC
        68-54773.
This work predates Mary Beard's better-known *Woman as a Force in History*
by fifteen years, but it is concerned with similar issues—namely, with the fact
that, despite the bias of historical records, women have been central to the
evolution of all that one would want to call human culture. In fact, Beard
argues, the "continuance and care of life," which have been primarily women's
responsibility, must be the most basic priority of *all* of society if it is to survive.

1616   Beauvoir, Simone de, 1908- . **The Second Sex.** New York: Knopf,
        1953. 732p. index. $15.00. ISBN 0394444159. LC 52-6407.
Probably the most important statement of woman's historical and contemporary
position in Western society, *The Second Sex* ranges over psychological, theological, anthropological, historical, and literary terrain, weaving brilliant arguments, synthesizing, sifting, concluding. De Beauvoir's subject is so vast that
she must be forgiven for repetition. Beginning with the biological views of
women, she moves through the psychoanalytic view to that of historical materialism. Her chapter on history explores patriarchal and matriarchal theories
from the nomads to French contemporary society (c. 1950s). She is particularly
brilliant when examining myths and in her analysis of the work of Motherlant,
Lawrence, Claudel, Breton, and Stendhal. While Book 1 explores Facts and
Myths, Book 2 looks at Woman's Life Today. Those who are familiar with de
Beauvoir's autobiographical works will know that the materials on childhood,
the young girl, sexual initiation, and lesbianism are drawn heavily from her
personal experiences. When she talks of the situation of women—whether the
married woman, the mother, the prostitute, or the aging woman—de Beauvoir's
analysis always takes into account the double-bind as defined by woman's
social and cultural milieu. She posits that woman's situation is essentially
immanent and inward, while man's is transcendent and outward. Narcissism,
being in love, and mysticism are strategies that women have used to gain a
measure of transcendence. Her conclusion on independence and liberation is
hopeful about the male-female relationship but calls for an abolition of false
division between the sexes. This is a translation of *Le deuxième sexe.*

1617   Bebel, August, 1840-1913. **Woman Under Socialism.** New York:
        Source Book Press, 1970. (Repr. of 1904 ed.). 379p. bibliog. $18.00.
        ISBN 0442810768. LC 70-134002.
"Woman and the workingman have, since old, had this in common—*oppression.*"
So opens this classic treatise on women's oppression and women's liberation
by the great leader of the German Social-Democratic movement, August Bebel.
First published in 1883, *Woman Under Socialism* was immediately popular and
had reached over fifty German editions and been translated into almost all
the major European languages by Bebel's death in 1913. At the heart of its
appeal is its popularization of arguments for women's liberation from a socialist

perspective. Women's politicization was envisaged by Bebel as a force that would combine with the working-class movement (which was strong and well-organized in the Germany of this period) to build a revolution. Bebel is essential reading for those interested in nineteenth-century perspectives on the "woman question."

1618   Bergman, Arlene Eisen. **Women of Viet Nam.** (Rev. ed.). San Francisco, CA: People's Press, 1975. 223p. bibliog. $3.95. ISBN 091475002X. LC 75-28221.
Dedicated to "the growing solidarity between women of Viet Nam and women of the United States," Bergman's book strives to help break down the ethnocentrism of a unitary focus on women in the U.S. and the developed world by providing a vivid descriptive and analytic history of the experience of Vietnamese women—from the ancient past, through the period of French colonialism, to the end of the war against the United States. The material on Vietnamese women's experiences following the partition of their country into a socialist north and a capitalist south is particularly valuable, as it contributes to an understanding of the relation between overall social structure and sexual inequality.

1619   Billings, Victoria, 1945- . **The Womansbook.** Los Angeles: Wollstonecraft, 1974. 266p. bibliog. $7.95. ISBN 0883810069. LC 73-82723.
Billings discusses the question of independence for women—what it means and how to achieve it—by focusing on issues such as relationships with men, sexuality, sex roles, motherhood, jobs and money, and personal needs. It is written in a chatty style for a general audience.

1620   Bird, Caroline. **Born Female: The High Cost of Keeping Women Down.** (Rev. ed.). New York: McKay, 1974. 340p. bibliog. index. $9.95. ISBN 0679502300. LC 71-134801.
"This is a frankly feminist book. It counts the social, moral and personal costs of keeping women down on the job and finds them high," writes Bird in her introduction. The book started off as an article for the *Saturday Evening Post*, which turned it down because it considered the tone strident. Bird succinctly addresses major issues of women's liberation in America: the ERA; the extent of women's participation in the labor force; equal pay for equal work; subtle forms of discrimination in education and employment, which Bird calls "the invisible bar"; "the sex map of the work world." Along the way, she offers interesting observations about spectacularly successful women and the parallels between discrimination against blacks and women. Bird offers interesting commentaries on the shifting sands of feminism during the '70s. She is particularly good in pinpointing issues on which there is agreement among feminists, and she articulates a moderate platform of women's issues that energized the women's movement in 1970.

1621   Birkby, Phyllis, et al., eds. **Amazon Expedition: A Lesbian Feminist Anthology.** Washington, NJ: Times Change Press; distr. New York: Monthly Review Press, 1973. 93p. $6.50. ISBN 0878105263. LC 73-79902.
Written from a lesbian-feminist perspective, this is an excellent collection of articles. Included are: "Lesbianism and Feminism," by Ti-Grace Atkinson; "The New

Misandry," by Joanna Russ; "Emily Dickinson Feminist," by Rebecca Patterson; "Return of the Amazon Mother," by Jill Johnston; and "The More Profound Nationality of Their Lesbianism: Lesbian Society in Paris in the 1920's," by Bertha Harris.

1622   Blanc, Marie Therese (de Solms), 1840-1907. **The Condition of Woman in the United States: A Traveller's Notes.** New York: Arno Press, 1972. (Repr. of 1895 ed.). 285p. $14.00. ISBN 040504447X. LC 72-2590.

"Under the pseudonym, Th. Bentzon, Marie Therese de Solms Blanc (1840-1907) wrote novels of great popularity in France. In her literary criticism she was especially concerned with American values and authors. During her travels in the United States she talked with organized women's groups, visited women's colleges, clubs, and private homes, and observed women at work in the industrial East" ("A Note about This Volume," A. K. Baxter and L. Stein, eds.). Blanc writes (1895) about Jane Addams and Hull House, the Woman's Club and the Fortnightly (a literary club) in Chicago, the Woman's Building at the Chicago Fair, her meeting with Mrs. Julia Ward Howe at the New England Woman's Club in Boston, women's colleges (the Woman's Annex of Harvard, Bryn Mawr, Wellesley), Knox College at Galesburg, Illinois (a coeducational school), and Sherborn Prison, a women's prison in Boston. Readers interested in European perspectives on nineteenth-century United States society will of course also want to look at De Tocqueville's famous *Democracy in America*, volume 2 of which includes his observations on women's education, women as wives, and equality of the sexes.

1623   Bluh, Bonnie Charles. **Woman To Woman: European Feminists.** New York: Starogubski Press, 1974. 317p. $3.95. LC 74-20184.

Bluh writes a very personal brand of reportage, weaving the interview techniques of journalism and the narrative filtering method of the novelist in this description of feminism as she found it in Ireland, England, Holland, France, Italy, and Spain. The theme that emerges is the quality of friendship in international feminism. She provides a brief list of women's centers and groups, which should be cautiously used given the compilation date.

1624   Blumhagen, Kathleen O'Connor and Walter D. Johnson, eds. **Women's Studies: An Interdisciplinary Collection.** Westport, CT: Greenwood Press, 1978. 142p. bibliog. index. $11.95. ISBN 0313200289. LC 77-18110.

This anthology grew out of the Women's Studies section at the 1976 meetings of the Western Social Science Association. The eleven articles are extremely diverse in topic and perspective. Among them are: Sarah Slavin Schramm, "Women's Studies: Its Focus, Idea Power, and Promise"; Mary Stewart and Pat Erickson, "The Sociology of Birth: A Critical Assessment of Theory and Research"; M. Jane Slaughter, "Women and Socialism: The Case of Angelica Balabanoff"; Sylvia Gonzales, "The White Feminist Movement: The Chicano Perspective"; and Susan K. Macmanus and Nikki R. Van Hightower, "The Impacts of Local Government Tax Structures on Women: Inefficiencies and Inequalities."

1625   Brenton, Myron. **The American Male.** Greenwich, CT: Fawcett Publications, 1975. 224p. bibliog. index. $1.50.

Acknowledging that it is difficult to generalize about the societal pressures on more than 88 million males, Brenton confines his observations to the American male. "This is a book about the plight of the contemporary American male . . . about the increasingly difficult choices he is having to meet, and, most of all, about the invisible straitjacket that still keeps him bound to antiquated patriarchal notions of what he must do or be in order to prove himself a man." Brenton sees males as pressured beings because society defines their major role as that of breadwinner; the success of their role largely measured in financial terms; their masculinity equated to job status. Topics that Brenton addresses in this book, which exhorts men to redefine their roles to avoid "enslavement" and psychic castration, are: woman in the workplace, the role of the American patriarch, the modern woman's demand for sexual gratification, and fatherhood. Brenton is extremely sympathetic to the trials of the male role; a typical example is his defense of the paradoxical paternal role of American men in his chapter "Every Day Is Mother's Day." Readers may also be interested in *For Men Against Sexism: A Book of Readings*, edited by Jon Snodgrass (Times Change Press; distr. Monthly Review Press, 1977).

1626   Brown, Rita Mae, 1944- . **A Plain Brown Rapper.** Oakland, CA: Diana Press, 1976. 236p. $5.00. ISBN 0884470113. LC 76-50589.

This collection of Rita Mae Brown's essays was written between 1969 and 1975 and originally published in *Rat, Come Out!, The Ladder, Off Our Backs, Women: A Journal of Liberation, The Furies,* and *Quest: A Feminist Quarterly.* The essays reflect the evolution of her thinking during these electrifying years on questions of feminism, lesbianism, race, class, the Left, political organizing and leadership, and more. She has also written a new introduction for the volume, telling the story of her life and changes since 1965, with particular focus on the experience of the Furies Collective. This is important feminist and movement history.

1627   Brownmiller, Susan. **Against Our Will: Men, Women, and Rape.** New York: Simon and Schuster, 1975. 472p. bibliog. index. $10.95. ISBN 0671220624. LC 75-12705.

Of the avalanche of work and writing on rape that has come out of the contemporary women's movement, Brownmiller's book probably was the most responsible (due to the publicity it attracted) for creating a *national* awareness of feminist views on rape. It offers both theoretical and historical analyses of the issue, including specific discussions of the two World Wars, Bangladesh, Vietnam, the American Revolution, mob violence against blacks, slavery, and prison rape.

1628*   Buck, Pearl (Sydenstricker), 1892-1973. **Of Men and Women.** New York: John Day, 1971. 210p. LC 75-159970.

Pearl Buck lived most of her life in China and is best known for her fiction on China. It was the impressions awakened by her return to the United States that induced her to write these essays (orig. 1941) about the relations of men and women. She tells us in her foreword that she "found two obvious things . . .

the general discontent of our women and the marked lack of enjoyment between men and women." In this volume, described as an important feminist statement by June Sochen (*Movers and Shakers*, 1973), Buck includes pieces on "The Home in China and America," "The American Man," "The American Woman," "Monogamy," "Women and War," and "Women and Freedom." An epilogue entitled "Women and Liberation" was added to the 1971 edition.

1629   Bunch, Charlotte, 1944- , and Nancy Myron, 1943- , comps. **Class and Feminism: A Collection of Essays from the Furies.** Baltimore, MD: Diana Press, 1974. 90p. $2.25. ISBN 0884470040. LC 74-13894.
This little book is important both for the ideas it explores and as a historical document of the U.S. women's movement. The essays reprinted here originally appeared in publications of a lesbian-feminist collective called The Furies and represent early attempts at dealing with the question of class differences between women—how class shapes women's experiences of sexism and the ways in which it can undermine unity in the women's movement.

1630   Burton, Gabrielle. **I'm Running Away From Home, But I'm Not Allowed to Cross the Street: A Primer of Women's Liberation.** Pittsburgh, PA: Know, 1972. 206p. $5.00. ISBN 0912786000. LC 76-182740.
Gabrielle Burton tells us her "primer" is "affectionately geared to the woman who was off scouring her sink when *The Feminine Mystique* began stirring deeper waters. . . . It is an invitation—read it in the tub—let it pick up jelly smudges from the kitchen table. It is a book to be kept by your back door." This is a very readable and often amusing discussion of one woman's introduction to women's liberation. Written in a personal style, with anecdotes about her own reactions and those of her husband and five daughters, the book covers basic topics like consciousness-raising and sisterhood, housework and childcare, sex-role socialization, abortion, equal pay for equal work, the nuclear family, and monogamy.

1631   Cade, Toni, comp. **The Black Woman: An Anthology.** New York: Pathfinder Press, n.d. $1.50.
Toni Cade [Bambara] introduces this anthology with a statement of impatience "with the fact that in the whole bibliography of feminist literature, literature immediately and directly relevant to us wouldn't fill a page." In drawing together this collection of poems, stories, essays, there has been a conscientious effort to seek out a diversity of contributors unified by the fact that they are living black women writing about such contemporary issues as "Double Jeopardy: To Be Black and Female"; "The Pill: Genocide or Liberation."

1632   Carden, Maren Lockwood. **The New Feminist Movement.** New York: Russell Sage Foundation, 1974. 234p. bibliog. index. $8.95. ISBN 0871541963. LC 73-83889.
In the foreword to this book about women's liberation and women's rights groups of the 1960s and 1970s, Jessie Bernard writes that Carden has written "the definitive study" of the movement. The author tells us that her ideas and analysis reflect a mixture of radical and conservative philosophies regarding the "woman question," and her conclusions attempt to take stock of the problems

and accomplishments of the new feminist movement. In the course of her research, Carden interviewed 104 movement participants and attended many women's conferences and meetings. She discusses the National Organization for Women (NOW), the National Women's Political Caucus (NWPC), and the Women's Equity Action League (WEAL), which she depicts as "Women's Rights Groups," and the thousands of very small, relatively unstructured consciousness-raising groups, which she calls "women's liberation." Other major topics handled are: The New Feminist; The New Feminism; and Feminism and American Society. Along with a useful bibliography on important feminist and anti-feminist works, Carden provides appendices on her methodology and a list of resource centers and of the women's rights organizations referred to in the text. This is essential reading for anyone seeking an understanding of the contemporary feminist movement.

1633   Cooke, Joanne, et al., comps. **The New Women: A Motive Anthology on Women's Liberation.** Greenwich, CT: Fawcett Publications, 1973. 222p. bibliog. $0.95.
Edited by Joanne Cooke, Charlotte Bunch-Weeks, and Robin Morgan, and based on a special double issue of *Motive* magazine (March-April 1969), this collection of essays, letters, and poems is especially interesting for the feeling it conveys of the very early period in the contemporary women's movement, and for the way it fills in on the early development of writers better known for their later work (e.g., Charlotte Bunch, Robin Morgan, Marlene Dixon, Marge Piercy). Several letters that were received in response to the special issue of *Motive* are reprinted here and convey the excitment of the time.

1634   Cooper, Anna Julia (Haywood), 1859-1964. **A Voice from the South, by a Black Woman of the South.** New York: Negro Universities Press, 1969. (Repr. of 1892 ed.). 304p. $13.00. ISBN 0837113849. LC 77-78762.
Anna Julia Cooper was a noted black educator who taught, in the course of her career, at Oberlin College; Wilberforce University; the M Street High School in Washington, D.C.; and Frelinghuysen University, a school for employed blacks run from Cooper's own home in Washington, D.C. She received a Ph.D. from the Sorbonne in Paris in 1925, at the age of 66, and lived to the age of 105. In addition to this long and energetic career, Cooper became well-known for her book, *A Voice from the South* (1892), which addresses the questions of racism in the United States and of the "hitherto voiceless Black Woman of America." In part 1, on the black woman, Cooper discusses: Womanhood a Vital Element in the Regeneration and Progress of a Race; The Higher Education of Woman; "Woman vs. the Indian"; and The Status of Woman in America. "Woman vs. the Indian" is of particular interest, as it addresses a problem still relevant within feminism today: the failure of white feminists to adequately embrace the needs and demands of all oppressed people within their movement. Cooper is here referring to a speech by the Rev. Anna Shaw in 1891 bearing the title "Woman vs. the Indian," which appealed to the racism of white men as the basis for white women's right to the vote. Cooper writes that "cause of freedom is not the cause of a race or a sect, a party or a class,—it is the cause of human kind, the very birthright of humanity. . . . It is not the intelligent woman vs. the

ignorant woman; nor the white woman vs. the black, the brown, and the red,—
it is not even the cause of woman vs. man. . . . Why should woman become
plaintiff in a suit versus the Indian, or the Negro or any other race or class who
have been crushed under the iron heel of Anglo-Saxon power and selfishness?"

1635   Cooper, James L., and Sheila McIsaac Cooper, comps. **The Roots of
        American Feminist Thought.** Boston: Allyn and Bacon, 1973. 298p.
        bibliog. $7.95. LC 72-92094.
Included in this collection of abridged statements by seven key theorists whose
work and writings helped form the basis of American feminist thought are
selections from Mary Wollstonecraft's *Vindication of the Rights of Woman*,
Sarah Grimké's *Letters on the Equality of the Sexes*, Margaret Fuller's *Woman
in the Nineteenth Century*, John Stuart Mill's *Subjection of Women*, Charlotte
Perkins Gilman's *Women and Economics*, Margaret Sanger's *Woman and the New
Race*, and Suzanne LaFollette's *Concerning Women*. The editors have provided
a general introduction to the collection and historical and biographical introductions (fifteen pages average) to each selection.

1636   Croll, Elizabeth J., ed. **The Women's Movement in China: A Selection
        of Readings, 1949-1973.** London: Anglo-Chinese Educational Institute,
        1974. 115p. bibliog. ISBN 0903193051. LC 75-330685.
Elizabeth Croll has excerpted and organized a collection of translated readings
drawn from daily newspapers and periodicals published in the People's Republic
of China from 1949 to 1973. The reader is thus able to discover how questions
of women's oppression and women's liberation are treated in China, from the
point of view of the Chinese press. Among the topics addressed are: the separate
political organization of women within the revolutionary process; marriage
and the family; housework; women's participation in production; political
participation; and ideological struggle and liberation. Croll has written brief
introductions to each section.

1637   Curtin, Katie. **Women in China.** New York: Pathfinder Press, 1975.
        95p. bibliog. $6.00. ISBN 0873484045. LC 74-14166.
Katie Curtin is a Canadian socialist feminist who has written a brief critical
appraisal of the transformation in the status of women since the 1949 liberation
in China. Chapters include: Women's Position in the Old Society; The Early
Women's Movement; The Communist Party and the Women's Movement Before
1949; The Policy Toward Women After the Revolution; Women and Education;
Women and the Work Force; Women in Management; Women in Politics; and
Abortion, Birth Control, and Sexuality. Another more recent and lengthier
treatment of this topic is Elizabeth J. Croll's *Feminism and Socialism in China*
(Routledge and Kegan Paul, 1978).

1638   Dall, Caroline Wells (Healey), 1822-1912. **The College, the Market
        and the Court; Or, Woman's Relation to Education, Labor and Law.**
        New York: Arno Press, 1972. (Repr. of 1867 ed.). 498p. $23.00.
        ISBN 0405044534. LC 72-2596.
"As a teen-ager, Caroline Wells Healey Dall (1822-1912) participated in Margaret
Fuller's weekly transcendental 'conversations' in Boston. But it was the mission

work of the Rev. Joseph Tuckerman that drew her to Boston's slums, where
for five years she operated a nursery for children of working women. Left
with two children by a husband whose church mission to India lasted 31 years,
she became a vigorous champion of women's rights. In this book she traces
cultural traditions and religious influences that have blocked women's entry
into the professions, attacking especially the hypocritical charity which restricted
woman's freedom to learn and to work" ("A Note about This Volume," by the
editors, A. K. Baxter and L. Stein). This series of lectures is pleasant reading,
and like the work of so many of the nineteenth-century feminists, will shock
the reader with the contemporary content and flavor of its arguments. There is
much intelligence and passion in these pieces; a characteristic passage: "I ask
for woman, then, free, untrammelled access to all fields of labor; and I ask it,
first, on the ground that she needs to be fed, and that the question which is at
this moment before the great body of working women is 'death or dishonor':
for lust is a better paymaster than the mill-owner or the tailor. . . . "

1639   Dalla Costa, Mariarosa, and Selma James. **The Power of Women and the
        Subversion of the Community.** (3rd ed.). Bristol, England: Falling
        Wall Press, 1975. 79p. ISBN 0950270245. LC 77-356275.
This pamphlet has become a classic of the women's movement, especially among
socialist feminists. It reprints two articles. "A Woman's Place," by Selma James,
originally published in 1952, is remarkable for the analysis it makes of the
relation and division of labor of men and women in marriage, especially remarkable
given that it was written in a period of reaction in the United States. Mariarosa
Dalla Costa's "Women and the Subversion of the Community" was first published
in Italian in 1972. Its appearance in English in that same year sparked great
controversy and debate among Marxist feminist theorists over the question of
how best to understand the significance and function of housework as it is
organized within capitalist societies. The pamphlet can be obtained from Falling
Wall Press Ltd., 79 Richmond Road, Montpelier, Bristol B56 5EP, England.

1640   Davin, Delia. **Woman-Work: Women and the Party in Revolutionary
        China.** Oxford, England: Clarendon Press, 1976. 244p. bibliog. index.
        $15.00. ISBN 0198272316. LC 76-363613.
Davin defines her term "woman-work" (a literal translation from the Chinese)
very broadly to include mobilization of women "for revolutionary struggle,
production, literacy and hygiene campaigns, social reform, and so on." Thus
her study actually amounts to an assessment of changes in the social relations
of the sexes in China during the course of the twentieth century, with particular
emphasis on the immediate post-liberation period (1949-1960). In an introductory chapter, Davin sets the historical context with a brief discussion of traditional Chinese society, early forms of feminism (e.g., the nineteenth-century
Taiping movement), the women's section of the early Kuomintang, and the
emergence of an alliance between revolutionary women intellectuals and working-
class/peasant women under the Communist Party. Chapter 1 gives an account
of Party policy toward women during the period of the Jiangxi Soviet, the Anti-
Japanese War, and the Civil War. Chapter 2 discusses the history of the Women's
Federation since 1949 and the contradictions that have arisen between its goals
and those of the state. In chapter 3, Davin considers the barriers to new marriage

and family patterns in the conservative countryside. Chapter 4 analyzes the relationship between women, production, and the land, noting in particular the positive impact of land reform and collectivization on women's economic status and relative independence. Davin's final chapter looks at women's lives in towns and the limits of orthodox Marxist solutions to their problems. As Davin notes, the material presented here on the impact of economic development on women's status in revolutionary China offers interesting comparisons with Ester Boserup's analysis in *Woman's Role in Economic Development* (1974).

1641   Deckard, Barbara Sinclair. **The Women's Movement: Political, Socio-**
        economic, and Psychological Issues. New York: Harper and Row, 1975.
        450p. bibliog. index. $8.95. ISBN 0060416114. LC 74-15669.
The Women's Movement makes for very good introductory reading in the history of women in the United States and of the U.S. women's movement, the history of evolving forms of sexual oppression (in primitive, slave, feudal, capitalist, and socialist societies), the nature of sexual oppression in the U.S. today, and the contemporary U.S. women's liberation movement, with its different theories of women's liberation (socialist feminism, radical feminism and "women's rights feminism"). Introductory women's studies courses would find this a useful text.

1642   DeCrow, Karen. **The Young Woman's Guide to Liberation: Alternatives**
        to a Half-Life While the Choice Is Still Yours. New York: Pegasus,
        1971. 200p. bibliog. $5.75. ISBN 0672636158. LC 72-141377.
DeCrow hands down the commandments of women's liberation in very simple form: e.g., stop voting for males; stop subscribing to male media messages. Drawing from popular media images and messages, DeCrow indicts the male-dominated culture for crippling women emotionally, psychologically, education-ally, legally, and economically. The book is important as a primer for consciousness-raising. Typical chapters include Sisterhood and Self-Love: 6000 Years of Vying for the King's Approval; Love and Marriage: The Canary's Cage.

1643   Decter, Midge. **The New Chastity and Other Arguments Against Women's**
        Liberation. New York: Putnam, 1974. bibliog. $2.65. ISBN 0399503072.
Decter makes a forceful argument against women's liberation using as a rationale her perception that the women's movement is childish in not coming to terms with the burden that the new freedom imposes—the burden of career, which she defines as another form of "adult anguish." She claims that women's liberation posits woman as victim. "The equality demanded by the self-proclaimed victim is equality of attribution only: not to be, but to be deemed equal—no matter what." She discounts all arguments that men are responsible for female exploi-tation in sex and marriage, dismissing this issue by indicting women for lacking "the courage to recognize the extent of one's frailty and dependence on others." She equates women's liberation with a variety of bizarre contemporary cults that use the vocabulary of social justice to win their points, and concludes that women's liberation is a false and destructive liberation.

1644   Delaney, Janice, et al. **The Curse: A Cultural History of Menstruation.**
        New York: E. P. Dutton, 1976. 276p. bibliog. index. $9.95. ISBN
        0876902220. LC 76-5461.
" . . . menstruation is a factor in the control of women by men not only in ancient
and primitive societies, where knowledge of physiology is rudimentary at best,
but also in our post-industrial world. Women are physically and emotionally
handicapped by menstruation, goes the argument, and therefore cannot and may
not compete with men" (from the introduction). The authors—Janice Delaney,
Mary Jane Lupton, and Emily Toth—believe that menstruation needs to be
brought out of the closet and made an openly acknowledged part of human
experience. In their book, they discuss the history of taboos surrounding the
menstruating woman, the physiology and psychology of menstruation, the
menstruating woman in the popular imagination and in literature, the menopause,
and men and menstruation. In their final chapter, "Lifting the Curse," they
describe some of the ways in which contemporary feminists have tried to change
cultural meanings of menstruation—for example, Judy Chicago, with her striking
lithograph of a woman removing a tampon, titled "Red Flag." Readers may also
want to look at Paula Weideger's *Menstruation and Menopause: The Physiology
and Psychology, The Myth and the Reality* (Knopf, 1976).

1645   Douglass, Frederick, 1817?-1895. **Frederick Douglass on Women's
        Rights.** Ed. by Philip S. Foner. Westport, CT: Greenwood Press, 1976.
        190p. bibliog. index. $13.50. ISBN 0837188954. LC 76-5326.
The intimate but conflicted relationship between the Abolition Movement and
the Woman Suffrage Movement is a central part of the history of nineteenth-
century feminism. This collection of writings by Frederick Douglass offers a
rare glimpse into a black male abolitionist's perspective on that relationship.
Douglass was born a slave in Maryland, escaping at the age of 21 and becoming
one of the century's most prominent abolitionists. Less familiar is the history
of his advocacy of women's rights, from his attendance at the first convention
at Seneca Falls in 1848 until his death. Douglass's long association with suffragists such as Susan B. Anthony, Elizabeth Cady Stanton, and Lucy Stone was
troubled during Reconstruction by his opposition to the inclusion of woman
suffrage as part of the Fifteenth Amendment. The ensuing split between the
black and women's movements is an unfortunate part of suffrage history.
Douglass is particularly important as a *black* man who spoke to both the com-
monalities and the differences between the struggles of blacks and of white
women against oppression. Foner writes a fine introduction to Douglass's writings.
The views of two black women on Douglass's role in the Woman Suffrage
Movement (1899 and 1908) are included in an appendix.

1646*   Dreifus, Claudia. **Woman's Fate: Raps from a Feminist Consciousness-
        Raising Group.** New York: Bantam Books, 1973. 277p. bibliog.
Most of the key issues that arise in these transcribed consciousness-raising
sessions have become very familiar since the late '60s, but here there is the
advantage that they are addressed in the course of women's conversations with
each other, rather than abstractly or theoretically. The following topics are
discussed: sex-role socialization, preadolescent sexuality, adolescent sexuality,

adult sexuality, love, marriage and children, work, birth control and abortion,
rape, and age and women.

1647   DuBois, Ellen Carol, 1947- . **Feminism and Suffrage: The Emergence
of an Independent Women's Movement in America, 1848-1869.** Ithaca,
NY: Cornell University Press, 1978. 224p. bibliog. index. $12.50.
ISBN 0801410436. LC 77-90902.

Ellen DuBois believes that the Woman Suffrage Movement is too frequently
underestimated or written off in a facile way by historians and feminists armed
with historical hindsight, which reveals the limitations of enfranchisement as
a route to liberation. From her perspective, we make a mistake to reduce the
social movement to the social *reform* the movement struggled for. DuBois argues
that in the mysterious process that brings a social movement to life, the transformations in the people involved and in social consciousness are at least as
important and probably more important than the ultimate victory or defeat of
their aims. In the case of the Woman Suffrage Movement, the fight for the vote,
while it did not achieve liberation, did bring into existence "the first independent
movement of women for their own liberation." Through her examination of
the Movement from 1848 to 1869, as it moved through coalitions or attempted
coalitions with abolitionism, the black suffrage movement, and the labor movement, DuBois shows the emergence of a consciousness among women that the
battle for women's rights and freedom was one that women themselves must
fight.

1648   Dworkin, Andrea. **Our Blood: Prophecies and Discourses on Sexual
Politics.** New York: Harper and Row, 1976. 118p. bibliog. $6.95.
ISBN 006011116X. LC 76-9187.

The author of *Woman Hating* writes of her family background, her becoming a
feminist, and theories of feminist art. Hers is a revolutionary feminism committed
"to ending the system of oppression called patriarchy; to ending the male sexual
model itself." To Dworkin, rape is the first model for marriage, firmly entrenched
in biblical law. She calls for an overthrow of the existing social order. Chapters
formed from texts for speeches delivered by Dworkin include: Feminism, Art
and My Mother Sylvia; Renouncing Sexual "Equality"; Remembering the Witches;
The Rape Atrocity and the Boy Next Door; Redefining Non-Violence; Lesbian
Pride; Our Blood: The Slavery of Women in Amerika.

1649   Eckstein—Diener, Berta [Diner, Helen]. **Mothers and Amazons: The
First Feminine History of Culture.** New York: Julian Press, 1965.
308p. index. $7.50. ISBN 0870970178. LC 65-21550.

First published in German in the early 1930s, *Mothers and Amazons* belongs to
a tradition of thinkers and writers who have questioned the historical precedence
or universality of patriarchy, looking to other cultures, contemporary and
ancient, to mythology and religion, for clues pointing to the existence of
matriarchy (others in this tradition include J. J. Bachofen, Lewis Henry Morgan,
Friedrich Engels, Robert Briffault, and Elizabeth Gould Davis; Diner—who
disdains to acknowledge her sources—does acknowledge a debt to Bachofen and
Briffault). Diner describes her work as "the first feminine history of culture,"
one that "endeavors to remain as one-sided as possible" inasmuch as "the other

side is fairly well known to anyone who takes an interest in intellectual things."
Her intention is to restore to women a cultural tradition. This aim takes her from
her opening chapter, "Parthenogenesis" ("In the beginning, there was woman"),
through discussions of the Mother, matriarchy, symbols, circumcision, totemism,
exogamy, the couvade, and Amazons, followed by chapters on a variety of specific
cultures, including Greece, India, China, Central and South America, Egypt,
and Rome. Diner concludes with a series of brief critical assessments of other
theories of matriarchy: J. J. Bachofen, H. Schulte-Vaerting and Dr. M. Vaerting,
Heinrich Schurtz, Leo Frobenius, and Marx and Engels.

1650   Eisenstein, Zillah R., ed. **Capitalist Patriarchy and the Case for Socialist
        Feminism.** New York: Monthly Review Press, 1978. 394p. bibliog.
        $16.50. ISBN 0853454191. LC 77-76162.
Eisenstein pulls together here a series of important and hard-to-locate essays
from the last ten years. As a whole, they represent a beginning attempt to
analyze how capitalism and sexism have come to be structurally integrated and
mutually dependent systems. The collection includes historical studies, analyses
of particular problems such as job segregation by sex and housework, and
theoretical pieces. Among the contributors are Ellen DuBois, Mary Ryan,
Linda Gordon, Heidi Hartmann, and Nancy Chodorow.

1651   Evans, Richard J., 1947- . **The Feminist Movement in Germany,
        1894-1933.** Beverly Hills, CA: Sage Publications, 1976. 310p. bibliog.
        index. $13.50. ISBN 0803999518. LC 75-31571.
Evans's aims are, first of all, to contribute to the comparative study of feminism,
which has until recently been largely restricted to movements in the United
States and England; and, secondly, to contribute to an analysis of feminism as
a complex ideology of several different political strains with conflicting conceptions of liberation. He thinks that feminism must be "seen as an integral part of
the social and political system within which it sought to achieve its aims. The
closest ties of feminism in the nineteenth and early twentieth centuries . . . were
to bourgeois liberalism, and it is to the success or failure of this creed . . . that
its fate was linked." The feminist movement in Germany is therefore taken as
material for a "case-study in the development of German liberalism from the
fall of Bismarck to the advent of Hitler"; the core of the analysis is concerned
with explaining the retreat from liberalism from 1908 onwards. The study
focuses primarily on the Federation of German Women's Associations (1894-1933),
relegating analysis of the status of German women and the history of the Social
Democratic women's movement to positions of secondary concern.

1652   Farrell, Warren. **The Liberated Man; Beyond Masculinity: Freeing Men
        and Their Relationships with Women.** New York: Bantam Books, 1975.
        353p. bibliog. index. $1.95. ISBN 055302275X.
The author begins with the admission that the process of writing a book on men's
liberation has changed his life. The book is sensitively written and addresses the
major issues men face in acknowledging and remedying personal sexist attitudes.
The author includes a useful questionnaire on feelings about women and masculinity, designed for men but possibly applicable to examine women's feelings
about their roles. Part 1, Beyond Masculinity, discusses topics such as the

masculine mystique, redefinition of the family, and masculine images in advertising. Part 2 concentrates on behavior changes necessary to achieve liberation for both sexes. Part 3 discusses strategies, problems, and topics in consciousness-raising groups. In addition to a bibliography of resources, Farrell includes a bibliography for starting a child-care center.

1653*   Figes, Eva. **Patriarchal Attitudes.** New York: Stein and Day, 1970. 191p.
         bibliog. index. ISBN 0812813324. LC 71-126974.
" . . . it was intended that this should be a book about women in relation to society as a whole, on the traditional role they have played for so long, the reasons for it, and the ways that I think this role should now change. It has turned out to be a book largely about men." Published in 1970, *Patriarchal Attitudes* now seems a bit dated, its scope broad and its focus diffuse, the analysis overfamiliar. Figes discusses "patriarchal attitudes" in relation to such writers as Rousseau, Darwin, Schopenhauer, Nietzsche, and Freud, as well as the attitudes of women writers such as Charlotte Brontë, George Eliot, and Virginia Woolf to their situations as women.

1654   Firestone, Shulamith. **The Dialectic of Sex: The Case for Feminist
         Revolution.** New York: Morrow, 1970. 274p. $2.95. ISBN 068806454X.
         LC 70-123149.
Firestone's book was, and continues to be, an important contribution to the development of radical feminist theory—i.e., theory that seeks to analyze and explain sexual power relations. Firestone's goal is "to develop a materialist view of history based on sex itself" and her sketch of what this means in the first chapter, The Dialectic of Sex, has been very influential. The weakness of the book lies in her (understandable) failure to fulfill this goal. Instead, the later chapters rove over topics such as Freudianism, children and child raising, romance and love.

1655   Foreman, Ann. **Femininity As Alienation: Women and the Family in
         Marxism and Psychoanalysis.** London: Pluto Press; distr. Southwest
         Book Service, 1977. 168p. bibliog. index. $9.95. ISBN 0904383636.
         LC 78-306339.
Arguing that "the ideas of freedom and women's liberation were opposed in liberal thought in the nineteenth century" because the freedom of men in the public sphere took its meaning from the restriction of women to the private, Foreman contends that "an index of the extent that revolutionary thought has broken from the limitations of its liberal heritage is the degree to which an understanding of women's oppression is integral to it." Foreman's extended essay represents an assessment as of the late '70s of progress made toward the development of an adequate socialist feminist theory and practice. This project carries her from a critical analysis of political theorists who have attempted an integration of Marx and Freud (Wilhelm Reich, Herbert Marcuse, Erich Fromm, and Juliet Mitchell—all of whom she finds guilty of preserving the dualism of the two theoretical systems); to the existentialist approach of Sartre and de Beauvoir, whom she praises for their highlighting of the problem of sexual relations but criticizes for their ahistorical explanation; and through the most recent

Marxist-feminist analyses of women's domestic and wage labor (Dalla Costa, Margaret Benston, Wally Seccombe, Jean Gardiner, and others).

1656* Freeman, Jo. **The Politics of Women's Liberation: A Case Study of an Emerging Social Movement and Its Relation to the Policy Process.** New York: McKay, 1975. 268p. bibliog. index. ISBN 0679302840. LC 74-25208.

Freeman says in her preface that "this is a book about social movements, public policy and feminism." She outlines her methodology as one consisting of observation, experience, some library research, historiography, and interviewing. The strength of this book lies in Freeman's careful analysis of the movement, though her conclusions about the public policy sphere are thoughtful and well-researched. Chapters include: The Roots of Revolt; the Origins of the Women's Liberation Movement; The National Organization for Women; The Small Groups; The Policy Impact of the Women's Liberation Movement.

1657 Freeman, Jo, ed. **Women: A Feminist Perspective.** Palo Alto, CA: Mayfield, 1975. 487p. bibliog. index. $11.95. ISBN 0874842905. LC 74-84579.

The essays in this anthology are grouped broadly under the following topics: the body, the family, the female experience in society, work, the arts, institutions, and feminism. Written by an impressive array of feminist scholars and theoreticians, these essays seek to define future possibilities for societal change and to criticize present limitations in the existing social structure. Among the essays are: Susan Griffin's "Rape: The All-American Crime"; Kathleen Gough's "The Origin of the Family"; Jo Freeman's "How to Discriminate Against Women Without Really Trying"; Francine Blau's "Women in the Labor Force: An Overview"; Lyvia Morgan Brown's "Sexism in Western Art"; Phyllis Chesler's "Marriage and Psychotherapy."

1658 Friedan, Betty. **The Feminine Mystique.** New York: Norton, 1974. 430p. bibliog. index. $10.00. ISBN 0393086852. LC 74-160840.

"It's frightening when you're starting on a new road that no one has been on before," writes Betty Friedan in her introduction to the 10th anniversary edition of *The Feminine Mystique.* Of course, hers wasn't a new, untraveled road, but one down which many forgotten women had preceded her, from all the nineteenth- and early twentieth-century feminists to Simone de Beauvoir. What is astonishing today is to realize that, in 1963, Friedan's message did seem new, as the feminist history and consciousness of fifty years before were deeply submerged beneath the "feminine mystique" in United States culture. Thus, the significance of Friedan's book in historical terms far outweighs the significance of its analysis, which is in fact a very partial one, drawing its generalizations about American women's experiences from a model of the white, middle-class suburban housewife. Nonetheless, there is a vividness in Friedan's depiction of "the problem that has no name" that still makes the reading worthwhile.

1659 Friedan, Betty. **It Changed My Life: Writings on the Women's Movement.** New York: Random House, 1976. 388p. $10.00. ISBN 0394463986. LC 75-10305.

"I did not set out consciously to start a revolution when I wrote *The Feminine Mystique*, but it changed my life, as a woman and as a writer, and other women tell me it changed theirs." Friedan asserts repeatedly in this diary of global experiences speaking and traveling on behalf of women that the women's movement is about being a part of the mainstream, the system. It is about changing the system, not withdrawing from it. This is a collage of experiences from 1949 tracing the personal effect that her book has had on her life, recording numerous political activities, speeches, and rallies in which she has been a prime mover. Her personal truth seems to be a recognition that men are not the enemy and that the women's movement makes a grave error when it adopts a politics of separatism. Her accounts of meetings with Indira Ghandi, Pope Paul VI, and Simone de Beauvoir are very interesting, as is her account of International Women's Year at Mexico City. Friedan never loses perspective on the ordinary woman's situation, problems, and vision of liberation—which usually include a husband and children.

1660   Garskof, Michele Hoffnung, comp. **Roles Women Play: Readings Toward Women's Liberation.** Belmont, CA: Brooks/Cole, 1971. 210p. bibliog. $5.95. ISBN 0818500093. LC 75-146974.
An anthology of women's liberation readings, this includes: "Woman as Secretary, Sexpot, Spender, Sow, Civic Actor, Sickie," by M. Salzman-Webb; "The Unmothered Woman," by E. Albert; "The Sex Map of the Work World," by C. Bird; "The Politics of Orgasm," by S. Lydon; "Psychology Constructs the Female, or the Fantasy Life of the Male Psychologist," by N. Weisstein; "Training the Woman to Know Her Place: The Power of a Nonconscious Ideology," by S. L. Bem and D. J. Bem; "Femininity and Successful Achievement: A Basic Inconsistency," by M. S. Horner; "The Social Construction of the Second Sex," by J. Freeman; "Equality Between the Sexes: An Immodest Proposal," by A. S. Rossi; "Why Women's Liberation?," by M. Dixon; "I Am Furious (Female)," by E. Cantarow, et al.; and "The Political Economy of Women's Liberation," by M. Benston.

1661   Gilder, George F., 1939- . **Sexual Suicide.** New York: Quadrangle Books, 1973. 308p. bibliog. index. $7.95. ISBN 0812903811. LC 73-79913.
George Gilder falls in a class with Ashley Montagu (*The Natural Superiority of Women*) and Amaury de Riencourt (*Sex and Power in History*)—that is, men who attempt to repudiate the visions and demands of feminism and to maintain the status quo not by declaring the unfitness of women for equality due to inferiority, but by asserting that women possess a "natural superiority" that necessitates their continued monopoly in those "most important" fields of human endeavor, childrearing and care of home and family. Equality or androgyny, they claim, spells suicide for the human race. Gilder writes in a popular style, gleefully trying to be provocative. His argument never leaves the realm of personal opinion and moralizing: in his horrified survey of the contemporary sexual scene, with all its confusion, experimentation, and pain, he is never able to take a historical view or an analytic approach. Sexuality exploited as a marketing tool by our corporate, mass production/mass consumption economy is indiscriminately thrown in alongside historical changes in family structure, childraising, and male/female relations produced by industrialization; within his view, all changes are equal and equally bad. Among the changes he

finds most appalling is the rise of gay liberation; homosexuality is, he says, an index of sexual frustration and societal failure. All in all, this is a book worthy of notice not for any merits of its own, but only as a document of the anti-feminist backlash.

1662   Gilman, Charlotte (Perkins) Stetson, 1860-1935. **The Home: Its Work and Influence.** New York: McClure, Phillips, 1903; repr. Urbana: University of Illinois Press, 1972. 347p. $7.95. ISBN 0252002784. LC 72-76863.

In his introduction to the reprint edition of *The Home* (originally 1903), William L. O'Neill argues that this book "is in some ways Mrs. Gilman's best book, and certainly the most pertinent today—because it deals with domestic life." Gilman had first developed a critique of the home and domestic mythology in her better-known *Women and Economics*. In that work, she went so far as to propose the socialization of meal preparation, child care, cleaning, and other services to free women so that they could achieve economic independence. In *The Home*, Gilman drops her proposals for change but extends her critical analysis of the home as she sees it. She makes clear that she is not criticizing the home *per se*, which she feels could and should be a source of comfort and security. Rather, she is attacking the failure of the home to keep pace with what she believed to be important forms of progress in her day: "In all this long period of progress the moving world has carried with it the unmoving home; the man free, the woman confined; the man specializing in a thousand industries, the woman still limited to her domestic functions."

1663   Gilman, Charlotte (Perkins) Stetson, 1860-1935. **The Man-Made World: Or, Our Androcentric Culture.** New York: Source Book Press, 1970. (Repr. of 1911 ed.). 260p. $10.00. ISBN 0442810857. LC 74-134187.

In this book, first published in 1911, Charlotte Perkins Gilman—best known for her earlier work, *Women and Economics*—explores and contrasts what she calls "The Androcentric Theory of Life" with a "Gynaecocentric Theory" (the terms are pulled from a chapter of Lester Ward's *Pure Sociology*). Gilman defines the gynaecocentric theory as positing "that the female is the race type, and the male, originally but a sex type, reaching a later equality with the female, and, in the human race, becoming her master for a considerable historical period. . . . " *The Man-Made World* "gives a series of studies of the effect upon our human development of this unprecedented dominance of the male, showing it to be by no means an unmixed good." Chapter headings are as follows: As to Humanness; The Man-Made Family; Health and Beauty; Men and Art; Masculine Literature; Games and Sports; Ethics and Religion; Education; "Society" and "Fashion"; Law and Government; Crime and Punishment; Politics and Warfare; Industry and Economics; A Human World.

1664   Gilman, Charlotte (Perkins) Stetson, 1860-1935. **Women and Economics.** Gloucester, MA: Peter Smith, n.d. $7.00. ISBN 0844621307.

Women and Economics represents a point of substantial advance in the evolution of feminist theory. First published in 1899, it posed the fundamental question of how sexual inequality originated and how it is maintained, beginning from the radical assumption that the structure of sexual relations was not a product of immutable nature but of social institutions. The social institutions that Gilman considered most important for women's oppression were economic— in particular, the economic relations of industrial capitalism which removed production from the home and thereby circumscribed women's productive activities. Gilman writes in her introduction to the 1920 edition that the essential argument of her book is "that women as a class are supported by men, in return for the fulfillment of feminine functions; . . . that this economic dependence of the female upon the male is the sufficient and continuous cause of the difficulties arising in the relations of the sexes . . . [and] that every woman should earn her own living." She admits to leaving two questions unanswered: 1) "Why should anyone work unless forced to it?" and 2) "How can women earn their own living and still do their duty to home and family?" The first of these is considered in her book *Human Work*, and the second, in *The Home*.

1665   Goldberg, Herb, 1937- . **The Hazards of Being Male: Surviving the Myth of Masculine Privilege.** New York: Nash, 1976. 200p. bibliog. index. $8.95. ISBN 0840213646. LC 74-28987.
This book appears to have at least three major limitations: Goldberg deals with the question of the disadvantages of the male sex role almost exclusively at the psychological level. He seems to assume that there *is* a generalizable male sex role, and this assumption camouflages the neglect of class, race, and ethnic differences (the assumed model is that of the middle- or upper-middle-class male "success object"). He also moves naively from the fact that sex roles, male and female, *do* confine and oppress to the belief that male privilege is a "myth." Nevertheless, with these limitations in mind, the reader can find here a description of some of the costs of masculinity and male/female power relations for the middle-class male, from a man's point of view.

1666   Goldberg, Steven. **The Inevitability of Patriarchy.** New York: Morrow, 1974. 318p. bibliog. index. $3.25. ISBN 0688051758. LC 73-7385; (rev. ed.). London: Temple Smith, 1977. 224p. bibliog. index. LC 78-305674.
Goldberg tries early on to fend off the inevitable attacks on his theory by protesting that, "like any scientific analysis, that presented here cannot and does not entail any ethical, social or political position. . . . To make judgments of what is good and what is bad, what should be and what should not be, is outside the realm of science; science can neither validate or invalidate subjective appraisals. Science speaks only of what is." "*What is*," according to Goldberg, what always has been, and, therefore, always will be, is *patriarchy*, defined as "any system of organization . . . in which the overwhelming number of upper positions in hierarchies are occupied by males." The development of his theory leads Goldberg through discussions of the universality of patriarchy and the limits of social variation, physiological differentiation, and social conformity to psychophysiological reality, the inadequacy of a non-physiological explanation, fallacies of "the" feminist analysis, and possible sexual differentiation in cognitive aptitudes. In addition, in the revised British edition, Goldberg addresses criticisms received by the 1973 United States edition. Goldberg sees his main opponents as feminists who wish to distort "science" to confirm "ideology." He either is blinded to or refuses to acknowledge the long history of debate

over the nature of the social sciences and whether "social fact" is separable from social value. Goldberg argues that "the theory presented in this book is either correct or incorrect, . . . its social effects are irrelevant to this, and . . . the same can be said of the motivations of its author." It's clear that many would be disturbed by this claim who are not in the least concerned with feminism.

1667*   Goldman, Emma, 1869-1940. **Red Emma Speaks: Selected Writings and Speeches.** Comp. and ed. by Alix Kates Shulman. New York: Random House, 1972. 413p. index. ISBN 0394470958. LC 77-37077.

Alix Kates Shulman has compiled an excellent collection of Emma Goldman's writings and speeches, from which the reader is able to gain a good introduction to her anarchist and feminist thought. Included are pieces on the nature of anarchism, a critical view of socialism, the individual society and the state, atheism, political violence, prisons, Goldman's disillusionment with the Soviet Union, plus the following writings on women: "The Tragedy of Woman's Emancipation"; "The Traffic in Women"; "Marriage and Love"; and "Jealousy: Causes and a Possible Cure." The reader might also want to consult another Goldman collection, *Anarchism and Other Essays*.

1668   Goldman, Emma, 1869-1940. **The Traffic in Women and Other Essays on Feminism.** New York: Times Change Press, 1971. 63p. bibliog. $2.25. ISBN 0878100016. LC 76-30014.

This small volume contains three important essays originally published in 1917 by the courageous anarchist and feminist, Emma Goldman. "The Traffic in Women" analyzes the problem of prostitution in terms of its roots in economic and sexual power relations that make women dependent upon men—whether it be one man in marriage, or many outside marriage. In "Marriage and Love," Goldman argues that the institution and the emotional tie "have nothing in common" and "are, in fact, antagonistic to each other," marriage being an oppressive institution of capitalism and the state. In the final essay, "Woman Suffrage," Goldman analyzes the limitations of the nineteenth-century women's movement, which became increasingly committed to the one reform of enfranchising women. In her view, the liberation of all women would require for more than the vote: it would require social revolution. These three essays are prefaced by Alix Kates Shulman's brief biography of Goldman, "The Most Dangerous Woman in the World." Readers may want to look at Shulman's full-length biography, *To the Barricades: The Anarchist Life of Emma Goldman* (Thomas Y. Crowell, 1971).

1669   Gornick, Vivian. **Essays in Feminism.** New York: Harper and Row, 1978. 240p. $10.00. ISBN 0060116277. LC 77-6884.

This collection of Gornick's essays, written mainly for the *Village Voice*, records the maturation of a feminist voice over a period of eight years. The essays are consistently interesting and well written, whether discussing the fear of success found in Radcliffe women or Gabrielle Russier's trial and suicide in France over her affair with a young male student. Alice Paul, Agnes Smedley, Margaret Fuller, and Virginia Woolf are among her vivid portraits. Gornick is at her best in catching the special glints of a notable feminist personality. Most convincing is her conviction that dogma and polemic will not do in coming to a feminist consciousness, which she chooses to term "self-possession." She recognizes that feminist critics can be dogmatic and mistaken, just as feminist writers can write poor poetry and prose. Though she calls her own writing "uneven," as journalistic writing can be in a collection of this sort, Gornick delivers provocative notes on the feminist experience and does it well.

1670   Gornick, Vivian, and Barbara K. Moran, comps. **Woman in Sexist Society: Studies in Power and Powerlessness.** New York: Basic Books, 1971. 515p. bibliog. index. $12.50. ISBN 0405091997. LC 70-157125.
Woman in Sexist Society and *Sisterhood Is Powerful* (Robin Morgan, editor) are probably the two best-known early anthologies of literature from the contemporary women's liberation movement. This collection has writings by Alta, Kate Millett, Vivian Gornick, Jessie Bernard, Pauline Bart, Naomi Weisstein, Alix Shulman, Phyllis Chesler, Sidney Abbott and Barbara Love, Shulamith Firestone, and many others. A wide range of issues is covered: prostitution, marriage, mental health, anthropology, psychology, women and work, lesbianism, racism. These early writings continue to offer some of the most acute analyses of the oppression of women.

1671   Greer, Germaine, 1939- . **The Female Eunuch.** New York: McGraw-Hill, 1971. 349p. bibliog. $9.95. ISBN 0070243727. LC 79-148988.
As an early (1971) and very general analysis of the oppression of women and women's liberation, *The Female Eunuch* may strike readers as dated. Popular and introductory it is, but also intelligent and well-written. Greer's flamboyant approach to her topic elicited the kind of media attention that—despite its condescending and anti-feminist slant—served to acquaint millions of people with some basic feminist issues. Greer argues that male supremacist society *castrates* women through the suppression and deflection of their energy. Revolution would require "the redeployment of energy, no longer to be used in repression, but in desire, movement and creation." Women must repudiate symbiotic, constricting heterosexual relations; if this requires "irresponsibility," " . . . when the stake is life and freedom, and the necessary condition is the recovery of a will to live, irresponsibility might be thought a small risk." Greer begins with a discussion of biology (Body), next considers socialization processes (Soul), then moves on to an analysis of idealized heterosexual relations (Love) and their cost (Hate). She concludes with a speculative chapter on Revolution. While Greer is gleefully idiosyncratic in political and ideological terms, she also demonstrates understanding of the feminist political spectrum and makes efforts to place herself in relation to conservative, liberal, and socialist positions.

1672   Grimké, Sarah Moore, 1792-1873. **Letters on the Equality of the Sexes and the Condition of Woman, Addressed to Mary S. Parker.** New York: B. Franklin, 1970. (Repr. of 1838 ed.). 128p. $12.50. ISBN 0833714597. LC 79-133542.
Written by the famous abolitionist and feminist, these letters dating from 1837 set forth arguments for the equality of women "based on the immutable truths of the Bible." Grimké says that she makes the letters public because she believes

"if they are acted upon, they will exalt the character and enlarge the usefulness of my own sex, and contribute greatly to the happiness and virtue of the other."

1673*   Guettel, Charnie. **Marxism and Feminism.** Toronto: Women's Press, 1974. 62p. bibliog. LC 74-177267.
In Guettel, one finds a contemporary statement of orthodox Marxist analysis of the oppression of women. Guettel develops her own argument through a critical analysis of the liberal tradition (John Stuart Mill), the Woman Suffrage Movement, socialist theory (Engels and Bebel), contemporary radical feminism (de Beauvoir, Kate Millett, and Shulamith Firestone), and socialist feminism (Juliet Mitchell). In her concluding section, Guettel proposes "A Marxist Alternative to Feminist Theory," in which she argues that "the oppression of women, while not primary, is nonetheless crucial to capitalism, and the liberation of women, while not primary, is nonetheless crucial for the *development* of socialism." Readers interested in feminist theory and debate among its various strains will want also to consult the recent anthology, *Capitalist Patriarchy and the Case for Socialist Feminism*, edited by Zillah Eisenstein (1978).

1674   Halimi, Gisele. **The Right to Choose.** St. Lucia, Queensland, Australia: University of Queensland Press, 1977. 178p. $9.95. ISBN 0702214345.
This is a translation of *La Cause des Femmes*, published in France in 1973. Halimi writes a very personal autobiographical account of her growing up in Tunisia, her early awareness of her oppression as a woman, her decision to become a lawyer, and her politicization as a leftist and a feminist. Her personal account merges with political history when her own struggle to become a lawyer yet have a sexual and family life on her own terms leads—via several abortions—to her commitment to the political struggle for women's reproductive freedom. Halimi was an important organizer of the famous "Manifesto of 343," a public admission by 343 French women (some of them famous, like Simone de Beauvoir) that they had had illegal abortions. The difficulties experienced by lesser-known signatories in the aftermath of the manifesto led to the founding of Choisir, an organization to promote contraception and legalized abortion. Halimi subsequently served as defense counsel in two French political trials on abortion in Bobigny and Grenoble. She is also well known for her militant commitment in the Algerian War. She concludes this stirring account with a statement of her personal view of women's struggles and women's liberation, in which she specifically addresses the question of the relation between these and socialist struggles.

1675   Hole, Judith, and Ellen Levine. **Rebirth of Feminism.** New York: Quadrangle Books, 1971. 488p. bibliog. index. $10.00. ISBN 0812902270. LC 70-162808.
Much of the material in this book has been covered elsewhere in women's movement literature. Section 1 deals with the origins and development of the contemporary movement, distinguishing the women's rights sector from women's liberation. Section 2 reviews feminist analyses of sex differences, sex stereotypes, and misogyny. Section 3 is worthy of note for its concise coverage of six major areas of action up to 1971: media, abortion, child care, education, professions, and the church. Lucinda Cisler's selected bibliography on women is reprinted

here; current only up to 1971, it covers general works, psychology and psychiatry, reproduction and its control, literature and literary criticism, works by and biographies of early feminists (to 1920), articles about the current women's movement, bibliographies and syllabi, and U.S. Government publications. Following their conclusion, Hole and Levine present a useful and concise chronology of the current feminist movement, from 1961 to 1971.

1676   Hope, Karol, and Nancy Young, eds. **Momma: The Sourcebook for Single Mothers.** New York: New American Library, 1976. 388p. $3.95. LC 75-29852.
"*Momma* is dedicated to all the women and men who find themselves in the mindboggling position of being the only adult in a house full of kids." Hope and Young, both single mothers, were instrumental in organizing MOMMA, a nationwide network of single mothers based in California, and in putting out the newspaper produced by that organization, also entitled *MOMMA*. This anthology is drawn from the best of *MOMMA* and from almost 100 interviews conducted with single mothers across the U.S. in 1974. In the transcripts, women talk about what it has meant and cost to survive as human beings and as parents alone. The *MOMMA* articles address topics such as: feminism and motherhood; single parenthood as an alternative lifestyle; divorce; puberty and the single mother; celibacy; welfare; going back to school; working in the skilled trades; child care; feelings about children; loneliness; and single fatherhood. The volume concludes with an essay on the history of MOMMA, by Lin Hartwell. This anthology is easy reading, with direct relevance to the realities of women's lives.

1677   Howe, Julia (Ward), 1819-1910. **Julia Ward Howe and the Woman Suffrage Movement.** Ed. by Florence Howe Hall. New York: Arno Press, 1969. (Repr. of 1913 ed.). 241p. $10.00. ISBN 0405001061. LC 71-79179.
This basic source for Julia Ward Howe's speeches and essays on woman suffrage and women's rights was edited, with introduction and notes, by her daughter, Florence Howe Hall. Among those included here are: "The Position of Women in Plato's Republic"; "Why Are Women the Natural Guardians of Social Morals?"; "The Change in the Position of Women"; "What the Nineteenth Century Has Done for Women"; "The Future of American Women"; and "Speech on Equal Rights."

1678   International Tribunal on Crimes against Women, Brussels, 1976. **Crimes against Women: Proceedings of the International Tribunal.** Comp. and ed. by Diana E. H. Russell and Nicole Van de Ven. Millbrae, CA: Les Femmes, 1976. 298p. $5.95. ISBN 0890879214. LC 76-25356.
The International Tribunal on Crimes Against Women was held in Brussels from March 4-8, 1976, bringing together over 2,000 women from forty countries. The Tribunal was intended as a feminist response to the UN-declared International Women's Year and its Mexico City meeting. The spirit of the Tribunal was internationalist and there was a marked commitment to revealing and working with differences such as those of nationality, culture, class, race, sexual preference, and age. Personal testimony was emphasized rather than abstract analysis. The crimes testified about are for the most part "not recognized as such by

patriarchal nations, indeed many of the crimes are enforced by our patriarchal laws." This volume presents the English-language edition of the Tribunal proceedings. In part 1, witnesses from around the world testify about forced motherhood, compulsory non-motherhood, persecution of non-virgins and unmarried mothers, crimes perpetrated by the medical profession, compulsory heterosexuality, crimes within the patriarchal family, economic crimes, double oppression of Third World women, double oppression of immigrant women, double oppression of women from religious minorities, violence against women (rape, forced incarceration in mental hospitals and marriage, clitoridectomy, political torture, brutal treatment in prison), and sexual objectification of women (prostitution, pornography). In part 2, proposals relating to particular crimes are presented, for example: "A Manifesto for Older Women, U.S.A."; "Rape, France"; "Women in Poverty, U.S.A."; "Wages for Housework"; "Women Political Prisoners, Iran"; "Permanent Tribunal, Chile"; and "Lesbian Network, U.S.A." Part 3 presents the "herstory" of the Tribunal and part 4, a series of critiques. Two appendices detail the publication contract agreement and the budget of the Tribunal.

1679   Irwin, Inez Haynes, 1873-1970. **The Story of the Woman's Party**. New York: Kraus Reprints, 1971. (Repr. of 1921 ed.). 486p. index. $27.00. ISBN 0527447005.

In 1912, Alice Paul, as chairman of the Congressional Committee of the National American Woman Suffrage Association, came to Washington at the period when the Suffrage Movement was at high pitch and when six states had granted the franchise. Paul, a remarkable scholar and organizer, organized the Woman's Party in 1913, garnered support, and made the Suffrage Amendment a national issue. Irwin's book (orig. 1921) concentrated on the Woman's Party during its peak period from 1913-1917. Since Alice Paul *was* the Woman's Party, much of the book contains biographical material about Paul, written by a woman who knew and worked with her. *The National Woman's Party Papers, 1913-1974* are now available on microfilm from Microfilm Corporation of America. This collection contains 450,000 pages of primary source material including correspondence, minutes, legal papers, financial records, printed materials, photographs, and the World Woman's Party Papers, 1938-1954, and provides the most detailed corpus of material for researching the Party and its founder, Alice Paul.

1680   Jaggar, Alison M., and Paula Rothenberg Struhl, eds. **Feminist Frameworks: Alternative Theoretical Accounts of the Relations Between Women and Men**. New York: McGraw-Hill, 1978. 333p. bibliog. index. $8.95. ISBN 0070322503. LC 77-11069.

Jaggar and Struhl have compiled an unusually valuable reader in feminist theory, constructed around a recognition of the important alternative perspectives in the women's movement: liberalism, orthodox Marxism, radical feminism, and socialist feminism. They argue very persuasively that selection of a preferred theory of women's oppression and women's liberation—and of the political practice that would follow from the theory—must be based on a rigorous analysis of its presuppositions about such things as human nature, history, justice, and change. Selections from writers representing each of these perspectives are chosen for the following topics: explanation of the roots of oppression; women and work; the family; and sexuality. The four variants of feminist theory are at each point also counterposed to a representative of the conservative perspective (which takes sexual inequality as a "natural" phenomenon). These statements on specific issues are preceded by a collection of articles presenting different arguments for the necessity of women's and men's liberation. The conservative viewpoint is represented by, among others, Freud, Steven Goldberg, Lionel Tiger, and Bruno Bettelheim; liberalism, by J. S. Mill, NOW, and Ann Crittenden Scott; orthodox Marxism, by Engels, Evelyn Reed, Lenin, and Margaret Benston; radical feminism, by Shulamith Firestone, Charlotte Bunch, Rita Mae Brown, and Ti-Grace Atkinson; and socialist feminism, by Juliet Mitchell, Gayle Rubin, Eli Zaretsky, and Sheila Rowbotham. One weakness of the volume is that articles are in some cases drastically shortened. However, the reader is carefully directed to the original sources and also to thoughtfully compiled suggestions for further reading.

1681   Janeway, Elizabeth. **Between Myth and Morning: Women Awakening.**
        New York: Morrow, 1974. 279p. bibliog. $8.95. ISBN 0688003117.
        LC 74-7166.
Attributing the causes of the women's liberation movement to the Industrial Revolution and its transformation of work, the family, and society, Janeway cautions that the task of liberation is a societal one, and that the attendant social and public problems cannot be readily resolved by personal solutions. Janeway explores the vast territory of woman's liberation and human liberation, reflecting on woman's history, her place in a changing world, the nature of the family, the women's movement, and Freudian-defined female sexuality. She works toward developing a parallel between the modification of man's world by women and the modification of the feudal world by the bourgeoisie in centuries past.

1682   Janeway, Elizabeth. **Man's World, Woman's Place: A Study in Social
        Mythology.** New York: Morrow, 1971. 319p. bibliog. index. $8.95.
        ISBN 068802047X. LC 73-142405.
" 'Woman's place' is a shorthand phrase which sums up a whole set of traits and attitudes and ways of presenting themselves which we think proper to women, along with the obligations and restrictions that it implies." Janeway's eloquent and scholarly exploration of social mythology, of the social system that creates the mythology, and of the definitions of women's roles takes issue with arguments of prominent social scientists such as David McClelland and Erik Erikson, who rationalize that societal health is contingent upon the split between man's "outer space" and woman's "inner space." According to Janeway, any discussion of woman's place as wife, housewife, and mother must take into account history, values, and facts. Even in the workplace, Janeway shows how the "feminine" job takes shape in supporting, nurturing patterns assigned to woman's role. As women's liberation breaks down old myths and challenges traditional patterns, what will be the emotional consequences for all role-players? Janeway calls for an understanding of the tremendous emotional power of myth in order to meet real crises and shifts in the social order. This is essential reading.

1683*   Jenness, Linda, comp. **Feminism and Socialism.** New York: Pathfinder
         Press, 1972. 160p. bibliog. LC 72-82948.
The other sides of feminism and socialism are male supremacy and capitalism,
and these are really the major foci of this collection of articles, which addresses
questions such as is women's liberation possible within capitalism? and, is
there a connection between the oppression of women, racism, and exploitation?
Among the articles here are: Mary-Alice Waters's "Are Feminism and Socialism
Related?"; Maxine Williams's "Why Women's Liberation Is Important to Black
Women"; Mirta Vidal's "Chicanas Speak Out—New Voices of La Raza"; Carol
Lipman's "Why Red-Baiting Hurts the Feminist Movement"; Kipp Dawson's
"A Revolutionary Perspective on the Oppression of Women"; Evelyn Reed's
"In Defense of Engels on the Matriarchy"; and Dianne Feeley's "Women and
the Russian Revolution."

1684   Johnston, Jill. **Lesbian Nation: The Feminist Solution.** New York:
        Simon and Schuster, 1973. 283p. bibliog. $7.95. ISBN 0671214330.
        LC 72-83934.
Lesbian Nation took lesbian feminism to its ultimate, exuberant conclusion:
all women are lesbians, though many don't realize it; feminism's the theory,
lesbianism, the practice. The book is a collection of different bits and pieces,
including journal entries, reminiscences, polemic, mythology, all written in
Johnston's inimitable style—lengthy stream-of-consciousness sentences without
the inhibiting intervention of paragraphs. As readers of the *Village Voice* will
already know, with Jill Johnston there's no skimming or picking up on a piece
in the middle; either you jump in with her at the start, or you skip it altogether.

1685   Klein, Viola. **The Feminine Character: History of an Ideology.** (2nd
        ed.). Urbana: University of Illinois Press, 1971. 202p. bibliog. index.
        $7.95. ISBN 0252002946. LC 72-83482.
Now with an introductory essay for the American edition by Janet Zollinger
Giele, this study was first published in 1946 as a volume in Karl Mannheim's
International Library of Sociology and Social Reconstruction. Klein's method
was, first, to set the stage with an historical survey of women's position in society
from the Industrial Revolution through the first half of the twentieth century,
and, second, to analyze a sequence of theoretical approaches to "the feminine
character" that emerged during that period. Klein writes in her preface to the
second edition, "Originally, the work was conceived of as the application of
the principles of Sociology of Knowledge to the study of a specific, clearly
delimited and topical issue. In other words, its main purpose was to demonstrate
that scholars—no matter how honestly they endeavour to pursue the truth and
nothing but the truth, pure and objective—are intellectually dependent on the
social, cultural and historical climate of their time. The book's subtitle, 'History
of an Ideology,' was meant to convey this idea." Included are essays on: The
Biological Approach: Havelock Ellis; A Philosophical Approach: Otto Weininger;
The Psycho-Analytical Approach: Sigmund Freud; First Investigations in Experimental Psychology: Helen B. Thompson; Psychometric Tests: L. M. Terman
and C. C. Miles; An Historical Approach: Mathias and Mathilde Vaerting; The
Anthropological Approach: Margaret Mead; and A Sociological Approach:

W. I. Thomas. Klein's other major work (now out of print) is *Britain's Married Women Workers* (Routledge and Kegan Paul/Humanities Press, 1965).

1686   Koedt, Anne, et al., comps. **Radical Feminism.** New York: Quadrangle
        Books, 1973. 424p. bibliog. $10.00. ISBN 0812962206. LC 72-91380.
Edited by Anne Koedt, Ellen Levine, and Anita Rapone, this collection (published in 1973) brings together writings from the first six years of the women's movement. Many of the articles were first published in *Notes*, an early annual journal of movement writings. Part 1, Liberating History, discusses the history of the nineteenth-century women's movement. Part 2, Women's Experience, addresses the issue of the political dimensions of women's "personal" experience. Part 3, Theory and Analysis, brings together articles analyzing specific problems, such as marriage, housework, abortion, and rape. Section 4, Building a Movement, discusses consciousness-raising, women's relation to the Left, and other movement questions. The final section, The Arts, includes articles on women writers such as Plath and Nin, and the attitudes of male critics toward these writers. Among the classic articles reprinted here are: "The Bitch Manifesto," by Joreen; "Why I want a Wife," by Judy Syfers; "The Myth of the Vaginal Orgasm," by Anne Koedt; "Housework: Slavery or Labor of Love," by Betsy Warrior; "The Woman-Identified Woman," by Radicalesbians; "Free Space," by Pamela Allen; "The Tyranny of Structurelessness," by Joreen; and "Fourth World Manifesto," by Barbara Burris.

1687   Kollontai, Aleksandra Mikhailovna, 1872-1952. **Selected Writings of
        Alexandra Kollontai.** Westport, CT: Lawrence Hall; distr. New York:
        Whirlwind Books, 1978. 335p. bibliog. index. $12.95. ISBN
        088208092X. LC 77-88786.
This is an invaluable collection of Alexandra Kollontai's writings, most of them appearing in English for the first time. The rediscovery of Kollontai is not just important to the writing of the history of socialist women and women in revolutionary movements. Kollontai stands out even among socialist women as one who fought bravely to assert the importance of a transformation of sexual relations, the family, and personal life as part of the Russian Revolution in its early days. Translator and editor Alix Holt includes selections from Kollontai's writings on the following topics: Social Democracy and the Woman Question (including excerpts from "Towards a History of the Working Women's Movement in Russia" and from "The Social Basis of the Woman Question"); Exile and War; The Revolution; Women and the Revolution (including "Working Woman and Mother" and an excerpt from "The Labour of Women in the Evolution of the Economy"); Crisis in the Party (on the Workers' Opposition); Morality and the New Society (including "Sisters," a short story, "Theses on Communist Morality in the Sphere of Marital Relations," "Sexual Relations and the Class Struggle," "Communism and the Family," "Prostitution and Ways of Fighting It," and "Make Way for Winged Eros: A Letter to Working Youth"); and Diplomatic Duties (including "Marriage and Everyday Life"). Holt has written a chronology of Kollontai's life, lengthy introductions to the volume and to each section, and has compiled a chronological bibliography of Kollontai's writings.

1688*   Kollontai, Aleksandra Mikhailovna, 1872-1952. **Sexual Relations and
         Class Struggle.** Montpelier, Bristol, England: Falling Wall Press, 1972.
         26p.

This pamphlet reprints two of the three essays originally published in the Soviet
Union in 1919 as *The New Morality and the Working Class*: "Sexual Relations
and the Class Struggle" and "Love and the New Morality." (The third essay,
"The New Woman," is available as part of Kollontai's *Autobiography*.) The two
essays "examine how the ways in which people relate to each other in the most
'private' of personal relationships are affected by the kind of society in which
they live. They were published as a contribution to a debate taking place in
Russia after the Revolution, at a time when their authoress, Alexandra Kollontai,
was arguing urgently for her belief that the Bolshevik party should be taking a
lead in understanding and explaining the nature of changes taking place in the
family and in personal relationships" (from the foreword).

1689*   Kollontai, Aleksandra Mikhailovna, 1872-1952. **Women Workers
         Struggle for Their Rights.** Montpelier, Bristol, England: Falling Wall
         Press, 1973. (3rd ed.). 35p. bibliog.

This pamphlet reprints two articles originally published by Kollontai before
World War I–"The Socialist Movement of Women Workers in Different Countries"
and "Forms of Organisation of Women Workers in the West." The historical
context faced by women now is different, but some of the key issues remain.
As Sheila Rowbotham points out in her introduction to the pamphlet, Kollontai's
writings remain relevant because of "her arguments with the left on the need
for the separate organisation of women, her stress not only on political emancipation and work, but also on the family and the psychological effect of centuries
of oppression on women's consciousness. . . . "

1690   Kraditor, Aileen S. **The Ideas of the Woman Suffrage Movement,
         1890-1920.** New York: Columbia University Press, 1965. 313p. bibliog.
         index. $15.00. ISBN 0231027559. LC 65-14410.

Kraditor's book remains widely read, though dated. The questions in which
she was interested and which, writing in 1964, she noted had remained unasked,
have since been considered by a variety of people from many different angles.
In search of the ideas that united the Woman Suffrage Movement, Kraditor
explored the views of women who were re-elected to national office in the
National American Woman Suffrage Association at least twice between 1890
and 1918; of women who were top leaders in the Woman's Party; the official
published works of the Association and the Woman's Party; testimony before
legislative committees in behalf of the two organizations; and the events within
the Association, as recorded in its *Proceedings* and in the *History of Woman
Suffrage* (Stanton, Elizabeth Cady, et al., eds.). The period under investigation
(1890-1920) was one of transition in the Movement: the original leaders were
retiring and new participants were giving a more conservative direction to the
struggle. Kraditor distinguishes the suffrage "argument from justice" from the
"argument from expediency" (which exploited racist, anti-labor, and xenophobic
sentiments) and describes the conditions of their coexistence within the suffrage
movement. Also considered are suffragist views on woman and the home, the
"new immigration" and labor, the "southern question," and political parties

and suffrage tactics. An appendix provides brief biographies of key suffrage figures. An extensive bibliography—including manuscript collections, government publications, periodicals, and other primary and secondary sources—is also appended.

1691   Kraditor, Aileen S., comp. **Up from the Pedestal: Selected Writings in the History of American Feminism.** Chicago: Quadrangle Books, 1968. 372p. bibliog. $8.95. ISBN 0812900626. LC 68-26443.

Kraditor's anthology of excerpted feminist writings concentrates primarily on the nineteenth century movement, with an emphasis on less accessible sources (as of the 1968 publication date). Part 1 brings together selections on the question of "woman's proper sphere" and early agitation (Grimké sisters, Margaret Fuller). Part 2 presents nineteenth-century writings which anchor the feminist cause in more specific issues such as education, religion, fashion, science, marriage, divorce, the home, economics, and motherhood. In part 3, writings representing pro- and anti-suffrage positions appear, including examples of attempts by white suffragists to enlist racism and xenophobia in their cause. Part 4, Unfinished Business, briefly looks at issues of public policy in this century and visions of the future. The final selection among those looking toward the future dates this anthology—the 1966 Statement of Purpose of the National Organization for Women. Kraditor (author of *The Ideas of the Woman Suffrage Movement, 1890-1920*) provides brief introductions to each major chapter and selection, as well as an overall introduction to the volume.

1692   La Follette, Suzanne. **Concerning Women.** New York: Arno Press, 1972. (Repr. of 1926 ed.). 306p. $16.00. ISBN 040504464X. LC 72-2610.

First published in 1926, *Concerning Women* is a highly cogent analysis of the oppression of women and an inspiring argument on the necessary conditions for their liberation. The central point is repeatedly driven home: women's liberation is necessarily a question of human liberation. La Follette writes that "every phase of the question of freedom for women is bound up with the larger question of human freedom. If it is freedom that women want, they can not be content to be legally equal with men; but having gained this equality they must carry on their struggle against the oppressions which privilege exercises upon humanity at large by virtue of an usurped economic power. . . . Woman tends to assume a position of equality with man only where the idea of property in human beings has not yet arisen or where it has disappeared: that is to say, only in extremely primitive or highly civilized communities." This is a very early indictment of feminist strategies that concentrate exclusively on legal rights and legal equality, and it represents an important statement of a socialist feminist perspective. La Follette carries the thread of this analysis through extended discussions of the following topics: The Beginnings of Emancipation; Woman's Status, Past and Present; Institutional Marriage and Its Economic Aspects; Woman and Marriage; The Economic Position of Women; What Is to Be Done; Signs of Promise.

1693   Lenin, Vladimir Ilich, 1870-1924. **The Emancipation of Women: From the Writings of V. I. Lenin.** New York: International Publishers, 1969. 153p. index. $1.65. ISBN 0717802906. LC 74-15197.

Brought together here are some of Lenin's writings on women's liberation, spanning the period from 1899 to 1922. All of the selections are brief and in many cases, they are excerpted from longer essays, with the result that together they make for scattered reading rather than a sequential, in-depth analysis. The writings are drawn from Lenin's *Women and Society* (International Pubs., 1938), *The Woman Question* (International Pubs., 1951—includes writings of Marx, Engels, and Stalin in addition to Lenin), and *Collected Works* (Lawrence and Wishart, 1963-1969). Among the selections are: "From *The Development of Capitalism in Russia*" (1899), "Capitalism and Female Labour" (1913), "Speech at the First All-Russia Congress of Working Women, November 19, 1918," "The Tasks of the Working Women's Movement in the Soviet Republic" (speech delivered at the Fourth Moscow City Conference of Non-Party Working Women, Sept. 23, 1919), "Soviet Power and the Status of Women" (1919), "On International Working Women's Day" (1920), and "From *The Fourth Anniversary of the October Revolution*" (1921). Also included are a preface by Nadezhda K. Krupskaya and "My Recollections of Lenin," by Clara Zetkin (from her *Reminiscences of Lenin*, International Pubs., 1934).

1694*   Liddington, Jill, and Jill Norris. **One Hand Tied behind Us: The Rise of the Women's Suffrage Movement.** London: Virago, 1978. 304p. bibliog. index. ISBN 086078007X.

Historians and media writers have a way of reducing complex social movements to the activities of a few charismatic leaders or to a series of sensationalist events. In *Feminist Revolution*, the New York radical feminist Redstockings expressed their anger at how the history of the current U.S. women's movement had already been subjected to a liberal rewrite less than ten years after its beginning. In *One Hand Tied behind Us*, Liddington and Norris undertook the difficult and important task of resurrecting the buried history of the women who struggled for the vote in England either prior to or outside of the Pankhursts' Women's Social and Political Union (WSPU). British suffrage history has been almost uniquely identified with the history of the London-based, middle-class, militant suffragettes of the WSPU. Liddington and Norris painstakingly unearthed from documents and oral histories the story of the working-class women of Manchester and Lancashire (whom they call "radical suffragists" by contrast with the "militants") who fought for the vote as part of their fight for the broader social goals of industrial rights or socialism.

1695   Lipshitz, Susan, ed. **Tearing the Veil: Essays on Femininity.** Boston: Routledge and Kegan Paul, 1978. 147p. bibliog. index. $6.75. ISBN 0710087217. LC 77-30323.

Multidisciplinary in approach, the essays in this book consider the topic of femininity in a patriarchal society using the perspectives of history, literature, psychoanalysis, and anthropology. Essayists are Dana Breen, Susan Lipshitz, Katherine Arnold, Mary Jacobus, Mandy Merck, and Barbara Taylor. They write about maternity, female illness, and prostitution in dealing with issues of sexuality and the body. Hardy's Tess, Amazons, and feminism in early English socialism are topics treating images of women. Each essay is preceded by an abstract and followed by copious notes and a bibliography.

1696   Mailer, Norman. **The Prisoner of Sex.** Boston: Little, Brown, 1971. 240p. bibliog. $5.95. ISBN 0316544132. LC 70-157475.
In the main, this is a rebuttal to Kate Millett's attack on Mailer in *Sexual Politics*. Mailer responds: "By any major literary perspective, the land of Millett is a barren and mediocre terrain, its flora reminiscent of a Ph.D. tract, its roads a narrow argument, and its horizon low." He quarrels with Millett over her interpretations, misreadings, and misquotings of Miller and Lawrence. He criticizes other feminist writers for their short-sighted views. Writing in the inimitable Mailer prose, the author struts and crows his various points across the pages, asserting that he believes in a sexuality that emphasizes humanity. He deplores the legalese of feminist marriage contracts and the like, and he rejects the rhetoric of female assertion from almost any quarter. Mailer concludes by equating the tenets of liberation with technological possibilities for tampering with human reproduction—artificial insemination, cloning, etc. Thus, he comes to the conclusion that much of the rhetoric of women's liberation speaks of unnatural transformations in society. Mailer is consistently interesting as well as egotistical. He seeks to be entertaining as the "victim" of four failed marriages and the consummate "prisoner of sex."

1697   Martin, Del, and Phyllis Lyon. **Lesbian/Woman.** San Francisco: Glide Publications, 1972. 283p. $7.95. ISBN 0912078200. LC 72-76532.
Del Martin and Phyllis Lyon are well known as founders of the Daughters of Bilitis (1955). They also had lived together as lovers for nineteen years as of the writing of this book. They bring their own personal experiences, as well as their vast experience with friends and women whom they've known through the DOB, to this book. The title, *Lesbian/Woman*, conveys their overall perspective on lesbianism: "In order to understand the Lesbian, it is therefore necessary that you think of her as a living, feeling, thinking human being: a woman. The Lesbian looks, dresses, acts, and *is* like any other woman. The only thing that distinguishes her as a Lesbian is her choice of another woman as her sex, love or life partner." This is a very different message from those that have emerged more recently within lesbian feminism, in which it is often the *differences* between the "woman-identified woman" and straight women that are emphasized. But it seems probable that Lyon and Martin's message is designed to reach and enlighten heterosexual readers, which may help explain the moderate tone. Chapter topics are: The Lesbian—Myth and Reality; Self-Image; Sexuality & Sex Roles; Life Styles; Lesbians are Mothers Too; Growing Up Gay; Lesbian Paranoia—Real & Imagined Fears; Lesbians United; Lesbian/Woman; Not Toleration—Lesbian Liberation.

1698   Martin, Wendy, comp. **The American Sisterhood: Writings of the Feminist Movement from Colonial Times to the Present.** New York: Harper and Row, 1972. 373p. bibliog. $7.95. ISBN 0060442344. LC 74-174528.
Martin makes the point that many of the essays in this volume have been ignored by historians and literary scholars and remained generally unavailable to the public, save in special collections. The purpose of the anthology is to lay a

historical and intellectual foundation for American feminism, and the editor has collected an array of fascinating documentation; preceding each segment is a short biographical commentary on the writer of the piece. The collection is divided between essays speaking to the legal, political and economic issues that have faced women and the sexual, social, and psychological questions. Among the feminist luminaries whose writing appears here are: Sarah Grimké, Lucy Stone, Lucretia Mott, Sojourner Truth, Elizabeth Cady Stanton, Natalie Shainess, Gloria Steinem, Emma Goldman, Florence Howe, Robin Morgan, and the Lower East Side Women's Liberation Collective. There are many excellent photographs depicting issues of women's change and progress, as well as individual portraits and photographs of the essay writers.

1699*   Marx, Karl, 1818-1883. **On Education, Women, and Children.** New
         York: McGraw-Hill, 1975. 164p. bibliog. index. LC 78-172260.
Several factors make one hesitant to recommend this reader: the rather silly introduction (by the editor of the series, The Karl Marx Library, Saul K. Padover); the assumptions underlying the volume's grouping of materials on education, women, and children together; and the pitfalls inherent in any such collection of excerpts from larger works. Nonetheless, the volume may prove helpful to readers seeking references to Marx's writings on women, especially if they return to the original sources to set these pieces in their proper context. Among the excerpts on women: "Sex and Marriage" (from "The Philosophical Manuscript of the Historical School of Law," 1842); "The Divorce Law Draft" (from *Rheinische Zeitung*, 1842); "The Community of Women" (from *Economic and Philosophic Manuscripts of 1844*); "The Condition of Women" (from *The Holy Family*, 1845); "The Sanctity of Marriage" and "Family" (from *The German Ideology*, 1845-1846); "The Bourgeois Family" (from *The Communist Manifesto*, 1848); plus a series of excerpts from *Capital*. Excerpts are so brief as to be unintelligible to the reader uninitiated in Marx. The excerpt titles are, of course, the editor's creation.

1700   Marx, Karl, 1818-1883, et al. **The Woman Question: Selections from
        the Writings of Karl Marx, Frederick Engels, V. I. Lenin and Joseph
        Stalin.** New York: International Publishers, 1951. 96p. bibliog. $1.25.
        ISBN 0717802566. LC 51-5114.
The editor of this volume has tried to achieve some continuity in these scattered selections by arranging them topically: The Enslavement of Women; The Exploitation of Women; The Bourgeois Family; Women in the Struggle for Socialism; Socialism and the Emancipation of Women; The Relation of the Sexes; and Women in Socialist Construction. Nonetheless, the reader should be cautious about forming impressions from these excerpts alone, out of the context of the writer's larger opus. The anthology is chiefly useful as a reference tool that can direct the reader to those works by Marx, Engels, Lenin, and Stalin that deal with women and sexual inequality in some fashion. Also of interest is the essay by Clara Zetkin, "Lenin on the Woman Question," included as an appendix.

1701   Millett, Kate, 1934- . **Sexual Politics.** New York: Avon Books, 1971.
        393p. bibliog. index. $2.95.

This remains one of the most powerful statements defining the theory of power and domination roles in sexual relationships and the concept of patriarchy as a political institution. In the section "Literary Reflection," Millett examines the works of D. H. Lawrence, Henry Miller, Norman Mailer, and Jean Genet. Her bibliography is excellent for its selection of core works in anthropology, biology, psychology, sociology, and the history and status of women. The reader may also want to look at Norman Mailer's response to *Sexual Politics*, in *Prisoner of Sex*.

1702   Mitchell, Juliet, 1940- . **Woman's Estate.** New York: Vintage Books, 1973. 182p. bibliog. $1.95. ISBN 0394719050. LC 72-10106.
"Radical feminism attempts to solve the problem of analyzing the oppression of women by making it *the* problem. . . . We have to see *why* women have always been oppressed, and *how* they are oppressed now, and how differently else-where. . . . We should ask the feminist questions, but try to come up with some Marxist answers" (p. 99). *Woman's Estate* is an expansion of Mitchell's well-known article from 1966, "Women: The Longest Revolution," which called for a differentiation of the separate "structures" of women's oppression—Production, Reproduction, Sexuality, and Socialization. In this book, Mitchell adds a section on the origins of the movement and its form in different countries. Her chapter "Psychoanalysis and the Family" is of interest as a first formulation of the ideas that she later developed in *Psychoanalysis and Feminism*.

1703   Montagu, Ashley, 1905- . **The Natural Superiority of Women.** (Rev. ed.). New York: Macmillan, 1968. 235p. bibliog. index. $7.95. LC 68-18873.
Montagu's book was first published in 1953, then twice revised since the rise of the contemporary women's movement. The author argues that "the natural superiority of women is a biological fact, and a socially unacknowledged reality. . . . These conclusions are based on incontrovertible evidence . . . [not] on the author's opinions." Despite these claims, this rather long-winded plea for social equality based on an assertion of "biological superiority" is replete with opinions such as the following: "Certainly, a wife should fulfill the obligations that are tradi-tionally expected of her, but she should also have a right to a life of her own"; "The sexes should not compete; they should cooperate and complement each other"; and "The most important of women's tasks is the making of human beings in cooperation with their husbands." Montagu develops his rather ambiva-lent and ambiguous thesis in the course of discussing the relative biological strengths and weaknesses, sexuality, emotionality, competence, intelligence, and creativity of men and women.

1704   Morgan, Robin. **Going Too Far: The Personal Chronicle of a Feminist.** New York: Random House, 1977. 333p. bibliog. index. $10.00. ISBN 0394482271. LC 76-53507.
Robin Morgan has collected a selection of her writings from the last ten years, which together show her own development as a feminist and the evolution of the women's movement itself. The prefatory comments she has written to introduce each section, and some individual selections, create a dialogue between

the writer and herself at different points in her life and consistently relate her
political to her personal involvements.

1705　Morgan, Robin, comp. **Sisterhood Is Powerful: An Anthology of Writings
　　　from the Women's Liberation Movement.** New York: Random House,
　　　1970. 602p. bibliog. $12.95. ISBN 0394452402. LC 70-117694.
This is one of the first anthologies to come out of the contemporary women's
movement and contains many of the best known early essays. Among the classic
pieces in the collection are: Susan Lydon's "The Politics of Orgasm," Naomi
Weisstein's " 'Kinde, Kuche, Kirche' as Scientific Law: Psychology Constructs
the Female," Martha Shelley's "Notes of a Radical Lesbian," Frances M. Beal's
"Double Jeopardy: To Be Black and Female," Marge Piercy's "The Grand Coolie
Damn," Pat Mainardi's "The Politics of Housework," and many more. There are
also collections of poetry and of historical documents (for example, the NOW
Bill of Rights, the SCUM Manifesto, and the Redstockings Manifesto). The
bibliography and list of movement contacts at the end of the book are, of
course, out of date. Another even earlier reader in women's liberation is Betty
and Theodore Roszak's *Masculine/Feminine: Readings in Sexual Mythology
and the Liberation of Women* (Harper and Row, 1969). The Roszak collection
combines pre-women's movement selections (by Freud, Strindberg, G. B. Shaw,
Havelock Ellis, Karen Horney, de Beauvoir, and others) with early movement
pieces, several of which duplicate selections from the Morgan anthology.

1706　Nichols, Jack. **Men's Liberation: A New Definition of Masculinity.**
　　　New York: Penguin Books, 1975. 333p. bibliog. $2.50. ISBN
　　　0140040366. LC 75-24159.
While lambasting stereotypical macho masculinity, the book recognizes men's
propensity to cling to past profiles as they struggle to escape from the cocoon
of conformity into an enlightened androgynous future. Self-examination and
the recognition of the need and desire to change are encouraged in a panoply
of areas suggested by chapter titles: Intellect; Feeling; Intuition; Mind; Roles;
Instincts; Playfulness; Competition; Violence; Work; Dominance; Politics;
Size and Status; Women; Sexuality; Ladies; Coupling; Fatherhood; Friendship;
and Body. Although ancient in origin, the codes of conduct, admonitions,
philosophies, perspectives on self and society, and observations about the human
condition are presented in the more recent context of a nuclear age. The principles
of liberation are treated at various levels, from the beginnings of attitude and
behavior modification to self-actualization and spanning the chronological and
cultural interval from Lao-Tsu to Walt Whitman. The central theme is that
masculinist values have outlived their usefulness and must be restructured or
destroyed by male activists, led by intelligent and persuasive male liberationists.
The author concludes that males must have their own liberation movement.

1707　O'Neill, William L. **Everyone Was Brave: The Rise and Fall of Feminism
　　　in America.** Chicago: Quadrangle Books, 1969. 369p. bibliog. index.
　　　$3.95. ISBN 0812961927. LC 71-78313.
"This book, then, is first of all an inquiry into the failure of feminism," writes
O'Neill in the preface. His assumption is that since parity of the sexes exists
nowhere in the world, the notion of equality is impossible to assess. He

differentiates between social feminists and extreme feminists by characterizing the former as subordinating women's rights to social reform. O'Neill concludes that the failure of feminism hinges on the faulty analysis made by feminists about their own movement and their misreading of societal organization. An excellent inquiry into the anatomy of social change. Chapters include: The Origins of American Feminism; The Demand for Equal Suffrage; The Structure of Social Feminism; Ten Who Led the Woman Movement; Feminism in the Progressive Era; The Woman Movement and the War; The Return to Normalcy; The Post-Suffrage Era; Toward the Feminine Mystique; An End and a Beginning.

1708   O'Neill, William L., ed. **The Woman Movement: Feminism in the United States and England.** New York: New Viewpoints/F. Watts, 1971. bibliog. index. $2.65. ISBN 0531064654.
Among the diversity included here are Elizabeth Cady Stanton, "The Bloomer Costume"; Laura Curtis Bullard, "The Slave-Women of America"; Charlotte Perkins Gilman, "The Home"; Josephine Woodward, "Woman's Clubs from a Reporter's Point of View"; Grover Cleveland, "Woman's Mission and Woman's Clubs"; and Vida Scudder, "Class Consciousness." Introductory essays explore the beginnings of feminism, the rise and maturation of social feminism, the winning of suffrage, the waning of feminism.

1709   Ossoli, Sarah Margaret (Fuller) Marchesa d' [Fuller, Margaret], 1810-1850. **Woman in the Nineteenth Century, and Kindred Papers Relating to the Sphere, Condition, and Duties of Woman.** New York: Source Book Press, 1970. (Repr. of 1855 ed.). 428p. $15.00. ISBN 0442810652. LC 70-134186.
"What Woman needs is not as a woman to act or rule, but as a nature to grow, as an intellect to discern, as a soul to live freely and unimpeded, to unfold such powers as were given her when we left our common home. . . . I believe that, at present, women are the best helpers of one another. Let them think; let them act; till they know what they need. We only ask of men to remove arbitrary barriers." So writes Fuller in this important nineteenth-century feminist statement—an extended essay that roves over a wide expanse of world history, literature, mythology, and anthropology in search of illustrations for the central argument expressed above. Fuller asserts that there is no "woman's" or "man's purpose," but only one overarching Purpose of Man (she takes "Man" to include both men and women), which is to realize a God-given potentiality. Further, Man is taken to encompass both the masculine and the feminine, energy and harmony, power and beauty, intellect and love. While Fuller's essay was and continues to be important historically, today her vision may seem somewhat ethereal; her demands, limited; her line of argument, shallow. Like her nineteenth-century contemporary, John Stuart Mill (*The Subjection of Women*), Fuller ultimately asks only for the removal of "arbitrary barriers" to women's achievements, admitting to the suspicion that most women would under these circumstances continue to choose the same life vocation as previously. "Mothers will delight to make the nest soft and warm. . . . The difference would be that *all* need not be constrained to employments for which *some* are unfit." In other words, Fuller ultimately is pleading the cause of the "exceptional" rather than the "common" woman.

1710   Parker, Gail, 1943- , comp. **The Oven Birds: American Women on Womanhood, 1820-1920.** Garden City, NY: Anchor Books, 1972. 387p. bibliog. $2.95. ISBN 0385047452. LC 72-171338.

The best thing about this anthology of writings by foremost American feminists from 1820 to 1920 is Gail Parker's introduction, in which she charts the waters of American feminism during the nineteenth and early twentieth centuries. Parker is particularly good at capturing personalities, and what she notes about women such as Catharine Beecher, Sarah Orne Jewett, and Charlotte Perkins Gilman is often surprising. Parker says that all were plagued by feelings of inadequacy and that they compared themselves negatively against their mothers and grandmothers. Parker's short sketches preceding the excerpts from the work of Lydia Maria Child, Angelina Grimké Weld, Catharine Beecher, Harriet Beecher Stowe, Sarah Orne Jewett, Elizabeth Cady Stanton, Jane Addams, and Charlotte Perkins Gilman are excellent for their capturing of the human qualities of these women and the human roots of their sentimentalism, anti-romanticism, radicalism, realism, or whatever strain of American feminism each possessed. The title is taken from the Robert Frost poem, "The Oven Bird": "The question that he frames in all but words/Is what to make of a diminished thing." This is an essential anthology.

1711   Peck, Ellen, 1942- , and Judith Senderowitz, comps. **Pronatalism: The Myth of Mom and Apple Pie.** New York: Thomas Y. Crowell, 1974. 333p. bibliog. $7.95. ISBN 0690004982. LC 74-6087.

Peck and Senderowitz bring together here a collection of readings on the subtle and not-so-subtle mechanisms deployed by male supremacist societies to coerce women to bear children. In some of the pieces, there is a tendency to equate the oppressive conditions under which women currently bear and raise children with childraising *per se*, resulting in an unnecessarily bleak view of the parent-child relationship. However, the volume as a whole makes an important contribution to an analysis of the social relations of reproduction—how they control women and effectively nullify reproductive (and hence life) choices. Among the specific topics addressed by contributors are pronatalism and U.S. population policy; pronatalism in women's magazine fiction, television, and textbooks; motivations for childbearing; parenthood as crisis; motherhood and political participation; the choice to remain childfree; and childfree marriages. Contributors include: Leta S. Hollingworth, Judith Blake, Ellen Peck, Edward Pohlman, Robert E. Gould, E. E. LeMasters, Naomi B. Lynn, and Cornelia B. Flora. Readers might also want to consult editor Ellen Peck's earlier book, *The Baby Trap* (B. Geis, 1971).

1712   Randall, Margaret, 1936- . **Cuban Women Now: Interviews With Cuban Women.** Toronto: Women's Press: Dumont Press Graphix; distr. Toronto: Canadian Women's Educational Press, 1974. 375p. $5.50. LC 75-315425.

This book is exciting to read and helpful in bringing to life the revolutionary process in Cuba, women's part in this process, and its impact on their lives. We are given verbatim portions of interviews that Randall conducted with fourteen women, mainly of worker-peasant background, aged seventeen to 47, black and white, married, divorced and single, and of the most diverse occupations. Discussion ranges over a large number of important topics, among them the transition from capitalist to socialist Cuba, marriage, relations with men, child care, education, work, and political life. The interviews are preceded by Randall's historical introduction. Readers may also be interested in Randall's *Part of the Solution: Portrait of a Revolutionary* (New Directions, 1973).

1713   Redstockings. **Feminist Revolution.** New York: Random House, 1976. $12.95. ISBN 0394408217. LC 76-16456.

Originally published in 1975 by Redstockings, this is an important document of the contemporary women's liberation movement in the United States. Red-stockings was one of the earliest radical feminist organizations, dating back to 1969. In this collection of essays, the predominant concerns are the cooptation of the movement by the liberal establishment and the consequent rewriting of the history of the movement in diluted form. The authors try to reestablish this history as they see it and to reenliven some theoretical insights that have either been forgotten or have had their meanings altered (for example, consciousness-raising and the "pro-woman line"). They also offer an analysis of the different tendencies that they saw in the movement in 1975 and a sketch of a program for the future. Authors include Kathie Sarachild, Pat Mainardi, Barbara Leon, Carol Hanisch, Judy Grahn, Ellen Willis, and others.

1714   Reed, Evelyn. **Problems of Women's Liberation: A Marxist Approach.** (5th and enl. ed.). New York: Pathfinder Press, 1971. 96p. $6.00. ISBN 0873481666. LC 78-143808.

This early collection of essays on women is by the Marxist anthropologist, Evelyn Reed. Included are: Women and the Family: A Historical View; The Myth of Women's Inferiority; How Women Lost Control of Their Destiny and How They Can Regain It; Women: Caste, Class or Oppressed Sex?; Cosmetics, Fashions, and the Exploitation of Women; and The Feminine Mystique. Some of the ideas explored here are further developed in Reed's major work, *Woman's Evolution* (1975), as well as in her most recent, *Sexism and Science* (1978).

1715   Reed, Evelyn. **Sexism and Science.** New York: Pathfinder Press, 1978. 190p. bibliog. index. $12.95. ISBN 0873485157. LC 77-92144.

Reed views this collection of articles (many previously published in the *International Socialist Review*) as "a sequel and supplement" to her earlier major work, *Woman's Evolution* (1975). Here she takes direct aim at the sexist, racist, and capitalist ideological underpinnings of science, especially "those branches of science that are closest to human life and its history and values . . . biology, sociology, anthropology, and the two younger sciences called sociobiology and primatology." Readers who have been following the widespread debate sparked by the publication of zoologist Edward O. Wilson's *Sociobiology: The New Synthesis* (1975) will especially appreciate Reed's critical analysis of this "new" perspective and of its theory of sexual inequality in her essay "Sociobiology and Pseudoscience" (1975). Other essays in the volume are "Primatology and Prejudice" (1977), "An Answer to 'The Naked Ape' and Other Books on Aggression" (1970), "Lionel Tiger's 'Men in Groups': Self-Portrait of a Woman-Hater" (1977), "Anthropology and Feminism: An Exchange of Views [between Howard Haymes and Reed]" (1975), "The Challenge of the Matriarchy" (1975), "The Misconceptions of Claude Lévi-Strauss on 'The Elementary Structures of

Kinship' " (1977), and "Evolutionism and Antievolutionism" (1957). For another recent discussion of sociobiology (which, however, does not address feminist issues), see Marshall Sahlins's *The Use and Abuse of Biology: An Anthropological Critique of Sociobiology* (1976).

1716*   Reiche, Reimut, 1941- . **Sexuality and Class Struggle.** New York: Praeger, 1971. 175p. bibliog. LC 74-163096.
Written by a political activist in West Germany at the beginning of the mass political mobilizations of the late '60s, *Sexuality and Class Struggle* is an analysis of "the change in the role of sexuality under the cultural dominance of late capitalism." It belongs to the tradition, largely identified with the theories of Wilhelm Reich (*Sex-Pol, Mass Psychology of Fascism, The Sexual Revolution*), that has explored possibilities for an integration of Marx and Freud. Writers in this tradition have found Marxist theory lacking in the psycho-logical dimension and psychoanalysis lacking in the social dimension, but they have recognized the complementary nature of the two and the similarity of their methods. Reich emphasized the role of sexual repression in the creation of authoritarian personality structure and saw this form of social control via the unconscious as but another expression of the hegemony of the ruling classes. Reimut Reiche wanted to explore the ways in which the manipulation of sexuality in capitalist society had changed from the 1930s of Reich to the late 1960s. His emphasis is on the capacity of the capitalist system to absorb demands for sexual liberation, reformulating them to serve its own ends. Among other current works readers will want to be aware of are Eli Zaretsky's *Capitalism, the Family, and Personal Life* (1976) and Juliet Mitchell's *Psychoanalysis and Feminism* (1974).

1717   Reid, Inez Smith. **"Together" Black Women.** New York: Third Press, 1975. 383p. $12.95. ISBN 0893881147. LC 73-83156.
Reid reports here on her questionnaire research in the early 1970s on "the militant Black woman," commissioned by the Black Women's Community Development Foundation. The questionnaire (filled out in in-depth interviews) delved into the women's views on the black struggle, marriage, women's liberation, the role of black women in the black struggle, contrasting political philosophies, and more. Interviews were conducted with 202 women from all regions of the United States who were involved in a wide variety of political activities, including black student unions, the Black Panther Party, neo-Panther groups, local black women's groups, traditional civil rights groups, day care centers, welfare rights, etc. Reid summarizes the main impressions to emerge from her study as: 1) a general distrust of or even hostility on the part of the women toward the women's liberation movement; 2) profound opposition to national and local political and social conditions in the U.S.; 3) a willingness to embrace violence as the only viable solution to black oppression; and 4) the sense of being in a "state of limbo" while awaiting the next stage of the black struggle. Reid has tried to write in a popular style and quotes extensively from the interviews.

1718   Rich, Adrienne Cecile. **Of Woman Born: Motherhood as Experience and Institution.** New York: Norton, 1976. 318p. bibliog. index. $8.95. ISBN 0393087506. LC 76-18744.

In the preface, Rich says, "But I did not choose this subject; it had long ago chosen me." This is a book about motherhood, daughterhood, sisterhood—womanhood. Rich writes from the perspective of a mother with a personal constellation of autobiographical mother and daughter experiences that she wishes to explore. It is grounded in intense historical research and analysis in an effort to demonstrate that much of the "objective scholarship" about women-as-mothers has never examined the experience of women except through a patriarchally distorted lens. She points out the dearth of primary sources on motherhood in Western culture. The most autobiographical chapter ("Anger and Tenderness") explores the conflicts Rich felt rearing children in the '50s and '60s, torn between being a poet and a mother. Other chapters deal with anthropological, psychological, historical, economic, and literary treatments of motherhood. Chapters include: The "Sacred Calling"; The Kingdom of the Fathers; The Primacy of the Mother; The Domestication of Motherhood; Alienated Labor; Mother and Son, Woman and Man; Motherhood and Daughterhood; Violence: The Heart of Maternal Darkness. Rich writes a very personal strain of history, and her reading of the "specialists" is always filtered through her perspective as woman/mother/poet.

1719   Rossi, Alice S., 1922- , comp. **Essays on Sex Equality.** By John Stuart
        Mill and Harriet Taylor Mill. Chicago: University of Chicago Press,
        1970. 242p. bibliog. $12.50. ISBN 0226525457. LC 78-133381.
Collected in this volume are three classic essays in the history of liberal feminism: "Early Essays on Marriage and Divorce" (1832), by John Stuart and Harriet Taylor Mill; "Enfranchisement of Women" (1851), by Harriet Taylor Mill; and "The Subjection of Women" (1869), by John Stuart Mill. These essays are normally attributed to John Stuart Mill alone, but Alice Rossi, editor of the volume, chose to restore joint authorship to Harriet Taylor on the basis of extensive research on the Mills' intellectual collaboration. Rossi's lengthy introductory essay, "Sentiment and Intellect: The Story of John Stuart Mill and Harriet Taylor Mill," is a sensitive study of the Mills' extraordinary relationship and makes this edition of the essays particularly valuable for the feminist library. "The Subjection of Women," best known of the three pieces, had significant impact on nineteenth-century debate on "the woman question." In this essay, John Stuart Mill comes through as a sensitive spokesman for the legal rights of women—equality in marriage and equal opportunity in public and intellectual realms of endeavor. His chief concern is that the "fundamental law" of modern social institutions—reward for merit, not birth, under conditions of competition—be applied to women as well as men. Although he concludes that most women would continue to choose marriage and motherhood as their vocation, he argues that the principle of free choice must be instituted for sexual justice to reign—and in the interests of "exceptional" women who would exercise that freedom.

1720   Rossi, Alice S., 1922- , comp. **The Feminist Papers: From Adams to
        de Beauvoir.** New York: Columbia University Press, 1973. 716p.
        bibliog. $15.00. ISBN 0231037953. LC 73-8828.
Rossi has compiled an anthology of representative writings of key feminist thinkers, American and European, whose lives span the years from 1744 to the

present. She introduces each author with a substantial essay in which she brings a feminist sociologist's questions to bear on the biography, the historical period, and the ideas in question. In many cases, this involves an exploration of the interfaces between personal, political, intellectual, and historical struggle and change. Part 1, Feminism and the Enlightenment Perspective, includes selections from the correspondence of Abigail and John Adams, Judith Sargent Murray, Mary Wollstonecraft, Frances Wright, Harriet Martineau, Margaret Fuller, and John Stuart Mill. Part 2, Feminist and Status Politics, has selections from the Grimké sisters, the Blackwells, Elizabeth Cady Stanton, Susan B. Anthony, and from the *History of Woman Suffrage*. Part 3, Bread Comes First, has selections from Friedrich Engels, August Bebel, Emma Goldman, Margaret Sanger, Suzanne LaFollette, Charlotte Perkins Gilman, and Jane Addams; and part 4, Sex Is a Many-Sided Thing, from Virginia Woolf, Margaret Mead, and Simone de Beauvoir. A list of references, including but not confined to the selections abridged for the volume, is appended. This is a fine, painstakingly edited anthology, essential for any women's studies collection and undoubtedly excellent as a text for courses in feminist theory.

1721   Rowbotham, Sheila. **A New World For Women; Stella Browne: Socialist Feminist.** London: Pluto Press, 1977. 128p. bibliog. index. $7.95. ISBN 094383555.

"I became interested in Stella Brown while writing *Hidden From History*. She fought for contraception and abortion as a feminist committed to sexual liberation. She asserted women's control over their own bodies against men's power of sexual ownership but understood that this was only one aspect of a more general social and economic struggle for liberation. She fought as a socialist as well as a feminist. . . . She tried to relate the specific oppression of women as a sex to the emancipation of the working class." Thus Rowbotham introduces this study of Stella Browne, the birth control campaign of the '20s in England, and its impact on the Left. This work represents a continuation of Rowbotham's commitment to unearthing the history of socialist feminist politics and to advancing a feminist materialist analysis of reproduction, its control, and reproductive freedom. Appended are two brief essays by Browne (which Rowbotham introduces): "The Sexual Variety and Variability Among Women" (1915) and "The Right to Abortion" (1935).

1722   Rowbotham, Sheila. **Woman's Consciousness, Man's World.** Harmondsworth: Penguin Books, 1973. 136p. bibliog. index. $1.95. ISBN 0140217177. LC 74-164441.

More an extended essay than an in-depth analysis, this book will be appreciated for its eloquence and clarity of perception. Sheila Rowbotham writes in part 1 about the patriarchal world women are born into, how women come to see themselves and men in these circumstances, and how they come to political consciousness. In part 2, she analyzes the complex web of power relations that makes patriarchy, capitalism, racism, and imperialism interdependent systems and tries to show how these systems shape people's daily lives.

1723   Rowbotham, Sheila. **Women, Resistance, and Revolution: A History
        of Women and Revolution in the Modern World.** New York: Pantheon
        Books, 1972. 287p. bibliog. $7.95. ISBN 0394475453. LC 72-3404.
"This is not a proper history of feminism and revolution. . . . Instead I have
tried to trace the fortunes of an idea. It is a very simple idea, but one with which
we have lost touch, that the liberation of women necessitates the liberation of
all human beings" (from the introduction). This book makes for exciting reading
as Rowbotham pursues historical connections between the rise of feminist
consciousness and other revolutionary upsurges. This pursuit takes her from the
Puritan revolution, through the French Revolution, through the progressive
movements in nineteenth-century Europe, to the Russian Revolution, the
Chinese Revolution, and finally, the anti-imperialist movements in Vietnam,
Cuba, and Algeria. Rowbotham reprints, at the end, part of a long and fine
bibliography previously published in pamphlet form in England under the title,
"Women's Liberation and Revolution."

1724   Ruether, Rosemary Radford. **New Woman, New Earth: Sexist Ideologies
        and Human Liberation.** New York: Seabury Press, 1975. 221p. bibliog.
        index. $8.95. ISBN 0816412057. LC 75-17649.
Rosemary Ruether has written extensively about liberation theology from a
socialist feminist perspective. This collection of essays (or sketches, as she looks
at them) represents a very important statement of this perspective and a contribution to the laying of "a groundwork for recognizing the interrelation of ideology
and social structure in the history of sexism" (p. xiv). She divides the book
into three parts. Part 1 addresses issues of religion and sexism; part 2 looks at
the parallels and differences between the forms of oppression experienced
historically by women, witches, Jews, and by blacks in the United States; part
3 presents a critical analysis of psychoanalytic, socialist, and ecological perspectives. Ruether's own point of view is that a liberation theory and movement must
address all forms of oppression within the society they confront, going beyond
exclusivistic, interest-group politics to a politics that is encompassing and
integrative. Readers may be interested in comparing Ruether's work with Mary
Daly's *Beyond God the Father*, which covers similar ground, but from a radical
feminist perspective. Ruether's more recent book is *Mary: The Feminine Face
of the Church* (Westminster Press, 1977).

1725   Saffioti, Heleieth Iara Bongiovani. **Women in Class Society.** New
        York: Monthly Review Press, 1978. 378p. bibliog. $16.50. ISBN
        0853454159. LC 77-76170.
Written by a Brazilian sociologist in 1966-1967, *Women in Class Society* prefigures
in its theoretical formulations much of the work by socialist feminists of the
last ten years. Saffiotti's perspective as a Third World woman is particularly
important for North American feminists, who tend to assume a framework of
advanced capitalist society in their analyses of women's oppression and women's
liberation. Saffiotti devotes almost one-third of her book to a case study of
women's position in Brazil, from colonial times to the present. But she takes
care throughout the entire study to make distinctions between the center
(advanced capitalist) countries and the underdeveloped periphery. As summarized
by Eleanor Burke Leacock in her excellent introduction to the English translation,

Saffiotti's concerns in this study "can be grouped under six topics: 1) the economic marginalization of women in capitalist society; 2) functions served by family organization (or kinship, as Saffiotti puts it) in capitalist society; 3) relations among sex, race, and class; 4) the organization of women in imperialist and in Third World nations; 5) science and the ideology of the 'feminine mystique'; and 6) women and the struggle for socialism." Theoretical sophistication combined with ponderousness of style (possibly exacerbated by poor translation) make this work difficult for readers unfamiliar with Marxist or Marxist-feminist literature. However, Leacock's introduction crystallizes in clear language the main thrust of Saffiotti's arguments, as well as updating them with references to relevant English-language work of the past ten years. Saffiotti's own bibliography is also valuable, though dated, as it includes numerous references in Portuguese, French, and Spanish.

1726   Safilios-Rothschild, Constantina, 1934- . **Women and Social Policy.**
        Englewood Cliffs, NJ: Prentice-Hall, 1974. 197p. bibliog. index.
        $6.95. ISBN 0139616985. LC 73-12215.
The author analyzes the network of social policies and practices designed to eliminate sexism from United States society. Research data and analyses are synthesized to describe the social actions, policies, and laws that are evolving. The term "sexism" is equated to "racism," and the intent is to raise the reader's consciousness and to stimulate corrective actions to eliminate discrimination. A basic assumption is that the Women's Liberation Movement in the U.S.A. and other Western nations will become increasingly more vocal, active, and efficacious in applying political and social pressures for eliminating tokenism and enlarging the sharing of power with women. The ten-page bibliography covers a wide variety of references. Chapters: The Theoretical Background of Social Policy Related to Women; Social Policy to Liberate Women; Social Policy to Liberate Men (the author refers to her spouse as a liberated husband); Social Policy to Liberate Marriage, the Institution of the Family, and Family Life; and Social Policy to Liberate the Society from Sexism.

1727   Salper, Roberta, comp. **Female Liberation: History and Current Politics.**
        Philadelphia, PA: Philadelphia Book Co., 1971. 246p. bibliog. $4.50.
        ISBN 0394315286. LC 74-157188.
Yet another women's liberation reader, this one combines the "essential historical writings" approach with selections from the contemporary movement. Among the excerpts included in part 1, History and Background, are: Mary Wollstonecraft, "The Rights of Woman"; Harriet Taylor Mill, "On the Enfranchisement of Women"; Frederick Douglass, "Life and Writings of Frederick Douglass"; Sojourner Truth, "Narrative of a Life"; Hal Draper, "Marx and Engels on Women's Liberation"; and Emma Goldman, "Anarchism and Other Essays." Part 2, The New Feminism, includes: Kathy McAfee and Myrna Wood, "Bread & Roses"; Roberta Salper, "The Development of the American Women's Liberation Movement, 1967-1971"; Marlene Dixon, "Why Women's Liberation—2?"; Frances Beal, "Double Jeopardy: To Be Black and Female"; Kate Ellis, "The Politics of Day Care"; and Barbara Burris, et al., "Fourth World Manifesto." The bibliography is brief and, of course, dated (1971). This is a good introductory anthology.

1727a   Sayers, Dorothy Leigh, 1893-1957. **Are Women Human?** Grand Rapids,
        MI: Eerdmans, 1971. 47p. $1.25. ISBN 0802813844. LC 73-27055.
The two essays reprinted in this volume have been taken from the author's collection of 21 essays entitled *Unpopular Opinions*. These essays ("Are Women
Human?" and "The Human-Not-Quite-Human") represent Sayers' views on the
position of women. Her only other published statement on the subject occurs
in her introduction to Dante's *Purgatory*. Her participation in the world of ideas
as a scholar, playwright, lecturer, theologian and, most notably, as a preeminent
writer of mystery stories, has perhaps muted her consciousness with regard to
the woman question. Sayers maintains that she is not a feminist, and that the
unique qualities of the individual are more important than changing sex roles.
She believes that males and females are uniquely suited to perform certain
functions as a result of biological differences, that men and women are certainly
equal but not comparable.

1727b   Schneir, Miriam, comp. **Feminism: The Essential Historical Writings.**
        New York: Random House, 1972. 360p. bibliog. $8.95. ISBN
        0394471911. LC 70-159371.
In this particularly fine anthology of feminist writings, the major segments are:
Eighteenth-Century Rebels; Woman Alone; An American Woman's Movement;
Men as Feminists; and Twentieth Century Themes. Schneir begins with the
assumption that most women are not acquainted with the essential historical
feminist writings and are thus deprived of their history and identity. Writers
represented are Abigail Adams, Mary Wollstonecraft, Frances Wright, George
Sand, Sarah Grimké, Harriet H. Robinson, Thomas Hood, Margaret Fuller,
Frederick Douglass, William Lloyd Garrison, Sojourner Truth, Lucretia Mott,
Lucy Stone, Susan B. Anthony, Victoria Woodhull and Tennessee Claflin,
John Stuart Mill, Henrik Ibsen, Frederich Engels, August Bebel, Thorstein
Veblen, Charlotte Perkins Gilman, Anna Garlin Spencer, Carrie Chapman Catt,
Emmeline Pankhurst, Emma Goldman, Margaret Sanger, Clara Zetkin and
Virginia Woolf. Some documents are included such as "Declaration of Sentiments
and Resolutions, Seneca Falls" and the "Married Women's Property Act, New
York, 1848."

1728   Schreiner, Olive, 1855-1920. **Woman and Labor.** New York: F. A.
        Stokes, 1911; repr. New York: Johnson Reprint, 1972. 299p. $14.00.
        ISBN 0384542808. LC 79-38699.
Woman and Labor is an important piece of feminist analysis, influential when
first published in 1911 (for example, Alice Clark acknowledged Schreiner's
influence as fundamental for her own classic work, *Working Life of Women
in the Seventeenth Century*) and still influential today, as it is rediscovered by
contemporary feminist historians. Schreiner viewed her work as merely "a
collection of musings," an underestimation perhaps but understandable when
one learns in her introduction that *Woman and Labor* was but a fragment of a
monumental treatise on women that Schreiner had spent decades writing but
which was burned during the Anglo-Boer War. The central concern in *Woman
and Labor* is the deterioration of women's place in production, which has
accompanied the development of industrial capitalism and which has created a
new form of oppressive dependence of women on men, called by Schreiner

"parasitism." She is at the same time concerned with society's lack of recognition and remuneration for the work with which women are burdened in the home. It is her particular approach to the interrelation between the history and evolution of production and the changing structure of women's oppression that has given this book its impact. After developing this perspective in her first chapter, "Parasitism," Schreiner goes on to discuss the probable effect of sexual equality upon the incidence of war, the question of sex differences, objections to the expansion of opportunities for women in employment, and "The New Woman and the New Man."

1729   Scott, Hilda. **Does Socialism Liberate Women? Experiences from Eastern Europe.** Boston: Beacon Press, 1974. 240p. bibliog. index. $4.95. ISBN 0807041637. LC 74-212.

Hilda Scott lived in Czechoslovakia for many years, and hence, her extensive research is further substantiated by personal experience. The study looks at the treatment of the "woman question" in the countries of Eastern Europe (but especially Czechoslovakia) since World War II and offers an illuminating critical analysis of orthodox Marxist theory of women's liberation. The principal weakness of the book is its failure to be equally critical in its analysis of Czechoslovak society as a whole, particularly of limitations in the process of socialist transformation that extend beyond problems of sexual inequality. Readers may also be interested in Ivan and Nancy Volgyes' *The Liberated Female: Life, Work, and Sex in Socialist Hungary* (Westview Press, 1977). Based both on interviews and statistical data, the Volgyes' study delves into the areas of women's employment, marriage and divorce, motherhood, sex, and retirement.

1730   Sidel, Ruth. **Women and Child Care in China: A Firsthand Report.** New York: Hill and Wang, 1972. 207p. bibliog. index. $7.95. ISBN 080909777X. LC 72-81286.

Sidel's book has become a classic women's studies text, largely because of her focus on the relationship between the organization of child care and changes in women's roles in China. She discusses pre-liberation China; women's liberation; marriage, pregnancy, and childbirth; the Cultural Revolution and the organization of child care; multiple mothering; socialization practices in nurseries and kindergartens; comparisons with the Soviet Union and Israel; and comparisons with the U.S. Other works of comparative interest are Hilda Scott's *Does Socialism Liberate Women?* (1974; not restricted to the issue of child care), Marvin Leiner's *Children Are the Revolution: Day Care in Cuba* (1978), and Karen Wald's *Children of Che: Childcare and Education in Cuba* (1978).

1731   Spencer, Anna (Garlin), 1851-1931. **Woman's Share in Social Culture.** New York: Arno Press, 1972. (Repr. of 1913 ed.). 331p. $17.00. ISBN 0405044798. LC 72-2623.

"New Englander Anna Carpenter Garlin Spencer (1851-1931) early revealed a talent for public speaking. In 1891 she became the first female ordained minister in Rhode Island. In later years she was associated with the New York Society for Ethical Culture, the New York School of Philanthropy (Social Work), the University of Wisconsin, the University of Chicago and Columbia University. She was concerned with factory laws, child labor and, as head of the Family

Relations Division of the American Social Hygiene Association, with prostitution" ("A Note about This Volume," A. K. Baxter and L. Stein, eds.). This collection includes essays on women in "primitive times," women in antiquity, the predicament of the woman genius, the spinster, economic discrimination against women workers, the sexual division of labor (which she terms "the vocational divide")—looking particularly at the consequences of women's responsibilities within the family—problems of marriage and divorce, and woman and the state. A page-by-page analysis of contents is appended at the end.

1732   Stanton, Elizabeth (Cady), 1815-1902, et al., eds. **History of Woman Suffrage.** New York: Arno Press, 1969. (Repr. of 1881-1922 ed.). 6v. $200.00. ISBN 040500107X. LC 73-79182.

This massive six-volume work—each volume of approximately 1,000 pages—is so comprehensive and so universally acknowledged as *the* authoritative source on the Woman Suffrage Movement that complete description won't be attempted here. Susan B. Anthony is generally credited with the original conception and it was she who, from the Movement's beginnings, preserved the important letters, speeches, newspaper clippings, accounts of conventions, and legislative and congressional reports. The first three volumes (v.1, 1848-1861, published 1881; v.2, 1861-1876, published 1881; v.3, 1876-1885, published 1886) were edited by Anthony, Elizabeth Cady Stanton, and Matilda Joslyn Gage. Contemporary feminists owe a profound debt to the vision and sense of history that prompted these three women to go ahead with the project in the face of the skepticism of those who said that the history mustn't be written by activists or before the story was "complete." In these three volumes, as in the subsequent three, documents are interspersed with a running historical account. Volume 4 (1883-1900, published 1902) was edited by Anthony and Ida Husted Harper. Volumes 5 and 6 (1900-1920, published 1922) were completed by Harper. Stanton, Anthony, and Gage originally set aside four months in 1876 for the writing of what they imagined would be a pamphlet of a few hundred pages. The project grew and grew and eventually outlived the three of them. Readers overwhelmed by the full six volumes may be interested in a recent one-volume condensation edited by Paul and Mari Jo Buhle, *The Concise History of Woman Suffrage* (University of Illinois Press, 1978).

1733   Stites, Richard. **The Women's Liberation Movement in Russia; Feminism, Nihilism, and Bolshevism, 1860-1930.** Princeton, NJ: Princeton University Press, 1977. 464p. bibliog. index. $37.50. ISBN 0691052549. LC 77-72137.

This massive work, the product of twelve years of research in the United States, Europe, and the Soviet Union, was begun as the author's dissertation in history. The study is extremely valuable both for its meticulous documentation (based on extensive use of archival, primary, and secondary sources in Russian and English) and for its theoretical perspective. Stites rejects the simplistic dichotomization of "bourgeois feminism" and socialism. Instead, he seeks to understand and sketch for the reader the complex interaction of social movements and ideologies in Russia during the last century: the educated, upper-class feminists with their charitable activities in the nineteenth century; the nihilists with their stress on personal liberation; the suffragists; the revolutionaries; the Bolsheviks. Arguing that "a clear understanding of social history is impeded by the traditional obeisance to the year 1917 as a watershed," Stites tries to assess the changing fortunes of Russian women's liberation in the twentieth century "in the light of pre-revolutionary aspirations, achievements, and failures; and in the light of the furious, if often untangential, debates between feminists and Marxists." While any interpretation of women's liberation in the Soviet Union is bound to provoke controversy, Stites's study recommends itself as essential background reading on the basis of its broad scope, its historical grounding, and its clear grip on the issues.

1734*   Thomas, Edith. **The Women Incendiaries.** New York: Braziller, 1966.
         274p. bibliog. index. LC 66-15754.
Originally published in France in 1963 as *Les Pétroleuses*, this is an emphatically feminist account of women's revolutionary struggles in the Paris Commune of 1871, written at a time when, as Thomas notes in her introduction, feminism was generally considered to be a nineteenth-century anachronism and women, peripheral to the historians's task. The accounts of contemporaries of the 1871 Revolution leave no doubt that women were anything but peripheral to that epic struggle (though the women are often pictured as debased creatures). For example, Maxime du Camp wrote: "During the final days, all of these bellicose viragos held out longer than the men did behind the barricades. . . . Many of them were arrested, with powder-blackened hands and shoulders bruised by the recoil of their rifles; they were still palpitating from the overstimulation of battle. . . . " Thomas sees her own participation in the French Resistance during World War II, and, in particular, in the demonstrations of the Union des Femmes Françaises against the Nazi occupation, as having laid the basis for her interest in the women of the Commune.

1735   Thompson, Mary Lou, ed. **Voices of the New Feminism.** Boston:
        Beacon Press, 1970. 246p. bibliog. $3.95. ISBN 0807041750. LC
        76-119679.
This anthology speaks to historical, ideological, and problematic aspects of feminism. It also discusses new lifestyles and the future of feminism. Contents: Joyce Cowley, "Pioneers of Women's Liberation"; Betty Friedan, "Our Revolution is Unique"; Roxanne Dunbar, "Female Liberation as the Basis for Social Revolution"; Alice Rossi, "Sex Equality: The Beginnings of Ideology"; Elizabeth Duncan Koontz, "Women as a Minority Group"; Pauli Murray, "The Liberation of Black Women"; Martha Griffiths, "Women and Legislation"; Doris L. Pullen, "The Educational Establishment: Wasted Women"; Mary Daly, "Toward Partnership in the Church"; Caroline Bird, "The Androgynous Life"; Mary Lou Thompson, "Forecast for Feminism"; Shirley Chisholm, "Women Must Rebel"; and Lucinda Cisler, "Women: A Bibliography."

1736   Thompson, William, 1775-1883. **Appeal of One Half the Human Race,
        Women, Against the Pretensions of the Other Half, Men, to Retain Them
        in Political, and thence in Civil and Domestic, Slavery; In Reply to
        a Paragraph of Mr. Mill's Celebrated "Article on Government."** New
        York: B. Franklin, 1970. (Repr. of 1825 ed.). 221p. index. $10.50.
        ISBN 0833735152. LC 71-134450.

William Thompson wrote his *Appeal* in 1825 in response to James Mill's *Article on Government*, which had set forth the argument that women had no need of political rights because men could sufficiently look after their interests. In his indictment of this argument as a typical attempt at self-justification by an oppressor, as well as in his outrage at the inequality imposed on women by law, in marriage, education, and employment, Thompson's thinking resembles that of Mary Wollstonecraft, whose *Vindication of the Rights of Woman* had appeared in 1792. However, Thompson's *Appeal* makes a significant break in the history of feminist thought because the description of women's oppression is integrated into an overall critique of the capitalist system and is combined with a positive vision of an alternative. One of the early utopian socialists, Thompson developed a critical analysis of the exploitation of workers under capitalism and advocated the right of workers to the product of their labor. His view of capitalist competition led him to conclude that the mere removal of legal barriers could never liberate women within capitalism, because "unequal powers under free competition must produce unequal effects." Under competitive conditions where wealth is the measure of power, women's weaker physique and childbearing function would always maintain inequality between the sexes. His vision of a future society stipulated economic independence and security for all people and collective responsibility for reproduction and childcare.

1737   Thonnessen, Werner, 1929- . **The Emancipation of Women: The Rise and Decline of the Women's Movement in German Social Democracy, 1863-1933.** London: Pluto Press, 1973; Urizen Books, distr. New York: E. P. Dutton, 1976. 185p. bibliog. index. $10.00. ISBN 0902818279. LC 74-180714.
Thonnessen's book is a case-study in the relation between socialist and feminist movements. He traces the history of the German Social Democratic Party (SPD) and of the German women's movement from the founding of the German Workers' Association in 1863 to the rise of Nazi power in 1933. A central focus is the impact of political developments within and outside the SPD on its attitude and policies toward women.

1738   Tobias, Sheila, et al., eds. **The Cornell Conference on Women: Proceedings.** Pittsburgh, PA: Know, 1969. 100p. $3.00. ISBN 0912786132.
This publication contains selected proceedings of the Cornell Conference on Women, held at Cornell University in Ithaca, New York, under the sponsorship of Cornell's College of Human Ecology and the University Administration. Transcripts of the panel discussions convey a sense of the spirit of the conference. Radical, angry, persistent discussions took place among participants who were knowledgeable about, but certainly not in agreement on, the issues around which the panels were centered: How Do Man Look at Women and How Do Women Look at Themselves?; The Political Dimension: Is the Question of Women a Political Question?; Equality and the Education of Women in America; The Psychological Differences Between Men and Women; The Black Woman in America. Panelists included Kate Millett, Betty Friedan, Dr. Howard Osofsky, Dr. Howard Feinstein, Prof. Andrew Hacker, Prof. Marguerite Fisher, Karen de Crow, Anne-Marie Berggren, and many others, including students, members of SDS, and community women. The coordinator was Sheila Tobias, then

assistant to the vice president for academic affairs. The organization of this conference provided a model for other conferences on women's issues on other campuses during the early '70s. "There were approximately 30 members of the organizing committee, 50 panel participants, and more than 2,000 in the audience. The Conference was followed by a student-run independent study seminar in the spring of 1969; a faculty seminar in the fall of 1969 and a course, The Evolution of Female Personality in the spring of 1970." The proceedings originally were reproduced primarily for students in the course.

1739   Trotskii, Lev, 1879-1940. **Women and the Family.** (2nd ed.). New
        York: Pathfinder Press, 1973. 78p. $1.25. ISBN 0873482182. LC
        72-92457.
In these selections from Trotsky's writings relevant to issues of women and the family are included: "From the Old Family to the New"; "A Letter to a Moscow Women Workers' Celebration and Rally"; "The Protection of Motherhood and the Struggle for Culture"; "To Build Socialism Means to Emancipate Women and Protect Mothers"; "Family Relations Under the Soviets"; and "Thermidor in the Family."

1740   Watson, Barbara Bellow, ed. **Women's Studies: The Social Realities.**
        New York: Harper's College Press, 1976. 255p. bibliog. $6.95. ISBN
        0061604216. LC 76-18176.
Beginning with a review of the classic texts—Wollstonecraft, Mill, Bernard Shaw, Woolf, and de Beauvoir—this book's intention is "to provide for students and teachers a convenient and reasonably authoritative collection of basic readings in the field, but this is neither an anthology nor an essay collection" (from the introduction). Watson has organized the material around the following foci: sociology, psychology, anthropology, the feminist movement to 1920, and the contemporary women's liberation movement. In each section, a scholar has assembled relevant, non-sexist materials, interpreted those materials, and provided an interdisciplinary context. Questions appear at the end of each section, along with a generous list of further readings. The section on social roles, for example, introduced and organized by Helen Mayer Hacker, begins with a definition of the sociological perspective and includes writings by Ralph Linton and E. T. Hiller, with numerous suggestions by Hacker for discussion questions, writing projects, and role-playing situations. The format lends itself to the classroom situation; the content, to the development and analysis of women's studies pedagogy.

1741   West, Uta, ed. **Women in a Changing World.** New York: McGraw-Hill,
        1975. 170p. $3.95. ISBN 0070694656. LC 75-22278.
Contributors to this anthology include Marge Piercy, Elizabeth Janeway, Doris Lessing, Jane Lazarre, Grace Paley, Anaïs Nin, Mary Daly, and others.

1742   West Coast Women's Studies Conference, California State University,
        Sacramento, 1973. **Report on the West Coast Women's Studies Conference.**
        Pittsburgh, PA: Know, 1974. 155p. $4.50. ISBN 0912786353.
The West Coast Women's Studies Conference at California State University, Sacramento, was held May 25-28, 1973. The Editorial Staff of the Women's Studies Board wisely decided to publish complete transcriptions of the addresses,

criticisms, and "open mike" contributions without editing or interpretation of their own; a series of interpretive essays that either were sent to the CSUS Women's Studies Board or appeared in women's publications following the conference also appear. What emerges is an electrifying documentary of confrontation within the women's movement, and a significant historical document as well. The conference was beset by a major rift between two groups, which came to be characterized by participants as the "Marxists" (socialist feminists) and the "Matriarchs" (cultural feminists). What gets played out in these pages is an emotional debate central to the women's movement, and still very much alive today, over the connections between sex, class, race, and lesbian oppression, in general, and over the uneasy relationship between academic feminists and the community, in particular. Major speakers at the conference were Joan Huff Wilson, Kirsten Amundsen, Florence Howe, Robin Morgan, and Rita Mae Brown.

1743   Wollstonecraft, Mary, 1759-1797. **A Vindication of the Rights of Woman: An Anthoritative Text, Backgrounds, Criticism.** New York: Norton, 1975. 240p. bibliog. $10.00. ISBN 0393044270. LC 75-37775.

In September of 1791, in the aftermath of the French Revolution, Talleyrand (former Bishop of Autun) called for a system of free education in France, making, however, no reference at all to the education of women. It is to Talleyrand that Mary Wollstonecraft dedicated her book, *A Vindication of the Rights of Woman*, hurriedly written and published in 1792. The era was one of tumultuous change, democratic upheaval, and heated debate over the nature of the "rights of man." Wollstonecraft's fiercely-stated argument was that the achievement of a new, more rational and just society necessitated a commitment to the rights of woman repeatedly denied or ignored by the treatises of the day: a new woman, as well as a new man, must be nurtured through proper education, based on the human capacity of Reason. Wollstonecraft was infuriated by Rousseau's ideas on the education of women (for men) as expressed in *Émile*, and she rebutted these in chapter 5 of *Vindication* ("Animadversions on Some of the Writers Who Have Rendered Women Objects of Pity, Bordering on Contempt"). Like Rousseau, however, Wollstonecraft did not see the emerging structure of capitalism, with its new class relations, which underlay the democratic movement of her time. She fails, therefore, to speak to questions of the exploitation of women and of class divisions between women; her political statement falls within the framework of liberal feminism.

1744   Wollstonecraft, Mary, 1759-1797. **A Wollstonecraft Anthology.** Ed. by Janet M. Todd. Bloomington: Indiana University Press, 1977. 269p. bibliog. $16.50. ISBN 0253366054. LC 77-72192.

Wollstonecraft's work is seeing more frequent current editions as her writings begin to get the attention they deserve. A woman who earned her living by writing, Wollstonecraft wrote reviews, fiction, and social commentary in addition to her controversial works, *A Vindication of the Rights of Woman* and *A Vindication of the Rights of Men*. Though reading Wollstonecraft completely and in a detailed manner is recommended, this volume provides a healthy sampling that can serve as a good introduction to her writings and thought. Included are selections from "Letters on the Management of Infants," from both *Vindications*; from her letters to Imlay, Godwin, and others; from her reviews; and from her fiction (*Mary: A Fiction* and *Maria, Or the Wrongs of Woman*). Janet Todd provides useful, brief commentary throughout.

1745*   **Women Unite!: An Anthology of the Canadian Women's Movement.**
Toronto: Women's Educational Press, 1972. 191p. bibliog. LC 75-306988.
The Canadian women's movement arose in the late 1960s, as did the movement in the United States, largely as a response of women in the New Left to the sexism that they experienced from leftist men. The similarities in the Canadian and U.S. movements extend further to the political schisms that quickly developed in each between socialist feminists (who attacked class exploitation and racism in addition to male supremacy) and radical feminists (who saw sexual oppression as primary and similarities between women as more important than differences). *Women Unite!* brings together writings of the Canadian women's movement, divided into three sections: Women in Canada; Strategies for Women's Liberation (including Alternatives to the Family, Economics of Working Women, and Politics of Sex); and a Selected Bibliography of Writings By and About Canadian Women.

1746   Yates, Gayle Graham, 1940- . **What Women Want: The Ideas of the Movement.** Cambridge, MA: Harvard University Press, 1975. 230p. bibliog. index. $10.00. ISBN 0674950771. LC 75-14018.
Yates has undertaken the task of analyzing and classifying the political theory of the contemporary women's movement. Her conclusions are bound to be controversial (as any would be), but her analysis will prove helpful to readers trying to sort out their own ideas on feminist theory. Yates sees feminist ideology as dividing into three types: the "feminist perspective" ("women equal to men"), the "women's liberationist perspective" ("women over/against men"), and the "androgynous perspective" ("women and men equal to each other"). She covers much ground rather quickly, and thus the book is probably most appropriate for readers who already have some familiarity with feminist theory. A good bibliography of basic sources is included.

1747   Young, Marilyn Blatt, comp. **Women in China: Studies in Social Change and Feminism.** Ann Arbor, MI: Center for Chinese Studies, University of Michigan, 1973. 259p. bibliog. $4.00. ISBN 0892640154. LC 73-623427.
"Of course it was necessary to give them [women] legal equality to begin with. But from there on, everything still remains to be done" (Mao Tse-tung to André Malraux, c. 1958, from *Anti-mémoires*). It is with this epigram that this excellent reader on women in China opens. Included are: Roxane Witke's "Mao Tse-tung, Women and Suicide" and "Woman as Politician in China of the 1920s"; Suzette Leith's "Chinese Women in the Early Communist Movement"; Delia Davin's "Women in the Liberated Areas"; Janet Salaff's "Institutionalized Motivation for Fertility Limitation"; Janet Salaff and Judith Merkle's "Women and Revolution: The Lessons of the Soviet Union and China"; Nancy Milton's "A Response to 'Women and Revolution' "; Jane Barrett's "Women Hold Up Half the Sky"; Soong Ching-ling's "Women's Liberation"; Lu Yu-lan's "Liberation of Women"; and Norma Diamond's "The Status of Women in Taiwan: One Step Forward,

Two Steps Back." An annotated bibliography of sources on women in both traditional and revolutionary China is appended.

1748   Zaretsky, Eli. **Capitalism, the Family, and Personal Life.** New York: Harper and Row, 1976. 156p. bibliog. index. $3.25. ISBN 0060905387. LC 76-21168.

This lengthy essay originally appeared as a series of articles in *Socialist Revolution*, nos. 13-15 (Jan.-June 1973). The book has become a classic, widely read in the women's movement, on the Left, and in college courses. Zaretsky gives us a sweeping historical interpretation of the process of capitalist development, of its impact on production and on the family, and of "the emergence of a sphere of personal life seemingly independent of the 'economy' and of 'production,'" the sphere in which male supremacy is rooted.

PERIODICALS

The journals and magazines described in this section are relatively new and have been selected from the array of dynamic women-related periodicals currently available. Most libraries are unable to pick up more than a smattering of the many unusual, often alternative-press women's periodicals representing the spectrum of the feminist movement. *Women's Studies Abstracts* thus becomes a first-choice selection, because it guides users to important literature in women's studies in an ongoing if perpetually belated way. *Women's Studies Newsletter, Signs,* and *Chrysalis* consistently feature good articles and reviews. Much informal sharing of information occurs in newsletters, too numerous to mention in separate annotations. Representative of the best in the newsletter approach for collection development assistance is *Women Are Human,* a monthly newsletter describing new materials received by Ohio State University's Women's Studies Library (published by that library). No single source surveys what is currently available in women's periodicals as thoroughly as Joan and Chesman's *Guide to Women's Publishing* (1978), a source that gives bibliographic information and editorial policies for the constantly expanding field of feminist journals.

1749   **Chrysalis.** v. 1, no. 1- . 1977- . 1727 North Spring Street, Los Angeles, CA 90012. Quarterly. $10.00.
Chrysalis; a Magazine of Women's Culture attempts to represent a wide variety of values, experiences, and lifestyles, recognizing that feminism is multi-faceted. In the first four numbers, it has managed to offer high calibre poetry, fiction, and articles. Represented among the contributors have been Marge Piercy, June Jordan, Robin Morgan, and Elizabeth Janeway. Excellent book reviews, and often, fine bibliographies on difficult-to-access materials are included.

1750   **Feminist Studies.** v. 1, no. 1-v. 3, no. 4. 1971-1974(?); v. 4, no. 1- . 1978- . Managing Editor, Women's Studies Program, University of Maryland, College Park, MD 20742. Triannually. $10.00.
Feminist Studies is an independent interdisciplinary journal founded for the purpose of encouraging scholarly and other analytic treatments of issues related to the status and condition of women. The June 1978 issue, for example, includes poetry, photography, and literary and historical articles, all related to motherhood. It is indexed in *America, History and Life*; *Historical Abstracts*; *Philosopher's Index*; *PMLA*; *Sociological Abstracts*; and *Women Studies Abstracts*.

1751   **Ms.** v. 1, no. 1- . Sept. 1972- . Subscription Dept., 123 Garden Street, Marion, OH 43302. Monthly. $10.00.
A mass market magazine that speaks with a feminist editorial voice, this is an attractive and intelligent magazine that deserves a place in every collection. It provides consistently knowledgeable reviews on trade books and major films, sensitive interviews, excellent fiction and poetry, and provocative articles by well-known feminist writers and personalities. It speaks to minority as well as to white women, though the tone is distinctly middle-class. It is indexed in *Readers' Guide* and *Women Studies Abstracts*.

1752   **off our backs.** v. 1, no. 1- . Sept. 1970- . 1724 - 20th Street, NW,
        Washington, DC 20009. Eleven issues per year. $6.00.
off our backs: A Women's News Journal is probably the best known of the radical
feminist tabloids and certainly one of the long-time survivors. Regular features
are: labor news, international news, health, poetry, reviews, "Chicken Lady,"
letters, and ads. Always original and fresh, recent articles include: commentaries
on lesbians, affirmative action, IWY, publishers, violence, love and feminism,
rape, and women's culture. It is indexed in *Women Studies Abstracts, Alternative
Press Index*, and *New Periodicals Index*.

1753   **Quest: A Feminist Quarterly.** v. 1, no. 1- . Summer 1974- . 2000 P
        Street, NW, Washington, DC 20036. Quarterly. $9.00.
Quest is a journal of feminist political analysis and theory that solicits contribu-
tions from both scholars and activists. Past contributors have included Charlotte
Bunch, Rita Mae Brown, Nancy Hartsock, Mary Daly, and Joanna Russ. Most
issues are devoted to a particular theme, for example: Processes of Change;
Women and Spirituality; Theories of Revolution; and International Feminism.
It is indexed in *Women Studies Abstracts, Access, Alternative Press Index*, and
Popular Periodical Index.

1754   **Signs.** v. 1, no. 1- . Autumn, 1975- . University of Chicago Press, 5801
        Ellis Avenue, Chicago, IL 60637. Quarterly. $20.00.
Signs: Journal of Women in Culture and Society is the most prestigious and
commercially successful of the scholarly journals publishing the new scholarship
on women. In the first number, the editors announced that "the form the work
will take may be reports of original research, contemplative essays, or a synthesis
of report and essay." *Signs* is multicultural and multi-disciplinary and features
the work of major feminist scholars. A must for all academic libraries, it is indexed
in *Women Studies Abstracts*.

1755   **The Spokeswoman.** v. 1, no. 1- . June 5, 1970- . 53 West Jackson,
        Chicago, IL 60604. Monthly. $12.00.
Brevity is the editorial policy of *The Spokeswoman*, which digests the latest
in legislation and suits affecting women on the issues of employment, ERA,
abortion, health, education, and other miscellaneous women's issues. Regular
features are a review section covering books, periodicals, and films, and a
Helpwanted section, which advertises professional openings. It is a basic,
objective source of information on the most important women's issues.

1756   **Women & Health.** v. 1, no. 1- . July/Aug. 1976- . SUNY/College at
        Old Westbury, Old Westbury, NY 11568. Six times a year.
Published by the Biological Science Program at SUNY, this journal features
informative and understandable articles on women's health care. A sampling
of recent articles: "Parental/Child Psychology—Delivery Alternatives"; "Options
in Maternity Care"; "The Risks of Sex Hormones as Drugs." Articles are written
by professionals in a variety of fields. Regular features are "Women, Health,
and Books" and "Women, Health, and Films."

1757   **Women and Literature.** v. 1, no. 1- . Spring 1973- . Dept. of English,
        Douglass College, Rutgers University, New Brunswick, NJ 08903.
        Semi-annual. $7.00.
A scholarly journal, this publishes short articles on the work of women writers.
It should be of interest to both graduate and undergraduate collections. An
annual bibliography of women and literature appears in the Fall issue of each
volume. Sample articles: Elaine Showalter, "A Passage to India as 'Marriage
Fiction': Forster's Sexual Politics"; Charlotte Goodman, "Women and Madness
in the Fiction of Joyce Carol Oates." It is indexed in *Women Studies Abstracts,
Abstracts of English Studies*, and *PMLA.*

1758   **Women Reviewing Women** (the only magazine devoted entirely to
        women's publications) will be issued four times yearly; order from Seagull
        Publications, 1736 E. 53rd Street, Brooklyn, NY 11234. $6.00.
The only magazine devoted entirely to women's publications, this new periodical
looks as if it will be promising in locating the best material for, about, and by
women.

1759   **Women Studies Abstracts.** v. 1- . Winter 1972- . Rush Publishing Co.,
        P.O. Box 1, Rush, NY 14543. Quarterly. $25.00.
This is the only abstracting and indexing service that searches the scholarly
literature on women. Bibliographic essays often appear. Special issues of journals
and reports, and special publications are identified and annotated. It provides
and cites book reviews for major titles of interest to women's studies scholars.

1760   **Women's Studies.** v. 1, no. 1- . 1972- . Gordon and Breach Science
        Publishers, Inc., One Park Avenue, New York, NY 10016. Three times/
        yr. $14.50.
"*Women's Studies* provides a forum for the presentation of scholarship and
criticism about women in the fields of literature, history, arts, sociology, law,
political science, economics, anthropology and the sciences." Book and film
reviews regularly appear, as do short stories, poetry, and photographs. Special
issues of recent date include numbers on Virginia Woolf, women's poetry,
androgyny, Victorian Englishwomen, and rites of passage. Like *Signs, Women's
Studies* is avowedly interdisciplinary. The editor is Wendy Martin, Department
of English, Queens College, CUNY, Flushing, NY 11367. It is indexed in *Women
Studies Abstracts.*

1761   **Women's Studies Newsletter.** v. 1, no. 1- . 1972- . The Feminist Press,
        Box 334, Old Westbury, NY 11568. Quarterly. $10.00.
Women's Studies is indeed fortunate to have this clearinghouse on information
pertaining to the scholarly study of women. Articles are of consistently high
quality. Sample articles from recent issues include: "On Teaching a Feminist
Writing Workshop"; "Finding and Studying Lesbian Culture"; "Women's
Studies in Its Second Phase"; "Images of Women in Renaissance Literature:
A Selected Bibliography of Scholarship." This is an absolute necessity for
institutions which support a Women's Studies program. Indexed: *Women
Studies Abstracts.*

1762   **Women's Work.** v. 1, no. 1- . Jan./Feb. 1975- . Women's Work, Inc.,
        1302 - 185 H Street, NW, Suite 203, Washington, DC 20036. Bi-monthly.
        $6.00.

Practical in tone and content, *Women's Work* is a magazine appropriate for any
library which serves women. The articles are short, written in a somewhat
breezy style, e.g., "Is Consulting for You?," "Work . . . and the Older Woman";
"Choosing a Mentor." Book reviews focus on practical titles aimed at women
in business. A regular feature is "Job Market Hotline: Reports from Major
Cities Job Market Resources."

1763   **Womensports.** v. 1, no. 1- . 1974- . 1660 South Amphlett Boulevard,
        Suite 266, San Mateo, CA. Monthly.

Ceased publication, v. 5, no. 2, February 1978. Worth getting a back-run for
the articles on current women sports figures. Indexed: *Women Studies Abstracts*;
Access.

AUTHOR INDEX

Numbers in the index refer to entry, not page, number. Boldface names are referred to but have no annotations themselves, e.g., **Anger, Jane.**

Tolchin, Martin, 1260
Tolchin, Susan, 1260
Tomalin, Claire, 158, 310
Tominaga, Thomas T., 1394
Tomkinson, William Shirley, 1885- , 592
Trahey, Jane, 382
Trask, Anne E., 410
Trautmann, Joanne, 311, 330
Trofimenkoff, Susan Mann, 1941- , 621
Trotskii, Lev, 1879-1940, 1739
Troubridge, Una Elena Taylor, Lady, 312
Tsuzuki, Chushichi, 208
Tuchman, Gaye, 1590
Tucker, Anne, 486
Tucker, Patricia, 1557
Tufts, Eleanor, 487
Turner, Darwin T., 1931- , 1395

Ullyot, Joan, 1940- , 1604
United States. Bureau of the Census, 1456
United States. Commission on Civil Rights, 1586
United States. Congress. House. Committee on Education and Labor. Special Subcommittee on Education, 444
United States. Congress. Senate. Committee on the Judiciary. Subcommittee on Constitutional Amendments, 658
United States. Equal Employment Opportunity Commission, 1457
United States. National Commission on the Observance of International Women's Year, 1975, 659
United States. President's Commission on the Status of Women, 383
United States. Women's Bureau, 1458, 1459, 1460
University of Wisconsin-Extension. Family Living Education and Women's Education Resources, 1461
Urdang, Constance, 1173

Van Doren, Dorothy (Graffe), 1896- , 313
Van de Ven, Nicole, 1678
Van Voris, Jacqueline, 314
Vasquez, Enrizueta Longeaux Y., 575
Veith, Ilza, 1304
Vequaud, Yves, 488
Vetterling-Braggin, Mary, 1486
Vicinus, Martha, 1939- , 622, 623
Vida, Ginny, 1939- , 1462
Vietor, Agnes C., 332
Vivien, Renée, 1877-1909, 982
Volgyes, Ivan, 1729
Volgyes, Nancy, 1729
Vorse, Mary Marvin Heaton, 315

Wade, Mason, 1913- , 316
Waehrer, Helen Youngelson, 1533
Wakoski, Diane, 1174, 1175, 1176
Wald, Karen, 428
　　See also: Leiner, Marvin
Walker, Alice, 1944- , 983, 984, 1177, 1178
Walker, Kathryn E., 1917- , 384
Walker, Margaret, 1915- , 672, 985, 1179, 1180, 1181
Wallace, Phyllis Ann, 385
Walsh, Mary Roth, 1235
Walsh, Thomas P., 1374
Walstedt, Joyce Jennings, 1396
Ward, David A., 1587
Wardle, Ralph Martin, 1909- , 317
Warner, Marina, 1946- , 1487
Warrior, Betsy, 1463
Wartofsky, Marx W., 1465, 1473
Washburne, Carolyn Kott, 1528
Washington, Mary Helen, 702
Wasserstrom, William, 1097
Waters, Clara Erskine Clement [Clement, Clara Erskine], 1834-1916, 463
Waters, Ethel, 1900- , 318
Waters, Mary-Alice, 1255
Watkins, Mel, 1588
Watson, Barbara Bellow, 1098, 1740
Watts, Emily Stipes, 1099
Webber, Jeannette L., 703
Weber, Carl J., 1370
Weber, Clara C., 1370
Weibel, Kathleen, 1589
Weibel, Kathryn, 1590
Weideger, Paula, 1193
Weil, Simone, 1909-1943, 1488
Weinberg, Martin S., 1190, 1345
Weiner, Annette B., 1933- , 60
Weinzberg, Marjorie, 1465
Weisbord, Robert G., 1261
Welch, Jeffrey, 1384
Weldon, Fay, 986, 987, 988
Wells, Anna Mary, 319
Wells, Ida B.
　　See: Barnett, Ida B. Wells, 1862-1931
Wells, Theodora, 361
Welter, Barbara, 555, 624, 625
Welty, Eudora, 1909- , 746, 989
Wengraf, Susan, 1309
Werner, Vivian L., 143
Werstein, Irving, 154
Wertheimer, Barbara M., 626
Wertz, Dorothy C., 627
Wertz, Richard W., 627
Wery, Mary K., 1388
West, Dorothy, 1909- , 990
West, Rebecca, pseud., 991, 992
West, Uta, 1741
West Coast Women's Studies Conference, California State University, Sacramento, 1973, 1742

TITLE INDEX

Numbers in the index refer to entry, not page, number. Boldface titles are referred to but have no annotations themselves, e.g., **Abortion.**

SUBJECT INDEX

Numbers in the index refer to entry, not page, number.

(continues on page 662)